A Collection of Papers from the
8th AIAA/CEAS Aeroacoustics Conference & Exhibit
Breckenridge, Colorado, USA
17-19 June 2002

Table of Contents

Paper No.	Title and Author	Page Number
AIAA-2002-2400	Simulation of Acoustic Characteristics and Mechanisms of Powered Resonance Tubes A. Cain, E. Kerschen, and G. Raman	1
AIAA-2002-2403	Computational and Experimental Investigations of Cavity Attenuation Using High Frequency Control N. Sinha, S. Arunajatesan, and J. Seiner	11
AIAA-2002-2404	High Frequency Acoustic Suppression - The Role of Mass Flow & The Notion of Superposition M. Stanek, G. Raman, J. Ross, J. Odedra, J. Peto, F. Alvi, and V. Kibens	23
AIAA-2002-2405	Experimental and Numerical Investigation of Confined Unsteady Supersonic Flow Over Cavities V. Babu, G. Anavaradham, B. Umesh Chandra, S. Chakravarthy, and S. Panneerselvam	53
AIAA-2002-2406	Airframe Noise Study of a CRJ-700 Aircraft Model in the NASA Ames 7- by 10- Foot Wind Tunnnel No. 1 P. Soderman, F. Kafyeke, N. Burnside, R. Chandrasekharan, S. Jaeger, and J. Boudreau	64
AIAA-2002-2407	Flow Survey of the Wake of a Commercial Transport Main Landing Gear W. Horne, K. James, and B. Storms	83
AIAA-2002-2408	Landing Gears and High Lift Devices Airframe Noise Research H. Remy, K. Mau, and L. Chow	92
AIAA-2002-2409	Research into Landing Gear Airframe Noise Reduction W. Dobrzynski, L. Chow, P. Guion, and D. Shiells	103

AIAA-2002-2410   Microphone Array Assessment of an Isolated, 26%-scale, High-fidelity Landing Gear
S. Jaeger, N. Burnside, P. Soderman, W. Horne, and K. James 113

AIAA-2002-2411   Unsteady Simulations of a Landing-Gear Flow Field
F. Li, M. Khorrami, and M. Malik 128

AIAA-2002-2412   Aeroacoustic Behaviour of a 1:11 Scale Airbus Model in the Open Anechoic Wind Tunnel CEPRA 19
R. Davy, F. Moens, and H. Remy......................141

AIAA-2002-2413   Numerical and Experimental Investigation of the Vibro-Acoustics of a Multi-Layered Plate Backed Cavity
N. Atalla, H. Osman, and C. Amedin......................156

AIAA-2002-2414   Analytical Modeling of Active/Passive Smart Foam Noise Control Treatment in Aerospace Vehicles
C. Chin, J. Lee, and G. Mathur......................164

AIAA-2002-2415   Effect of Fluid Wall Shear Stress on Nonlinear Vibration and Acoustic Radiation
A. Frendi and W. Buhler......................174

AIAA-2002-2416   Noise Transmission Characteristics of Damped Plexiglas Windows
G. Gibbs, R. Buehrle, J. Klos, and S. Brown......................186

AIAA-2002-2417   Creation of a Markup Language for Vibroacoustic Data
C. Musser......................195

AIAA-2002-2418   Finite Element Modeling of the NASA Langley Aluminum Testbed Cylinder
F. Grosveld, J. Pritchard, R. Buehrle, and R. Pappa......................201

AIAA-2002-2419   A Parametric Study of Fine-Scale Turbulence Mixing Noise
A. Khavaran, J. Bridges, and J. Freund 212

AIAA-2002-2421   Sound Radiation from a Subsonic Turbulent Plane Jet
Z. Hu, C. Morfey, and N. Sandham......................228

AIAA-2002-2422   The Prediction of Three-Dimensional Jet Flows for Noise Applications
S. Birch, A. Secundov, A. Lebedev, D. Lyubimov, V. Maslov, and B. Mineev 236

AIAA-2002-2423   Turbulent Jet Noise: Shear noise, Self-noise, and Entropic Contributions
J. Freund......................245

AIAA-2002-2424   On Modelling the Near-Field Noise of the High-speed Jet
Exhausts of Combat Aircraft
M. Harper-Bourne 258

AIAA-2002-2425   Further Consideration of the Limitations and Validity of the
Acoustic Analogy Theory
C. Tam 269

AIAA-2002-2426   Fan Noise Source Diagnostic Test - Rotor Alone Aerodynamic
Performance Results
C. Hughes, R. Jeracki, R. Woodward, and C. Miller.....................280

AIAA-2002-2427   Fan Noise Source Diagnostic Test -- Far-field Acoustic Results
R. Woodward, C. Hughes, R. Jeracki, and C. Miller......................302

AIAA-2002-2428   Fan Noise Source Diagnostic Test - Tone Modal Structure
Results
L. Heidelberg...328

AIAA-2002-2429   Fan Noise Source Diagnostic Test - Wall Measured
Circumferential Array Mode Results
J. Premo and P. Joppa..349

AIAA-2002-2430   Fan Noise Source Diagnostics Test - Vane Unsteady Pressure
Results
E. Envia...362

AIAA-2002-2431   Fan Noise Source Diagnostic Test- LDV Measured Flow Field
Results
G. Podboy, M. Krupar, C. Hughes, and R. Woodward 377

AIAA-2002-2432   Control of Inflow Distortion in a Scarf Inlet
C. Gerhold, L. Clark, and R. Biedron...406

AIAA-2002-2433   Acoustic Wave Attenuation Through Glow Discharge Plasma
V. Otugen, V. Sheverev, V. Stepaniuk, C. Tarau, G. Raman,
and V. Soukhomlinov 416

AIAA-2002-2434   Simulation on Effect of Surface Impedance for Reducing
Aerodynamic Sound from Circular Cylinder
I. Yahathugoda and S. Akishita 424

AIAA-2002-2435   Effect of Trailing Edge Geometry on Vortex Shedding and
Acoustic Radiation
T. Mueller, D. Lynch, C. Kunze, and W. Blake 435

AIAA-2002-2436   Numerical Simulation of Trailing Edge Receptivity
M. Barone and S. Lele 444

AIAA-2002-2437 Impedance of Perforated Screens with Bias Flow
V. Bellucci, C. Paschereit, and P. Flohr 458

AIAA-2002-2438 Towards Arbitrary Accuracy Inviscid Surface Boundary
Conditions
R. Dyson and R. Hixon.................................467

AIAA-2002-2439 Finite Element Implementation of Nonreflecting Far-field
Conditions for Unsteady Aerodynamics and Aeroacoustics
H. Atassi and R. Susan-Resiga.................................477

AIAA-2002-2441 Evaluation of Far-Field Boundary Conditions for the Gust
Response Problem
J. Scott, K. Kreider, and J. Heminger.................................488

AIAA-2002-2442 Open Boundary Conditions of Predictor-Corrector Type for
External Flows
S. Karabasov and T. Hynes 509

AIAA-2002-2443 Effect of Grazing Flow and SPL on Impedance of 2-DOF
Resonators
A. Hersh, B. Walker, and J. Celano.................................520

AIAA-2002-2444 Hard Strips in Lined Ducts
T. Elnady and H. Bodén.................................530

AIAA-2002-2445 Near Cut-on/Cut-off Transition in Lined Ducts with Flow
N. Ovenden.................................541

AIAA-2002-2446 Effects of Liner Geometry on Acoustic Impedance
M. Jones, M. Tracy, W. Watson, and T. Parrott 550

AIAA-2002-2447 Grazing Flow Acoustic Impedance Testing for the NASA AST
Program
J. Gallman and R. Kunze 560

AIAA-2002-2448 Buzz-saw
Alan. A, Mike. M, and Brian. B 569

AIAA-2002-2449 Modelling Tone Propagation from Turbofan Inlets - The Effect of
Extended Lip Liners
R. Astley, J. Hamilton, N. Baker, and E. Kitchen.................................580

AIAA-2002-2450 High Speed Jet Noise Reduction Using Microjets
A. Krothapalli, A. Arakeri, B. Greska, and T. Joseph.................................591

AIAA-2002-2451 Analysis of Three-Dimensional, Nonlinear Development of
Wave-Like Structure in a Compressible Round Jet
M. Dahl and R. Mankbadi.................................603

AIAA-2002-2452   Selection of Acoustic Modes in the Vicinity of Supersonic Jets
C. Millet and G. Casalis..614

AIAA-2002-2454   Spatial Scale Decomposition of Shear Layer Turbulence and the
Sound Sources Associated with the Missing Scales in a Large-
Eddy Simulation
D. Bodony and S. Lele 621

AIAA-2002-2455   Prediction of the Acoustic Field Associated with Instability
Wave Source Model for a Compressible Jet
V. Golubev, R. Mankbadi, and M. Dahl 634

AIAA-2002-2456   Large Jet-Noise Reductions Through Distributed Nozzles
R. Gaeta, K. Ahuja, D. Schein, and W. Solomon 642

AIAA-2002-2457   Evaluation and further analysis of unsteady pressure response
measurements on an airfoil at angle of attack
P. Mish and W. Devenport 658

AIAA-2002-2460   Trailing Edge Noise Measurements and Prediction for Subsonic
Loaded Fan Blades
M. Roger and S. Moreau..681

AIAA-2002-2461   Designing a Dual Waveguide Normal Incidence Tube Utilizing
Energy and Modal Methods
J. Betts 696

AIAA-2002-2462   The Reflection Canceller - Phased Array Measurements in a
Reverberating Environment
S. Guidati, C. Brauer, and S. Wagner 708

AIAA-2002-2463   Signal Processing for In-flow Measurement of Acoustic Velocity
by LDV
A. Minotti, F. Simon, J. Piet, and P. Millan 718

AIAA-2002-2464   Determination of Absolute Levels from Phased Array
Measurements Using Spatial Source Coherence
S. Oerlemans and P. Sijtsma 727

AIAA-2002-2465   Uncertainty Analysis of the Two-Microphone Method for
Acoustical Impedance Testing
T. Schultz, L. Cattafesta, T. Nishida, and M. Sheplak........................738

AIAA-2002-2466   Design, Construction, and Validation of an Aeroacoustic
Anechoic Test Facility
L. Cattafesta, D. Jansson, J. Hubner, and M. Sheplak......................749

AIAA-2002-2467   Computation of Trailing Edge Noise via LES and Acoustic
Perturbation Equations
R. Ewert, M. Meinke, and W. Schroeder 760

AIAA-2002-2468   Slat-Cove Noise Modeling: A Posteriori Analysis of Unsteady
RANS Simulations
M. Choudhari, M. Khorrami, D. Lockard, and G. Lilley 773

AIAA-2002-2469   Reduction of Flap Side Edge Noise by Active Flow Control
L. Koop, K. Ehrenfried, A. Dillmann, and U. Michel..........................787

AIAA-2002-2470   Validation of a Semiempirical Airframe Noise Prediction Method
Through Dedicated A319 Flyover Noise Measurements
M. Pott-Pollenske, W. Dobrzynski, H. Buchholz, B. Gehlhar,
and F. Walle 796

AIAA-2002-2471   Trailing-edge Noise Prediction by SATIN on the Basis of Steady
RANS Solutions
J. Ostertag, A. Celic, and S. Wagner 807

AIAA-2002-2472   Measurement of Trailing Edge Noise Using Directional Array
and Coherent Output Power Methods
F. Hutcheson and T. Brooks 817

AIAA-2002-2473   Vortex Element Methods and Kutta Conditions for Slat Noise
Predictions
Z. Zheng and B. Tan 833

AIAA-2002-2475   Computation of Spinning Modal Radiation from an Unflanged
Duct
X. Zhang, X. Chen, C. Morfey, and P. Nelson.....................................844

AIAA-2002-2476   Aerodynamic Noise Induced by Laminar and Turbulent
Boundary Layers over Rectangular Cavities
X. Gloerfelt, C. Bogey, C. Bailly, and D. Juve 856

AIAA-2002-2477   Trailing Edge Noise Prediction Based on a New Acoustic
Formulation
J. Casper and F. Farassat...868

AIAA-2002-2480   Numerical Study of the Impact of Streamwise Vorticity on Jet
Noise
M. Soteriou, R. Reba, and T. Maeder 880

AIAA-2002-2481   Aeroacoustics of Hot Jets
K. Viswanathan 893

AIAA-2002-2482   Effects of Vortex Generating Tabs on Noise Sources in an
Ideally Expanded Mach 1.3 Jet
M. Samimy and J. Hileman 904

AIAA-2002-2483   Forward Flight Effects on Heated and Unheated Rectangular Jets
K. Massey and K. Ahuja...916

AIAA-2002-2484   Turbulence Measurements of Separate Flow Nozzles with Mixing Enhancement Features
J. Bridges and M. Wernet...929

AIAA-2002-2485   Measurement of Correlation Between Flow Density, Velocity and Density*velocity2 with Far Field Noise in High Speed Jets
J. Panda, R. Seasholtz, and K. Elam 940

AIAA-2002-2487   Correlating Model-Scale & Full-Scale Test Results of Dual Flow Nozzle Jets
E. Nesbitt, R. Elkoby, T. Bhat, P. Strange, and C. Mead 961

AIAA-2002-2488   Broadband Theory for Coupled Fan Stages Including Blade Row Reflection/Transmission Effects
D. Hanson 974

AIAA-2002-2489   Fan Noise Source Diagnostic Test - Computation of Rotor Wake Turbulence Noise
M. Nallasamy, E. Envia, S. Thorp, and A. Shabbir............................990

AIAA-2002-2490   Fan Broadband Self Noise Prediction Model
P. Gliebe 1003

AIAA-2002-2491   Fan Noise Prediction Using Unsteady CFD Analysis
N. Tsuchiya, Y. Nakamura, A. Yamagata, H. Kodama, K. Yamamoto, O. Nozaki, and T. Nishizawa 1017

AIAA-2002-2492   Low-Speed Fan Noise Reduction with Trailing Edge Blowing
D. Sutliff, D. Tweedt, E. Fite, and E. Envia.....................................1027

AIAA-2002-2493   Active Noise Control in Axial Turbomachines by Flow Induced Secondary Sources
J. Schulz, W. Neise, and M. Möser 1062

AIAA-2002-2494   Phase Determination of Reverberant Structural-Acoustic Systems Using Pole and Zero Distribution
J. Betts and C. Fuller..1071

AIAA-2002-2495   Active Vibration Isolation System for Helicopter Interior Noise Reduction
R. Maier, F. Hoffmann, S. Tewes, and M. Bebesel 1080

AIAA-2002-2496   Active Control of Turbulent Boundary Layer Induced Sound Radiation from Multiple Aircraft Panels
G. Gibbs and R. Cabell 1090

AIAA-2002-2497   Experimental Feedback Control of Flow Induced Cavity Tones
R. Cabell, M. Kegerise, D. Cox, and G. Gibbs 1098

AIAA-2002-2498   Noise Reduction in a Flow Duct by Active Control of Wall
Impedance
M. Galland, O. Hilbrunner, and N. Sellen 1108

AIAA-2002-2499   Active Control of the Aerodynamic and Acoustic Performance
of Axial Turbomachines
L. Neuhaus and W. Neise 1118

AIAA-2002-2500   Active Control of Fan Noise in Ducts Using Magnetic Bearings
J. Watkins, J. Nelson, and G. Piper..1127

AIAA-2002-2501   Investigation of Aircraft Wake Vortices with Phased Microphone
Arrays
P. Böhning and U. Michel...1134

AIAA-2002-2502   A Novel Onsite Narrowband Tool for Flight Test Acoustic Data
Processing
S. Uellenberg, M. Czech, E. Nesbitt, and Y. Abdelhamid.................1143

AIAA-2002-2503   Recent Advances in Large Scale Aeroacoustic Wind Tunnels
E. Duell, J. Walter, J. Yen, and S. Arnette 1152

AIAA-2002-2504   Identification of the Characteristic Parameters of Porous Media
Using Active Control
N. Sellen, M. Galland, and O. Hilbrunner 1166

AIAA-2002-2505   New Beam-forming Algorithm for High Speed Jet Flows
T. Suzuki and G. Bulter 1176

AIAA-2002-2506   Localization of the Acoustic Sources of the A340 with a Large
Phased Microphone Array During Flight Tests
J. Piet, U. Michel, and P. Böhning..1189

AIAA-2002-2509   A Family of Low Dispersive and Low Dissipative Explicit
Schemes for Computing Aerodynamic Noise
C. Bogey and C. Bailly 1200

AIAA-2002-2510   A New Class of Higher Order Accurate Non-Oscillatory Implicit
Time Integration Schemes
K. Duraisamy and J. Baeder 1211

AIAA-2002-2511   Reconstructed Sub-Grid Methods for Acoustics Predictions at
all Reynolds Numbers
P. Batten, U. Goldberg, and S. Chakravarthy 1223

AIAA-2002-2514 Two-dimensional Wave Analysis of the Discontinuous Galerkin Method with Non-Uniform Grids and Boundary Conditions
F. Hu and H. Atkins 1232

AIAA-2002-2515 Accuracy and Efficiency in FEM Modeling of Turbofan Acoustic Radiation
W. Eversman and E. Listerud 1243

AIAA-2002-2516 A Method for Optimizing Non-Axisymmetric Liners for Multi-Modal Sound Sources
W. Watson, M. Jones, T. Parrott, and J. Sobieski 1254

AIAA-2002-2517 Forward Flight Effects on the Internal Noise of an Ejector Nozzle
K. Massey and K. Ahuja 1265

AIAA-2002-2518 A New Conceptual Design for Active Noise Control with Controllable Impedance Liners
M. Zhuang and S. Zheng 1277

AIAA-2002-2520 The Webster Equation Revisited
S. Rienstra 1284

AIAA-2002-2521 On the Azimuthal Mode Propagation in Axisymmetric Duct FLows
X. Li, C. Schemel, U. Michel, and F. Thiele...................................1294

AIAA-2002-2523 Turbulence Suppression in the Noise Producing Region of a M = 0.9 Jet
A. Krothapalli, V. Arakeri, L. Lourenco, V. Siddavaram,
and M. Alkislar..1304

AIAA-2002-2524 Noise Control Using Adjoint-based Optimization
J. Freund and M. Wei..1312

AIAA-2002-2525 Progress in Jet Turbulence Modeling for Aero-Acoustic Applications
S. Dash, D. Kenzakowsli, J. Papp, W. Calhoon, S. Arunajatesan,
C. Kannepalli, and J. Seiner...1319

AIAA-2002-2526 Sound Produced by Vortex Ring Pairing: Prediction Based on Particle Image Velocimetry
C. Schram, A. Hirschberg, and M. Riethmuller..............................1325

AIAA-2002-2527 Computation of Shock Induced Noise in Imperfectly Expanded Supersonic Jets
B. Imamoglu and P. Balakumar..1337

AIAA-2002-2529 An Investigation of the Flow Structure of Tone Producing Supersonic Impinging Jets
B. Henderson, J. Bridges, and M. Wernet.....................................1348

AIAA-2002-2530   A Numerical Study of Shock-Associated Noise
C. Lui and S. Lele..1359

AIAA-2002-2532   Numerical Simulation of Unsteady Cavity Flow Using Lattice
Boltzmann Method
D. Ricot, V. Maillard, and C. Bailly 1371

AIAA-2002-2535   Nonlinear Analysis of Airfoil High-Intensity Gust Response
Using a High-Order Prefactored Compact Code
V. Golubev, R. Mankbadi, A. Crivellini, L. Povinelli, J. Scott,
and R. Hixon 1382

AIAA-2002-2536   Simulation of 3-D Acoustic Scattering with a Pentadiagonal
Compact-Difference Method
P. TenPas and N. Edgar 1392

AIAA-2002-2538   Finite-Element Based LES of the Near-Nozzle Region of a
Compressible Round Jet
T. Maeder, R. Reba, and K. Jansen...1402

AIAA-2002-2539   A Velocity-Potential-Based Boundary-Element Method for the
Aeroacoustic Analysis of Rotors and Propellers in Arbitrary
Motion
L. Morino, G. Bernardini, and M. Gennaretti 1413

AIAA-2002-2540   A Study of Noise Abatement Procedures Using Ames B747-400
Flight Simulator
K. Elmer, J. Wat, G. Gershzohn, B. Shivashankara, J. Clarke,
L. Tobias, and D. Lambert...1424

AIAA-2002-2541   A Computational Study of Ignition Over-Pressure for Launch
Vehicles
A. Frendi and F. Canabal 1434

AIAA-2002-2542   Prediction of Sonic Boom Signature Using Euler-Full Potential
CFD with Grid Adaptation and Shock Fitting
O. Kandil, Z. Yang, and P. Bobbitt 1444

AIAA-2002-2543   Prediction of Rod-Airfoil Interaction Noise Using the FW-H
Analogy
D. Casalino, M. Jacob, and M. Roger 1464

AIAA-2002-2544   Tiltrotor BVI Noise Reduction Through Flight Trajectory
Management & Configuration Control
M. Gervais and F. Schmitz..1475

AIAA-2002-2545   The Aeroacoustics of Transonic Helicopter Blades
A. Morgans and A. Dowling...1487

AIAA-2002-2548 Flow-Induced Noise Around the A-pillar of an Idealized Car Greenhouse
M. Janssens, J. Heck, L. van Lier, C. Rops, G. Strumolo, and M. Snellen 1497

AIAA-2002-2549 Sound Radiation of the Vortex Flow Past a Generic Side Mirror
F. Thiele, J. Yan, T. Rung, and D. Eschricht 1505

AIAA-2002-2550 Simulation and Design of Automobile Sunroof Buffeting Noise Control
R. Singh and K. Karbon 1515

AIAA-2002-2551 Aero-Vibro-Acoustics: Problem Statement and Methods for Simulation–based Design Solution
P. Bremner and J. Wilby 1521

AIAA-2002-2553 Two-Point Correlations and Acoustic Measurements of High-Speed Axisymmetric Jets
M. Doty and D. McLaughlin 1532

AIAA-2002-2554 A Computational and Experimental Investigation of Serrated Coaxial Nozzles
G. Page, N. Hughes, J. McGuirk, M. Hossain, and M. Trumper 1546

AIAA-2002-2555 Experiments and Analyses of Distributed Exhaust Nozzles
K. Kinzie, D. Schein, and W. Solomon 1557

AIAA-2002-2557 Noise Suppression in Moderate-Speed Multistream Jets
D. Papamoschou and E. Abbey 1568

AIAA-2002-2558 Experimental Investigation of Jet Noise and Core Noise Using a Small Gas Turbine Engine
V. Tesson, M. Doty, and D. McLaughlin 1585

AIAA-2002-2559 Scattering of Acoustic and Vorticity Disturbances by an Unloaded Annular Cascade in a Swirling Flow
H. Atassi, A. Ali, and O. Atassi 1597

AIAA-2002-2560 High Frequency Sound Radiation from an Annular Cascade in Swirling Flows
H. Atassi and B. Elhadidi..1608

AIAA-2002-2562 Buzz-Saw Noise Spectra and Directivity from Flyover Tests
H. Siller and U. Michel...1619

AIAA-2002-2563 Inlet Mode Measurements with an Inflow Control Device Microphone Array
J. Lan, J. Premo, and D. Sutliff...1626

AIAA-2002-2564   Duct Mode Measurements on the TFE731-60 Full Scale Engine
D. Sutliff, K. Konno, and L. Heidelberg..1637

AIAA-2002-2565   An Empirical Spectral Model of Surface-Pressure Fluctuations
that Includes Reynolds Number Effects
M. Goody 1652

AIAA-2002-2566   Phase Synchronization and Desynchronization of Structural
Response Induced by Turbulent and External Sound
L. Maestrello 1666

AIAA-2002-2568   Aerodynamic Noise Prediction in Internal Flows Using LES and
Linear Euler Equations
P. Lafon, T. Buchal, F. Crouzet, and D. Laurence............................1683

AIAA-2002-2569   A Correlation Length Scale for the Prediction of Aeroacoustic
Response
T. Mueller, D. Lynch, and W. Blake..1689

AIAA-2002-2570   Thermoacoustic Properties of Can Annular Combustors
S. Bethke, W. Krebs, P. Flohr, and B. Prade 1702

AIAA-2002-2571   Character of Mach Wave Radiation and Convection Velocity
Estimation in Supersonic Shear Layers
T. Rossmann, G. Mungal, and R. Hanson 1713

AIAA-2002-2572   Visualization of Aerodynamic Sound Source with Compact
Green's Function
A. Iida, C. Kato, and A. Mizuno 1722

AIAA-2002-2573   Numerical Prediction of Airfoil Aerodynamic Noise
E. Manoha, C. Herrero, S. Ben Khelil, I. Mary, P. Guillen,
and P. Sagaut 1730

AIAA-2002-2574   A Component Based Empirical Model for Airframe Noise
Prediction
Y. Guo, K. Yamamoto, and R. Stoker 1743

AIAA-2002-2575   Investigation of the Physical Mechanisms of Tonal Sound
Generation by Slats
A. Agarwal and P. Morris 1753

AIAA-2002-2576   Array Design and Performance for a Large Scale Airframe Noise
Study
N. Burnside, W. Horne, S. Jaeger, P. Soderman, and B. Reinero ...1764

AIAA-2002-2577   Dense Compact Rigid Object in a Turbulent Flow: Application of
Curle's Theory
D. Leclercq and M. Symes 1775

AIAA-2002-2578   Simulation of Sound Generation by Vortices Passing the
Trailing Edge of Airfoils
M. Lummer, J. Delfs, and T. Lauke 1786

AIAA-2002-2579   Time-Accurate Simulations and Acoustic Analysis of Slat Free-
Shear-Layer: Part II
M. Khorrami, B. Singer, and D. Lockard..1796

AIAA-2002-2580   A Comparison of Ffowcs Williams-Hawkings Solvers for
Airframe Noise Applications
D. Lockard...1807

AIAA-2002-2581   Validation of a Prediction Model for Aerodynamic Noise from
Aircraft Landing Gears
M. Smith and L. Chow..1818

AIAA-2002-2582   Acoustic Source Terms for the Linear Euler Equations on
Conservative Form
M. Billson, L. Eriksson, and L. Davidson 1826

AIAA-2002-2583   Parallelization Strategy for an Explicit Computational
Aeroacoustics Code
R. Hixon, M. Nallasamy, and S. Sawyer 1835

AIAA-2002-2584   On the Use of Characteristics in Computational Aeroacoustics
J. Schulten 1849

AIAA-2002-2586   Large Scale Frequency Domain Numerical Simulation of Aircraft
Engine Tone Noise Radiation and Scattering
D. Stanescu, M. Hussaini, and F. Farassat.......................................1859

AIAA-2002-2587   A Frequency-Domain Numerical Method for Noise Radiation
from Ducted Fans
Y. Ozyoruk, E. Alpman, V. Ahuja, and L. Long 1870

AIAA-2002-2589   Acoustic Insertion Loss Measurement of HQ-Tube Liner
H. Kwan, R. Burdisso, S. Chiou, E. Chien, J. Yu, and S. Byrne.......1881

AIAA-2002-2590   The Absorption of Sound by Helmholtz Resonators with and
without Flow
I. Dupere and A. Dowling 1890

AIAA-2002-2591   Environmental Monitoring via Infrasound
M. Gilinsky and J. Hardin 1901

AIAA-2002-2593   Application and Verification of Broadband Time Domain
Impedance Boundary Conditions in Multi-Dimensional Acoustic
Problems
M. Zhuang and S. Zheng 1912

AIAA-2002-2594   Numerical Prediction of Minor Losses in High Amplitude
Acoustic Resonators
S. Boluriaan and P. Morris 1920

AIAA-2002-2596   General Aviation IC Engine Dimensionless Exhaust Noise
Spectrum
H. Patrick and H. Tada...1932

AIAA-2002-2598   Recent Progress Towards a Large Eddy Simulation Code for Jet
Aeroacoustics
A. Uzun, G. Blaisdell, and A. Lyrintzis...1943

AIAA-2002-2599   Comprehensive 3D Unsteady Simulations of Subsonic and
Supersonic Hot Jet Flow-Fields: Part 1: Aerodynamic Analysis
F. Vuillot, A. Biancherin, G. Rahier, and N. Lupoglazoff...................1955

AIAA-2002-2600   Comprehensive 3D Unsteady Simulations of Subsonic and
Supersonic Hot Jet Flow-Fields: Part 2: Acoustic Analysis
F. Vuillot, A. Biancherin, N. Lupoglazoff, and G. Rahier...................1966

AIAA-2002-2601   Low-Dimensional Description of an Underexpanded
Rectangular Jet
M. Alkislar, L. Lourenco, D. Moreno, and A. Krothapalli...................1977

AIAA-2002-2602   Simulation of Jet Noise with OVERFLOW CFD Code and
Kirchhoff Surface Integral
M. Kandula and R. Caimi 1986

AIAA-2002-2603   Jet Noise at Take-Off and Landing
C. Tam and N. Pastouchenko 2001

AIAA-2002-2604   Aeroacoustic Measurements of a Wing/Slat Model
J. Mendoza, T. Brooks, and W. Humphreys.....................................2009

AIAA-2002-2605   Influence of Small Steps on Wall Pressure Fluctuation Spectra
Measured on Tu-144LL Flying Laboratory
R. Rackl, B. Efimtsov, A. Golubev, S. Rizzi, A. Andersson,
and E. Andrianov...2027

AIAA-2002-2606   Absorbing Layers and Radiation Boundary Conditions for Jet
Flow Simulations
T. Hagstrom and I. Nazarov 2036

AIAA 2002-2530

A NUMERICAL STUDY OF SHOCK-ASSOCIATED NOISE

Calvin Lui [*] and Sanjiva K. Lele [†]
Department of Mechanical Engineering
Stanford University, Stanford, California 94305

June 18, 2002

Abstract

The interaction between a spatially developing, turbulent shear layer ($M_c = 0.6$) and an isolated oblique compression wave ($\Delta P / P_1 = 0.2$) was studied by direct numerical simulation. Effects of rapid compression on the shear-layer turbulence were investigated in detail to explore the generation mechanism of shock-associated noise. It was found that both the Reynolds streamwise $(\overline{u'_x u'_x})$ and transverse $(\overline{u'_y u'_y})$ normal stresses are enhanced across a localized region within the incident compression wave which is bounded by the mean sonic line and the boundary of the shear layer on the supersonic side while the dominant Reynolds shear stress $(\overline{u'_x u'_y})$ is inhibited in the same region. However, these Reynolds stress components recover back to their respective pre-compression levels immediately after the compression suggesting the changes in the Reynolds stresses are primarily due to the unsteady motion of the compression wave over a localized region. Spectral analyses reveal that the enhancement in the streamwise velocity fluctuation across the compression wave occurs over a frequency range which is slightly higher than the observed spectral peak of the shock-associated noise. Overall results suggest that the source of shock-associated noise is located in the the compressive region of the shock-cell structure where the shear-layer turbulence is not negligible. Due to the minimal motion associated with the compression wave, the source region is localized in nature while its spatial extent depends on the width of the supersonic portion in the turbulent shear layer.

[*]Graduate research assistant, e-mail: luical@stanford.edu
[†]Associate professor, e-mail: lele@stanford.edu

1 Introduction

In addition to the turbulent mixing noise, supersonic jets emit additional noise components under imperfectly expanded conditions [17]. They are generated by the interaction between the jet turbulence and the shock-cell structure contained in the supersonic portion of the jet. Hence, they are termed shock-associated noise components. As the turbulence-associated hydrodynamic and thermodynamic fluctuations pass through and interact with the quasi-periodic pattern of compression and expansion in the shock-cell structure, additional dilatational and rotational disturbances are generated. While the rotational disturbances are convective in nature, the dilatational disturbances can be radiating. The radiating portion of the dilatational disturbances is perceived as shock-associated noise in the far field.

In general, shock-associated noise consists of a discrete, high-amplitude screech tone and a broad-band component. The fundamental difference between screech and broad-band shock noise, as far as generation mechanism is concerned, is that screech is produced by a self-sustained feedback mechanism in the jet [11] while the broad-band component is generated by the weak interaction between the downstream propagating jet turbulence and the quasi-periodic shock-cell structure [18]. The present investigation is focused on the broad-band component.

The leading effort in understanding the broad-band shock noise dates back to the seminal experimental and modeling work by Harper-Bourne & Fisher [3]. They recognized the importance of the quasi-periodicity of the shock-cell structure and extended the idea by Powell [11] to model the acoustic source as individual point sources placed at the tip of each shock-expansion unit. The spatial coherence of the disturbance field was incorporated as a key element into their model to account for the radiation pattern observed in the far field. The phases of the adjacent point sources are assumed to be correlated by the convective time delay from one point source to another. Due to the difference in the propagation path length and the difference in the time origin of acoustic emission, the sound generated from adjacent point sources can be in phase (constructive interference) or out of phase (destructive interference) when they reach the observer, depending on the observer's location and the frequency of sound. This simple and yet important concept becomes a crucial aspect in the modeling of broad-band shock noise.

Later, Tam [17] formulated in detail the dynamical problem of the non-linear interaction between the jet turbulence (regarded as a superposition of instability waves) and the time-independent shock-cell modes (obtained by multiple-scales expansion) as the source of broad-band shock noise. Due to the vast computational demands, its solution was not pursued ultimately. Instead a model of the near-field pressure fluctuation was proposed based on physical arguments. While his stochastic model and its subsequent refinement are successful in capturing many important aspects of the noise spectra and its directivity pattern, the semi-empiricism of the model makes it less trivial to be applied to general configuration where co-flowing streams are present.

Beside the major modeling contributions from Harper-Bourne & Fisher, and Tam, the experimental works by Tanna [19], Tam & Tanna [18], Seiner & Norum [12] [13] and Seiner & Yu [14] contribute greatly to our fundamental knowledge of shock noise, including the shift of dominant frequency with angular position, the scaling of shock noise intensity and the dominant source location. However, little numerical work has been done to investigate the shock-turbulence interaction problem from the acoustic point of view. This research was initiated to pursue fundamental understanding of the sound generation mechanism from first-principle numerical simulation.

As a first step to understand the intricate sound generation mechanism of the shock-turbulence interaction, a model problem was formulated which contains the two most essential elements pertinent to shock noise generation, namely the shear-layer turbulence and the rapid compression. Figure 1 depicts this model problem in a succinct manner. In this idealized problem, the shock cell is modeled as a two-dimensional compression wave with finite thickness. This simplification is well justified by the experimental observation that the dominant source of broad-band shock noise is located close to the end of the jet potential core where the pressure gradients are found to be relatively smooth. In view of this,

the terms "shock" and "compression" will be used interchangeably throughout this paper.

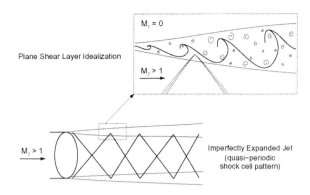

Figure 1: Flow in an imperfectly expanded jet

In our earlier work [8], analyses were performed on three different elements of the shock-turbulence interaction problem: the oblique compression-expansion wave, the acoustic field and the shear-layer turbulence. Major results include minimal shock oscillation during the interaction and the omni-directionality of the shock noise component. This work is a continuation of our on-going effort on this problem. The objective of this paper is to investigate the mutual effects of the shock-turbulence interaction so that insights into the shock noise generation mechanism can be gained. Major aspects of this interaction include

- effects of compression on the mean flow

- effects of compression on the turbulence

- effects of turbulence on the compression-expansion wave

Our goal is to incorporate some of our findings from this study in a physics-based noise source model which can hopefully be applied to a wider range of problems in industrial applications. Hence, this work can be viewed as a part of an integrated effort in modeling shock noise.

2   Methodology

The near-field shock-turbulence interaction and its acoustic field are studied by a direct numerical simulation (DNS) approach. The fully three-dimensional, time-dependent, compressible Navier-Stokes equations are solved in its conservative form. All physical length and time scales are resolved without any turbulence model. The governing equations are non-dimensionalized using the inflow vorticity thickness

(δ_ω^0) as the length scale, the speed of sound (a_1) and the density (ρ_1) on the quiescent stream as the velocity scale and reference density, respectively.

Full description of the numerical method is documented by Lui & Lele [7]. It is briefly described here as a summary. High band-width spatial discretization and time advancement schemes are employed to capture the relevant physics with the highest efficiency. An optimized, compact sixth order finite difference scheme with spectral-like accuracy [6] is used in the inhomogeneous streamwise and transverse directions while a Fourier spectral scheme is used in the homogeneous spanwise direction to discretize the flow field. A fourth order low-dissipation-dispersion Runge-Kutta scheme ([4], [15]) is used to advance the solution in time. This combined numerical method gives very low dissipative and dispersive errors, which is crucial in obtaining reliable numerical solutions for both the turbulence dynamics and the acoustic propagation.

In the numerical boundary treatment, a combination of Thompson's non-reflecting boundary conditions [20] and damping sponge is used to absorb the outgoing acoustic radiation in the free-stream on the quiescent side and to impose the compression wave on the supersonic side. The compression wave is positioned at approximately 70 δ_ω^0 downstream of the inflow boundary with a 20 % pressure rise across it. The location of the interaction site is strategically chosen such that the shear layer can develop into a fully turbulent state before the interaction and a large portion of the sound field can be captured in the primarily upstream direction (a region where shock noise is expected to play a dominant role). The damping sponge treatment is also used at the inflow boundary zone to introduce inflow turbulence seeding through the time-dependent reference state. In the present study, a total of 40 pairs of oblique eigen-modes, obtained from linear stability theory, with equal amplitude and random phases are introduced at the inflow to perturb the shear layer. The forcing frequency, $f\delta_\omega^0/a_1$, of the 40 eigen-mode ranges from 0.04 to 0.11. In the outflow zone, a combination of grid stretching and numerical filtering [2] is used to attenuate the vortical flow structures before they exit the outflow boundary. Due to the mixed subsonic-supersonic flow condition, an artificial convective term [10] is added to the Navier-Stokes equations in the outflow boundary zone, which ensures all characteristics to be outgoing. For clarity, a schematic which summarizes the overall boundary treatment is included in Figure 2.

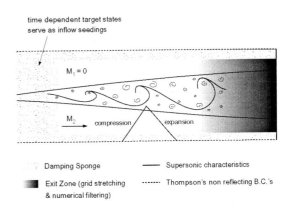

Figure 2: Overview of boundary treatment

3   Results

In the present study, the supersonic stream on the lower side of the shear layer is at Mach 1.2 while the stream on the upper side is quiescent. The flow Reynolds number is 500, based on the velocity difference between the two streams and the inflow vorticity thickness, δ_ω^0. The temperature ratio between the two streams is unity, the gas specific heat ratio is 1.4, Prandtl number and Schmidt number are taken to be 0.7 and 1.0 respectively. The boundaries of both the computational and the physical domains are summarized in Table 1 for reference. A structured computation mesh of size $704 \times 320 \times \times 48$ is used to resolve the flow.

Direction	Computational	Physical
Streamwise	[0, 130]	[20, 90]
Transverse	[-15, 50]	[-10, 45]
Spanwise	[-5, 0]	[-5, 0]

Table 1: Boundary location of computational and physical domains (in terms of δ_ω^0)

Turbulence statistics were collected after the inflow disturbances convect through the domain four times. This provides enough time for the initial transients to settle down and a stationary turbulent flow to develop. A total of 16800 instantaneous flow field samples were gathered over a period of 350 convection time units and then averaged to give the statistical results. They span approximately four flow-through times of the physical domain and 14 periods of the lowest forcing frequency mode in the turbulence seeding.

3.1 Visualization

Figure 3 below is an instantaneous composite visualization showing three distinct elements of this interaction problem: the spatially developing, turbulent shear layer in colored contours, the oblique compression-expansion wave in colored map and the associated dilatation field in grey scale map. Over the upstream transition region, the large turbulent scales break down and generate a distinct set of downstream propagating acoustic waves which originates from around $x = 30\,\delta_\omega^0$. The intensity of this set of acoustic waves is much stronger than the shock noise component originated downstream. This phenomenon illustrates one necessary complexity in any shock noise study: the presence of mixing noise in the background. It inevitably makes the postprocessing of the acoustic data much more difficult.

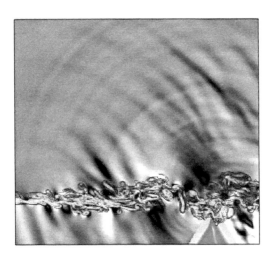

Figure 3: Visualization of shock-noise generation and the associated acoustic field.

Regardless of the strong mixing noise component, the shock-associated noise is very distinguishable in the visualization. It appears as a set of circular waves originated from the interaction site at $x = 70\,\delta_\omega^0$ and it radiates in an omni-directional manner. Upon careful examination of a sequence of visualization frames, the "apparent" source region of the shock noise was found to be slightly downstream of the mean tip position of the compression-expansion wave extending from $x = 70\,\delta_\omega^0$ to $x = 76\,\delta_\omega^0$. An explanation of this streamwise displacement will be given Section 4.

3.2 Effects of Compression on Mean Flow

3.2.1 Mean Pressure

Figure 4 shows the contour plot of the mean pressure, with the mean sonic line plotted in black solid line. The mean sonic line first develops towards the supersonic side before the compression-expansion reflection and then deflects upwards by the interaction. This deflection is caused by the successive acceleration of the transverse velocity component across both the compression and expansion. The dip in the sonic line near the shock cell is caused by the rapid deceleration of the streamwise velocity at the compression and the relatively gradual acceleration at the expansion fan. It should be mentioned that the dip of the mean sonic line occurs at the same position of the compression-expansion reflection of the mean pressure field. Hence, the region upstream of the dip is compressive while the region downstream is expansive in the mean sense. This observation will be very useful in interpreting the later results.

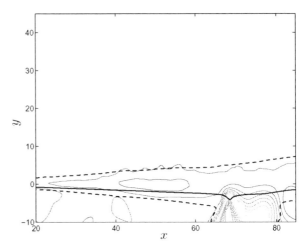

Figure 4: Contour plot of mean normalized pressure field ($\overline{P}/P_1$) with maximum value at 1.26 (red) and minimum at 1.00 (blue). The mean sonic line is plotted in black solid line while the lower and upper 2 % mean streamwise velocity lines are in black dashed lines.

For ease of reference, the lower and upper 2 % of the mean streamwise velocity contours are also plotted in black dashed lines in Figure 4 to outline the boundaries of the turbulent shear layer. The linear growth rate of the shear layer thickness (a requirement for self-similarity) is evident from the straight line pattern of the two boundaries. On the quiescent side, there is a mild change in the slope of the upper shear layer boundary slightly before the tip of the compression-expansion reflection. The deflection is "sensed" on the subsonic side even before the interaction due to flow communication in the upstream direction.

There is a mild pressure reflection off the lower boundary of the computational domain. It is caused by the inadequacy of the non-reflection boundary conditions at the lower boundary and could have been minimized by choosing a stronger damping sponge in the simulation.

3.2.2 Mean Streamwise Velocity

Contour plot of the mean streamwise velocity is shown in Figure 5. The feature of mean flow deflection at the interaction is much easier to observe.

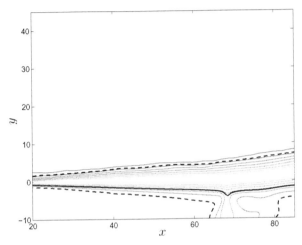

Figure 5: Contour plot of mean streamwise velocity field.

Due to the low supersonic Mach number of the lower stream, the spatial region between the mean sonic line and the mean shear layer boundary is very small in the present study. This is the region where appreciable turbulence and shock-cell structure coexist. Hence, it is expected to be the dominant region of shock-turbulence interaction. The larger this region is, the more intense the shock noise can be. However, due to the limited volume of interaction in this study, the intensity of the associated shock noise is expected to be low accordingly.

3.2.3 Mean Streamline

In our investigation on the effects of compression on turbulence, it is appropriate to observe the evolution along the mean streamlines. They give the direction of fluid parcels as they pass through the compression-expansion wave and define the fluid motion in the mean sense. Based on the mean stream-

wise ($\overline{U}_x$) and transverse ($\overline{U}_y$) velocities, the trajectory of thirteen equally spaced streamlines are plotted in Figure 6. They are traced from the common starting streamwise location at $x = 50\,\delta_\omega^0$. The trajectories are basically horizontal for the most part before the interaction and gradually deflected upward in the compression-expansion wave.

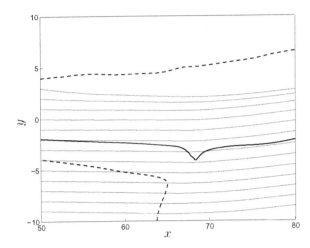

Figure 6: Mean streamline trajectory

As a summary, the major effect of compression on the mean flow is the injection of positive transverse velocity into the shear layer which causes an upward deflection in the flow direction after the interaction.

3.3 Effects of Compression on Turbulence

Due to the strong gradients of both thermodynamic properties and velocity components associated with the compression, the effects of compression on the thermodynamic and hydrodynamic fluctuations of turbulence will be investigated separately in this section.

3.3.1 Thermodynamic Fluctuations

The effects of compression on the thermodynamic fluctuations display very similar characteristics: a spatially compact region of intense fluctuation is located in the compressive region bounded by the mean sonic line and the shear layer boundary on the supersonic side. Its spatial extent and location is clearly shown in Figure 7 which is a magnified view of the interaction location. Pressure and density variances are chosen because they have the highest levels of fluctuation while the distribution of temperature variance displays very similar behavior.

The existence and location of such a localized region of intense fluctuation can be understood by

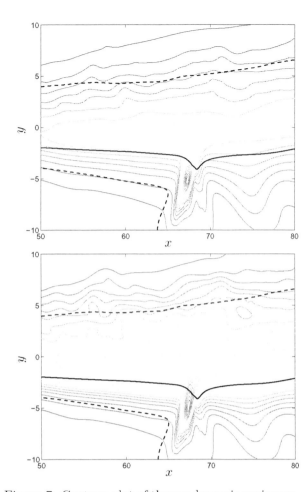

Figure 7: Contour plot of thermodynamic variances. Top: pressure $(\overline{P'P'}/P_1^2)$ with maximum value at 0.0153 (red); bottom: density $(\overline{\rho'\rho'}/\rho_1^2)$ with maximum value at 0.0076 (red).

recalling the steep positive gradient of thermodynamic properties (pressure, density and temperature) across the compression. Any small amount of shock motion can lead to a large fluctuation to the local thermodynamic properties. However, the spatial compactness of the intense region has two immediate implications. Firstly, the quick recovery back to the pre-compression values downstream of the compression indicates that the fluctuations were not generated and then convected, but caused by the unsteady shock oscillations. Secondly, it can be concluded that the shock motion is minimal which is consistent with an observation made in our previous study [8]. Instead of the large-amplitude flapping motion of the shock commonly observed in jet screech [9], this type of shock motion is best represented by the small-amplitude motion associated with the shock tip. Nevertheless, this highly localized compressive region naturally becomes the re-

gion of special interests in investigating the effects on hydrodynamic fluctuations.

3.3.2 Hydrodynamic Fluctuations

Different velocity component interacts with the compression wave in a different manner. For example, the velocity component parallel to the shock front is expected to be unchanged while the one normal to it will be abruptly altered by the interaction. Hence, the effects of compression on the Reynolds stress components do not all display similar behavior. The contour plots of the streamwise normal stress and dominant shear stress are shown in Figure 8 which displays an enhancement in the former component and an inhibition in the latter one.

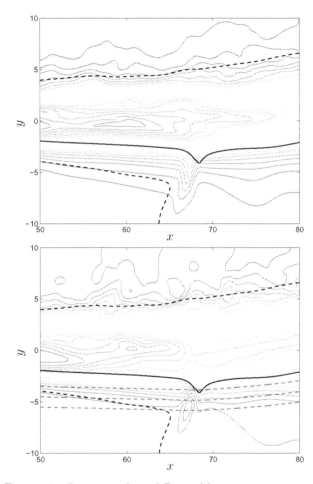

Figure 8: Contour plot of Reynolds stress components. Top: streamwise normal stress $(\overline{u'u'}/(\Delta U)^2)$ with maximum value at 0.0269 (red); bottom: dominant shear stress $(\overline{u'v'}/(\Delta U)^2)$ with maximum value at 0.0091 (red).

However, the features in the hydrodynamic fluctuations are not as distinct as those observed in the thermodynamic fluctuations. The reason for the difference can be explained as follows. Firstly, the flow is an isothermal shear layer. The variation in mean thermodynamic properties is essentially negligible in the flow. Hence, the compressive region is the sole location with appreciable gradients. Secondly, the shock-turbulence interaction occurs in a limited region on the supersonic side of the shear layer. As pointed out previously, this region is very small in the present study due to the low supersonic Mach number of the flow. Moreover, this region resides in the "off peak" portion of the shear-layer turbulence, with the bulk of the Reynolds stress located on the subsonic side of the shear layer. This is apparent from the relative contour magnitude in Figure 8. Even in the presence of the shock, the resulting fluctuation level is still low compared with the peak turbulence level in the center of the shear layer. However, one may imagine the situation to be significantly different if the flow speed is high enough that a substantial portion of the Reynolds stress lies between the sonic line and the supersonic boundary of the shear layer. As shown in Figure 8, the streamwise normal stress ($\overline{u'_x u'_x}$) is enhanced by the interaction (similar behavior is observed in the transverse normal stress ($\overline{u'_y u'_y}$)) while the shear stress ($\overline{u'_x u'_y}$) is inhibited.

To observe the evolution of these Reynolds stress components more closely, one needs to follow the mean streamline coordinate mentioned in the previous sub-section. An example of such streamline traces is shown as three evenly spaced red dashed lines on the $\overline{u'_x u'_y}$ contour plot of Figure 8. As we follow these mean streamlines and pass through the compression, the evolution of the various Reynolds stress components are obtained. Figure 9 shows the evolution of the normal stresses while Figure 10 displays that of the dominant shear stress. The streamline variable, s, in both figures is computed by integrating along the streamlines from the starting location at $x = 64\delta_\omega^0$ and $y = y^*$, where $y^* = -4\delta_\omega^0, -5\delta_\omega^0, -6\delta_\omega^0$ for the three streamlines shown starting from the top one.

The enhancement in the streamwise and transverse normal stresses and inhibition in the shear stress are clearly shown in Figure 9. The degree of enhancement differ between the two normal components with a higher level in the streamwise component. This observation can be understood by recalling that the compression wave is at an oblique angle of roughly 60 degrees to the horizontal at this flow Mach number. This implies the transverse component is more aligned with the mean shock front than the streamwise component. Hence, that results in

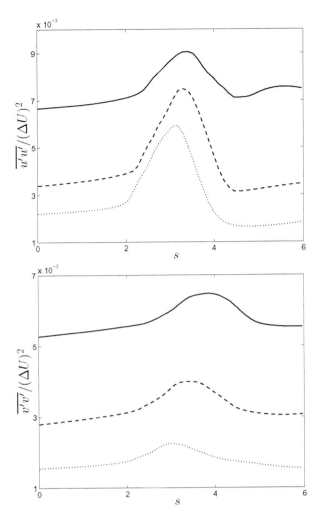

Figure 9: Streamwise variation of Reynolds normal stress components.

a lower level of enhancement. Upon close examination of the changes in the Reynolds stress components across the compression, a slight overshoot is observed on the downstream side of the compression before returning to the pre-compression values. Similar behavior was also observed in the interaction of isotropic turbulence with shock waves by Lee et al. [5].

3.3.3 Spectral Evolution Across the Compression

Recall that sound is generated when the turbulent structures are changed as they convect. The observed changes in the Reynolds stress components over the compressive region suggest a mechanism for the generation of shock-associated noise. For any claim to be made about a sound generation mechanism, it is crucial to check the change in the

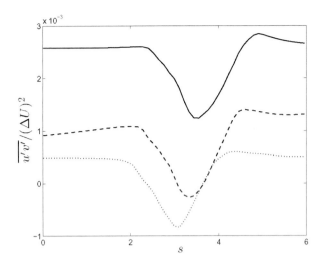

Figure 10: Streamwise variation of dominant Reynolds shear stress component.

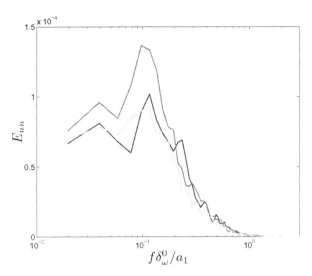

Figure 11: Evolution of streamwise velocity energy spectrum across the compression. Before compression (blue); at compression (red); after compression (green).

spectral content of the velocity fluctuation from the pre-compression to the post-compression conditions. "Over what frequency range does the enhancement in velocity fluctuation occur?", "Does the frequency range correlate in any way to the frequency peak of the observed acoustic field?" are two fundamental questions one needs to answer. It is our goal in this sub-section to address these questions.

During the course of the simulation, probe measurements were recorded at every time step at some pre-determined locations around the interaction location and the acoustic field. The posterior identification of the potential source region helps to select the relevant probes of interest. For this purpose, three different probes were chosen for the spectral analyses. They are located at

1. before compression: $x = 62\,\delta_\omega^0, y = -3\,\delta_\omega^0$

2. within compression: $x = 67\,\delta_\omega^0, y = -3\,\delta_\omega^0$

3. after compression: $x = 71\,\delta_\omega^0, y = -3\,\delta_\omega^0$

The evolution of the streamwise velocity fluctuation as the turbulence convects across the compression is shown in Figure 11.

The enhancement of the energy spectrum within the compression is observed to be over the non-dimensional frequency range (based on acoustic speed and inflow vorticity thickness) centered at $f = 0.1$. With the post-compression spectrum returns back to the pre-compression level, the effects of compression on the turbulence spectral content is unambiguously displayed. No definitive enhancement was observed in the energy spectrum of the transverse velocity fluctuation. Hence, the change

in the spectrum of streamwise velocity fluctuation is the most significant observation in the spectral analyses. However, it should be noted that as the supersonic Mach number increases, the compression wave will becomes increasingly oblique and the effect of a higher level of transverse velocity fluctuation will be expected.

3.3.4 Correlation Between Near-Field and Acoustic-Field Spectra

A direct comparison with the spectrum of shock noise is necessary to determine if the frequency range associated with the spectral enhancement of the streamwise velocity is related to the generation of shock noise. In the present study, this task is not as simple as it may seem. As shown in the visualization of Figure 3, the acoustic field contains a strong component of turbulent mixing noise radiating in the downstream direction, in addition to the shock noise component of interest. Currently, our best strategy in obtaining a reliable measurement of the shock noise component is by extracting information from the most upstream probe in the acoustic field. This probe is taken to be located at a radial distance of $50\,\delta_\omega^0$ and an inlet angle (ϕ) of 40 degrees from the "intended" interaction location at $x = 70\,\delta_\omega^0$ and $y = 0\,\delta_\omega^0$. The pressure signal at this probe location shows a systematic drift with respect to time and is shown in Figure 12.

This observation is attributed to the artifact of the numerical boundary treatment used in the com-

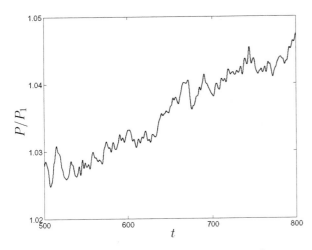

Figure 12: Systematic drift of pressure in the upstream acoustic field field. Probe is located at $r = 50, \phi = 40$ degs, $z = 0$.

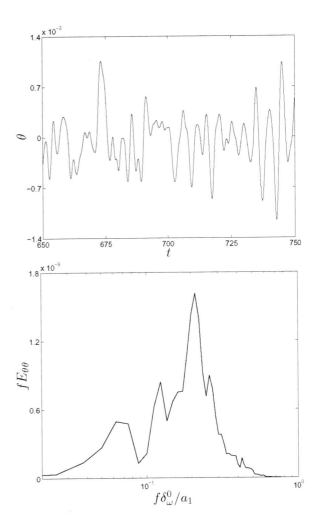

Figure 13: Dilatation measurement at upstream location ($r = 50, \phi = 40$ degs, $z = 0$). Top: time history; bottom: energy spectrum

putation.

Despite the linear trend observed in the pressure measurements, the dilatation record appears to be statistically stationary and direct Fourier transform can be performed to estimate its spectrum. The time history of dilatation at the same probe location is shown in Figure 13 along with its spectrum to demonstrate this point. The frequency peak of the shock noise component in dilatation is centered around a non-dimensional frequency of 0.2, which is slightly higher than the spectral peak observed in streamwise velocity fluctuation.

However, it should be emphasized that dilatation is directly related to the time rate of change of pressure in the acoustic field through

$$\theta = -\frac{\partial P}{\partial t}$$

in non-dimensional form and their spectra are related through the second power of the angular frequency factor:

$$\left|\hat{\theta}\right|^2 = \omega^2 \left|\hat{P}\right|^2 \tag{1}$$

In an attempt to recover the true pressure spectrum of the shock noise component, two different methods were used and their results will be compared in this section. The first method is to "derive" the pressure spectrum by directly processing the dilatation spectrum according to Equation 1. Results of this "derived" pressure spectrum (E_{PdPd}) is shown in Figure 14. Due to the division by a quadratic frequency factor, it is inevitable to magnify any uncertainty inherent in the estimation of the spectrum in the low frequency end. Despite this reservation, the "derived" pressure spectrum has a spectral peak around a non-dimensional frequency of 0.06 which is lower than the enhancement peak observed in the streamwise velocity fluctuation.

The second method is to perform a linear regression on the pressure measurement and then subtract out the linear trend to obtain the "filtered" pressure fluctuation. The time history of the "filtered" pressure fluctuation is plotted in Figure 15 while its spectrum (E_{PfPf}) is plotted in Figure 16 along with the spectrum of the "derived" pressure for a direct comparison between the two methods. Results from these two methods agree very well with each other and consistently give a spectral peak around a non-dimensional frequency of 0.06.

As a summary, the major effect of compression on the turbulence is observed in a spatially compact re-

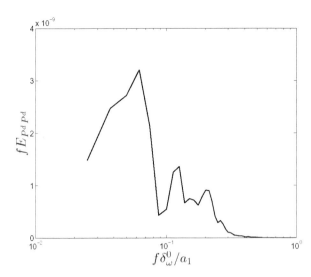

Figure 14: Spectrum of "derived" pressure at upstream location ($r = 50\,\delta_\omega^0, \phi = 40$ degs).

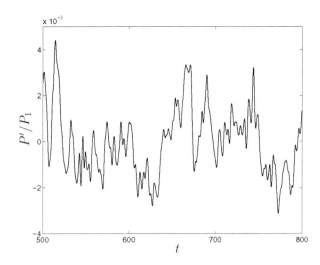

Figure 15: Pressure fluctuation obtained by subtracting the linear trend from the measurement. Probe is located at $r = 50, \phi = 40$ degs, $z = 0$.

gion on the compressive side of the shock cell which is upper bounded by the mean sonic line and lower bounded by the shear layer boundary on the supersonic side. Over this compact region, all thermodynamic variances, streamwise and transverse normal stresses are enhanced while the Reynolds shear stress is inhibited. The increase in streamwise normal stress is observed to occur over a frequency range which is slightly higher than the observed pressure spectral peak of shock noise. Further work on the shock noise pressure spectrum is necessary before a definitive statement can be drawn on the relationship between the streamwise velocity enhancement and the generation mechanism of shock-associated noise.

3.4 Effects of Turbulence on Compression

While the interaction between the shear-layer turbulence and the compression wave is mutual, it would be informative to examine the effects of turbulence on the compression wave. In this regard, a separate two-dimensional simulation was performed to obtain the laminar shock solution at the same flow conditions in the absence of any inflow disturbance. However, it should be emphasized that a direct comparison between the mean turbulent field and the two-dimensional laminar solution deserves great caution. The mean turbulent statistics are averaged over time and the homogeneous spanwise direction and represent the mean turbulent state whereas the laminar shock solution is the steady state solution to the Navier-Stokes equation. Hence, a direct comparison

between the two entities may be misleading. Nevertheless, a qualitative comparison between the two may shed insight into the potential issue on the prediction of mean shock-cell structure in a turbulent flow. For this reason, the pressure field is chosen for a qualitative comparison in Figure 17.

Besides the difference in the width of the compression-expansion wave which is mainly caused by the smearing effect of the averaging process, the most significant differences occur at the location of the sonic line and the compression-expansion reflection site. In the laminar case the compression wave penetrates much deeper into the shear layer due to the lack of mixing and dissipation mechanisms while the turbulent mean field gives a significantly different reflection site: one that is located more upstream and towards the supersonic side. This observation suggests that the turbulent viscosity used in any turbulence model will be a critical factor in predicting the location of the sonic line, hence, the correct compression-expansion reflection location. Furthermore, any misalignment in the preceding shock-cell prediction will directly influence the prediction of the shock cells downstream, *i.e.* the error in a shock-cell prediction is propagated or compounded in the streamwise direction. The experimental finding that the dominant source of shock-associated noise is located many shock cells from the nozzle exit imposes great challenges to the prediction. Choi & Lele [1] applied the parabolized stability equation (**PSE**) approach to predict the stationary shock-cell structure and found that the level of eddy-viscosity used in the **PSE** is the most important parameter in determining the decay rate of the shock-cell structure.

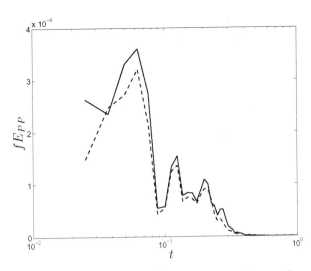

Figure 16: Comparison of pressure spectrum obtained by two different methods. Solid line: trend removal; dashed line: derived from dilatation measurement.

4   Discussions

The shock-turbulence interaction problem was studied by performing direct numerical simulation on a model problem formulated around the vicinity of the interaction location between a turbulent shear layer and an oblique compression wave. The goal of this research is to fundamentally understand the generation mechanism of shock-associated noise. Results presented in this paper suggest that the acoustic source of shock noise is located in the spatially compact, compressive region of the shock cell which is bounded by the sonic line and the shear layer boundary on the supersonic side. The size of this region depends primarily on the width of the supersonic portion of the turbulent shear layer. In the present study, a low supersonic stream of Mach 1.2 was chosen. Hence, this source region is very limited in size which explains the relatively low intensity of shock noise measured. Shock motion is minimal throughout the simulation and no large-scale flapping motion of the compression wave was observed. It implies that this source region will stay localized on the compressive side of the shock cell.

The suggestion of this *real* noise source location offers a good explanation to the *apparent* noise source location observed downstream of the compression-expansion tip in the flow visualization. The acoustic waves generated by the shock-turbulence interaction take time to travel from this source location on the supersonic side to the subsonic side before they radiate out of the shear layer. During this "escape" process, these acoustic waves are convected down-

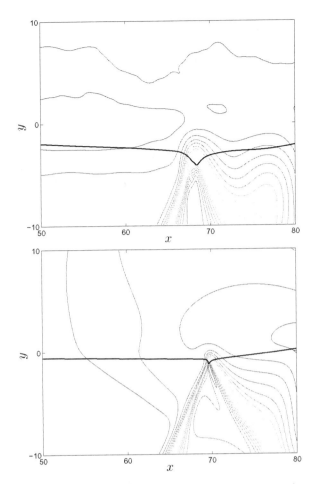

Figure 17: Comparison of pressure contour associated with the shock-cell structure. Top: turbulent mean field; bottom: laminar solution obtained without any inflow disturbance.

stream by an observable distance due to the high convection speed on the supersonic side.

Turbulence enhancement in the streamwise and transverse normal stresses were observed over the source region. The enhancement in the streamwise (largest) component occurs over a frequency range which is slightly higher than the observed spectral peak of the shock noise component. Further research will be pursued on this issue before a definitive conclusion can be reached. Moreover, causality correlation between the near-field acoustic source and the acoustic field is planned in the immediate future.

Acknowledgments

This research is sponsored by the Boeing Company under Contract B283357. Computational resources are generously granted by the U.S. Army Engineer Research and Development Center-Major

Shared Resource Center (ERDC MSRC) and the Army Research Laboratory-Major Shared Resource Center (ARL MSRC) under the Department of Defense.

References

[1] Choi, M.R. and Lele, S.K. "Prediction of Shock-Cell Structure Using Parabolized Stability Equations", *AIAA Paper 2001-0744*, 2001.

[2] Colonius, T., Lele, S.K. and Moin, P. "Boundary Conditions for Direct Computation of Aerodynamic Sound", *AIAA Journal* **31**, No. 9, 1574-1582, 1993.

[3] Harper-Bourne, M. and Fisher, M.J. "The Noise from Shock Waves in Supersonic Jets", *Proceedings No. 131 of the AGARD Conference on Noise Mechanisms, Brussels, Belgium*, 1973.

[4] Hu, F.Q., Hussaini, M.Y. and Manthey, M. "Low-Dissipation and -Dispersion Runge-Kutta Schemes for Computational Acoustics", *Journal of Computational Physics* **124**, 177-191, 1996.

[5] Lee, S.S., Lele, S.K. and Moin, P. "Interaction of Isotropic Turbulence with Shock Waves: Effect of Shock Strength", *Journal of Fluid Mechanics* **304**, 225-247, 1997.

[6] Lele, S.K. "Compact Finite Difference Schemes with Spectral-Like Resolution", *Journal of Computational Physics* **103**, 16-42, 1992.

[7] Lui, C., and Lele, S.K. "Direct Numerical Simulation of Spatially Developing, Compressible, Turbulent Mixing Layers", *AIAA Paper 2001-0291*, 2001.

[8] Lui, C., and Lele, S.K. "A Numerical Investigation of Broad-Band Shock Noise", *AIAA Paper 2002-0074*, 2002.

[9] Manning, T.A. and Lele, S.K. "A Numerical Investigation of Sound Generation in Supersonic Jet Screech", *AIAA Paper 2000-2081*, 2000.

[10] Ta'asan, S. and Nark, D.M. "An Absorbing Buffer Zone Technique of Acoustic Wave Propagation". *AIAA Paper 95-0164*, 1995.

[11] Powell, A. "On the Mechanism of Choked Jet Noise". *Proceedings of the Physical Society of London B.* **66**, 1039-1056, 1953.

[12] Seiner, J.M. and Norum, T.D. "Experiments on Shock Associated Noise of Supersonic Jets". *AIAA Paper 1979-1526*, 1979.

[13] Seiner, J.M. and Norum, T.D. "Aerodynamic Aspects of Shock Containing Jet Plumes". *AIAA Paper 1980-0965*, 1980.

[14] Seiner, J.M. and Yu, J.C. "Acoustic Near-field Properties Associated with Broadband Shock Noise" *AIAA Journal* **22**, 1207-15, 1984.

[15] Stanescu, D. and Habashi, W.G. "2N-Storage Low Dissipation and Dispersion Runge-Kutta Schemes for Computational Acoustics", *Journal of Computational Physics* **143**, 674-681, 1998.

[16] Tam, C.K.W. "Supersonic Jet Noise", *Annual Review of Fluid Mechanics.* **27**, 17-43, 1995.

[17] Tam, C.K.W. "Stochastic Model Theory of Broadband Shock Associated Noise from Supersonic Jets", *Journal of Sound and Vibration* **116**(2), 265-302, 1987.

[18] Tam, C.K.W. and Tanna, H.K. "Shock Associated Noise of Supersonic Jets from Convergent-Divergent Nozzles", *Journal of Sound and Vibration* **81**(3), 337-358, 1982.

[19] Tanna, H.K. "An Experimental Study of Jet Noise Part II: Shock Associated Noise", *Journal of Sound and Vibration* **50**(3), 429-444, 1977.

[20] Thompson, K.W. "Time Dependent Boundary Conditions for Hyperbolic Systems", *Journal of Computational Physics* **68**, 1-24, 1987.

Numerical simulation of unsteady cavity flow using Lattice Boltzmann Method

Denis Ricot[*], Virginie Maillard[†] and Christophe Bailly[‡]

*, †   Direction de la Recherche, Renault S.A.

TCR RUC 4 05, 1 avenue du golf

78288 Guyancourt cedex, France.

‡   Laboratoire de Mécanique des Fluides et d'Acoustique

Ecole Centrale de Lyon & UMR CNRS 5509

BP 163, 69131 Ecully cedex, France.

Abstract

A lattice Bolzmann code based on the two-dimensional nine-velocity model has been developed for computational aeroacoustic studies. The connection between the continuous and lattice Boltzmann equations is completely described for this model. A discrete-velocity Boltzmann equation is first derived and is integrated along a characteristic. The fully explicit equations of the LBM are recovered by introducing equivalent distribution functions. Using the discrete velocity Boltzmann equation, a free field boundary is proposed to minimize the reflection of vortical and acoustic perturbations on the limit of the calculation domain. The numerical stability problem for under-resolved sheared flow is overcome by adding a selective viscosity filter that damps the spurious high frequency numerical oscillations. The first validation cases are the pulse propagation in a uniform flow and a cavity excited by a laminar grazing flow. The results show that the LBM could be used for aeroacoustic computations of low subsonic flows.

1. Introduction

The lattice Boltzmann method (LBM) is an innovative numerical method based on kinetic theory to simulate various hydrodynamic systems. The scheme is particularly successful in fluid applications[10] involving interfacial dynamics, multiphase, multicomponent flows and particle suspension which are usually difficult problems for traditional numerical schemes. But in its simplest form, the lattice Boltzmann method simulates the time-dependent motion of a perfect gas at low Mach number that is governed by the compressible Navier-Stokes equations. Then, LBM is a reasonable candidate for simulation of turbulence, flow-induced noise and sound propagation. For example, the response of a two-dimensional Helmholtz cavity under grazing flow has been investigated[32] with the commercial code PowerFLOW based on the LBM. The acoustic coupling between the vortex shedding and the cavity resonance has been predicted by the solver. This preliminary result encouraged the authors to study in more details this numerical method in the framework of computational aeroacoustics.

The development of the lattice Boltzmann equation (LBE) was independent of the continuous Boltzmann equation. It was introduced[9,29] to solve some of the difficulties of the Lattice Gas Automata (LGA).[16] A parameter matching procedure (see appendix of reference [23]) based on the Chapman-Enskog analysis of the LGA allowed to construct a set of relaxation equations so that the correct hydrodynamic equations are derived. But recently, the connection between the LBE models and the continuous Boltzmann equation has been explicitly shown.[1,21] This new approach is presented in the second part of this paper. The boundary conditions for aeroacoustic simulations are investigated in the third part. The stability problem of LBM for low viscosity is discussed in part 4. Then, the aeroacoustic test case of a pulse in a uniform flow is studied in part 5. In part 6, the self-sustained oscillation of a laminar flow over rectangular cavities is calculated.

2. Theory of the Lattice Boltzmann Method

2.1 The continuous Boltzmann equation

In kinetic theory,[24] a monoatomic gas is represented as a cloud of like point particles and is fully described by its continuous distribution function $f_m(\mathbf{x}, \mathbf{c}, t)$, which represents the number of particles whose positions and velocities are $\mathbf{x}$ and $\mathbf{c}$ at time t. Then one can define the density distribution function $f(\mathbf{x}, \mathbf{c}, t) = m f_m(\mathbf{x}, \mathbf{c}, t)$, with m the molecular mass of the gas. It is a mesoscopic description of the fluid, intermediate between the microscopic and macroscopic ones. For a dilute (or rarefied) gas where only binary collisions between particles occur,

---

*PhD student

†Research Engineer, Renault S.A.

‡Assistant Professor, Member AIAA

the evolution of the distribution function is governed by the Boltzmann equation[6] :

$$\frac{\partial f}{\partial t} + c_i \frac{\partial f}{\partial x_i} = \Omega(f) \tag{1}$$

where $\Omega(f)$ is a bilinear collision operator which determines physics of the flow. The fluid density ρ, velocity $\mathbf{u}$ and internal energy e are defined via moments of the distribution function :

$$\rho = \int f d\mathbf{c} \tag{2}$$

$$\rho\mathbf{u} = \int \mathbf{c} f d\mathbf{c} \tag{3}$$

$$\rho e + \frac{1}{2}\rho|\mathbf{u}|^2 = \frac{1}{2}\int |\mathbf{c}|^2 f d\mathbf{c} \tag{4}$$

In case of elastic collisions, the mass, momentum and kinetic energy are conserved. For the collision operator $\Omega(f)$ to be mass, momentum and energy conservative, it is required that :

$$\int \Psi_p \Omega(f) d\mathbf{c} = 0 \tag{5}$$

for $\Psi_0 = 1, \Psi_1 = c_1, \Psi_2 = c_2, \Psi_3 = c_3, \Psi_4 = |\mathbf{c}|^2$, which are frequently called the elementary collision invariants. Hence, it is possible to derive all the continuous equations by multiplying the Boltzmann equation (1) by Ψ_p, $p = 0, ..., 4$ and integrating over all velocities. Using relations (2), (3) and (4), we obtain successively :

$$\frac{\partial \rho}{\partial t} + \frac{\partial \rho u_i}{\partial x_i} = 0$$

$$\frac{\partial \rho u_j}{\partial t} + \frac{\partial (\rho u_i u_j + P_{ij})}{\partial x_i} = 0 \tag{6}$$

$$\frac{\partial \left[\rho\left(\frac{1}{2}u^2 + e\right)\right]}{\partial t} + \frac{\partial \left[\rho u_i\left(\frac{1}{2}u^2 + e\right) + P_{ij}u_j + q_i\right]}{\partial x_i} = 0$$

where P_{ij} is the total stress tensor and $\mathbf{q}$ is the heat flux which expressions depend on $\mathbf{c}$ and f :

$$P_{ij} = \int (c_i - u_i)(c_j - u_j) f d\mathbf{c} \tag{7}$$

$$q_i = \frac{1}{2}\int (c_i - u_i)|\mathbf{c} - \mathbf{u}|^2 f d\mathbf{c} \tag{8}$$

It is worth noting that the derivation of these equations does not depend on the exact form of the collision operator. Of course, the above conservation equations are *not* the hydrodynamic equations : the stress tensor and heat flux cannot be a priori calculated only in term of ρ, $\mathbf{u}$ and e. The closure problem consists in finding such relations and it was tackled via the expansion methods of Chapman-Enskog[7] and Hilbert. Rigorous mathematical derivation of compressible Navier-Stokes equations with formal expressions of the transport coefficients (shear and bulk viscosities, heat conductivity) can be found in literature.[4,15,19] In this paper, an outline of the Chapman-Enskog (or Hilbert) expansion will be given within the framework of discrete-velocity Boltzmann equation with the nine-speed model and a simplified collision operator.

Boltzmann's equation can be use to derive the fundamental conservation laws but it also contains a natural notion of entropy and entropy production. This can be seen by considering the function $H(t) = \int f \ln f d\mathbf{c}$. The entropy of the system can be written as $S(t) = -k_B H(t) + \alpha$, where k_B is the Boltzmann's constant and α is also a constant. Differentiating H with respect to time and using Boltzmann's equation to replace the time derivative of f in the integral, it can be shown[7] that $\partial H/\partial t \leq 0$. This means that H can never increase, and consequently that the entropy can never decrease, and is known as Boltzmann's H-theorem. It can be also shown that H is bounded below. Then H decreases until f reaches an equilibrium state f^{eq} defined by $\partial H/\partial t = 0$. The solutions of this equation are the global (constant in both time and space) and local Maxwellian equilibrium functions. The local Maxwellian is :

$$f^{eq} = \rho\left(\frac{m}{2\pi k_B T}\right)^{D/2} \exp\left[\frac{-m|\mathbf{c} - \mathbf{u}|^2}{2k_B T}\right] \tag{9}$$

with T the fluid temperature and D the spatial dimension. We introduce the normalized temperature $\theta = rT$, with r the gas constant given by $r = k_B/m$.

The complicated analytical form of the particle collision term $\Omega(f)$ leads to tedious calculations for the closure problem. In fact, a large amount of the details of the two-body interaction is unlikely to influence significantly the values of macroscopic quantities. It is therefore assumed[6] that $\Omega(f)$ can be replaced by a simplified collision operator. The H-theorem shows that the collision operator drives the distribution function f toward the local Maxwell-Boltzmann equilibrium distribution f^{eq}. The most straightforward choice of collision operator is the linearized collision operator with a single relaxation time λ or the Bhatnagar-Gross-Krook (BGK) approximation[6] :

$$\Omega(f) = -\frac{f - f^{eq}}{\lambda} \tag{10}$$

By considering the collision invariant condition (5), it appears that the three moments (2), (3) and (4) still hold if f is replaced by f^{eq}. In other words, the non-equilibrium part $(f - f^{eq})$ of the distribution function do not contribute to the macroscopic fluid variables.

2.2 The discrete-velocity Boltzmann equation

Noting that the mass and momentum conservation equations involve moments of up to second order, an effective equilibrium function is obtained[1,21] by a truncation at order 2 of the small velocity Taylor expansion of (9) :

$$f^{eq} = \rho \frac{1}{(2\pi\theta)^{D/2}} \exp\left[-\frac{|\mathbf{c}|^2}{2\theta}\right]$$
$$\cdot \left\{1 + \frac{\mathbf{c}\cdot\mathbf{u}}{\theta} + \frac{(\mathbf{c}\cdot\mathbf{u})^2}{2\theta^2} - \frac{\mathbf{u}^2}{2\theta}\right\} + O\left(\left(\frac{|\mathbf{u}|}{\sqrt{\theta}}\right)^3\right)$$

Of course, in order to construct a non-isothermal model, a third-order expansion would be considered.[2,8]

As for the original derivation of LBE,[9,29] the polynomial form of the equilibrium function is necessary for the explicit calculation of weighting factors associated with the discrete velocities. As shown in the next section, the evaluation of the stress tensor and heat flux needs the calculation of the third and fourth moments of f^{eq} respectively. Considering the linear form of the equilibrium function, all the integrals (2), (3), (4), (7) and (8) can be expressed as linear combination of terms :

$$\int_{\Re^3} \xi_{x_1}^n \xi_{x_2}^m \xi_{x_3}^p e^{-(\xi_1^2 + \xi_2^2 + \xi_3^2)} dx_1 dx_2 dx_3 , \quad \boldsymbol{\xi} = \frac{\mathbf{c}}{\sqrt{2\theta}}$$

with $0 \le n, m, p \le 7$ in the more general case. The one-dimensional integrals can be calculated using a Gaussian quadrature formulae.[21] If the third-order Hermite formula[12] is used, we obtain :

$$\int_{\Re} \xi_{x_i}^n e^{-\xi_i^2} dx_i = \sum_{k=1}^{3} \omega_k \xi_k^n \quad \text{for } i = 1, 2, 3$$

where $\xi_{1,2,3} = \left(-\sqrt{3/2}, 0, \sqrt{3/2}\right)$ are the abscissas of the quadrature points with the corresponding weights $\omega_{1,2,3} = (\sqrt{\pi}/6, 2\sqrt{\pi}/3, \sqrt{\pi}/6)$. This quadrature is exact only up to $n = 6$, then it can not be applied for thermal simulations. If we consider now the two-dimensional case ($D = 2$), the moment integrals of the continuous equilibrium function can be evaluated by performing the moment summations over the nine velocities $\mathbf{c}_\alpha = \sqrt{(2\theta)} (\xi_k, \xi_l)$ of the discrete-velocity equilibrium functions given by :

$$f_\alpha^{eq} = \frac{\rho h_\alpha}{2\pi\theta} \left\{1 + \frac{\mathbf{c}_\alpha \cdot \mathbf{u}}{\theta} + \frac{(\mathbf{c}_\alpha \cdot \mathbf{u})^2}{2\theta^2} - \frac{\mathbf{u}^2}{2\theta}\right\} \quad (11)$$

with $h_\alpha = 2\theta\omega_k\omega_l$, $\alpha = 0, ..., 8$. This discretization of the velocity space and the discrete equilibrium functions correspond exactly to the classical so-called nine-speed lattice Boltzmann model.[29] Since only the values of the distribution functions at the discrete speeds are needed for the evaluation of the moments, the continuous Boltzmann equation (1) may be replaced by a discrete-velocity Boltzmann equation :

$$\frac{\partial f_\alpha}{\partial t} + c_{\alpha,i} \frac{\partial f_\alpha}{\partial x_i} = -\frac{1}{\lambda}(f_\alpha - f_\alpha^{eq}) \quad (12)$$

Since we are only concerned with isothermal simulations, the energy equation is no more considered in the following. The discrete forms of the density, momentum and stress tensor are :

$$\rho = \sum_{\alpha=0}^{8} f_\alpha , \quad \rho\mathbf{u} = \sum_{\alpha=0}^{8} \mathbf{c}_\alpha f_\alpha \quad (13)$$

and

$$P_{ij} = \sum_{\alpha=0}^{8} (c_{\alpha,i} - u_i)(c_{\alpha,j} - u_j) f_\alpha \quad (14)$$

The continuous moments of f can be evaluated by the discrete moments of $f(\mathbf{x}, \mathbf{c}_\alpha, t) = f_\alpha(\mathbf{x}, t)$ at the velocity nodes because, in the limit of slow variations in space and time of the distribution function around the equilibrium state, f can be expressed as a function of f^{eq}. This important result is shown in the next section.

2.3 Derivation of the Navier-Stokes equations

The treatment of the closure problem appeals to the expansion of the distribution function as regard to the Knudsen number of the flow. The Knudsen number is the ratio of the collision mean free path to the macroscopic length scale :

$$\epsilon = \frac{\lambda_0 \sqrt{\theta_0}}{L}$$

where λ_0 is a characteristic relaxation time (the average time between collisions), θ_0 is the characteristic temperature and L is the hydrodynamic length scale. Considering the dimensionless variables $\hat{t} = t\sqrt{\theta_0}/L$, $\hat{\lambda} = \lambda/\lambda_0$, $\hat{x} = x/L$, $\hat{\mathbf{c}} = \mathbf{c}/\sqrt{\theta_0}$ and $\hat{f}_\alpha = f_\alpha/\rho_0$ the following rescaled Boltzmann equation can be written :

$$\frac{\partial \hat{f}_\alpha}{\partial t} + \hat{c}_{\alpha,i} \frac{\partial \hat{f}_\alpha}{\partial \hat{x}_i} = -\frac{1}{\epsilon\hat{\lambda}}\left(\hat{f}_\alpha - \hat{f}_\alpha^{eq}\right) \quad (15)$$

For simplicity, all hats will be dropped in the following. The Chapman-Enskog or Hilbert expansion allows to find successive approximate solutions of equation (15) in term of small parameter ϵ. The formal expansion of f_α is :

$$f_\alpha = f_\alpha^{(0)} + \epsilon f_\alpha^{(1)} + \epsilon^2 f_\alpha^{(2)} + ... \quad (16)$$

Inserting (16) in (15) and balancing order by order in ϵ leads to :

Order -1 :
$$f_\alpha^{(0)} = f_\alpha^{eq} \qquad (17)$$

Order 0 :
$$\frac{\partial f_\alpha^{(0)}}{\partial t} + c_{\alpha,i} \frac{\partial f_\alpha^{(0)}}{\partial x_i} = -\frac{1}{\lambda} f_\alpha^{(1)} \qquad (18)$$

Order 1 :
$$\frac{\partial f_\alpha^{(1)}}{\partial t} + c_{\alpha,i} \frac{\partial f_\alpha^{(1)}}{\partial x_i} = -\frac{1}{\lambda} f_\alpha^{(2)} \qquad (19)$$

In the Chapman-Enskog analysis[7] the distribution function is supposed to be a normal solution, which is constrained by :

$$\sum_\alpha \Psi_{\alpha,p} f_\alpha^{(n)} = 0 \qquad n = 1, 2, \dots \qquad (20)$$

Considering only the first order expansion of f_α, we remark that in case of the BGK collision operator, the solvability condition for $f_\alpha^{(1)}$ is ensured by construction and traduces the conservation of collision invariants (equation (5)). In the general mathematical approach,[4,15,19] the solvability condition (20) for $f_\alpha^{(n)}$ is viewed as a compatibility condition to ensure the existence of the next term $f_\alpha^{(n+1)}$ of the expansion. The interest of equations (17), (18) and (19) is that they provide an explicit expression of the $(n+1)$-th order term of the expansion of f_α as a function of the n-th order term.

Taking the first two moments, $\sum \Psi_{\alpha,p} (\cdot)$ for $p = 0, \dots, 2$, of the equation (15) truncated at the order zero and using relation (17) and (20) for $n = 1$, we immediately obtain the mass and momentum conservation equations (6) with :

$$P_{ij}^{(0)} = \sum_\alpha \left(c_{\alpha,i} - u_i \right) \left(c_{\alpha,j} - u_j \right) f_\alpha^{eq} = \rho\theta\delta_{ij} \qquad (21)$$

The details of the calculations of $P_{ij}^{(0)}$ can be found in reference [23]. Noting that the thermodynamic pressure is $p = \rho\theta$ (equation of state of an ideal gas), the exact Euler equations have been recovered by this procedure. Now, if we take the first two moments of the rescaled Boltzmann equation, neglecting term in $O\left(\epsilon^2\right)$ and using (20) for $n = 1, 2$ the conservation equations are obtained with :

$$P_{ij} = \sum_\alpha \left(c_{\alpha,i} - u_i \right) \left(c_{\alpha,j} - u_j \right) \left(f_\alpha^{(0)} + \epsilon f_\alpha^{(1)} \right) \qquad (22)$$

Inserting relations (17), (18) and (21), the stress tensor becomes :

$$P_{ij} = p\delta_{ij} - \epsilon\lambda \left(\frac{\partial}{\partial t} \sum_\alpha c_{\alpha,i} c_{\alpha,j} f_\alpha^{eq} + \frac{\partial}{\partial x_k} \sum_\alpha c_{\alpha,i} c_{\alpha,j} c_{\alpha,k} f_\alpha^{eq} \right)$$

The temporal derivative $\partial/\partial t \sum c_{\alpha,i} c_{\alpha,j} f_\alpha^{eq} = \partial/\partial t \left(\rho\theta\delta_{ij} + \rho u_i u_j \right)$ is calculated as a function of spatial derivatives using the mass and momentum conservation equations at the Euler level. Since the energy conservation equation is not considered, the temperature must be supposed to be constant. The third-order moment can be calculated using the symmetry properties of the discrete velocity system.[23] The final expression of the stress tensor for the isothermal flow is :

$$P_{ij} = p\delta_{ij} - \epsilon\lambda \left(\rho\theta \left(\frac{\partial u_i}{\partial x_j} + \frac{\partial u_j}{\partial x_i} \right) - \frac{\partial \rho u_i u_j u_k}{\partial x_k} \right)$$

The unphysical cubic nonlinear term in the stress tensor can be neglected in case of low Mach flows. More complicated lattice Boltzmann models have been proposed in order to remove this spurious term.[30] The small Mach number hypothesis is also used for the Taylor expansion of the equilibrium function. Then, we can conclude that the Navier-Stokes equations can be derived from the discrete-velocity Boltzmann equation with an accuracy of $O\left(\epsilon^2\right)$ and $O\left(\mathrm{Ma}^3\right)$. The viscous stress tensor is given by :

$$\tau_{ij} = 2\mu S_{ij} + \left(\eta - \frac{2}{3}\mu \right) S_{kk}\delta_{ij}$$

with $S_{ij} = \left(\partial u_i/\partial x_j + \partial u_j/\partial x_i \right)/2$. The shear viscosity is $\mu = \tau\rho\theta$, with $\tau = \epsilon\lambda$. The density-dependent behavior of μ could be removed by noting that in dilute gas, the collision time-scale τ is inversely proportional to the local density.[14] Unlike in usual fluid as air (Stoke's hypothesis), the second viscosity coefficient $\eta = 2\mu/3$ (sometimes called bulk viscosity) is nonzero. This difference directly results from the isothermal hypothesis.[14]

2.4 Integration of the discrete-velocity Boltzmann equation

To achieve a fully discrete lattice Boltzmann equation, we must approximate (15) in **x** and t. For example, the discrete-velocity Boltzmann equation can be calculated numerically using an Euler time step in conjunction with a first order upwind spatial discretization.[36] A Lagrangian behavior is then obtained by imposing $\Delta x/\Delta t = |\mathbf{c}_\alpha|$. But this approach does not allow to show that the LBM is in fact a second order method. In the classical approach of LBM,[9,10,29] the second order accuracy is theoretically shown by Taylor expanding in time and space the kinetic discrete equation (see below equation (25)). In the framework of Chapman-Enskog procedure, both the temporal derivative operator and the distribution functions are expanded as a function of the Knudsen number.[2,10,23] At the Navier-Stokes level, it appears that the numerical diffusion due to second order terms can be included in the viscous tensor. The result is that the coefficient τ in the transport coefficients is simply replaced by $\tau - 1/2$. Thus, the numerical contribution to the viscosity for the lattice Boltzmann scheme is negative, requiring that the relaxation time τ to be greater than one half to maintain positive viscosity.

But the second order accuracy of the LBE and the effective value of the relaxation time can be recovered[14] directly from the discrete-velocity Boltzmann equation. The idea is to integrate equation (15) along the characteristic (the direction of $\mathbf{c}_\alpha$) for a time interval Δt. The integral of the BGK collision operator is approximated by the trapezium rule which is a second order accuracy method :

$$f_\alpha \left(\mathbf{x} + \mathbf{c}_\alpha \Delta t, t + \Delta t \right) - f_\alpha \left(\mathbf{x}, t \right) =$$
$$-\frac{\Delta t}{2\tau} \{ f_\alpha \left(\mathbf{x} + \mathbf{c}_\alpha \Delta t, t + \Delta t \right) - f_\alpha^{eq} \left(\mathbf{x} + \mathbf{c}_\alpha \Delta t, t + \Delta t \right)$$
$$+ f_\alpha \left(\mathbf{x}, t \right) - f_\alpha^{eq} \left(\mathbf{x}, t \right) \} + O\left(\Delta t^3 \right) \quad (23)$$

This equation is implicit because of the presence of the term $f_\alpha^{eq} \left(\mathbf{x} + \mathbf{c}_\alpha \Delta t, t + \Delta t \right)$. By a change of variables :

$$g_\alpha \left(\mathbf{x}, t \right) = f_\alpha \left(\mathbf{x}, t \right) + \frac{\Delta t}{2\tau} \left(f_\alpha \left(\mathbf{x}, t \right) - f_\alpha^{eq} \left(\mathbf{x}, t \right) \right) \quad (24)$$

we can find an equivalent explicit equation :

$$g_\alpha (\mathbf{x} + \mathbf{c}_\alpha \Delta t, t + \Delta t) = \left(1 - \frac{\Delta t}{\tau_g} \right) g_\alpha (\mathbf{x}, t) + \frac{\Delta t}{\tau_g} g_\alpha^{eq} (\mathbf{x}, t) \quad (25)$$

with $\tau_g = \tau + \Delta t / 2$ and $g_\alpha^{eq} = f_\alpha^{eq}$. For the calculation of the moments of g_α, it is interesting to note that $g_\alpha = f_\alpha - \Delta t \Omega \left(f \right) / 2$. Then, equation (5) shows that the first two moments of g_α give exactly the same macroscopic density and momentum than f_α. Solving the distribution functions g_α by equation (25) with a relaxation time τ_g allows to calculate the fluid variables for a flow of which the distribution functions f_α are described by the discrete-velocity Boltzmann equation (15) with the relaxation time τ. In particular, the kinematic viscosity of the simulated flow is $\nu = \theta \left(\tau_g - \Delta t / 2 \right)$.

2.5 Spatial and temporal discretizations

In this part, we write again the dimensionless variables with hat. The time $\hat{t}$ is discretized with a time step $\hat{\Delta} t$ and a space grid is defined such as if $\hat{\mathbf{x}}_k$ is a grid node then the points $\hat{\mathbf{x}}_k + \hat{\mathbf{c}}_\alpha \Delta t$, $\alpha = 0, ..., 8$ are also on the lattice. In case of the two-dimensional nine speed model (see part 2.2), this condition leads to a mesh with square cells of length $\Delta x = \sqrt{3\hat{\theta}} \hat{\Delta} t$. This shows that temperature must be supposed constant. Thermal simulations can not be performed with a "single energy"

discrete velocity scheme. To include temperature variations, it is necessary to use a multispeed model.[2,8,10]

We can re-write the relation between time and space increments in term of variables with physical dimension :

$$c_s = \frac{1}{\sqrt{3}} \frac{\Delta x}{\Delta t} \quad (26)$$

where $c_s = \sqrt{\theta}$ is the speed of sound for an "athermal" fluid. The kinematic viscosity also depends on the space and time increments :

$$\nu = \frac{1}{3} \left(\tilde{\tau}_g - \frac{1}{2} \right) \frac{\Delta x^2}{\Delta t} \quad \text{with} \quad \tilde{\tau}_g = \frac{\tau_g}{\Delta t} \quad (27)$$

However, the lattice Boltzmann equation (25) is calculated in its dimensionless form. Using the relation between Δx, Δt and θ, the discrete equilibrium distribution functions given by (11) can be written as :

$$\hat{g}_\alpha^{eq} = \rho h_\alpha \left\{ 1 + 3 \tilde{\mathbf{c}}_\alpha \cdot \tilde{\mathbf{u}} + \frac{9}{2} \left(\tilde{\mathbf{c}}_\alpha \cdot \tilde{\mathbf{u}} \right)^2 - \frac{3}{2} \tilde{\mathbf{u}}^2 \right\} \quad (28)$$

where $\tilde{\mathbf{u}} = \mathbf{u} \Delta t / \Delta x$ and $\tilde{\mathbf{c}}_\alpha = (0,0)$ for $\alpha = 0$, $\tilde{\mathbf{c}}_\alpha = (\sin\left((\alpha - 1)\pi/2 \right), \cos\left((\alpha - 1)\pi/2 \right))$ for $\alpha = 1,2,3,4$, $\tilde{\mathbf{c}}_\alpha = \sqrt{2} (\sin\left((2\alpha - 1)\pi/4 \right), \cos\left((2\alpha - 1)\pi/4 \right))$ for $\alpha = 5,6,7,8$. The corresponding weights are $h_\alpha = 4/9$ for $\alpha = 0$, $h_\alpha = 1/9$ for $\alpha = 1,2,3,4$ and $h_\alpha = 1/36$ for $\alpha = 5,6,7,8$. The tilde denotes a dimensionless variable with respect to the lattice length Δx and time step Δt.

3. Boundary Conditions

For a node on a boundary, some of its neighboring nodes lie outside the flow domain. Therefore, the distribution functions associated with the inward-pointing velocities (velocities which are on the directions pointing into the flow) are not defined. In case of the nine-velocity model, there are three unknown distribution functions on a plane boundary. The simplest way to determine these unknown functions for a no-slip wall condition is to use the bounce-back scheme, that was originally taken from the LGA method[10] : when a particle distribution streams to a wall node, the particle distribution scatters back to the node it came from. Then, the unknown inward-pointing distributions $\hat{g}_\alpha^{in}$ are defined directly from the outward-pointing distributions : $\hat{g}_\alpha^{in} = \hat{g}_\alpha^{out}$, with $\tilde{\mathbf{c}}_\alpha^{in} = -\tilde{\mathbf{c}}_\alpha^{out}$. Unfortunately, it was found that the bounce-back condition is only a first-order accuracy scheme. In order to improve the numerical accuracy, other boundary treatments have been proposed. For example, Noble $et\ al$[27] suggested using the hydrodynamic variables to calculate the unknown distributions (equation (13)). If the fluid velocity is known ($\mathbf{u} = 0$ for a no-slip wall) it is necessary to enforce a pressure constraint to obtain a system of three equations with three unknowns. The pressure enforcing can be avoided by adding some supplementary rules on the distribution functions. Zou and He[41] supposed that the bounce-back condition could be apply for the non-equilibrium part of the particle distribution normal to the boundary. If the components of the fluid velocity must also be calculated (frictionless wall, fluid boundary conditions), extrapolation schemes can be used to evaluated some particle distributions[26] or macroscopic fluid variables[41] in order to obtain as many equations as unknowns.

3.1 An extended equilibrium distribution for wall boundary conditions

As it is done for the initialization of populations, the inward-pointing distributions $\hat{g}_\alpha^{in}$ can also be supposed equal to the equilibrium values $\hat{g}_\alpha^{eq}$ which are known in term of $\hat{\rho}$ and $\tilde{\mathbf{u}}$ (equation (28)). In fact, this method for evaluating the unknown distributions can be considered as an application of the lattice Boltzmann equation (25) with $\tilde{\tau}_g = 1$. Therefore, a systematic error is made on the viscous fluxes at the boundary if the relaxation time in the fluid domain is not equal to one. But it can be shown[14,35,39] that the transport coefficients can be controlled independently of the relaxation time by adding "non-equilibrium" terms in the equilibrium populations. For example,[35,39] the following extended equilibrium distribution functions can be used :

$$g_\alpha^{eq\star} = \hat{g}_\alpha^{eq} + \epsilon\hat{\rho}\left(r\left(\alpha\right)\tilde{c}_{\alpha,i}\tilde{c}_{\alpha,j}\frac{\partial\tilde{u}_i}{\partial\tilde{x}_j} + s\left(\alpha\right)\frac{\partial\tilde{u}_i}{\partial\tilde{x}_i}\right)$$

with $r\left(0\right) = 0$ and $s\left(0\right) = s_0$; $r\left(\alpha\right) = r_1$ and $s\left(\alpha\right) = s_1$ for $\alpha = 1,2,3,4$; $r\left(\alpha\right) = r_2$ and $s\left(\alpha\right) = s_2$ for $\alpha = 5,6,7,8$. Using the symmetric properties of the discrete velocity tensors, it appears that the momentum is conserved by this new expression of the equilibrium distributions while the condition $s_0 + 4s_1 + 4s_2 + 2r_1 + 4r_2 = 0$ is necessary for the mass conservation. Recalling that $\hat{f}_\alpha^{eq\star} = \hat{g}_\alpha^{eq\star}$, the modified stress tensor can be calculated with equation (22). Neglecting terms in $O\left(\epsilon^2\right)$ and choosing $r_2 = r_1/4$, the viscous stress tensor can be written as :

$$\tilde{\tau}_{ij}^* = 2\rho\left(\tilde{\nu} - \epsilon r_2\right)\tilde{S}_{ij} - 2\epsilon\left(r_2 + s_1 + 2s_2\right)\tilde{S}_{kk}\delta_{ij}$$

On a boundary, $\tilde{\tau}_g$ can be set equal to one and the coefficients $\epsilon r\left(\alpha\right)$ and $\epsilon s\left(\alpha\right)$ are calculated such that $\tilde{\nu} - \epsilon r_2$ is equal to the shear viscosity of the inside fluid and $2\epsilon\left(r_2 + s_1 + 2s_2\right) = 0$. The parameter ϵs_2 is freely chosen $\epsilon s_2 = \epsilon s_1/4$ for simplicity. The coefficient ϵs_0 is calculated by the mass conservation condition. This approach for the calculation of inward-pointing distributions requires the macroscopic fluid variables be known on the boundary. In case of a plane boundary parallel to a Cartesian axis, the density does not depend on the inward-pointing distributions (equation (13)) :

$$\hat{\rho} = \frac{1}{1 - \mathbf{n}\cdot\tilde{\mathbf{u}}}\left(\hat{g}_0 + \sum_{\alpha_\parallel}\hat{g}_\alpha + 2\sum_{\alpha^{out}}\hat{g}_\alpha\right)$$

where $\mathbf{n}$ is the inward-pointing normal of the boundary and $\alpha_\parallel$ are the indices of the velocities that are parallel to the boundary. For example, if $\mathbf{n} = \left(0,1\right)$, then $\alpha_\parallel = 1,3$ and $\alpha^{out} = 4,7,8$. In our simulations, the calculation of inward-pointing populations by the extended equilibrium method is only made on no-slip walls. The nonzero velocity gradients are computed using second order asymmetric finite differences. For fluid boundaries where the velocity is not imposed, an other method must be used.

3.2 Finite difference method for non-reflective boundary conditions

In lattice Boltzmann literature, it does not exist boundary scheme to model non-reflective boundary condition for vortical and acoustic perturbations. In this case, six variables must be evaluated : the three inward-pointing distribution functions and the three macroscopic variables. Since the explicit relaxation/convection algorithm (25) can not be applied for inward-pointing populations, one can try to integrate directly the discrete-velocity Boltzmann equation (15) using classical time and space discretization schemes. This approach has been already applied for the calculation of the whole flow using finite difference[31] or finite volume[40] schemes. But since the relation (24) between the distributions $\hat{g}_\alpha$ and $\hat{f}_\alpha$ is known, an hybrid method for the boundary treatment can be constructed. An explicit fourth-order Runge-Kutta time-marching is chosen.[38] The spatial derivatives are evaluated with second order central and asymmetric finite differences. Since the distribution functions of the inner points are not calculated with the Runge-Kutta scheme, their values at the intermediate times of the time-step are unknown. Then, the asymmetric finite differences that are used to calculated the normal spatial derivative at the boundary are only introduced in the last stage of the temporal integration procedure. For example, the numerical scheme for a boundary parallel to the x-axis is :

$$\hat{f}_\alpha^k = \hat{f}_\alpha^{k-1} + a_k\left(\Omega^{k-1} - \tilde{c}_{\alpha,x}\frac{\partial\hat{f}_\alpha^{k-1}}{\partial\tilde{x}}\right) \quad \text{for } k = 1,..,3$$

$$\hat{f}_\alpha\left(\tilde{\mathbf{x}}, \tilde{t}+1\right) = \hat{f}_\alpha^0 + a_4\left(\Omega^3 - \tilde{c}_{\alpha,x}\frac{\partial\hat{f}_\alpha^3}{\partial\tilde{x}} - \tilde{c}_{\alpha,y}\frac{\partial\hat{f}_\alpha^0}{\partial\tilde{y}}\right)$$

with

$$\hat{f}_\alpha^0 = \hat{f}_\alpha\left(\tilde{\mathbf{x}}, \tilde{t}\right) \quad \text{and} \quad \Omega^k = -\frac{\hat{f}_\alpha^k - \hat{f}_\alpha^{eq,k}}{\tilde{\tau}}$$

The coefficients of the Runge-Kutta method are $a_1 = 1/4$, $a_2 = 1/3$, $a_3 = 1/2$, $a_4 = 1$. Unfortunately, the asymmetric finite difference scheme applied to normal component of the inward-pointing function gradient is a downwind scheme that is unconditionally unstable. It is therefore necessary to suppose that

$$\frac{\partial \hat{f}_\alpha^{in}}{\partial n} = 0 \qquad (29)$$

Moreover, Reider[31] showed that the stability condition for a direct discretization of equation (15) is not imposed by the classical CFL requirement but by the constraint that populations are not allowed to evolve far from equilibrium. Then the time-step must be preferably lower than the collision time, or at least we must have $\Delta t = O(\tau)$. Since we are interesting in high Reynolds number and low Mach number flows, this condition is very restrictive and can be overcome by using a space dependent collision time. In the bulk flow, the value of $\tilde{\tau}_g$ is close to $1/2$ (i.e. $\tau \ll \Delta t$) in order to reach low viscosity and on fluid boundaries, a minimal value of $\tilde{\tau}_g = 1$ can be imposed. To ensure the continuity, an exponential increase of $\tilde{\tau}_g$ on the nearest boundary nodes is defined.

Even if the condition (29) is not a physical constraint, the boundary treatment described above appears to be a comparatively effective scheme to model non-reflective conditions. For example, the figure 1 shows the behavior of this boundary condition under acoustic excitation (see part 5 for the details of the calculation). The total amplitude of the outcoming wave is about 20 Pa. Only the contour-lines -1 and -2 Pa are altered by the spurious incoming waves. It can be deduced that the reflection rate is about 10%.

4. Short wave damping with artificial viscosity

In this paper, the simulated fluid is air with $\rho_0 = 1.22$ kg/m^3, $c_s = 340$ m/s and $\nu = 1.5 \times 10^{-5}$ m^2/s. Expressions (26) and (27) show that the time and space increments are inversely proportional to $\tilde{\tau} = \tilde{\tau}_g - 1/2$. Consequently, for a given number of lattice nodes, the Reynolds number of the flow can be increased only by decreasing $\tilde{\tau}_g$ toward $1/2$. But it is well known[36] that the system can become unstable when the lattice relaxation time is close to $1/2$. Most of time, the computation diverges when some high frequency oscillations become too strong. These oscillations can be associated

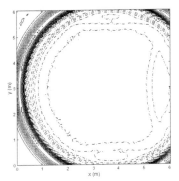

Figure 1: Pressure isocontours of a pulse in a uniform flow at $M = 0.2$. $\tilde{\tau} = 1.25 \times 10^{-6}$ and $\tilde{t} = 100$. The domain size is 100×100. ——— positive contours. – · – · negative contours. The pressure step between two contour-lines is 1 Pa.

to unphysical spurious invariants[28] and are generated in under-resolved regions.[14] Then numerical instabilities are generated when there is a lack of spatial resolution in a strongly-sheared region of the flow. In order to perform simulations at high Reynolds number, the numerical oscillations must be damped. In our model, these high frequency instabilities are reduced by applying a selective viscosity filter[37] on the macroscopic variables $v = \rho$, $\tilde{u}_x$ and $\tilde{u}_y$:

$$v\left(\tilde{x}, \tilde{y}\right) = v\left(\tilde{x}, \tilde{y}\right) - \tilde{\nu}_a \sum_{j=-3}^{j=3} \left(d_j v\left(\tilde{x}+j, \tilde{y}\right) + d_j v\left(\tilde{x}, \tilde{y}+j\right)\right)$$

where $\tilde{\nu}_a$ is the artificial viscosity. Another solution proposed by Dellar[14] is to use an enhanced bulk viscosity. Indeed, the bulk viscosity can be readily adjusted by using the extended equilibrium functions (see part 3.1).

5. Pulse propagation in a uniform flow

Simulations of sound waves with LBM were studied previously[5,14] but with an emphasis on non-linear steepening at finite amplitude[5] and energy decay of high frequency plane waves due to viscous dissipation.[5,14] For very small values of $\tilde{\tau}$, it is possible to simulate low frequency wave with a limited number of nodes. The viscous dissipation of long wave acoustic perturbations is negligible and the results of LBM computations can be compared to the solutions of Euler equations. For example, the analytical expression of the linear propagation of a Gaussian pressure pulse in a uniform flow is known.[20] A Gaussian density source of half-width b and amplitude $10^{-3}\rho_0$ is introduced at the center of the computational domain. For an Euler problem, numerical oscillations are very weak because the distribution functions are always close to the equilibrium, therefore the artificial viscosity is not applied. Figure 2 shows the

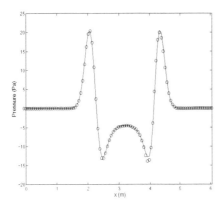

Figure 2: Pressure pulse in a uniform flow at $M = 0.2$. $\tilde{\tau} = 1.25 \times 10^{-6}$ and $\tilde{t} = 30$. The domain size is 100×100. —— Analytical solution. ○ LBM simulation.

pressure profile along the centerline of the domain for a convection flow at $M = 0.2$. The agreement between the analytical and calculated profiles is quite good. Using the reference analytical solution p_{ref}, the convergence of the numerical method can be investigated as a function of the lattice discretization. Since the time and spatial steps are linearly linked by (26), the accuracy is only expressed in term of Δx. The constant CFL number is a characteristic of LBM and must be taken into account in the convergence study.[31] Indeed, a smaller spatial lattice size requires an increase in the number of time iteration needed for the same flow evolution.

The half-width of the pulse and the domain size are kept constant at $b = 19.3$ cm and $N_x \times N_y = 16 \, (b \times b)$. The definition of the error norm is :

$$Err = \left(\frac{1}{N_x} \sum_{k=1}^{N_x} \left(p\left(k, N_y/2\right) - p_{ref}\right)^2 \right)^{1/2}$$

In figure 3, if the convergence rate for the largest spatial size is first considered, we see that the error decay is almost in power three. This result is in agreement with equation (23). However, the error saturates at a certain level as the mesh is refined and even increases if the error is measured at a given physical time. The linear error increase is due to the cumulative sum of the errors made at each iteration. The convergence saturation of LBM has also been pointed out in previous works.[25,31,35] It can be associated with several effects such as the influence of higher order terms in $O\left(M^3\right)$ and $O\left(\epsilon^2\right)$ (the so-called compressibility errors) or the numerical round-off error.[35] Further investigations would be necessary to study the cause of the error saturation in our particular case.

Despite this limitation, the lattice Boltzmann method appears to be a fairly good numerical scheme for acoustic propagation.

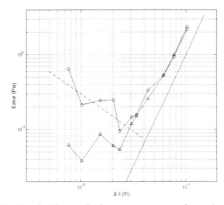

Figure 3: Evolution of the error as a function of Δx. ○ Error at a given physical time. △ Error at a given lattice time ($\tilde{t} = 20$). —— line with slope = 3. - - - line with slope = -1.

6. Simulations of flow-excited cavities

In order to assess the ability of the lattice Boltzmann method to simulate practical flow problems at low subsonic speeds, we study the case of a flow-excited cavity. Even if the introduction of a subgrid viscosity for turbulence modeling is not difficult,[22] the two-dimensional hypothesis does not allow to compute actual turbulent phenomenon. Then, laminar flows are chosen in this validation.

6.1 Cavity flow oscillation at very low Mach number

We try to reproduce the experiments of Sarohia[34] who investigated a laminar flow oscillation over an axisymmetric non-resonant cavity. Flow oscillations over rectangular cavities at very low Mach numbers and comparable Reynolds numbers have been also studied by Gharib & Roshko[17] and Rockwell & Knisely.[33] The simulations are performed at $Re_{\theta_0} = 240$ where θ_0 is the momentum thickness of the boundary layer at separation. The Mach number is $M = 0.044$. The depth of the cavity $D/\theta_0 = 80$ is kept constant. A cavity with length to depth ratio $L/D = 1$ is meshed with 50×50 points. The mesh size is 300×200 outside the cavity. The relaxation time is $\tilde{\tau} = 1.6 \times 10^{-4}$ and the artificial viscosity is $\tilde{\nu}_a = 0.1$. The initial condition is a polynomial expression of the laminar Blasius boundary layer. A typical computation is 6 hours long on a SGI workstation with a 250 MHz R10000 processor.

Figure 4 shows the transverse velocity signals obtained with four L/θ_0 ratios. The Strouhal numbers for the simulations at $L/\theta_0 = 61$, $L/\theta_0 = 80$ and $L/\theta_0 = 104$ are respectively $St = fL/U_0 = 0.57$, 0.91 and 1.01. Figure 5 depicts the variation of the phase difference Φ for probes located along the cavity opening near the

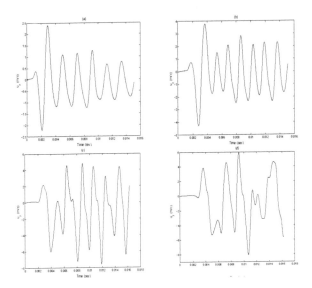

Figure 4: Time history of the transverse velocity for a point at $y/\theta_0 = 1.5$ and (a) $x/\theta_0 = 48$, $L/\theta_0 = 61$; (b) $x/\theta_0 = 64$, $L/\theta_0 = 80$; (c) $x/\theta_0 = 93$, $L/\theta_0 = 104$; (d) $x/\theta_0 = 112$, $L/\theta_0 = 134$.

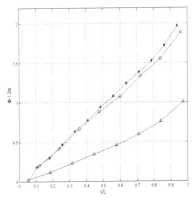

Figure 5: Streamwise variation of the transverse velocity phase at $y/\theta_0 = 6.5$. $\triangle$, $L/\theta_0 = 61$, mode I; $\circ$, $L/\theta_0 = 80$, mode II; $*$, $L/\theta_0 = 104$, mode III.

outside edge of the shear layer. Between the two corners of the cavity, the characteristic phase difference[17] of $2n\pi$ with $n = 1, 2$ is found. Then for $L/\theta_0 = 61$ the flow oscillates in mode I and for $L/\theta_0 = 80$ and $L/\theta_0 = 104$ the oscillation is in mode II (figure 6 (a)). This behavior well corresponds to experimental observations.[17,34] For $L/\theta_0 = 61$, the oscillation phenomenon tends to disappear (figure 4). It is consistent with experimental data, where the first mode appears to not be a stable stage of oscillation in certain conditions. As L/θ_0 further increases, the transition from mode II to mode III is obtained for $L/\theta_0 = 122$ in experiments.[17] Then for $L/\theta_0 = 134$, the flow normally oscillates in mode III while temporal signal (figure 4) and flow visualization (figure 6 (b)) indicates that the cavity flow is in the wake mode.[17] This non-coherent organization of the

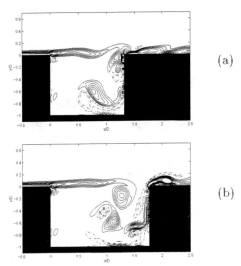

Figure 6: Instantaneous vorticity contours. (a) $L/\theta_0 = 104$, mode II; (b) $L/\theta_0 = 134$, wake mode. ——— negative contours; — · — · positive contours.

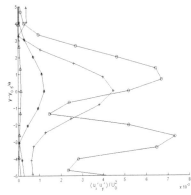

Figure 7: Reynolds stress profiles for $L/\theta_0 = 80$. $\triangle$, $x/\theta_0 = 14$; $*$, $x/\theta_0 = 38$; $+$ $x/\theta_0 = 54$; $\circ$, $x/\theta_0 = 70$.

flow only appears at $L/\theta_0 = 160$ in experiments. The transition to wake mode for too low ratios L/θ_0 has been also observed in other numerical simulations[11] and it is probably due to the two-dimensional hypothesis of the computations.

For the self-sustained oscillation conditions, the growth of the momentum thickness θ of the shear layer have been measured. As in experimental studies,[17,33,34] θ is found to grow linearly with x/θ_0 and for all cases, the growth rate is almost constant at $d\theta/dx = 0.021$ which is very close to the value found by Sarohia ($d\theta/dx = 0.022$). Figure 7 represents the streamwise evolution of the transverse profile of the shear stress for $L/\theta_0 = 80$. The amplitude and the existence of the second peak in the lower portion of the shear layer compare very well with the measurements of Gharib & Roshko.

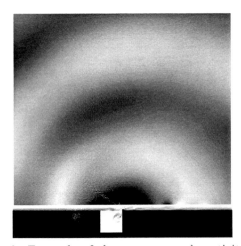

Figure 8: Example of the pressure and vorticity fields produced by an unsteady cavity flow. $L/D = 1$, $L/\theta_0 = 60$, $M = 0.25$. The pressure is drawn for values between -200 and 200 Pa. The negative pressures are in dark gray.

6.2 The acoustic field radiated by a cavity flow

The sound field radiated by a flow-excited cavity can also be calculated by the code. In order to reduced the ratio between the acoustic wavelength and the domain size, calculations are performed with Mach number $M = 0.25$. We keep the parameters $\tilde{\tau}$, $\tilde{\nu}_a$ of the previous computations and a cavity with the same characteristic size is simulated. The outside domain size is inceased up to 500×500 mesh points. The Reynolds number is $Re_{\theta_0} = 2250$. Figure 8 shows the acoustic pressure field radiated by a cavity flow for $L/D = 1$ and $L/\theta_0 = 60$. The oscillation frequency is $fL/U_0 = 0.81$.

For this cavity length-to-depth ratio and Mach number, there is no available numerical data to compare precisely our acoustic field. Most of cavity noise computations have been performed[11,18] for shallow cavities ($L/D \geq 2$) at higher Mach numbers. But, as in these simulations, the acoustic field is centered at the downstream edge of the cavity : the noise is generated by the periodic impingement of coherent vortices upon the corner. Even if the radiated sound of our computation is not omni-directional, the very strong upstream directivity[11,18] is not recovered. This difference can be explained by a lower effect of the free stream convection and a different acoustic inteference pattern inside the cavity.

7. Concluding remarks

In this paper, the lattice Boltzmann method is investigated for aeroacoustic simulations. The recent approach that allows to derive a discrete-velocity Boltzmann equation is presented. The Navier-Stokes equa-tions can be recovered using exactly the same mathematical procedure as that applied in the continuous Boltzmann kinetic theory. The second order accuracy equations of the LBM are found by integrating the discrete velocity model and introducing equivalent population functions: the populations that are calculated by the LBM are not the populations of the discrete velocity equation but give the same macroscopic variables. This procedure allows very large time-steps compared to the fluid collision time, which is not possible if the discrete-velocity Boltzmann equation is directly solved. Specific treatments for aeroacoustic computations at high Reynolds number have been added to the two-dimensional model. With small computational efforts, a quite good agreement between numerical results and analytical or experimental data is obtained. Of course, further validations and comparisons with the other CAA methods would be necessary but this first application of Boltzmann methods for computational aeroacoustics is encouraging. The new explicit link of the LBM to the continuous kinetic theory offers new opportunities for future developments of kinetic boundary conditions[3] and maybe for turbulence modeling.[13]

References

[1] ABE, T., 1997. Derivation of the lattice Boltzmann method by means of the discrete ordinate method for the Boltzmann equation. *J. Comput. Phys.*, **131**, 241-246.

[2] ALEXANDER, F.J., CHEN, S. & STERLING, J.D., 1993. Lattice Boltzmann thermohydrodynamics. *Phys. Rev. E*, **47**, R2249.

[3] ANSUMALI, S. & KARLIN, I.V., 2002. Kinetic boundary conditions in the lattice Boltzmann method. *Preprint*.

[4] BARDOS, C., GOLSE, F. & LEVERMORE, D., 1991. Fluid dynamic limits of kinetic equations I : Formal derivations. *J. Stat. Phys.*, **63**, 323-344.

[5] BUICK, J.M., GREATED, C.A. & CAMPBELL, D.M., 1998. Lattice BGK simulation of sound waves. *Europhys. Lett.*, **43**(3), 235-240.

[6] CERCIGNANI, C., 1988. The Boltzmann equation and its applications. *Spinger Verlag, New York*.

[7] CHAPMAN, S. & COWLING, T.G., 1970. The mathematical theory of non-uniform gases. *Cambridge University Press*.

[8] CHEN, H., TEIXEIRA, C. & MOLVIG, K., 1997. Digital Physics approach to computational fluid dynamics : some basic theoretical features. *Int. J. Mod. Phys. C*, 8(4), 675-684.

[9] CHEN, S., CHEN, H., MARTINEZ D. & MATTHAEUS, W., 1991. Lattice Boltzmann model for simulation of magnetohydrodynamics. *Phys. Rev. Lett.*, **67**, 3776-3779.

[10]CHEN, S. & DOOLEN, G.D., 1998. Lattice Boltzmann Method for fluid flows. *Annu. Rev. Fluid Mech.*, **30**, 329-364.

[11]COLONIUS, T., BASU, A.J. & ROWLEY, C.W., 1999. Numerical investigation of the flow past a cavity. *AIAA Paper* **99-1912**.

[12]DAVIS, P.J. & RABINOWITZ, P., 1984. Methods for Numerical Integration. *Academic, New York, 2nd ed.*

[13]DEGOND, P. & LEMOU, M., 2002. Turbulence models for incompressible fluids derived from kinetic theory. *to appear in* J. Math. Fluid Mech.

[14]DELLAR, P.J., 2001. Bulk and shear viscosities in lattice Boltzmann equations. *Phys. Rev. E*, **64**, 031203.

[15]ESPOSITO, R., LEBOWITZ, J.L. & MARRA, R., 1999. On the derivation of hydrodynamics from the Boltzmann equation. *Phys. Fluids*, **11**(8), 2354-2366.

[16]FRISCH, U., HASSLACHER, B. & POMEAU, Y., 1986. Lattice-Gas Automata for the Navier-Stokes equation. *Phys. Rev. Lett.*, **56**(14), 1505-1508.

[17]GHARIB, M. & ROSHKO, A., 1987. The effect of flow oscillations on cavity drag. *J. Fluid Mech.*, **117**, 501-530.

[18]GLOERFELT, X., BAILLY, C. & JUVÉ, D., 2001. Computation of the noise radiated by a subsonic cavity using direct simulation and acoustic analogy. *AIAA Paper* **01-2226**.

[19]GOLSE, F., 1998. From kinetic to macroscopic models. *Session "L'Etat de la Recherche" de la S.M.F., Orléans*, www.dma.ens.fr/~golse/qcours.html.

[20]HARDIN, J.C., RISTORCELLI, J.R. & TAM, C.K.W., 1995. Workshop on benchmark problems in computational aeroacoustics. ICASE/LaRC. NASA CP - 3300.

[21]HE, X. & LUO, L.-S., 1997. Theory of the lattice Boltzmann method: From the Boltzmann equation to the lattice Boltzmann equation. *Phys. Rev. E*, **56**, 6811-6817.

[22]HOU, S., STERLING, J., CHEN, S. & DOOLEN, G.D., 1996. A lattice Boltzmann subgrid model for high Reynolds number flows. *Fields Inst. Comm.*, **6**, 151-166.

[23]HOU, S., ZOU, Q., CHEN, S., DOOLEN, G.D. & COGLEY, A.C., 1995. Simulation of cavity flow by the lattice Boltzmann method. *J. Comp. Phys.*, **118**, 329-347.

[24]HUANG, K. 1963. Statistical Mechanics. *Wiley, New York.*

[25]MAIER, R.S & BERNARD, R.S., 1997. Accuracy of the lattice-Boltzmann method. *Int. J. Modern Phys. C*, **8**(4), 747-752.

[26]MAIER, R.S, BERNARD, R.S. & GRUNAU, D.W., 1996. Boundary conditions for the lattice Boltzmann method. *Phys. Fluids*, **8**(7), 1788-1801.

[27]NOBLE, D.R., CHEN, S., GEORGIADIS, J.G. & BUCKIUS, R.O., 1995. A consistent hydrodynamic boundary condition for the lattice Boltzmann method. *Phys. Fluids*, **7**(1), 203-209.

[28]QIAN, Y.-H., 1997. Fractional propagation and the elimination of staggered invariants in lattice-BGK models. *Int. J. Modern Phys. C*, **8**(4), 753-761.

[29]QIAN, Y.-H., D'HUMIÈRES, D. & LALLEMAND, P., 1992. Lattice BGK models for Navier-Stokes equation. *Europhys. Lett.*, **17**(6), 479-484.

[30]QIAN, Y.-H. & ZHOU, Y., 1998. Complete Galilean-invariant lattice BGK models for the Navier-Stokes equation. NASA/CR-1998-208701, ICASE Report No. 98-38.

[31]REIDER, M.B. & STERLING, J.D., 1995. Accuracy of discrete-velocity BGK models for the simulation of incompressible Navier-Stokes equations. *Comput. Fluids*, **24**, 459-467.

[32]RICOT, D., MAILLARD, V. & BAILLY, C., 2001. Numerical simulation of the unsteady flow past a cavity and application to the sunroof buffeting. *AIAA Paper* **01-2112**.

[33]ROCKWELL, D. & KNISELY, C., 1979. The organized nature of flow impingement upon a corner. *J. Fluid Mech.*, **93**(3), 413-432.

[34]SAROHIA, V., 1977. Experimental investigation of oscillations in flows over shallow cavities. *AIAA J.*, **15**(7), 984-991.

[35]SKORDOS, P.A., 1993. Initial and boundary conditions for the Lattice Boltzmann Method. *Phys. Rev. E*, **48**, 4823-4842.

[36]STERLING, J.D & CHEN, S., 1996. Stability analysis of lattice Boltzmann methods. *J. Comp. Phys.*, **123**, 196-206.

[37]TAM, C.K.W., WEBB, J.C & DONG, Z., 1993. A study of the short wave components in computational acoustics. *J. Comput. Acoust.*, **1**(1), 1-30.

[38]WILLIAMSON, J.H., 1980. Low-storage Runge-Kutta schemes. *J. Comput. Phys.*, **35**, 48-56.

[39]WOLFRAM, S., 1986. Cellular automata fluids 1: Basic theory. *J. Stat. Phys.*, **45**(3), 471-526.

[40]XI, H., PENG, G. & CHOU, S.-H., 1999. Finite-volume lattice Boltzmann schemes in two and three dimensions. *Phys. Rev. E*, **60**(3), 3380-3388.

[41]ZOU, Q. & HE, X., 1997. On pressure and velocity boundary conditions for the lattice Boltzmann BGK model. *Phys. Fluids*, **9**, 1591-1598.

AIAA 2002-2535

NONLINEAR ANALYSIS OF AIRFOIL HIGH-INTENSITY GUST RESPONSE USING A HIGH-ORDER PREFACTORED COMPACT CODE

A. Crivellini*
Universita Degli Studi Di Ancona, Italy
V.V. Golubev[†], R.R. Mankbadi[‡]
Embry-Riddle Aeronautical University
J.R. Scott[§], R. Hixon[¶], L. A. Povinelli[#]
NASA Glenn Research Center

ABSTRACT

The nonlinear response of symmetric and loaded airfoils to an impinging vortical gust is investigated in the parametric space of gust dimension, intensity, and frequency. The study, which was designed to investigate the validity limits for a linear analysis, is implemented by applying a nonlinear high-order prefactored compact code and comparing results with linear solutions from the GUST3D frequency-domain solver. Both the unsteady aerodynamic and acoustic gust responses are examined.

INTRODUCTION

Most unsteady aerodynamic and aeroacoustic analyses considering interaction of upstream flow nonuniformities with downstream structural components follow linear theory wherein the unsteady part of the flow is considered a small perturbation about the steady mean flowfield. This approach, which relies on solutions to the linearized Euler equations, is adopted, for example, in problems dealing with rotor-stator interactions where the rotor wakes are represented as low-intensity flow disturbances (vortical gusts) convected by the mean flow. This paper examines the limits of the linear theory when the unsteady vortical flow velocity component is, in fact, not too small compared to the steady mean flow velocity. Thus, the interaction problem is investigated by imposing a finite-amplitude gust on the mean flow, and a nonlinear flow

*Research Associate
†Assistant Professor, Member of AIAA
‡Professor, Associate Fellow of AIAA
§Senior Research Scientist, Senior Member of AIAA
¶Senior Research Associate, Member of AIAA
#Chief Scientist, Fellow of AIAA

analysis is then applied to examine possible deviations from the linear theory predictions. The problem of gust-airfoil interaction is selected for this study as it presents a widely used benchmark in unsteady aerodynamics.

To the authors' best knowledge, no detailed, systematic study of high-intensity gust response has been conducted so far (at least for realistic airfoil profiles), although nonlinear Euler and Navier-Stokes solvers have been in use for unsteady problems in turbomachinery for at least a decade (see [1] for a good review of the subject). A fully nonlinear viscous study of gust-airfoil interaction has been previously conducted by Lockard and Morris [2] with assumption of a small-amplitude perturbation. Hence, most observed nonlinear effects in [2] were related to gust-triggered instabilities in the viscous wake. In fact, in the present study, a similar mechanism giving rise to *inviscid* wake instability remains a crucial factor in describing the nonlinear response effects. In general, such effects to be investigated may include (e.g., [3], pp.863-873) generation of higher harmonics (both for single and multiple frequency input) and combination tones (for multiple-frequency input) resulting from nonlinear self-interaction and exchange of energy between multiple imposed frequencies. In certain cases, the effects of nonlinear interaction between the imposed harmonic(s) and the mean flow, including exchange of energy, can also be present. It is expected that these effects combined should become increasingly more noticeable at higher gust intensities when they would thus produce a more significant impact on the unsteady airfoil response, particularly on the unsteady aerodynamic loading and the acoustic directivity pattern.

The present work extends the analysis of the gust-airfoil interaction problem first presented in [4] and [5]. Results of the nonlinear inviscid analysis based on explicit time marching with prefactored sixth-order compact scheme for spatial differences, are compared with solutions from a frequency-domain linearized Euler solver GUST3D [6]. The unsteady response to one-dimensional and two-dimensional gusts is examined for both loaded and unloaded thick Joukowski airfoils in a subsonic flow.

FORMULATION

The analysis of nonlinear inviscid gust-airfoil interaction is based on the numerical solution to the nonlinear Euler equations which can be written in two-dimensional Cartesian coordinates as

$$\frac{\partial Q}{\partial t} + \frac{\partial E}{\partial x} + \frac{\partial F}{\partial y} = 0, \tag{1}$$

where Q is the solution vector, and F and G are the flux vectors:

$$Q = \begin{bmatrix} \rho \\ \rho u \\ \rho v \\ E \end{bmatrix},$$

$$E = \begin{bmatrix} \rho u \\ \rho u^2 + p \\ \rho uv \\ u(E+p) \end{bmatrix}, \tag{2}$$

$$F = \begin{bmatrix} \rho v \\ \rho uv \\ \rho v^2 + p \\ v(E+p) \end{bmatrix},$$

and

$$p = (\gamma - 1)\left(E - \frac{1}{2}\rho(u^2 + v^2) \right) \tag{3}$$

Since the gust response is investigated for the complex-shaped Joukowksi airfoil, it requires recasting the equations in generalized curvilinear coordinates, with the chain-rule curvilinear Euler equations written as

$$\frac{\partial Q}{\partial t} + \frac{\partial \xi}{\partial x}\frac{\partial E}{\partial \xi} + \frac{\partial \eta}{\partial x}\frac{\partial E}{\partial \eta} + \frac{\partial \xi}{\partial y}\frac{\partial F}{\partial \xi} + \frac{\partial \eta}{\partial y}\frac{\partial F}{\partial \eta} = 0 \tag{4}$$

The numerical formulation established in [4] and [5] uses the low-storage 4th order 5-6 Low Dispersion and Dissipation Runge-Kutta scheme [7] for time marching, and the prefactored 6th order compact scheme and explicit boundary stencils for spatial derivatives [8]. A 10th order explicit filter is used at every stage of the Runge-Kutta solver to provide dissipation.

For the analysis of the gust response problem, a C-grid 2D topology is used for the 12% thick Joukowski airfoil, with the grid extending at least 10 chords away from the surface in each direction. All the meshes are generated as single blocks by the GridPro commercial software [9]. More details on the numerical implementation are included below.

GUST AND AIRFOIL CONFIGURATIONS AND FLOW INITIALIZATION

In the current work, the nonlinear gust response is examined for a series of imposed gust intensities and frequencies. Each vortical gust harmonic is initially imposed on the mean flow with the following distribution:

$$u_{gust} = -\left(\frac{\varepsilon \beta M}{\sqrt{\alpha^2 + \beta^2}} \right) \cos(\alpha x + \beta y - \omega t)$$

$$v_{gust} = -\left(\frac{\varepsilon \alpha M}{\sqrt{\alpha^2 + \beta^2}} \right) \cos(\alpha x + \beta y - \omega t) \tag{5}$$

where ε is the gust intensity relative to the mean flow, α and β are the gust wave numbers in the x and y directions, and ω is the imposed gust frequency. The mean flow is defined far upstream from the airfoil as:

$$\begin{aligned} \overline{\rho} &= 1 \\ \overline{u} &= M \\ \overline{v} &= 0 \\ \overline{p} &= \frac{1}{\gamma}(\overline{\rho}^{\gamma}) \end{aligned} \tag{6}$$

where M is the upstream mean flow Mach number, and $\gamma=1.4$. For this paper's computations, the Mach number is fixed at $M=0.5$.

The flow is initialized throughout the physical domain, with the gust superimposed on the mean flow. In addition, at the inflow boundary, the acoustic radiation condition given by Tam and Webb [10] is applied to the outgoing perturbation which is defined, e.g., for u-component as $u_{BC} = u_{boundary} - \overline{u} - u_{gust}$.

The following two configurations for the airfoil geometry are considered:

(A1) Unloaded symmetric 12%-thick Joukowski airfoil (no angle of attack);

(A2) Loaded 12%-thick 2%-cambered Joukowski airfoil at a two-degree angle of attack.

Two configurations for the impinging gust are examined:

(G1) One-dimensional (1D) transverse gust with $\alpha = 2k, \beta = 0, \omega = 2kM$ in (5);

(G2) Two-dimensional (2D) gust with $\alpha = 2k, \beta = 2k, \omega = 2kM$ in (5),

where k is the reduced frequency of the gust non-dimensionalized by the half-chord and the upstream flow velocity. In the computations, both the gust intensity and reduced frequency are varied.

RESULTS AND DISCUSSION

The focus of this study is on nonlinear effects of high-intensity gust interaction with an airfoil. Hence, it is important to provide comparison for different gust intensity levels, with the corresponding low-intensity results assumed to fall within the linear response limits. At first, the results of the numerical analysis for all gust and airfoil configurations are validated against the GUST3D linear analysis calculations. Following this, a systematic study of gust intensity effects on various nonlinear response aspects is carried out, with the most important findings discussed and illustrated below.

Numerical Implementation

The computational code performing nonlinear unsteady analysis is written in Fortran 90 and uses the MPI library for parallelization. Numerical solutions are obtained through parallel implementation on the Beowulf-type Linux Athlon cluster consisting of eight dual-processor 1.4GHz AMD compute nodes, each with 1GB of PC2100DDR memory. The nodes are connected by five full duplex fast ethernet connections to the other nodes in the cluster using a symmetric interconnection scheme. The MPICH implementation of MPI is used [11].

The parallel performance of the code is shown in Figure 1, with the noticeable decrease in the computational efficiency observed when more then eight processors are involved in the computations. This is due to the fact that the cluster starts to utilize both processors of the single nodes sharing the same bus allocation on the motherboard. For instance, the same computation performed with two processors from different nodes is observed to have the parallel efficiency of 95 %,

compared to 73 % when two processors from the same node are used. This trend is typical of communication-intensive numerical implementations.

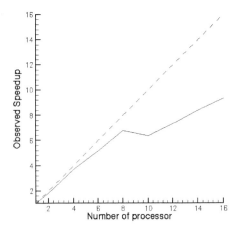

Figure 1: Observed speedup for parallel runs.

In this work, the simulations are run for longer time periods compared to [4] since stable, time-accurate solutions are sought not only for imposed gust frequencies but also for higher harmonics and combination tones. In terms of the non-dimensional time (normalized by the airfoil half-chord and the speed of sound), the values between 360 and 450 are found necessary for the more slowly converging loaded airfoil simulations to accurately resolve the mean flowfield and the acoustic field. More time iterations are required for lower gust frequency cases in order to march through an adequate number of longer periods. Some small differences in results compared to the similar cases in [4] can be attributed to longer convergence histories in the present runs. Finally, to quantify the computational effort, a 16-hour numerical run is required to march to the non-dimensional time value of 360, which corresponds to 70,000 iterations on the 600x240 grid using all sixteen processors.

Validation

The validation of the nonlinear code results with the linear solutions from the GUST3D solver has been previously accomplished in [4], where thorough grid density and domain size sensitivity studies have also been conducted. The reader is referred to this paper for more details. In the present work, this validation is further extended to numerical simulations on meshes with grid densities 600x240 (for the cambered airfoil cases) and 591x238 (for the symmetric airfoil cases). Similar to [4], the grids are generated by GridPro using algebraic clustering around the profile in the normal direction (Δn=0.01) and near the trailing edge

($\Delta x=0.01$), with the stretching ratio of 1.05 used to expand to the far field. Note that some oscillations and loss of accuracy are found near the trailing edge, which is due to the singularity treatment in the grid topology. Nevertheless, a careful clustering of grid points near the trailing edge may help to keep these effects localized, with minimal impact on the overall solution.

The results are presented for two reduced frequencies of the gust, k=0.1 in Figures 2 and 3, and k=1.0 in Figures 4 and 5. For the selected airfoil and gust configurations (A1-G1), (A1-G2), (A2-G1), (A2-G2), Figures 2 and 4 show the acoustic intensity of the unsteady response at a distance of one chord length away from the centerpoint of the airfoil, while Figures 3 and 5 show results for the same quantity at a distance of four chord lengths. For each case, three results are compared including the low-intensity gust response (for $\varepsilon=0.02$), the high-intensity gust response (for $\varepsilon=0.20$), and the GUST3D linear solution [6,12].

A detailed discussion of the high-intensity gust results is presented in the following paragraphs. The low-intensity solutions match well with GUST3D predictions, with only the case of high frequency and cambered profile showing apparent discrepancy (also in line with comparison in [4]).

In general, the comparison is better for the unloaded airfoil cases. It should be also mentioned that the unsteady pressure distribution on the airfoil shows an excellent match for all the considered cases, with results nearly identical to the previous comparison in [4].

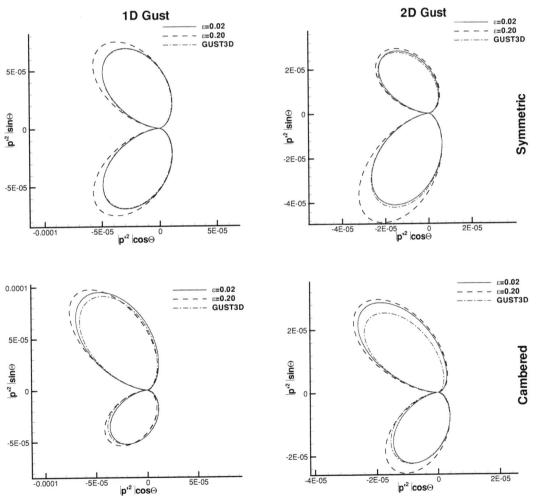

Figure 2:Disribution of $|p'^2|$ at R=1 (k=0.1)

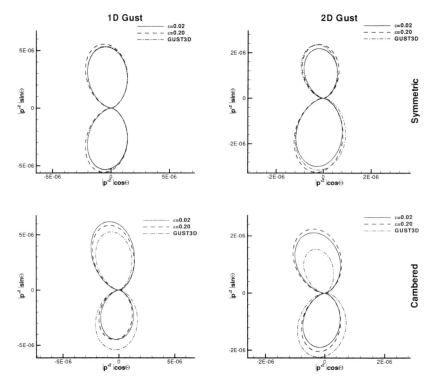

Figure 3:Disribution of $|p'^2|$ at R=4 (k=0.1)

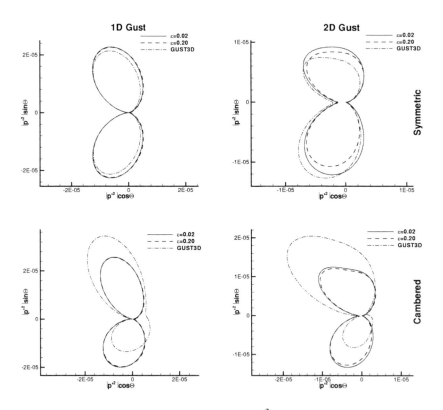

Figure 4:Disribution of $|p'^2|$ at R=1 (k=1.0)

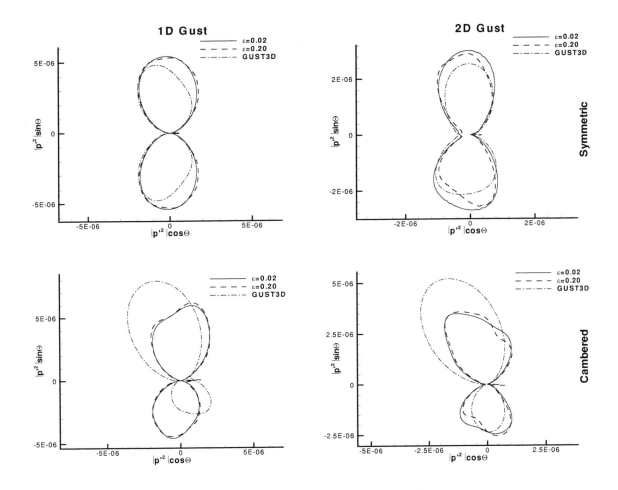

Figure 5: Disribution at R=4 (k=1.0)

Single-Frequency Gust

Figures 2-5 also introduce a comparison between the solutions obtained for the low (ε=0.02) and high (ε=0.2) gust disturbance amplitudes. All the results in these and the following figures are scaled to the gust amplitude ε=0.02 for proper comparison. Note that at the low reduced frequency of k=0.1, the directivity patterns for all the cases retain the same shape, but, at least in the near field for R=1, show a notable overall increase in the lobe acoustic intensity magnitudes, less evident in the far field (R=4). For the higher reduced frequency of k=1.0, the situation actually reverses, with only small lobe variation noticeable in the near field but rather significant change in the directivity *shape* in the far field, especially for the 2D gust cases. To examine this effect in more detail, Figure 6 shows the variation of the acoustic intensity in the far field over a range of 2D gust amplitudes for the loaded airfoil case.

Note that multiple lobes start to develop in the directivity pattern with increasing gust amplitude, which may point to the appearance of new non-compact sources in the domain. Indeed, the numerical analysis indicates that this phenomenon is connected to the development of the inviscid wake instability triggered by the breakdown of the gust at the airfoil surface (first noticed by Lockard and Morris [2] for the viscous case).

To illustrate this phenomenon, Figures 7-10 show contour plots for the instantaneous vertical velocity component. The results imply an increasing vorticity downstream in the wake, with the growth much more rapid for higher ε.

Moreover, a similar trend is noted in Figure 11 for the RMS unsteady pressure fluctuations in the wake, which gives rise to the spike in the directivity pattern across the wake region, observed in Figure 6.

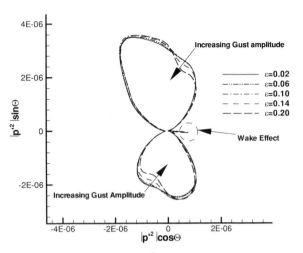

Figure 6: Effect of ε on $|p'^2|$ Disribution at R=4 (k=1.0, 2D gust, cambered airfoil)

Thus, the lobe distortion in Figure 6 is apparently attributed to the wave-like instability development in the wake as the radiation pattern from such instability waves may develop a multi-lobe response (this phenomenon is examined in [13] using an integral Kirchhoff technique). Also, from Figures 3 and 5, one may notice that the 2D gust produces a more significant nonlinear effect on directivity, which may possibly be attributed to the fact that the longitudinal gust component induces additional shear in the wake thus contributing to instability development. All these hypotheses will be validated in a future analysis. Note that the near-field results (R=1) do not reveal these directivity distortions since major nonlinear wake evolution occurs further downstream.

Figure 12 illustrates the contours of the calculated instantaneous unsteady pressure distribution in the domain. In order to examine the higher harmonics of the unsteady gust response, the FFT of the unsteady lift coefficient is carried out for all the test cases. Figure 13 shows the results scaled to the same input gust amplitude for comparison. In the analysis, the FFT is performed over a period corresponding to the non-dimensional time of 40π. For this period, the code switches from an adjustable time step (satisfying the stability criteria) to the fixed one, using small steps to march through more than 30,000 iterations. It is obvious from Figure 13 that the level of higher

harmonics is greatly increased at the higher gust intensity. A single case of unsteady response of the cambered airfoil to the 1D gust with amplitude $\varepsilon=0.20$ also reveals harmonics of an unexplained spurious frequency.

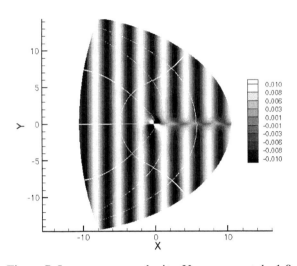

Figure 7: Instantaneous velocity, Y-component: k=1.0, 1D gust, $\varepsilon=0.02$, symmetric airfoil.

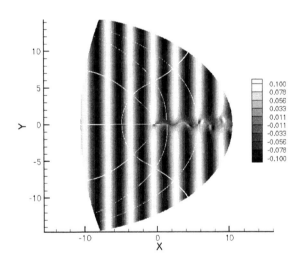

Figure 8: Instantaneous velocity, Y-component: k=1.0, 1D gust, $\varepsilon=0.20$, symmetric airfoil.

1388

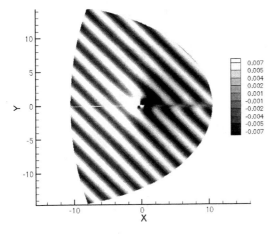

Figure 9: Instantaneous velocity, Y-component: k=1.0, 2D gust, ε=0.02, cambered airfoil.

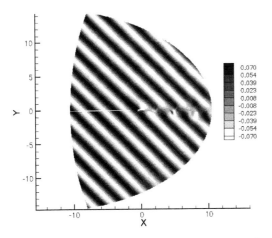

Figure 10: Instantaneous velocity, Y-component: k=1.0, 2D gust, ε=0.20, cambered airfoil.

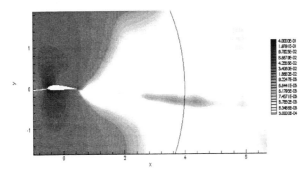

Figure 11: RMS unsteady pressure response contours downstream of airfoil (with R=4 line shown). 2D gust, k=1.0, ε=0.20, cambered airfoil.

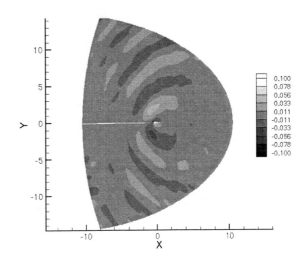

Figure 12: Contours of instantaneous unsteady pressure response. 2D gust, k=1.0, ε=0.20, cambered airfoil.

It should be mentioned that for gust intensities higher than ε=0.2 and for higher gust frequencies, the nonlinear simulations start failing to converge as the spurious reflections start building up in the computational domain. This is attributed to the currently used formulation for the acoustic radiation boundary conditions based on the linear theory and the point source assumption. Future work will focus on resolving this issue to extend the analysis. This aspect is especially important because of the need to examine the nonlinear response at higher gust frequencies more typical of rotor/stator unsteady interactions.

Multiple-Frequency Gust

In order to further investigate the nonlinear response at high gust amplitudes, several simulations have been run with superposition of two different gust frequencies. Only the loaded airfoil is considered. In Figure 14, the FFT of the lift coefficient is presented for two superimposed 2D gust frequencies with k=0.6 and k=1.0. The gusts are imposed with equal amplitudes, and comparison is presented for two cases with ε=0.06 and ε=0.1. As expected, the unsteady response reveals the presence of combination tones with k=0.4 and k=1.6, in addition to higher harmonics. All of them reveal higher amplitudes at higher gust intensities. Finally, for the same imposed gust amplitudes, Figure 15 compares the unsteady responses due to the superposition of 1D vs. 2D gusts. Clearly, the superposition of 2D gusts generates higher levels of nonlinear response.

ε=0.02   ε=0.20

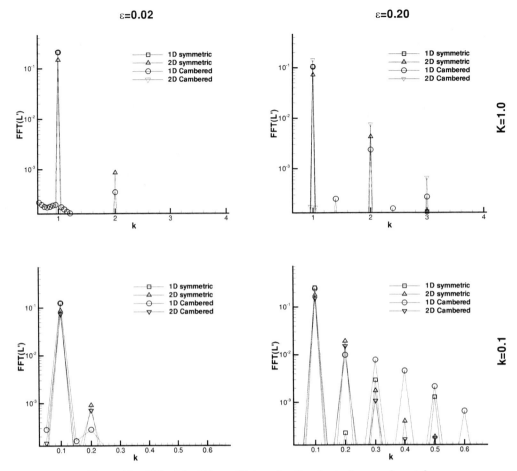

Figure13: FFT of the lift coefficient for the single imposed gust frequency.

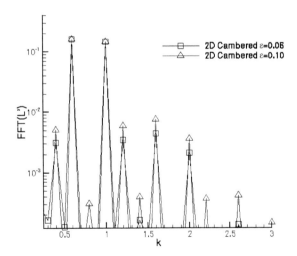

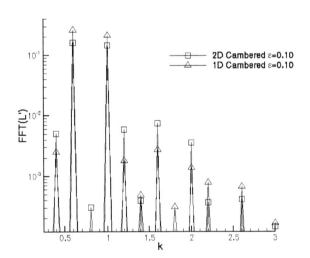

Figure 14: FFT of the lift coefficient for k=0.6+1.0. Cambered airfoil, 2D gusts, cases with ε=0.06 and ε=0.1

Figure 15: FFT of the lift coefficient for k=0.6+1.0. Cambered airfoil, 1D and 2D gust cases, ε=0.1

CONCLUSIONS

This study focused on nonlinear effects of high-intensity gust interaction with an airfoil. To investigate the limits of validity for the linearized approach, results of the nonlinear inviscid analysis were compared with the linearized Euler solutions in the parametric space of gust dimension, intensity, and frequency. Both loaded and unloaded airfoils in a subsonic flow were considered.

Among the nonlinear effects, generation of higher harmonics and combination tones associated with nonlinear self-interaction and exchange of energy between multiple imposed frequencies was observed for gust amplitudes approaching 20% of the mean flow. At low reduced frequency of k=0.1, the double-lobe directivity patterns tended to retain its shape but increased the overall acoustic intensity magnitudes. On the other hand, for the higher reduced frequency of k=1.0, most significant changes occurred in the directivity shapes starting to develop multiple lobes. This effect was attributed to the development of inviscid wake instability acting as a new non-compact source.

Overall, no significant deviation from the small-perturbation predictions was observed for gust amplitudes up to about 10% of the mean flow. It was further determined that, compared to the 1D transverse gust, the 2D gust produced more significant nonlinear effects on the acoustic directivity in all cases considered, with the difference more pronounced at the higher reduced frequency. Nevertheless, no clear conclusion on the effects of gust frequency and airfoil loading on nonlinear response could be derived at this point. Future work is planned to extend this analysis to higher frequencies more typical of unsteady rotor-stator interactions, which will require development of a new approach to the acoustic boundary condition treatment more adequate for nonlinear computations. Effects of viscosity on nonlinear response particularly in the wake region will be examined with introduction of implicit time marching in the existing structure of the Very Large Eddy Simulation code used in this paper. The remaining discrepancies between the nonlinear analysis at low gust intensity and linear GUST3D solutions will be further investigated.

ACKNOWLEDGEMENTS

The authors would like to thank Rich Riendeau for his help and support in developing the Linux cluster for parallel computations. Dr. Golubev and Mr. Crivellini would like to acknowledge the support of the Ohio Aerospace Institute in this work.

REFERENCES

1. Verdon, J.M., "Review of Unsteady Aerodynamic Methods for Turbomachinery Aeroelastic and Aeroacoustics Applications," AIAA Journal, Vol. 31, pp. 235-250, 1993.
2. Lockard, D.P. and Morris, P.J., "Radiated Noise from Airfoils in Realistic Mean Flows," AIAA Journal, Vol.36, pp. 907-914, 1998.
3. Morse,P.M. and Ingard, K.U., "Theoretical Acoustics," Princeton Univ. Press, 1986.
4. Hixon, R., Mankbadi, R.R. and Scott, J.R., "Validation of a High-Order Prefactored Compact Code on Nonlinear Flows with Complex Geometries," AIAA Paper 2001-1103, Reno, NV, January 2001.
5. Hixon, R., Shih, S.-H., Mankbadi, R.R., and Scott, J.R., "Time Domain Solution of the Airfoil Gust Problem Using a High-Order Compact Scheme," AIAA Paper 98-3241, Cleveland, OH, 1998.
6. Scott, J.R. and Atassi, H.M., "A Finite-Difference, Frequency-Domain Numerical Scheme for the Solution of the Gust-Response Problem," Journal of Computational Physics, Vol. 119, pp.75-93, 1995.
7. Stanescu, D. and Habashi, W.G., "2N-Storage Low Dissipation and Dispersion Runge-Kutta Schemes for Computational Acoustics," Journal of Computational Physics, Vol.143, pp.674-681, 1998.
8. Hixon, R., "A New Class of Compact Schemes," AIAA Paper 98-0367, Reno, NV, January 1998.
9. GridPro™, Program Development Corporation, White Plains, NY.
10. Tam, C.K.W. and Webb, J.C., "Dispersion-Relation-Preserving Finite Difference Schemes for Computational Acoustics," Journal of Computational Physics, Vol. 107, pp.262-281, 1993
11. Gropp, W., Lusk, E., Doss, N., and Skjellum, A., "A High-Performance, Portable Implementation of the MPI Message-Passing Interface Standard," Parallel Computing, Vol. 22(6), pp. 789-828, 1996.
12. Hariharan, S.I., Scott, J.R., and Kreider, K.L., "A Potential-Theoretic Method for Far-Field Sound Radiation Calculations," Journal of Computational Physics, Vol. 164, pp. 143-164, 2000.
13. Golubev, V.V., Mankbadi, R.R., and Dahl, M.D., "Prediction of the Acoustic Field Associated with Instability Wave Source Model for a Compressible Jet," accepted for presentation at the AIAA/CEAS Aeroacoustics Conference, June 2002.

SIMULATION OF 3-D ACOUSTIC SCATTERING WITH A PENTADIAGONAL COMPACT-DIFFERENCE METHOD

Nathan B. Edgar* and Peter W. TenPas[+]

*College of Engineering
Arkansas State University
State University, Arkansas 72467

[+]Department of Mechanical Engineering
University of Kansas
Lawrence, Kansas 66045-7526

ABSTRACT

A compact finite-difference method based upon pentadiagonal matrices for the computation of spatial derivatives and a 4/6 alternating step Low-Dissipation and Low-Dispersion Runge-Kutta (LDDRK 4/6) time integration scheme is described and formulated for the three-dimensional linearized Euler equations. Results are presented for 1-D, 2-D, and 3-D model problems, including linear wave propagation, scattering from a circular cylinder, and reflected waves from a periodic source near a wall with a uniform crossflow. The far-field boundary conditions are approximated by the Perfectly-Matched-Layer (PML) equations, which provide a numerical zone to absorb all outgoing waves. Wall boundary conditions are formulated using the standard central difference form of the compact stencil by using 'ghost points' adjacent to the computational domain. Results indicate that the use of the tenth-order pentadiagonal scheme provides a 30% to 50% grid reduction compared to the eighth-order tridiagonal scheme. Dispersion characteristics for the combined compact-difference scheme and LDDRK 4/6 temporal integration are examined for periodic boundary conditions.

INTRODUCTION

The requirements to accurately model the propagation and scattering of an acoustic signal depend on minimizing dispersion and dissipation error in the proposed solution methodology. These solution procedures involve the computation of spatial derivatives and a method to advance the solution forward in time. A number of high-order spatial differencing schemes have been developed and used for computational aeroacoustics (CAA) including compact[1], DRP[2], and ENO[3] methods which generally possess superior dissipation and dispersion characteristics compared to lower-order methods traditionally used for CFD. Because these higher-order spatial differences possess only a minimal damping mechanism, all instabilities generated in the computational domain will continue to grow if left untreated. Thus, the implementation of numerical boundary conditions is of critical importance. A number of damping[4,5] and filtering[6,7] techniques have been proposed to limit the growth rate of instabilities generated at or near boundary nodes.

In the present work, implicit high-order compact differencing schemes as described by Lele[1] are used to compute the spatial derivatives required by the linearized Euler equations. These high-order compact schemes are able to accurately resolve wave content using comparatively coarse grids at the cost of factoring a tridiagonal or pentadiagonal matrix. While the tridiagonal form is commonly used, results with the pentadiagonal form have not been widely reported.

The numerical solution is marched forward in time using an alternating-step Low-Dissipation and Low-Dispersion Runge-Kutta (LDDRK) integration scheme developed by Hu, Hussaini and Manthey[8]. This technique provides a larger time step for a given level of accuracy when compared to the traditional fourth-order Runge-Kutta integration scheme.

* Instructor, Member AIAA
[+] Associate Professor, Senior Member AIAA

Two types of boundary conditions are of interest for the examples in the present work. The modeling of an infinite domain is carried out by using the Perfectly Matched Layer (PML) equations, first developed by Berenger[9] for use in computational electromagnetics and adapted by Hu[10] for use with the Euler equations. Dietiker, Hoffmann, Agarwal and Papadakis[11] have recently reported results with this technique for three-dimensional flow. The PML equations absorb outgoing wave content without production of spurious numerical reflection into the computational domain.

Walls and lines-of-symmetry are modeled using the standard centered compact stencil by implementation of ghost points adjacent to the computational boundary.

The goal of the present study is to show that utilization of a tenth-order pentadiagonal compact difference operator provides a significant reduction in grid requirements for some three-dimensional CAA problems when compared to an eighth-order tridiagonal compact operator. The increase in computational cost in factoring a pentadiagonal coefficient matrix as opposed to a tridiagonal matrix is more than offset by the increase in allowable grid spacing for these problems. This work is an extension of a previous study by TenPas, Schwalm and Agarwal.[12]

Numerical results are presented for wave propagation using the 1-D linear wave equation, 2-D scattering of an acoustic pulse off of a cylinder, and scattering of a periodic 3-D acoustic source off a flat plate in a uniform mean flow.

GOVERNING EQUATIONS

The dimensionless form of the equations describing the propagation of a small acoustic perturbation in a uniform mean flow is given below for a Cartesian reference frame. This specific form is developed by linearizing the compressible Euler equations about the uniform mean flow.

$$\frac{\partial \mathbf{U}}{\partial t} + \frac{\partial \mathbf{E}}{\partial x} + \frac{\partial \mathbf{F}}{\partial y} + \frac{\partial \mathbf{G}}{\partial z} = \mathbf{S} \qquad (1)$$

where $\mathbf{U}^T = [u, v, w, p]$ are the perturbation velocities and pressure. The flux components are:

$$\mathbf{E} = \begin{Bmatrix} M_x u + p \\ M_x v \\ M_x w \\ u + M_x p \end{Bmatrix} \quad \mathbf{F} = \begin{Bmatrix} M_y u \\ M_y v + p \\ M_y w \\ v + M_y p \end{Bmatrix} \quad \mathbf{G} = \begin{Bmatrix} M_z u \\ M_z v \\ M_z w + p \\ w + M_z p \end{Bmatrix} \qquad (2)$$

with M_x, M_y, and M_z representing the mean velocity components normalized by the speed of sound.

Boundary Conditions

The boundary conditions needed for the examples in the present work include a mechanism to model an infinite domain and the representation of solid walls and lines-of-symmetry. The Perfectly Matched Layer (PML) equations have been implemented here to model an infinite medium by adding layers of nodes adjacent to the computational domain. This layer acts to absorb outgoing wave content normal to the computational boundary, while leaving the tangential wave components unaffected. The absorption effect is accomplished by defining a source term composed of an absorption coefficient, σ, and the normal component of the outgoing wave. The 3-D form of the PML equations for a Cartesian geometry is shown below.

$$\frac{\partial \mathbf{U}_1}{\partial t} + \frac{\partial \mathbf{E}_1}{\partial x} + \frac{\partial \mathbf{F}_1}{\partial y} + \frac{\partial \mathbf{G}_1}{\partial z} = \mathbf{S}_1 \qquad (3.a)$$

$$\frac{\partial \mathbf{U}_2}{\partial t} + \frac{\partial \mathbf{E}_2}{\partial x} + \frac{\partial \mathbf{F}_2}{\partial y} + \frac{\partial \mathbf{G}_2}{\partial z} = \mathbf{S}_2 \qquad (3.b)$$

$$\frac{\partial \mathbf{U}_3}{\partial t} + \frac{\partial \mathbf{E}_3}{\partial x} + \frac{\partial \mathbf{F}_3}{\partial y} + \frac{\partial \mathbf{G}_3}{\partial z} = \mathbf{S}_3 \qquad (3.c)$$

where the primary variables are split as shown below along with the split form for the flux components.

$$\mathbf{U}_1 = \begin{Bmatrix} u_1 \\ v_1 \\ w_1 \\ p_1 \end{Bmatrix} \quad \mathbf{U}_2 = \begin{Bmatrix} u_2 \\ v_2 \\ w_2 \\ p_2 \end{Bmatrix} \quad \mathbf{U}_3 = \begin{Bmatrix} u_3 \\ v_3 \\ w_3 \\ p_3 \end{Bmatrix}$$

such that, $\mathbf{U} = \mathbf{U}_1 + \mathbf{U}_2 + \mathbf{U}_3$ and,

$$\mathbf{E}_1 = \begin{Bmatrix} M_x u + p \\ M_x v \\ M_x w \\ u + M_x p \end{Bmatrix} \quad \mathbf{F}_2 = \begin{Bmatrix} M_y u \\ M_y v + p \\ M_y w \\ v + M_y p \end{Bmatrix} \quad \mathbf{G}_3 = \begin{Bmatrix} M_z u \\ M_z v \\ M_z w + p \\ w + M_z p \end{Bmatrix}$$

$$\mathbf{E}_2 = \mathbf{E}_3 = 0 \qquad \mathbf{F}_1 = \mathbf{F}_3 = 0 \qquad \mathbf{G}_1 = \mathbf{G}_2 = 0$$

The source terms are defined as

$$\mathbf{S}_1 = -\sigma_x \mathbf{U}_1 \qquad \mathbf{S}_2 = -\sigma_y \mathbf{U}_2 \qquad \mathbf{S}_3 = -\sigma_z \mathbf{U}_3$$

where σ_x, σ_y, and σ_z are the absorption coefficients defined in layers adjacent to the computational boundaries. The magnitudes of these coefficients are defined by their relative position within the PML zone, with a value of zero at the interface with the computational boundary. See Hayder, Hu and Hussaini[13] or Nizampatnam, Hoffmann, Papadakis and Agarwal[14] for details. Note that if the absorption coefficients are zero, then equations (3.a-c) can be recombined to get the original describing equations (1).

Solid walls and lines-of-symmetry are approximated by using 'ghost points' adjacent to the computational boundary. The ghost points are assigned values whose magnitudes correspond to values of interior variables, and whose sign is dependent on whether symmetry or asymmetry is being enforced. The maximum number of ghost points used is three, which accommodates a seven-point stencil at a boundary node.

Spatial Discretization

The centered compact differencing operators developed by Lele[1] are utilized in the present work for the computation of spatial derivatives on the grid interior as well as the computational boundaries. The implicit pentadiagonal compact difference operator (CDO) on a uniform grid with a 7-point stencil is given by:

$$\beta f'_{i-2} + \alpha f'_{i-1} + f'_i + \alpha f'_{i+1} + \beta f'_{i+2} = \frac{a}{2h}\left(f_{i+1} - f_{i-1}\right) + \frac{b}{4h}\left(f_{i+2} - f_{i-2}\right) + \frac{c}{6h}\left(f_{i+3} - f_{i-3}\right) \qquad (4)$$

where α, β, a, b, and c are constants, and h is the grid spacing between consecutive nodes. The commonly used tridiagonal schemes are obtained with $\beta = 0$.

The relationship between the constants are determined by grouping the coefficients of like-ordered terms of a Taylor series expansion developed for each primary variable and its derivative. The constants are then manipulated to nullify the desired coefficients, yielding a remainder term that determines the order of the differencing scheme. For a 7-point stencil, tridiagonal schemes of up eighth-order and pentadiagonal schemes of up to tenth-order are possible.

In the present work, comparisons are made between the eighth-order tridiagonal compact difference operator (CDO3/8) and the tenth-order pentadiagonal scheme (CDO5/10). The constants for each scheme are:

CDO3/8: $\beta = 0$, $\alpha = 3/8$, a = 75/48, b = 1/5, c = -1/180

CDO5/10: $\beta = 1/20$, $\alpha = 1/2$, a = 17/12, b = 101/150, c = 1/100

The numerical resolution characteristics may be found in numerous literature citations. The combined resolution characteristics for these compact schemes and LDDRK integration are presented in the numerical examples for the linear wave equation with periodic boundary conditions.

Temporal integration

Runge-Kutta integration has been a popular choice for temporal integration in CAA. The primary objective of any temporal integration method is to march the solution forward in time without adversely affecting the resolution characteristics of the spatial discretization scheme. Hu, Hussaini and Manthey[8] developed an optimal integration technique by specifying a baseline formal order of accuracy, and then using any free parameters to minimize the square of the error between the numerical and exact amplification factor via a least-squares minimization process. The result was development of a p-stage Low-Dissipation and Low-Dispersion Runge-Kutta (LDDRK) integration technique. The specific form of the p-stage LDDRK scheme for linear problems is given by:

$$\mathbf{U}^{n+1} = \mathbf{U}^n + \mathbf{K}_p \qquad (5)$$

where,

$$\mathbf{K}_i = \Delta t\left(\mathbf{U}^n + \overline{\beta}_i \mathbf{K}_{i-1}\right), \quad i = 1,2,....,p$$

See the previously cited reference for complete details of the minimization process and the derived constants.

Hu, et al[8] reported that by using alternate p-stage LDDRK schemes at each time step, further reduction in dissipation and dispersion error could be achieved. Therefore, a 4/6 alternating-step LDDRK scheme (RK-4/6) is implemented in the present work, with the traditional fourth-order 4-stage Runge-Kutta integration scheme (RK-4) for the first step and an optimized 6-stage fourth-order LDDRK scheme for the second step.

NUMERICAL RESULTS

Results are now presented for propagation and scattering of acoustic perturbations in quiescent and uniform mean flow using implicit high-order compact difference method coupled with alternating-step LDDRK integration. A 1-D linear wave equation is used to demonstrate the potential reduction in grid requirements using the pentadiagonal scheme. Scattering of an acoustic pulse from a 2-D cylinder is used to demonstrate anomalies in the curved-wall boundary conditions, and scattering of a 3-D acoustic pulse from a flat plate in a uniform mean flow is used to demonstrate the computational savings realized by using the pentadiagonal scheme.

1-D Linear wave propagation

The accuracy of the method is now demonstrated by analysis of one-dimensional wave propagation. The errors in wave speed of the fourth-order through tenth-order compact difference operators in tridiagonal and pentadiagonal form are shown in Figure 1. Numerical tests were performed for the wave propagation benchmark problem of a Gaussian pulse[15]. The wave equation is given by:

$$\frac{\partial u}{\partial t} + c\frac{\partial u}{\partial x} = 0 \qquad (6)$$

where u is the wave amplitude and c is the wave speed. A Gaussian pulse is initially prescribed and represented as:

$$u(x,0) = \frac{1}{2}\exp\left[-\ln(2)\left(\frac{x}{3}\right)^2\right]$$

The error trend with respect to spatial grid refinement is shown in Figure 2 for the numerical solution with c =1 at t = 400. A small CFL number is employed to eliminate time-step error. The results show at least an order-of-magnitude reduction in error, up to unit grid spacing, for the tenth-order pentadiagonal compact difference operator (CDO5/10) compared to the eighth-order tridiagonal (CDO3/8) scheme for this problem. Therefore, for the same level of accuracy, CDO5/10 provides a 30% reduction in grid spacing compared to CDO3/8 for the problem considered here.

Figure 3 shows error with respect to CFL number to compare the 4/6 alternating-step LDDRK (RK-4/6) with the classic 4-stage Runge-Kutta method (RK-4) for spatial grids of $\Delta x = 0.25$ and 1.0. Both methods converge at a 4th order rate to the limit set by the spatial error for the given grid sizes. For CFL number ranging from 0.3 to 1.0 the RK-4/6 shows an error reduction factor of 36 as compared to RK-4 for either grid size. Thus, for the same level of accuracy, 2.45 RK-4 steps are required for every RK-4/6 step. Since RK-4/6 requires 1.25 the computational effort as RK-4, the computational reduction using RK-4/6 is approximately 50% (1.25/2.45).

Example wave profiles are shown in Figure 4 using CDO3/8 and CDO5/10, and show the 30% reduction in

grid spacing for an error level of 10^{-2}. The solution was computed using RK-4/6 with a CFL number or 0.8.

Figures 5 and 6 show the dispersion characteristics for the combined compact difference operators coupled with LDDRK integration. CDO3/8 and CDO5/10 for various CFL number are shown, and it is noted that for CFL numbers less than 1.0, the dispersion characteristics of the combined scheme are essentially the same as those of the compact operator, i.e. the LDDRK integration does not degrade the resolution characteristics of the compact operator. For details of the combined resolution characteristics, see Edgar.[16]

This 1-D study indicates that substantial computational savings may be realized by utilizing CDO5/10 for multi-dimensional problems. Even a 10% reduction in grid requirement in one dimension, translates to a 27% reduction for a 3-D problem.

2-D Scattering from a cylinder

Solution of the idealized fuselage scattering benchmark problem[17] is used to evaluate wall boundary conditions for a curved geometry. The problem is a cylinder of diameter, D, located at the origin, with a line source positioned four cylinder diameters from the origin as shown in Figure 7. The pressure disturbance is defined as a single pulse with Gaussian distribution:

$$p(r,\theta,t=0) =$$
$$\sin(\omega t)\exp\left(-\ln(2)\left[\frac{(r\cos(\theta)-4.0)^2 + (r\sin(\theta))^2}{(0.2)^2}\right]\right)$$

with additional initial conditions of:

$$U(r, \theta, 0) = V(r, \theta, 0) = 0$$

The numerical solution is well represented on an O-type grid with mesh-spacings of $\Delta r/D$ of 0.05 and $\Delta\theta$ of $\pi/180$ for both CDO3/8 and CDO5/10. These grid dimensions were chosen so that the source would be properly represented by the mesh. A drawback of using this type of mesh is the unnecessary grid refinement near the cylinder wall. This limits the time step that may be used due to the stability limit of the RK-4/6 integration scheme.

At the curved wall boundary, ghost points are employed to accommodate the seven point compact stencil. Since these ghost points take on values of corresponding interior nodes, with sign dependent on symmetry or asymmetry, the effective implementation corresponds to a dispersive one-sided difference scheme. The nodes near the boundary produce spurious high-frequency errors, which are spatially damped in the radial direction, but in some instances, can be supported by the fine resolution of the transverse mesh spacing. While the errors introduced are comparatively small, they can interfere with the accuracy of the background pressure field for periodic test cases. Selective damping near the curved wall boundary can be used to minimize these errors. Examples can be found in Edgar[16].

Figure 8 shows a typical snapshot of the instantaneous wave pattern, at t = 6.25, showing the initial diffracted wave and the wall reflection. The top half of the contour plot was computed with CDO3/8 and the bottom half was computed using CDO5/10.

The benchmark required the solution for the instantaneous pressure transient at a radius of 5 units from the cylinder center at $\theta = \pi/2$, $3\pi/4$, and π. These are shown in Figures 9–11, and are compared to the analytic solution due to Kurbatskii[18]. Both operators show excellent agreement with the computed analytic solution.

3-D Scattering from plate

This test case models waves from a periodic pressure source reflecting from a flat plate with a uniform flow imposed in the axial direction. The source is located a distance of two units above the plate, and symmetry is used about the XY-plane to model the source. PML boundary conditions are imposed upstream and downstream of the source at x = -4 and x = 4. PML conditions are also applied in the XY-plane at z = 4, and above the source (XZ-plane) at y = 4.

Figure 12 illustrates the physical dimensions of the problem, with the plate located in the y = 0 plane. The Gaussian source distribution has a period of 0.5 with a pulse width of 0.1 and is given by:

$$p(x, y, z, t) =$$
$$\sin(\omega t)\exp\left(-\ln(2)\frac{\left(x^2 + (y-2)^2 + z^2\right)}{pw^2}\right)$$

where ω is the angular frequency and pw is the pulse width.

A uniform flow with Mach number, $M_x = 0.5$ is imposed, resulting in an apparent upstream source wavelength of $\lambda_u = 0.25$ ($\lambda_u = (1 - M_x)\lambda$) and an apparent downstream wavelength of 0.75. Therefore, the grid requirements will be controlled by the resolution needed to properly model the upstream portion of the domain.

Computations were executed with CDO3/8 and CDO5/10 for CFL = 0.5 to determine the minimum grid requirements. For comparable levels of accuracy near the source, CDO3/8 required a nominal 8 points per wavelength (ppw) yielding an effective grid spacing of 4 ppw in the upstream section, while CDO5/10 required a nominal grid spacing of 6 ppw, or 3 ppw upstream.

A series of instantaneous pressure contour plots at t = 30 are shown to illustrate the impact that phase error has on the solution computed by CDO3/8 as compared to CDO5/10. Figure 13 shows the YZ-plane normal to the flow at x = 0 which contains the source center. The left half of the figure is the CDO3/8 solution using 8 ppw and the right half is the computed solution using CDO5/10 and 6 ppw. In this plane, there is no discernable difference in the solutions. Figure 14, located at 1.5 units (6 effective wavelengths) upstream of the source shows the comparison between the solutions is still fairly good. Figures 15 and 16 display contours at 2.5 and 3.5 units upstream of the source, and begin to show a slight phase error for the CDO3/8 solution.

An increase in CFL number has a stronger effect on CDO3/8 as compared to CDO5/10. A comparison with the analytic solution is shown in Figure 17 for CFL = 0.8. The pressure at a point located at x = -3.5 and y = 3.5 is compared to the analytic pressure solution. The analytic solution was computed by superposition of two distributed sources located 4 units apart ($y_s = \pm 2$) in the y-direction. The analytic solution for a single source is computed by the spatial convolution of the source distribution with the 3-D convective Green's function. The specific form of the Green's function may be found in Wu and Lee[19] as:

$$G_c = \frac{e^{-ik\frac{\sqrt{\left(x - x_p\right)^2 + (1 - M_x^2)\left[(y - y_p)^2 + (z - z_p)^2\right]} - M_x(x - x_p)}{1 - M_x^2}}}{4\pi\sqrt{(x - x_p) + (1 - M_x^2)\left[(y - y_p)^2 + (z - z_p)^2\right]}}$$

where x_p, y_p, and z_p represent the source location, k is the wavenumber, with uniform flow, corresponding to $M_x = 0.5$, in the positive x-direction. Details on the spatial convolution to find the pressure or velocity potential can be found in Ziomek[20], or see Bailly and Juve[21] for similar treatment of a 2-D source.

As shown in Figure 17, the amplitudes of the pressure waves are comparable, with CDO3/8 having the greater amount of phase error directly upstream of the source.

CONCLUDING REMARKS

The 1-D and 2-D numerical examples demonstrate the ability of the high-order compact difference operators and LDDRK time integration method to propagate acoustic signals with high-fidelity over large distances and long integration times. The pentadiagonal operators can be introduced into computational procedures utilizing the tridiagonal schemes in a straightforward manner, however some care in the treatment of wall boundaries is necessary. The superior accuracy produces a greater rate of convergence toward exact results, or permits coarser grid resolution for a given error tolerance.

The 3-D numerical example presented here shows that for certain problems in CAA, the use of high-order pentadiagonal compact difference operators provides both a computational and storage savings when compared to tridiagonal schemes. For this case use of the pentadiagonal compact scheme resulted in a 53% reduction in the spatial grid requirement (and associated memory space) compared to the tridiagonal scheme. The CPU penalty for using the pentadiagonal scheme is approximately 1.56. With this penalty factored in, the decrease in actual computational time is 27% by using CDO5/10 compared to CDO3/8 for the same level of solution accuracy. These reductions are in addition to the 50% savings in CPU time achieved by adopting the RK-4/6 LDDRK time-integration in place of RK-4. Because 3-D problems tax the storage requirements of a system, the reduction in nodal requirements offered by the pentadiagonal scheme may be as important as the CPU savings.

Acknowledgements

The work presented here was supported by a NASA-EPSCOR grant. The authors wish to thank Dr. Ramesh Agarwal for leading that effort.

REFERENCES

1. Lele, S.K., "Compact Finite Difference Schemes with Spectral-like Resolution", *Journal of Computational Physics*, 103, 16-42, 1992.

2. Tam, C.K. and Webb, J.C., "Dispersion-Relation-Preserving Schemes for Computational Aeroacoustics", *Journal of Computational Physics*, 107, 262-281, 1993.

3. Casper, J., "Using High-Order Essentially Non-oscillating Schemes for Aeroacoustic Applications", AIAA *Journal*, 34, 244-250, 1994.

4. Tam, C.K. and Shen, H., "Direct Computation of Nonlinear Acoustic Pulses Using High-Order Finite Difference Schemes", AIAA Paper 93-4325, 1993.

5. Tam, C.K., Aurialt, L., and Camberli, F., "Perfectly Matched Layer as Absorbing Boundary Condition for Linearized Euler Equations in Open and Ducted Domains", AIAA Paper 98-0183, 1998.

6. Koutsavdis, E.K., Blaisdell, G.A., and Lyrintzis, A.S., "On the Use of Compact Schemes with Spatial Filtering in Computational Aeroacoustics", AIAA Paper 99-0360, 1999.

7. Visbal, M.R. and Gaitonde, D., "Very High-Order-Accurate Methods for Complex Unsteady Subsonic Flows", AIAA *Journal*, Vol. 37, No. 10, 1231-1239, 1999.

8. Hu, F.Q., Hussaini, Y.M., and Manthey, J.L., "Low-Dissipation and Low-Dispersion Runge-Kutta Schemes for Computational Aeroacoustics", *Journal of Computational Physics*, 124, 177-191, 1996.

9. Berenger, J.P., "A Perfectly Matched Layer for the Absorption of Electromagnetic Waves", *Journal of Computational Physics*, 114, 185-200, 1994.

10. Hu, F.Q., "On Absorbing Boundary Conditions for Linearized Euler Equations by a Perfectly Matched Layer", *Journal of Computational Physics*, 129, 201-219, 1996.

11. Dietiker, J.F., Hoffmann, K.A., Agarwal, R.K. and Papadakis, M., "Development of Three-Dimensional PML Boundary Conditions for Aeroacoustics Applications", AIAA Paper 2001-2790, 2001.

12. TenPas, P.W., Schwalm, S.E., and Agarwal, R.K., "Development of a High-Order Compact Algorithm for Aeroacoustics Employing PML Absorbing Boundaries", AIAA Paper 98-221, 1998.

13. Hayder, M., Hu, F.Q., and Hussaini, Y.M., "Toward Perfectly Matched Boundary Conditions for Euler Equations", AIAA Paper 97-2075, 1997.

14. Nizampatnam, L.S., Hoffmann, K. A., Papadakis, M. and Agarwal, R.K., "Investigation of Boundary Conditions for Computational Aeroacoustics", AIAA Paper 99-0357, 1999.

15. ICASE/LaRC Workshop on Benchmark Problems in Computational Aeroacoustics, NASA CP 3300, Eds. Hardin, J.C., Ristorcelli, J.R., and Tam, C.K.W., 1995.

16. Edgar, N.B., *A Study of the Accuracy and Stability of High-Order Compact Difference Methods for Computational Aeroacoustics*, Ph.D. Dissertation, University of Kansas, 2002.

17. ICASE/LaRC Second Workshop on Benchmark Problems in Computational Aeroacoustics, NASA CP 3352, Eds. Tam, C.K.W. and Hardin, C., 1997.

18. Kurbatskii, K.A., "Analytical Solutions of Category 1, Benchmark Problems 1 and 2", ICASE/LaRC Second Workshop on Benchmark Problems in Computational Aeroacoustics, NASA CP 3352, Eds. Tam, C.K. and Hardin, J.C., 9-17, 1997.

19. Wu, T.W., and Lee, L., "A Direct Boundary Integral Formulation for Acoustic Radiation in a Subsonic Uniform Flow", *Journal of Sound and Vibration*, **175**, No. 1, 51-63, 1994.

20 Ziomek, L.J., *Fundamentals of Acoustic Field Theory and Space-Time Signal Processing*, CRC Press, 1995.

21. Bailly, C. and Juve, D., "Numerical Solution of Acoustic Propagation Problems Using Linearized Euler Equations", AIAA *Journal*, Vol. 38, No. 1, 22-29, 2000.

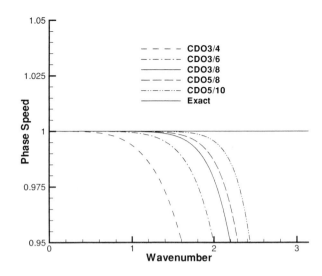

Figure 1. Numerical phase speed for families of tridiagonal and pentadiagonal compact difference operators as a function of wavenumber.

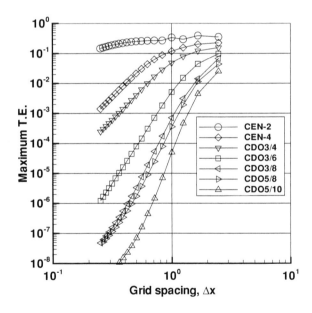

Figure 2. Maximum truncation error with respect to spatial grid refinement for linear wave equation solution at t = 400.

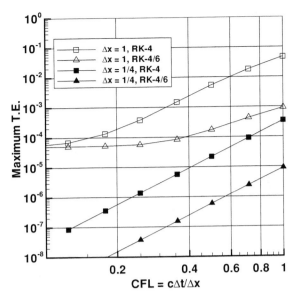

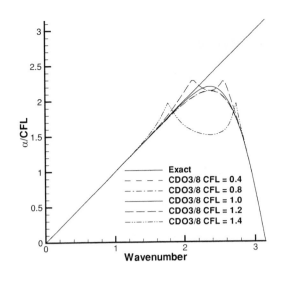

Figure 3. Maximum truncation error with respect to CFL number for linear wave equation at t = 400 with spatial grids of Δx = 0.25 and 1.0, using CDO5/10 and RK-4 and RK-4/6.

Figure 5. Dispersion characteristics for combined CDO3/8 and RK-4/6 integration for linear wave equation and periodic boundary conditions.

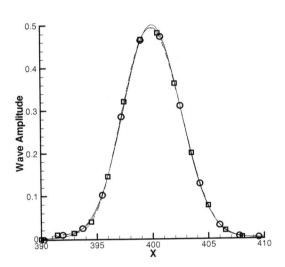

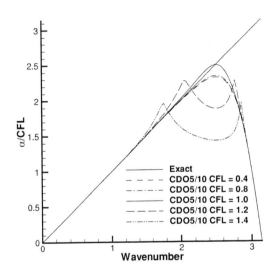

Figure 4. Comparison of CD03/8 and CDO5/10 numerical solutions at t = 400 for 1-D linear wave equation with Gaussian initial pulse.

Figure 6. Dispersion characteristics for combined CDO5/10 and RK-4/6 integration for linear wave equation and periodic boundary conditions.

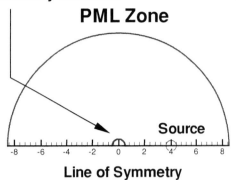

Figure 7. Schematic of 2-D cylindrical scattering of a transient pulse.

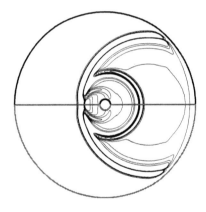

Figure 8. Pressure contours for transient pulse problem. Numerical solution at t = 6.25. Top half computed with CDO3/8 and bottom half with CDO5/10.

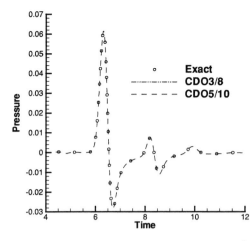

Figure 9. Pressure history at $r = 5$, $\theta = 90°$ for 2-D transient pulse problem.

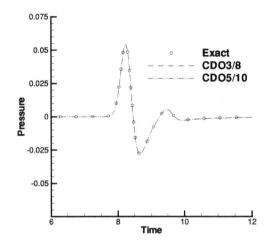

Figure 10. Pressure history at $r = 5$, $\theta = 135°$ for 2-D transient pulse problem.

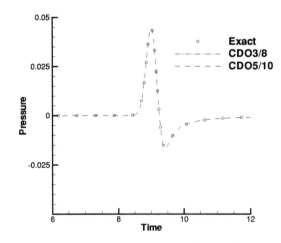

Figure 11. Pressure history at $r = 5$, $\theta = 180°$ for 2-D transient pulse problem.

Instantaneous Pressure Field
Note: Only positive pressure contours are shown

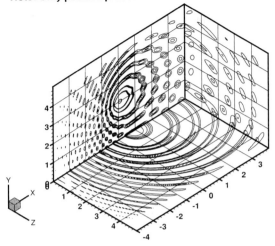

Figure 12. Scattering from a flat plate in uniform flow. Source centered at x = 0, y = 2, z = 0. Wall is located in XZ-plane at y = 0. Mach number, M_x=0.5.

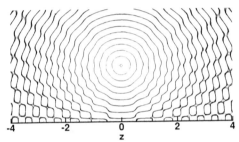

Figure 13. Positive pressure contours in the YZ-plane at x = 0. Left half CDO3/8 solution, right half CDO5/10. t = 30, CFL=0.5

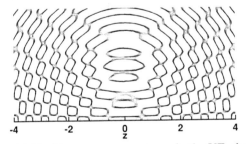

Figure 14. Positive pressure contours in the YZ-plane at x=-1.5. L-Side CDO3/8 solution, R-Side CDO5/10. t = 30, CFL = 0.5

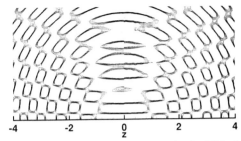

Figure 15. Positive pressure contours in the YZ-plane at x =-2.5. L-Side CDO3/8 solution, R-Side CDO5/10. t = 30, CFL = 0.5

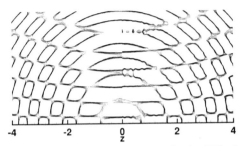

Figure 16. Positive pressure contours in the YZ-plane at x =-3.5. L-Side CDO3/8 solution, R-Side CDO5/10. t = 30, CFL = 0.5

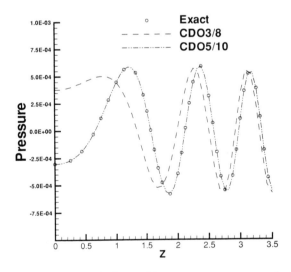

Figure 17. Comparison of instantaneous pressure in the XY-plane at x = -3.5 and y = 3.5 for CDO3/8 and CDO5/10. RK-4/6 integration, CFL = 0.8.

FINITE-ELEMENT BASED LARGE-EDDY SIMULATION OF THE NEAR-NOZZLE REGION OF A COMPRESSIBLE ROUND JET

K. Jansen[*]

Rensselaer Polytechnic Institute

Troy, NY 12180

T. Maeder, R. Reba

United Technologies Research Center

East Hartford, CT 06018

Abstract

The near-nozzle region of a compressible high Reynolds number ($Re \quad 10^6$) turbulent cold round jet has been numerically simulated. A finite-element based large-eddy simulation technique has been used on a fully unstructured mesh. The computational domain has been restricted to a 20-degree azimuthal sector that includes the end part of a converging nozzle. Results for the flow in the first diameter downstream of the nozzle lip are in qualitative agreement with experimental data. A frequency-domain formulation of the Lighthill analogy has been used to compute the far-field pressure spectrum. Sources of discrepancy with experimental data have been identified and improvement strategies are addressed.

Introduction

Aircraft noise is a problem of continuing concern due to the steadily augmenting volume of air transport, and due to increasing stringency in national and international noise regulations. In many situations, jet exhaust noise is a dominant contributor to the overall noise of the aircraft. The design of jet noise reduction devices continues to rely heavily on extensive experimental testing. In recent years, however, computational techniques for modeling noise generation by jet flows have emerged as useful tools for both understanding fundamental physical mechanisms and for practical design.[1-3] Among these, large-eddy simulation (LES) offers a promising alternative to direct numerical simulation (DNS), which is prohibitively expensive for Reynolds numbers of practical interest, and to Reynolds-averaged Navier-Stokes simulation (RANS), which does not yield dynamical information. A review of some problems and promises of computational aeroacoustics is found in Lele.[4]

To date, application of LES to jet noise analysis has focused on downstream regions of the jet domain, while ignoring details of nozzle geometry and of the initial shear-layer development. Only very recently a LES of a high Reynolds number supersonic jet was undertaken, where the entire nozzle geometry was included in the computational domain.[5] The simulation uses a structured grid extending more than 12 diameters downstream of the nozzle lip with 1.5 million points and a finite-difference numerical scheme with a compressible form of Smagorinsky's subgrid-scale model. The agreement of the mean flow with experimental data is relatively good, but unfortunately neither turbulence statistics nor dynamical flow information are shown. The authors of that simulation recognize that there is much room for improvement, especially by enhancing the subgrid-scale model.

Understanding the dynamics of the near-nozzle region is important from the standpoint of designing passive noise reduction devices such as tabs. Recent studies show that while the dominant noise generation occurs at the end of the jet potential core, EPNL (Effective Perceived Noise Level) sensitive high-frequency noise is produced within the first few jet diameters.[6,7] Hence, the objective of the current research is to develop LES capability for simulating the effects of real geometry (e.g. nozzle and tabs) on initial jet

---

* Associate Professor

development and noise. Note that the accurate flow information provided by LES is extremely valuable to develop and validate reduced-order models, e.g. vortex models.[8,9]

In this paper, we present results of a finite-element based LES of the near-nozzle region of a Mach 0.6 cold turbulent round jet at a Reynolds number of approximately 10^6. The computational domain is a 20-degree azimuthal sector extending 2 jet diameters D downstream of an axisymmetric converging nozzle, and roughly $0.1D$ inside the nozzle. The grid is fully unstructured. The far-field pressure is computed by applying the Lighthill acoustic analogy.

Numerical method

The compressible Navier-Stokes equations are filtered in space (with the density weighted Favre average) to arrive at transport equations for the large eddies in the simulation. The non-linear convective term gives rise to a new term, the subgrid scale stress, which is modeled with the dynamic approach of Germano *et al.*,[10] extended to unstructured grids by Jansen.[11] The filtered equations are:

$$\overline{}_{,t} + \left[\,\overline{}\,\tilde{u}_i\right]_{,i} = 0 \tag{1}$$

$$\left[\overline{}\,\tilde{u}_i\right]_{,t} + \left[\overline{}\,\tilde{u}_i\tilde{u}_j\right]_{,j} = \left[\;\overline{p}\;_{ij} + \;_{ij}\right]_{,j} \tag{2}$$

$$\left[\overline{}\,\tilde{e}_{tot}\right]_{,t} + \left[\overline{}\,\tilde{u}_i\tilde{e}_{tot}\right]_{,i} = \left[\;\overline{p}\tilde{u}_i + \;\overline{}_{ij}\tilde{u}_j \quad q_i^{heat}\right]_{,i} \tag{3}$$

where is the density, u_i the velocity component in Cartesian direction i, p the pressure, $_{ij}$ the Kronecker delta function, $_{ij}$ the stress tensor, e_{tot} the total energy per unit mass and q_i^{heat} the component of the heat flux in direction i. Here a tilde denotes quantities that are formed with a density weighted filter while quantities with a bar are filtered without a density weight (simple filtering).

The fluid is assumed to be Newtonian with a total viscosity μ_T^{visc} given as the sum of molecular μ^{visc} and eddy viscosity μ_e^{visc} (given by the dynamic model). The stress tensor is then

$$_{ij} = 2\mu_T^{visc}(S_{ij} \quad \frac{1}{3}S_{kk} \;_{ij}) \tag{4}$$

where S_{ij} is the strain rate tensor

$$S_{ij} = \tfrac{1}{2}\left(\tilde{u}_{i,j} + \tilde{u}_{j,i}\right). \tag{5}$$

The heat flux q_i^{heat} is similarly augmented by an eddy conductivity which is related to the eddy viscosity given by the dynamic model through a turbulent Prandtl number.

The fluid is assumed to be an ideal gas, for which pressure, temperature and density are related as

$$\overline{p} = \overline{}R\tilde{T} \tag{6}$$

where R is the gas constant for the fluid.

The equations described above can be written as a vector system

$$\mathbf{U}_{,t} + \mathbf{F}_{i,i} = \mathbf{U}_{,t} + \mathbf{F}_{i,i}^{adv} \quad \mathbf{F}_{i,i}^{diff} = \mathbf{0} \tag{7}$$

with

$$\mathbf{U} = \begin{matrix} \overline{} \\ \overline{}\tilde{u}_1 \\ \overline{}\tilde{u}_2 \\ \overline{}\tilde{u}_3 \\ \overline{}\tilde{e}_{tot} \end{matrix}, \quad \mathbf{F}_i^{adv} = \begin{matrix} \overline{}\tilde{u}_i \\ \overline{}\tilde{u}_1\tilde{u}_i + \overline{p}\;_{1i} \\ \overline{}\tilde{u}_2\tilde{u}_i + \overline{p}\;_{2i} \\ \overline{}\tilde{u}_3\tilde{u}_i + \overline{p}\;_{3i} \\ \overline{}\tilde{e}_{tot}\tilde{u}_i + \overline{p}\tilde{u}_i \end{matrix},$$

$$\mathbf{F}_i^{diff} = \begin{matrix} 0 \\ _{1i}(\tilde{\mathbf{u}}) \\ _{2i}(\tilde{\mathbf{u}}) \\ _{3i}(\tilde{\mathbf{u}}) \\ \tilde{u}_j\left(\;_{ij}(\tilde{\mathbf{u}})\right) + \;\tilde{T}_{,i} \end{matrix}. \tag{8}$$

This system of partial differential equations is discretized via a finite element method

$$\int\left(\mathbf{W}\;\mathbf{U}_{,t} \quad \mathbf{W}_{,i}\;\mathbf{F}_i\right)d \quad + \int\left(\mathbf{W}\;\mathbf{F}_i\right)\mathbf{n}_i\,d = 0 \tag{9}$$

where $\mathbf{W}$ is a vector of weight functions that are left arbitrary. It is more practical to interpolate the solution with primitive variables, such as $\mathbf{Y} = \{\,p\;u_j\;T\,\}^T$. The transformation for the time derivative and the advective flux term is obtained using the chain rule

$$\mathbf{U}_{,t} = \mathbf{U}_{,Y}\mathbf{Y}_{,t} \quad \mathbf{A}_0\mathbf{Y}_{,t} \tag{10}$$

$$\mathbf{F}_{i,i}^{adv} = \mathbf{F}_{i,Y}^{adv}\;\mathbf{Y}_{,i} \quad \mathbf{A}_i\mathbf{Y}_{,i}. \tag{11}$$

For the term that involves a time derivative of $\mathbf{U}$, the Euclidean metric $\mathbf{A}_0$ is multiplied by the time derivative of $\mathbf{Y}$. For the advective flux term, which involves three spatial derivatives of $\mathbf{U}$, there exist Jacobians $\mathbf{A}_i$ for each of the three spatial derivatives of the primitive variables. The diffusive flux is constructed in a similar fashion

$$\mathbf{F}_{i,i}^{diff} = \left[\Gamma_{ij}\mathbf{Y}_{,j} \right]_{,i} . \qquad (12)$$

The scheme described above is unstable in its present formulation. This is remedied by adding a stabilization term

$$\int \mathbf{L}^T \mathbf{W} \, \tau \, (\mathbf{L}\mathbf{Y}) d\Omega \qquad (13)$$

to the residual, with the operator

$$\mathbf{L} = \mathbf{A}_0 \frac{\partial}{\partial t} + \mathbf{A}_i \frac{\partial}{\partial x_i} - \frac{\partial}{\partial x_i} \Gamma_{ij} \frac{\partial}{\partial x_j} . \qquad (14)$$

The design of the stabilization matrix τ is described in Franca & Frey.[12] It does no harm to the exact formulation, since $\mathbf{L}\mathbf{Y} = 0$ for the exact solution.

At this point, the continuum problem must be reduced to the final discrete problem. Instead of finding a field (with infinite degrees of freedom) that satisfies the Reynolds-averaged Navier Stokes equations, only a set of nodal values needs to be determined for which the residual,

$$\mathbf{G}_B = \int_\Omega \left[N_B\left(\mathbf{U}_{,t}\right) - N_{B,i}\mathbf{F}_i \right] d\Omega +$$

$$\int_\Omega \mathbf{L}N_B \, \tau \, (\mathbf{L}\mathbf{Y}) d\Omega + \int_\Gamma \left(N_B \mathbf{F}_i \right) n_i d\Gamma \qquad (16)$$

is minimized.

Results and discussion

To exploit the power of the finite element method, fully unstructured grids are employed. Since we are interested in the flow very near the lip we must resolve the boundary layer on the interior of the nozzle, requiring the use of highly anisotropic boundary layer meshes.

The near lip region of a jet flow is characterized by widely varying length scales, which represent a challenge for the flow modeling. The thickness of the boundary layer and the finite thickness of the nozzle lip set the length scale of the smallest eddy that even a large-eddy simulation of a near lip region must capture. In our case, the lip is $0.004D$ thick (D is the nozzle exit diameter) and the boundary layer thickness at the lip is approximately $0.01D$. To even marginally resolve this scale requires spacing of $0.001D$ in all directions at the nozzle lip.

At the other extreme is the extent of the domain to be considered. In keeping with the objective of having one diameter of the after-lip flow accurately simulated, the downstream boundary was placed two diameters downstream. Gradual growth of the element size, in keeping with the growth of the large-eddies as they mature in the shear layer is possible with the unstructured grid as can be seen in Figure 1. The radial extent of this refinement followed by gradual coarsening was bounded by an estimation of the radial extent of the shear layer.

While the experiment starts a boundary layer prior to the converging nozzle (following a series of screens), it would be impractical to perform the simulation of that long domain, owing to the strict grid requirements of wall-bounded flows in LES. Instead, the results from a RANS simulation of the entire domain are used to provide inlet profiles to the LES, which starts only $0.12D$ upstream of the nozzle lip. This modeling choice has consequences that will be discussed more fully below. As the boundary layer and the shear layer remain relatively thin, the computational domain is reduced to only a 20-degree azimuthal sector, which in the region of interest provides sufficient decay of the two-point correlation for the application of axisymmetric-periodic boundary conditions (see below). A broader sector would be needed for accurate representation of the shear layer beyond one diameter downstream of the nozzle lip, where the shear layer would "outgrow" the azimuthal extent of the present domain.

Flow field

Mean streamwise velocity profiles are represented at X/D=0 and 1 in Figure 2 and compared with the experimental data of Narayanan et al.[7] The boundary-layer thickness at the exit is well captured, but the computation proves to have a too high spreading rate, as indicated by the overpredicted shear layer thickness at X/D=1. This is believed to be the result of a too early and aggressive grid coarsening. A simulation with an extended and improved grid is currently in progress. The exaggerated spreading rate is also seen in Figure 3 with the profile of streamwise velocity fluctuations. The location of the peak fluctuations is seen to be slightly further away from the centerline in the LES, and the profile is broader. The peak fluctuation level is roughly 2.7 times higher in the LES compared with the experimental data. This situation is also visible at the nozzle lip, where the peak turbulence in the LES is approximately twice as high as the one measured experimentally, which is around 3 to 5%.

We suspect that a spurious feedback mechanism between the inflow plane inside the nozzle and the shear-layer excite the flow in an artificial way. We have indications that the short inflow section combined with stiff boundary conditions (velocity and temperature from a RANS simulation) might be responsible for non-physical wave reflection at the inflow plane. Also, we have noticed that the mean flow seems not to have reached a perfectly steady state, which affects the quality of the fluctuations statistics.

The streamwise evolution of the shear layer is illustrated in Figure 4. The instantaneous radial velocity field in the vertical centerline plane shows the formation and pairing process of vortices. The azimuthal extent of those flow structures is represented in Figure 5. In this section normal to the centerline at $X/D=0.5$, the azimuthal correlation length is seen to be sufficiently smaller than the corresponding domain extent at the lip location. The autocorrelation functions of the azimuthal velocity component, illustrated in Figure 6, support the above-mentioned observation. The two-dimensional (streamwise direction – time) autocorrelation functions of the radial velocity component in the shear layer (Figure 7) show a clear increase of correlation length when going downstream. If the correlation time scale is defined as the first separation where the autocorrelation function becomes zero, one gets $t_{cor} = 0.08$ at $X/D=0.24$ and $t_{cor} = 0.2$ at $X/D=0.74$, with a convection velocity $v_{conv} \approx 0.5$ (t_{cor} and v_{conv} normalized with the jet diameter D and mixed velocity U).

Near-field streamwise velocity spectra are shown in Figure 8 and compared with data of Narayanan et al.[8] The velocity signal is taken in the shear layer at two streamwise locations. As the experimental signal was not calibrated, it has been rescaled with the peak amplitude of the simulation data at each considered location. The LES data show a decrease in peak frequency when going downstream, as observed in the experiment. However, the peak frequency in the simulation is systematically lower than in the experiment. This may be related to the higher spreading rate of the shear-layer, where a thicker shear layer accommodates larger structures with a smaller characteristic frequency, which is proportional to the convective velocity divided by the shear-layer thickness.

Far-field pressure

A frequency-domain formulation of Lighthill's acoustic analogy[13] was used to compute the far-field pressure. To simplify the problem, the sound

is computed for an observer located at an angle of 90 degrees from the jet axis. This allows consideration of only one component of the Lighthill acoustic 'source' term T_{ij} given by

$$T_{ij} = u_i u_j + \left(p - c_0^2 \rho \right) \delta_{ij} \quad . \tag{17}$$

For the cold jet considered here, the second term in (17) has been neglected. With the far-field approximation, the density fluctuations are

$$\rho(\mathbf{x},t) = \frac{1}{4\pi c_0^4} \frac{x_i x_j}{|\mathbf{x}|^3} \int \frac{\partial^2}{\partial t^2} T_{ij}(\mathbf{y},t_r)\, d\mathbf{y} \tag{18}$$

where $\mathbf{x}$ is the observer location, $\mathbf{y}$ the source field location, c_0 the speed of sound in the acoustic propagation region and t_r the retarded time

$$t_r = t - \frac{|\mathbf{x}|}{c_0} + \frac{\mathbf{x}\cdot\mathbf{y}}{|\mathbf{x}| c_0} \quad . \tag{19}$$

The sound pressure spectrum

$$P(\mathbf{x},\omega) = \frac{1}{p_{ref}^2} \int \langle p(\mathbf{x},t)\, p(\mathbf{x},t+\tau) \rangle e^{i\omega\tau}\, d\tau \tag{20}$$

is then computed as

$$P(\tilde{\mathbf{x}},\omega) = \frac{\rho_0^2 U^7 D}{p_{ref}^2 c_0^4} \frac{\omega^4}{16\pi^2} \frac{\tilde{x}_i \tilde{x}_j \tilde{x}_k \tilde{x}_l}{|\tilde{\mathbf{x}}|^6} \frac{2}{\tilde{T}}$$
$$\left\langle \int \tilde{T}_{ij}(\tilde{\mathbf{y}},\omega)\exp\left(-iM\omega\tilde{\mathbf{x}}\cdot\tilde{\mathbf{y}}/|\tilde{\mathbf{x}}| \right)d\tilde{\mathbf{y}} \right. \tag{21}$$
$$\left. \left\{ \int \tilde{T}_{kl}(\tilde{\mathbf{y}},\omega)\exp\left(-iM\omega\tilde{\mathbf{x}}\cdot\tilde{\mathbf{y}}/|\tilde{\mathbf{x}}| \right)d\tilde{\mathbf{y}} \right\}^* \right\rangle$$

where the symbols with a tilde have been non-dimensionalized with the nozzle exit diameter D and the mixed velocity U, and M is the Mach number U/c_0. The Fourier transformation of T_{ij} in time is given by

$$T_{ij}(\omega) = \int_0^T T_{ij}(t) e^{i\omega t}\, dt \quad . \tag{22}$$

The reference pressure p_{ref} is $2\ 10^{-5}\ Pa$ and the observer is located 12 nozzle diameters away from the jet axis at an angle of 90 degrees.

The noise produced by the full jet section is approximated by the addition of the 18 contributions of the 20-degree sector, which has been rotated without overlap to describe the full section. Considering the reconstructed full section would introduce artificial azimuthal correlation and acoustic interference effects. The linear addition of acoustic power from the individual contributions on the other hand cannot represent azimuthal structures larger than the arc spanned by the computational domain, and the corresponding noise will not be captured. This will typically be visible as a deficit at low frequencies, but this effect is expected to be small, as the flow within the first jet diameter has not had enough time to develop such large azimuthal structures.

In order to accommodate the non-periodic samples with a Fourier transformation, the data is filtered in time (Hanning filter) and space (Gaussian filter in the spanwise direction and Gaussian or combined filters in the streamwise direction). The sound pressure level computed with the above-described method is shown in Figure 9 and compared with phased-array data from Narayanan *et al.*[7] The phased array technique provides an axial noise source distribution, which allows the determination of the noise contribution from each longitudinal "slice" of the jet. Given the limited streamwise extent of our computational domain, the phased-array data for the corresponding flow region offer a better comparison than the far-field noise spectrum of the full jet. The non-dimensional sampling rate is $St = 82$, and 7 records (with 50% overlap) of length $T=1.56$ have been used. The considered flow history corresponds to roughly 3 flow-through times through a domain of 1 diameter streamwise extent. The overpredicted noise level is consistent with the high fluctuation level observed in the near field. The velocity fluctuations are roughly two to three times too high, which gives a 12-14 dB difference when translated directly in squared pressure fluctuations. The observed maximal difference of roughly 8dB shows that not all the excess near-field fluctuations have made their way to the far field. Note however that the peak frequency range is in good agreement with data.

Several streamwise filters (illustrated in Figure 10) have been applied to assess the influence of artificially truncating the flow structures at the domain exit. In general, the effects of windowing will become less important as the number of "correlation volumes" contained within the domain increases. It is clear that in this case the Gaussian filter is too abrupt, decaying over a scale short compared to the typical local streamwise correlation scale (Figure 7), and generates significant spurious noise. Results obtained with the less aggressive filters show lower noise levels and reduced sensitivity to filter shape.

Conclusions

The challenging problem of simulating the near-nozzle region (including the end of the nozzle itself) of a round jet at a Reynolds number of 10^6 and a Mach number of 0.6 has been addressed using a FEM-based LES technique in a 20-degree sector with a fully unstructured mesh. Very careful gridding has appeared to be essential for the physical meaningfulness of the resulting flow-field. Due to insufficient resolution of some regions of the shear-layer and spurious wave reflection at the inflow boundary, fluctuation levels in the shear layer are overpredicted by approximately a factor of 2 to 3, resulting in an overprediction of shear-layer growth rate. An improved boundary region treatment based on the implementation of numerical sponges enforcing a previously computed mean solution is being tested. Consistent with the high fluctuation level in the near field, the far-field pressure spectrum computed with the Lighthill analogy is overpredicted. The peak frequency range is however in relatively good agreement with experimental data.

These preliminary results, while falling short of completely describing the physics and matching experimental data, have provided much information to what further improvements are necessary. A new simulation is underway, in which the near-lip region has been further refined. The refinement region has now a wider radial extent to ensure that the unsteady shear layer does not "wag" out of that region. Within the shear-layer refinement region (particularly between $X/D=0.5$ and 1.0), the growth rate of the spacing has been reduced. The outflow boundary has been extended to five diameters downstream of the nozzle lip, while the far-field boundary has been pushed to four diameters in the radial direction. Finally, the inflow region has been extended upstream to the same location as the screens in the experiment (with a hybrid RANS/LES/DES treatment of the region between the inflow and $0.12D$ upstream of the nozzle). Figure 11 provides a view of the new mesh and computational domain.

This work is jointly funded by the United Technologies Research Center and Pratt & Whitney. The authors acknowledge R. H. Schlinker and W. Lord for their support, thank T. Colonius and S. Narayanan for constructive discussions, and M. Yaworski for assistance in processing the results.

References

1. J. Gilson, V. Saxena, G. Kohlenberg, A. Rangwalla, A. Nedungadi and C. K. W. Tam, "Prediction of three dimensional jet noise", AIAA Paper 2001-2118, 2001.

2. T. Colonius and J. B. Freund, "Application of Lighthill's equation to a Mach 1.92 turbulent jet", AIAA J., Vol. 38(2), pp. 368-370, 2000.

3. J. B. Freund, "Noise sources in a low Reynolds number turbulent jet at Mach 0.9", J. Fluid Mech., Vol. 438, pp. 277-305, 2001.

4. S. K. Lele, "Computational aeroacoustics: a review", AIAA Paper 97-0018, 1997.

5. J. R. DeBonis and J. N. Scott, "A large-eddy simulation of a turbulent compressible round jet", AIAA Paper 2001-2254, 2001.

6. J. C. Simonich, S. Narayanan, T. J. Barber and N. Nishimura, "Aeroacoustic characterization, noise reduction, and dimensional scaling effects of high subsonic jets", AIAA J., Vol. 39(11), pp. 2062-2069, 2001.

7. S. Narayanan, T. J. Barber and D. R. Polak, "High subsonic jet experiments: Turbulence and noise generation studies", AIAA J., Vol. 40(2), pp. 430-437, 2002.

8. S. Narayanan, B. R. Noack and E. Meiburg, "Reduced-order dynamical modeling of sound generation from a jet", AIAA Paper 2002-0073, 2002.

9. M. C. Soteriou, R. Reba and T. Maeder, "Numerical study of the impact of streamwise vorticity on jet noise", AIAA Paper 2002-2480, 2002.

10. M. Germano, U. Piomelli, P. Moin and W. H. Cabot, "A dynamic subgrid-scale eddy viscosity model", Phys. Fluids, Vol. A3, pp. 1760-1765, 1991.

11. K. E. Jansen, "A stabilized finite element method to compute turbulence", Comput. Methods Appl. Mech. Engrg., Vol. 174, pp. 299-317, 1999.

12. L. P. Franca and S. Frey, "Stabilized finite element methods: II. The incompressible Navier-Stokes equations", Comput. Methods Appl. Mech. Engrg., Vol. 99, pp. 209-233, 1992.

13. M. J. Lighthill, "On sound generated aerodynamically I. General theory", Proc. Roy. Soc. London, Series A, Vol. 211, pp. 564-581, 1952.

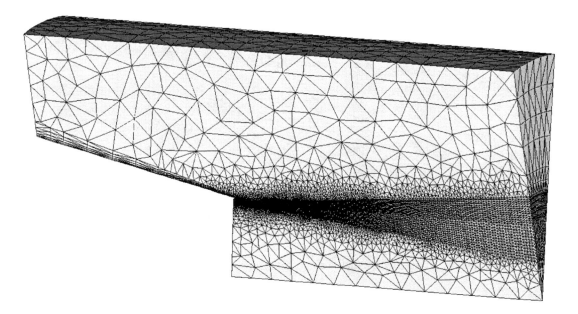

Figure 1: Unstructured grid extending 2 nozzle diameters downstream of the nozzle exit plane.

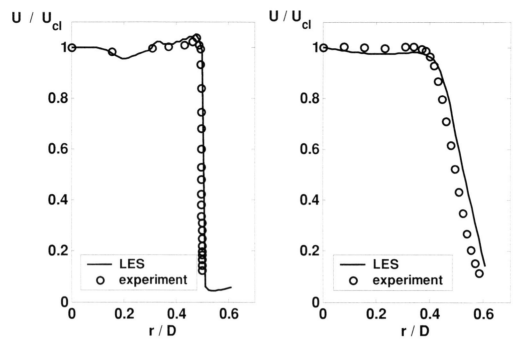

Figure 2: Mean streamwise velocity profile at the nozzle exit plane $X/D = 0$ (left) and at $X/D=1$ (right).

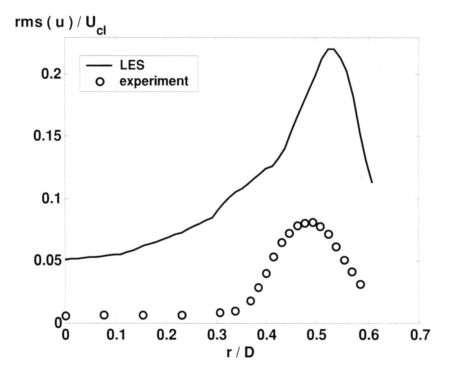

Figure 3: Mean streamwise velocity fluctuations one diameter downstream of nozzle exit plane ($X/D=1$).

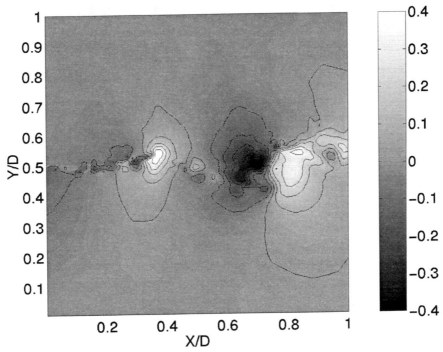

Figure 4: Instantaneous radial velocity field in the vertical x-y centerline plane (*X*=0 is the nozzle exit).

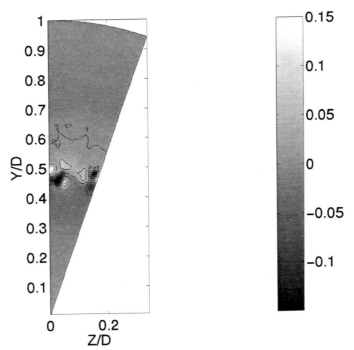

Figure 5: Instantaneous radial velocity field in the vertical y-z plane half a diameter downstream of the nozzle exit plane.

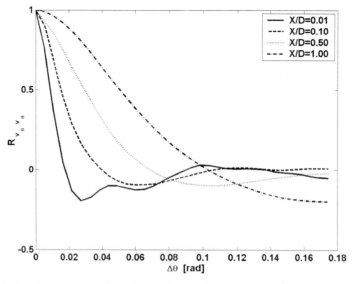

Figure 6: Autocorrelation function for the azimuthal velocity component in the shear layer at different streamwise locations. The maximum azimuthal separation $\Delta\theta'_{max}$ corresponds to half the sector aperture angle.

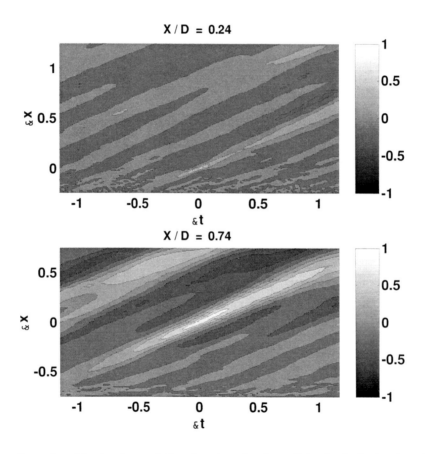

Figure 7: Two-dimensional (x-t) autocorrelation functions for the radial velocity in the shear-layer at different streamwise locations ($X=0$ is the nozzle lip).

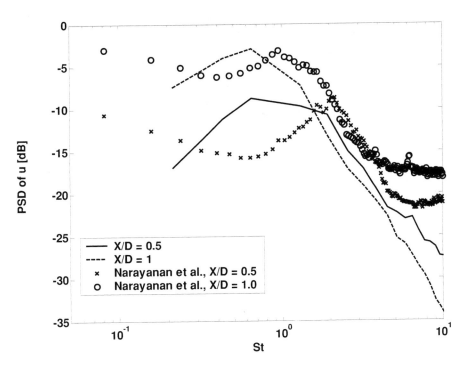

Figure 8: Power spectral density of streamwise velocity *u* in the shear layer; amplitude of experimental data normalized with peak simulation value.

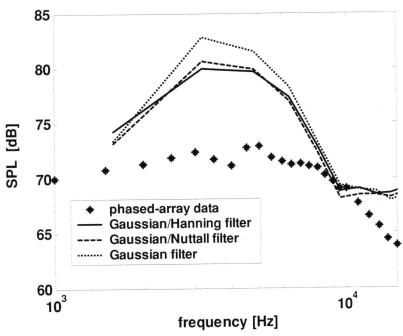

Figure 9: Sound pressure level (SPL) of the first jet diameter for an observer located 12 nozzle diameters away from the jet axis at 90 degrees. The different spatial filters used in the streamwise direction are illustrated in Figure 10.

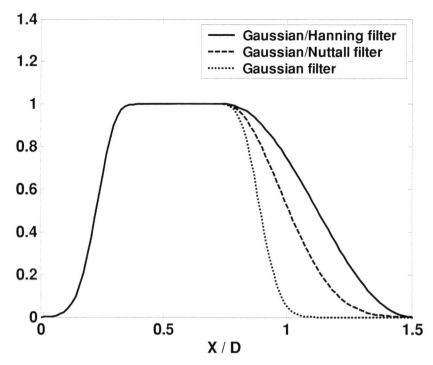

Figure 10: Spatial streamwise filters used to compute the sound pressure levels of Figure 9.

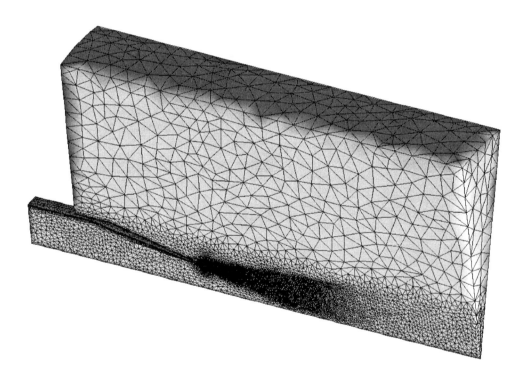

Figure 11: Improved LES mesh.

A VELOCITY–POTENTIAL–BASED BOUNDARY–ELEMENT METHOD FOR THE AEROACOUSTIC ANALYSIS OF ROTORS AND PROPELLERS IN ARBITRARY MOTION

L. Morino, G. Bernardini and M. Gennaretti
Università *Roma Tre*
via Vasca Navale 79 – 00146 Rome, Italy

ABSTRACT

A new boundary integral formulation for the aerodynamic and aeroacoustic analysis of a body (in particular, a tiltrotor) in arbitrary motion is presented. The formulation is based on the velocity potential for compressible flows, and as such is an extension of past work of the authors. The distinguishing feature is that the boundary integral representation is written for a surface in arbitrary motion with respect to a frame of reference which in turns moves in arbitrary motion with respect to the undisturbed air. Thus, the integrals are evaluated on the *emission surface*, which is the locus of the emitting points at the locations that they had (in the moving frame) when the signal influencing a given point at a given time was emitted. The differences with respect to others formulations (*e.g.*, Ffowcs Williams and Hawkings) are outlined; also, the advantages of the formulation with respect to the preceding formulations by the authors are discussed.

INTRODUCTION

The objective of this paper is to present a formulation for the aerodynamic and aeroacoustic analysis of a body in arbitrary motion with emphasis on propellers and helicopter rotors. The formulation is related to those used in the past by the authors and their collaborators, in that it is based on the solution of the equation for the velocity potential, via a boundary integral equation. Two approaches have been used in the past by the authors and their collaborators. In the original work by [7], the integral representation is written for a surface moving in arbitrary motion with respect to a space of reference in uniform translation. A more general approach is used in [9], where the integral formulation is written for a surface that moves in arbitrary motion with

respect to a frame of reference that in turns moves in arbitrary motion; the compressible–flow applications however are limited to rotors in hover. A related formulation is presented in [5], which includes numerical applications to forward flight (see also [6], which includes numerical applications to aeroacoustics). For all the numerical compressible–flow results presented in these papers, the surface is fixed with respect to the frame of reference chosen for that surface, *i.e.*, a body frame is used for the rotor, whereas for the wake, different frames are used for hover and forward flight; specifically, in hover, a body frame of reference is used, as the wake is fixed in such a frame, whereas in forward flight an air frame is used as the wake may be considered fixed in such a frame, as long as the roll–up may be neglected. This fact causes problems for the transition from hover to forward flight or for forward flight cases with low advance ratios (where neither one of the two formulations is applicable).

These problems are the main motivations for the present work. Specifically, it is desirable to have a formulation in which a single frame of reference (*e.g.*, body frame, or air frame) is used for the blade and/or its wake throughout the transition. This implies that, with the exception of a propeller in axial flow and a helicopter rotor in hover, one needs a formulation in which the boundary surface (*i.e.*, the blade and/or the wake surface) moves with respect to the frame of reference. The distinguishing feature of the formulation presented here is that the surface is assumed to be moving with respect to an arbitrary moving auxiliary frame of reference which in turn is moving with respect to the undisturbed air. Hence, the integrals are evaluated on the *emission surface*, which is here defined as the locus of all the *emission points* at the location they had when the signal reaching a given *receiving point* at a given time was emitted. As mentioned above, this feature is present in the formulations of both [9] and [5]. The present work contains features from both of these papers (specifically, in Eq. 4 the operators are outside the integrals as in [9], whereas the transformation, based on Eq. 16, is from [5]).

The fact that the integrals are evaluated on the emission surface implies that the mathematics used in the present formulation for obtaining the integral formulation is closely related to the emission–surface (or retarded–surface) algorithms used in aeroacoustics for the integration of the Ffowcs Williams and Hawkings [4] equation for the acoustic pressure (see for instance Farassat [2], Farassat and Myers [3], and Brentner [1]). However, the present formulation is written in a moving frame of reference (whereas in aeroacoustics the *emission surface* is defined with respect to the undisturbed air). In addition, the formulation is written in terms of the velocity potential and may therefore be used not only for aeroacoustics but also for aerodynamics, indeed providing a useful tool for an integrated analysis of both aerodynamics and aeroacoustics.

A preliminary version of this paper, with results limited to aerodynamics, was presented in [8].

BOUNDARY INTEGRAL FORMULATION

An inviscid nonconducting flow, which is initially isentropic and irrotational, remains isentropic and irrotational at all times (Kelvin's theorem), with the exception of the points emanating from the trailing edge, which form a surface, $\mathcal{S}_\mathrm{W}$, called the wake. In this case, the velocity field may be expressed in terms of a velocity potential, $\varphi(\mathbf{x}, t)$, as $\mathbf{v} = \nabla_{\mathbf{x}}\varphi$, for $\mathbf{x} \in \mathcal{V}_\mathrm{F}\backslash\mathcal{S}_\mathrm{W}$, where $\mathcal{V}_\mathrm{F}$ is the fluid volume.[1] The motion of an object of arbitrary shape in a potential flow is governed by the equation for the velocity potential which is a nonlinear wave equation. Neglecting the non–linear terms we have

$$\nabla_{\mathbf{x}}^2\varphi - \frac{1}{c^2}\frac{\partial^2\varphi}{\partial t^2} = 0 \qquad (\mathbf{x} \in \mathcal{V}_\mathrm{F}\backslash\mathcal{S}_\mathrm{W}), \qquad (1)$$

where c is the undisturbed speed of sound.

Next, consider the boundary conditions. The impermeability boundary condition on the boundary surface (body) implies $\partial\varphi/\partial n = \mathbf{v}_\mathrm{B} \cdot \mathbf{n}$ ($\mathbf{x} \in \mathcal{S}_\mathrm{B}$), where $\mathbf{v}_\mathrm{B}$ is the velocity of the boundary at $\mathbf{x}$ and $\mathbf{n}$ is the normal to $\mathcal{S}_\mathrm{B}$, also at $\mathbf{x}$. The boundary condition at infinity is $\varphi = 0$. The boundary conditions on the wake, a surface of discontinuity for the potential φ,

---

[1]We use $\mathbf{x}$ and t to denote collocation point and time (in the air space), whereas space and time variables of integration are denoted by $\mathbf{y}$ and τ in the air space and by $\bar{\mathbf{y}}$ and $\bar{\tau}$ in the auxiliary moving space.

are $\Delta\left(\partial\varphi/\partial n\right) = 0$, and $\Delta\varphi =$ constant following a wake point.

Following Ffowcs Williams and Hawkings [4], we replace the above boundary–value problem with an equivalent infinite–space problem. Introducing the domain function, $E(\mathbf{x}, t) = 1$ outside $\mathcal{S}_\mathrm{B}$, $E(\mathbf{x}, t) = 0$ inside $\mathcal{S}_\mathrm{B}$, yields

$$\nabla_{\mathbf{x}}^2(E\varphi) - \frac{1}{c^2}\frac{\partial^2(E\varphi)}{\partial t^2} = \nabla_{\mathbf{x}}\varphi \cdot \nabla_{\mathbf{x}}E + \nabla_{\mathbf{x}} \cdot (\varphi\nabla_{\mathbf{x}}E)$$
$$- \frac{1}{c^2}\frac{\partial\varphi}{\partial t}\frac{\partial E}{\partial t} - \frac{1}{c^2}\frac{\partial}{\partial t}\left(\varphi\frac{\partial E}{\partial t}\right), \qquad (2)$$

with $\mathbf{x} \in \mathbb{R}^3$. Introducing the fundamental solution for the acoustic (wave) equation,

$$G_\mathrm{A} = G\delta(\tau - t + r/c), \qquad (3)$$

with $G = -1/4\pi r$ and $r = \|\mathbf{x} - \mathbf{y}\|$, one obtains the following integral representation for the velocity potential:

$$
\begin{aligned}
E(\mathbf{x}, t)\varphi(\mathbf{x}, t) &= \int_0^t\int_{\mathbb{R}^3} G_\mathrm{A}\nabla_{\mathbf{y}}\varphi \cdot \nabla_{\mathbf{y}}E d\mathcal{V}d\tau \\
&+ \nabla_{\mathbf{x}} \cdot \int_0^t\int_{\mathbb{R}^3} G_\mathrm{A}\varphi\nabla_{\mathbf{y}}E d\mathcal{V}d\tau \\
&- \frac{1}{c^2}\int_0^t\int_{\mathbb{R}^3} G_\mathrm{A}\frac{\partial\varphi}{\partial\tau}\frac{\partial E}{\partial\tau}d\mathcal{V}d\tau \\
&- \frac{1}{c^2}\frac{\partial}{\partial t}\int_0^t\int_{\mathbb{R}^3} G_\mathrm{A}\varphi\frac{\partial E}{\partial\tau}d\mathcal{V}d\tau. \quad (4)
\end{aligned}
$$

In obtaining Eq. 4, we have followed [4], in that we have (*i*) performed an integration by parts, (*ii*) used the facts that $\nabla_{\mathbf{x}}G_\mathrm{A} = -\nabla_{\mathbf{y}}G_\mathrm{A}$ and $\partial G_\mathrm{A}/\partial t = -\partial G_\mathrm{A}/\partial\tau$, and (*iii*) moved the operators $\nabla_{\mathbf{x}}$ and $\partial/\partial t$ outside the integral signs.

MOVING–FRAME FORMULATION

Equation 4 is an integral representation of the solution of Eq. 1. Note that this expression contains two Dirac delta functions: one from the fundamental solution G_A, and the other arising from $\nabla_{\mathbf{y}}E$ and $\partial E/\partial\tau$. Thus, the four–dimensional integrals may be reduced to two–dimensional ones. In order to accomplish this, it is convenient to introduce suitable coordinate transformations. This is achieved in two steps. First, we introduce a change of variables of integration, from the air space to the auxiliary moving space discussed in the preceding section, (this is done in this section); then, we introduce a second transformation, using time–dependent body–fitted curvilinear coordinates, and perform time and space integrations, for the general case of a surface moving with respect to the moving space (this is done in the following section).

Specifically, referring only to the variables of integration, let $(\mathbf{y}, \tau)$ denote the event in the air space and $(\check{\mathbf{y}}, \check{\tau})$ that in the moving space. Let

$$\mathbf{y} = \mathbf{y}_{\text{M}}(\check{\mathbf{y}}, \check{\tau}) = \mathbf{R}(\check{\tau})\check{\mathbf{y}} + \mathbf{y}_0(\check{\tau}); \quad \tau = \check{\tau} \quad (5)$$

indicate the transformation relating the two systems. In the above equation, $\mathbf{R}$ denotes an orthogonal isomorphism (rigid–body rotation): hence, $\mathbf{R}\mathbf{R}^{\mathsf{T}} = \mathbf{I}$. In general, for any other vector $\mathbf{a}$ (i.e., except for $\mathbf{y}$, see the equation above), we use the notation $\check{\mathbf{a}} := \mathbf{R}^T \mathbf{a}$. Thus, for any two arbitrary vectors $\mathbf{a}$ and $\mathbf{b}$, we have, $\check{\mathbf{a}} \cdot \check{\mathbf{b}} = \mathbf{a} \cdot \mathbf{b}$. Note that the Jacobian of the above transformations equals one. Let

$$\check{\mathbf{y}} = \check{\mathbf{y}}_{\text{M}}^{-1}(\mathbf{y}, \tau) = \mathbf{R}^{\mathsf{T}}(\tau)[\mathbf{y} - \mathbf{y}_0(\tau)]; \quad \check{\tau} = \tau \quad (6)$$

denote the inverse transformation.

In addition, for any function $g[\check{\mathbf{y}}_{\text{M}}^{-1}(\mathbf{y}, \tau), \tau]$, we have $\nabla_{\mathbf{y}} g = \mathbf{R} \nabla_{\check{\mathbf{y}}} g$ and $\partial g/\partial \tau = \partial g/\partial \check{\tau} + \check{\mathbf{v}}_{\mathbf{y}} \cdot \nabla_{\check{\mathbf{y}}} g =: d_{\text{M}} g/d\check{\tau}$, where $\partial g/\partial \check{\tau} := \partial g/\partial \tau|_{\check{\mathbf{y}}}$, whereas $\check{\mathbf{v}}_{\mathbf{y}} = \partial \check{\mathbf{y}}_{\text{M}}^{-1}/\partial \tau$ is the moving–space vector of the velocity of the air–space point $\mathbf{y}$ relative to the moving space. Note that, using $d(\mathbf{R}\mathbf{R}^{\mathsf{T}})/d\tau = 0$, we have

$$\begin{aligned}
\check{\mathbf{v}}_{\mathbf{y}} &= \frac{d\check{\mathbf{y}}_{\text{M}}^{-1}}{d\tau} = \frac{d\mathbf{R}^{\mathsf{T}}}{d\tau}(\mathbf{y} - \mathbf{y}_0) - \mathbf{R}^{\mathsf{T}} \frac{d\mathbf{y}_0}{d\tau} \\
&= -\mathbf{R}^{\mathsf{T}} \frac{d\mathbf{R}}{d\tau}\mathbf{R}^{\mathsf{T}}(\mathbf{y} - \mathbf{y}_0) - \mathbf{R}^{\mathsf{T}} \frac{d\mathbf{y}_0}{d\tau} \\
&= -\mathbf{R}^{\mathsf{T}} \left(\frac{d\mathbf{R}}{d\check{\tau}}\check{\mathbf{y}} + \frac{d\mathbf{y}_0}{d\check{\tau}} \right) = -\mathbf{R}^{\mathsf{T}} \frac{\partial \mathbf{y}_{\text{M}}}{\partial \check{\tau}}, \quad (7)
\end{aligned}$$

or $\check{\mathbf{v}}_{\mathbf{y}} = -\mathbf{R}^{\mathsf{T}}\mathbf{v}_{\text{M}} = -\check{\mathbf{v}}_{\text{M}}$, where $\mathbf{v}_{\text{M}}(\check{\mathbf{y}}, \tau)$ denotes the air–space velocity vector of the moving–space point $\check{\mathbf{y}}$ relative to the air space, $\mathbf{v}_{\text{M}}(\check{\mathbf{y}}, \tau) = \partial \mathbf{y}_{\text{M}}(\check{\mathbf{y}}, \tau)/\partial \check{\tau}$. Combining the above equations we have

$$\frac{d_{\text{M}} g}{d\check{\tau}} := \frac{\partial g}{\partial \tau} = \frac{\partial g}{\partial \check{\tau}} - \check{\mathbf{v}}_{\text{M}} \cdot \nabla_{\check{\mathbf{y}}} g. \quad (8)$$

Next, note that the argument of the Dirac delta function in Eq. 3, when expressed in terms of the moving–space variables is given by

$$h_{\text{M}} = h_{\text{M}}(\mathbf{x}, t, \check{\mathbf{y}}, \check{\tau}) := \check{\tau} - t + \frac{1}{c} \|\mathbf{x} - \mathbf{y}_{\text{M}}(\check{\mathbf{y}}, \check{\tau})\|. \quad (9)$$

Using $\nabla_{\mathbf{y}} g = \mathbf{R} \nabla_{\check{\mathbf{y}}} g$ and Eqs. 8, and 9, Eq. 4 may be rewritten in the new variables as

$$\begin{aligned}
E(\mathbf{x}, t)\varphi(\mathbf{x}, t) &= \int_0^t \int_{\mathbb{R}^3} G_{\text{M}} \delta(h_{\text{M}}) \nabla_{\check{\mathbf{y}}} \varphi \cdot \nabla_{\check{\mathbf{y}}} E d\mathcal{V} d\check{\tau} \\
&+ \nabla_{\mathbf{x}} \cdot \int_0^t \int_{\mathbb{R}^3} G_{\text{M}} \delta(h_{\text{M}}) \varphi \mathbf{R} \nabla_{\check{\mathbf{y}}} E d\mathcal{V} d\check{\tau} \\
&- \frac{1}{c^2} \int_0^t \int_{\mathbb{R}^3} G_{\text{M}} \delta(h_{\text{M}}) \frac{d_{\text{M}}\varphi}{d\check{\tau}} \frac{d_{\text{M}} E}{d\check{\tau}} d\mathcal{V} d\check{\tau} \\
&- \frac{1}{c^2} \frac{\partial}{\partial t} \int_0^t \int_{\mathbb{R}^3} G_{\text{M}} \delta(h_{\text{M}}) \varphi \frac{d_{\text{M}} E}{d\check{\tau}} d\mathcal{V} d\check{\tau}, \quad (10)
\end{aligned}$$

with h_{M} given by Eq. 9. Also, $G_{\text{M}} = -1/4\pi\|\mathbf{r}_{\text{M}}\|$, where $\mathbf{r}_{\text{M}} = \mathbf{x} - \mathbf{y}_{\text{M}}(\check{\mathbf{y}}, \check{\tau})$. As mentioned above, the integrals in Eq. 10 contain two Dirac delta functions, one stemming from the fundamental solution for the wave equation and the other one from the derivatives of the function E. Thus, two integrations may be performed in closed form. This is examined in the following section.

PERFORMING THE INTEGRATIONS

In this section, we perform the integration related to the two Dirac delta functions for the general case in which the surface moves in arbitrary motion within the moving space. In order to perform the two integrations in the four–dimensional integrals of the type given in Eq. 10, following Gennaretti [5], it is convenient to introduce a time–dependent body–fitted right–handed coordinate system ξ^α ($\alpha = 1, 2, 3$). Let the mapping $\check{\mathbf{y}} = \check{\mathbf{y}}_{\text{R}}(\xi^\alpha, \check{\tau})$ (to be used only within an infinitesimally thin layer, $\mathcal{L}_\varepsilon$, around the surface $\mathcal{S}_{\text{B}}$, see Eq. 19) be such that the equation

$$\check{\mathbf{y}} = \check{\mathbf{y}}_{\text{R}_0}(\xi^1, \xi^2, \check{\tau}) = \check{\mathbf{y}}_{\text{R}}(\xi^1, \xi^2, 0, \check{\tau}) \quad (11)$$

describes the location of the points of the boundary surface relative to the moving space. For simplicity, we assume that ξ^3 is the arclength η along the unit normal $\check{\mathbf{n}}$ (for instance, we may use $\check{\mathbf{y}}_{\text{R}}(\xi^1, \xi^2, \xi^3, \check{\tau}) := \check{\mathbf{y}}_{\text{R}_0}(\xi^1, \xi^2, \check{\tau}) + \xi^3 \check{\mathbf{n}}(\xi^1, \xi^2, \check{\tau})$ where $\check{\mathbf{n}}$ is the unit normal to $\mathcal{S}_{\text{B}}$). Let $\xi^\alpha = \xi^\alpha(\check{\mathbf{y}}, \check{\tau})$ define the inverse of $\check{\mathbf{y}} = \check{\mathbf{y}}_{\text{R}}(\xi^\alpha, \check{\tau})$ with $\check{\tau}$ constant.

In the air space, the location of the grid point (identified by ξ^1, ξ^2, and ξ^3) is given by $\mathbf{y} = \mathbf{y}_{\text{B}}(\xi^\alpha, \check{\tau}) := \mathbf{y}_{\text{M}}[\check{\mathbf{y}}_{\text{R}}(\xi^\alpha, \check{\tau}), \check{\tau}]$. Hence, the air–space velocity vector of the grid point relative to the air space is (see Eq. 5)

$$\begin{aligned}
\mathbf{v}_{\text{B}} &= \frac{\partial \mathbf{y}_{\text{B}}}{\partial \check{\tau}} = \frac{\partial}{\partial \check{\tau}} \mathbf{y}_{\text{M}}[\check{\mathbf{y}}_{\text{R}}(\xi^\alpha, \check{\tau}), \check{\tau}] = \mathbf{R} \frac{\partial \check{\mathbf{y}}_{\text{R}}}{\partial \check{\tau}} + \frac{\partial \mathbf{y}_{\text{M}}}{\partial \check{\tau}} \\
&= \mathbf{v}_{\text{R}} + \mathbf{v}_{\text{M}}, \quad (12)
\end{aligned}$$

with $\mathbf{v}_{\text{R}} = \mathbf{R}\check{\mathbf{v}}_{\text{R}}$, where $\check{\mathbf{v}}_{\text{R}} = \partial \check{\mathbf{y}}_{\text{R}}(\xi^\alpha, \check{\tau})/\partial \check{\tau}$ is the moving–space vector of the velocity of a grid point $\check{\mathbf{y}}_{\text{R}}(\xi^\alpha, \check{\tau})$ relative to the moving space. Next, note that (see also footnote 6) $\nabla_{\check{\mathbf{y}}} E = \delta(\eta)\check{\mathbf{n}}$ and $\partial E/\partial \tau = -\delta(\eta)v_n^{\text{R}}$. Hence (see Eq. 8)

$$\begin{aligned}
\frac{d_{\text{M}} E}{d\check{\tau}} &= \frac{\partial E}{\partial \tau} - \check{\mathbf{v}}_{\text{M}} \cdot \nabla_{\check{\mathbf{y}}} E = -\delta(\eta)(v_n^{\text{R}} + v_n^{\text{M}}) \\
&= -\delta(\eta)v_n^{\text{B}}, \quad (13)
\end{aligned}$$

with $v_n^{\text{R}} := \check{\mathbf{v}}_{\text{R}} \cdot \check{\mathbf{n}}$, $v_n^{\text{M}} := \check{\mathbf{v}}_{\text{M}} \cdot \check{\mathbf{n}}$, $v_n^{\text{B}} := \check{\mathbf{v}}_{\text{B}} \cdot \check{\mathbf{n}}$. Thus, the integrals in Eq. 10 are of the type

$$\int_0^t \int_{\mathbb{R}^3} \ldots \delta(h_{\text{M}})\delta(\eta) d\mathcal{V}(\check{\mathbf{y}}) d\check{\tau}. \quad (14)$$

In order to evaluate these types of integrals, it is convenient to use, as variables of integration, ξ^1, ξ^2, $\xi^3 = \eta$, and h_M. Therefore, we need the Jacobian J_4 of the four–dimensional mapping from (ξ^α, h_M) to $(\check{\mathbf{y}}, \check{\tau})$, with $(\mathbf{x}, t)$ constant. It is convenient to evaluate J_4 as the reciprocal of the Jacobian of the inverse mapping, i.e., that from $(\check{\mathbf{y}}, \check{\tau})$ to (ξ^α, h_M), still with $(\mathbf{x}, t)$ constant. This mapping is given by

$$\xi^\alpha = \xi^\alpha_R(\check{\mathbf{y}}, \check{\tau}) \quad (\alpha = 1, 2, 3);$$
$$h_M = \check{\tau} - t + \frac{1}{c}\|\mathbf{x} - \mathbf{y}_M(\check{\mathbf{y}}, \check{\tau})\|. \quad (15)$$

In order to evaluate the Jacobian of this mapping we need $\partial \xi^\alpha_R / \partial \check{\tau}|_{\check{\mathbf{y}}}$. To this end, note that, if $\check{\mathbf{y}}$ is constant, then (Einstein's convention on repeated indices is used here; the sum is over the range 1,2,3) $\partial \check{\mathbf{y}}_R / \partial \xi^\beta|_{\check{\tau}} d\xi^\beta + \partial \check{\mathbf{y}}_R / \partial \check{\tau}|_{\xi^\alpha} d\check{\tau} = 0$; or, introducing the base vectors $\check{\mathbf{g}}_\alpha(\check{\mathbf{y}}, \tau) = \partial \check{\mathbf{y}}_R(\check{\mathbf{y}}, \tau)/\partial \xi^\alpha$, and recalling that $\check{\mathbf{v}}_R = \partial \check{\mathbf{y}}_R / \partial \check{\tau}|_{\xi^\alpha}$, we have $\check{\mathbf{g}}_\beta d\xi^\beta + \check{\mathbf{v}}_R d\check{\tau} = 0$. Hence, (recalling that $\partial / \partial \check{\tau}$ implies that $\check{\mathbf{y}}$ is kept constant) one obtains $\partial \xi^\beta / \partial \check{\tau} = -\check{v}^\beta_R$, where $\check{v}^\beta_R$ are the contravariant components of $\check{\mathbf{v}}_R$, which are such that $\check{\mathbf{v}}_R = \check{v}^\beta_R \check{\mathbf{g}}_\beta$. Using the above equations, and introducing the contravariant base vectors $\check{\mathbf{g}}^\alpha(\check{\mathbf{y}}, \tau) = \nabla_{\check{\mathbf{y}}}\xi^\alpha_R(\check{\mathbf{y}}, \check{\tau})$, we have[2]

$$J_4^{-1} = \frac{\partial(h_M, \xi^1, \xi^2, \xi^3)}{\partial(\check{\tau}, \check{y}_1, \check{y}_2, \check{y}_3)}$$
$$= \begin{vmatrix} 1 - M^M_r & -\check{v}^1_R & -\check{v}^2_R & -\check{v}^3_R \\ \check{\mathbf{e}}_r/c & \check{\mathbf{g}}^1 & \check{\mathbf{g}}^2 & \check{\mathbf{g}}^3 \end{vmatrix}$$
$$= \frac{1 - M^M_r - M^R_r}{\sqrt{g}} = \frac{1 - M^B_r}{\sqrt{g}}, \quad (16)$$

with $\sqrt{g} = \mathbf{g}_1 \times \mathbf{g}_2 \cdot \mathbf{g}_3 = \check{\mathbf{g}}_1 \times \check{\mathbf{g}}_2 \cdot \check{\mathbf{g}}_3 = 1/\mathbf{g}^1 \times \mathbf{g}^2 \cdot \mathbf{g}^3 = 1/\check{\mathbf{g}}^1 \times \check{\mathbf{g}}^2 \cdot \check{\mathbf{g}}^3$. In deriving Eq. 16, we have used the fact that, for $\mathbf{x}$, t, and τ constant, we have (see Eqs. 5 and 15) $\nabla_{\check{\mathbf{y}}} h_M = -\mathbf{R}^T\mathbf{r}_M/\|\mathbf{r}_M\| = -\check{\mathbf{e}}_r$, where $\mathbf{e}_r := \mathbf{r}_M/\|\mathbf{r}_M\|$ is the unit vector in direction $\mathbf{r}_M = \mathbf{x} - \mathbf{y}_M(\check{\mathbf{y}}, \check{\tau})$; in addition, we have introduced the notations $M^R_r := v^R_r/c$, $M^M_r := v^M_r/c$, $M^B_r := v^B_r/c$, where $v^R_r := \check{\mathbf{v}}_R \cdot \check{\mathbf{e}}_r$, $v^M_r := \check{\mathbf{v}}_M \cdot \check{\mathbf{e}}_r$, $v^B_r := \check{\mathbf{v}}_B \cdot \check{\mathbf{e}}_r$, and used the relationship

$$\sqrt{g}(\check{v}^1_R \check{\mathbf{e}}_r \cdot \check{\mathbf{g}}^2 \times \check{\mathbf{g}}^3 + \check{v}^2_R \check{\mathbf{e}}_r \cdot \check{\mathbf{g}}^3 \times \check{\mathbf{g}}^1 + \check{v}^3_R \check{\mathbf{e}}_r \cdot \check{\mathbf{g}}^1 \times \check{\mathbf{g}}^2)$$
$$= (\check{v}^1_R \check{\mathbf{e}}_r \cdot \check{\mathbf{g}}_1 + \check{v}^2_R \check{\mathbf{e}}_r \cdot \check{\mathbf{g}}_2 + \check{v}^3_R \check{\mathbf{e}}_r \cdot \check{\mathbf{g}}_3)$$
$$= \check{v}^\alpha_R \check{\mathbf{g}}_\alpha \cdot \check{\mathbf{e}}_r = \check{\mathbf{v}}_R \cdot \check{\mathbf{e}}_r = v^R_r \quad (17)$$

(recall that $\check{\mathbf{g}}_\alpha = \sqrt{g} \, \check{\mathbf{g}}^\beta \times \check{\mathbf{g}}^\gamma$, with $(\alpha, \beta, \gamma) = (1, 2, 3), (2, 3, 1), (3, 1, 2)$).

---

[2]Note that, on $\mathcal{S}_B$, $J_4 > 0$, since $\sqrt{g} > 0$ (right–handed coordinate system) and $M^B_r < 1$ (subsonic assumption).

THE SUBSONIC CASE

For the sake of simplicity, in the following we limit ourselves to the subsonic case. Specifically, we assume that the velocity $\mathbf{v}_B$ (relative to the air space) of each grid point that affects $\varphi(\check{\mathbf{x}}, \check{t})$ is subsonic. This implies (by definition of subsonic) that (for ξ^α, $\mathbf{x}$, and t fixed) the argument, h_B, of the Dirac delta function arising from the fundamental solution G_A vanishes for only one value of $\check{\tau}$, say for $\check{\tau} = t - \theta_B$ with $\theta_B = \theta_B(\xi^\alpha, \mathbf{x}, t)$, where $\theta_B(\xi^\alpha, \mathbf{x}, t)$ is implicitly defined by

$$h_B(\mathbf{x}, t, \xi^\alpha, \theta_B) := -\theta_B + \frac{1}{c}\|\mathbf{r}^\theta_B\| = 0, \quad (18)$$

with $\mathbf{r}^\theta_B = \mathbf{x} - \mathbf{y}_B(\xi^\alpha, t - \theta_B)$. Finally, recalling that $\xi^3 = \eta$ is an arclength and hence $\check{\mathbf{g}}_3 = \check{\mathbf{n}}$, we have $\sqrt{g}|_{\eta=0} = \|\check{\mathbf{a}}_1 \times \check{\mathbf{a}}_2\| =: \sqrt{a}$, where $\check{\mathbf{a}}_\alpha = \partial \check{\mathbf{y}}_{R_0}/\partial \xi^\alpha$, with $\check{\mathbf{y}}_{R_0}$ defined by Eq. 11. Then (see Eq. 16, and recall the definition of $\mathcal{L}_\varepsilon$ given above Eq. 11), we have, for any function $f(\check{\mathbf{x}}, \check{\tau})$,

$$\int_0^t \int_{\mathbb{R}^3} f(\check{\mathbf{x}}, \check{\tau})\delta(h_M)\delta(\eta)d\mathcal{V}(\check{\mathbf{y}})d\check{\tau}$$
$$= \int_0^t \int_{\mathcal{L}_\varepsilon} f_R(\xi^\alpha, \check{\tau})\delta(h_B)\delta(\eta)J_4 d\xi^1 d\xi^2 d\eta dh_B$$
$$= \int_{\xi^\alpha} [f_R(\xi^\alpha, \check{\tau})J_4]_{h_B=\eta=0} d\xi^1 d\xi^2$$
$$= \int_{\mathcal{S}^\theta_R} \left[f_R(\xi^\alpha, \check{\tau})\frac{\kappa}{1 - M^B_r} \right]_\theta d\mathcal{S}^\theta_R(\xi^\alpha),$$

where now in the definition of M^B_r one should use $\mathbf{e}_r := \mathbf{r}_B/\|\mathbf{r}_B\|$; also $f_R(\xi^\alpha, \check{\tau}) = f(\check{\mathbf{y}}_R(\xi^\alpha, \check{\tau}), \check{\tau})$, where the subscript θ denotes evaluation at $\check{\tau} = t - \theta_B$,

$$[\ldots]_\theta = [\ldots]|_{\check{\tau}=t-\theta_B}. \quad (19)$$

In addition, the *emission* (or retarded) surface $\mathcal{S}^\theta_R$ is defined by

$$\check{\mathbf{y}} = \check{\mathbf{y}}^\theta_{R_0}(\xi^1, \xi^2, \mathbf{x}, t)$$
$$:= \check{\mathbf{y}}_{R_0}\left(\xi^1, \xi^2, t - \theta_B(\xi^1, \xi^2, \mathbf{x}, t)\right). \quad (20)$$

Its element is given by $d\mathcal{S}^\theta_R = \sqrt{a^\theta}d\xi^1 d\xi^2$ where $\sqrt{a^\theta} = \|\check{\mathbf{a}}^\theta_1 \times \check{\mathbf{a}}^\theta_2\|$, with

$$\check{\mathbf{a}}^\theta_\alpha = \frac{\partial \check{\mathbf{y}}^\theta_{R_0}}{\partial \xi^\alpha} = \frac{\partial \check{\mathbf{y}}_{R_0}}{\partial \xi^\alpha} - \frac{\partial \check{\mathbf{y}}_{R_0}}{\partial \check{\tau}}\frac{\partial \theta_B}{\partial \xi^\alpha} = \check{\mathbf{a}}_\alpha - \theta_{B,\alpha}\check{\mathbf{v}}_R, \quad (21)$$

where $\theta_{B,\alpha} = \partial \theta_B/\partial \xi^\alpha$ and $\check{\mathbf{v}}_R$ is understood evaluated on the boundary surface (i.e., $\check{\mathbf{v}}_R = \partial \check{\mathbf{y}}_{R_0}/\partial \tau = \partial \check{\mathbf{y}}_R/\partial t|_{\eta=0}$). Finally, $\kappa = \sqrt{a/a^\theta}$.

Using Eq. 19, Eq. 10 yields

$$E(\mathbf{x}, t)\varphi(\mathbf{x}, t) = \int_{\mathcal{S}^\theta_R} \left[\frac{\partial \varphi}{\partial n}\kappa \right]_\theta \hat{G}_\theta d\mathcal{S}^\theta_R$$

$$+\nabla_{\mathbf{x}} \cdot \int_{\mathcal{S}_{\mathrm{R}}^{\theta}} [\varphi \mathbf{n} \kappa]_{\theta} \hat{G}_{\theta} d\mathcal{S}_{\mathrm{R}}^{\theta}$$

$$+\frac{1}{c} \int_{\mathcal{S}_{\mathrm{R}}^{\theta}} \left[\frac{d_{\mathrm{M}}\varphi}{d\tilde{\tau}} M_n^{\mathrm{B}} \kappa \right]_{\theta} \hat{G}_{\theta} d\mathcal{S}_{\mathrm{R}}^{\theta}$$

$$+\frac{1}{c} \frac{\partial}{\partial t} \int_{\mathcal{S}_{\mathrm{R}}^{\theta}} [\varphi M_n^{\mathrm{B}} \kappa]_{\theta} \hat{G}_{\theta} d\mathcal{S}_{\mathrm{R}}^{\theta} \qquad (22)$$

where $\hat{G}_{\theta} = \hat{G}_{\theta}(\mathbf{x}, \xi^{\alpha}) = \left[G_{\mathrm{B}}/(1 - M_r^{\mathrm{B}}) \right]_{\theta}$, or, using $G_{\mathrm{B}} = -1/4\pi \|\mathbf{r}_{\mathrm{B}}\|$, and recalling that according to Eq. 19, $f_{\mathrm{R}}(\xi^{\alpha}, \tilde{\tau}) = f(\check{\mathbf{y}}_{\mathrm{R}}(\xi^{\alpha}, \tilde{\tau}), \tilde{\tau})$, we have that

$$\hat{G}_{\theta} = \left[\frac{-1}{4\pi(\|\mathbf{r}_{\mathrm{B}}\| - \mathbf{v}_{\mathrm{B}} \cdot \mathbf{r}_{\mathrm{B}}/c)} \right]_{\theta}. \qquad (23)$$

Equation 22 is the desired boundary integral representation for φ.

For numerical implementations, it is convenient, akin to Gennaretti [5], to have the operators $\nabla_{\mathbf{x}}$ and $\partial/\partial t$ inside the integral signs. In order to accomplish this, it is convenient to rewrite the integrals as (recall $\kappa = \sqrt{a^{\theta}/a}$)

$$\int_{\mathcal{S}_{\mathrm{R}}^{\theta}} [\dots \kappa]_{\theta} d\mathcal{S}^{\theta}(\mathbf{y}) = \int_{\mathcal{D}_{\mathrm{R}}(\xi^{\alpha})} [\dots \kappa]_{\theta} \sqrt{a^{\theta}} d\xi^1 d\xi^2$$

$$= \int_{\mathcal{D}_{\mathrm{R}}(\xi^{\alpha})} [\dots \sqrt{a}]_{\theta} d\xi^1 d\xi^2, \qquad (24)$$

where $\mathcal{D}_{\mathrm{R}}(\xi^{\alpha})$ is the domain of integration in the ξ^{α} plane (image of $\mathcal{S}_{\mathrm{R}}^{\theta}$ in the ξ^{α} plane), which is independent of the variables $\mathbf{x}$ and t. Thus, the derivatives may be moved under the integral sign (it should be noted that, in the process, $\nabla_{\mathbf{x}}$ is now to be understood with t, ξ^{α}, and $\tilde{\tau}$ constant, whereas $\partial/\partial t$ is to be understood with $\mathbf{x}$, ξ^{α}, and $\tilde{\tau}$ constant).

Thus, assuming for simplicity $(\sqrt{a})^{\cdot}$ to be negligible (nearly rigid–body motion), we have

$$\nabla_{\mathbf{x}} \cdot \left(\left[\varphi \sqrt{\check{a}} \mathbf{n} \right]_{\theta} \hat{G}_{\theta} \right) = \qquad (25)$$

$$\left[\varphi \mathbf{n} \cdot \nabla_{\mathbf{x}} \hat{G}_{\theta} - (\varphi \dot{\mathbf{n}} + \dot{\varphi} \mathbf{n}) \cdot \nabla_{\mathbf{x}} \theta_{\mathrm{B}} \hat{G}_{\theta} \right]_{\theta}$$

where, for any g, $\dot{g} = \partial g/\partial\tilde{\tau}|_{\xi^{\alpha}}$ (note the difference with respect to $\partial g/\partial\tilde{\tau} := \partial g/\partial\tilde{\tau}|_{\check{\mathbf{y}}}$). Note that $\nabla_{\mathbf{x}} \theta_{\mathrm{B}} = \mathbf{e}_r/c(1 - M_r^{\mathrm{B}})$.[3] Hence

$$\nabla_{\mathbf{x}} \cdot \left[\varphi \mathbf{n} \hat{G}_{\theta} \right]_{\theta} = \left[\varphi \mathbf{n} \cdot \nabla_{\mathbf{x}} \hat{G}_{\theta} \right. \qquad (26)$$

$$\left. -\frac{1}{c} \left(\varphi \dot{\mathbf{n}} \cdot \mathbf{e}_r + \dot{\varphi} n_r \right) \frac{\hat{G}}{1 - M_r^{\mathrm{B}}} \right]_{\theta}.$$

Also,

$$\frac{\partial}{\partial t} \left[\varphi M_n^{\mathrm{B}} \hat{G}_{\theta} \right]_{\theta} = \qquad (27)$$

$$\left[\varphi M_n^{\mathrm{B}} \frac{\partial \hat{G}_{\theta}}{\partial t} + (\varphi \dot{M}_n^{\mathrm{B}} \hat{G}_{\theta} + \dot{\varphi} M_n^{\mathrm{B}} \hat{G}_{\theta})(1 - \frac{\partial\theta_{\mathrm{B}}}{\partial t}) \right]_{\theta}.$$

Hence, noting that $1 - \partial\theta_{\mathrm{B}}/\partial t = 1/(1 - M_r^{\mathrm{B}})$,[4] one obtains

$$\frac{\partial}{\partial t} \left[\varphi M_n^{\mathrm{B}} \hat{G}_{\theta} \right]_{\theta} = \left[\varphi M_n^{\mathrm{B}} \frac{\partial \hat{G}_{\theta}}{\partial t} \right. \qquad (28)$$

$$\left. + \left(\varphi \dot{M}_n^{\mathrm{B}} + \dot{\varphi} M_n^{\mathrm{B}} \right) \frac{\hat{G}_{\theta}}{1 - M_r^{\mathrm{B}}} \right]_{\theta}.$$

Also, note that (Eq. 8) $d_{\mathrm{M}}\varphi/d\tilde{\tau} = \partial\varphi/\partial\tilde{\tau} - \check{\mathbf{v}}_{\mathrm{M}} \cdot \nabla_{\check{\mathbf{y}}}\varphi = \dot{\varphi} - \check{\mathbf{v}}_{\mathrm{B}} \cdot \nabla_{\check{\mathbf{y}}}\varphi$. Then, setting $\hat{\chi} = \partial\varphi/\partial n - M_n^{\mathrm{B}} \check{\mathbf{v}}_{\mathrm{B}} \cdot \nabla_{\check{\mathbf{y}}}\varphi/c$, and collecting terms in $\hat{\chi}$, φ, and $\dot{\varphi}$, we have

$$E(\mathbf{x}, t)\varphi(\mathbf{x}, t) = \int_{\mathcal{S}^{\theta}} \mathcal{K}_{\hat{\chi}}(\mathbf{x}, t, \check{\mathbf{y}})\hat{\chi}_{\theta} d\mathcal{S}^{\theta}$$

$$+ \int_{\mathcal{S}^{\theta}} \mathcal{K}_{\varphi}(\mathbf{x}, t, \check{\mathbf{y}})\varphi_{\theta} d\mathcal{S}^{\theta}$$

$$+ \int_{\mathcal{S}^{\theta}} \mathcal{K}_{\dot{\varphi}}(\mathbf{x}, t, \check{\mathbf{y}})\dot{\varphi}_{\theta} d\mathcal{S}^{\theta}, \qquad (29)$$

where

$$\mathcal{K}_{\hat{\chi}}(\mathbf{x}, t, \check{\mathbf{y}}) = [\hat{G}_{\theta}\kappa]_{\theta} \qquad (30)$$

$$\mathcal{K}_{\varphi}(\mathbf{x}, t, \check{\mathbf{y}}) = \left[\left(\mathbf{n} \cdot \nabla_{\mathbf{x}} \hat{G}_{\theta} + \frac{\partial \hat{G}_{\theta}}{\partial t} M_n^{\mathrm{B}} \right) \kappa \right.$$

$$\left. + \frac{1}{c} \left(-\dot{\mathbf{n}} \cdot \mathbf{e}_r + \dot{M}_n^{\mathrm{B}} \right) \frac{\hat{G}_{\theta}\kappa}{1 - M_r^{\mathrm{B}}} \right]_{\theta}$$

$$\mathcal{K}_{\dot{\varphi}}(\mathbf{x}, t, \check{\mathbf{y}}) = \left[\frac{1}{c} \left(-n_r + M_n^{\mathrm{B}}(2 - M_r^{\mathrm{B}}) \right) \frac{\hat{G}_{\theta}\kappa}{1 - M_r^{\mathrm{B}}} \right]_{\theta}$$

Note that $\mathbf{n}$ is the unit normal to the surface $\mathcal{S}_{\mathrm{B}}$ (and not to $\mathcal{S}^{\theta}$).

Equation 29 is an integral representation for the potential φ at a point $\mathbf{x}$ in the field, in terms of $\chi = \partial\varphi/\partial n$, as well φ and its derivatives on $\mathcal{S}_{\mathrm{B}}$. If $\mathbf{x}$ approaches the surface $\mathcal{S}$, the above equation yields a boundary integral equation for φ, with $\chi = \partial\varphi/\partial n$ known from the body boundary conditions. The contribution of the wake is examined in Appendix B. Once φ on $\mathcal{S}_{\mathrm{B}}$ is known, the potential in the field may be obtained from Eq. 29, and the pressure from Bernoulli's theorem, which in the linearized form gives $p - p_{\infty} = -\rho\dot{\varphi}$ (thereby providing the

---

[3]Indeed, using the derivatives of implicit functions, Eq. 18 yields $-\nabla_{\mathbf{x}}\theta_{\mathrm{B}} + (\mathbf{r}_{\mathrm{B}} + \mathbf{r}_{\mathrm{B}} \cdot \mathbf{v}_{\mathrm{B}} \nabla_{\mathbf{x}}\theta_{\mathrm{B}})/c\|\mathbf{r}_{\mathrm{B}}\| = 0$.

[4]Indeed, Eq. 18 yields $-\partial\theta_{\mathrm{B}}/\partial t - \mathbf{r}_{\mathrm{B}} \cdot \mathbf{v}_{\mathrm{B}}(1 - \partial\theta_{\mathrm{B}}/\partial t)/c\|\mathbf{r}_{\mathrm{B}}\| = 0$, or $\partial\theta_{\mathrm{B}}/\partial t = -M_r^{\mathrm{B}}/(1 - M_r^{\mathrm{B}})$.

integrated approach to aerodynamics and aeroacoustics).

NUMERICAL VALIDATION

Investigation about aerodynamics

In this section, we present some numerical results for the validation of the above formulation. The discretization is obtained by dividing into elements the body surface (N_1 elements along the chord, and N_2 along the span), as well as the wake surface and assuming χ, φ and $\Delta\varphi$ to be piece–wise constant. All the results are preliminary in that they are obtained for a one–bladed rotor in axial flow, with an undeformed wake surface (i.e., neglecting the wake roll–up). Specifically, we compare the solutions obtained using different frames of reference in the computation of blade and wake contributions. The rotor has a rectangular blade with radius $R = 1\,m$, chord $c = 0.1\,m$, and NACA 0012 section. The geometric angle is of $82°$ at the root, and of $26°$ at the tip; this corresponds to a root–to–tip twist angle of $-56°$. In addition, the rotor moves with an angular velocity equal to $100\,rad/s$ and an axial velocity equal to $40\,m/s$, which yield an angle of $6°$ at the root and one of $4°$ at the tip, with a tip Mach number equal to 0.55. The wake roll–up is neglected so that the wake is the locus of the points swept by the trailing edge.

The body or the air frame of reference may be used for either body or wake. Because of space limitations, here we concentrate on the formulation which, as of now, in our experience appears to be the best candidate, i.e., a body frame of reference for the body and an air frame of reference for the wake. Note that there exist two formulations for the wake, based respectively on Eqs. 43 and 49.

The results in Figure 1 are obtained with a body frame for the body, whereas for the wake we use the air–frame formulation based upon Eq. 43. Both surfaces are time–independent in these frames of reference. Figure 1 depicts the convergence analysis of the solution in terms of the pressure coefficient distribution at the blade section located at $0.75\,R$, as the blade panels are increased. It is apparent that the solution has an excellent rate of convergence and that the solution obtained with $N_1 = 12$ and $N_2 = 10$ is very close to the converged one.

Next, we compare the above results with those obtained using the body frame of reference for both the blade and its wake. This second algorithm has shown a convergence similar to that presented in Figure 1. For $N_1 = N_2 = 14$, Figure 2 shows the agreement between the results from the double–frame formulation and the body–frame one. The agreement is excellent.

Then, in order to assess the "retarded–surface" feature, we examine the wake formulation based upon Eq. 49. In this case, no line contribution appears, but some wake elements are distorted; this causes the need for a special algorithm to capture the contributions of such distorted elements. Specifically, in this preliminary analysis, all the wake panels (not only the distorted ones) are subdivided into $N_s \times N_s$ subpanels (with obvious increase in computational time). The results presented in Figure 3 are for $N_1 = 10$ and $N_2 = 6$ and different values of N_s and are compared with those of Figure 1. The results are encouraging. However, the number of sub–elements appears to be excessive. Further analysis is warranted.

Finally, we have also considered a hovering rotor having the same geometry of the propeller described above, but with angular velocity equal to $240\,rad/s$, root angle of attack equal to $6°$ and tip angle of attack equal to $4°$. The convergence analyses performed for this hovering rotor have shown the same behavior of the propeller case (see Figures 1 and 3). Therefore, in Figure 4 we depict the comparison between the double–frame formulation and the body–frame one in terms of pressure coefficient at $0.75\,R$ in steady conditions, whereas in Figure 5 the same comparison is shown in terms of the evolution of circulation at $0.75\,R$, for rotor starting from rest. Hence, the agreement between the two formulations appear to be very good also for unsteady hovering analysis.

Investigation about aeroacoustics

For the aeroacoustic validation of the formulations presented above, we have considered a hovering rotor with a NACA0012–section rectangular blade having radius $R = 1.829\,m$ and chord $c = 0.1334\,m$. The angle of attak at the root is $14.1°$, the angle of attak at the tip is $4.1°$ whereas the angular velocit is equal to $135\,rad/s$ that corresponds to a tip Mach number equal to 0.73. For the aeroacoustic investigation we have also considered an helicoidal undistorted rotor wake and an observer placed on the rotor disc at a distance of $3\,m$ from the rotor hub.

For a blade discretization of $N_1 = 8$ and $N_2 = 10$ elements, in Figure 6 we present the acoustic signature predicted using different wake lengths. Observing these results it is apparent that for the acoustic analysis it is necessary to include the effects coming from the very far wake and at least a 20 wake spirals have to be considered. Note that this is in contrast with the aerodynamic predictions where, for this case a 3 wake spirals proved to be sufficient. Note also that these results have been computed using body–frame descriptions for both blade and wake, but identical type of convergence has been also computed by using the air frame formulation. Next, in Figure 7, for a 30–spiral wake, we present the convergence analysis of the acoustic signature with respect to the radial discretization of the wake. In this case, with no difference with respect to the aerodynamic analysis, about 10 spanwise elements seems to give converged results. Finally, in Figure 8, for $N_1 = 8$ and $N_2 = 10$ and a 30-spiral wake we compare the results obtained from blade and wake body–frame formulation and blade and wake air–frame formulation. These two results are in very good agreement, thereby validating the arbitrary frame formulation presented. It is worth pointing out that in this case the air–frame body and wake effects have been computed without the further subdivision of panels needed in the aerodynamic analysis (see Figure 3). This is attributed to the larger distance between collocation point and panels in the aeroacoustic analysis with respect to that in the aerodynamic one where singular contributions are present.

CONCLUDING REMARKS

In this paper we have presented a general formulation for the aerodynamic and aeroacoustic analyses of deformable bodies in arbitrary motion. A distinguishing feature of the formulation is that body and wake contributions may be described in different frames with respect to which the surfaces can be fixed or not. The aerodynamic analyses of a propeller and hovering rotors have shown that body and air frame descriptions may have different convergence behavior, but give, in both cases, the same converged solution (both for steady and unsteady flows). Identical converged solutions have also been obtained in the aeroacoustic analysis were the strong dependence of the prediction upon the wake length has also been demostrated. For the aeroacoustic analysis air frame descriptions have shown a much higher rate of convergence with respect to the aerodynamic one.

APPENDIX A: A RELATED FORMULATION

In this appendix we compare the formulation presented in the main body of this work with that used by [9]. First, we derive briefly the results of [9]. [This is accomplished in two steps. In the first, we perform the integration with respect to the time variable, exploiting the Dirac delta function in the fundamental solution. In the second we reduce the volume integrals into surface integrals, exploiting the Dirac delta function arising from the derivatives of E.] Then, we compare these results with those obtained in the main body of the paper.

Note that, for any two functions $g(\check{\tau})$ and $h(\check{\tau})$,

$$
\int_0^t g(\check{\tau})\delta[h(\check{\tau})]d\check{\tau} = \sum_i g(\check{\tau}_i)\kappa_{\text{M}}(\check{\tau}_i)
$$
$$
= \sum_i \int_0^t g(\check{\tau})\kappa_{\text{M}}(\check{\tau})\delta(\check{\tau} - \check{\tau}_i)d\check{\tau} \qquad (31)
$$

where the $\check{\tau}_i$'s are the roots of $h(\check{\tau}) = 0$, whereas $\kappa_{\text{M}} = |dh/d\check{\tau}|^{-1}$. In the specific case considered here, $h(\check{\tau})$ is given by Eq. 9. In the following, for the sake of simplicity, we assume that the equation $h(\check{\tau}) = 0$ yields only one root, $\check{\tau} = t - \theta$, with $\theta = \theta_{\text{M}}(\check{\mathbf{y}}, \mathbf{x}, t)$, with $\theta_{\text{M}}(\check{\mathbf{y}}, \mathbf{x}, t)$ defined implicitly by

$$
-\theta_{\text{M}} + \frac{1}{c}\|\mathbf{x} - \mathbf{y}_{\text{M}}(\check{\mathbf{y}}, t - \theta_{\text{M}})\| = 0 \qquad (32)
$$

Then, $1/\kappa_{\text{M}} = |\partial h/\partial \check{\tau}| = (1 - M_r^{\text{M}}) > 0$, since $M_r^{\text{M}} = \mathbf{e}_r \cdot \mathbf{v}_{\text{M}}/c < 1$. Combining Eqs. 10 and 31 one obtains

$$
E(\mathbf{x},t)\varphi(\mathbf{x},t) = \int_{\mathbf{R}^3} [G\nabla_{\check{\mathbf{y}}}\varphi \cdot \nabla_{\check{\mathbf{y}}} E\kappa_{\text{M}}]_\theta \, d\mathcal{V}
$$
$$
+ \nabla_{\mathbf{x}} \cdot \int_{\mathbf{R}^3} [G\varphi\mathbf{R}\nabla_{\check{\mathbf{y}}} E\kappa_{\text{M}}]_\theta \, d\mathcal{V}
$$
$$
- \frac{1}{c^2}\int_{\mathbf{R}^3}\left[G\frac{d_{\text{M}}\varphi}{d\check{\tau}}\frac{d_{\text{M}}E}{d\check{\tau}}\kappa_{\text{M}}\right]_\theta d\mathcal{V}
$$
$$
- \frac{1}{c^2}\frac{\partial}{\partial t}\int_{\mathbf{R}^3}\left[G\varphi\frac{d_{\text{M}}E}{d\check{\tau}}\kappa_{\text{M}}\right]_\theta d\mathcal{V} \qquad (33)
$$

Next, we perform the integration related to the second Dirac delta function for the general case in which the surface moves in arbitrary motion within the moving space. Let $\mathcal{S}_{\text{R}}$ denote the boundary surface as seen in the moving space, and let $f(\check{\mathbf{y}}, \check{\tau})$ be a continuously differentiable function that is positive outside $\mathcal{S}_{\text{R}}$, negative inside $\mathcal{S}_{\text{R}}$, and zero on $\mathcal{S}_{\text{R}}$. Thus, the equation $f(\check{\mathbf{y}}, \check{\tau}) = 0$ defines the motion of the surface within the moving space, whereas $\check{\mathbf{n}} = \nabla_{\check{\mathbf{y}}}f/\|\nabla_{\check{\mathbf{y}}}f\|$ denotes the moving–space unit vector normal to $\mathcal{S}_{\text{R}}$. Note that, if $\check{\mathbf{v}}_{\text{R}}$ denotes the velocity of a point $\check{\mathbf{y}}$ of the moving surface $\mathcal{S}_{\text{R}}$ in the moving space, then $\partial f/\partial \check{\tau} + \check{\mathbf{v}}_{\text{R}} \cdot \nabla_{\check{\mathbf{y}}}f = 0.$[5] Hence the velocity v_n^{R} of the surface $\mathcal{S}_{\text{R}}$ within the air space is given by

$$
v_n^{\text{R}} := \check{\mathbf{v}}_{\text{R}} \cdot \check{\mathbf{n}} = \check{\mathbf{v}}_{\text{R}} \cdot \frac{\nabla_{\check{\mathbf{y}}}f}{\|\nabla_{\check{\mathbf{y}}}f\|} = \frac{-1}{\|\nabla_{\check{\mathbf{y}}}f\|}\frac{\partial f}{\partial \check{\tau}} \qquad (34)
$$

Note that the definition of $E(\mathbf{x})$ implies $E(\check{\mathbf{y}}, \check{\tau}) = H[f(\check{\mathbf{y}}, \check{\tau})]$, where $H[...]$ denotes the Heaviside function. Hence $\nabla_{\check{\mathbf{y}}}E = \delta(f)\nabla_{\check{\mathbf{y}}}f$, where $\delta(f) = dH/df$.

---

[5]In order to avoid proliferation of symbols, we use the same notations introduced above with a slightly different meaning, *i.e.*, the value at $\xi^3 = 0$, which ultimately is the only case of interest here.

In addition, for any two smooth functions f and g, in analogy with Eq. 31 (recall that the directional derivative in the direction of $\nabla_{\check{\mathbf{y}}} f$ is given by $df/d\eta = \|\nabla_{\check{\mathbf{y}}} f\|$), we have, denoting by η the arclength along the normal to $\mathcal{S}$,

$$\int_{\mathbb{R}^3} g\delta(f) d\mathcal{V} = \int_{\mathcal{S}} \int_{-\epsilon}^{\epsilon} g\delta(f) d\eta d\mathcal{S}$$
$$= \int_{\mathcal{S}} g \frac{1}{\|\nabla_{\check{\mathbf{y}}} f\|} d\mathcal{S} \quad (35)$$

where $\mathcal{S}$ is the surface defined by $f = 0$.[6] This implies

$$\int_{\mathbb{R}^3} [g\nabla_{\check{\mathbf{y}}} E]_\theta \, d\mathcal{V} = \int_{\mathbb{R}^3} [g\nabla_{\check{\mathbf{y}}} f \, \delta(f)]_\theta \, d\mathcal{V}$$
$$= \int_{\mathbb{R}^3} [g\nabla_{\check{\mathbf{y}}} f]_\theta \, \delta(f_\theta) d\mathcal{V}$$
$$= \int_{\mathcal{S}_{\mathrm{R}}^\theta} [g\check{\mathbf{n}}\kappa_{\mathrm{R}}]_\theta \, d\mathcal{S}_{\mathrm{R}}^\theta \quad (36)$$

where, for a given point $\check{\mathbf{y}}$ and a given time $\check{\tau}$, the *emission surface*, $\mathcal{S}_{\mathrm{R}}^\theta$, is defined by $f_\theta(\check{\mathbf{y}}) = 0$ with $f_\theta(\check{\mathbf{y}}, \mathbf{x}, t) := f[\check{\mathbf{y}}, t - \theta_{\mathrm{M}}(\check{\mathbf{y}}, \mathbf{x}, t)]$, whereas, using the above definition for v_n^{R},

$$\frac{1}{\kappa_{\mathrm{R}}} = \frac{\|\nabla_{\check{\mathbf{y}}} f_\theta\|}{\|\nabla_{\check{\mathbf{y}}} f\|} = \frac{1}{\|\nabla_{\check{\mathbf{y}}} f\|} \left\| \nabla_{\check{\mathbf{y}}} f - \frac{\partial f}{\partial \check{\tau}} \nabla_{\check{\mathbf{y}}} \theta_{\mathrm{M}} \right\| \quad (37)$$
$$= \left\| \check{\mathbf{n}} + v_n^{\mathrm{R}} \nabla_{\check{\mathbf{y}}} \theta_{\mathrm{M}} \right\|$$

Similarly, noting that $d_{\mathrm{M}} f / d\check{\tau} = \partial f / \partial \check{\tau} - \check{\mathbf{v}}_{\mathrm{M}} \cdot \nabla_{\check{\mathbf{y}}} f = -(v_n^{\mathrm{R}} + v_n^{\mathrm{M}})\|\nabla_{\check{\mathbf{y}}} f\| = -v_n^{\mathrm{B}}\|\nabla_{\check{\mathbf{y}}} f\|$, we have

$$\int_{\mathbb{R}^3} \left[g\frac{d_{\mathrm{M}} E}{d\check{\tau}} \right]_\theta d\mathcal{V} = \int_{\mathbb{R}^3} \left[g\frac{d_{\mathrm{M}} f}{d\check{\tau}}\delta(f) \right]_\theta d\mathcal{V}$$
$$= \int_{\mathbb{R}^3} \left[g\frac{d_{\mathrm{M}} f}{d\check{\tau}} \right]_\theta \delta(f_\theta) d\mathcal{V}$$
$$= -\int_{\mathcal{S}_{\mathrm{R}}^\theta} \left[gv_n^{\mathrm{B}} \kappa_{\mathrm{R}} \right]_\theta d\mathcal{S}_{\mathrm{R}}^\theta \quad (38)$$

Combining Eqs. 33, 36, and 38 one obtains Eq. 22, where now $\kappa = \kappa_{\mathrm{M}} \kappa_{\mathrm{R}} (1 - M_r^{\mathrm{B}})$. A simpler expression may be obtained by noting that $\nabla_{\check{\mathbf{y}}} \theta_{\mathrm{M}} = -\check{\mathbf{e}}_r / c (1 - M_r^{\mathrm{M}})$.[7] Thus, combining with $1/\kappa_{\mathrm{M}} = 1 - M_r^{\mathrm{M}}$ and Eq. 37, one obtains

$$\kappa = \frac{1 - M_r^{\mathrm{B}}}{\|(1 - M_r^{\mathrm{M}})\check{\mathbf{n}} - M_n^{\mathrm{R}}\check{\mathbf{e}}_r\|}. \quad (39)$$

Finally, we wish to show that the expression for $\kappa = \sqrt{a/a^\theta}$ is equivalent to that given above. To this

---

[6] Equation 35 and $\nabla_{\mathbf{y}} E = \delta(f)\nabla_{\check{\mathbf{y}}} f$ imply $\nabla_{\check{\mathbf{y}}} E = \delta(\eta)\check{\mathbf{n}}$, whereas Eq. 34 implies $\partial E/\partial \check{\tau} = -\delta(\eta)v_n^{\mathrm{R}}$.

[7] Indeed, Eq. 32 yields $\nabla_{\check{\mathbf{y}}} \theta_{\mathrm{M}} = -(\mathbf{R}^{\mathrm{T}}\mathbf{r}_{\mathrm{M}} - \mathbf{r}_{\mathrm{M}} \cdot \mathbf{y}_{\mathrm{M}} \nabla_{\check{\mathbf{y}}} \theta_{\mathrm{M}})/\|\mathbf{r}_{\mathrm{M}}\|$.

---

end, note that, recalling the expression for $\check{\mathbf{a}}_\alpha^\theta$ (Eq. 21) and using $\check{\mathbf{a}}_1 = -\sqrt{a}\check{\mathbf{n}} \times \check{\mathbf{a}}^2$ and $\check{\mathbf{a}}_2 = \sqrt{a}\check{\mathbf{n}} \times \check{\mathbf{a}}^1$ as well as $\mathbf{a} \times (\mathbf{b} \times \mathbf{c}) = \mathbf{b}\,\mathbf{a} \cdot \mathbf{c} - \mathbf{c}\,\mathbf{a} \cdot \mathbf{b}$, one obtains

$$\sqrt{a^\theta} = \left\| \left(\check{\mathbf{a}}_1 - \check{\mathbf{v}}_{\mathrm{R}}\theta_{\mathrm{B},1}\right) \times \left(\check{\mathbf{a}}_2 - \check{\mathbf{v}}_{\mathrm{R}}\theta_{\mathrm{B},2}\right) \right\|$$
$$= \sqrt{a} \left\| \mathbf{n} - \check{\mathbf{v}}_{\mathrm{R}} \times (\check{\mathbf{n}} \times \check{\mathbf{a}}^2)\theta_{\mathrm{B},2} - \check{\mathbf{v}}_{\mathrm{R}} \times (\check{\mathbf{n}} \times \check{\mathbf{a}}^1)\theta_{\mathrm{B},1} \right\|$$
$$= \sqrt{a} \left\| \check{\mathbf{n}} - \check{\mathbf{v}}_{\mathrm{R}} \times (\check{\mathbf{n}} \times \nabla_{\check{\mathbf{y}}}\theta_{\mathrm{B}}) \right\| \quad (40)$$
$$= \sqrt{a} \left\| \check{\mathbf{n}}(1 - \check{\mathbf{v}}_{\mathrm{R}} \cdot \nabla_{\check{\mathbf{y}}}\theta_{\mathrm{B}}) + \check{\mathbf{v}}_{\mathrm{R}} \cdot \check{\mathbf{n}}\nabla_{\check{\mathbf{y}}}\theta_{\mathrm{B}} \right\|,$$

where we have used the expression for the gradient in curvilinear coordinates $\nabla_{\check{\mathbf{y}}} = \check{\mathbf{g}}^\alpha \partial/\partial\xi^\alpha$ and taken advantage of the fact that the normal component of $\nabla_{\check{\mathbf{y}}}\theta_{\mathrm{B}}$ is inessential. Therefore, recalling that $\theta = \theta_{\mathrm{B}}(\xi^\alpha, t, \mathbf{x})$ is defined implicitly by Eq. 18, we have (see Eq. 12) $\theta_{\mathrm{B},\alpha} = -\check{\mathbf{e}}_r \cdot \left(\check{\mathbf{g}}_\alpha - \check{\mathbf{v}}_{\mathrm{B}}\theta_{\mathrm{B},\alpha}\right)/c$ or $\theta_{\mathrm{B},\alpha} = -\check{\mathbf{e}}_r \cdot \check{\mathbf{g}}_\alpha/c\left(1 - M_r^{\mathrm{B}}\right)$, and hence $\nabla_{\check{\mathbf{y}}}\theta_{\mathrm{B}} = -\check{\mathbf{e}}_r/c\left(1 - M_r^{\mathrm{B}}\right)$ (note the difference between $\nabla_{\check{\mathbf{y}}}\theta_{\mathrm{B}}$ and $\nabla_{\check{\mathbf{y}}}\theta_{\mathrm{F}}$). Thus, from Eq. $\kappa = \sqrt{a/a^\theta}$, one obtains, using $M_r^{\mathrm{B}} = M_r^{\mathrm{M}} + M_r^{\mathrm{R}}$,

$$\frac{1 - M_r^{\mathrm{B}}}{\kappa} = (1 - M_r^{\mathrm{B}}) \left\| \left(1 + \frac{M_r^{\mathrm{R}}}{1 - M_r^{\mathrm{B}}}\right)\check{\mathbf{n}} + \frac{M_n^{\mathrm{R}}\check{\mathbf{e}}_r}{1 - M_r^{\mathrm{B}}} \right\|$$
$$= \|(1 - M_r^{\mathrm{M}})\check{\mathbf{n}} - M_n^{\mathrm{R}}\check{\mathbf{e}}_r\|, \quad (41)$$

in agreement with the expression for κ given in Eq. 39. Thus, we have shown that the present formulation is equivalent to that of [9].

APPENDIX B: THE WAKE

In the formulation above, for clarity, the contribution of the wake has been ignored. Here, we examine briefly how the formulation is modified in order to include the effects of the wake. To this end, apply Eq. 22 to a surface that surrounds both body and wake. Then, $E(\mathbf{x},t)\varphi(\mathbf{x},t) = \mathcal{I}_{\mathrm{B}} + \mathcal{I}_{\mathrm{W}}$ where $\mathcal{I}_{\mathrm{B}}$ and $\mathcal{I}_{\mathrm{W}}$ denote, respectively, the body and wake contributions. Proceeding as in Section "The subsoni case", the contribution of the body may be rewritten as in Eq. 29, as long as the boundaries of the ξ^α–image of the surface (or of the subsurfaces) are independent of $\mathbf{x}$ and t, as it was implicitly assumed in the same section. In the limit as the surrounding surface approaches the (open) wake surface $\mathcal{S}_{\mathrm{R_W}}$, the wake contribution $\mathcal{I}_{\mathrm{W}}$ is given by (taking into account that the normals on the two sides of the surface have opposite signs)

$$\mathcal{I}_{\mathrm{W}} = \nabla_{\mathbf{x}} \cdot \int_{\mathcal{S}_{\mathrm{R_W}}^\theta} \left[\mathbf{n}\hat{G}\Delta\varphi\kappa \right]_\theta dS_{\mathrm{R_W}}^\theta$$
$$+ \frac{1}{c}\int_{\mathcal{S}_{\mathrm{R_W}}^\theta} \left[\hat{G}\Delta\frac{d_{\mathrm{M}}\varphi}{d\check{\tau}}M_n^{\mathrm{B}}\kappa \right]_\theta dS_{\mathrm{R_W}}^\theta$$

$$+ \quad \frac{1}{c}\frac{\partial}{\partial t}\int_{\mathcal{S}_{\scriptscriptstyle{R_W}}^{\theta}}\left[\hat{G}\Delta\varphi M_n^{\scriptscriptstyle B}\kappa\right]_{\theta}d\mathcal{S}_{\scriptscriptstyle{R_W}}^{\theta} \qquad (42)$$

For the wake contribution the situation is more subtle and the issue is addressed in the following. For the sake of simplicity, we discuss only the formulation in the air frame of reference (since the extension to a moving frame of reference is relatively simple). In order to describe the wake geometry, let us introduce a right–handed system of curvilinear coordinates, ξ^1 and ξ^2, over the surface of the wake. Note that the wake surface coincides with the locus of the material points generated by the trailing edge during its motion (streak surface). Thus, a possible choice is to identify one of the two coordinate, ξ^1, with the time at which the trailing edge generated a given line and the other coordinate, ξ^2 with the arclength along the trailing edge. In other words, the line ξ^1=constant identifies the locus of the material points that were on the trailing edge at a certain time, $\tau = \xi^1$, whereas the line ξ^2=constant identifies the streak line generated by a trailing edge point. Also, note that the wake surface grows progressively in time because of the sweeping motion of the trailing edge. Then, the wake surface, at a given time τ, may be described by

$$\mathbf{y} = \mathbf{y}_{\scriptscriptstyle W}(\xi^1,\xi^2,\tau) \quad [\xi^1 \in (0,\tau); \xi^2 \in (\xi_{\scriptscriptstyle A}^2,\xi_{\scriptscriptstyle B}^2)] \quad (43)$$

$\xi_{\scriptscriptstyle A}^2$ and $\xi_{\scriptscriptstyle B}^2$ are the trailing–edge extremes.

Because of the fact that, in compressible flows, a signal has a finite speed of propagation, a point $\mathbf{x}$ at time t will be influenced by the not entire wake surface generated up to time t, but only by the points that where present at the retarded time $\tau = t - \theta_{\scriptscriptstyle TE}$, where $\theta_{\scriptscriptstyle TE}(\xi^2,\mathbf{x},t)$ is defined by $\theta_{\scriptscriptstyle TE} = \mathbf{x} - \mathbf{y}_{\scriptscriptstyle TE}(\xi^2,t - \theta_{\scriptscriptstyle TE})$. Indeed, using these coordinates, Eq. 44 becomes (see Eq. 24)

$$\mathcal{I}_{\scriptscriptstyle W} = \nabla_{\mathbf{x}} \cdot \int_{\mathcal{D}_{\scriptscriptstyle{R_W}}(\xi^\alpha)}\left[\mathbf{n}\hat{G}\Delta\varphi\sqrt{a}\right]_{\theta}d\xi^1 d\xi^2$$

$$+ \quad \frac{1}{c}\int_{\mathcal{D}_{\scriptscriptstyle{R_W}}(\xi^\alpha)}\left[\hat{G}\Delta\left(\frac{d_{\scriptscriptstyle M}\varphi}{d\tilde{\tau}}\right)M_n^{\scriptscriptstyle B}\sqrt{a}\right]_{\theta}d\xi^1 d\xi^2$$

$$+ \quad \frac{1}{c}\frac{\partial}{\partial t}\int_{\mathcal{D}_{\scriptscriptstyle{R_W}}(\xi^\alpha)}\left[\hat{G}\Delta\varphi M_n^{\scriptscriptstyle B}\sqrt{a}\right]_{\theta}d\xi^1 d\xi^2, \quad (44)$$

where $\mathcal{D}_{\scriptscriptstyle{R_W}}(\xi^\alpha)$ is the domain of integration in the ξ^α plane (image of $\mathcal{S}_{\scriptscriptstyle{R_W}}^{\theta}$ in the ξ^α plane), defined by $\xi^1 \in (0, t - \theta_{\scriptscriptstyle TE})$ and $\xi^2 \in (\xi_{\scriptscriptstyle A}^2, \xi_{\scriptscriptstyle B}^2)$. In contrast with the assumption made for the body, $\mathcal{D}_{\scriptscriptstyle{R_W}}(\xi^\alpha)$ is not independent of the variables $\mathbf{x}$ and t. Thus, moving the derivatives inside the integrals yields line integral. Specifically,

$$\nabla_{\mathbf{x}} \cdot \int_{\mathcal{D}_{\scriptscriptstyle{R_W}}(\xi^\alpha)}\left[\mathbf{n}\hat{G}\Delta\varphi\sqrt{a}\right]_{\theta}d\xi^1 d\xi^2 \qquad (45)$$

$$= \int_{\mathcal{D}_{\scriptscriptstyle{R_W}}(\xi^\alpha)}\nabla_{\mathbf{x}} \cdot \left[\mathbf{n}\hat{G}\Delta\varphi\sqrt{a}\right]_{\theta}d\xi^1 d\xi^2 + \Delta\mathcal{I}_{\scriptscriptstyle W_1}$$

where, noting that $\nabla_{\mathbf{x}}\theta_{\scriptscriptstyle TE} = \mathbf{e}_r/c(1 - M_r^{\scriptscriptstyle TE})$, with $M_r^{\scriptscriptstyle TE} = \mathbf{v}_{\scriptscriptstyle TE} \cdot \mathbf{e}_r/c$ where $\mathbf{v}_{\scriptscriptstyle TE} = \partial\mathbf{y}_{\scriptscriptstyle TE}/\partial\tau$,[8]

$$\Delta\mathcal{I}_{\scriptscriptstyle W_1} = \int_{\xi_{\scriptscriptstyle A}^2}^{\xi_{\scriptscriptstyle B}^2}\left[\hat{G}\Delta\varphi\sqrt{a}\,\mathbf{n} \cdot \nabla_{\mathbf{x}}\theta_{\scriptscriptstyle TE}\right]_{\theta}d\xi^2$$

$$= -\frac{1}{c}\int_{\xi_{\scriptscriptstyle A}^2}^{\xi_{\scriptscriptstyle B}^2}\left[n_r\hat{G}\Delta\varphi\frac{\sqrt{a}}{1 - M_r^{\scriptscriptstyle TE}}\right]_{\theta}d\xi^2 . \quad (46)$$

Similarly, one obtains

$$\frac{\partial}{\partial t}\int_{\mathcal{D}_{\scriptscriptstyle{R_W}}(\xi^\alpha)}\left[M_n^{\scriptscriptstyle B}\hat{G}\Delta\varphi\sqrt{a}\right]_{\theta}d\xi^1 d\xi^2 \qquad (47)$$

$$= \int_{\mathcal{D}_{\scriptscriptstyle{R_W}}(\xi^\alpha)}\frac{\partial}{\partial t}\left[M_n^{\scriptscriptstyle B}\hat{G}\Delta\varphi\sqrt{a}\right]_{\theta}d\xi^1 d\xi^2 + \Delta\mathcal{I}_{\scriptscriptstyle W_2}$$

where, noting that $1 - \partial\theta_{\scriptscriptstyle TE}/\partial t = 1/(1 - M_r^{\scriptscriptstyle TE})$,

$$\Delta\mathcal{I}_{\scriptscriptstyle W_2} = \int_{\xi_{\scriptscriptstyle A}^2}^{\xi_{\scriptscriptstyle B}^2}\left[M_n^{\scriptscriptstyle B}\hat{G}\Delta\varphi\sqrt{a}\right]_{\theta}\left(1 - \frac{\partial\theta_{\scriptscriptstyle TE}}{\partial t}\right)d\xi^2$$

$$= \int_{\xi_{\scriptscriptstyle A}^2}^{\xi_{\scriptscriptstyle B}^2}\left[M_n^{\scriptscriptstyle B}\hat{G}\Delta\varphi\frac{\sqrt{a}}{1 - M_r^{\scriptscriptstyle TE}}\right]_{\theta}d\xi^2. \quad (48)$$

The present formulation reduces to that of [6], for the specific case examined in these papers (*i.e.*, undeformed wake and formulation in the air frame).

Next, note that the numerical evaluation of the line contribution requires considerable attention. Thus, it is desirable to consider an alternate formulation that does not yield a line contribution. This may be obtained using the following description for the wake geometry:

$$\mathbf{y} = \mathbf{y}_{\scriptscriptstyle W}(\tau - \xi^1,\xi^2,\tau) \quad [\xi^1 \in (0,\tau); \xi^2 \in (\xi_{\scriptscriptstyle A}^2,\xi_{\scriptscriptstyle B}^2)], (49)$$

where now the variable ξ^1 originates from the current location of the trailing edge and may be identified with a backward time shift ($\xi^1 = \tau$ identifies the material points which at time $\tau = 0$ were on the trailing edge). In this case, following the procedure above, we obtain that the line contributions are to be evaluated at the initial location of the trailing edge, where however $\Delta\varphi$ vanishes. Thus, in this case there are no line contributions.

---

[8] In order to evaluate $\sqrt{a}$, note that the above choice made for the coordinates ξ^1 and ξ^2 implies that on the wake, at the trailing edge, $\mathbf{a}_1 = \partial\mathbf{y}_{\scriptscriptstyle W}/\partial\xi^1 = \mathbf{v}_{\scriptscriptstyle TE} - \mathbf{v}_{\scriptscriptstyle W}$, where $\mathbf{v}_{\scriptscriptstyle W} = \partial\mathbf{y}_{\scriptscriptstyle W}/\partial\tau$, and $\mathbf{v}_{\scriptscriptstyle TE} = \partial\mathbf{y}_{\scriptscriptstyle TE}/\partial\tau$ because $\mathbf{y}_{\scriptscriptstyle TE}(\xi^2,\tau) = \mathbf{y}_{\scriptscriptstyle W}(\tau,\xi^2,\tau)$. In addition $\mathbf{a}_2 = \partial\mathbf{y}_{\scriptscriptstyle W}/\partial\xi^2$ is the unit tangent, $\mathbf{e}_{\scriptscriptstyle TE}$ to the trailing edge at time $t = \xi^1$. Hence $\sqrt{a} = \|\mathbf{a}_1 \times \mathbf{a}_2\| = \|(\mathbf{v}_{\scriptscriptstyle TE} - \mathbf{v}_{\scriptscriptstyle W}) \times \mathbf{e}_{\scriptscriptstyle TE}\|$.

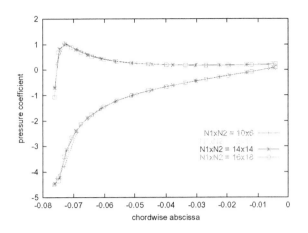

Figure 1: Chordwise pressure coefficient distribution: section at $0.75\,R$

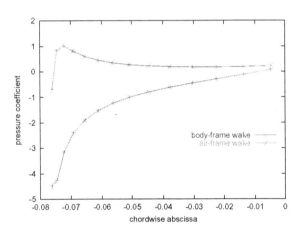

Figure 2: Chordwise pressure coefficient distribution: section at $0.75\,R$

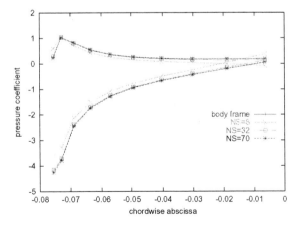

Figure 3: Chordwise pressure coefficient distribution: section at $0.75\,R$

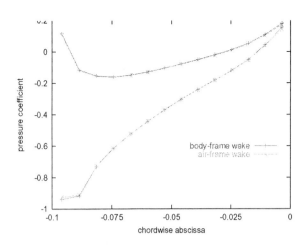

Figure 4: Chordwise pressure coefficient distribution: section at $0.75\,R$

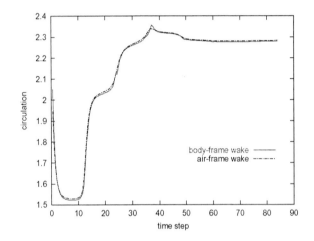

Figure 5: Time history of circulation, $\Delta\varphi_{\text{TE}}$, at $r/R = 0.75$ for $M = 0.7$

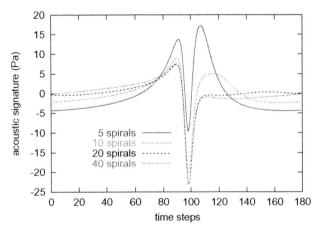

Figure 6: Acoustic signature: convergence analysis with respect to wake length

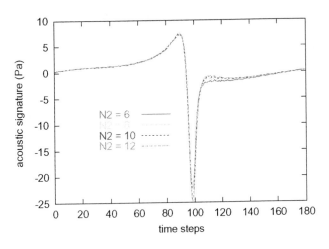

Figure 7: Acoustic signature: convergence analysis with respect to spanwise wake elements

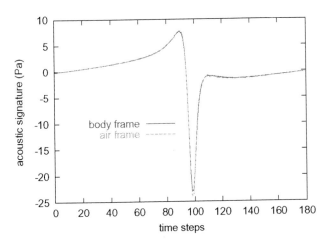

Figure 8: Acoustic signature: comparison betweeen body-frame and air-frame formulations

REFERENCES

1. Brentner, K. S. (1997). Numerical Algorithms for Acoustic Integrals with Examples for Rotor Noise Prediction. *AIAA Journal*, vol 35(no 4):pp 625–630.

2. Farassat, F. (1975). Theory of Noise Generation from Moving Bodies with an Application to Helicopter Rotors. *NASA TR–R–45*.

3. Farassat, F., and Myers, M. K. (1988). Extension of Kirchhoff's Formula to Radiation from Moving Surfaces. *Journal of Sound and Vibration*, vol 123:pp 451–460.

4. Ffowcs Williams, J. E., and Hawkings, D. L. (1969). Sound Generation by Turbulence and Surfaces in Arbitrary Motion. *Philosophical Transactions of the Royal Society*, vol A264(no 1151):pp 321–542.

5. Gennaretti, M. (1993). Una Formulazione Integrale di Contorno per la Trattazione Unificata di Flussi Aeronautici Viscosi e Potenziali. *Doctoral thesis, Department of Applied Mechanics, University of Roma "La Sapienza"*.

6. Gennaretti, M., Luceri, L., and Morino, L. (1997). A Unified Boundary Integral Methodology for Aerodynamics and Aeroacoustics of Rotors. *Journal of Sound and Vibration*, vol 200:pp 467–489.

7. Morino, L. (1974). A General Theory of Unsteady Compressible Potential Aerodynamics. *NASA CR–2464*.

8. Morino, L., Bernardini, G., and Gennaretti, M. (2002). A Boundary Element Method for the Aerodynamic Analysis of Rotors in Arbitrary Motion. *Symposium of the International Association of Boundary Element Method*, Austin, Texas.

9. Morino, L., Bharadvaj, B. K., Freedman, M. I., and Tseng, K. (1989). Boundary Integral Equation for Wave Equation with Moving Boundary and Applications to Compressible Potential Aerodynamics of Airplanes and Helicopters. *Computational Mechanics*, vol 4:pp 231–243.

AIAA 2002-2540

A STUDY OF NOISE ABATEMENT PROCEDURES USING AMES B747-400 FLIGHT SIMULATOR

Kevin Elmer, Joseph Wat, Gary Gershzohn, Belur Shivashankara,
The Boeing Company

John-Paul Clarke, Nhut Ho,
Massachusetts Institute of Technology

Leonard Tobias, David Lambert,
NASA Ames Research Center

Abstract

In the summer of 2001, a team of researchers from Boeing, MIT, and NASA Ames conducted a study to evaluate the noise impact and the operational characteristics of current and proposed noise abatement procedures (NAPs). The major component of this study was a series of Pilot-in-the-loop simulations conducted at the NASA Ames Research Center's Crew-Vehicle Simulation Research Facility's (CVSRF) Boeing 747-400 flight simulator. The noise under the flight path was displayed in real-time using the output of a noise calculation program, which was installed at the CVSRF. Community noise as well as flight crew acceptability, performance, and workload were measured. The noise results show that departure and arrival NAPs are effective in reducing community noise levels and noise contour variability when compared with standard procedures. The pilot surveys and performance data indicate that all NAPs were acceptable to the airline pilot subjects although preferences were specified.

Introduction

The proliferation of air travel in the latter half of the 20th century has fostered the implementation of noise mitigation measures at airports around the world. Differences in the specific makeup of airport communities and the degree to which local authorities impose airport noise regulations have led to the development of a large variety of noise abatement procedures. For safety and efficiency considerations, the FAA has allowed operators to define two standardized NAPs that they could adopt for departure operations at noise sensitive airports, namely a distant and a close-in community noise abatement departure procedure (NADP).[1] The International Civil Aviation Organization (ICAO) has defined two similar procedures (ICAO-A and ICAO-B).[2] Implementation of these procedures are limited due to concerns for safety and increased workload.

Local airport authorities typically implement noise restrictions only after years of noise complaints lodged by private citizens or a planned change in operations forces them to conduct a costly environmental impact study. Such a study may result in the levying of restrictions on operations based on measured noise levels, number of operations, aircraft type, and time of day curfews, or alternatively costly community relocation or soundproofing programs. Once noise regulations at an airport are in place, the NAP offers an operator one last recourse to avert non-compliance penalties.

With the continued development of new quieter aircraft, the focus of community noise is shifting to include airport arrival operations as well as departures. Several European airport authorities, for example, have implemented NAPs that apply to arrivals as well as those for departures.[3] With projected increases in air traffic and noise regulations, the trend towards increased implementation of NAPs will continue in the 21st century.

The goal of this project was to assess the noise reduction benefit, and to examine the operational characteristics and the flight crew human factors issues, of existing and proposed NAPs at a noise sensitive airport. The airport selected for this study was London Heathrow (LHR). A total of three departure and four arrival NAPs were evaluated under various conditions. Eight airline pilots served as test subjects in order to create a statistical database of pilot performance, acceptability, and workload as well as aircraft performance and community noise. The departures were flown at the 747-400's maximum takeoff gross weight whereas the arrivals were flown at its minimum approach weight (in order to meet some of the performance requirements of the NAPs tested).

In addition to the real time noise predictions, the aircraft performance was also recorded for later community noise analysis using the FAA's Integrated Noise Model (INM).[4] This noise data was used to determine the effectiveness of the NAPs in reducing community noise as well as determining the variability in noise associated with each procedure due to pilot performance.

Pilot performance was evaluated by recording aircraft performance variables, controls movement, and autopilot events. Statistical distributions were derived for specific pilot activities such as when turns were made, when the thrust was reduced, when the pitch was reduced, when climb and descents were initiated and when systems such as the Autopilot Flight Director System were activated.

Method

Subjects – Eight B-747-400 qualified airline captains and first officers participated in the experiment. The mean age and flight times of the pilots were 49.5 years and 11,875 hours respectively. The age ranged from 37 to 60 years and the flight time ranged from 3700 to 20,000 hours.

Flight Simulator – The NASA Ames Research Center's CVRSF B-747-400 full motion FAA certified Level D flight simulator was used. It represented a full-fidelity aircraft configured for line operations. Used primarily in this experiment were the Primary Flight Display, NAV display, Flight Management System (FMS), Mode Control Panel

(MCP), Autopilot Flight Director System (AFDS), and Multifunction Control Display Unit (MCDU).

Experimental Design – The experiment was partitioned into two parts, one for departure NAPs and one for arrival NAPs.

LHR was loaded into the simulator and the BUZ 3J and BUZ 2K Standard Instrument Departures shown in figure 1 were used.[5] All arrivals and landings were to LHR Runway 27R.[6]

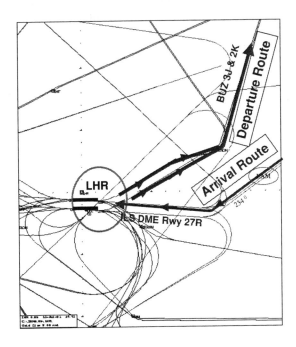

Figure 1: LHR Departure and Arrival routes

The Departure NAP experiment was a 3 X 2 X 2 within-subjects design. The three independent variables were:

1. NAP with three levels [ICAO-A, ICAO-A 1000, and Minimum Climb Gradient (MCG)] (see Table 1)
2. Lateral Navigation (LNAV) with two levels [Early Turn and Late Turn after departure at 500 ft above ground level (AGL) and 1000 ft AGL, respectively]
3. Control Mode with two levels [AFDS plus autothrottle (AUTO) and flight director only (MAN)]. In the AUTO level, the pilot controlled the autopilot with the MCP and the autothrottle with the MCDU. The MAN level consisted of hand flying only.

Table 1. Departure NAPs

NAP	Definition
ICAO-A	Climb at V_2 +10 to 3000 ft AGL. At 1500 ft AGL, reduce to climb thrust. At 3000 ft AGL, retract flaps on schedule and accelerate to Ref_{30}+100K.
ICAO-A 1000	Climb at V_2 +10 to 3000 ft AGL. At 1000 ft AGL, reduce to climb thrust. At 3000 ft AGL, retract flaps on schedule and accelerate to Ref_{30}+100K.
MCG	Climb at V_2 +10 to 3000 ft AGL. At 1000 ft AGL, reduce to 1.7% climb gradient thrust. At 3000 ft AGL, increase to climb thrust. At 3000 ft AGL, retract flaps on schedule and accelerate to Ref_{30}+100K.

Table 2. Arrival NAPs

NAP	Definition
STD	Cross Lambourne (LAM) in level flight at 7000 ft mean sea level (MSL); descend, slow, and extend flaps/gear at pilot's discretion; intercept glide slope (GS) at 2500 ft; cross 4-nautical mile (nm) final at 160K; complete ILS approach to landing.
CDA1	Cross LAM in level flight at 7000 ft MSL; intercept GS at 7000 ft; slow and extend flaps/gear according to predetermined schedule; cross 4-nm final at 160K; complete ILS approach to landing. Maintain idle thrust from GS intercept to 4-nm final.
TSA	Cross LAM in level flight at 7000 ft MSL; descend late at a 3.7 deg flight path angle to intercept the GS from above at 10-nm final; slow and extend speed brakes/flaps/gear at pilot's discretion; cross 4-nm final at 160K; complete ILS approach to landing.
CDA2	Cross LAM in level flight at 7000 ft MSL; intercept GS at 7000 ft; slow and extend flaps/gear according to predetermined schedule; cross 4-nm final at 160K; complete ILS approach to landing. Maintain low-to-idle thrust from GS intercept to 4-nm final.

The Arrival NAP experiment was a 4 X 2 within-subjects design. The two independent variables were:

1. NAP with four levels [Standard, Ideal Continuous Descent Approach (CDA1), Two-Segment Approach (TSA), and a more practical Continuous Descent Approach (CDA2)] (see Table 2)

2. Control Mode with two levels (AUTO and MAN)

The departure and arrival trials were presented in separate blocks. The order of presentation of trials for each was counterbalanced to account for order and learning effects.

Procedure – The pilot was given a ground school briefing on aircraft weight, airport conditions, and procedures. Each pilot was administered one practice trial for each NAP prior to experimental runs.

Departure Trials – LHR runways 9L/R were employed.[5] At brake release, the pilot applied takeoff thrust and followed the proscribed NAP until 5000 ft at which point the trial ended.

Arrival Trials – The LHR ILS-DME Runway 27R approach with LAM transition was employed.[6] The aircraft began the trial 3.0 nm northeast of LAM at 7000 ft. At LAM, a 234 degree (deg) outbound course was used and the pilot controlled the aircraft according to the NAP. The LAM transition intercepted the ILS-DME final approach course at 10.1-nm final from where the pilot followed the ILS to a landing.

Data Collection – There were three main dependent variables: pilot workload, pilot flying accuracy/compliance with the NAP, and noise. The CVRSF recording system collected data for pilot reaction time, aircraft parameters (e.g., trajectory and speed), and noise.

In addition, a 10-point Cooper/Harper-type questionnaire tailored to NAP operations was administered to assess pilots' subjective evaluations.[7] Pilots were requested to select a numerical rating that corresponded to a text description that best described their opinion or observation of their flying experience. The definitions of numerical ratings are shown in Table 3. The ratings most often selected were 1, 2, 3, and 10.

Table 3. Questionnaire Numerical Ratings Most Often Selected by Pilots

Rating	Definition
1	Excellent; no pilot effort required
2	Good; negligible deficiencies; pilot effort not a factor
3	Fair; mild deficiencies; minimal pilot effort required for desired performance
4	Minor deficiencies; moderate pilot effort required for desired performance
5	Objectionable deficiencies, Considerable pilot effort required for desired performance
6	Very objectionable deficiency, Extensive pilot effort required for desired performance
7	Major deficiencies, Adequate performance not attainable with maximum effort
8	Major deficiencies, Minor errors experienced with maximum effort
9	Major deficiencies, Major errors experienced with maximum effort
10	Impossible; unacceptable; pilot cannot complete task

Noise Measurements - A noise calculation program, which makes use of tabulated noise – power-distance (NPD) data for the B-747-400 aircraft, was used to predict noise under the flight path. The aircraft performance was also recorded for further community noise analysis INM.[4] The noise data were used to determine the effectiveness of the NAPs in reducing community noise as well as determining the variability in noise associated with each NAP due to pilot performance. It should be noted, however, that this study was not designed to address existing noise problems at LHR because the population distribution as well as the adherence to all aerodrome flight restrictions were not considered.

Results And Discussion

Departures

The results of the pilot questionnaire and human factors evaluation are given in greater detail in a forthcoming paper.[8] Subject opinions showed that each NAP was acceptable in terms of workload, situation awareness, ease of performance, and safety, with the MCG perceived to be slightly more difficult and less safe than the ICAO-A or ICAO-A 1000 procedures. Ratings indicated that early and late turns both were executed with acceptable workload. And as for control mode, there was a slight tendency to favor AUTO as opposed to MAN.

Each NAP was executed within normal ranges of required performance using airspeed error as the main metric. There were no statistically or operationally significant performance differences between ICAO-A, ICAO-A1000, and MCG. For the LNAV performance evaluation, a significant difference was found only for the ICAO-A 1000 and MCG first segment where less accurate performance was associated with the turn at 500 ft compared to 1000 ft. For the control mode the only significant difference found was for the ICAO-A first segment. A less accurate performance was associated with AUTO compared to MAN control mode.

According to the responses to the questionnaire, most of the subjects had a certain degree of experience prior to the test with departure NAPs. For example, MCG is a procedure similar to that used at Orange County Airport (SNA), California; and ICAO-A is the recommended departure procedure for United's B747-400 operations at San Francisco Airport (SFO), California. The ICAO-A 1000 procedure was the recommended departure procedure for LHR as well. Thus, all subjects had no problem performing these NAPs and produced consistent noise signatures on the ground.

Figure 2 depicts a noise contour comparison from a typical subject. The external INM noise tool was used to calculate these noise contours based on the subject's flight performance data. Figure 3 illustrates the real time display of four performance parameters of these flight tests. This display was used for the test monitoring and to provide the test subject with feedback after the questionnaire and debriefing session. The % changes of contour area at different maximum A-weighted noise levels

(L_AMAX) shown in Table 4 depict a typical and consistent result of these NAPs. The ICAO-A procedure was the reference procedure since it is the most common operational noise procedure in Europe. An earlier cutback (e.g. ICAO-A 1000 and MCG) produced a noise reduction near the airport, i.e. a smaller 90 dB L_AMAX contour. For the MCG procedure, the increase in engine power to climb thrust at 12 NM distance and 3000 ft altitude induced an increase of contour area (at 70 and 75 dB as shown in the Figure 2). This phenomenon was reflected in Table 4 as a large increase of % L_AMAX at 70 dB.

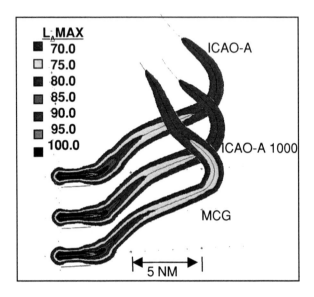

Figure 2. A-weighted noise level contour comparison for typical departure operations (Manual and early turn departures by subject 3)

These results illustrate the variation in sizes of the noise contour area as a function of the specific procedure and the procedure's parameters such as height and thrust. Because of this variation, it is critical to evaluate the noise impact at a specific location to determine the procedure that provides the most noise reduction for the community around that particular airport.

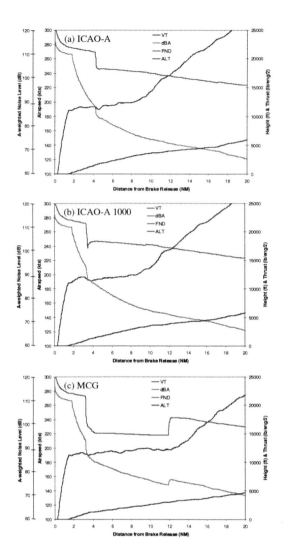

Figure 3 Corresponding aircraft performance parameter of procedures in Figure 2

Table 4 % L_AMAX Contour Area Change Due to NAP with Early Turn and Manual Conditions (Subject 3 Only)

	ICAO-A	ICAO-A 1000	MCG
70 dB	Reference	+1.10	+16.39
80 dB	Reference	+1.48	-2.22
90 dB	Reference	-2.82	-4.52

Arrivals

Arrival NAPs were rated by subjects using 12 questions. Overall, subject opinions showed that each NAP was acceptable in terms of workload, situation awareness, ease of performance, and safety. The subjects preferred the CDA1 and CDA2 procedures over the STD procedure for their stabilized flight path, in contrast to the STD procedure where multiple level-off and descent segments increased the probability for pilot error. The subjects also did not favor the TSA procedure because of the high descent rate and small flight safety margin.

Lateral course error, vertical path error, and Control Mode were analyzed. Each NAP was executed within normal ranges of required performance with the exception of the TSA. The CDA and LPLD were associated with the most accurate performance and the TSA was associated with the least accurate performance.

Unlike the departure NAP test, the eight subjects in this study had no previous experience with advanced arrival NAPs. The subjects familiarized themselves with the NAPs during the pre-test briefing, the review of flight bug-cards just prior to each simulation, and during the practice flights. On average, these pilots could fly the procedures as instructed. Since each simulation started from a fixed initial position (from Lambourne (LAM) at 7000, proceeding outbound on LAM R-234 and intercepting the LOC at IRR D10.1), all flight tests showed an insignificant lateral flight track variation. The type of NAP employed therefore drove the vertical flight track variations and their impact on ground noise levels.

The accuracy of the INM is a concern at low and/or idle engine thrust conditions, such as those near and before the stabilization point of these procedures.[9] The NPD used in the present study did not account for the contribution of varying operational configurations of the aircraft at low power setting, e.g. airframe noise contribution.

Figure 4 shows the noise under the flight path of the STD, CDA1, CDA2, and TSA procedure. The figure illustrates significant noise reductions in L_AMAX between 60 and 80 dB in the three advanced NAPs in comparison to the STD procedure. The TSA approach provides the highest noise reduction at the expense of higher

workload. The noise reduction shown is up to 5 dB for communities between 10 and 20 nautical miles from the airport.

Table 5 shows the % L_AMAX contour area reduction of NAPs. There are significant reductions in the area exposed to noise between 65 dB and 70 dB, which is consistent with Figure 4. The CDA2 provides slightly smaller noise contour area reduction compared to CDA1 as a result of using extra thrust for additional aircraft control before the stabilization point.

There are two important points to note when trying to interpret the results in Figure 4 and Table 5:

- In an actual Standard arrival, the pilot may descends to the intermediate approach segment at 2500 ft sooner, and the resulting longer level flight segment would in turn produces a larger noise contour area.
- The uncommon initial descending angle (~3.7°) of the TSA procedure caused most of the subjects to overshoot and capture the final glide slope from above, consequently the resulting higher flight paths than designed produced smaller noise contour areas.

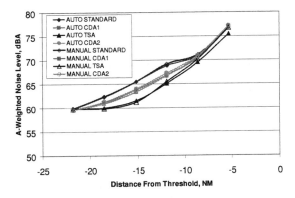

Figure 4 Averaged A-weighted noise level under the flight path (all subjects)

Table 5 % L$_A$MAX Contour Area Reduction of
NAPs (Mean Values for All Subjects)

	Standard	CDA1	CDA2	TSA
65 dB Auto	Reference	-14.92	-8.93	-25.88
65 dB Man	Reference	-11.45	-10.92	-24.45
70 dB Auto	Reference	-20.07	-8.81	-24.08
70 dB Man	Reference	-13.99	-13.20	-21.15

Figure 5 depicts a comparison of the noise contours from these NAPs for a typical subject. Advanced NAPs provided significant reductions in the 65 and 70 L$_A$MAX contour areas. Figure 6 shows the corresponding flight performance charts for these arrival cases. The level flight segment in Figure 6a could be elongated if the pilot chose to step down early as instructed. The required thrust to maintain a stabilized flight, in this case, should extend the 65 and 70 L$_A$MAX contour area significantly. The additional thrust used before stabilization in the CDA2 procedures was obvious when comparing Figure 6b and c. In a normal operation, e.g. higher landing weight than that used in the present test, the CDA2 is the practical NAP with the current B747-400 FMS.[10] Additional landing weights (430,000, 530,000, and 630,000 lb) were tested successfully with the CDA2. The advantage of TSA was its higher than normal altitude before intercepting the 3° glide slope. From the community noise point of view, an ideal arrival NAP is one that stays as high as possible, delays final stabilization to an acceptable point, and approaches with minimum throttle during decent.

Figures 7 depicts the variation in MAN control mode of each NAP's altitude, speed, and weighted peak noise at six final DME locations. Although there were no strict altitude and speed (Figure 7a and 7b) requirements other than 160 knots at 4 DME, the CDA1 and CDA2 procedures exhibited

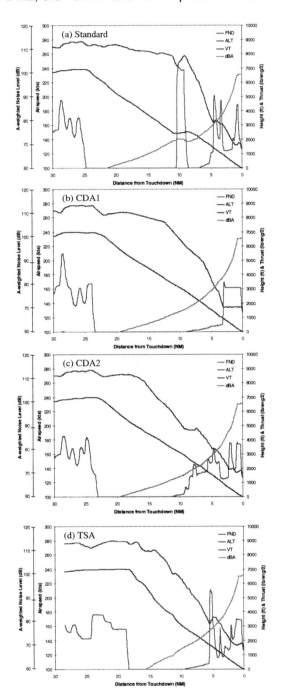

Figure 6. Corresponding aircraft performance parameter of procedures in Figure 5

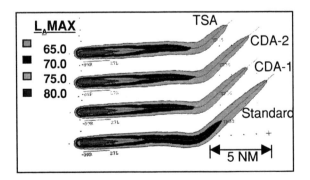

Figure 5. A-weighted noise level contour comparison for arrival operations (Subject 3)

greatest consistency. Although a supplementary test showed that additional training could reduce the scattering of the more difficult TSA procedure, we concluded that CDA1 (and CDA2) were better procedures in terms of performance and noise (Figure 7c) accuracy. As stated earlier, the performance accuracy is becoming more important in many airports where a narrow flying corridor is designed for the purpose of community noise reduction.

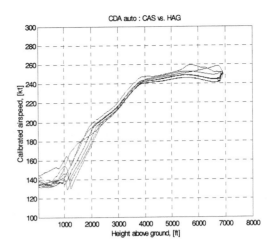

Figure 8: Speed profiles of CDA procedure in autopilot mode.

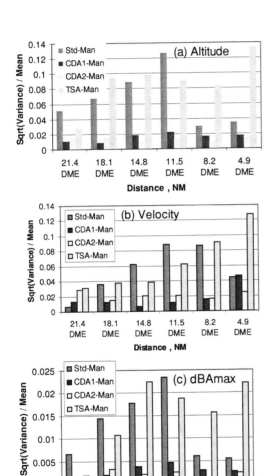

Figure 7 CDA1 and CDA2 had the least noise scattering near final approach

Figure 8 illustrates the different speed profiles, flown by eight different pilots, of the CDA in autopilot mode. While all the profiles' speeds prior to the point of intercepting the glide slope were at the instructed speed of 250 knots, the speeds immediately after glide slope interception varied by 5 knots. Closer examination revealed that this variability was the result of the order in which the pitch and speed were reduced. Specifically, if the aircraft pitch was reduced before the thrust was reduced to idle, the speed immediately after intercepting the glide slope is higher than 250 knots due the sudden partial loss of lift. Conversely, if the thrust was reduced to idle before the aircraft pitch was reduced, the speed is slower than 250 knots immediately after the glide slope was intercepted.

Additional simulator flight tests (by a NASA test pilot in a supplemental noise sensitivity test) showed that the initial Top of Descent (TOD) altitude and speed were important for aircraft descent rate and speed control at higher landing weights. A higher initial altitude also gave additional time for the pilot to react to the flight descending slope transition of the TSA procedure. The TOD condition, however, is usually restricted by the local airport airspace requirement. On the other hand, it could be used to control the estimated arrival time (EAT) from initial descent of the aircraft. In a more complicated fleet mix system where standard and CDA procedures are both used with different type of aircraft, the EAT could be used to establish a proper separation requirement by the ATC during final approach. Thus, the initial condition should be an important consideration for future arrival NAP and air traffic integration.

Summary

The goal of this project was to examine the effectiveness in community noise reduction, the operational feasibility and flight crew human factors issues of existing and proposed NAPs at a noise sensitive airport. Results from the study have enhanced the databases for NASA's programs, such as QAT, and Boeing's Community Noise Programs.

Results are based on the specific aircraft, density altitude conditions, and NAPs used in this study. The aircraft was a B-747-400 at maximum takeoff gross weight (873,000 pounds) for departures and very light landing weight (436,000 pounds) for approaches. London Heathrow airport was used in standard day conditions. Any extrapolation of results and conclusions to other aircraft and density altitudes must consider differences in relative aircraft performance. Operational acceptability of these NAPs for some aircraft in certain conditions may be substantially different than that described here.

Three departure NAPs were examined: ICAO-A, ICAO-A 1000, and MCG. Overall, data showed that each NAP was acceptable in terms of pilot acceptability, ease of performance, workload, flying performance accuracy, and safety.

Performance differences among them were insignificant. However, pilots rated the MCG as the most difficult and least safe.

Four approach NAPs were examined: STD, CDA1, TSA, and CDA2. Overall, data showed that each NAP was acceptable in terms of pilot acceptability and safety. However, the TSA measured significantly higher for performance difficulty, workload, and flying performance inaccuracy.

Pilot ratings and flying performance for the STD were somewhat lower than those were for CDA1 and CDA2. Pilots rated workload higher and were concerned with the potential for human error that could result from multiple step-down segments.

With limited practice runs, all subjects performed various NAPs and produced expected noise signatures on the ground. Better performance accuracy (flight path and noise) could be achieved with adequate training and an advanced FMS. Arrival NAPs are more critical from a future NAP development point of view, especially for envisioned FMS/ATM. Among all arrival NAPs, CDA1 and CDA2 provided the most consistent noise benefit and had better flight control characteristics. In general, the pilots liked to operate CDA1 and CDA2. TSA provides better noise reduction, but has a higher workload and requires additional training. Current 747-400 FMS does not provide sufficient flight guidance to adequately handle CDA1 and TSA.

For this single event flight test, the NPD in the INM method may not be adequate for an accurate noise prediction when the engine thrust setting is low or idle and has a large throttle fluctuation. The propagation algorithm in the INM method needs improvements for an advanced NAP and ATM integration as well.

The Ames flight simulator has proven to be a useful tool for community noise studies. Realistic and detailed aircraft performance data were generated for difficult procedures with multi-flight segments. The implementation of a noise prediction tool in the simulator provided an instant feedback to the test subject. The NASA Ames test site also provided an unprecedented opportunity for communication with different community noise stakeholders. Through this Phase I and II period, we have contacted and worked with airport officers, pilots, airlines, air traffic controller's avionics engineers, ATM, and the FAA.

Recommendations

Results of this study suggest that future research should be directed at evaluating and refining the most-promising NAPs. This may be any of the three departure NAPs and the CDA2. Study of the TSA may also be worthwhile if its design is developed correctly. Future NAP should be tailored to advanced FMS development as well. Variations and derivatives of the concepts used in this and other studies should be subjects for examination.

Because some of the aspects of this simulation did not represent line operations, it would be well for future efforts to maximize realism. In addition, the inclusion of air traffic control operations and relevant advanced technologies will provide a valid setting for more-focused evaluations. Some of the features suggested for future simulations and/or actual operation include the following:

(1) operation at multiple airports

(2) use of the FMS as appropriate to line operations (e.g., modified with required CDA2 data, flap extension schedule, and real-time profile progress status)

(3) use of AFDS as appropriate to line operations (LNAV/VNAV modes)

(4) employment of a modified primary flight display and/or NAV display(s) to show CDA2 data as necessary

(5) provisions for an increase in workload using line-oriented conditions (weather, traffic, communications)

(6) inclusion of NASA Ames' Center-TRACON (Terminal Radar Approach Control) Automation Systems (CTAS) environment options

The noise modeling development of an improved INM tool maintains as the most important task for improvement on this and European Sourdine studies. This tool development is also part of the SAE A21 committee activity of which Boeing will evidently become a more active participant in the near future. While ATM and FMS research groups are working on an integrated plan for future NAP development, the noise team should have a role to monitor any new NAP design and to conduct its flight simulator test, either single event or integration CTAS test.

Acknowledgements

This research was supported by NASA QAT Program, NASA Ames Aviation System Research and The Boeing Company. The authors would like to thank the crews of the B747-400 Simulator at the Ames CVSRF facility and the United Airline pilots for their participation in this study.

References

1. FAA AC 91-53A, Noise Abatement Departure Profiles, July 1993

2. ICAO Doc 8168-OPS/611, Procedures for Air Navigation Services, Aircraft Operations, Volume 1, Flight Procedures

3. Erkelens, L. J. J., "Development of noise abatement procedures in the Netherlands," Based on a paper presented at the New Aviation Technologies, International Symposium, Zhukovsky, Moscow Region, Russia, August 17-22, 1999.

4. Gulding, et al, FAA. Integrated Noise Model (INM) Version 6.0 User's Guide, Sep 1999.

5. Jeppesen Sanderson, Inc. London, UK, BUZAD THREE JULIET/BUZAD TWO KILO, Standard instrument departure chart 10-3B. May 15, 1998.

6. Jeppesen Sanderson, Inc. EGLL Heathrow, London, UK, ILS DME Rwy 27R approach chart 11-4. Sep 10, 1999.

7. Clarke, J. P.,"A System Analysis Methodology for Developing Single Events Noise Abatement Procedures," Ph. D. thesis, Department of Aeronautics and Astronautics, MIT, January 1997

8. Gerszhon, G. et. al., "Advanced Noise Abatement Procedures: An Experimental Study of Flight Operational Acceptability", AIAA 2002 not yet published.

9. TRB/NRC Transportation Research Circular Number 473, Aircraft Noise Modeling, May 1997

10. Kershaw, A., Rhodes, D. and Smith, N., "The influence of ATC in approach noise abatement," 3rd USA/Europe Air Traffic Management R&D Seminar, Napoli, June 13-16, 2000

A COMPUTATIONAL STUDY OF THE IGNITION OVER-PRESSURE FOR LAUNCH VEHICLES

Francisco Canabal
NASA Marshall Space Flight Center
Huntsville, AL 35889

Abdelkader Frendi
University of Alabama in Huntsville
Huntsville, AL 3589

8th AIAA/CEAS Aeroacoustics Conference and Exhibit
17-19 June 2002
Breckenridge, Colorado

1. ABSTRACT

Accurate predictions of ignition over-pressure for the Minuteman and Titan Silo launchers with comparisons to test data and Broadwell and Tsu's model predictions [1] are presented. Initial over-pressure results, using the current model, are in much better agreement with the test data for both launchers. The current one-dimensional and two-dimensional axi-symmetric models are able to handle wave reflections from the top and bottom of silos without any empirical constants. This is not the case for the Broadwell and Tsu model, which introduces empirical constants to account for after-burning and momentum losses. Qualitative results for launch vehicle take-off are also given.

2. INTRODUCTION

It is well known that during the ignition sequence leading up to launch vehicle take-off, a large blast wave is generated and propagates up the vehicle. A similar problem is also encountered in silo missile launchers, where the sudden release of mass, momentum and energy generates a large over-pressure that can lead to increased structural vibration, sonic fatigue and potential structural failure. In the case of launch vehicles, this may severely damage the sensitive payloads stored in the cargo bay area. Therefore, it is important to understand the mechanisms that generate the blast wave and its subsequent propagation.

There exists many ways of generating a blast wave in a gas mixture; heat addition, mass addition and momentum addition. When heat is added to a volume of gas the density of the gas is reduced, this in turn causes an expansion of the volume occupied by the heated gas, which results in a blast wave. G. I. Taylor[1] studied the propagation and decay of blast waves generated by a detonating explosive. He defined a blast wave as a sharp wave front followed by a suction wave. This sharp wave front is also known as the blast wave over-pressure. He found that the spatial decay of the maximum over-pressure was inversely proportional to the distance from the source. Sakurai[2] later studied the propagation and decay of spherical blast waves. He used a power series expansion approach to solve the hydrodynamic equations. He found that the decay of the blast waves was inversely proportional to the cubic power of the distance from the source. The maximum over-pressures generated by Sakurai's blast waves were much higher than that studied by G. I. Taylor. Frendi[3] studied the blast waves generated by a spark ignition device in a chemically reacting gas mixture. He found that the maximum over-pressure increased by increasing the energy input or decreasing the ignition time.

Broadwell and Tsu[4] developed an analytical model to study the ignition over-pressure generated by silo launchers such as the Titan and the Minuteman. Their one-dimensional model needed two empirical constants in order to be used; one that accounts for combustion in the exhaust gases, the other for momentum loss. Once these constants were fixed, reasonably good agreement with measured data was obtained.

Following, the first space shuttle flight (STS-1), it became apparent to NASA engineers that the problem of ignition over-pressure needed immediate attention. Several experimental studies were initiated to look into ways to alleviate this problem. Dougherty et al[5] studied the effects of water addition to the solid rocket motor exhaust plume. This was found to be effective in reducing the over-pressure and was subsequently used in STS-2. Additional numerical and experimental studies followed in order to understand the effects of water addition to the exhaust plume.[6-9]

In this paper, results from a one-dimensional and tow-dimensional axis-symmetric studies on the ignition over-pressure for a Minuteman and a Titan silo launchers are presented. The use of one spatial dimension is only to compare with Broadwell and Tsu's model. The remainder of the paper is organized as follows; the mathematical model is described in the next section, followed by the method of solution. The various results are discussed next and finally the concluding remarks are given.

3. FORMULATION OF THE MODEL

The computational domain shown on Fig. 1 represents a silo launcher configuration, which can be described as a missile positioned coaxially inside a slender cylindrical cavity. During the transient start of a silo launch the engine exhaust fills the bottom of the silo sending acoustic waves toward the bottom and the top of the silo.

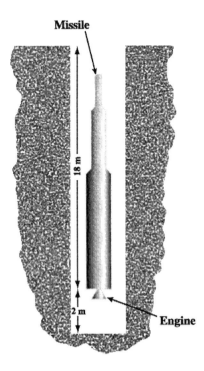

Figure 1. Silo Launcher Configuration

The model used to describe this problem is based on the nonlinear Euler equations written in one space dimension as

$$\frac{\partial U}{\partial t} + \frac{\partial F_i}{\partial x_i} = B \qquad (1)$$

where

$$U = \begin{bmatrix} \rho \\ \rho v_j \\ \rho E \end{bmatrix} \quad \text{and} \quad F_i = \begin{bmatrix} \rho v_i \\ \rho v_i v_j + P\delta_{ij} \\ \rho v_i(E + P/\rho) \end{bmatrix} \qquad (2)$$

and $E = c_v T + \frac{1}{2}\rho v_i v_i$. The closure is formed with the equation of state for an ideal gas, $P = \rho RT$. The vector B is defined according to the case under consideration. For the one-dimensional simulations the vector B represents the source of mass, momentum and energy as follows

$$B = \begin{bmatrix} \dot{m}''' \\ \dot{m}''' g I_{sp} \\ \dot{m}''' Y_f \Delta h_c \end{bmatrix} \qquad (3)$$

whereas for the two-dimensional axi-symmetric simulation this vector is defined as

$$B = \frac{1}{y}\begin{bmatrix} \rho v \\ \rho v u \\ \rho v v \\ \rho v(E + P/\rho) \end{bmatrix} \qquad (4)$$

where y is the coordinate away from the axi.

The quantities $\dot{m}'''$, g_c, I_{sp}, Y_f and Δh_c are the volumetric mass flow rate, gravitational constant, specific impulse at sea-level, fuel mass fraction and enthalpy of combustion per unit mass of fuel, respectively. In order to make accurate comparisons with test data and Broadwell and Tsu results, the source terms are obtained through

$$\dot{m}''' = (\dot{m}''')_{ss} \frac{P_c}{(P_c)_{ss}} \qquad (5)$$

where $(\dot{m}''')_{ss}$ is the steady-state engine mass flow rate. Input data for these source terms are obtained from the various published reports on the engines used in the Titan and Minuteman. When calculating the exhaust gas total enthalpy, complete combustion of the fuel is assumed. The ratio $P_c/(P_c)_{ss}$ represents the unsteady, non-dimensional combustion chamber pressure and is obtained from the test data published in reference. [4]

4. METHOD OF SOLUTION

The numerical technique used to solve Eq. (1) is described as a combination of a temporal discretization scheme, a spatial discretization scheme and a discontinuity-capturing scheme. In the time discretization scheme, the value of ΔU is calculated using equation

$$\Delta U^{l+1} = \Delta t\left(\left.\frac{\partial U}{\partial t}\right|^l + s_1\left.\frac{\partial \Delta U}{\partial t}\right|^{l+1}\right)$$
$$+ \frac{\Delta t^2}{2}\left((1-2s_1)\left.\frac{\partial^2 U}{\partial t^2}\right|^l + s_2\left.\frac{\partial^2 \Delta U}{\partial t^2}\right|^{l+1}\right) \qquad (6)$$

where $0 \le (s_1, s_2) \le 1$ are parameters designed to control the implicit and explicit levels of the scheme. [10]

The spatial discretization is performed using a Galerkin finite element method in which the integrated weighted-residual is minimized.

The domain is discretized in a number of finite elements formed by nodes at the vertices. Within the elements, high order polynomials are used to interpolate the values of U from the nodes. These polynomials known as shape functions are denoted by Φ_α where α is the global node number. Thus, the value of U at any point within the domain is given by $U(x) = \Phi_\alpha(x)U_\alpha$, where U_α is the discrete nodal value of U at the node α.

To resolve discontinuities in the flow field a convective flux correction term is devised following the work of Davis.[11] This is achieved by introducing upwind biased discretization of the convective fluxes. Also, the use of nonlinear limiters make it possible to maintain high order accuracy without introducing the oscillations or dispersion error characteristic of high order schemes.

The boundaries for the one-dimensional simulation are at the bottom and top (exit) of the silo (Fig. 2). For the Minuteman silo the boundary at the bottom is treated as a rigid wall in which the mass and energy fluxes are set equal to zero. At the exit, the flow field is simulated using the method of characteristics to account for the far-field conditions. The plume expansion rate (see Fig. 1b) is approximated as

$$\frac{1}{S_e}\frac{dS}{dx}\bigg|_e = (M_e^2 - 1)\frac{1}{u_e}\frac{du}{dx}\bigg|_e$$
$$\approx (M_e^2 - 1)\frac{1}{u_e}\frac{u_\infty - u_e}{l} \tag{7}$$

where the subscript e identifies quantities evaluated at the silo exit. Also, following the work of Broadwell & Tsu, the value of l is defined as $\pi d/8$, which represents the effective length. Unlike the Minuteman silo, the configuration of the Titan silo introduces an arrangement of channels connecting the bottom of the silo to the exterior of the silo. Therefore, for this configuration, the exit and bottom boundaries are both treated the same using equation (7) with different values for l at the exit and bottom. At the exit the value of l is defined as $\pi d/8$, whereas at the bottom l corresponds to the length of the channel.

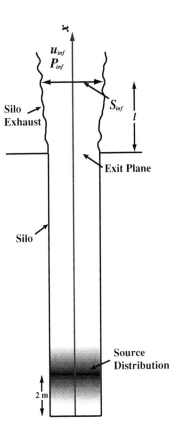

Figure 2. One-Dimensional Silo Model

Figure 3 shows the boundaries for the two-dimensional axi-symmetric simulation. All solid surfaces are treated as slip-walls. At the engine chamber inlet (chamber faceplate) the total pressure and total temperature were approximated as

$$\frac{T_o}{(T_o)_{ss}} \approx \frac{P_o}{(P_o)_{ss}} \approx \frac{P_c}{(P_c)_{ss}} \tag{8}$$

At the far-field the total condition were fixed at the ambient conditions.

Another axi-symmetric configuration considered in this study is that of a generic vehicle on an open launch pad as opposed to a closed one as in the silo case. Figure 4 shows a representative launch pad and vehicle configuration. The geometry for this vehicle and the boundary conditions are similar to those used in the silo simulation. Similarly, the assumption on equation 8 was also used for this configuration.

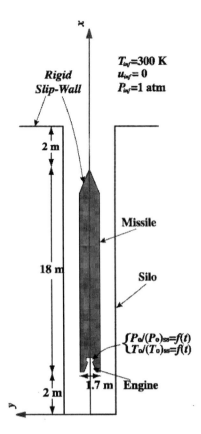

Figure 3. Two-Dimensional Silo Model

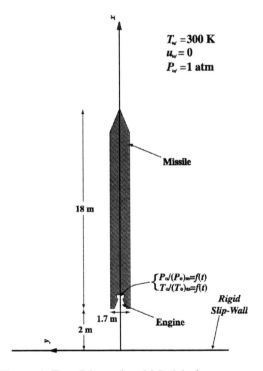

Figure 4. Two-Dimensional Model of a Representative Launch Pad and Vehicle Configuration

5. RESULTS AND DISCUSSIONS

The simulation begins with the entire silo filled with stagnant air at atmospheric conditions. This represents the trivial solution at $t = 0$. For $t > 0$, the engine chamber pressure continues increasing until reaching its steady-state value.

For the one-dimensional simulation the source term, B, is evaluated according to equations (3) and (5) and the data for the particular engine or motor under consideration. The mass flow rate, thrust and enthalpy of combustion of the first stage Minuteman motor are 679 lbm/sec, 161000 lb and 1.5×10^9 lb-ft/sec, respectively. For the Titan engine these values are 1215 lbm/sec, 300000 lb and 5×10^9 lb-ft/sec for the engine mass flow rate, thrust and enthalpy of combustion, respectively. The calculated source term, B, was distributed axially according to a Gaussian distribution. This distribution spans for two meters and it is centered two meters above the sillo bottom as shown in Fig. 2.

Fig. 5 shows the measured unsteady, non-dimensional combustion chamber pressure for the 16 ft Minuteman silo launcher. Fig. 6 shows the pressure in the silo as a function of time at a location near the missile base resulting from the chamber pressure input of Fig. 5. The first peak corresponds to the ignition over-pressure, which is about 6 psi. Our model not only predicts the over-pressure accurately but also the low amplitude oscillations that follows it.

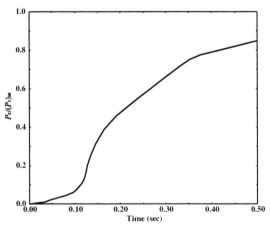

Figure 5. Measured Chamber Pressure for the 16-foot Silo

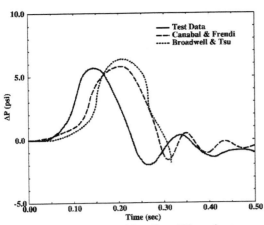

Figure 6. Measured and Predicted Transient Pressure at a Station Near the Missile Base

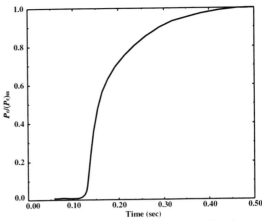

Figure 7. Measured Chamber Pressure for the 12-foot Silo

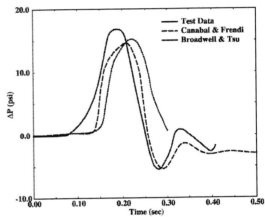

Figure 8. Measured and Predicted Transient Pressure at a Station Near the Missile Base

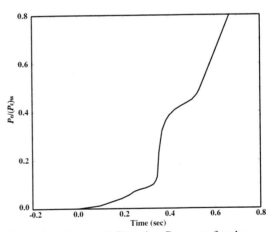

Figure 9. Measured Chamber Pressure for the Titan Silo

Similar results are shown on Figs. 7 and 8 for the 12 ft diameter Minuteman silo launcher. In this case the ignition over-pressure is of the order of 16 psi. Even though the same engine is used for both, the 12 and 16-foot silos, it is interesting to note that the 12-foot silo experiences an over pressure almost two and a half times higher than that experience by the 16-foot silo. This increase in over-pressure is attributed to a smaller volume inside the silo.

Both Minuteman silo predictions show a retarded response relative to the experimental data. For instance, according to the experimental data for the 12-foot Minuteman silo, the pressure near the missile base begins its rapid increase at about 0.1 seconds whereas the predicted value indicates that this would occur at about 0.15 seconds. It is not surprising that the predictions indicate 0.15 seconds as the time for the beginning of the rapid pressure increase since it is after about 0.13 seconds that the chamber pressure begins to increase as shown in Fig. 7. At this point it is unknown why the experimental data of the pressure near the missile base begins to increase before the chamber pressure.

Figures 9 and 10 show the measured, unsteady chamber pressure input (Fig. 9) and the measured and predicted over-pressure at a location near the middle of the missile for the Titan silo launcher (Fig. 10). The combustion chamber pressure for the Titan silo launcher is still increasing rapidly (Fig. 9), whereas that for the Minuteman silo launchers is nearing a steady state value (Figs. 5, 7). Our model predictions are, for all the cases, in good agreement with the test data.

1439

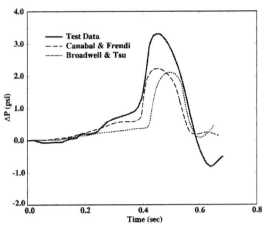

Figure 10. Measured and Predicted Transient Pressure at a Station Near the Missile Base

In the two-dimensional simulations, instead of modeling the engine as a source term, the engine is now simulated. Like in the one-dimensional calculation, the simulation begins with the entire silo at ambient conditions. For $t>0$ the engine total pressure is varied according to measured chamber pressure. Using the test data for the 16-foot silo and the configuration shown in figure 3 a simulation of the first 0.5 sec of the test was performed. The steady-state chamber pressure is 800 *psi* and the steady-state chamber temperature is estimated as 2600 K. Figure 11 shows a sequence of nine pressure distributions taken at nine equal time intervals within the 0.5 sec interval. In this figure the time increases from left to right and from top to bottom. Also, the range of the pressure contours have been narrowed to the interval from 1 to 10 *atms*. The first three slides at the top show approximately the first 0.15 sec of the simulation where the chamber has gone from zero to approximately 30% of its steady-state value (see Fig. 4). The following three slides correspond to the time interval where the engine undergoes a rapid increase in chamber pressure. It is within this interval (from approximately 0.2 to 0.3 seconds) that the missile is subjected to the maximum over-pressure. At the end of this interval it is clearly shown in the third slide the formation of the rarefaction wave. This wave travels toward the bottom of the silo inducing a rapid decrease in pressure. The last set of time slides show a relatively smaller pressure variation consistent with a slower rate of chamber pressure increase.

Figures 12 and 13 show the transient pressure distributions at a location near the missile base and near the missile nose, respectively.

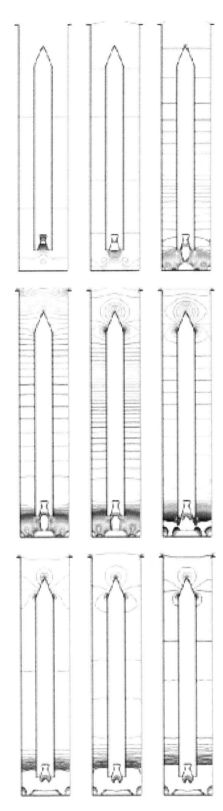

Figure 11. Pressure Distributions at Nine Different Times (time increases from Left to Right, Top to Bottom)

1440

In the open launch pad configuration the chamber pressure was varied according to the test data shown on figure 7. The far-field total pressure and total temperature was fixed at 1 *atm* and 300 K, respectively. The steady-state chamber pressure is 800 *psi* and the steady-state chamber temperature is estimated as 2600 K. Figures 14 and 15 shows the pressure and Mach number distributions, respectively, at t=0.5 seconds. These represent a near steady-state flow field. Figure 16 shows ten time slides at ten equally spaced time intervals. Time increases from left to right and from top to bottom the time increment between slides is 0.05 seconds.

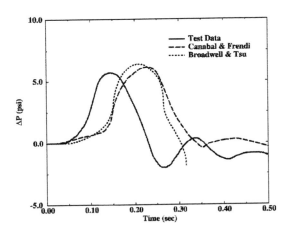

Figure12. Measured and Predicted Transient Pressure at a Station Near the Missile Base

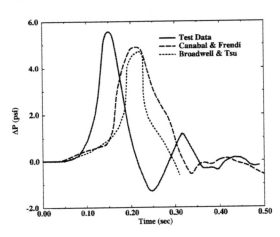

Figure13. Measured and Predicted Transient Pressure at a Station Near the Missile Nose

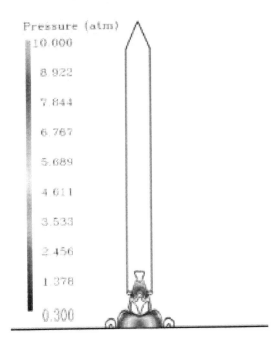

Figure 14. Pressure Distribution at t=0.5 seconds

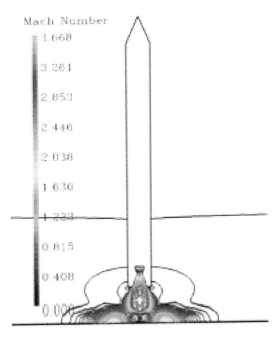

Figure 15. Mach Number Distribution at t=0.5 seconds

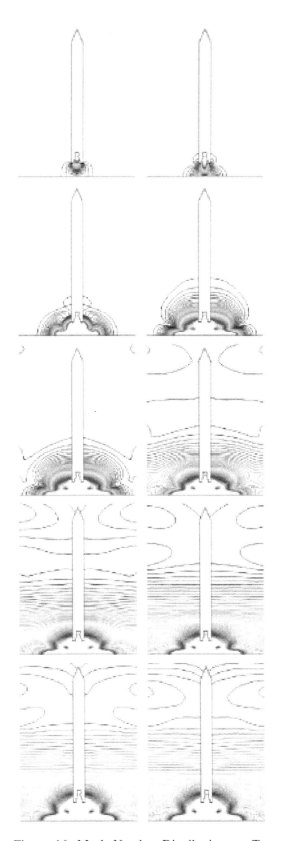

Figure 16. Mach Number Distributions at Ten Different Time Slides (Left to Right, Top to Bottom)

6. CONCLUDING REMARKS

A simple model capable of accurately predicting the ignition over-pressure in silo launchers has been presented. This model does not require the use of empirical constants. The over-pressure results obtained using this model are in good agreement with test data for the Minuteman and Titan silo launchers.

7. ACKNOWLEDGEMENTS

The second author would like the acknowledge the support of NASA Langley Research Center through grant number NAG-1-01008 with Drs. Bart Singer and Rich Silcox as the technical monitors.

8. REFERENCES

[1]Taylor, G.I., "Aerodynamics and the Mechanics of Projectiles and Explosions", The Scientific papers of G.I. Taylor Edited by G.K. Batchelor, Cambridge, Vol. III, 1939, pp. 221-250.

[2]Sakurai, A., "Propagation and Decay of Spherical Blast Waves", *Journal of the Physical Society of Japan*, Vol. 8, No. 5, 1953, pp. 662-700.

[3]Frendi, A., "Flammability Limits of Premixed Gases at Zero Gravity", Ph.D. Dissertation, Brown University, 1990, Providence, Rhode Island.

[4]Broadwell, J.E., and Tsu, C.N., "Transient Pressure Caused by Rocket Start and Shutdown in Ducted Launchers", *Journal of Spacecraft*, Vol. 4, No. 10, 1967, pp. 1323-1328.

[5]Dougherty, N.S., Nesman, T.E. and Guest, S.H., "Shuttle SRB Over-pressure: Model Suppression Test Program and Flight Results", 13th JANNAF conference, NASA Johnson Space Center, 1982.

[6]Shapiro A.H., and Hawthorne, W., "The Mechanics and Thermodynamics of Steady One-dimensional Gas Flow", *Journal of Applied Mechanics*, Vol. 14, 1947, pp. A317-336.

[7]Woo, J., Jones, J.H., and Guest, S.H., "A Study of the Effects of Water Addition on Supersonic Gas Streams", 13th JANNAF conference, NASA Johnson Space Center, 1982.

[8]Jones, J.H., "Scaling of Ignition Startup Pressure Transients in Rocket Systems as Applied to the Space Shuttle Over-pressure Phenomenon", 13th JANNAF conference, NASA Johnson Space Center, 1982.

[9]Lai, S., and Laspesa, F.S., "Ignition Over-pressure Measured on STS Lift-Off and Correlation with Subscale Model Tests", 13th JANNAF conference, NASA Johnson Space Center, 1982.

[10]Schunk, G., Canabal, F., Heard, G., and Chung, T.J., "Unified CFD Methods Via Flowfield-Dependent Variation Theory", 30th AIAA Fluid Dynamics Conference, Norfolk, VA, 1999.

[11]Davis, Stephen F., "A Simplified TVD Finite Difference Scheme Via Artificial Viscosity", SIAM J. Sci. Stat. Comput., Vol 8, No. 1, January 1987.

AIAA 2002-2542

PREDICTION OF SONIC BOOM SIGNATURE USING EULER-FULL POTENTIAL CFD WITH GRID ADAPTATION AND SHOCK FITTING*

O. A. Kandil [1] and Z. Yang [2], Old Dominion University, Norfolk, VA 23529
and
P. J. Bobbitt [3] Eagle Aeronautics, Inc., Hampton, VA 23666

Abstract

A computational fluid dynamics (CFD) methodology has been formulated and a prototype computer code has been developed to propagate Euler-equations-based, near-field supersonic pressure calculations to the ground through a real atmosphere. This near-field supersonic flow is propagated to the ground using the full-potential equation. The scheme is called the Euler-full potential (EFP) scheme. Once shocks are captured, a grid adaptation scheme, based on the density gradient, is implemented to obtain a crisper shock. This is followed by a shock-fitting scheme that is based on the Rankine-Hugoniot conservation equations. Computational results for uniform (isothermal) and non-uniform (standard) atmospheric conditions are presented. For computational validation, the far-field results of the Euler equations for a two-dimensional biconvex airfoil are compared with the results of the far-field potential equation. The results on the ground are in excellent agreement with each other. The three-dimensional capability of the code is illustrated by calculations of on and aft track ground pressure distributions for a three-dimensional delta wing cruising at 52,000 feet altitude and at a Mach number of 2.01.

Symbols

C   wing or airfoil chord
H   distance below source location
M_∞ Mach number
p   static pressure
q_∞ dynamic pressure
r   radial distance from aircraft
S   wing area
U, V,W longitudinal, lateral, and vertical velocity
X   longitudinal or streamwise coordinate

Y   lateral distance
Z   vertical distance
C_D drag coefficient $= drag/ q_\infty S$
C_L lift coefficient $= lift/ q_\infty S$
C_P $= (p - p_\infty) / q_\infty$
Δp $p - p_\infty$
ρ Ambient density
ϕ Velocity potential

Abbreviations
RMS   root mean square
CFD   computational fluid dynamics
EFP   Euler-Full Potential
GASF grid adaptation and shock fitting

Subscripts
∞ freestream
x, y, z derivative relative to these coordinates
ξ, η, ζ derivative relative to these coordinates

Introduction

A number of methods and computer codes are available for predicting the evolution of supersonic aircraft's pressure signature as it propagates to the ground through a "real" stratified atmosphere [1-8]. The most utilized sonic boom propagation codes are based on linear acoustic ray tracing and the Blokhintsev invariant. If, in addition, equivalent axisymmetric-body, F-function methodology is utilized, then the code developed by Hayes (ref. l) is employed. Where a pressure distribution is available, then the Thomas code (ref. 6) is the preferred approach. This method is also based on the acoustic ray tracing methodology but employs several waveform parameters to describe the evolution of the pressure wave. It is this latter code that is normally used in combination with a near-field Euler CFD calculation to propagate sonic boom signatures to the ground.

---

*Work performed under Lockheed-Martin contract Number EM1424560E to Eagle Aeronautics, Inc.
[1] Professor & Eminent Scholar, Associate Fellow AIAA.
[2] Graduate Research Assistant, Member AIAA
[3] Director of Aerodynamics, Fellow AIAA

One of the problems in matching (or connecting) the Thomas propagation code to an Euler near-field solution is that the Thomas solution in the near-field has a $\frac{1}{\sqrt{r}}$ pressure dependency (r is radial distance). Near-field Euler solutions generally do not reach this "asymptotic" state at the outer boundary of the calculated flow field where the match is made. Consequently, there is an error introduced. One improvement is provided by the introduction of a mid-field pressure propagation routine that more exactly matches the Euler solution rate of radial decay as well as the $\frac{1}{\sqrt{r}}$ decay at the other boundary where the Thomas waveform code is implemented.

Reference 11 describes a modified propagation code based on the multipole linear scheme of George (Ref. 12). While this is clearly a more accurate method to propagate the pressure signature than connecting the ray tracing code directly to the CFD solution, there is still a concern. If the linear multipole solution is matched to the CFD solution where there are still significant nonlinear effects, then one would expect some error to creep in as the multipole solution is propagated to the far-field. Clearly, the further one can take the CFD solution (larger radial distance) into the mid-field, the more accurate will be the multipole solution. It will also be easier to match to the CFD pressures with the multipole solution. While the multipole solution can be matched to the CFD pressures, no *comparisons* were given in Ref. 11 of the radial pressure gradients, which are intrinsic to the multipole method, with those at the CFD boundary. In addition, results were only given for a simple triangular wing. Since the publication of Ref. 11 the multipole method has been used for a wide range work and gradually thought to be an improvement over the direct coupling of near and far-field solutions.

The precision with which a complex near field solution with the nonlinear effects and radial gradients can be matched and propagated can still be improved. Use of a higher order methodology in both the near field and far field is feasible and desirable. Ideally, this "higher order" solution would be matched to the near field solution point for point including radial gradients and shock jumps. The study described herein provides such a solution.

In this paper, a computational fluid dynamics (CFD) method and a solver have been developed to accurately compute the propagation of an aircraft's sonic boom pressure wave through a real atmosphere. The near field flow is predicted by using the Euler equations while the far-field flow is predicted by using the full-potential equation. This scheme is called the Euler full-potential (EFP) scheme. Once shocks are captured, a grid adaptation scheme, based on the density gradient, is implemented to obtain a crisper shock. This is followed by a shock-fitting scheme that is based on a searching algorithm and the Rankine-Hugoniot conservation equations of mass, momentum and energy equations. The repetitive solution cycles of the grid-adaptation and shock-fitting (GASF) schemes minimize the root mean square of relative errors percentage in the mass, momentum and energy equations across the shock.

The methodology of EFP and GASF has been applied to a biconvex airfoil with a 5 percent thickness ratio and to a *60* degree Delta wing with a 5 percent thickness ratio thickness ratio biconvex airfoil section. The wing has a chord length of 50 feet and is at 52,000-foot altitude, a Mach number of 2.01 and an angle of attack of 0°.

Near Field Calculation

As noted in reference 13, "If one calculates the near field of an aircraft using a CFD Euler code, the shock jumps are consistent with the Rankine-Hugoniot equations. With this "constraint" there are shocks of different shape and strength followed by pressure recoveries of different strengths (rates of recovery). Normally CFD calculations are made with grids that are stretched radially as one moves to the outer boundaries, since the flow gradients become smaller and far-field boundary conditions can be imposed. Outer boundaries are typically placed one to two body lengths from the centerline depending on the Mach number and shape. Solution schemes are generally of the shock capturing variety. All of this combines for most solution schemes, to smear the shocks and reduce their maximum pressure jumps from their proper value at the outer boundary." Reference 13 further stated "That shock-fitting schemes are more appropriate and have been available for many years. However, they are not normally used or needed where the primary interest is the pressures on the configuration itself. Whether a procedure can be formulated to recover an "accurate" finite shock jump at the near field boundary from a smeared one is not clear. Lacking a "shock fitted" Euler (or Navier-Stokes) code it is desirable to utilize a grid that conforms as close as possible to the shocks and to have as high a concentration of grid points in the vicinity of the shocks as can be accommodated. The latter is desirable since shock jumps are usually resolved in three or four grid points. The use of a grid adaptation scheme in an Euler code with a shock capturing solution algorithm is one way of further improving resolution. The combination of shock capturing and shock fitting is the preferred or ideal approach."

In the present study an early version of NASA Langley's CFL3D code was modified to include both grid adaptation as well as shock fitting. Shock fitting yields the most accurate flow solution available. It provides a procedure for explicitly computing the jump conditions across shocks. It locates the shocks and treats them as boundaries between regions where the solution is "regular." Moretti developed a method known as floating shock fitting where shocks "float" during the iterative calculation. A number of papers treating the Euler equations with shock fitting have been published over the years and the technique is fairly well established. Shock fitting has also been applied to various versions of the potential equations for both transonic and supersonic flows (Refs. 14 and 15).

Adaptive Grid

In order to have an accurate shock jump calculation, using a shock-fitting technique, the shock jump should first be resolved as accurately as possible using the basic solution algorithm. A two-step adaptive grid scheme has been employed, along with the pseudo-time shock-capturing solution methodology of the basic code to solve for the flow about a simple slab-sided delta wing. Its effect on the shock jumps, lift, drag, and solution convergence has been examined. Figures 1 and 2 show pressure distributions on the centerline and near the tip of a slab-sided delta wing at a Mach number of 2.01 and an angle of attack of 5 degrees. Results are given for the original grid and after the first and second grid

adaptations. Figure 3 shows color contour plots of the pressure field for the same 3-grid configurations. As in Figs. 1 and 2, there is a significant difference between the original grid and the first grid adaptation and not much difference between the first and second. Of equal importance is the effect of grid adaptation on convergence. Figure 4 shows that once the grid is adapted, lift and drag converge after only 30 or 40 time steps; several hundred were needed for the fixed grid.

Shock Fitting

The three-dimensional shock fitting is based on the pseudo-time captured shock with adaptive grid. First, the captured shock is located using a searching algorithm. Once the shock is located, shock-fitting equations are implemented. Shock-fitting equations are based on the Rankine-Hugoniot conservation equations of mass, momentum and energy. The equations are used to fit the three-dimensional shock surface. Next, the grid is adapted around the fitted shock surface and the flow is recomputed. This cycle is repeated and the errors in mass, momentum and energy are monitored until they reach certain minima.

Figure 5, for the same slab-sided delta wing of the earlier figures, shows a comparison of C_L and C_D histories for the original grid case, the adaptive grid-only case, and the shock-fitting along with the adaptive grid. It is observed that the latter technique requires about 25 iteration cycles to obtain the shock. The adaptive grid requires about 45 cycles and the original grid requires about 65 cycles. Figure 6 shows comparisons of the relative errors in mass, momentum and energy across the projected shock surface. The figures show the relative errors as viewed by an observer looking upstream at the shock surface. It is clear that shock fitting coupled with an adaptive grid technique produces the minimum relative errors. The root-mean square of the relative errors in mass, momentum, and energy for adaptive grid-only and shock fitting with grid adaptation for 1 of 5 cycles of iteration is given in the following table.

	Mass.	Momentum	Energy
Adaptive	4.86E-002	3.00E-002	7.93E-003
Fitting (1 iteration)	2.65E-003	1.54E-003	6.49E-004
Fitting (5 iterations)	1.24E-003	1.13E-003	3.94E-004

Figure 7 shows a comparison of the root-mean square of the relative errors in mass, momentum, and energy or the adaptive grid-only and the shock fitting with grid adaptation for several iterative cycles. Figure 8 shows a comparison of shock thickness as obtained by grid adaptation only and shock fitting with grid adaptation.

Full Potential Equation Solution for Flow Field Propagation

The full potential equation is used to propagate, to the ground, the near field signature calculated using the Euler equations. Since the Euler equations solution does not exactly satisfy the potential equations, a methodology is formulated to determine the potential and its derivatives at the interface between the Euler and potential "domains." The conservative form of the potential equation is solved using a space marching, upwind scheme (see Refs. 15-19). This scheme is "augmented" by a sub-block technique, which facilitates the treatment of the varying speed of sound.

Details of the Solver

Governing Equation

The 3D full-potential equation written in conservation-law form is given by [15]

$$(\rho \phi_x)_x + (\rho \phi_y)_y + (\rho \phi_z)_z = 0 \tag{1}$$

$$\rho = \left[1 + \tfrac{\gamma-1}{2}M_\infty^2(1 - \phi_x^2 - \phi_y^2 - \phi_z^2)\right]^{\frac{1}{\gamma-1}}$$

In computational domain, it can be written as

$$\left(\rho \frac{U}{J}\right)_\xi + \left(\rho \frac{V}{J}\right)_\eta + \left(\rho \frac{W}{J}\right)_\zeta = 0 \tag{2}$$

where

$$\begin{Bmatrix} U \\ V \\ W \end{Bmatrix} = \begin{bmatrix} a_{11} & a_{12} & a_{13} \\ a_{21} & a_{22} & a_{23} \\ a_{31} & a_{32} & a_{33} \end{bmatrix} \begin{Bmatrix} \phi_\xi \\ \phi_\eta \\ \phi_\zeta \end{Bmatrix} \tag{3}$$

$$a_{11} = \xi_x^2 + \xi_y^2 + \xi_z^2$$

$$a_{12} = a_{21} = \xi_x \eta_x + \xi_y \eta_y + \xi_z \eta_z$$

$$a_{13} = a_{31} = \xi_x \zeta_x + \xi_y \zeta_y + \xi_z \zeta_z$$

$$a_{22} = \eta_x^2 + \eta_y^2 + \eta_z^2 \tag{4}$$

$$a_{23} = a_{32} = \eta_x \zeta_x + \eta_y \zeta_y + \eta_z \zeta_z$$

$$a_{33} = \zeta_x^2 + \zeta_y^2 + \zeta_z^2$$

$$J = \frac{\partial(\xi, \eta, \zeta)}{\partial(x, y, z)} = \begin{bmatrix} \xi_x & \xi_y & \xi_z \\ \eta_x & \eta_y & \eta_z \\ \zeta_x & \zeta_y & \zeta_z \end{bmatrix} \tag{5}$$

Space Marching Scheme

a. Treatment of $\left(\dfrac{\rho U}{J}\right)_\xi$

Upwind scheme is used. Consider the direction ξ to be the marching direction. Since ρU is a function of ϕ and the unknown $(\rho U)_{i+1}$, the latter can be expanded as

$$(\rho U)_{i+1} \approx \rho_i \left[\left(a_{11} - \frac{U^2}{a^2}\right)_i \frac{\partial(\Delta\phi)}{\partial \xi} + \left(a_{12} - \frac{UV}{a^2}\right)_i \frac{\partial(\Delta\phi)}{\partial \eta} + \left(a_{13} - \frac{UW}{a^2}\right)_i \frac{\partial(\Delta\phi)}{\partial \zeta} + U_i \right] \tag{6}$$

where $\Delta\phi = \phi_{i+1} - \phi_i$. Using upwind differencing

$$\frac{\partial(\ )}{\partial \xi} = \frac{1}{\Delta\xi}\{(\ )_{i+1} - (\ )_i\}$$

this approximation produces the positive artificial viscosity

$$\frac{\rho}{Ja^2}\left(1 - \frac{a^2 a_{11}}{U^2}\right)U^2 \phi_{\xi\xi\xi}\Delta\xi \quad \text{if} \quad \frac{U^2}{a^2} > a_{11}$$

b. Treatment of $\left(\dfrac{\rho V}{J}\right)_\eta$

The 2nd order central differencing is used here. A second-order finite-difference approximation is given by

$$\left(\frac{\rho V}{J}\right)_\eta = \left(\frac{\hat{\rho} V}{J}\right)_{j+\frac{1}{2}} - \left(\frac{\hat{\rho} V}{J}\right)_{j-\frac{1}{2}} \tag{7}$$

The artificial density is given by

$$\hat{\rho}_{j+\frac{1}{2}} = (1-\nu)\rho_{j+\frac{1}{2}} + \frac{1}{2}\nu(\rho_{j+2m} + \rho_{j-1+2m}) \tag{8}$$

where

$$m = \begin{cases} 0, V > 0 \\ 1, V < 0 \end{cases} \quad \nu = \begin{cases} 0 & \text{for } a_{22} - \frac{V^2}{a^2} > 0 \\ 1 - \frac{a^2 a_{22}}{V^2} & \text{for } a_{22} - \frac{V^2}{a^2} > 0 \end{cases}$$

The treatment of the term of $\left(\frac{\rho W}{J}\right)_\zeta$ is similar to

the one described above.

Implicit Algorithm

A fully implicit model will be

$$\left[1 + \frac{A_3}{\beta\Delta\xi}\frac{\partial}{\partial\zeta} + \frac{1}{\beta}\frac{\partial}{\partial\zeta}\left(\frac{\bar{\rho}a_{31}}{J\Delta\zeta}\right) + \frac{1}{\beta}\frac{\partial}{\partial\zeta}\frac{\bar{\rho}a_{33}}{J}\frac{\partial}{\partial\zeta}\right]$$
$$\left[1 + \frac{A_2}{\beta\Delta\xi}\frac{\partial}{\partial\eta} + \frac{1}{\beta}\frac{\partial}{\partial\eta}\left(\frac{\hat{\rho}a_{21}}{J\Delta\xi}\right) + \frac{1}{\beta}\frac{\partial}{\partial\eta}\frac{\hat{\rho}a_{22}}{J}\frac{\partial}{\partial\eta}\right]\Delta\phi = R \tag{9}$$

where

$$A_1 = \frac{\rho_i}{J}\left(a_{11} - \frac{U^2}{a^2}\right)_i, \quad A_2 = \frac{\rho_i}{J}\left(a_{12} - \frac{UV}{a^2}\right)_i, \tag{10}$$
$$A_3 = \frac{\rho_i}{J}\left(a_{13} - \frac{UW}{a^2}\right)_i, \quad \beta = \frac{A_1}{(\Delta\xi)^2}$$

Ref. 15 gives the detail of equations and solution method.

Interface Conditions Between Euler Solution and Full Potential Solution

In the sonic boom computation, the near field is calculated using an Euler solver (CFL3D) and the far field is calculated using the developed full potential solver. At the interface, the velocity components (u, v, w) of the Euler solution are transformed into a velocity potential that is used for the initial condition of the full potential solver. The figures and the steps below give the detailed procedure:

Step A. Cut planes at $x = X_0, X_0 + \Delta x, X_0 + 2\Delta x$ from 3D Euler solution and obtain the velocity (u, v, w) on the cutting planes by interpolation.

Step B. Generate a new grid for the full potential solver. The new grid is totally independent of the grid used in 3D Euler solution. But the first three planes of the new grid are at the same locations of the cutting planes of the Euler grid $x = X_0, X_0 + \Delta x, X_0 + 2\Delta x$, respectively. Then the velocity is interpolated from the cutting planes to the first three planes of the new grid.

Step C. For the first three planes in the new grid, calculate the velocity potential ϕ from velocity (u, v, w). This is accomplished by rewriting the full potential equation in terms of ϕ_η, ϕ_ζ as unknowns on the left hand side and the remaining terms as source terms and the equation is solved using an ADI scheme. Once ϕ is obtained on the third plane, backward differencing is used to obtain ϕ on the second and first planes. The details of the procedure are given below: Rewrite full potential equation, Eq.(2)

$$\frac{\partial}{\partial\eta}\left[\frac{\rho}{J}\left(a_{22}\phi_\eta + a_{23}\phi_\zeta\right)\right] +$$
$$\frac{\partial}{\partial\zeta}\left[\frac{\rho}{J}\left(a_{32}\phi_\eta + a_{33}\phi_\zeta\right)\right] = R \tag{11}$$

where

$$R = -\frac{\partial}{\partial\xi}\left[\frac{\rho}{J}\left(a_{11}\phi_\xi + a_{12}\phi_\eta + a_{13}\phi_\zeta\right)\right]$$
$$-\frac{\partial}{\partial\eta}\left[\frac{\rho}{J}\left(a_{21}\phi_\xi\right)\right] - \frac{\partial}{\partial\zeta}\left[\frac{\rho}{J}\left(a_{31}\phi_\xi\right)\right] \tag{12}$$

and R can be calculated using $\phi_\xi, \phi_\eta, \phi_\zeta$, which can be derived from u, v, w by

$$\begin{Bmatrix} \phi_\xi \\ \phi_\eta \\ \phi_\zeta \end{Bmatrix} = \begin{bmatrix} x_\xi & x_\eta & x_\zeta \\ y_\xi & y_\eta & y_\zeta \\ z_\xi & z_\eta & z_\zeta \end{bmatrix} \begin{Bmatrix} u \\ v \\ w \end{Bmatrix} \tag{13}$$

For the third plane in new grid, Eq. (11) can be discretized using a 2nd order central differencing scheme. For the 2nd and 1st planes in new grid, ϕ can be obtained by

$$\phi_i = \phi_{i+1} - \phi_\xi\Delta\xi \tag{14}$$

1448

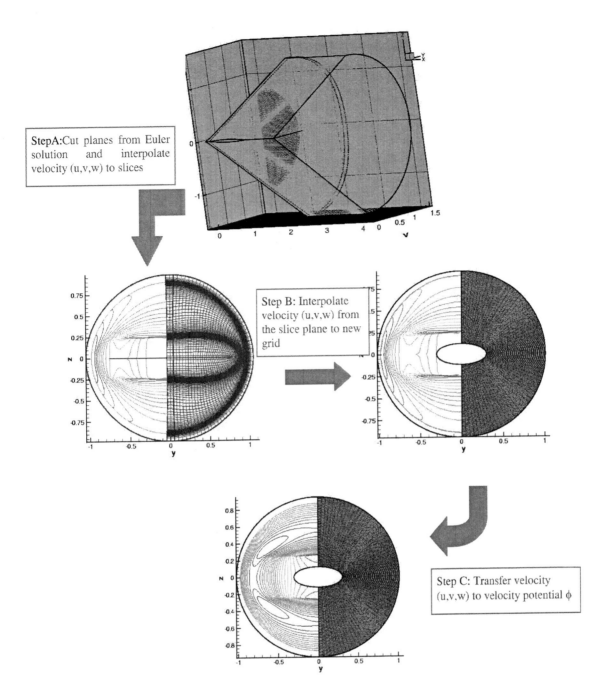

StepA: Cut planes from Euler solution and interpolate velocity (u,v,w) to slices

Step B: Interpolate velocity (u,v,w) from the slice plane to new grid

Step C: Transfer velocity (u,v,w) to velocity potential ϕ

Because only ϕ at 3rd plane and ϕ_ζ at 2nd plane will be used in full potential solver, the method above should produce the correct initial condition for full potential space-marching scheme.

Interface Conditions for the Sub-Blocks

The atmospheric conditions are varying continuously with the altitude. To simulate the real flow, a sub-block technique has been developed to account for this variation. In each sub-block, flow is assumed as uniform flow and the free-stream conditions are determined from the altitude conditions at the midpoint altitude of this sub-block. To transfer the shock from one block to other block, the pressure jump introduced by shock has been kept the same across the interface. This means that

$$P_A^* - P_{A\infty}^* = P_B^* - P_{B\infty}^* \qquad (15)$$

where A and B refer to the sub-blocks on the two sides of interface. Consider

$$\frac{P}{P_\infty} = \left[1 + \tfrac{\gamma-1}{2}M_\infty^2(1 - \phi_x^2 - \phi_y^2 - \phi_z^2)\right]^{\frac{\gamma}{\gamma-1}} \qquad (16)$$

Equation (15) can be rewritten as

$$P_{A\infty}^{*}\left\{\left[1-\tfrac{\gamma-1}{2}M_{A\infty}^{2}\left(\widetilde{V}_{A}^{2}-1\right)\right]^{\frac{\gamma}{\gamma-1}}-1\right\}=$$

$$P_{B\infty}^{*}\left\{\left[1-\tfrac{\gamma-1}{2}M_{B\infty}^{2}\left(\widetilde{V}_{B}^{2}-1\right)\right]^{\frac{\gamma}{\gamma-1}}-1\right\}\qquad(17)$$

where $P_{A\infty}^{*}$ and $P_{B\infty}^{*}$ are the dimensional free-stream pressure at sub-blocks A and B, respectively; $\widetilde{V}_{A}^{2}$ and $\widetilde{V}_{B}^{2}$ are total velocities at sub-blocks A and B. If $\widetilde{V}_{A}^{2}$ in sub-block A is known, $\widetilde{V}_{B}^{2}$ can be calculated by using Eq. (17).

Two types of interfaces are used: one is the interface in marching direction (Interface Type I) and the other is the interface in the perpendicular direction (Interface Type II).

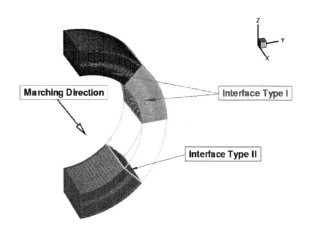

Interface Type I

For Interface Type I, the flow is supersonic and the direction of flow is perpendicular to the interface. Iteration is not needed here. Assume the sub-block A is the upwind block and the sub-block B is the downstream block. To satisfy Eq. (15), the total velocity $\widetilde{V}_{B}^{2}$, which is calculated from velocity potential ϕ_{B}, must satisfy Eq. (17), where ϕ_{B} is derived from Eq. (17) and ϕ_{A} is known.

There are three planes in this interface. First, assume $\phi_{B}=\phi_{A}$ at the 3rd plane. Considering Eq. (3), we have

$$U_{B}-U_{A}=a_{11}(\phi_{B\xi}-\phi_{A\xi})$$
$$V_{B}-V_{A}=a_{21}(\phi_{B\xi}-\phi_{A\xi})\qquad(18)$$
$$W_{B}-W_{A}=a_{31}(\phi_{B\xi}-\phi_{A\xi})$$

at plane No.3. Then, by using

$$\widetilde{V}^{2}=U\phi_{\xi}+V\phi_{\eta}+W\phi_{\zeta},$$

we can find

$$\widetilde{V}_{B}^{2}-\widetilde{V}_{A}^{2}=U_{B}\phi_{B\xi}-U_{A}\phi_{A\xi}+$$
$$a_{21}\phi_{\eta}(\phi_{B\xi}-\phi_{A\xi})+a_{31}\phi_{\zeta}(\phi_{B\xi}-\phi_{A\xi})\qquad(19)$$

Let $\Delta\phi_{\xi}=\phi_{B\xi}-\phi_{A\xi}$, Eq. (19) becomes

$$a_{11}\Delta\phi_{\xi}^{2}+2U_{A}\Delta\phi_{\xi}+(\widetilde{V}_{A}^{2}-\widetilde{V}_{B}^{2})=0\qquad(20)$$

Solving for $\Delta\phi_{\xi}$ and considering $\phi_{B\xi}=\phi_{B3}-\phi_{B2}$ and $\phi_{A\xi}=\phi_{A3}-\phi_{A2}$, we can get

$$\phi_{B2}=\phi_{A2}-\Delta\phi_{\xi}\qquad(21)$$

where 2 and 3 represent planes No. 2 and No.3, respectively. Similarly, ϕ_{B1} can be obtained.

Interface Type II

For Interface Type II, the flow perpendicular to interface is subsonic flow and iteration is needed. This means that after sub-block A is done, velocity potential is re-created based on sub-block A and Eq. (17). These values are used as boundary conditions for sub-block B. After sub-block B is done, using the same procedure, this process is iterated until the error is less than a prescribed tolerance.

The procedure of re-creating velocity potential is: First, Eq. (17) is applied to get total velocity $\widetilde{V}_{B}^{2}$ at the interface. Second, the velocity component directions are assumed fixed. Thus, the velocity components are

$$u_{B}=u_{A}\sqrt{\frac{\widetilde{V}_{B}^{2}}{\widetilde{V}_{A}^{2}}},\ v_{B}=v_{A}\sqrt{\frac{\widetilde{V}_{B}^{2}}{\widetilde{V}_{A}^{2}}},\ w_{B}=w_{A}\sqrt{\frac{\widetilde{V}_{B}^{2}}{\widetilde{V}_{A}^{2}}}$$

Then doing similarly to what have been done in Eq. (11)– (14), the velocity potential at interface is obtained.

Results for 2D Biconvex Airfoil

Propagation calculations were first carried out for two-dimensional flow. They were done to establish the grid adaptation and shock-fitting techniques, developed for the Euler equations, for the potential equation formulation. The geometry that was used is a biconvex airfoil with t/c of 5 percent with a 50 feet chord. The match between the Euler and potential equation solutions for the potential propagation was made at 3 chord lengths (150 feet) below the wing. The angle-of-attack was zero degrees and the Mach number is 2.01. The calculation was started at an altitude of approximately 52,000 feet. Both Euler and potential-equation propagations were done to "check" the accuracy of the potential equation results. The Euler calculation is, of course, very time consuming but doable in two dimensions. No such check would be practical for the 3D propagation. Finally, propagation calculations were made for both uniform (isothermal) and non-uniform (standard) atmospheres.

Figure 9 shows the results for a uniform (isothermal) atmosphere. It illustrates the grid, density contours and pressure distribution for both the Euler and potential calculations side by side. The results are for 9.8 miles below the airfoil (-52,000 ft.). The initial pressure jump at this distance for the Euler calculation is 1.908 psf and that for the potential calculation 1.898 psf. Computation time for the Euler code on a 1.4 GHz PC was approximately 5 days; and for the potential equation, approximately one half hour. Note that no ground reflection factor has been used on the pressure distribution at 9.8 miles. Also, note that the pressures are plotted against vertical distance; consequently, the duration of the pressure signal on the ground cannot be obtained directly from these plots.

Results for the non-uniform (standard) atmosphere are given in Figure 10. The results are for 9.8 miles below the airfoil. The Figure shows that the initial pressure jump for the Euler formulation was 7.142 psf while that for the potential was 7.230 psf. Computation times were only slightly larger than those for the uniform atmosphere.

Results for Delta Wing

The delta wing used in the present calculations had a t/c of 5 percent and a root chord of 50 feet. The angle-of-attack was zero degrees. The Mach number

was 2.01 and the starting altitude was 52,000 feet (9.8 mi). The match between the Euler and potential solutions was made at 1.8 chord lengths (90 feet) below the wing. As with the two-dimensional configuration, both uniform (isothermal) and non-uniform (standard) atmosphere results were obtained and the pressures are plotted against vertical distance. Figure 11 gives plots of the mesh, pressure contours and centerline (on-track) pressure distributions for both of these atmospheres side by side for two distances. Figure 11a is for a distance of 5000 feet (0.9 mi) below the wing; Figure 11b is for 52,000 feet (9.8 mi) below the wing. A plot of the variation of pressure jump with altitude is given in Fig. 12. It is similar in character to the results obtained by wave propagation methods (see Fig. 4 of Ref. 20).

Figure 13 gives the grid and pressure distributions along the ground at the symmetry plane (without reflection factor) for the uniform (isothermal) and non-uniform (standard) atmospheres. It is approximately 4.2 chord lengths long (210 ft.) which converts to 108 milliseconds in duration; consistent with experimental data for an aircraft of this size. Off-track pressure distributions (without reflection factor) are given in figures 14 and 15 for the uniform (isothermal) and non-uniform (standard) atmospheres, respectively. Plots are given for one, two, three, four and five hundred chord lengths (50 feet) off the plane of symmetry. Initial Δp values are tabled at the end of each figure.

Concluding Remarks

The methodology developed in this study represents a giant step forward in our ability to predict the sonic boom signatures of supersonic configurations. No longer will linear mid-field codes be required to link up with a nonlinear near field code on one side and linear far field code on the other that assumes a cosine-like lateral variation of pressure. The basis has been established to treat complex configurations that attempt to modify the off-track pressure distributions, with much greater precision. Configurations that intuitively ought to have lower booms can now be analyzed with a confidence not heretofore possible.

Acknowledgement

The authors wish to thank the Lockheed-Martin Skunkworks for their support of this research. Work performed under Lockheed-Martin contract number EM1424560E to Eagle Aeronautics, Inc.

References

1. Hays, W.D., Haefeli, R. C.; and Kulsrud, H. E., "Sonic Boom Propagation in a stratified Atmosphere, With Computer Program," NASA CR 1299, Aero. Res. Associates. of Princeton, Inc., April 1969.

2. Hayes, Wallace D.; and Runyan, Harry L., Jr., "Sonic Boom Propagation Through a Stratified Atmosphere," Journal of Acoustical. Soc. of America, Vol 51, No. 2 (part 3), pp. 695-701, 1972.

3. Randall, D. C., "Sonic Bang Intensities in a Stratified, Still Atmosphere," J. Sound Vibrations, No. 8, pp.196-214, 1968. Also RAE Tech. Report. No. 66002, 1966.

4. Friedman, Manfred P., "A Description of a Computer Program for the Study of Atmospheric Effects on Sonic Booms," NASA CR-157, MIT, Feb. 1965.

5. Friedman, M. P.; Kane, E. J.; and Sigalla, A., "Effects of Atmosphere and Aircraft Motion on the Location and Intensity of Sonic Boom," AIAA Jour., Vol. 1, p. 13-27, June 1963.

6. Thomas, Charles L., " Extrapolation of Sonic Boom Pressure Signatures by the Waveform Parameter Method," NASA TN D-6832, June 1972.

7. Chambers, James P.; Cleveland, Robin, O.; Bass, Henry E.; Blackstock, David T. and Hamilton, Mark F., " Comparison of Computer Codes for the Propagation of Sonic Booms Through Realistic Atmospheres Utilizing Actual Acoustic Signatures," NASA Conference Publication 3335, pp. 151-175, July 1996.

8. Plotkin, K, J.; and Cantril, J. M., " Prediction of Sonic Boom at a Focus," Wyle Laboratories Res. Staff Report. WR 75-7, Oct. 1975.

9. Cliff, Susan E.: On the Design and Analysis of Low Sonic Boom Configurations. NASA Conf. Pub. 10133, Ames Research Center, May 12-14, 1993.

10. Siclari, M. J.; and Fouladi, Karoran: A CFD Study of Component Configuration Effects on the Sonic Boom of Several High-Speed Civil Transport Concepts. NASA Conf. Pub. 10133, Ames Research Center, May 12-14, 1993.

11. Page, Juliet A.; and Plotkin, Kenneth J., " An Efficient Method for Incorporating Computational Fluid Dynamics Into Sonic Boom Prediction," AIAA paper 91-3275, Baltimore, MD, September 23-25 1991.

12. George, A. R, " Reduction of Sonic Boom by Azimuthal Redistribution of Overpressure," AIAA Paper No. 68-159, 1968.

13. Maglieri, Domenic J.; and Bobbitt, Percy J., "History of Sonic Boom Technology, Including Minimization," Eagle Aeronautics, Inc. under Lockheed Martin Contract EM1424560E, Nov. 2001.

14. Hafez, M. M.; and Murman, E. M., " A Shock-Fitting Algorithm for the Full Potential Equation," AIAA Paper 77-632, 1977.

15. Shankar, Vijaya, " Conservative Full Potential, Implicit Marching Scheme for Supersonic Flows," AIAA Jour., Vol. 20, No. 11, pp. 1508 - 1514, Nov. 1982.

16. Shankar, Vijaya and Osher, Stanley, "An Efficient, Full-Potential Implicit Method Based on Characteristics for Supersonic Flows," AIAA Jour., Vol. 21, No. 9, pp. 1262-1270, Sept. 1983.

17. Holst, T. L and Ballhaus, W. F., " Fast, Conservative Schemes for the Full-Potential Equation Applied to Transonic Flows," AIAA Jour., Vol. 17, No. 2, pp. 145-152, Feb. 1979.

18. Holst, T. L., "Fast Conservative Algorithm for Solving the Transonic Full-Potential Equation," AIAA Jour., Vol. 18, No. 12, pp. 1431-1439, Dec. 1980.

19. Hirsch, Charles, "Numerical Computation of Internal and External Flows," John Wiley and Sonic, Ltd., Vol. 2, 1990.

20. Thomas, Charles L, "Extrapolation of Wind-Tunnel Sonic Boom Signatures Without Use of a Whitham F-Function," NASA SP 255, pp. 205-217, 1970

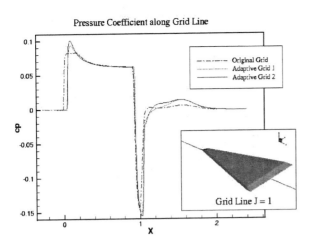

Figure 1. Pressure distribution for slab-sided delta wing along grid line J = 1 determined with and without grid adaptation.

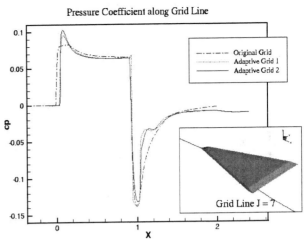

Figure 2. Pressure distribution for slab-sided delta wing along grid line J = 7 determined with and without grid adaptation.

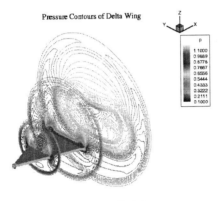

Original Grid

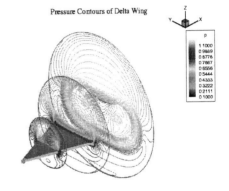

Adaptation 2

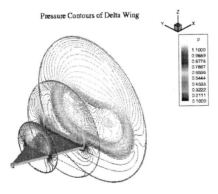

Adaptation 1

Figure 3. Pressure contour plots for slab-sided delta wing with and without grid adaptation.

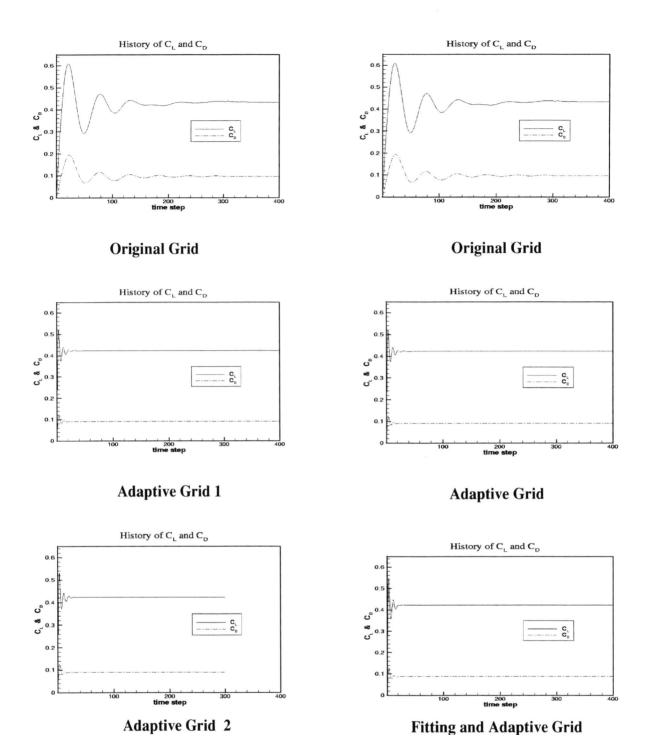

Original Grid   **Original Grid**

Adaptive Grid 1   **Adaptive Grid**

Adaptive Grid 2   **Fitting and Adaptive Grid**

Figure 4. Variation of CL and CD with time step for slab-sided delta wing with and without grid adaptation.

Figure 5. Comparison of lift and drag coefficient history for slab-sided delta wing with and without grid adaptation and shock fitting.

1454

Original Grid   **Adaptive Grid**   **Fitting and Adaptive Grid**

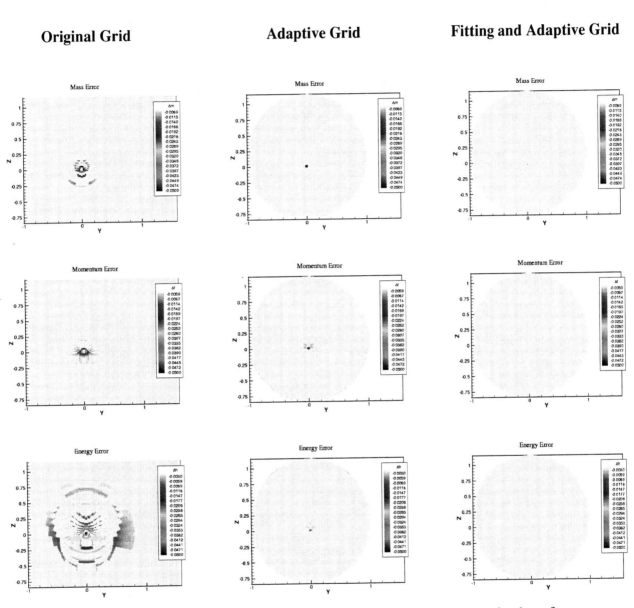

Figure 6. Comparison of relative errors in mass, momentum and energy across shock surface
For a slab-sided delta wing with and without grid adaptation and shock fitting.

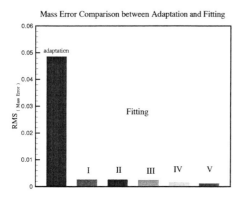

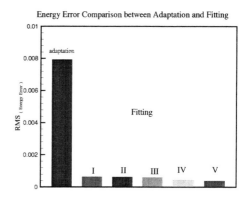

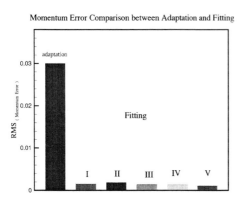

Figure 7. Comparison of root-mean square, RMS, of mass, momentum and energy relative errors

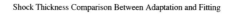

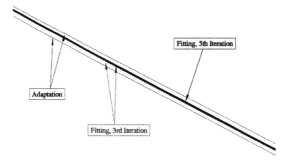

Figure 8. Comparison of shock thickness between adaptive grid only and shock fitting with grid adaptation.

On ground, H = 9.8 mi below the source location

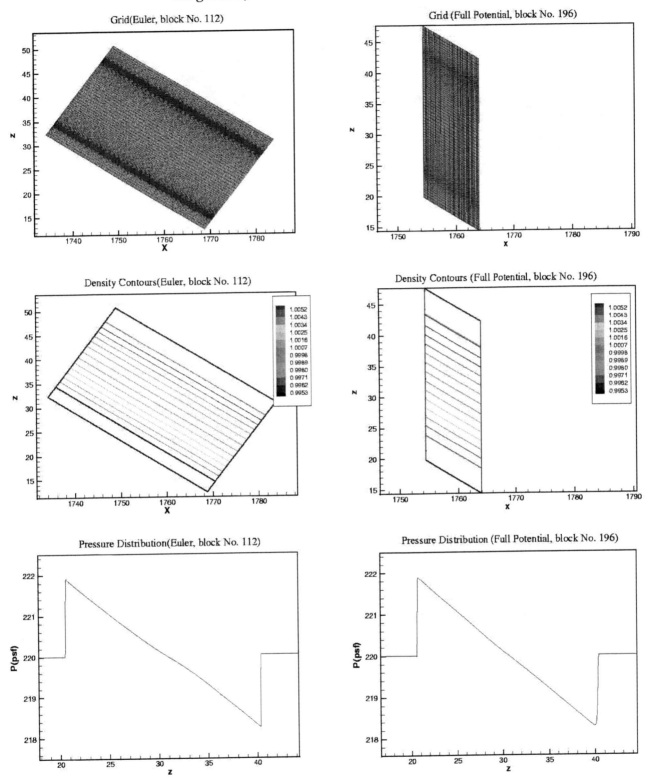

Figure 9. Two-dimensional far field computation using full potential code and comparison with Euler Code for uniform (isothermal) atmosphere at $\alpha = 0$, M = 2.01, initial altitude 52,000 ft.

On ground, H = 9.8 mi below the source location

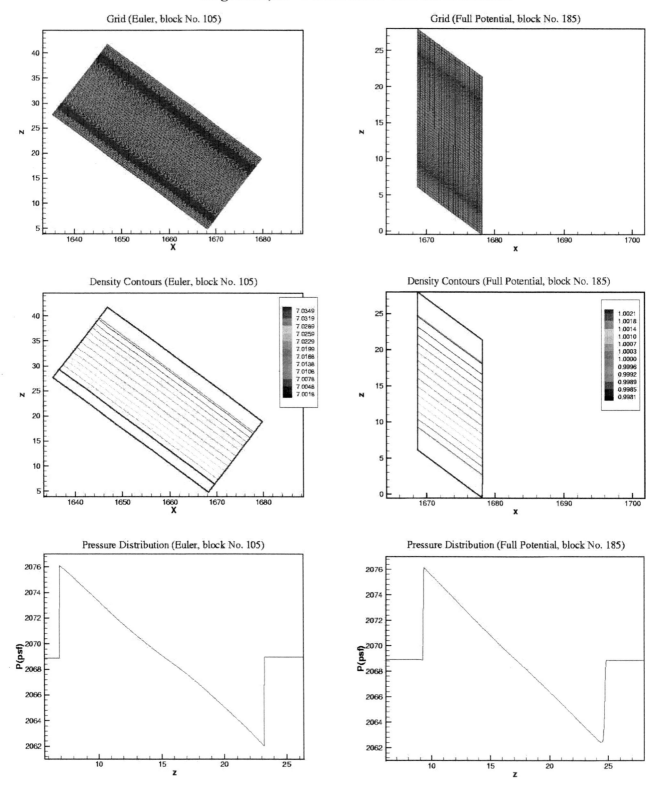

Figure 10. Two-dimensional far field computation using full potential code and comparison with Euler Code for non-uniform (standard) atmosphere at $\alpha = 0$, M = 2.01, initial altitude 52,000 ft.

Uniform (isothermal) Flow ΔP = 0.90 psf   Non-uniform (standard) Flow ΔP = 0.9709 psf

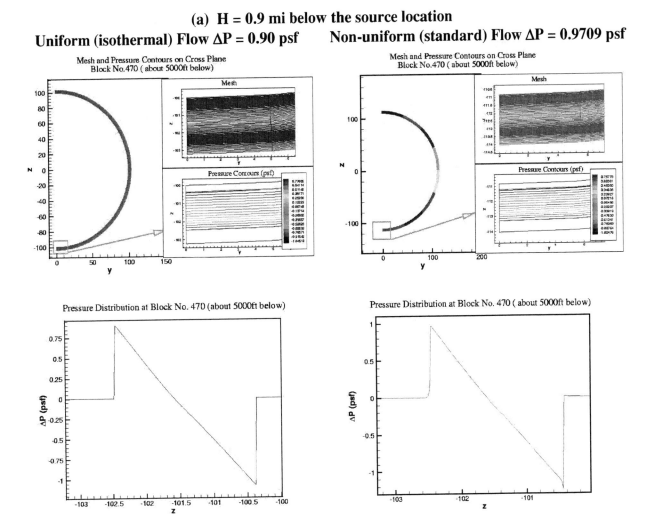

Figure 11. Comparison of uniform (isothermal) and non-uniform (standard) atmosphere sonic boom pressure for a 60-degree delta wing with 5 percent biconvex profile at α = 0, M∞ = 2.01, initial altitude of 52,000 ft

(b) H = 9.8 mi below the source location: Near Ground with No Reflection Factor
Uniform (isothermal) Flow ΔP = 0.150 psf   Non-uniform (standard) Flow ΔP = 0.3285 psf

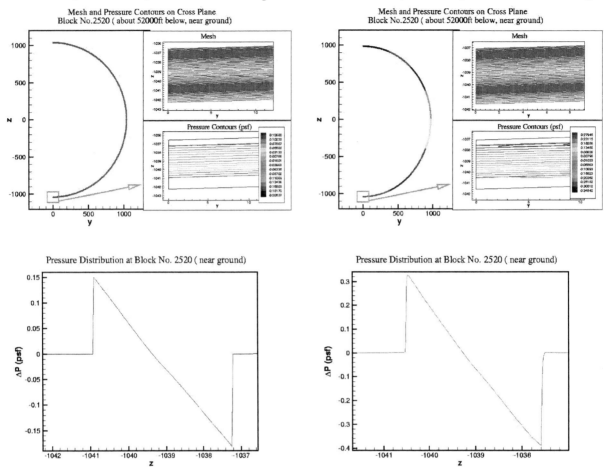

Figure 11. Concluded.

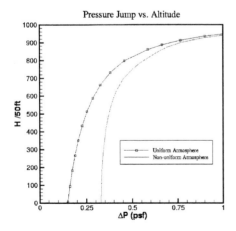

Figure 12. Variation of pressure jump with altitude for initial altitude of 52,000 ft., $\alpha = 0$, $M_\infty = 2.01$, uniform (isothermal) and non-uniform (standard) atmospheres.

Uniform (isothermal) Atmosphere

Mesh Near the Ground (at symmetry plane)

Pressure Distribution Near the Ground (at symmetry plane)

Non-uniform (standard) Atmosphere

Mesh Near the Ground (at symmetry plane)

Pressure Contours Near the Ground (at symmetry plane)

Figure 13. Ground pressure distribution and grid blocks for a 60-degree delta wing with 5 percent biconvex profile at $\alpha = 0$, $M = 2.01$, initial altitude 52,000 ft. No reflection factor.

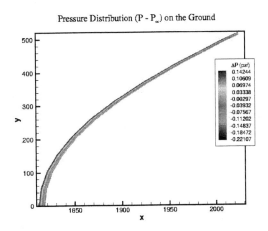

Pressure Distribution ($P - P_\infty$) on the Ground

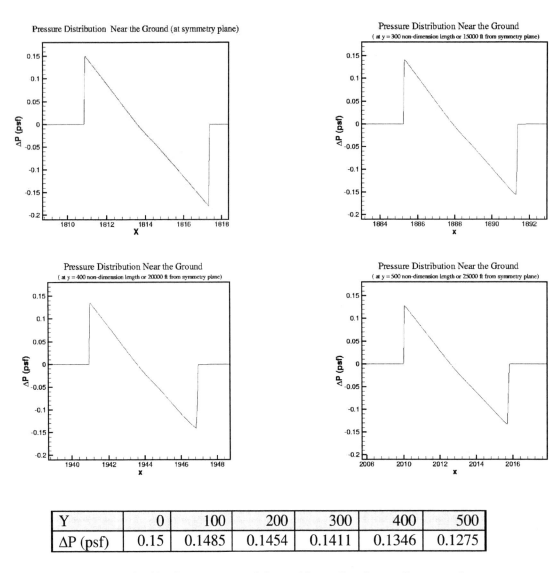

Y	0	100	200	300	400	500
ΔP (psf)	0.15	0.1485	0.1454	0.1411	0.1346	0.1275

Figure 14. Pressure distribution on ground for uniform (isothermal) atmosphere

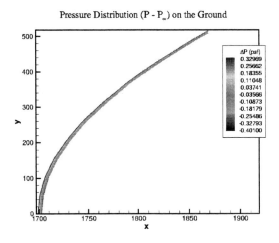

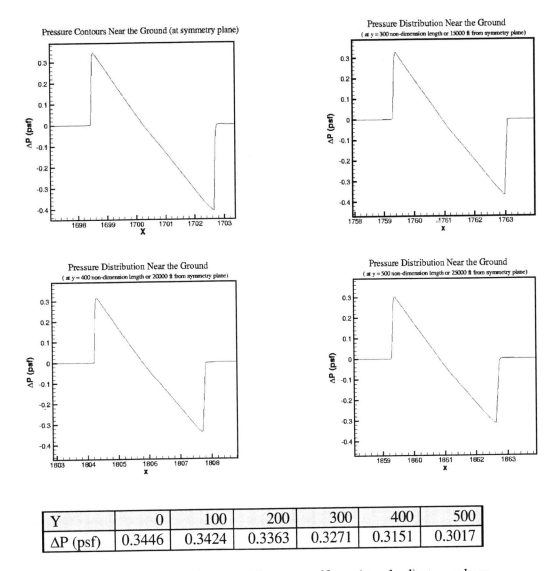

Y	0	100	200	300	400	500
ΔP (psf)	0.3446	0.3424	0.3363	0.3271	0.3151	0.3017

Figure 15. Pressure distribution on ground for non-uniform (standard) atmosphere

AIAA 2002-2543

PREDICTION OF ROD-AIRFOIL INTERACTION NOISE USING THE FW-H ANALOGY

Damiano Casalino [*] Marc Jacob [†] Michel Roger [‡]

Laboratoire de Mécanique des Fluides et Acoustique

Ecole Centrale de Lyon

69131 ECULLY Cedex, France

ABSTRACT

Aerodynamic noise generated by an airfoil embedded in the wake of a rod is the object of a numerical investigation. The acoustic field is computed in the time domain by applying the Ffowcs Williams & Hawkings analogy to aerodynamic data computed on various contours around the source region. The flow field is obtained from a 2D Reynolds-Averaged Navier-Stokes calculation and three-dimensionality is partially recovered by assuming the aerodynamic field to undergo a Gaussian correlation in the spanwise direction. Acoustic results are compared to measurements obtained from an accompanying experiment.

NOMENCLATURE

c	Airfoil chord
C_p	Pressure coefficient
d	Rod diameter
f	Frequency
$f = 0$	Integration surface
k	Kinetic turbulent energy
l	Span length
L_g	Gaussian correlation length
M_∞	Inflow Mach number
M_i	Mach number of $f = 0$
M_{ref}	Reference Mach number
M_{oi}	Observer Mach number vector
$\hat{n}_i$	Unit outward normal vector to $f = 0$
p, p_∞	Pressure and inflow pressure
p'	Acoustic pressure
p_d	Reference dynamic pressure
q_i	Dimensionless relative flow momentum
r	Observation distance
R	Dimensionless observation distance
St	Strouhal number
u_i	Flow velocity (also (u, v))

$\tilde{u}_i$	Flow velocity relative to $f = 0$
V_i	Dimensionless velocity of $f = 0$
V_∞	Inflow velocity
$\mathbf{X}$	Dimensionless observer position
$\mathbf{Y}$	Dimensionless source position
w	Gaussian variance
ϕ	Angular rod co-odinate
$\tilde{\varphi}$	Vortex shedding phase
η	Spanwise dimensionless co-ordinate
λ_i, χ_i	Loading noise source terms
θ	Observation angle and dimensionless time
ρ	Correlation coefficient
ρ_∞	Inflow density

Superscripts

$\cdot$	Dimensionless time derivative

Subscripts

n	Projection in the normal direction
r	Projection in the radiation direction

Abbreviations

CFD	Computational Fluid Dynamics
FW-H	Ffowcs-Williams & Hawkings
RANS	Reynolds-Averaged Navier Stokes
2D	Two-dimensional
3D	Three-dimensional

[*]Aerospace Engineer

[†]Assistant Professor at Université C. Bernard, Villeurbanne, France

[‡]Professor

1. INTRODUCTION

Unsteady aerodynamics of wings are due to various mechanisms. They come down to two types of phenomena encountered in wing aerodynamics. One is related to flow detachment either at the trailing edge or, if the wing is stalled, on the suction side. The other unsteady mechanism is due to oncoming disturbances which might interact with the airfoil. In strongly perturbed flows at reasonable angles of attack, this latter mechanism is dominant in means of unsteady loading and resulting sound radiation. There are two approaches to study such interactions, depending on the context. In helicopter aeroacoustics, a major perturbation might occur when the main rotor blades chop their own tip vortices: these interactions are classically investigated by considering the impulsive interaction between a blade and a single vortex. In turbomachinery applications, noise sources are often due to the repeated interactions between an oncoming unsteady flow and the blades. In such a case, the incoming disturbance is more or less periodic with some randomness depending on the stage. These flow-blade interactions are often modeled by means of a spectral decomposition of the incoming disturbance, including its random part. Each Fourier mode is a sinusoidal velocity perturbation which is called a gust in the present context. Many theories using this approach are concerned with connecting the unsteady pressure field to the velocity field (Possio,[1] Sears,[2] Filotas[3]) and to predict the sound radiated into the far field (Amiet[4]).

These theories generally assume the disturbances to be 2D without any spanwise effect, which is usually not the case in practical applications. Therefore, one goal of the present study is to model the influence of such 3D effects onto the sound field. In order to take into account these 3D effects, an *ad hoc* spanwise statistical model is introduced into a permeable surface acoustic analogy (Brentner & Farassat[5]). In the present paper, the approach is validated on a relevant test configuration: a rod is placed upstream of a symmetric airfoil. The rod sheds a von Kármán street of counter rotating vortices at a nearly constant Strouhal number $St = f_0 d / V_\infty \simeq 0.2$. The resulting flow disturbance is nearly sinusoidal and can be thus considered as a gust. In fact, the experiment is operated at quite high rod based Reynolds numbers ($Re_d = 2.2 \times 10^4$) where the rod wake almost immediately becomes turbulent as the vortices are formed.[6] Thus the gust which hits the airfoil is a more or less periodic perturbation with significant spanwise perturbations. The analogy is applied to a 2D unsteady RANS computation and compared to far field measurements allowing the 3D model to be validated.

After a brief description of the experiment and of the aerodynamic computation in sections 2 and 3, the aeroacoustic model is discussed in section 4. The computed steady flow and the statistics of its fluctuations are briefly analyzed in section 5. In section 6, results of the acoustic analogy are shown: first the influence of the integration surfaces is discussed for a deterministic flow (without the statistical model). Second, the analogy both with and without spanwise model is tested against experimental data far a given set of integration surfaces.

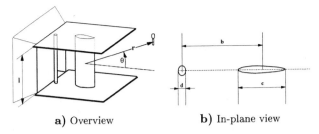

a) Overview   b) In-plane view

Fig. 1 **Rod-airfoil configuration and experimental set-up:** $d = 0.016\,\mathrm{m}$, $c = 0.1\,\mathrm{m}$, $b = 0.162\,\mathrm{m}$, $l = 0.3\,\mathrm{m}$, $r = 1.38\,\mathrm{m}$, $V_\infty = 20\,\mathrm{m/s}$. **The airfoil chord is parallel to the inflow direction.**

2. EXPERIMENT

The rod-airfoil experiment is carried out in the small anechoic room of the Ecole Centrale de Lyon (6m × 5m × 4m), where air is supplied by a low speed subsonic anechoic wind tunnel. The experiment goal is to provide data against which aeroacoustic numerical results can be checked.

The reference configuration is a NACA-0012 airfoil downstream of a rod. Both the airfoil and the rod are fixed between two parallel plates and placed into the potential core of a partially flanged rectangular jet. The inflow velocity is $V_\infty = 20\,\mathrm{m/s}$, corresponding to $M_\infty = 0.06$. The rod diameter is $d = 0.016\,\mathrm{m}$ and the airfoil chord is $c = 0.1\,\mathrm{m}$, providing the Reynolds numbers $Re_d = 2.2 \times 10^4$ and $Re_c = 1.37 \times 10^5$, respectively. The distance between the airfoil mid point and the center of the rod is $b = 0.162\,\mathrm{m}$. Both the airfoil and the rod extend by $l = 0.3\,\mathrm{m}$ in the spanwise direction. The experimental set-up is sketched in Fig.1.

Acoustic measurements are performed at a distance $r = 1.38\,\mathrm{m}$ from the airfoil mid point, at various observation angles in the mid span plane. A Brüel & Kjaer type 4191 microphone with a Brüel & Kjaer type 2669 preamplifier is used for these measurements. Data acquisitions are carried out with a spectral resolution of 2 Hz, from 0 to 6400 Hz, and the number of averages is 300. The Brüel & Kjaer software *Pulse* is used for the signal acquisition and analysis. The rod-alone configuration noise (no airfoil) is also measured in order to check the airfoil contribution to the rod-airfoil configuration noise.

Measurements of wall pressure fluctuations are performed on the rod in order to investigate the statistical behaviour of the vortical flow in the wake of the rod. 6 pressure pinholes are drilled on the rod at 90° away from the streamwise direction. Hence, two-point statistical measurements are taken with different spacing along the rod span. The coherence at the Strouhal

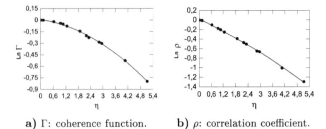

a) Γ: coherence function.   b) ρ: correlation coefficient.

Fig. 2 Spanwise coherence and correlation coefficient on the rod. ••Experimental data, —— Gaussian interpolation.

frequency and the correlation coefficient are plotted in Fig.2. Both these quantities are defined in Appendix A. The reference probe is at $\eta = 0$, η denoting the distance from the mid-span plane made dimensionless by d. Data are fitted by a Gaussian $\exp\left(-\eta^2/2L_g^2\right)$ function, with $L_g = 4.7$ for the coherence function, and $L_g = 6.6$ for the correlation coefficient. The vortex shedding process is therefore correlated upon a distance of about 6.5 d.

3. AERODYNAMIC COMPUTATION

The finite volume compressible RANS code *Proust*[7] is used in the current investigation. Both the convective fluxes and the viscous terms are evaluated using a second order centered scheme. The solution is advanced in time by using an explicit second order scheme based on a five-step Runge-Kutta factorization.

Non reflecting boundary conditions and grid stretching in the outer domains are used in order to limit spurious reflections of acoustic waves.

The turbulence model used is the two-equations Wilcox'[8] $k - \omega$ model, where k is the turbulent kinetic energy and ω is related to the turbulent dissipation.

The inflow conditions and the flow parameters are $\rho_\infty = 1.225\,\mathrm{kg/m^3}$, $V_\infty = 20\,\mathrm{m/s}$, $p_\infty = 101253.6\,\mathrm{Pa}$ and $\mu_\infty = 1.78 \times 10^{-5}\,\mathrm{kg/ms}$. The turbulent kinetic energy has a uniform initial value of 1%, as measured in experiments. The inflow boundary conditions remain the same throughout the computation.

An approximated steady potential flow is used as initial solution. Furthermore, a strong line-vortex in proximity of one rod separation point is added to the initial field in order to induce a vortex shedding as soon as the computation is started. The computational mesh is based on 54640 grid points and is split into 5 structured domains. An overview of the mesh is plotted in Fig.3. The grid around the rod is circumferentially clustered in the wake region. The minimum circumferential spacing, at the rod base point ($\phi = 0$), is $9.07 \times 10^{-3}\,d$, and the thickness of the mesh wall

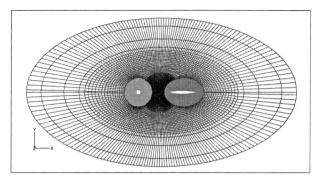

Fig. 3 Overview of the computational mesh.

layer is $7.50 \times 10^{-4}\,d$. The airfoil grid is build around a NACA-0012 airfoil. The thickness of the mesh wall layer varies from $6.40 \times 10^{-5}\,c$, at the leading edge, to $1.42 \times 10^{-3}\,c$, at the thickest airfoil section. A parallel computation is performed with one processor per domain. The computational time-step is $6 \times 10^{-8}\,\mathrm{s}$, corresponding to about 6.5×10^4 iterations per aerodynamic cycle. 1024 aerodynamic fields are stored for the acoustic computation, covering $3.15 \times 10^{-2}\,\mathrm{s}$.

4. ACOUSTIC COMPUTATION

The rotor noise code *Advantia*[9] is used for the acoustic prediction. For the purposes of the present investigation, only surface integrals are computed, provided that at low Mach numbers the volume sources give a vanishing contribution to the acoustic radiation. The consistency of this approximation is checked by comparing acoustic results obtained from different integration surfaces.

For the sake of the present work *Advantia* exploits the retarded time penetrable FW-H formulation proposed by Brentner & Farassat,[5] extended to a moving observer by Casalino.[9]

By introducing a reference length l_{ref}, a reference velocity U_{ref}, a reference time $l_{\mathrm{ref}}/U_{\mathrm{ref}}$ and a reference dynamic pressure p_d, the thickness and loading noise expressions, say p'_Q and p'_L, take the form

$$
\frac{2\pi}{p_d} p'_Q(\mathbf{X},\theta) = \int_{f=0} \left[\frac{\dot{V}_i\,\hat{n}_i + \dot{q}_i\,\hat{n}_i + (V_i + q_i)\,\dot{\hat{n}}_i}{R\,(1 - M_r)^2} \right]_{\mathrm{ret}} \mathrm{d}S
$$

$$
+ \int_{f=0} \left[\frac{(V_n + q_n)\left\{ R\,\dot{M}_r + \frac{M_r - M^2}{M_{\mathrm{ref}}} \right\}}{R^2\,(1 - M_r)^3} \right]_{\mathrm{ret}} \mathrm{d}S
$$

$$
- \int_{f=0} \left[M_{or}\,\frac{\dot{V}_i\,\hat{n}_i + \dot{q}_i\,\hat{n}_i + (V_i + q_i)\,\dot{\hat{n}}_i}{R\,(1 - M_r)^2} \right]_{\mathrm{ret}} \mathrm{d}S
$$

$$-\int\limits_{f=0}\left[\frac{M_{o\,r}\,\dot{M}_r\,(V_i+q_i)\,\hat{n}_i}{R\,(1-M_r)^3}\right]_{\rm ret}{\rm d}S$$

$$-\int\limits_{f=0}\left[\frac{2\,M_{o\,r}\,M_r\,(V_i+q_i)\,\hat{n}_i}{M_{\rm ref}\,R^2\,(1-M_r)^3}\right]_{\rm ret}{\rm d}S$$

$$+\int\limits_{f=0}\left[\frac{M_{o\,r}\,M^2\,(V_i+q_i)\,\hat{n}_i}{M_{\rm ref}\,R^2\,(1-M_r)^3}\right]_{\rm ret}{\rm d}S$$

$$+\int\limits_{f=0}\left[\frac{M_{o\,i}\,M_i\,(V_i+q_i)\,\hat{n}_i}{M_{\rm ref}\,R^2\,(1-M_r)^2}\right]_{\rm ret}{\rm d}S$$

$$+\int\limits_{f=0}\left[\frac{M_{o\,r}\,M_r^2\,(V_i+q_i)\,\hat{n}_i}{M_{\rm ref}\,R^2\,(1-M_r)^3}\right]_{\rm ret}{\rm d}S$$

$$-\int\limits_{f=0}\left[\frac{M_{o\,r}\,(V_i+q_i)\,\hat{n}_i}{M_{\rm ref}\,R^2\,(1-M_r)}\right]_{\rm ret}{\rm d}S \qquad (1)$$

$$\frac{2\pi}{p_d}\,p_L'(\mathbf{X},\theta)=\int\limits_{f=0}\left[\frac{M_{\rm ref}\,\chi_r}{R\,(1-M_r)^2}\right]_{\rm ret}{\rm d}S$$

$$+\int\limits_{f=0}\left[\frac{\lambda_r-\lambda_M}{R^2\,(1-M_r)^2}\right]_{\rm ret}{\rm d}S$$

$$+\int\limits_{f=0}\left[\frac{M_{\rm ref}\,\lambda_r\left\{R\,\dot{M}_r+\frac{M_r-M^2}{M_{\rm ref}}\right\}}{R^2\,(1-M_r)^3}\right]_{\rm ret}{\rm d}S \qquad (2)$$

Dots on quantities denote time derivative with respect to the dimensionless source time. Square brackets enclose quantities evaluated at the retarded time $\theta_{\rm ret}$ obtained from the dimensionless retarded time equation

$$\theta_{\rm ret}=\theta-(\mathbf{X}(\theta)-\mathbf{Y}(\theta_{\rm ret}))\,M_{\rm ref} \qquad (3)$$

Quantities in Eqs.(1) and (2) are all described in Appendix B.

1024 aerodynamic fields are used for the acoustic computation (about 9 vortex shedding cycles, $t_{\rm fin} = 3.15\times10^{-2}$ s and $\Delta f = 32.5\,{\rm Hz}$). The observation distance from the airfoil mid point is $r = 1.38\,{\rm m}$ ($kr = 6.37$ for a typical Strouhal number $St = 0.2$).

Both the observer $\mathbf{X}$ and the integration surface $f = 0$ move at the constant velocity $c\mathbf{M}_o = -V_\infty\hat{\mathbf{i}}$ and the flow at infinity is at rest.

Integrations are performed upon the rod and the airfoil surface, and upon penetrable surfaces around the airfoil and the rod-airfoil system. The aerodynamic field on both physical and penetrable surfaces is extracted directly from the CFD solution. In addition, the aerodynamic data are interpolated upon penetrable surfaces which do not coincide with mesh surfaces.

In order to deal with truncated time series, data are multiplied by the Tukey weighting function $w(t) = 0.815\,[1-\cos{(2\pi\,t/t_{\rm fin})}]$ before performing Fourier analyses. The energy of the original signals is preserved by scaling the windowed data.

4.1 Spanwise statistical model

The flow past a circular cylinder remains 2D up to Reynolds numbers of about 180. At higher values, 3D fluctuations are imposed on the dominant vortex shedding and the wall pressure signals exhibit a random amplitude modulation.

At very low Reynolds numbers this behaviour is presumably related[10] to a cellular structure of the vortex shedding, accompanied by *vortex dislocations* and oblique vortex shedding. At higher Reynolds numbers cellular shedding has never been observed, despite the fact that pressure and velocity signals exhibit a randomly modulated behaviour.[11]

An oblique vortex shedding causes a spanwise variation of the vortex shedding phase. Furthermore, as shown in Ref.,[12] a statistical analogy exists between a random amplitude modulation and a spanwise dispersion of the vortex shedding phase. Hence, an *ad-hoc* statistical model for the vortex shedding phase has been proposed by Casalino.[12] The model permits to perform aeroacoustic predictions by using a 2D flow, but accounting to some extent for the 3D character of the flow. It is based on a relationship between the statistical properties of a given spanwise random dispersion of the vortex shedding phase and a given spanwise loss of coherence.

By denoting as $\rho(\eta)$ the correlation coefficient at the vortex shedding frequency and by $w(\eta)$ the variance distribution of the vortex shedding phase, it results that

$$w(\eta)=-2\ln{\{\rho(\eta)\}} \qquad (4)$$

In particular, a Gaussian dispersion of the phase with a quadratic variance distribution, i.e.

$$w(\eta)=w_{\max}\left(\frac{2d}{l}\,\eta\right)^2 \qquad (5)$$

provides the Gaussian correlation coefficient

$$\rho=\exp{\left(-\eta^2/2\,L_g^2\right)} \qquad (6)$$

with

$$w_{\max}=\left(2\,\frac{d}{l}\,L_g\right)^{-2} \qquad (7)$$

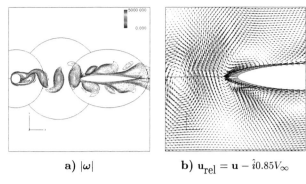

a) $|\boldsymbol{\omega}|$ b) $\mathbf{u}_{\mathrm{rel}} = \mathbf{u} - \hat{i}0.85V_\infty$

Fig. 4   Rod-airfoil flow: enstrophy (left), relative velocity (right). The vector field has been interpolated on a coarser grid.

The correlation length L_g can be experimentally determined and related to the maximum value $w_{\max}$ of the variance at the rod extremities. Details of the spanwise statistical model are given in Appendix A.

Eq.(4) provides the variance law which can be used to generate a random phase sequence $\tilde{\varphi}(\eta_i, \tau_j)$ along the rod span. Consistently with the observed features of the vortex shedding process, phase jumps are allowed to occur sporadically every two-three aerodynamic cycles. Furthermore, jump synchronization at two different spanwise sections is avoided by randomizing the time at which the phase jump occurs. The random phase is then converted into a random perturbation of the retarded time by writing

$$\tilde{\theta}_{\mathrm{ret}}(\eta, \theta) = \theta_{\mathrm{ret}}(\eta) + \frac{\tilde{\varphi}(\eta, \theta_{\mathrm{ret}}(\eta))}{2\pi\, \mathrm{St}} \qquad (8)$$

where $\theta_{\mathrm{ret}}(\eta)$ denotes the deterministic retarded time defined in Eq.(3).

The aeroacoustic prediction is then performed by forcing into equations (1) and (2) a spanwise random dispersion of the retarded time $\tilde{\theta}_{\mathrm{ret}}(\eta, \theta)$. This is equivalent to introduce a loss of coherence into the spanwise repetition of the 2D aerodynamic field.

Interestingly, the same 2D aerodynamic field can be used to predict the acoustic pressure by using different seeds of the random phase distribution. Then averaged acoustic spectra can be computed in a similar way as in the experiments.

In the present investigation, a Gaussian correlation length of $5\,d$ is used for both the rod and the airfoil. The acoustic spectra are obtained by averaging over 100 spectra.

5. AERODYNAMIC RESULTS

A snapshot of the enstrophy field in Fig.4(a) shows the vortex street downstream of the rod, undergoing a

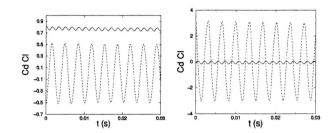

Fig. 5   Force on the rod (left) and the airfoil (right):——C_d, - - - -C_l. Reference length: d

nearly direct interaction with the airfoil leading edge. The corresponding relative velocity (with respect to the vortex convection speed) is plotted in Fig.4(b). Such a vortical flow induces the force plotted in Fig.5 on the rod-airfoil system. Both the rod and the airfoil lift depend on the vortex sign, whereas the drag does not. Hence, the lift and the drag main frequencies are $f_{St} \simeq 300\,\mathrm{Hz}$ and $2f_{St}$, respectively. The airfoil lift is about 6 times higher than the rod lift.

Counter-rotating vortices are shed from the rod at a Strouhal number $St = 0.24$. The overprediction of the vortex shedding frequency from a 2D rod is a common CFD result[13] that can be explained to some extent. As argued by Roshko,[14] the length of the mean recirculating region behind the rod results from an equilibrium between the base suction coefficient and the mean Reynolds stresses $\rho u'v'$ in the separated region. Hence, higher Reynolds stresses correspond to shorter mean recirculating regions. In a 3D flow a part of the energy extracted from the mean flow is used to maintain spanwise velocity fluctuations. As a consequence, the mean recirculating region is longer and its frequency is smaller than in a computed 2D flow.

Letting $\langle\rangle$ denote the local average of a quantity over a vortex shedding period, the following quantities are plotted in Figs.6 through 8:
- mean pressure coefficient, i.e.

$$\langle Cp \rangle = \frac{\langle p - p_\infty \rangle}{\frac{1}{2}\rho_\infty V_\infty^2} \qquad (9)$$

- root-mean-square pressure coefficient, i.e.

$$Cp_{\mathrm{rms}} = \sqrt{\left\langle \left(Cp - \langle Cp \rangle\right)^2 \right\rangle} \qquad (10)$$

- dimensionless mean velocity. i.e.

$$\langle V \rangle = \frac{\sqrt{\langle u \rangle^2 + \langle v \rangle^2}}{V_\infty} \qquad (11)$$

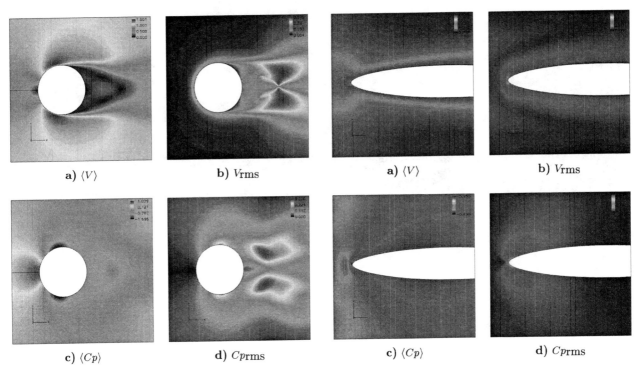

| a) $\langle V \rangle$ | b) $V_{\rm rms}$ | a) $\langle V \rangle$ | b) $V_{\rm rms}$ |

| c) $\langle Cp \rangle$ | d) $Cp_{\rm rms}$ | c) $\langle Cp \rangle$ | d) $Cp_{\rm rms}$ |

Fig. 6   Mean and fluctuating flow past the rod.

Fig. 7   Mean and fluctuating flow past the airfoil.

- dimensionless root-mean-square velocity, i.e.

$$V_{\rm rms} = \sqrt{\left\langle \left(u\, n_x/V_\infty + v\, n_y/V_\infty - \langle V \rangle \right)^2 \right\rangle + \frac{2}{3}\langle k \rangle}$$
$$(12)$$

where $n_x = \langle u \rangle / \langle V \rangle$ and $n_y = \langle v \rangle / \langle V \rangle$ are the component of the mean flow direction and $\langle k \rangle$ denotes the mean kinetic turbulent energy[§].

The mean velocity past the rod in Fig.6(a) shows the recirculating region behind the rod. Interestingly, the downstream point of minimum $\langle V \rangle$ at $(x/d = 1.27, y = 0)$ coincides with the point of maximum $V_{\rm rms}$. Conventionally, such a point defines the *vortex formation length*. Measurements made by Szepessy & Bearman[11] over a wide range of Reynolds numbers and rod aspect ratios show a vortex formation length of about 1.5. Thus, consistently with Roshko's[14] model, a two-dimensional computation provides a smaller mean recirculating region behind the rod.

The mean and fluctuating flow past the airfoil is plotted in Fig.7. Higher fluctuations occur in a very narrow region close to the leading edge where a

[§]Eq.12 is based on the hypothesis of local isotropy of the turbulent velocity field, i.e. $k = \frac{3}{2}\overline{u'u'}$, where u' is the Reynolds fluctuating component of the velocity field in the x−direction. Clearly, in the framework of unsteady RANS modeling, a fluctuating k only reaches sense if the averaging time is longer than that associated with the slowest turbulent motions, but is much smaller than the time scale of the flow unsteadiness (the vortex shedding period in the present study).

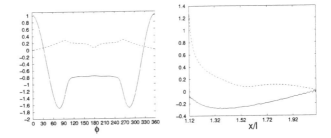

Fig. 8   Pressure field on the rod (left) and the airfoil (right) surface: —— $\langle Cp \rangle$, - - - - $Cp_{\rm rms}$.

strong vortex distortion is accompanied by high velocity gradients and where the stagnation point oscillates around the leading edge.

Fig.8(a) shows the pressure field on the rod surface. The $Cp_{\rm rms}$ peaks at $\phi = 95.5^o$, which marks the mean location of the separation point. The pressure field on the airfoil surface is plotted in Fig.8(b). Interestingly, $Cp_{\rm rms}$ peaks near the leading edge, decreasing fast downstream. The fluctuating pressure level at the leading edge is about 159 times higher than that at the trailing edge. Furthermore, the maximum $Cp_{\rm rms}$ on the airfoil is 4.5 times higher than the maximum on the rod. Therefore, the stronger aeroacoustic sources in the rod-airfoil configuration are likely to be found near the airfoil leading edge.

6. ACOUSTIC RESULTS

The integration surfaces used in the present investi-

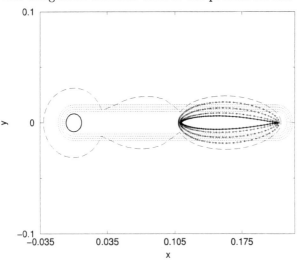

Fig. 9 Integration surfaces: —— R, ••A1...A4, - - - - RAi1...RAi4, — — RAe.

gation are plotted in Fig.9. They are:

- **R**: rod physical surface (200 points);
- **A1...A4**: surfaces around the airfoil extracted from the CFD mesh (200 points), **A1** coinciding with the airfoil surface;
- **RAi1...RAi4**: surfaces around the rod-airfoil upon which the aerodynamic data are obtained by interpolating the CFD solution (520 points);
- **RAe**: surface around the rod-airfoil extracted from the CFD mesh (595 points).

6.1 Influence of the integration surface

In this subsection acoustic computations are performed on the base of a 2D flow (no spanwise effects).

In Fig.10 the acoustic spectrum at $\theta = 90^o$ obtained from different integration surfaces is shown. First, the rod **R** and the airfoil **A1** contributions are compared in Fig.10(a) to the noise obtained by integrating upon **RAi1**, which surrounds the rod-airfoil system. The aerodynamic data on **RAi1** are obtained from a space interpolation of the CFD solution. This causes an unphysical behaviour at $1000\,\mathrm{Hz} \lesssim f$. Interestingly, as shown in Fig.10(b), integrations upon **RAi1...RAi4** provide unphysical but consistent results. Then, results obtained by integrating upon **A1...A4** are compared in Fig.10(c). Only small differences appear at even harmonics, showing again the consistency of the penetrable FW-H formulation. Finally, in Fig.10(d) the rod **R** and the airfoil **A1** contributions are compared to that obtained from the surface **RAe**, which is

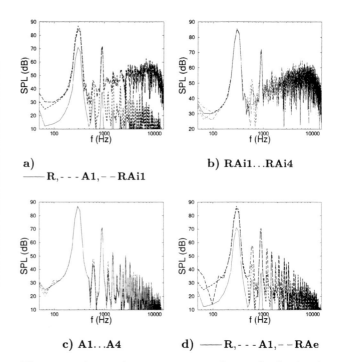

a)
—— R, - - - A1, - - RAi1

b) RAi1...RAi4

c) A1...A4

d) —— R, - - - A1, - - RAe

Fig. 10 Acoustic spectrum at $\theta = 90^o$ obtained from various integration surfaces. 2D aerodynamic field.

extracted from the CFD mesh and surrounds the rod-airfoil system. Now, the rod-airfoil spectrum exhibits a physically reliable behaviour.

Fig.10(d) shows that at $\theta = 90^0$ the airfoil is $86.9 - 71.1 = 15.8$ dB louder than the rod. This corresponds to a lift amplitude ratio of 6.16, provided that at low Mach numbers the acoustic radiation is essentially dipolar. Interestingly, such a value is in good agreement with that found in Fig.5.

In Fig.11(a) the rod **R** and the airfoil **A1** acoustic signals are checked against that obtained from **RAe**. Surprisingly, the rod-airfoil system is quieter than the airfoil alone. This is because the rod and the airfoil signals are in a partial phase opposition and because the computed shedding and the rod wake are deterministic. The directivity in Fig.11(b) shows that, at $\theta = 90^o$, the rod-airfoil sound pressure level is about 2 dB lower than that generated by the airfoil alone.

In order to further check the consistency of the penetrable FW-H prediction, Fig.12 shows the relative difference between the **RAe** noise and the sum of the rod **R** and the airfoil **A1** contributions. The spectrum of $\Delta p'/\max(p')$ exhibits an enveloped broadband behaviour with harmonics peaks, the even ones being slightly higher. Such a difference may be due to numerical as well as physical effects, namely, nonlinear contributions from the flow field inside **RAe**. The even

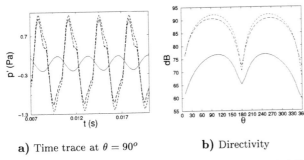

a) Time trace at $\theta = 90^o$ **b)** Directivity

Fig. 11   **Acoustic field:** ——— **rod,** - - - - **airfoil,** — — **rod-airfoil. 2D aerodynamic field.**

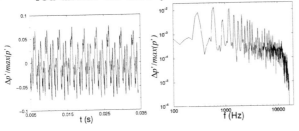

Fig. 12   **Relative difference between the rod-airfoil noise RAe and the sum of the rod R and the airfoil A1 contributions at $\theta = 90°$. Signal (left), spectrum (right). 2D aerodynamic field.**

harmonics effect has been observed also in Fig.10(c) by integrating upon surfaces surrounding the airfoil alone. This fact plays in favor of the possible physical reliability of Fig.12.

6.2 Comparison with acoustic measurements

In this subsection acoustic computations are performed by forcing statistical 3D effects into the aerodynamic field.

In Figs.13 through 16, acoustic results are checked against experimental data. Both the rod alone and the rod-airfoil noise are plotted. The numerical rod-airfoil noise is indeed the airfoil contribution obtained from **A1**. This is justified by the small difference previously observed between the computed airfoil noise and the rod-airfoil noise. Moreover, such a difference is even smaller if a deterministic phase opposition is smeared by some statistical effects.

The numerical prediction is performed by assuming a 2D aerodynamic field (2D), and an aerodynamic field undergoing a Gaussian correlation along the rod and the airfoil spans (3D). The measured power spectral densities have been integrated upon intervals of $\Delta f = 32.5$ Hz in order to provide sound levels against which the numerical ones can be checked. Furthermore, the aerodynamic Strouhal frequency overprediction is taken into account by scaling the numerical

results (f, dB) to (f', dB'), i.e.

$$f' = \frac{\text{St}_{\exp}}{\text{St}_{\text{num}}} f, \quad dB' = dB + 20 \log \left(\frac{\text{St}_{\exp}}{\text{St}_{\text{num}}} \right) \quad (13)$$

where the level correction accounts for the fact that the sound level is proportional to the vortex shedding frequency.

In Fig.13 the rod noise spectrum at $\theta = 90^o$ is plotted. The Strouhal peak is well predicted by both the 2D and 3D computations. Conversely, the second and third harmonic peaks are not well predicted. Comparing 2D and 3D results shows that the statistical model allows a quite accurate prediction of the broadband spectral behaviour. This is because the spanwise random distribution of the vortex shedding phase results in a random amplitude modulation of the acoustic signal. The second and third harmonic levels in the measurements are likely to be contaminated by installation effects. In fact, as pictured in Fig.1(a), the rod is slightly downstream of the duct end. Hence, diffraction effects may be responsible for a different acoustic behaviour with respect to that of an isolated rod.

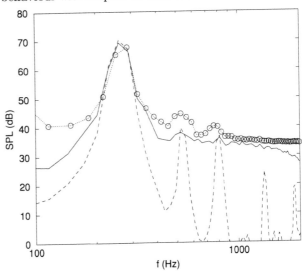

Fig. 13   **Rod noise spectrum at $\theta = 90°$. Comparison between: o Experimental data, - - - - 2D prediction, ——— 3D prediction.**

In Fig.14 the rod-airfoil noise spectrum at $\theta = 90^o$ is plotted. Computations provide an overprediction of about 3 dB of the Strouhal peak. This is not surprising for the airfoil alone prediction. In fact, as previously discussed, the rod-airfoil system is about 2 dB quieter than the airfoil alone. The 3D results show improvements in the prediction of the third harmonic peak. Moreover, the broadband spectral behaviour is quite well featured by the 3D computation.

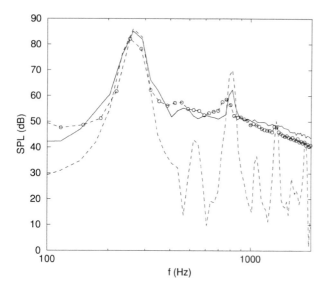

Fig. 14 Rod-airfoil noise spectrum at $\theta = 90^o$. Comparison between: o Experimental data, - - - - 2D prediction, —— 3D prediction.

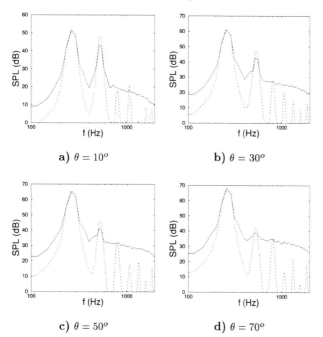

a) $\theta = 10^o$

b) $\theta = 30^o$

c) $\theta = 50^o$

d) $\theta = 70^o$

Fig. 15 Rod noise spectrum. Comparison between: - - - - 2D prediction, —— 3D prediction.

In Fig.15 the predicted rod noise spectra at different observation angles are plotted. Comparing 2D and 3D results shows that the spanwise statistical model contributes to the broadening of the main peak, reduces the higher harmonic peaks and generates a broadband spectral behaviour.

Finally, in Fig.16 the airfoil noise prediction is compared to rod-airfoil noise measurements at different

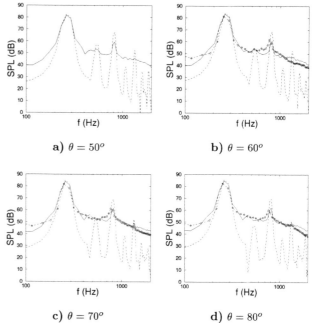

a) $\theta = 50^o$

b) $\theta = 60^o$

c) $\theta = 70^o$

d) $\theta = 80^o$

Fig. 16 Rod-airfoil noise spectrum. Comparison between: o Experimental data, - - - - 2D prediction, —— 3D prediction.

observation angles. As for the rod noise computation, the random phase dispersion results in a better prediction of both the higher harmonic peaks and the broadband spectral behaviour.

7. CONCLUSIONS

This study shows how a statistical model can be used in an acoustic analogy to account for 3D spanwise effects which are not featured by a 2D flow computation. Sound predictions are significantly improved and the broadband part of the sound field is quite well predicted. The model requires only an a priori knowledge of the spanwise correlation length and shape.

A particular point is that a fully correlated (2D) sound computation predicts partial cancelations between rod and airfoil contributions which are not likely to be found in the non deterministic 3D flow.

Moreover, interesting results are found or confirmed about the choice of a suitable integration surface:
- it should coincide with grid points of the CFD domain;
- in low Mach number applications, volume sources are negligible with respect to surface sources and the physical surfaces are thus good integration surfaces.

In the rod-airfoil configuration, the airfoil contribution is dominant and gives a good estimate of the overall noise.

This statistical analogy is an interesting tool for

complex flow configurations where only unsteady but deterministic RANS computations can be carried out

ACKNOWLEDGEMENTS

This work was partially supported by the European Community as part of the project TurboNoise-CFD.

REFERENCES

[1]Possio, C., "L'azione aerodinamica sul profilo oscillante in un fluido compressibile a velocitá iposonora," *L'Aerotecnica*, Vol. 18, No. 4, 1938, pp. 441–458.

[2]Sears, W. R., "Some Aspects of Non-Stationary Airfoil Theory and its Practical Application," *Journal of the Aeronautical Sciences*, Vol. 8, No. 3, 1941, pp. 104–108.

[3]Filotas, L. T., "Oblique Compressible Sears Function," *American Institute of Aeronautics and Astronautics Journal*, Vol. 12, No. 11, 1974, pp. 1601–1603.

[4]Amiet, R. K., "Acoustic Radiation from an Airfoil in a Turbulent Stream," *Journal of Sound and Vibration*, Vol. 41, No. 4, 1975, pp. 407–420.

[5]Brentner, K. S. and Farassat, F., "Analytical Comparison of the Acoustic Analogy and Kirchhoff Formulation for Moving Surfaces," *American Institute of Aeronautics and Astronautics Journal*, Vol. 36, No. 8, 1998, pp. 1379–1386.

[6]Williamson, C. H. K., "Vortex Dynamics in the Cylinder Wake," *Annual Review of Fluid Mechanics*, Vol. 28, 1996, pp. 477–539.

[7]Ferrand, P., Aubert, S., Smati, L., Bron, O., and Atassi, H. M., "Nonlinear Interaction of Upstream Propagating Sound with Unsteady Transonic Flow in a Nozzle," *American Institute of Aeronautics and Astronautics Paper 98-2213*, 1998.

[8]Wilcox, D. C., "Comparison of Two Equations Turbulence Models for Boundary Layers with Pressure Gradient," *American Institute of Aeronautics and Astronautics Journal*, Vol. 31, No. 8, 1993, pp. 1414–1421.

[9]Casalino, D., "An Advanced Time Approach for Acoustic Analogy Predictions," *Submitted to the Journal of Sound and Vibration*, 2002.

[10]Williamson, C. H. K., "Oblique and Parallel Modes of Vortex Shedding in the Wake of a Circular Cylinder at Low Reynolds Numbers," *Journal of Fluid Mechanics*, Vol. 206, 1989, pp. 579–627.

[11]Szepessy, S. and Bearman, P. W., "Aspect Ratio and End Plate Effects on Vortex Shedding from a Circular Cylinder," *Journal of Fluid Mechanics*, Vol. 234, 1992, pp. 191–217.

[12]Casalino, D., *Analytical and Numerical Methods in Vortex-Body Aeroacoustics*, PhD Thesis, Politecnico di Torino and Ecole Centrale de Lyon, 2002.

[13]Kato, C. and Ikegawa, M., "Large Eddy Simulation of Unsteady Turbulent Wake of a Circular Cylinder Using the Finite Element Method," *Advances in Numerical Simulation of Turbulent Flows, ASME, FED*, Vol. 117, 1991, pp. 49–56.

[14]Roshko, A., "Perspectives on Bluff Body Aerodynamics," *J. Wind Ind. Aerodyn.*, 1993, pp. 49–79.

A: COHERENCE AND CORRELATION

The coherence function Γ_{xy} between two signals $x(t)$ and $y(t)$ is defined as

$$\Gamma_{xy}(f) = \frac{|S_{xy}(f)|}{\sqrt{S_{xx}(f)\,S_{yy}(f)}} \qquad (14)$$

where $S_{xy}(f)$ is the cross-power spectral density $S_{xy}(f) = \text{TF}\{C_{xy}(\tau)\}$, with

$$C_{xy}(\tau) = \lim_{T \to \infty} \frac{1}{T} \int_0^T x(t)\,y(t-\tau)\,\mathrm{d}t \qquad (15)$$

and TF denoting a Fourier transform. For an ergodic process $C_{xy}(\tau)$ can be interpreted as the correlation function between $x(t)$ and $y(t)$. The correlation coefficient ρ is defined as

$$\rho = \frac{C_{xy}(0)}{\sqrt{C_{xx}(0)\,C_{yy}(0)}} = \frac{\int_{-\infty}^{\infty} S_{xy}(f)\,\mathrm{d}f}{\sqrt{\int_{-\infty}^{\infty} S_{xx}(f)\,\mathrm{d}f}\sqrt{\int_{-\infty}^{\infty} S_{yy}(f)\,\mathrm{d}f}} \qquad (16)$$

In the case of two tuned monochromatic signals it results that $\rho = \Gamma_{xy}(f_0)$.

The fluctuating pressure on the rod surface at 90° away from the streamwise direction is representative of the fluctuating lift behaviour. Thus, considering two points at different spanwise locations, the pressure can be written as $p_1(t) = P\cos(2\pi f_0 t + \tilde{\varphi}_1)$ and $p_2(t) = P\cos(2\pi f_0 t + \tilde{\varphi}_2)$, where $\tilde{\varphi}$ accounts for a random spanwise phase variation. The related cross-correlation function is given by

$$
\begin{aligned}
C_{12}(\Theta) &= \mathcal{E}\left[p_1(t)\,p_2(t+\Theta)\right] = \\
&= \frac{P^2}{2}\mathcal{E}\left[\cos\tilde{\varphi}_1\,\cos\tilde{\varphi}_2\right]\cos(2\pi f_0\Theta) \\
&- \frac{P^2}{2}\mathcal{E}\left[\cos\tilde{\varphi}_1\,\sin\tilde{\varphi}_2\right]\sin(2\pi f_0\Theta) \\
&+ \frac{P^2}{2}\mathcal{E}\left[\sin\tilde{\varphi}_1\,\cos\tilde{\varphi}_2\right]\sin(2\pi f_0\Theta) \\
&+ \frac{P^2}{2}\mathcal{E}\left[\sin\tilde{\varphi}_1\,\sin\tilde{\varphi}_2\right]\cos(2\pi f_0\Theta)\ (17)
\end{aligned}
$$

where $\mathcal{E}[\,]$ denotes the expected value.

Consider a spanwise phase distribution with a Gaussian probability density $\mathcal{P}$, whose variance w is zero at the cylinder half-span ($\eta = 0$) and increases symmetrically towards the cylinder extremities ($\eta = \pm\frac{l}{2d}$), i.e.

$$\mathcal{P}(\tilde{\varphi}, \eta) = \frac{\exp\left(-\frac{\tilde{\varphi}^2}{2\,w(\eta)}\right)}{\sqrt{2\pi\,w(\eta)}} \qquad (18)$$

Taking the first point in $\eta = 0$ and setting $\tilde{\varphi}_2 = \tilde{\varphi}$, Eq.(17) reduces to¶

$$C_{12}(\Theta) = \frac{P^2}{2}\mathcal{E}\left[\cos\tilde{\varphi}\right]\cos(2\pi f_0\Theta)$$

¶The flow around the rod can be approximately supposed to be statistically homogenous and the random phase $\tilde{\varphi}$ denotes a phase shift between two spanwise locations.

1473

$$- \frac{P^2}{2} \mathcal{E}\left[\sin \tilde{\varphi}\right] \sin(2\pi f_0 \Theta) \qquad (19)$$

whose related correlation coefficient is

$$\rho(\eta) \equiv C_{1\,2}(0) = \mathcal{E}\left[\cos \tilde{\varphi}\right] \qquad (20)$$

Moreover, the coherence function is given by

$$\begin{aligned}
\Gamma(\eta, f) &= \frac{|S_{1\,2}(\eta, f)|}{\sqrt{S_{1\,1}}\sqrt{S_{2\,2}}} \\
&= \mathcal{E}\left[\cos \tilde{\varphi}\right] \delta(f - f_0) \\
&\quad - \mathcal{E}\left[\sin \tilde{\varphi}\right] \delta(f - f_0)
\end{aligned} \qquad (21)$$

Since $\tilde{\varphi}$ has a symmetric probability density, it follows that $\mathcal{E}\left[\sin \tilde{\varphi}\right] = 0$. Hence, the coherence function can be interpreted as the correlation coefficient, i.e.

$$\Gamma(\eta, f) = \rho(\eta)\,\delta(f - f_0) \qquad (22)$$

In order to determine the correlation coefficient (20), consider the Taylor series of $\cos \tilde{\varphi}$ and write

$$\mathcal{E}\left[\cos \tilde{\varphi}\right] = \mathcal{E}\left[\sum_{n=0}^{\infty} \frac{(-1)^n}{(2n)!}\,\tilde{\varphi}^{2n}\right] = \sum_{n=0}^{\infty} \frac{(-1)^n}{(2n)!} \mathcal{E}\left[\tilde{\varphi}^{2n}\right] \qquad (23)$$

Since $\tilde{\varphi}$ has a Gaussian density probability, it results that

$$\mathcal{E}\left[\tilde{\varphi}^{0}\right] = 1 \quad \text{and, for } n \geq 1$$
$$\mathcal{E}\left[\tilde{\varphi}^{2n-1}\right] = 0$$
$$\mathcal{E}\left[\tilde{\varphi}^{2n}\right] = (2n-1)(2n-3)\cdot \ldots \cdot 3 \cdot 1 \cdot w^n$$

Thus, substituting into Eq.(23) and performing some algebra, i.e.

$$\begin{aligned}
\mathcal{E}\left[\cos \tilde{\varphi}\right] &= \sum_{n=0}^{\infty} \frac{(-1)^n}{(2n)!}\,(2n-1)\cdot \ldots \cdot 3 \cdot 1 \cdot w^n \\
&= \sum_{n=0}^{\infty} \frac{(-w)^n}{2n\,(2n-2)(2n-4)\cdot \ldots \cdot 4 \cdot 2} \\
&= \sum_{n=0}^{\infty} \frac{\left(-\frac{w}{2}\right)^n}{n\,(n-1)(n-2)\cdot \ldots \cdot 3 \cdot 1} \\
&= \sum_{n=0}^{\infty} \frac{1}{n!}\left(-\frac{w}{2}\right)^n \equiv \exp\left(-\frac{w}{2}\right)
\end{aligned} \qquad (24)$$

the two-point correlation coefficient takes the form

$$\rho(\eta) = \exp\left(-\frac{w}{2}\right) \qquad (25)$$

B: SYMBOLS IN THE FW-H ANALOGY

The aerodynamic field is introduced into Eqs.(1) and (2) in terms of conservative quantities: the flow density ρ, the linear momentum $\rho \tilde{u}_i$, $\tilde{u}_i$ being the relative velocity of the flow with respect to the integration surface $f = 0$, the specific total internal energy ρE and the specific kinetic turbulent energy ρk. A description of all the involved quantities is reported below.

$$p_d = \frac{1}{2}\rho_0 U_{\text{ref}}^2, \quad \theta = t\,U_{\text{ref}}/l_{\text{ref}}, \quad M_{\text{ref}} = U_{\text{ref}}/c$$

$$V_i = v_i/U_{\text{ref}}, \quad V_n = V_i \hat{n}_i, \quad \tilde{u}_i = u_i - v_i$$

$$\mathbf{X} = \mathbf{x}/l_{\text{ref}}, \quad \mathbf{Y} = \mathbf{y}/l_{\text{ref}}$$

$$\hat{r}_i = \frac{X_i - Y_i}{|\mathbf{X} - \mathbf{Y}|}, \quad R = |\mathbf{X} - \mathbf{Y}|$$

$$M_i = v_i/c, \; M_r = M_i \hat{r}_i, \; \dot{M}_r = \dot{M}_i \hat{r}_i, \; M_{o\,r} = M_{o\,i}\hat{r}_i$$

$$\sigma = \frac{\rho}{\rho_0}, \; q_i = \frac{(\rho \tilde{u}_i)}{(\rho_0 U_{\text{ref}})}, \; e = \frac{(\rho E)}{(\rho_0 U_{\text{ref}}^2)}, \; k = \frac{(\rho K)}{(\rho_0 U_{\text{ref}}^2)}$$

$$C_p = 2\left\{(\gamma - 1)\left[e - \frac{q_i q_i}{2\sigma} - k\right] - \frac{p_0}{2 p_d}\right\}$$

$$\dot{C}_p = 2(\gamma - 1)\left[\dot{e} - \frac{q_i \dot{q}_i}{\sigma} + \dot{\sigma}\frac{q_i q_i}{2\sigma^2} - \dot{k}\right]$$

$$\lambda_i = \frac{C_p}{2}\hat{n}_i + V_i q_n + \frac{q_i q_n}{\sigma}$$

$$\chi_i = \frac{\dot{C}_p}{2}\hat{n}_i + \frac{C_p}{2}\dot{\hat{n}}_i + \dot{V}_i q_n + V_i\,(\dot{q}_i \hat{n}_i) + V_i\left(q_i \dot{\hat{n}}_i\right)$$

$$+ \frac{\dot{q}_i q_n}{\sigma} + \frac{q_i\,(\dot{q}_i \hat{n}_i)}{\sigma} + \frac{q_i\left(q_i \dot{\hat{n}}_i\right)}{\sigma} - \frac{q_i q_n}{\sigma^2}\dot{\sigma}$$

$$q_n = q_i \hat{n}_i, \quad \lambda_M = \lambda_i M_i, \quad \lambda_r = \lambda_i \hat{r}_i, \quad \chi_r = \chi_i \hat{r}_i$$

In these expressions p_0 and ρ_0 are the quiescent fluid pressure and density, respectively, the term $\mathbf{M}_o$ denotes the observer Mach number, $\hat{n}_i$ is the unit vector pointing out of the integration surface and upper dots denote derivatives with respect to the dimensionless time θ. The loading-noise term χ_i is the dimensionless time derivative of the term λ_i.

Other details concerning the rotor noise code *Advantia* and the implemented FW-H formulation can be found in Ref.[9] and Ref.[12]

TILTROTOR BVI NOISE REDUCTION THROUGH
FLIGHT TRAJECTORY MANAGEMENT & CONFIGURATION CONTROL

Marc Gervais[*] & Fredric H. Schmitz[†]
University of Maryland
College Park, MD 20742

Abstract

A longitudinal performance model has been developed to study the potential of flight trajectory management and configuration control in reducing tiltrotor Blade-Vortex Interaction (BVI) noise during approach. The concept of a generalized miss-distance is related to the net inflow through the rotors to obtain a qualitative assessment of the likelihood of BVI noise radiation. Two types of constraints are imposed on the problem: deceleration limits relating to passenger/crew comfort and rotor inflow limits relating to the likelihood of BVI noise. For constant fuselage pitch angle and flap deflection, the nacelle tilt-rate is shown to strongly influence the deceleration while flight path angle and tilt-rate both influence the rotor inflow. It is shown that the nacelle tilt-rate must be progressively made smaller as the nacelles tilt-up and the airspeed decreases in order to limit the deceleration. Under the same conditions, it is also established that the glideslope must be flattened for a short time in order to limit the inflow and therefore reduce the likelihood of strong BVI noise.

Notation

AR = wing aspect ratio
AR_{blade} = blade aspect ratio
$C_{Lw'}$ = 3-D lift curve slope of the wing
C_T = individual rotor thrust coefficient
d = miss-distance
D = total airframe drag (lb)
D_f = flap drag (lb)
D_i = wing induced drag (lb)
D_o = wing profile drag (lb)
di_N/dt = nacelle tilt-rate (deg./sec.)
e = Oswald's wing efficiency factor
f_e = equivalent flat plate area (ft^2)
g = gravitational constant (g = 32.2 ft/sec^2)
H = net force in the rotor plane (lb)
i_N = nacelle tilt (deg.)
L = total airframe lift (lb)
m = vehicle mass (lb sec/ft^2)
q = dynamic pressure (lb/ft^2)
S_w = wing area (ft^2)

t = time (sec.)
T = total thrust of the rotors (lb)
V = airspeed (kts)
$\dot{V}$ = acceleration (ft/sec.^{2})
v_{i_ROTOR} = rotor induced velocity (ft/sec.)
$v_{i\ WING}$ = wing induced velocity at the rotor (ft/sec.)
W = vehicle gross weight (lb)

$_{TPP}$ = tip-path-plane angle (deg., positive nose-up)
$_f$ = flap deflection angle (deg.)
= flight path angle (deg., negative in descent)
$_\&$ = rate of change of flight path angle (deg./sec.)
= net rotor inflow (positive upwash)
$_{i\ WING}$ = net rotor inflow due to the wing
= advance ratio
μ = fuselage pitch attitude (deg.)
= blade azimuth location (deg.)
R = rotor tip speed (ft/s)

Introduction

The ability of the tiltrotor to takeoff and land vertically, as well as fly fast and on long distances makes it suitable for many civil and military missions. In civil service, this type of aircraft has been envisioned as a solution to the nearing air transport gridlock. Indeed, short haul fixed-wing aircraft operations account for a large portion of the total aircraft operations at hub airports, although they are responsible for only a small fragment of the passenger transport. Many therefore believe that Runway Independent Aircraft (RIA), such as helicopters, tiltrotors, or STOL aircraft, could be used to alleviate the congestion at hub airports by simultaneously operating on stub runways, helipads, or from smaller regional airports.

One of the main obstacles for the acceptance of tiltrotors as a commercial aircraft is the high level of external noise radiation associated with rotorcraft. Fortunately, the tiltrotor operates most of the time in airplane mode, where it cruises like a turboprop at low tip Mach numbers and has relatively low levels of noise radiated to the ground. The takeoff phase (climb in helicopter mode) has also been identified by previous research as a rather quiet phase.[1-4] However, the tiltrotor still has a "loud" phase which occurs during an approach to land.

---

[*] Graduate Research Assistant, AIAA student member.
[†] Minta Martin Professor of Rotorcraft Acoustics, AIAA fellow.

During the descent phase, the aircraft experiences a widely known phenomenon labeled Blade-Vortex Interaction (BVI) noise. The basic cause of BVI noise is fairly well understood:[5] when any of the rotating blades encounter the tip vortices previously shed by one or more preceding blades, large short duration impulsive loads are induced on the surface of the blade causing rapid changes in blade surface pressures that lead to impulsive noise radiation. This type of noise is often considered to be the most disruptive and annoying form of noise emitted by rotorcraft. The phenomenon produces a loud popping sound (or slapping sound) that contains a lot of acoustic energy and is efficiently radiated in the acoustic far-field. Since it occurs mostly during descent (or sometimes during maneuvering flight), BVI noise is usually produced at fairly low altitudes within the terminal area and close to neighboring communities. Consequently, for years it has been at the center of many noise reduction efforts for conventional helicopters.

Different techniques have been devised and tested in order to reduce BVI noise. These techniques can generally be grouped into three categories dealing with: the strength and size of the shed vortices, the response of the blade to the shed vortices and finally, the distance between the shed vortices and the rotor blades at the time of the interaction (termed miss-distance). The focus of this research is on the use of flight trajectory management and configuration control to develop noise-abating approaches for tiltrotors by increasing the value of the miss-distance. Previous theoretical and experimental studies on conventional helicopters have shown that flight trajectory management can be used to minimize BVI noise during the approach/landing phase.[6-11]

A tiltrotor aircraft has a broader range of trajectory and configuration controls than a conventional helicopter. The ability to tilt the nacelle from $0°$ to $90°$ (airplane mode to helicopter mode) and the presence of a flapped wing allow the aircraft to be statically trimmed at chosen combinations of airspeed and climb rates in a non-unique manner. These additional control freedoms can be used to "control" the miss-distance and thus alter BVI noise radiation. In fact, the use of the unique nacelle tilt degree of freedom of tiltrotors has been regarded as a possible noise abatement control for many years.[1-4] It was also shown that the inflow through the rotor strongly influences BVI noise radiation and that flight path control is useful in mitigating BVI noise radiation for tiltrotors.[1] In addition to this theoretical background, a NASA/Army/Bell Helicopter team conducted an extensive series of flight tests on the XV-15 research aircraft between 1995 and 1999.[12-14] The first set of flight tests identified regions of minimum,

moderate, and maximum noise within the XV-15 conversion envelope where it was determined that the approach condition was the main area of concern for noise issues.[12] A second and third phase of the program was conducted to design and refine low noise approach profiles.[13-14] Approach profiles that utilize a combination of flight path angle and nacelle tilt control were designed, showing that these controls could be used to reduce tiltrotor BVI noise radiation. Shallow approaches and shallow-to-steep segmented approaches were identified as providing the best noise reduction potential.

Reference 15 provided a basic understanding of the physical mechanisms involved in the tiltrotor airplane-to-helicopter descending approach by using a simplified longitudinal quasi-static performance model. This analysis allowed for a qualitative assessment of the potential for tiltrotor BVI noise reduction during approach using the available non-unique controls (flight path angle, flap deflection, fuselage pitch, airspeed, and deceleration, along with the nacelle tilt).

The present paper uses the same performance model[15] in a time-varying way to develop noise abatement strategies. The goal of the analysis is to determine how certain trajectory and configuration controls can be used to fly a tiltrotor aircraft in a way that minimizes BVI noise during an approach to land. The paper also introduces nacelle tilt-rate as one of the non-unique controls. Low noise approaches are achieved through flight trajectory management (flight path angle) and configuration control (nacelle tilt-rate). To gain a basic level of understanding, the fuselage pitch angle and the flap deflection are chosen to be constant throughout the approach maneuver. Constraints are imposed on the resulting inflow and deceleration during a converting approach, thereby introducing a way to limit BVI noise while maintaining passenger and crew comfort. The purpose of this paper is not to predict the exact magnitude of the radiated noise but to obtain trends useful in developing noise abatement trajectories. Thus, a simple technique is used to relate the performance-state of the tiltrotor to its noise radiation characteristics.

Generic Tiltrotor

The vehicle used for the analysis is a generic tiltrotor referred herein as Maryland TiltRotor (MTR). This aircraft does not represent an extensive design effort, but rather a scalable vehicle useful in conducting parametric studies. The MTR is configured similarly to the XV-15 or V-22 (in fact, it can be considered a scaled-up XV-15 or a scaled-down V-22). The MTR is slightly larger than the XV-15 and has a capacity of 15 passengers. Just as the XV-15 and V-22, the MTR has two three-bladed rotors mounted on wing tip nacelles that rotate to achieve conversion from airplane to helicopter mode. The helicopter-mode disk loading of the MTR is approximately 14 psf. compared to 13 psf. for the XV-15. This leads to similar inflow characteristics between the two aircraft. The main features of the aircraft are shown in Figure 1 as compared to those of the XV-15 and V-22.

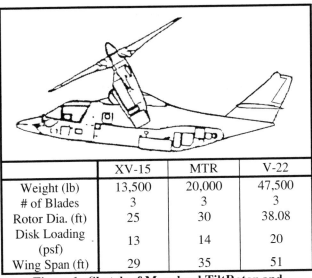

	XV-15	MTR	V-22
Weight (lb)	13,500	20,000	47,500
# of Blades	3	3	3
Rotor Dia. (ft)	25	30	38.08
Disk Loading (psf)	13	14	20
Wing Span (ft)	29	35	51

Figure 1. Sketch of Maryland TiltRotor and comparison with XV-15 and V-22.

Rotor Inflow Modeling

The inflow through each rotor is assumed to be uniform and is estimated using momentum theory. In addition, based on the assumption that the inflow changes are slow during slow maneuvering flight and can be modeled in a quasi-static manner, the transient inflow (unsteady aerodynamic) terms are neglected. Figure 2 graphically shows the components of the rotor inflow model.

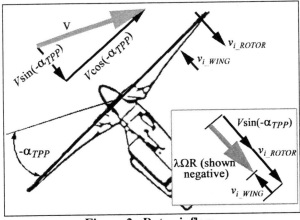

Figure 2. Rotor inflow.

For tiltrotors, the variation of the nacelle tilt is found to greatly alter the rotor's inflow. As shown in equation (1) below, the net inflow through the rotor disk is mainly governed by three factors: (a) the airspeed and rotor's tip-path-plane, (b) the rotor induced velocity, and (c) the induced effect due to the presence of the wing. As can be seen from Figure 2, the inflow is defined as (the convention used here is to denote the inflow as negative when the flow is downward through the rotor):

$$R = V \sin_{TPP} \quad v_{i\_ROTOR} + v_{i\_WING} \qquad (1)$$
$$(a) \qquad\qquad (b) \qquad (c)$$

Dividing the inflow by the rotor tip speed and using momentum theory to represent the rotor induced velocity, the non-dimensional expression for the inflow used in this paper is obtained:

$$= \frac{V \sin_{TPP}}{R} \quad \frac{C_T}{2\sqrt{\mu^2 + {}^2}} + {}_{i\_WING} \qquad (2)$$

It was previously shown in reference 15 that the induced inflow effect due to the presence of the wing ($_{i\_WING}$) does not alter the trends and only slightly changes the magnitude of the inflow results. Therefore, it is not included in this analysis. Examining equation (1) in more detail is a valuable exercise. In airplane mode ($_{TPP}$ -90°), the net total inflow is dominated by term (a) in the equation. The tip-path-plane and the airspeed are very large, causing the inflow to tend towards the value of the advance ratio. Such a large inflow leads to a large miss-distance; therefore BVI noise is not a concern in this regime. As the aircraft converts to helicopter mode, the airspeed reduces and the tip-path-plane angle becomes smaller, making term (b) of equation (1) more important.[15] As a result, the inflow curve for level un-accelerated flight becomes similar in shape to the typical momentum theory result of a conventional helicopter; a strong function of the tip-path-plane angle at low speeds.

Inflow and Miss-Distance as a Measure of BVI Noise

In order to obtain a measure of the likelihood of strong BVI, the concept of "miss-distance" is used. Miss-distance is defined as the perpendicular distance between a passing rotor blade and a shed vortex at the time of their interaction. Figure 3 shows the top and side views of the geometry of the blade-vortex interactions for a three-bladed rotor in forward flight at a given advance ratio. From the top view, it is seen that at the instant shown the blade at the 60° azimuth location has so far experienced two interactions on the advancing side, and is currently encountering a third interaction termed a "near-parallel" interaction. Parallel or near-parallel interactions, as opposed to highly "oblique" interactions, are known to cause high levels of BVI noise. As the rotor continues to rotate and move forward, other oblique and near-parallel interactions will occur, both on the advancing and retreating side (in the case shown, a blade will encounter a total of six interactions on the advancing side and three on the retreating side during one rotor revolution). The side view in Figure 3 graphically shows the concept of miss-distance. In the case sketched below, the miss-distance for the most parallel interaction is the smallest.

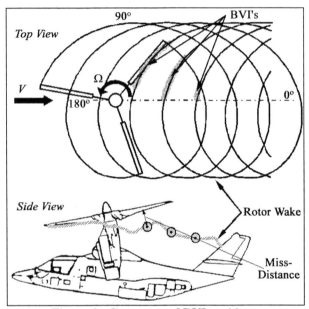

Figure 3. Geometry of BVI problem.

Obviously, the closer the vortex is to the blade, the stronger the aerodynamic disturbance on the blade and the louder the noise radiated to the far-field. In this paper, a "generalized" miss-distance is used, corresponding to the miss-distance associated with parallel or near-parallel interactions. This allows for a simpler analysis that relates miss-distance to the strongest possible BVI's (all BVI's are assumed to occur when the generalized miss-distance is small). The generalized miss-distance is from this point on referred to only as "miss-distance." In this trend-based analysis, a miss-distance of zero corresponds to the maximum radiated BVI noise, whereas an extremely large miss-distance would, in the limit, correspond to no BVI noise at all. Therefore, maximizing the miss-distance minimizes the likelihood of BVI noise. This is herein achieved by controlling the orientation of the rotor with respect to its shed wake system.

The miss-distance is governed by the inflow through the rotor ( ), a strong function of the aircraft's performance-state.

In order to relate inflow to BVI noise likelihood, a simple expression relating the perpendicular distance traveled by a vortex to the inflow after any given time is first obtained:

$$d = \quad _0 \quad R \, dt \qquad (3)$$

For constant rotor RPM, the wake age (azimuth) can be related to time as: $dt = d$. Also, since only uniform inflow is considered, the inflow is constant around the disk. This leads to the following expression:

$$\frac{d}{R} = \quad _0 \quad d \quad = \quad _0 \, d \qquad (4)$$

The previous equation can be written in terms of blade chords using the blade aspect ratio ($AR_{blade} = R/c$):

$$\frac{d}{c} = \quad (AR_{blade}) \quad _0 \, d \qquad (5)$$

To obtain inflow limits related to miss-distance limits, we now consider the strongest possible BVI, which is assumed to occur during a parallel interaction at a moderate advance ratio on the advancing side. For this particular aircraft and for the flight conditions studied in this paper, it was determined that the strongest possible BVI occurs at a wake age of approximately one rotor revolution. Therefore, equation (5) becomes (with $AR_{blade} = 9.8$):

$$\frac{d}{c} = 9.8 \quad _0 ^2 \, d \qquad d \quad 60 \quad c \qquad (6)$$

To gain an understanding of BVI noise level trends, values of miss-distance relating to the likelihood of strong BVI are defined. Since this is a trend-based analysis, the exact value of those limits is not of critical importance. For this analysis, the following values were used:

$d < 1.0c$ High likelihood of strong BVI
$1.0c \quad d < 2.0c$ Moderate likelihood of strong BVI
$d \quad 2.0c$ Low likelihood of strong BVI

Using equation (6), these limits can be directly related to inflow values:

		< 0.016	High likelihood of strong BVI
0.016		< 0.03	Moderate likelihood of strong BVI
		0.03	Low likelihood of strong BVI

Note that in the case of a tiltrotor, pushing the wake far above the rotor (positive inflow) is a valid way of increasing the miss-distance.[11] However, due to the tiltrotor's high disk loading, high sink rates are needed to achieve a positive inflow. These high sink rates can force the tiltrotor to unsafely operate outside the normal flight envelope for commercial operations. For this reason, this paper will focus on keeping the inflow below the rotor (negative inflow).

Simplified Quasi-Static Tiltrotor Performance Model

The general tiltrotor performance model is built by simultaneously solving the X and Z-force balance equations in a wind axis system as shown in Figure 4. The moment balance equation is also solved, but is decoupled from the force balance equation by verifying that the elevator power available is sufficient to trim-out moments and that there is sufficient rotor cyclic to maintain the tip-path-plane angle parallel to the rotor shaft. In addition, the change in Z-force balance due to elevator deflection is neglected because it is small compared to the total lift for slow maneuvering flight typical of commercial tiltrotor operations.

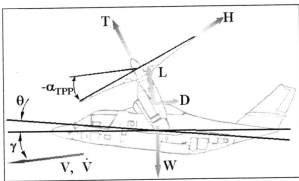

Figure 4. Set-up of the longitudinal force balance.

Examining Figure 4 gives the X and Z-force balance equations:

$$X \qquad T\sin(\ _{TPP}) = W\sin\ + D + m\dot{V} + H\cos(\ _{TPP}) \tag{7}$$

$$Z \qquad T\cos(\ _{TPP}) = W\cos\ \ L + mV \& \ H\sin(\ _{TPP}) \tag{8}$$

In the above equations it cannot be assumed that the rotor thrust equals the weight, and that the tip-path-plane angle is small because of the potential for large nacelle tilts and the presence of a lift-carrying wing. It should be noted that the drag term is very dependent on the aircraft's configuration (nacelle tilt and flap settings). In this analysis, the longitudinal flapping with respect to the shaft is assumed negligible by assuming that the pilot and/or the flight control system minimizes the longitudinal flapping throughout the flight. This assumption greatly simplifies the analysis by yielding a simple geometric relation between the nacelle tilt angle and the tip-path-plane angle:

$$i_N = \ _{TPP} + \frac{\ }{2} + \ \tag{9}$$

Because the transition from airplane mode to helicopter mode occurs relatively slowly, it is also assumed that the governing flow can be represented by quasi-steady aerodynamics. The wing lift is given by:

$$L_W = qS_W C_{L_w} \tag{10}$$

where C_{Lw} is the 3-D lift-curve slope, corrected for Mach number, the presence of the nacelles and the deflection of the flaps. The added lift due to the flaps is modeled as an increase in maximum lift coefficient and a decrease in zero-lift angle of attack. The lift of the horizontal tail is calculated similarly, but is corrected for the effect of the wing's downwash. Also, reference 15 showed that for the airspeed and nacelle tilt ranges considered (i.e., no hover or very slow forward flight), the rotor downwash does not impinge directly on the wing. Consequently, no changes in wing lift and drag due to rotor downwash are included.

The total drag of the vehicle is calculated using a combination of theoretical and empirical approaches. The expression for the total drag is:

$$D = q\ f_e + D_o + D_i + D_f \tag{11}$$

where f_e is the vehicle flat plate area (without the wing), D_o is the wing profile drag, D_i is the wing induced drag and D_f is the added drag due to the flaps. The flat plate area varies greatly with nacelle tilt and was approximated and scaled by interpolating power-off wind tunnel data of the XV-15.[16] The wing profile and induced drag are given by:

$$D_o = C_{Do}\ S_W\ q \tag{12}$$

$$D_i = \frac{C_{L_w}^{\ 2}}{AR\ e} S_W\ q \tag{13}$$

The drag increment due to the flaps is based mainly on empirical design data.

At this point, a few simplifying assumptions can also be made. First, because very slow speed flight ($V < 40$ knots) is not studied, the flight path angles considered are small. Thus, $\sin \gamma \approx \gamma$, $\cos \gamma \approx 1$. Second, the H-force term is small compared to lift and drag when resolved in the tip-path-plane during approach, so it is neglected ($H \approx 0$). Thirdly, $\dot{\gamma} \approx 0$. This last assumption is valid since only relatively small and gradual changes in flight path are considered.

The system of two equations given by the force balance (equations (7) and (8)) can be reduced to one equation by eliminating thrust, an unknown on the left-hand side of both the X and Z-force balance equations. This is accomplished by dividing the X-force equation by the Z-force equation, thus yielding a tangent function for the tip-path-plane angle.[17] Equation (9) is also used to introduce the nacelle tilt as a parameter in the equation:

$$\tan(\alpha_{TPP}) = \tan(\frac{\pi}{2} - i_N + \gamma) = \frac{W\gamma + D + m\dot{V}}{W - L} \tag{14}$$

Equation (14) is a nonlinear equation because of the squared airspeed within the lift and drag terms and is coupled since drag is dependent (mainly because of the nacelle drag) on the tip-path-plane angle. It is also a first-order differential equation in V because of the deceleration term ($\dot{V}$).

Solving equation (14) is equivalent to solving an under-determined system of one equation and six unknowns (V, $\dot{V}$, i_N, γ, θ and δ_f). As stated previously, the fuselage pitch and the flap deflection are both held fixed in the present paper, thereby reducing the system to one equation and four unknowns. In order to solve this system three control variables must be specified, leaving one unknown. Many different combinations of these controls can exactly solve equation (14). This characteristic of tiltrotors is referred to as "non-unique performance," or more commonly, "non-unique trim." Moreover, the parameters that allow the aircraft to achieve a non-unique trim are termed "non-unique controls." Due to the non-uniqueness of its performance-states, the tiltrotor has long been regarded as having great potential for noise reduction. Indeed, the various non-unique controls could be used to change from a "noisy" condition to a quieter one without a significant change in the flight trajectory. In order to avoid confusion, it must be pointed out that such "non-unique controls" are mathematical controls that dictate the behavior of the force and moment balance, and not piloting controls such as cyclic and collective.

Once equation (14) has been solved for the chosen unknown, the value of the total thrust required can be obtained by substituting back into either equation (7) or (8). Inflow, the parameter that controls the likelihood of BVI noise, can now be calculated since all values needed to solve equation (2) are determined by solving for the performance-state of the vehicle.

In reference 15, the effects of V, $\dot{V}$, γ, and δ_f on the nacelle tilt and inflow were parametrically studied. Note that since the deceleration was in this case one of the non-unique controls, the force balance reduced to an algebraic equation ($\dot{V}$ being simply a number that was specified). In order to study steady-state flight, the acceleration term in equation (14) was simply set to zero. Using this method, it was discovered that during a converting approach, a tiltrotor aircraft crosses a region where a combination of nacelle tilt and airspeed leads to severe BVI noise likelihood; a region of minimum inflow. Figure 5 shows a sample result of the quasi-static analysis for the case of a steady-state, $6°$ descent, converting from airplane mode ($i_N = 0°$) to helicopter mode ($i_N = 90°$). The resulting nacelle tilt schedule and inflow are shown on the same figure.

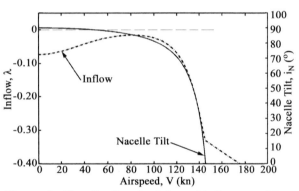

Figure 5. Nacelle tilt schedule and inflow resulting from steady-state analysis.

By observing the inflow curve, it is clear that the minimum inflow region (the inflow "hump") is restricted to a certain airspeed and nacelle tilt interval. This indicates that for a decelerating approach, the noise abating "mechanism" needs to be used only while the nacelle tilt is between certain values and not through the entire conversion corridor. Figure 5 shows that the region of minimum inflow is restricted to near helicopter mode flight (between $i_N = 75°$ and $i_N = 90°$). This fact is used to limit the present study cases from $60°$ to $90°$ nacelle tilt, which also corresponds to most test flights on the XV-15.[12-14] Other findings from this study showed that steep flight path angles and steep decelerations led to a more severe inflow condition while crossing the inflow "hump." Flap deflections and positive fuselage attitudes were found to be useful in delaying the conversion from airplane to helicopter mode, thus reducing the width of the minimum inflow region.

Because the scope of the analysis in reference 15 did not require time-dependent results, the airspeed and deceleration were specified independently of each other. However, because the goal of the present paper is to develop concrete and quantifiable approach trajectories, the use of a time-dependent analysis is important. In order to obtain time-dependent results, additional integral equations relating deceleration to airspeed and nacelle tilt-rate to nacelle tilt are introduced (the time-rate of change of the flight path angle is assumed negligible):

$$V(t) = \int \dot{V}(t) \ dt \qquad (15)$$

$$i_N(t) = \int di_N(t)/dt \ dt \qquad (16)$$

The nacelle tilt-rate is therefore a new unknown introduced in the system. The system is now comprised of three equations (14, 15, and 16) and five time-dependent unknowns ($V(t)$, $\dot{V}(t)$, $i_N(t)$, $di_N(t)/dt$, and $\gamma(t)$).

Nacelle Tilt-Rate and Flight Path Angle as Controls

In order to solve the above-mentioned system, two of the unknowns must be specified as control variables. To relate this research to an actual tiltrotor flight, the nacelle tilt-rate and flight path angle are chosen as controls. Equations (14-16) are simultaneously solved for the deceleration, airspeed, and nacelle tilt time-histories. Initial conditions are imposed on the deceleration, airspeed and nacelle tilt: $\dot{V}(0) = 0$, $V(0) = 110$ knots, and $i_N(0) = 60°$. Initial trimmed flight ($\dot{V}(0) = 0$) is achieved by adjusting the fuselage pitch angle and flap deflection to satisfy the force balance equation (in this case $\theta = 0.5°$ and $\delta_f = 40°$). The fuselage pitch angle and flap deflection are thereafter held constant. The nacelle tilt-rate is held at zero for ten seconds to start the simulation. After ten seconds in steady-state flight, the tilt-up of the nacelle is started at a constant 4.5 deg./sec. nacelle tilt-rate (the maximum tilt-rate of the XV-15 is 7.5 deg./sec.).[18] The nacelle tilt-up is stopped when the aircraft reaches helicopter mode ($i_N = 90°$). The flight path angle is held at -6° throughout the flight. A fourth-order Runge-Kutta scheme is used to numerically solve the system for $\dot{V}(t)$, $V(t)$, and $i_N(t)$. This case is considered the baseline approach against which other approaches will be compared.

Figure 6 shows the results of the baseline case. A considerably large maximum deceleration ($\dot{V} \approx -0.15$ g's) is obtained for this case due to the fairly high and constant nacelle tilt-rate. This flight profile and configuration also yield values of the net inflow that cross the zero-inflow line, indicating that the wake of the rotor could move through the rotor and cause high BVI noise. Clearly, both the deceleration and inflow reach values that are undesirable either in terms of passenger and crew comfort or BVI noise radiation levels.

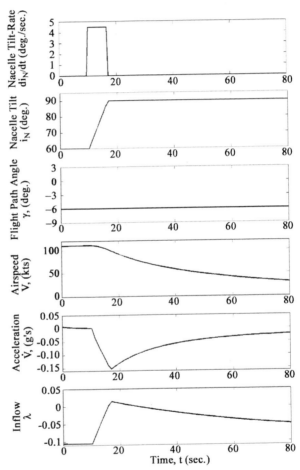

Figure 6. Results from the baseline approach.

Deceleration Constraint

Figure 6 has shown that a constant nacelle tilt-rate and flight path angle can lead to large decelerations. Therefore, a deceleration inequality constraint is imposed on the problem in order to maintain passenger and crew comfort level. An additional equation specifying the maximum deceleration is included in the system ($|\dot{V}| \leq \dot{V}_{max}$). If this constraint equation is violated, the maximum deceleration is enforced and the system becomes over-specified, i.e. a degree of freedom is lost. One of the specified variables (either the nacelle tilt-rate or flight path angle) must therefore be released to solve the system. The choice is here made to release the nacelle tilt-rate, since it intuitively has the strongest effect on the deceleration.[18]

Figure 7 shows the nacelle tilt-rate resulting from a constant 0.05 g's decelerating 6° descent (the 0.5 g's deceleration limit is considered acceptable for commercial flight operations). The figure shows that in order to maintain a constant deceleration, the nacelle tilt-rate cannot be held constant (linear nacelle tilt schedule). In fact, the nacelle tilt-rate must be progressively reduced as the airspeed reduces.

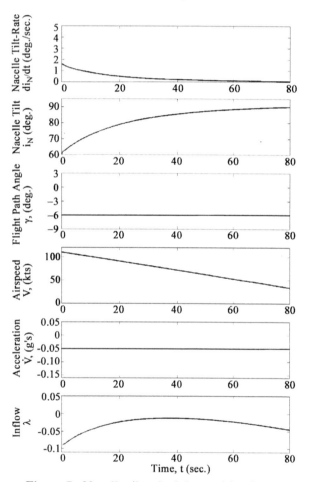

Figure 7. Nacelle tilt schedule resulting from a constant 0.05 g's deceleration.

The reduction in nacelle tilt-rate also has the beneficial effect of reducing the maximum value of the inflow. However, reducing the inflow below a certain threshold by using nacelle tilt-rate alone would yield very small values of the tilt-rate, and would lead to impractically long conversion times.

Inflow Constraint

In order to constrain the inflow an additional equation specifying the constraint is included in the system ($|\ |_{min}$). Once again, if this constraint equation is violated, the minimum inflow is enforced and the system becomes over-specified. Again, one of the specified variables must be released to solve the system. Since Figure 7 showed that nacelle tilt-rate is not a practical or effective choice to reduce the inflow, the flight path angle is released in order to satisfy the constraint. If both the deceleration and inflow constraints are violated, the system is comprised of six equations (four governing equations, that now include the inflow equation and two inequality constraint equations) and six unknowns ($V(t)$, $\dot{V}(t)$, $i_N(t)$, $di_N(t)/dt$, (t), and (t)).

The result of a constant 0.05 g's decelerating approach, with an inflow constraint corresponding to a moderate likelihood of strong BVI ($|\ |\ 0.02$), is shown below.

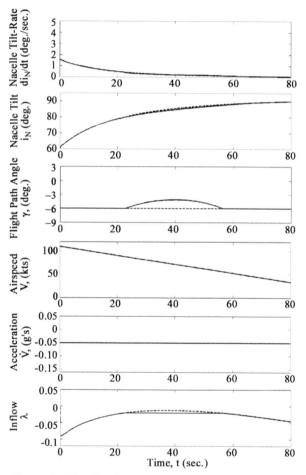

Figure 8. Nacelle tilt schedule and flight path angle schedule for $\dot{V}$ = -0.05 g's and ($|\ |\ 0.02$).

1482

As the figure indicates, achieving the constrained inflow requires flattening the flight path angle from a 6° descent to a 4° descent for a few seconds. The figure also shows that adding an inflow constraint has two effects: it barely changes the nacelle tilt schedule but appreciably changes the flight path angle (since the nacelle tilt-rate is small). In this case, because nacelle tilt-rates are almost zero, the only method of reducing inflow is through changes in flight path angle. These results suggest that for a constant deceleration approach with small nacelle tilt-rates, the flight path angle dominantly controls the inflow.

<u>Constrained Approaches Results</u>

This section presents results for approaches that are constrained by both inflow and deceleration. The baseline, unconstrained case shown in Figure 6 is also shown here in dashed lines along with the constrained results. The first constrained approach considers a deceleration constraint judged a limit for commercial operations ($|\dot{V}|$ 0.05 g's) and is shown in Figure 9.

As can be seen from the previous figure, the deceleration boundary is hit fairly early in the flight as the nacelle tilt reaches approximately 68°. To follow the deceleration constraint, the nacelle tilt-rate is reduced. The resulting constant deceleration also leads to a more favorable value of the inflow during certain segments of the flight. However, for this particular case reducing the nacelle tilt-rate is in itself not sufficient to keep the inflow from reaching undesirable values ($|\lambda|$ 0.16). As mentioned previously, achieving a stringent inflow constraint by only reducing tilt-rate would be impractical (even impossible) because it would require very small tilt-rates and lead to long conversion times. An additional drawback of the constrained approach shown in Figure 9 is that the most critical value of the inflow (the minimum inflow) now occurs at lower speeds. In a typical approach, this would occur closer to the surrounding communities.

The second constrained case has an inflow constraint ensuring a low likelihood of strong BVI, ($|\lambda|$ 0.03), while still maintaining an acceptable deceleration limit in terms of passenger comfort, ($|\dot{V}|$ 0.05 g's).

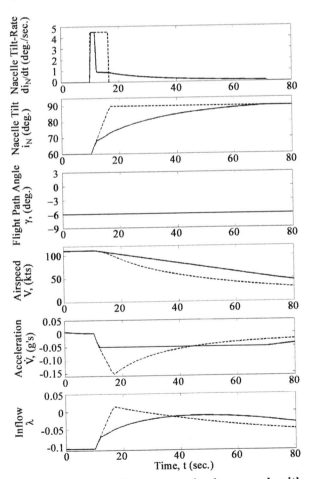

Figure 9. Results from constrained approach with $|\dot{V}|$ 0.05 g's.

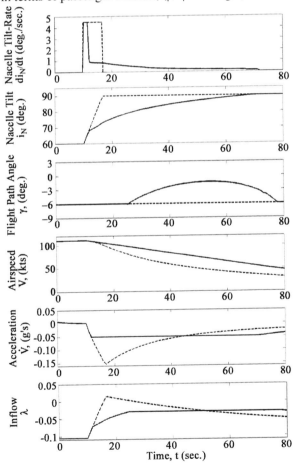

Figure 10. Results from constrained approach with $|\dot{V}|$ 0.05 g's and ($|\lambda|$ 0.03).

The case shown in Figure 10 uses a combination of tilt-rate and flight path changes to achieve constrained flight. In a real flight, this approach could be implemented as a combination of three or four progressively smaller tilt-rates and a segment of "flattened" flight path angle from a 6° descent to a 2° descent. This technique would be effective in reducing the likelihood of BVI noise radiation while maintaining acceptable comfort levels. One drawback of this approach is the long conversion time required by the deceleration constraint (60° to 90° in approximately sixty seconds).

The third case studies the effect of achieving a low likelihood of strong BVI, ($|\lambda| \geq 0.03$), while relaxing the deceleration constraint to $|\dot{V}| \leq 0.10$ g's in order to achieve a quicker conversion to helicopter mode. The resulting time-histories are presented in Figure 11.

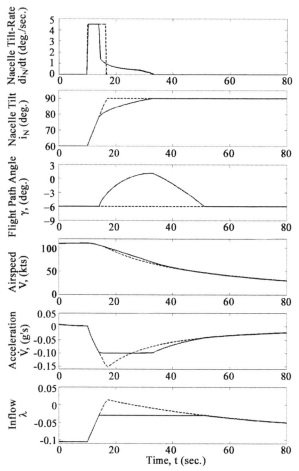

Figure 11. Results from constrained approach with $|\dot{V}| \leq 0.10$ g's and ($|\lambda| \geq 0.03$).

The previous figure shows that the relaxed deceleration constraint requires a fairly small change in tilt-rate. In fact, in an actual flight the required change in tilt-rate

could be approximately accomplished by a combination of two or three tilt-rates. However, the stringent inflow constraint requires a large change in flight path angle. As seen, the flight path angle must be increased from a 6° decent to an approximately 1.5° climb in order to stay on the inflow constraint. This might seem unusual but at second glance, it is intuitive. The climb angle has a strong influence on the rotor inflow at these nacelle tilt angles. The relationship between nacelle tilt and BVI noise has also been demonstrated experimentally.[12-14] It should be noted that the actual climb segment is quite short (3 sec.). What is important is that the 6° descent angle is being reduced to increase the absolute value of the inflow. This particular trajectory may also be limited by the potential for large time-rates of change of the flight path angle which were neglected in this analysis.

The next figure graphically depicts the trajectories produced by the three different constrained approaches previously presented. The figure illustrates the effects of flattening the descent angle (or even climbing in one of the cases). Although the three cases start their conversion at the same point, the different deceleration and flight path values result in different altitude and range covered in 80 seconds. Therefore, in order to arrive at the same landing point, the conversion for the three different approaches would have to be started at different altitudes and distances away from the landing point.

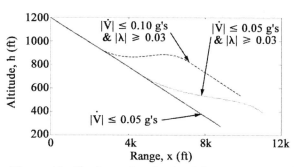

Figure 12. Trajectories obtained from the cases of Figures 9, 10 and 11.

These parametric studies have shown the importance of several flight path and vehicle control parameters on the reduction of BVI noise. However, they have also demonstrated the importance of knowing the relationship between BVI noise and the state of the rotor, especially the inflow through the rotor disk. This suggests that additional effort to quantitatively determine the causal relationship between BVI noise and the rotor state is needed before specific flight trajectories and controls that minimize BVI noise can be confidently counted on to reduce noise.

Conclusions

A quasi-static tiltrotor performance model had previously shown that flight path angle, fuselage pitch, flap angle and deceleration could all be used to control the net inflow through the rotor. In order to limit the scope of this research, fuselage pitch and flap deflection were both held constant. Flight path angle control and nacelle tilt-rate control were used to achieve constrained approaches that limit both the deceleration and the inflow. It was found that:

- A constant tilt-rate, constant flight path angle approach (unconstrained case) can yield undesirable values of deceleration and inflow that may exceed passenger and crew comfort limits, as well as create high levels of BVI noise radiation.

- In order to achieve a constant deceleration, the nacelle tilt-rate must be decreased as the airspeed decreases and the nacelle tilt increases. Also, a constant inflow can be obtained by increasing the flight path angle as the negative inflow becomes close to zero.

- Small deceleration values can be achieved by reducing the nacelle tilt-rate, but this leads to a long conversion time and moves the minimum inflow to slower airspeed (i.e. closer to surrounding communities during an approach).

- Large values of the inflow (keeping the inflow far below the rotor) can be achieved by flattening the flight path angle (and even climbing) during a segment of the approach.

- A typical constrained approach that does not appear to be very difficult to implement uses a combination of progressively smaller tilt-rates to limit deceleration and a short segment of flattened glideslope to limit the BVI noise level.

One of the most important conclusions of this study is that in order to reduce BVI noise likelihood, it is not necessary to apply flight trajectory management throughout the approach. Rather, the technique can be used only when needed, i.e. when the wake of the rotor becomes very close to the rotor itself. This leads to a better use of noise abatement strategies. For example, a shallow flight path angle is known to yield quieter approach.[12-14] However, flying shallower implies flying closer to the ground for a longer time, which is not a desirable feature when flying over a residential area. This research has shown that steeper descents can be flown quietly by controlling the flight path angle only when needed to avoid near-zero inflow conditions.

The additional controls of fuselage pitch angle (by means of cyclic and elevator control) and flap deflection were held constant throughout all approaches considered, but should also be coupled within the low noise approach strategy. This is subject to further research.

The research presented herein is a trend-based analysis based on a generic tiltrotor. Therefore, the actual implementation and selection of flight trajectories and aircraft configurations are case specific and need further study, experimentation, and refinement.

Acknowledgments

The authors appreciate and wish to acknowledge the fruitful discussions with Bryan Edwards of Bell Helicopter Textron, Dave Conner of the Army Aeroflightdynamics Directorate, NASA Langley and William Decker of NASA Ames.

References

1. Schmitz, F.H., Stepniewski, W.Z., Gibs, J., Hinterkeuser, E., "A Comparison of Optimal and Noise-Abatement Trajectories of a Tilt-Rotor Aircraft," NASA CR-2034, January 1972.

2. Brieger, John T., Maisel, Martin D., Gerdes, Ronald, "External Noise Evaluation of the XV-15 Tiltrotor Aircraft," American Helicopter Society National Specialists' Meeting on Aerodynamics and Aeroacoustics, Arlington, TX, February 25-27, 1987.

3. George, Albert R., Smith, Charles A., Maisel, Martin D., Brieger, John T., "Tilt Rotor Aircraft Aeroacoustics," American Helicopter Society 45th Annual Forum, Boston, MA, May 22-24, 1989.

4. Edwards, B. D., "XV-15 Tiltrotor Low Noise Characteristics," American Helicopter Society 46th Annual Forum, Washington, DC, May 21-23, 1990.

5. Schmitz, F.H.: Book chapter entitled "Rotor Noise" in Aeroacoustics of Flight Vehicles: Theory and Practice, edited by H. Hubbard, NASA RP 1258, 1991 & WRDC Technical Report 90-3052, August 1991 also re-published by the Acoustical Society of America, 1995.

6. Hawles, D. R., "Flight Operations to Minimize Noise," American Helicopter Society-AIAA-University of Texas at Arlington Joint Symposium on Environmental Effects of VTOL Designs, Arlington, Texas, November 16-18, 1970, and Vertiflite, February 1971.

7. Chen, R.T.F., Hindson, W.S., and Mueller, A.W., "Acoustic Flight Tests of Rotorcraft Noise-Abatement Approaches Using Local Differential GPS Guidance," presented at the American Helicopter Society Specialists Conference on Rotorcraft Aeromechanical Technologies, Fairfield County, Conn., Oct 11-13, 1995.

8. Lappos, N., Arnold, J., Erway, P., and McConkey, E.," The Development of a Decelerating Helicopter Instrument Landing system Using Differential GPS", American Helicopter Society 56th Annual National Forum, Virginia Beach, VA, May 2-4, 2000.

9. Janikaram, R. D. and Khan, H., "Prediction and Validation of Helicopter Descent Flyover Noise," American Helicopter Society 56th Annual Forum, Virginia Beach, VA, May 2-4, 2000.

10. Schmitz, F.H., Gopalan, G., and Sim, B.W., "Flight Path Management and Control Methodology to Reduce Helicopter Blade-Vortex Interaction (BVI) Noise," *Journal of Aircraft*, Vol. 39, No. 2, pp.193-205, March-April 2002.

11. Schmitz, F. H. "Reduction of Blade-Vortex Interaction (BVI) Noise through X-Force Control", *J. American Helicopter Society*, Vol. 43, Number 1, Jan. 1998.

12. Conner, D.A., Marcolini, M.A., Edwards, B.D., and Brieger, J.T., "XV-15 Tiltrotor Low Noise Terminal Area Operations," American Helicopter Society 53rd Annual Forum, Virginia Beach, VA, April 29-May 1, 1997.

13. Conner, D.A., Marcolini, M.A., Decker, W.A., Cline, J.H., Edwards, B.D., Nicks, C.O., and Klein, P.D., "XV-15 Tiltrotor Low Noise Approach Operations," American Helicopter Society 55th Annual Forum, Montreal, Quebec, Canada, May 25-27, 1999.

14. Conner, D.A., Edwards, B.D., Decker, W.A., Marcolini, M.A., and Klein, P.D., "NASA/Army/Bell XV-15 Tiltrotor Low Noise Terminal Area Operations Flight Research Program," AIAA/CEAS 6th Aeroacoustics Conference, Lahaina, Hawaii, June 2000.

15. Gervais, M. "Tiltrotor Blade-Vortex Interaction (BVI) Noise Control Through Non-Unique Longitudinal Force Trim," Presented at the Tiltrotor/Runway Independent Aircraft Technology and Applications Specialists' Meeting of the American Helicopter Society, Arlington, Texas, March 2001.

16. Weiberg, J.A., and Maisel, M.D., "Wind-Tunnel Tests of the XV-15 Tilt Rotor Aircraft," NASA TM-81177, April 1980.

17. Abelló, Juan C., George, Albert R., "Rotorcraft BVI Noise Reduction by Attitude Modification," Presented at the 5th AIAA/CEAS Aeroacoustics Conference and Exhibit, Bellevue, WA, May 10-12, 1999.

18. Lambert, Mark, "Flying the XV-15 and V-22 Tilt-Rotors," Interavia, Vol. 43, pp. 1282-1286, Dec. 1988.

AIAA 2002-2545

THE AEROACOUSTICS OF TRANSONIC HELICOPTER BLADES

A. S. Morgans *and A. P. Dowling [†]

Department of Engineering
University of Cambridge
Cambridge, CB2 1PZ
United Kingdom

ABSTRACT

One of the most important issues facing the helicopter industry today is helicopter noise, in particular transonic rotor noise. It is the main factor limiting cruise speeds, and there is real demand for efficient and reliable prediction methods which can be used in the rotor design process. This paper considers the Ffowcs Williams-Hawkings equation applied to a permeable control surface. The surface is chosen to be as small as possible, while enclosing both the blade and any transonic flow regions. This allows the problematic quadrupole term to always be neglected, and requires only near field CFD input data. It is therefore less computationally intensive than existing prediction methods, and moreover retains the physical interpretation of the sources in terms of thickness, loading and shock-associated noise. A computer program has been developed which implements the permeable surface form of retarded time formulation. The program has been validated and subsequently used to validate an acoustic 2-D CFD code. It is fast and reliable for subsonic motion, but it is demonstrated that it cannot be used at high subsonic or supersonic speeds. A second computer program implementing a more general formulation has also been developed and is presently being validated. This general formulation can be applied at high subsonic and supersonic speeds, except under one specific condition.

NOMENCLATURE

A $\quad = J|\nabla_{\boldsymbol{y}}f|/|\nabla_{\boldsymbol{\eta}}f|$

A_0 $\quad$ area of blade section, m^3

c $\quad$ speed of sound in undisturbed fluid, ms^{-1}

f $\quad f = 0$ defines location of S

g $\quad = t - \tau - r(\tau)/c$

J $\quad$ Jacobian of $\boldsymbol{y} \to \boldsymbol{\eta}$ coordinate change

L_i $\quad = p_{ij}n_j + \rho u_i(u_n - v_n)$

$\boldsymbol{M}$ $\quad$ Mach number

$\boldsymbol{n}$ $\quad$ unit vector normal to S

p $\quad$ absolute pressure, Pa

p_{ij} $\quad$ compressive stress tensor, Pa

Q $\quad$ monopole source strength, $kgm^{-3}s^{-2}$

$\boldsymbol{r}(\tau)$ $\quad = |\boldsymbol{x}(t) - \boldsymbol{y}(\tau)|$, radiation vector, m

$r(\tau)$ $\quad = |\boldsymbol{r}(\tau)|$, magnitude of r, m

S $\quad$ integration surface

t $\quad$ observer time, s

T_{ij} $\quad$ Lighthill stress tensor

$\boldsymbol{u}$ $\quad$ fluid velocity, ms^{-1}

U_i $\quad = (1 - \rho/\rho_0)v_i + \rho/\rho_0 u_i$

v $\quad$ velocity of S, ms^{-1}

$\boldsymbol{x}$ $\quad$ observer location, m

$\boldsymbol{y}$ $\quad$ source location, m

α $\quad$ angle of attack, degrees

η $\quad$ coordinates in which S is stationary

λ $\quad = c\tau$, m

λ $\quad$ the 4-D space given by $(\boldsymbol{\eta}, \lambda)$

ρ $\quad$ density, kgm^{-3}

θ $\quad$ angle between $\boldsymbol{r}$ and $\boldsymbol{v}$, radians

Θ $\quad$ angle between $\nabla(f)$ and $\nabla(g)$, radians

σ $\quad$ intersection of $g = 0$ and $f = 0$

τ $\quad$ source time, s

$\tau*$ $\quad$ retarded time $= t - r(\tau*)/c$

$()$ $\quad$ generalised variable

$()_0$ $\quad$ value in undisturbed fluid

$()'$ $\quad$ fluctuation about undisturbed level

$()_r$ $\quad$ component in radiation direction

$()_n$ $\quad$ component in surface normal direction

$\Box^2$ $\quad$ wave operator $= \nabla^2 - \frac{1}{c^2}\frac{\partial^2}{\partial t^2}$

INTRODUCTION

Helicopter noise is an increasingly important issue for helicopter designers. Factors such as community tolerance of noise levels, passenger comfort and acoustic detectability mean that quiet helicopters have a competitive advantage in both the civil and military helicopter markets. Shock associated rotor noise is generally the dominant source of noise at present cruise speeds, and will become increasingly so with higher cruise speeds planned for the future. There is consequently demand for a method of predicting shock associated rotor noise which is sufficiently accurate, fast and physically insightful to be useful as a design tool.

In the past, helicopter noise prediction has been

*Graduate Student, Department of Engineering

[†]Professor and Head of the Division of Energy, Fluid Mechanics and Turbomachinery, Department of Engineering

based on either the Kirchhoff method or the Ffowcs Williams - Hawkings equation. The Kirchhoff method involves integration over a control surface located in the linear flow regime, which is typically far from the blade for transonic flow.[1,2] It is capable of accurate noise prediction, but the computational times involved are restrictive as it requires a CFD solution which remains accurate and well-resolved as far out as the control surface.[3,4] It also does not offer any physical insight into the noise generation.

The Ffowcs Williams - Hawkings (FW-H) equation expresses the noise in terms of a distribution of monopole and dipole sources over a control surface, and a distribution of quadrupole sources over the volume outside of this surface.[1] When the control surface is chosen to coincide with the blade surface, the monopole distribution represents the noise due to blade thickness, the dipole distribution represents the noise due to blade loading and the quadrupole distribution represents the noise due to flow non-linearities and entropy variations. The noise from the quadrupole distribution is negligible except where the flow is transonic;[5] in these regions it may contribute significantly to the overall noise. To compute and integrate the quadrupole term is both difficult and computationally time consuming,[6] and is the main drawback of the impermeable surface form of the FW-H equation when applied to transonic blades.

To avoid calculation and integration of the quadrupole term in transonic problems, the FW-H equation can be applied to a permeable control surface which is not coincident with the blade surface. If the control surface is chosen to enclose all transonic flow regions, the flow outside it is always subsonic and the quadrupole distribution can be neglected. The permeable surface form of the FW-H equation has recently been used to predict transonic helicopter noise,[3,7] but in these cases the control surface was chosen to be a Kirchhoff-type surface which was far from the blade. This is far from optimal and consequently the advantages of the permeable form of the FW-H equation have not yet been fully exploited.

The permeable form of the FW-H equation is now applied to a control surface which is as small as possible while enclosing both the blade and any transonic flow regions. It is anticipated that this choice of control surface will allow the quadrupole term to be neglected. This is because even though the term is strictly negligible only at very low Mach numbers, it has been shown that significant quadrupole noise is in practice a transonic phenomenon.[5] The computational time associated with this choice of control surface will be small because the quadrupole noise does not need to be calculated and furthermore because accurate CFD data is required only close to the blade.

THE PERMEABLE SURFACE FORM OF THE FW-H EQUATION

The permeable surface form of the Ffowcs Williams-Hawkings equation follows from the fluid conservation laws in the same way as the more familiar impermeable surface form.[1]

A permeable control surface, S, is considered which is defined by the equation $f(x, t) = 0$. S encloses all solid boundaries and moves with velocity v.

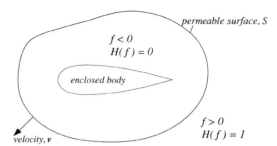

Fig. 1 Permeable control surface

Generalised flow variables (denoted by an overbar) which hold over infinite space are defined using generalised functions.[8–10] Outside the surface, S, the generalised variables are equal to the real flow variables, while inside the surface they have the value zero. Using these generalised variables, the continuity and momentum equations valid over all space can be written as,

$$\frac{\partial \overline{\rho'}}{\partial t} + \frac{\partial(\overline{\rho u_i})}{\partial x_i} = (\rho_0 u_n + \rho'(u_n - v_n))\delta(f)|\nabla_{\boldsymbol{x}} f| \quad (1)$$

$$\frac{\partial(\overline{\rho u_i})}{\partial t} + \frac{\partial}{\partial x_j}(\overline{p_{ij}} + \overline{\rho u_i u_j}) = \\ (p_{ij}n_j + \rho u_i(u_n - v_n))\delta(f)|\nabla_{\boldsymbol{x}} f| \quad (2)$$

Following the notation of di Francescantonio,[7] new variables, U_i and L_i are introduced to simplify the algebra. These can be thought of as a modified velocity and a modified stress tensor respectively. They account for the flow through S.

$$L_i = p_{ij}n_j + \rho u_i(u_n - v_n) \qquad (L_m = L_i M_i) \\ U_i = (1 - \rho/\rho_0)v_i + \rho/\rho_0 u_i \quad (3)$$

By subtracting the divergence of (2) from the time derivative of (1), an inhomogeneous wave equation is obtained.

$$\Box^2 p'(\boldsymbol{x}, t) = \frac{\partial^2 \overline{T_{ij}}}{\partial x_i \partial x_j} - \frac{\partial}{\partial x_i}\left(L_i \delta(f)|\nabla_{\boldsymbol{x}} f|\right) \\ + \frac{\partial}{\partial t}\left(\rho_0 U_n \delta(f)|\nabla_{\boldsymbol{x}} f|\right) \quad (4)$$

This is the differential form of the FW-H equation. $\overline{T_{ij}}$ is the generalised Lighthill stress tensor, which has value $T_{ij} = \rho u_i u_j + p_{ij} - c^2 \rho' \delta_{ij}$ outside of the surface S and is zero within it. The substitution $p' = c^2 \rho'$

has been made on the left side of the equation, requiring linearity and no entropy variation at the observer location.

The FW-H equation describes the generation and propagation of sound. On the right hand side, surface monopole, surface dipole and volume quadrupole distributions act as acoustic sources, while on the left the wave operator describes the propagation of sound from these sources to the observer location.

The equation is valid in all of three dimensional space, owing to the fact that generalised variables have been used. The integral form of the FW-H equation can therefore be obtained by convolving with the free space, 3-D Green's function for the wave equation, which has the well known form $\delta(t-|\boldsymbol{x}|/c)/(4\pi|\boldsymbol{x}|)$.[11]

$$
\begin{aligned}
p'(\boldsymbol{x},t) = {} & \frac{\partial^2}{\partial x_i \partial x_j} \int_{-\infty}^{+\infty} \frac{\overline{T_{ij}}\delta(g)}{4\pi r} \, d^3\boldsymbol{y}\, d\tau \\
& - \frac{\partial}{\partial x_i} \int_{-\infty}^{+\infty} \frac{L_i \delta(f)\delta(g)|\nabla_{\boldsymbol{y}} f|}{4\pi r} d^3\boldsymbol{y}\, d\tau \\
& + \frac{\partial}{\partial t} \int_{-\infty}^{+\infty} \frac{\rho_0 U_n \delta(f)\delta(g)|\nabla_{\boldsymbol{y}} f|}{4\pi r} d^3\boldsymbol{y}\, d\tau
\end{aligned}
\tag{5}
$$

where $r = |\boldsymbol{x} - \boldsymbol{y}(\tau)|$ and $g = t - \tau - r/c$

The first term in equation (5) can be neglected as $\overline{T_{ij}}$ is zero by definition inside the control surface, and is negligible outside it if the control surface has been chosen to be sufficiently large. A coordinate change from fixed coordinates, $\boldsymbol{y}$, to coordinates which move with the control surface, $\boldsymbol{\eta}$, allows the source strengths to be considered in a frame moving with the surface. The Jacobian for the coordinate change is J, and represents the ratio of volume elements in the $\boldsymbol{\eta}$ and $\boldsymbol{y}$ spaces.

$$
\begin{aligned}
p'(\boldsymbol{x},t) = {} & -\frac{\partial}{\partial x_i} \int_{-\infty}^{+\infty} \frac{L_i \delta(f)\delta(g)|\nabla_{\boldsymbol{y}} f|J}{4\pi r} d^3\boldsymbol{\eta}\, d\tau \\
& + \frac{\partial}{\partial t} \int_{-\infty}^{+\infty} \frac{\rho_0 U_n \delta(f)\delta(g)|\nabla_{\boldsymbol{y}} f|J}{4\pi r} d^3\boldsymbol{\eta}\, d\tau
\end{aligned}
\tag{6}
$$

Equation (6) is the most general integral form of the permeable FW-H equation. It is a four-dimensional integral (over three space dimensions and one time dimension) containing two one-dimensional delta functions. Integration will therefore ultimately be carried out over just two dimensions; the choice of these is determined by the formulation used.

THE PERMEABLE SURFACE FORM OF THE RETARDED TIME FORMULATION

The retarded time formulation is based on treating the space and time dimensions in (6) quite distinctly, using time to integrate one delta function and a single space dimension to integrate the other.

Since the surface, S, is fixed in η coordinates, the $\delta(f)$ term is unaffected by integration over τ. Integrating (6) over τ and using the fact that $|\partial g/\partial \tau| = |1 - M_r|$ gives,

$$
\begin{aligned}
p'(\boldsymbol{x},t) = {} & -\frac{\partial}{\partial x_i} \int_{-\infty}^{+\infty} \left[\frac{L_i \delta(f)|\nabla_{\boldsymbol{y}} f|J}{4\pi r|1 - M_r|} \right]_{\tau*} d^3\boldsymbol{\eta} \\
& + \frac{\partial}{\partial t} \int_{-\infty}^{+\infty} \left[\frac{\rho_0 U_n \delta(f)|\nabla_{\boldsymbol{y}} f|J}{4\pi r|1 - M_r|} \right]_{\tau*} d^3\boldsymbol{\eta}
\end{aligned}
\tag{7}
$$

Here r is the radiation direction, $r = |\boldsymbol{x} - \boldsymbol{y}(\tau)|$, M_r is the component of the Mach number in the radiation direction and $\tau*$ is the retarded time, given implicitly by the relationship,

$$
\tau* = t - \frac{r(\tau*)}{c} = t - \frac{|\boldsymbol{x}(t) - \boldsymbol{y}(\tau*)|}{c}
\tag{8}
$$

Sound emitted by the source at retarded time $\tau*$ will reach the observer at the time of interest, t. For a fixed observer position and time, $\tau*$ can only have one value if the source motion is subsonic, but can have many if the source motion is supersonic.

Integrating over one space dimension using the remaining delta function gives,

$$
\begin{aligned}
p'(\boldsymbol{x},t) = {} & -\frac{\partial}{\partial x_i} \int_S \left[\frac{L_i A}{4\pi r|1 - M_r|} \right]_{\tau*} dS(\boldsymbol{\eta}) \\
& + \frac{\partial}{\partial t} \int_S \left[\frac{\rho_0 U_n A}{4\pi r|1 - M_r|} \right]_{\tau*} dS(\boldsymbol{\eta})
\end{aligned}
\tag{9}
$$

where $A = J|\nabla_{\boldsymbol{y}} f|/|\nabla_{\boldsymbol{\eta}} f|$ and represents the ratio of area elements in the $\boldsymbol{\eta}$ and $\boldsymbol{y}$ spaces. If the surface is undistorted in motion then A is equal to unity.

Equation (9) is the permeable surface form of the retarded time formulation with the quadrupole term neglected. The time histories of the pressure, density and velocity are needed as input data.

When the integration surface is impermeable ($u_n = v_n$ so $L_i = p_{ij}n_j$ and $U_n = v_n$), only the time history of the blade pressure is required. A significant amount of past work has covered the impermeable surface form of the retarded time formulation. The computer codes developed as a result of this have proven to be robust, accurate and computationally relatively fast[4,12] when applied to subsonic rotor problems.

Computing the Retarded Time Formulation

By taking the derivatives inside the integrals in equation (9), numerical differentiation of the integrals can be avoided and the speed and accuracy of the computation is improved.[13]

The $\partial/\partial x_i$ can be replaced using (10). The integration surface, $S(\boldsymbol{\eta})$, is independent of t and so the time derivatives can be taken inside the integrals and replaced with $\partial/\partial\tau$ terms using (11).

$$
\frac{\partial}{\partial x_i} \int_S Q_i \, dS = \frac{\partial}{\partial t} \int_S \frac{Q_i r_i}{cr} \, dS + \int_S \frac{Q_i r_i}{r^2} \, dS
\tag{10}
$$

$$\frac{\partial [Q(\tau)]_{\tau*}}{\partial t} = \left[\frac{1}{(1-M_r)}\frac{\partial Q(\tau)}{\partial \tau}\right]_{\tau*} \quad (11)$$

Differentiating and gathering terms together gives,

$$p'(\boldsymbol{x},t) = \frac{1}{4\pi}\int_S \left[\frac{\rho_0(\dot{U}_n + U_{\dot{n}})}{r(1-Mr)^2}\right]_{\tau*} dS(\boldsymbol{\eta}) +$$

$$\frac{1}{4\pi}\int_S \left[\frac{\rho_0 U_n(r(\partial \boldsymbol{M}/\partial \tau)_r + c(M_r - |\boldsymbol{M}|^2))}{r^2(1-M_r)^3}\right]_{\tau*} dS(\boldsymbol{\eta})$$

$$+ \frac{1}{4\pi c}\int_S \left[\frac{\dot{L}_r}{r(1-Mr)^2}\right]_{\tau*} dS(\boldsymbol{\eta})$$

$$+ \frac{1}{4\pi}\int_S \left[\frac{L_r - L_m}{r^2(1-Mr)^2}\right]_{\tau*} dS(\boldsymbol{\eta}) +$$

$$\frac{1}{4\pi c}\int_S \left[\frac{L_r(r(\partial \boldsymbol{M}/\partial \tau)_r + c(M_r - |\boldsymbol{M}|^2))}{r^2(1-M_r)^3}\right]_{\tau*} dS(\boldsymbol{\eta})$$

$$(12)$$

Here it has been assumed that motion of the integration surface is subsonic so $|1 - M_r| = 1 - M_r$. It has also been assumed that the integration surface is undistorted in motion, so that $A = 1$ and $\partial A/\partial \tau = 0$. While it would, in theory, be possible to use an integration surface which distorted depending on the extent of the transonic region, this has not been considered here.

Equation (12) is the form of the impermeable retarded time formulation that has been used for numerical computation.

2-D CFD TEST CASES

Design of Test Cases

A computer program has been developed to numerically implement the permeable surface form of the retarded time formulation; the flow variables on the control surface are acquired from an unsteady CFD code ‡ .[14]

It is common practice to develop and validate CFD codes in two dimensions before progressing to three. It is therefore useful if the retarded time formulation program can utilise 2-D CFD data, allowing both the 2-D CFD code and the retarded time formulation program to be validated acoustically. The problem is that the integral form of the FW-H equation is based on use of the 3-D Green's function and thus applies specifically to 3-D problems and thus 3-D CFD data.

While it is possible to use the integral form of the FW-H equation based on the 2-D Green's function,[15] this is incompatible with using acoustic codes developed for use in 3-D, such as the retarded time formulation program. A better option is to consider a 2-D problem as an equivalent 3-D problem but with the length scale being infinite in the extra dimension. This in theory involves integration over an infinite length, but the length can be limited in practice by ensuring

‡developed by S. A. Karabasov and T. P. Hynes, Department of Engineering, University of Cambridge, UK

that the surface source terms are only non-zero beyond a certain time. Then, at any finite time, there is a maximum length from where sound arriving at any observer location originates. Surface sources with initial value zero can be achieved if the surface velocity starts from zero since the pressure, density and velocity fluctuations are zero when the surface is stationary.

To validate both the retarded time formulation program and the 2-D CFD code, an infinitely long blade of constant cross section moving with a velocity "pulse" which starts from zero is considered. The retarded time formulation is applied to several different control surfaces, all of which are close to the blade and enclose transonic flow regions. Each control surface is taken to have a constant cross section and be infinitely long.

Analytical Approximation

An analytical approximation to the noise from a subsonic, non-lifting blade can be used to ensure that the retarded time formulation prediction is of the correct order. This approximation assumes that the blade section is acoustically compact and that the observer is in the far acoustic field.

With the quadrupole term neglected and $u_n = v_n$, the differential form of the FW-H equation is,

$$\Box^2 p'(\boldsymbol{x},t) =$$
$$-\frac{\partial}{\partial x_i}\left(p_{ij}\delta(f)\frac{\partial f}{\partial x_j}\right) + \frac{\partial}{\partial t}\left(\rho_0 v_i\delta(f)\frac{\partial f}{\partial x_i}\right) \quad (13)$$

The body moves without distortion so $\partial v_i/\partial x_i = 0$. Also $\partial/\partial t = D/Dt - v_j\partial/\partial t$.

$$\Box^2 p'(\boldsymbol{x},t) = -\frac{\partial}{\partial x_i}\left(p_{ij}\delta(f)\frac{\partial f}{\partial x_j}\right) -$$
$$\rho_0\frac{\partial}{\partial x_i}\left((1-H)\frac{\partial v_i}{\partial t}\right) + \rho_0\frac{\partial^2}{\partial x_i \partial x_j}\left(v_i v_j(1-H)\right)$$
$$(14)$$

The integral form of this equation can be found by convolving with the Green's function in the normal way. Replacing the $\partial/\partial x_i$ in the second term, the retarded time formulation up as far as the integration over τ is,

$$p'(\boldsymbol{x},t) = -\frac{\partial}{\partial x_i}\int_{-\infty}^{+\infty}\left[\frac{p_{ij}n_j\delta(f)|\nabla_{\boldsymbol{y}}f|J}{4\pi r|1-M_r|}\right]_{\tau*}d^3(\boldsymbol{\eta})$$

$$+ \rho_0\frac{\partial}{\partial t}\int_{-\infty}^{+\infty}\left[\frac{(1-H)\frac{\partial v_i}{\partial \tau}r_i|\nabla_{\boldsymbol{y}}f|J}{4\pi cr^2|1-M_r|}\right]_{\tau*}d^3(\boldsymbol{\eta})$$

$$+ \rho_0\int_{-\infty}^{+\infty}\left[\frac{(1-H)\frac{\partial v_i}{\partial \tau}r_i|\nabla_{\boldsymbol{y}}f|J}{4\pi r^3|1-M_r|}\right]_{\tau*}d^3(\boldsymbol{\eta})$$

$$+ \rho_0\frac{\partial^2}{\partial x_i \partial x_j}\int_{-\infty}^{+\infty}\left[\frac{v_i v_j(1-H)|\nabla_{\boldsymbol{y}}f|J}{4\pi r|1-M_r|}\right]_{\tau*}d^3(\boldsymbol{\eta})$$

$$(15)$$

For a non-deforming blade, $J|\nabla_{\boldsymbol{y}}f| = 1$. The first term in (15) can be neglected for a non-lifting blade

1490

with a compact section, as the integral of $p_{ij}n_j$ will be very small. The last term is negligible for a compact blade section and far field observer as it is a quadrupole distribution over the volume occupied by the blade. Taking the second term time derivative inside the integral as before and considering the far field approximation leaves,

$$p'(\boldsymbol{x},t) = \frac{\rho_0}{4\pi c} \int_{-\infty}^{+\infty} \left[\frac{(1-H)r_i}{r^2(1-M_r)^2} \right. \tag{16}$$
$$\left. \left(\frac{\partial^2 v_i}{\partial \tau^2} + \frac{1}{1-M_r} \frac{\partial v_i}{\partial \tau} \left(\frac{\partial \boldsymbol{M}}{\partial \tau} \right)_r \right) \right]_{\tau*} d^3(\boldsymbol{\eta})$$

The $(1-H)$ means that volume integration is only performed over the volume enclosed by the blade. If the blade section is acoustically compact then there is no variation in $\tau*$ over this section, and the volume integral becomes a length integral multiplied by the section area. The final approximation is therefore,

$$p'(\boldsymbol{x},t) = \frac{\rho_0 A_0}{4\pi c} \int_{-\infty}^{+\infty} \left[\frac{r_i}{r^2(1-M_r)^2} \right. \tag{17}$$
$$\left. \left(\frac{\partial^2 v_i}{\partial \tau^2} + \frac{1}{1-M_r} \frac{\partial v_i}{\partial \tau} \left(\frac{\partial \boldsymbol{M}}{\partial \tau} \right)_r \right) \right]_{\tau*} dl$$

Results

For the subsonic non-lifting test case, the noise from a NACA0012 blade section moving with the velocity "pulse" described in (18) is considered. The blade has zero incidence.

$$\boldsymbol{v}(\tau) = \begin{cases} (0,0,0) & \text{if } \tau < 0 \\ (-100(1-\cos(34\tau)),0,0) & \text{if } 0 \le \tau \le \pi/17 \\ (0,0,0) & \text{if } \tau > \pi/17 \end{cases} \tag{18}$$

The pressure fluctuation at a variety of observer positions is calculated by applying the retarded time formulation program to the different integration surfaces shown in figure 2. The analytical approximation is also calculated to ensure that the noise predictions were of the order expected. The results are shown in figure 3.

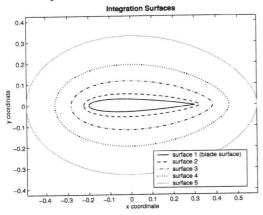

Fig. 2   Integration surfaces - subsonic cases

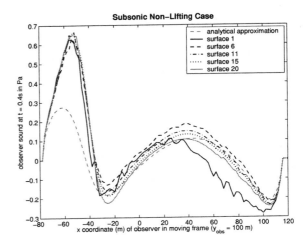

Fig. 3   Observer pressure predictions - subsonic non-lifting case

For the subsonic, lifting case, a NACA0012 blade section moving with same velocity profile but this time having varying pitch, $\alpha(t) = 3.66(1 + cos(34t))$, is considered. The integration surfaces shown in figure 2 are again used and the results shown in figure 4.

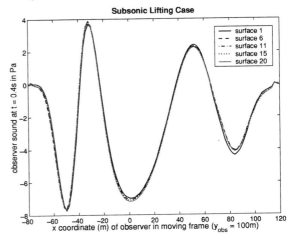

Fig. 4   Observer pressure predictions - subsonic lifting case

For the transonic lifting test case, the blade section moves with the velocity profile described in (19). The pitch is constant at 3.66 degrees. The maximum blade Mach number during this profile is $M = 0.8$ and so transonic effects are observed.

$$\boldsymbol{v}(\tau) = \begin{cases} (0,0,0) & \text{if } \tau < 0 \\ (-139(1-\cos(34\tau)),0,0) & \text{if } 0 \le \tau \le \pi/17 \\ (0,0,0) & \text{if } \tau > \pi/17 \end{cases} \tag{19}$$

So as to always enclose the shock, the integration surfaces are chosen to be further from the blade as shown in figure 5. Surfaces 4 and 5 represent optimum type surfaces - they are almost as small as possible while always enclosing both the blade and transonic flow regions. The blade surface is shown on this plot for comparison purposes only - it is not used as an integration surface. The results are shown in figure 6.

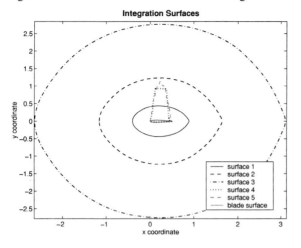

Fig. 5 Integration surfaces - transonic case

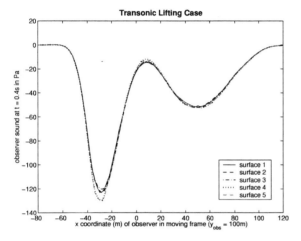

Fig. 6 Observer pressure predictions - transonic lifting case

Discussion

For the subsonic non-lifting test case, the predictions from all of the integration surfaces are very similar. They are of the same order and shape as the analytical approximation, particularly after the initial peak. The blade surface results are slightly noisier than those from the outer surfaces, probably due to a numerical boundary layer on the blade surface. This level of sensitivity is due to the very low noise levels. There is no shock associated noise and little loading noise as symmetric non-lifting blades have a symmetric pressure distribution and so loading noise arises only due to the variation of $p'n_x$ over the blade surface. Only thickness noise is significant.

For the subsonic lifting case, the noise predictions from the five integration surfaces are almost indistinguishable and are significantly larger than for the subsonic non-lifting blade. This is due to larger loading

noise levels - for lifting blades the pressure distributions on the upper and lower blade surfaces are very different.

The noise predictions from the surfaces in the transonic lifting test case are also in good agreement, with noise levels significantly higher again due to shock-associated noise. The shock weakly penetrates surface 1, but the noise predicted by this surface is still in fairly good agreement with other predictions, suggesting that the quadrupole noise associated with a weak shock is small. All other surfaces fully enclose the shock. The smaller optimum style surfaces, which are partly coincident with the blade itself, predict noise variations which are very similar to those from the outer surfaces.

These results validate the 2-D CFD code acoustically and also confirm that the retarded time formulation is being computed correctly. They verify that it is possible to capture shock associated noise with surfaces which are close to the blade but which enclose the shock.

DRAWBACK OF THE RETARDED TIME FORMULATION

In terms of predicting transonic rotor noise, the retarded time formulation has some serious limitations. These arise from the $\tau \rightarrow g$ coordinate change involved in integrating over the $\delta(g)$ in equation (6). This coordinate change involves division by $|\partial g / \partial \tau| = |1 - M_r|$, which becomes division by zero when $M_r = 1$. This clearly results in integrand singularities near the condition $M_r = 1$, and is unlikely to be the best choice close to it. The result is that the retarded time formulation cannot be used when the FW-H surface moves at supersonic speeds.

As well as being impossible to use at supersonic surface speeds, the retarded time formulation also becomes impractical to use at high subsonic Mach numbers. This is a significant drawback of the formulation, as high subsonic speeds are of particular importance to transonic problems. The reason this is that the variation of $\tau*$ across a given panel on the integration surface increases as the surface Mach number increases.[16] To maintain accuracy, the panel size must be reduced by increasing the number of grid points. This requires more computational time. Eventually, at a certain Mach number, the number of grid points required to obtain acceptable accuracy will result in impractical computational times and the retarded time formulation cannot be used.

Figure 7 shows how the error in the retarded time formulation prediction increases with Mach number. The observer sound due to the presence of a single translating monopole is plotted against the Mach number of the monopole. The sound due to a monopole has an analytical solution and so the error in the prediction from the retarded time formulation is straightforward to calculate. The error is plotted for fixed numbers of grid points on the integration surface. It can clearly be seen that error increases with Mach number for a fixed number of grid points, and that the error increases more slowly the larger the number of grid points.

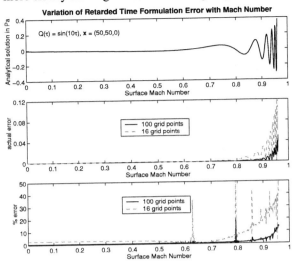

Fig. 7 The variation of error in the retarded time formulation with Mach number

THE GENERAL FORMULATION

Rather than performing coordinate changes to integrate the delta functions in (6), a more general formulation is obtained by using the idea that an integral containing two delta functions, $\delta(g)$ and $\delta(f)$, is equivalent to an integral over the subspace $g = 0, f = 0$.[1]

To obtain the general formulation from equation (6), the time dimension must firstly be transformed into an equivalent space dimension using $\lambda = c\tau$. This ensures that the dimensions of all the integration variables are the same, allowing the problem to be considered a four dimensional spatial integral over the $\boldsymbol{\lambda} = (\boldsymbol{\eta}, \lambda)$ space.

$$
p'(\boldsymbol{x}, t) = -\frac{\partial}{\partial x_i} \int_{-\infty}^{+\infty} \frac{L_i \delta(f)\delta(g)|\nabla_{\boldsymbol{y}} f| J}{4\pi rc} \, d^3\boldsymbol{\eta}\, d\lambda
$$
$$
+ \frac{\partial}{\partial t} \int_{-\infty}^{+\infty} \frac{\rho_0 U_n \delta(f)\delta(g)|\nabla_{\boldsymbol{y}} f| J}{4\pi rc} \, d^3\boldsymbol{\eta}\, d\lambda \qquad (20)
$$

Defining the σ subspace as the intersection of $g = 0$ and $f = 0$, integration over σ can be carried out to give,

$$
p'(\boldsymbol{x}, t) = -\frac{\partial}{\partial x_i} \int_{-\infty}^{+\infty} \frac{L_i |\nabla_{\boldsymbol{y}} f| J}{4\pi rc D} \, d\sigma
$$
$$
+ \frac{\partial}{\partial t} \int_{-\infty}^{+\infty} \frac{\rho_0 U_n |\nabla_{\boldsymbol{y}} f| J}{4\pi rc D} \, d\sigma \qquad (21)
$$
$$
\text{where} \quad D^2 = (\nabla g)^2 (\nabla f)^2 - (\nabla g \nabla f)^2
$$

The symbol ∇ is the gradient operator in the four-dimensional $\boldsymbol{\lambda}$ space. If the angle between ∇g and ∇f is Θ then D can be re-written as $D = |\nabla_{\boldsymbol{\lambda}} g||\nabla_{\boldsymbol{\lambda}} f| \sin\Theta$. Since f does not depend on λ, a further simplification can be made. If θ is the angle between the normal and radiation directions then D becomes,

$$
D = |\nabla_{\boldsymbol{\eta}} f| \left[\left(\frac{\partial g}{\partial \lambda} \right)^2 + \left(\frac{\partial g}{\partial \eta_i} \right)^2 \sin^2 \theta \right]^{\frac{1}{2}} \qquad (22)
$$

For an integration surface which is stationary in the blade fixed frame, it is straightforward to show that,

$$
\frac{\partial g}{\partial \lambda} = \frac{-1 + M_r}{c} \quad \text{and} \quad \frac{\partial g}{\partial \eta_i} = \frac{r_i}{rc} \qquad (23)
$$

Combining equations (21), (22) and (23) and substituting for the $\partial / \partial x_i$ term using (10), gives,

$$
p'(\boldsymbol{x}, t) = \frac{\partial}{\partial t} \int_{-\infty}^{+\infty} \frac{(L_r + \rho_0 c U_n)A}{4\pi rc\left((1-M_r)^2 + \sin^2\theta\right)^{\frac{1}{2}}} \, d\sigma
$$
$$
+ \int_{-\infty}^{+\infty} \frac{L_r A}{4\pi r^2 \left((1-M_r)^2 + \sin^2\theta\right)^{\frac{1}{2}}} \, d\sigma \qquad (24)
$$

Note that in the first term, it is not possible to take the time derivative inside the integral without generating the undesirable $1/(1 - M_r)$ term. For this reason, it is necessary to calculate this time derivative numerically.

This is the most general formulation of the FW-H equation. Although it may be conceptually difficult to envisage the $f = 0, g = 0$ surface in four dimensional space, the benefit is that any integrand singularities correspond exactly to singularities in the integrand of the full FW-H equation, rather than being the result of a poor choice of coordinate change.

Equation (23) shows that an integrand singularity in this general formulation occurs when $M_r = 1$ and $\sin\theta = 0$ simultaneously. This corresponds to the radiation and surface normal directions being parallel, and the Mach number component along the radiation direction being unity. At this condition, the wavelength of the emitted sound becomes zero since the observer frequency is equal to the source frequency divided by $1 - M_r$, and thus becomes infinite.

Computing the General Formulation

To compute equation (24), a method based on the "marching cubes" algorithm is used. This algorithm was originally developed within the field of computer graphics[17] and was first applied to acoustic integrals by Brentner.[16, 18] The method outlined here is essentially the same as Brentner's, but uses triangular rather than quadrangular surface panels. Geometric arguments are used to firstly locate the σ surface and then to perform the integration.

Identification of the σ surface within the four dimensional $\boldsymbol{\lambda} = (\boldsymbol{\eta}, \lambda)$ space is a difficult task. Physically, the surface represents those points which both lie on the FW-H surface and also emit sound which reaches the observer at the time of interest t.

Consider first the $f = 0$ subspace, representing the four-dimensional location of the FW-H surface. At a given value of λ, the equation $f = 0$ describes a surface which is perpendicular to the λ axis; the η coordinates of this surface are independent of λ.

If the surface is comprised of a grid of triangular panels then each panel is planar and can be described entirely using just two orthogonal coordinates, η_1 and η_2. These coordinates are both orthogonal to λ as well as each other, allowing the problem to be reduced to just three dimensions (an advantage unique to planar surface panels). The 3-D volume swept out by the planar $f = 0$ surface between times τ and $\tau + \Delta\tau$ can then be represented geometrically as shown.

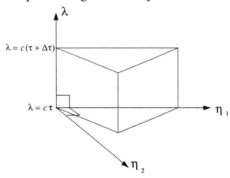

Fig. 8   The volume swept out by the $f = 0$ surface

The corresponding element of the surface σ is formed by the intersection of this volume and the $g = 0$ surface. The intersection can have several possible patterns or topologies, and it is necessary to know which is being dealt with before numerical integration can be carried out.

The topology is best identified methodically. Each volume has six vertices at which the values of both g and the integrands in equation (24) are known from CFD data. It is helpful to consider each vertex as having one of two possible states relative to the surface $g = 0$, these being $g < 0$ or $g \geq 0$. If the state of adjacent vertices differs then the surface $g = 0$ must intersect the edge between them.

A volume with six vertices, each having two possible states relative to a surface, can be intersected by the surface in $2^6 = 64$ possible ways. These 64 ways do not correspond to 64 topologies since the volume exhibits both complementary and rotational symmetries. Complementary cases, in which the $g < 0$ and $g \geq 0$ vertices are interchanged, have identical topologies. This means that to identify all topologies, only those cases in which zero to three vertices have the state $g < 0$ need to be considered, thus halving the number of cases to 32. By inspection, rotational symmetry further reduces this number to eight. These correspond to the eight possible topologies and are shown in figure 9.

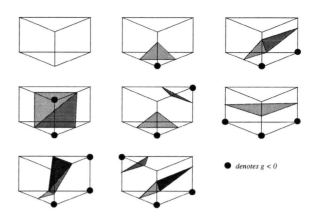

Fig. 9   The intersection surface topologies

Once the intersection topology for a given volume is known, approximation of the σ surface can be carried out. It is known that the $g = 0$ surface intersects those edges which have vertices of differing states at either end. The locations of the $g = 0$ edge intersections are approximated using linear interpolation, and are connected by a set of triangular surfaces. These surfaces approximate the surface σ for the volume, and it can be seen in figure 9 that up to three may be required.

Numerical integration is the final step in the process, and involves summing the products of area and central integrand value for each triangle. The integrand values at the triangle centres are found using linear interpolation between the vertex values, which are known from CFD data.

This process of volume generation, topology identification, σ surface approximation and numerical integration must be carried out for all possible times and all surface sections. Unless some information is provided which limits the range of times needing to be considered, this is a much more time intensive process than computation of the retarded time formulation.

Initial Validation

To initially validate the basic program implementing the general formulation, monopole test cases with analytical solutions are used. The observer pressures calculated at a variety of observer times using the general formulation are shown in figure 10. The monopole motion is subsonic and a spherical integration surface has been used. The analytical and calculated pressures agree, confirming that the formulation is being computed correctly. On close inspection, the errors from the general formulation are seen to be slightly larger than those from the retarded time formulation for the same number of grid points. This is probably due primarily to the errors incurred in evaluating the time derivative numerically, but could also be because computation of the general formulation is more complicated and thus results in more accumulation of rounding errors.

The above test case validates the general formulation program for subsonic motion, but also suggests

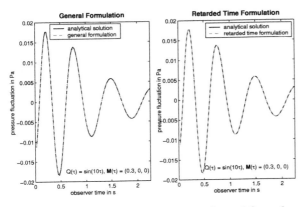

Fig. 10 Comparison of analytical results and formulation predictions

that the retarded time formulation is in general preferable at subsonic speeds as it is faster and more accurate to compute.

It should also be possible to validate the general formulation for high subsonic and supersonic speeds, the conditions under which it is likely to be used. This is likely to require a more complicated test case than one in which the monopole and integration surface have the same motion, as the analytical monopole solution itself suffers from the Doppler singularity, thus making the flow variables on the integration surface difficult or even impossible to compute when the monopole moves at high subsonic or supersonic speeds. Work on this validation is currently in progress.

CONCLUSIONS

By using the permeable surface form of the Ffowcs Williams-Hawkings equation, it should be possible to develop a transonic noise prediction method which offers a better compromise between speed and design guidance than existing prediction methods. This will be achieved by locating the control surface as close to the blade as possible while enclosing all transonic regions of flow. It has been shown that this allows the problematic quadrupole term to always be neglected, while retaining physical insight into the source mechanisms.

A computer program has been developed which implements the retarded time formulation of the FW-H equation in its less familiar permeable surface form. This program has been validated, and in turn used to acoustically validate a 2-D CFD code. For subsonic motion, the program computations are fast, reliable and conceptually easy to understand. However, the drawback is that use of the retarded time formulation becomes impossible at supersonic speeds and impractical at high subsonic speeds, cases of particular importance to transonic noise. The reasons for these limitations are understood.

A more general formulation of the FW-H equation has been considered, which should be practical to use at high subsonic and supersonic speeds except under one specific condition. A previously developed means of computing such integrals, based primarily on geometric arguments, has been adapted for computation of this formulation. A computer program has been written to perform this computation, and has been validated for subsonic speeds. Validation for transonic and supersonic speeds is ongoing.

It is anticipated that the advantages of the two formulations can be combined by applying them on different parts of the integration surface. Where M_r is sufficiently subsonic, the retarded time formulation will be used and where M_r is close to or beyond sonic, the general formulation will be applied.

ACKNOWLEDGEMENTS

The authors are grateful to Dr T. P. Hynes and Dr S. A. Karabasov[14] for making their CFD results readily available. The financial support of the Engineering and Physical Sciences Research Council (EPSRC), Westland Helicopters Ltd and Thales Underwater Systems Ltd is gratefully acknowledged.

REFERENCES

[1] Williams, J. E. F. and Hawkings, D. L., "Sound Generation by Turbulence and Surfaces in Arbitrary Motion," *Philosophical Transactions of the Royal Society*, Vol. A264, 1969, pp. 321–342.

[2] Lyrintzis, A. and Xue, Y., "Versatile Kirchhoff Code for Aeroacoustic Predictions," *AIAA Journal*, Vol. 35, No. 1, 1997.

[3] Brentner, K. S. and Farassat, F., "Analytical Comparison of the Acoustic Analogy and Kirchhoff Formulation for Moving Surfaces," *AIAA Journal*, Vol. 36, No. 8, 1998, pp. 1379–1386.

[4] Brentner, K. S., Lyrintzis, A. S., and Koutsavdis, E. K., "Comparison of Computational Aeroacoustic Prediction Methods for Transonic Rotor Noise," *Journal of Aircraft*, Vol. 34, No. 4, 1997, pp. 531–538.

[5] Hanson, D. B. and Fink, M. R., "The Importance of Quadrupole Sources in Prediction of Transonic Tip Speed Propeller Noise," *Journal of Sound and Vibration*, Vol. 62, No. 1, 1979, pp. 19–38.

[6] Brentner, K. S., "An Efficient and Robust Method for Predicting Helicopter High-Speed Impulsive Noise," *Journal of Sound and Vibration*, Vol. 203, No. 1, 1997, pp. 87–100.

[7] di Francescantonio, P., "A New Boundary Integral Formulation for the Prediction of Sound Radiation," *Journal of Sound and Vibration*, Vol. 202, No. 4, 1997, pp. 491–509.

[8] Gel'fand, I. M. and Shilov, G. E., *Generalized Functions Volume 1: Properties and Operations*, Academic Press: London, 1964.

[9] Farassat, F., "Introduction to Generalized Functions With Applications in Aerodynamics and Aeroacoustics," Tech. Rep. TP-3428, NASA, 1994.

[10] Farassat, F., "Discontinuities in Aerodynamics and Aeroacoustics: The Concept and Applications of Generalized Derivatives," *Journal of Sound and Vibration*, Vol. 55, 1977, pp. 165–193.

[11] Crighton, D. G., Dowling, A. P., Williams, J. E. F., Heckl, M., and Leppington, F. G., *Modern Methods in Analytical Acoustics*, Springer-Verlag, 1992.

[12] Brentner, K. S., "Prediction of Helicopter Rotor Discrete Frequency Noise - A Computer Program Incorporating Realistic Blade Motions and Advanced Acoustic Formulation," Tech. Rep. TM 87721, NASA, 1986.

[13] Farassat, F. and Succi, G. P., "The Prediction of Helicopter Rotor Discrete Frequency Noise," *Vertica*, Vol. 7, No. 4, 1983, pp. 309–320.

[14] Karabasov, S. A. and Hynes, T. P., "Open Boundary Conditions of Predictor - Corrector Type for External Flows," *8th AIAA/CEAS Aeroacoustics Conference*, No. 2002-2442, Breckenridge, CO, USA, June 2002.

[15]Lockard, D. P., "An Efficient, Two-Dimensional Implementation of the Ffowcs Williams and Hawkings Equation," *Journal of Sound and Vibration*, Vol. 229, No. 4, 2000, pp. 897–911.

[16]Brentner, K. S., "Numerical Algorithms for Acoustic Integrals with Examples for Rotor Noise Prediction," *AIAA Journal*, Vol. 35, No. 4, 1997, pp. 625–630.

[17]Lorenson, W. E. and Harvey, H. E., "Marching Cubes: A High Resolution 3D Surface Construction Algorithm," *Computer Graphics*, Vol. 21, No. 4, July 1987.

[18]Brentner, K. S., "A New Algorithm for Computing Acoustic Integrals," *Fourteenth IMACS World Congress*, Atlanta, GA, July 1994.

FLOW-INDUCED NOISE AROUND THE A-PILLAR OF AN IDEALIZED CAR GREENHOUSE

M. Snellen[*]
L. van Lier[†]
C. Rops[‡]
M.H.A. Janssens[§]
J. van Heck[¶]
G.S. Strumolo[#]

Due to the successes in reducing motor and tire noise as perceived inside cars and trucks, aerodynamically generated noise becomes more and more important. Some time ago the study of aero-acoustics in and around these vehicles was mainly done by wind tunnel test. Nowadays, computational methods become available that allow for numerical simulations of the aerodynamically generated noise. At TNO, a new computational aero-acoustics approach has been developed. This method provides a relatively fast assessment of the aerodynamically generated broadband noise and wall pressure fluctuations. At the same time it is capable of handling complex geometries. The method consists of three steps: 1) time-averaged RANS calculations, 2) unsteady acoustic source generation based on the RANS data, and 3) calculation of the propagation of the pressure fluctuations using the linearized Euler equations on an unstructured mesh. This paper gives an application example of the method and a comparison with results obtained from wind tunnel tests. The case at hand is an idealized shape of a car greenhouse; a rectangular block with a wedged front, representing the windscreen. Simulations have been carried out for two wind speeds: 55 and 70 mph. The calculation results are presented and discussed. Also a comparison with measurements is presented: good agreement between measurement and calculations is found.

1. INTRODUCTION

Various aspects determine the comfort inside a truck or a car cabin. One of these is the interior noise that is experienced by the driver. Due to continuous research efforts with respect to engine noise and road/tire noise, significant reductions are gained in that field. As a result, the aerodynamic noise ('wind noise') has become more important, and hence requires attention in order to achieve a further noise reduction.

The aerodynamic noise around vehicles is generated by turbulent airflow. This turbulent airflow causes local pressure fluctuations in the air adjacent to the vehicle. Part of these local pressure fluctuations results in a propagating pressure fluctuation: sound. This sound propagates into the external environment of the vehicle. Further, the local pressure fluctuations that act on a structural object, such as the windscreen, will cause that object to vibrate and to radiate sound inside the vehicle cabin.

The properties of turbulence, and hence the sound, strongly depend on the shape of the objects that are present in the flow. Some time ago the study of aero-acoustics in and around vehicles was mainly done by wind tunnel tests. Nowadays, computational methods become available that allow for numerical simulations. Nevertheless, computing the aerodynamic noise on the basis of data 'from the drawing board' is not common practice yet. Being able to support design decisions based on such computations has a strong cost-reduction potential for the vehicle design process.

At TNO TPD a state-of-the-art tool is developed for performing Computational Aero-Acoustics (CAA) calculations, see Ref 1. In terms of CPU time and applicability to complex geometries, the

---

[*] Research Scientist, Division of Sound and Vibration, TNO TPD, P.O.Box 155, 2600 AD, Delft, The Netherlands, Phone: +31 15 269 29 29, Fax +31 15 269 21 11, e-mail: snellen@tpd.tno.nl.

[†] Research Scientist, Division of Sound and Vibration, TNO TPD, P.O.Box 155, 2600 AD, Delft, The Netherlands, Phone: +31 15 269 20 66, Fax +31 15 269 21 11, e-mail: vlier@tpd.tno.nl.

[‡] Research Scientist, Division of Materials and Processes, TNO TPD, P.O.Box 155, 2600 AD, Delft, The Netherlands, Phone: +31 15 269 21 03, Fax +31 15 269 21 11, e-mail: rops@tpd.tno.nl.

[§] Research scientist, Division Sound and Vibration, TNO TPD, P.O.Box 155, 2600 AD, Delft, The Netherlands, Phone: +31 15 269 24 19, Fax +31 15 269 21 11, e-mail: janssens@tpd.tno.nl.

[¶] PhD, Research Engineer, Noise and Vibration, DAF Trucks NV, P.O.Box 90065, Eindhoven The Netherlands, Phone + 31 40 214 26 41, Fax +31 40 214 43 85, e-mail: jos.van.heck@daftrucks.com

[#] Senior Staff Technical Specialist, Group Leader Accident Avoidance, Safety Research & Development, Ford Motor Co, Dearborn, MI, USA.

method is positioned in between full, time-accurate simulations (Direct Numerical Simulations and Large Eddy Simulations) on the one hand and methods based on Green's functions on the other hand. Some background of the method will be presented in Section 2.

The study presented here aims to illustrate the application of this method and to compare its results with actual wind tunnel data. To this end simulations have been carried out to estimate the surface pressure fluctuations on a wedge-shaped block, being a highly schematized representation of a truck cabin or a car green house. The geometry is described in more detail in Section 3.

In Section 4 the results of the simulations are presented and a comparison with the measurements is made. Section 5 presents the conclusions.

The study was performed by TNO TPD in co-operation with DAF Trucks NV and Ford Motor Co, the latter providing the experimental results from wind tunnel tests and results obtained from an alternative (vortex lattice based) method.

2. APPROACH FOR CAA

This section briefly describes the approach used for predicting the noise generated by a turbulent flow. The assumption made for the current approach is that the turbulence is not influenced by the acoustics, i.e. there is no feedback, and therefore the turbulence is regarded as an autonomous source of sound, only fed by the mean flow. Several steps can be discerned within the calculation, see Figure 1.

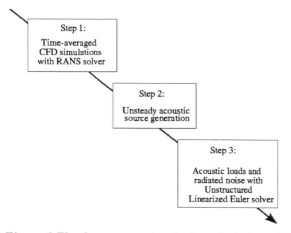

Figure 1 *The three steps taken in the calculation of the acoustic loads.*

The first step consists of a CFD calculation: for the results presented here a so-called Reynolds Averaged Navier-Stokes (RANS) calculation is performed. This RANS computation provides the time-averaged properties of the flow.

As a second step, the time-accurate acoustic sources for the Linearized Euler equations are calculated using the time-averaged properties of the flow, resulting from the RANS calculation. The source terms are computed from a reconstruction of the time-dependent turbulent flow. This is achieved by regarding the turbulence as a pseudo-stochastic phenomenon with many different length scales and time scales. The turbulent velocity fluctuations can be written as an infinite sum of sinusoidal components:

$$\mathbf{u}(\mathbf{x},t) = \int_{\mathbf{k},\omega} \hat{\mathbf{u}}(\mathbf{k},\omega)\exp(i\,\mathbf{k}\cdot\mathbf{x}+i\omega t)d\mathbf{k}d\omega \qquad (1)$$

with $\mathbf{u}(\mathbf{x},t)$ the turbulent velocity distribution, and $\hat{\mathbf{u}}(\mathbf{k},\omega)$ its Fourier transform as a function of the wavevector $\mathbf{k}$ and the angular frequency ω. Following a similar method as in Ref. 2 in our stochastic turbulence model, the integral is then replaced by a finite sum of modes, each with its own wave vector $\mathbf{k}_n$, its own angular frequency ω_n, and its own velocity amplitude and direction, $2\hat{u}_n$ and $\mathbf{i}_n$, respectively:

$$\mathbf{u}(\mathbf{x},t) = \sum_n 2\hat{u}_n\mathbf{i}_n\cos(i\mathbf{k}_n\cdot\mathbf{x}+i\omega_n t)d\mathbf{k}d\omega \qquad (2)$$

It is assumed that the turbulent velocity distribution is locally homogeneous, meaning that the variation of the turbulent kinetic energy k and of the turbulent integral length scale Λ is small across distances of the order of Λ. A Von Karman spectrum can thus be assumed for the turbulent velocity spectrum. For the frequency dependence of the spectrum, a moving axis spectrum is employed in a similar way as in Ref. 3.

As a third step, the radiation of the acoustic sources is determined by solving the linearized Euler equations (LEE):

$$\mathbf{L}(\mathbf{U}) = \frac{\partial}{\partial t}\mathbf{U} + \frac{\partial}{\partial x_j}\mathbf{F}_j(\mathbf{U}) = \mathbf{S} \qquad (3)$$

describing the perturbation $\mathbf{U}$ with respect to the mean flow $\mathbf{U}_0$, where

$$\mathbf{F}_j(\mathbf{U}) = \mathbf{A}_j(\mathbf{U}_0)\mathbf{U} \qquad (4)$$

with initial and boundary conditions. Here $\mathbf{S}(\mathbf{x},t)$ is the source for the LEE, computed from the turbulent field in step 2, $\mathbf{U} = (\rho',u_1',u_2',u_3',p')^{\mathrm{T}}$, the aero-acoustic density, velocity, and pressure perturbations, respectively. The matrices $\mathbf{A}_j$ are defined as:

$$A_j = \begin{bmatrix} u_{0_j} & \delta_{j1}\rho_0 & \delta_{j2}\rho_0 & \delta_{j3}\rho_0 & 0 \\ 0 & u_{0_j} & 0 & 0 & \delta_{1j}\rho_0^{-1} \\ 0 & 0 & u_{0_j} & 0 & \delta_{2j}\rho_0^{-1} \\ 0 & 0 & 0 & u_{0_j} & \delta_{3j}\rho_0^{-1} \\ 0 & \delta_{j1}\gamma p_0 & \delta_{j2}\gamma p_0 & \delta_{j3}\gamma p_0 & u_{0_j} \end{bmatrix} \quad (5)$$

The LEE are applicable since the propagation of sound is hardly influenced by turbulent and viscous effects. The Euler equations are solved on an unstructured tetrahedronal grid, which allows for complex geometries to be handled. The numerical method for solving the equations is based on a quadrature-free implementation of the Discontinuous Galerkin finite-element method. Further details on the LEE solver can be found in Ref.1.

As mentioned above, the approach is capable of handling complex geometries, and is therefore a very useful method for automotive and aerospace applications. One of the advantages of this three-step approach is that the computational domain can be chosen and optimized in each step. So that for each step the domain can be limited to the relevant area of interest. This results in quite different domains, and in fact to a significant reduction in domain size, and hence computer resources demands, for steps 2 and 3 relative to step 1. This is illustrated in Figure 2 for the object described in the next section.

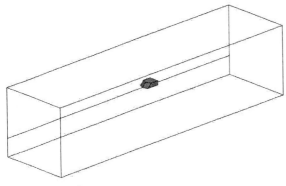

1) RANS domain

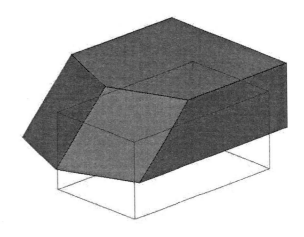

2) Source domain

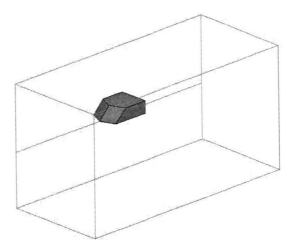

3) Propagation domain

Figure 2 *Illustration of tailoring the domain size of each computational step.*

3. TEST CASE CONFIGURATION

The case considered here is a basic shaped wedge-block, see Figure 3, and the goal is to determine the surface pressure levels resulting from the external flow around the object. This block can be seen as a highly schematic form of a car green house. The dimensions of the block are given in feet and inches. Ford performed wind tunnel experiments for this block. Two conditions are considered here both with frontal airflow onto the block, with flow speeds of 55 mph and 70 mph, respectively.

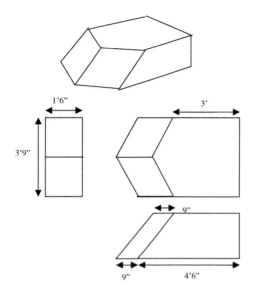

Figure 3 Wedge-block geometry (drawing not to scale; dimensions in feet (') and inches (")). The block is suspended in air 2'2" above a solid horizontal plane. The block has smooth surfaces and sharp edges.

From the wind tunnel experiment results are available in the form of measured surface pressure levels at various positions, see Figure 4. Data is available for two positions at the 'windscreen' (C3 and C5), for two positions adjacent to the A-pillar (D5 and D3), and three positions further downstream at the 'side window' (G3, G5 and I5). The results are available on a narrowband scale with a frequency resolution of 16 Hz in the range 0 to 8000 Hz.

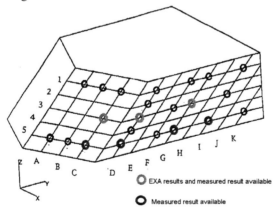

Figure 4 Measurement positions are located on a regular grid as shown. Circles indicate positions at which measured data is available.

Besides the experimental data, computational results are available for positions C3, G5 and I5. These results are generated by Ford USA using an alternative method based on vortex lattice, denoted by alternative method in the remaining of this paper. This enables a further comparison of the CAA approach presented here with an alternative approach.

For all TNO TPD calculations a symmetry plane has been assumed, and only half of the object has been considered. To test the influence of the boundary conditions on the acoustics, the symmetry plane has been modelled both as a reflecting and as a non-reflecting plane. The results were found to be very similar for the two boundary conditions. Use was made of the non-reflecting boundary for the calculations presented here.

4. RESULTS

4.1 CFD Results

As stated in Section 2 the first step in the CAA calculation is to determine the flow distribution. The inputs needed for the next step in the CAA calculation are: the velocity distribution (x-, y-, z-velocity), the pressure distribution, the turbulent energy distribution, k, and the turbulence dissipation distribution, ε. These quantities are obtained by solving the steady state Reynolds Averaged Navier Stokes (RANS) equations.

Several considerations are of interest with respect to using a RANS calculation in relation to CAA application. First, the most important areas of the flow will be those areas containing large shear stresses, such as wakes and near-wall flows. These have to be modeled in detail, and correspondingly their presence has to be accounted for when creating the mesh. Due to the importance of the shear stresses, the viscous boundary layer near the wall has to be modeled fully. In many applications it is common to use so-called wall functions for these layers. These wall functions represent the effects of the viscous boundary layer, but require far less grid points. However, since the effect of production and dissipation of turbulence is of major importance for CAA applications, the viscous boundary layer should preferably be taken into account totally in the RANS calculation, at least in the areas of interest.

Secondly, the important properties of the flow should be captured as well. The areas of special interest are those containing high shear stresses such as wakes (detachment and reattachment) and flow impingement. In these areas the streamlines are very much curved. In order to capture for this situation the turbulent properties properly a Reynolds Stress Model can be used. The more common and simpler k-ε model is not sufficient in this case. Figure 5 illustrates the curved streamlines for the wedge block.

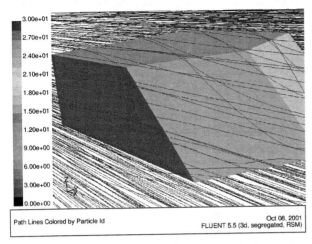

Figure 5 *The curved stream lines around the wedge shaped block (70 mph).*

Figure 6 shows the results of the RANS calculations. The upper picture shows the velocity distribution in a plane close to the side of the wedge shaped block (70 mph). The red area is an area indicating a recirculation zone. The middle picture shows the areas of high turbulent kinetic energy and in the lower picture the turbulent dissipation is visible. In this figure the region of the A-pillar vortex is visible as an area with high turbulence levels. The turbulent dissipation occurs in approximately the same areas, as well as in the boundary layer, as shown in the lower figure.

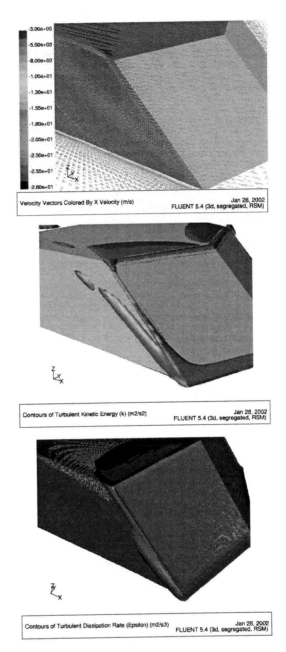

Figure 6 *The RANS results for the wedge shaped block (70 mph). Upper plot: velocity vectors. Middle plot: isosurface of turbulent kinetic energy. Lower plot: isosurface of turbulence dissipation.*

4.2 Acoustic computations

The second step in the CAA calculation is the derivation of source terms, based on the RANS results. In this step the temporal behavior is re-introduced into the calculations. Figure 7 shows a snap shot of source terms at a plane just besides (2.5 cm distance) the wedge block.

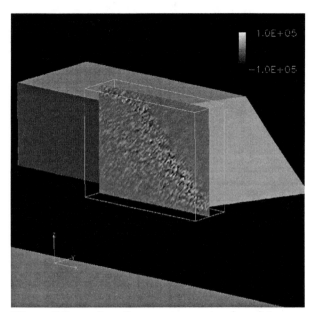

Figure 7 *Snap shot of source terms at a plane 2.5 cm away from the wedge block side surface.*

In the third and final step the pressure variations in the domain are determined by solving the LEE with the source terms calculated in step 2.

4.3 Sensitivity to model parameters

As mentioned in Section 2, a choice needs to be made for the source domain. Of course, the results may depend on the particular choice of the source domain, which is arbitrary to some extent.

To study this influence for the current case, calculations are performed for varying source domains, see Figure 8.

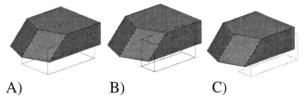

A)   B)   C)

Figure 8 *Three variants for the source domain for step 2 in CAA calculations.*

Table 3-1 presents the variation due to varying source domain in the surface sound pressure levels, as well as the measured levels, at various positions. It appears that the exact choice of the source domain has hardly any influence on the final results for those microphones that are located in the source domain for all three source domains considered. For microphone I5, which is located outside the source domain for domains A and B, but inside source domain C (see Figure 8), the variation of source domain does have a significant influence on the acoustic loads. Comparison of the calculated and measured spectra for this microphone (not shown here) shows an excellent agreement when use is made of the large source domain.

At microphone position C5 the calculated surface sound pressure level are higher than the levels obtained from the measurements. The measured surface sound pressure level at this microphone is about 40 dB lower, relative to position D5. This large dynamic range was not reproduced by the calculations.

Tabel 3-1 *Overview of measured and calculated overall surface pressure levels in dB(lin) for variation in modelling parameters.*

	Position	Measured Level [dB(lin)]	Calculated Level [dB(lin)]	Difference Range [-/+ Δ dB]
70 Mph	D5	133	132 – 135	-1 / +2
70 Mph	G5	129	128 – 133	-1 / + 4
70 Mph	I5	124	117 – 124	-7 / + 0
70 Mph	C5	94	113 – 117	+ 19 / +23
55 Mph	D5	128	127	-1
55 Mph	G5	121	120	-1

4.4 Surface pressure results

Figure 9 shows the power spectral density functions of the pressure fluctuations calculated at various positions at the wedge block surface. The measured and calculated spectra are shown at the two flow speeds, i.e., 55 mph and 70 mph, and for two microphones positions D5 and G5. It can be seen that for both flow speeds the agreement between the calculated and measured spectra is excellent.

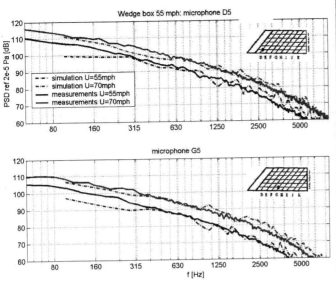

Figure 9 Spectra calculated for microphones D5 and G5 for two flow speeds (dashed/dotted lines). Also shown, as solid lines, are the measured spectra.

This illustrates that the current CAA method is capable of assessing the influence of the flow speeds on the surface pressure fluctuations.

At position C5 the surface sound pressure levels are over predicted (see Figure 11). The cause for this over prediction of the levels for this specific microphone is still under investigation. A possible explanation can lie in differences between the experimental flow field, and the flow field as predicted by the RANS calculation. An example of such a difference is relaminarization. If this happens in the experimental configuration, but is not (or not correctly) captured by the RANS calculation, this might give rise to a difference in measured and predicted levels as seen for position C5.

Besides the results at various predefined positions, the current CAA tool also allows for obtaining an overview of the acoustic loads on the surface of the object. This is important information, which can be obtained from wind tunnel measurements only by employing a large amount of microphones. Figure 10 presents the surface pressure levels at the wedge block for a speed of 55 mph. The pressure level is expressed in color.

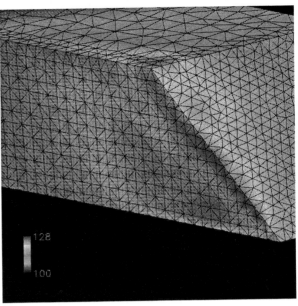

Figure 10 Overall surface sound pressure level in dB (re 2e-5 Pa) for 55 mph. The color scale ranges from 100 to 128 dB.

4.5 Comparison with an alternative method

Ford USA has performed calculations of the surface pressure fluctuations for this wedge block, using the alternative method mentioned in the introduction. These calculations are available for a mean flow speed of 70 mph. Here, the results of the alternative method and the TNO TPD CAA code are compared.

Figure 11 shows the measured spectra, the spectra predicted by the current TNO TPD CAA tool, and those by the alternative method. Since the microphone positions considered by the two methods are not exactly equal, each sub-plot presents results for microphones located close to each other. It is seen that for microphones located at the side of the wedge block, the spectra predicted by the TNO TPD CAA method agree very well with the measured spectra. The alternative method underestimates the surface pressure levels.

As already mentioned in Section 4.4, the measured level for the microphone located on the front surface of the block is much lower (40 dB) than the levels measured on the side of the block. For this microphone the TNO TPD CAA tool over predicts the pressure levels. The alternative method predicts the correct levels.

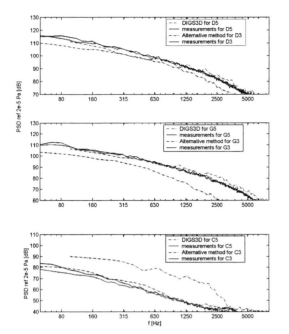

Figure 11 *Spectra calculated by the TNO TPD CAA prediction tool DIGS3D and with an alternative method for microphones D5/D3 (located close towards each other), G5/G3 (located close towards each other), and C5/C3 (located close towards each other).*

5. CONCLUSIONS

A CAA tool developed by TNO TPD is presented and applied to a wedge shaped block configuration in a flow. This case resembles the A-pillar of a car greenhouse or truck cabin. The results of the calculations are the surface pressures at the front and side face of the block (windscreen and side window). For a car or truck such surface pressure variations induced by the flow, cause those panels to vibrate and radiate sound into the interior.

For the wedge shape block, two flow speeds have been considered, 55 mph and 70 mph. At the front of the block ('windscreen') an overestimate of the pressure fluctuations was found. The comparison of measurements and calculations showed an excellent agreement in the surface sound pressure levels in the A-pillar vortex region, where the surface sound pressure levels are highest. The change in the measured surface pressure levels due to the change in flow speed was reproduced very well by the computations.

Based on the current results it is concluded that the TNO TPD CAA tool seems a powerful engineering tool, allowing for generating wind induced noise generated around complex geometries. Both qualitative and quantitative aspects of the results give a

thorough insight in the aero-acoustic phenomena to be controlled during the design process.

REFERENCES

[1] C.P.A. Blom, B.T. Verhaar, J.C. van der Heijden, and B.I. Soemarwoto, *A Linearized Euler method based predication of turbulence induced noise using time-averaged flow properties*, AIAA paper 2001-1100.

[2] M. Karweit, Ph. Blanc-Benon, D. Juvé, and C. Comte-Bellot, *Simulation of the propagation of an acoustic wave through a turbulent velocity field: a study of phase variance*, J. Acoust. Soc. Am., Vol. 89(1), pp. 52-62, 1991.

[3] W. K. Blake, *Mechanics of flow-induced sound and vibration, Volume I: General concepts and elementary sources*, Academic Press, Applied Mathematics and Mechanics, Vol. 17-I, 1986.

AIAA 2002-2549

SOUND RADIATION OF THE VORTEX FLOW PAST A GENERIC SIDE MIRROR

Th. Rung *, D. Eschricht, J. Yan and F. Thiele[†]

ABSTRACT

The paper assesses the predictive capabilities of a two-step noise generation and propagation simulation approach. The focal point of the investigation is a comparison between different methodologies for the analysis of the noise-generation problem by means of unsteady CFD, viz. Detached-Eddy Simulation and the Unsteady Reynolds Averaged Navier-Stokes equations. Results are reported for the aeroacoustic sound generated by the flow around a surface-mounted generic car-side mirror at $Re = 5.2 \times 10^5$ in comparison with experiments. The investigated configuration features massive separation due to shedding vortices and is deliberately unsteady, with no indication for a separation of time scales between mean-transient and residual-turbulence phenomena. The study reveals the limitations of the traditional URANS approaches in aeroacoustic applications, even when best-practice turbulence models for unsteady flows are employed. Moreover, it demonstrates the benefits of DES in conjunction with physics-based noise predictions at moderate computational costs.

INTRODUCTION

The prediction of noise generation is of ever-increasing importance for vehicle and airframe manufacturers. Additionally to its negative impact on passenger comfort, the emitted noise is a major contributor to present and future operating restrictions. Today's environmental provisions are likely to become more restrictive in the near future – some aim to implement an over-all noise reduction of approximately 6-10 dB within the next 5 years – which poses a significant challenge to transportation industry. Due to their large variation with velocity, the contribution of aeroacoustic sources is of particular relevance for high-speed transportation systems cruising beyond 250 km/h. Moreover, impressive noise reductions have been achieved in the area of vibro-acoustics, decreasing the audible threshold towards flow-induced noise even for lower speeds. Thus, transportation industry has a vital interest to improve today's highly empirical aeroacoustic prediction methods by means of feasible, physics-based noise-prediction tools. Related investigations pertain to external- and internal-flow problems, i.e. HVAC systems (fans and tube bundles), high-speed trains (pantographs and bogies), cars (A-pillars, sunroofs or side mirrors) and aircrafts (landing gears and high-lift systems).

*CoC Aerodynamics and Thermodynamics, Bombardier Transportation GmbH, Am Rathenaupark, D-16761 Hennigsdorf, Germany. E-mail thomas.rung@de.transport.bombardier.com

†Technical University of Berlin, Hermann-Föttinger-Institute for Fluid Dynamics, Müller-Breslau-Str. 8, D-10623 Berlin, Germany. E-mail thiele@pi.tu-berlin.de

Feasible simulation practices for industrial problems rely on a separation of the noise generation and propagation problem. Following a detailed, unsteady CFD analysis of the flow field in the vicinity of the aeroacoustic sources, the propagation of sound into the far field is predicted by an appropriate acoustic model utilizing an acoustic-analogy approach.

In industrial aeroacoustics, the relevant frequency range usually spans 5-6 octaves and no distinct spectral gap between mean-transient and residual-turbulence phenomena is observed. Thus, the predictive accuracy for the noise-generation mechanism depends on the turbulence-modelling capabilities with regards to the resolution of turbulence/transient interaction.

The present effort aims to scrutinize the capabilities of the recently developed Detached-Eddy Simulation (DES) approach[1-3] to model the unsteady turbulent flow field in comparison with a best-practice unsteady Reynold-Averaged Navier-Stokes (RANS) method.[4,5] Both approaches employ identical numerics and grids. Attention is confined to the prediction of sound generated by the flow around a generic car side mirror.[6,7]

ACOUSTIC MODEL

Based on the work of Lighthill[8] and Ffowcs-Williams and Hawkings[9] the unsteady pressure and velocity fluctuations in the flow field constitute the sources of an inhomogeneous wave-equation governing the noise propagation problem. These fluctuating values were obtained by CFD.

The acoustic model employed in the present effort is based on the equation of Ffowcs-Williams and Hawkings[9] (FWH), which can directly and without any additional assumptions be derived from the continuity and Navier-Stokes equations. In case of rigid bodies it may be written as

$$\left(\frac{1}{c^2}\frac{\partial^2}{\partial t^2} - \frac{\partial^2}{\partial x_i^2}\right)\left\{p'(\underline{x},t)H(f)\right\} =$$
$$+ \frac{\partial}{\partial t}\left\{\rho_o v_n \delta(f)|\nabla f|\right\} - \frac{\partial}{\partial x_i}\left\{P_{in}\,\delta(f)\,|\nabla f|\right\}$$
$$+ \frac{\partial^2}{\partial x_i \partial x_j}\left\{T_{ij}H(f)\right\}, \quad (1)$$

with $P_{ij} = p'\delta_{ij} - \tau_{ij}, \ T_{ij} = \rho u_i u_j + P_{ij} - c^2 \rho'\delta_{ij}$.

p'	acoustic pressure	c	sound speed
ρ_o	mean density	ρ	density, $\rho = \rho_0 + \rho'$
u_i	fluid velocity	v_i	surface velocity
$\delta(f)$	Dirac distribution	n_i	surface normal
$H(f)$	Heaviside function	P_{in}	$P_{ij}n_j$

The first two terms on the right hand side of equation (1) represent sources located on the surface, whereas the third term represents sources in the surrounding volume. In the present acoustic effort, effects of volume sources (T_{ij}) and of unsteady shear stress (τ_{ij}) have been neglected.[6] By utilizing the free-space Green's function for the wave operator on the left hand side of equation (1), an integral representation for the pressure fluctuations induced by sources on the surface can be obtained. For rigid bodies in subsonic motion, this may be written as (Farassat[10, 11]):

$$4\pi\, p'(\underline{x},t) =$$
$$\int_S \left[\frac{p'}{c(1-M_r)}\left(\frac{\partial}{\partial \tau}\left\{\frac{\hat{\underline{r}}\cdot\underline{n}}{r(1-M_r)}\right\} + \frac{c\,(\hat{\underline{r}}\cdot\underline{n})}{r^2}\right)\right]_{ret} dS$$
$$+ \int_S \left[\frac{1}{c(1-M_r)}\frac{\partial p'}{\partial \tau}\frac{\hat{\underline{r}}\cdot\underline{n}}{r(1-M_r)}\right]_{ret} dS$$
$$+ \int_S \left[\frac{\rho_o}{(1-M_r)}\frac{\partial}{\partial \tau}\left\{\frac{v_n}{r(1-M_r)}\right\}\right]_{ret} dS, \quad (2)$$

where $[\dots]_{ret}$ denotes quantities that have to be evaluated at retarded time $\tau = t - r/c$ and position $\underline{y}$. The acoustic pressure at a fixed position $\underline{x}$ and time t can now be obtained by evaluating the integrals in equation (2).

$\underline{x}$	observer position
$\underline{y}$	source position
r	$|\underline{x} - \underline{y}|$
$\hat{\underline{r}}$	unit vector in radiation direction
M_r	surface Mach number in radiation direction

FLOW-PHYSICS MODEL

The existence of a spectral gap between resolved coherent and modelled random structures is a formal prerequisite for the application of traditional Reynolds averaged Navier-Stokes approaches. The latter is often violated in unsteady flow fields of aeroacoustic relevance. In conclusion, an Unsteady RANS (URANS) can be questionable for aeroacoustic simulations. The principal drawback of statistical approaches is their rigid interface between resolved and modelled eddies, which is manifested by the complete independence of the turbulence model from the grid-resolution parameters.

Direct Numerical Simulation (DNS) and Large-Eddy Simulation (LES) methods are both natural candidates for an adequate description of the unsteady flow field in the vicinity of the acoustic sources. The computational effort associated with DNS, however, exceeds the feasibility threshold by many orders of magnitude. A full-domain LES requires the resolution of boundary-layer structures by the numerical grid, which approximately scales with $Re^{1.9}$. Hence, LES still remains prohibitively expensive for external aerodynamic applications beyond $Re \geq 10^5$. Time-scale restrictions follow similar arguments,[1] although they are usually irrelevant for aeroacoustic applications due to the associated transient resolution requirements.

The Detached-Eddy Simulation introduced by Spalart and his co-workers[1-3] offers a viable approach to model the vicinity of the aeroacoustic sources by means of a hybrid, non-zonal LES/URANS formulation. The DES essentially couples a near-wall URANS with an LES of the detached (massively separated) flow regime. Transition to LES usually occurs at a distance of a typical boundary-layer thickness (e.g. $5\ \theta$). The blend is realised by a limitation of the length scale inherent to the employed turbulence closure based on the local grid spacing. Further details can be obtained from Strelets.[12] Like LES, DES is inherently unsteady and three-dimensional. With the exception of extremely slender (high-aspect ratio) bodies, the computational effort of the approach is similar to URANS. The amount of grid points typically scales with $Re^{1.3}$. A fairly general estimation of the required time step is $\Delta t = 0.02T$, where $T = L/U$ is a typical time unit. Reasonable statistical averaging usually requires approximately 100 time units.

The DES has been found to be insensitive with regards to the underlying turbulence/SGS model. The present DES is thus confined to an efficient Spalart-Allmaras[13] one-equation model. In contrast to the DES methodology, the predictive quality returned by URANS hinges on seemingly subtle modelling details. There exists some body of evidence, that an inaccurate modelling of crucial, non-transient aspects might significantly deteriorate the predicted gross characteristics in unsteady-seperated flows.[14, 15] The most relevant issues are: (a) the surpression of a premature transition to turbulence due to irrotational strain, (b) an elaborate stress-strain relation featuring the ability to account for rotational (curvature) and non-eqilibrium (pressure-gradient) aspects, (c) a robust low-Re approach. The predictive failure of URANS is particularly pronounced when the modelled stresses overwhelm the unsteady contributions.[16] As standard

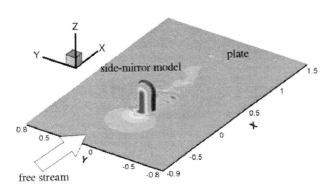

Fig. 1   Sketch of experimental setup.

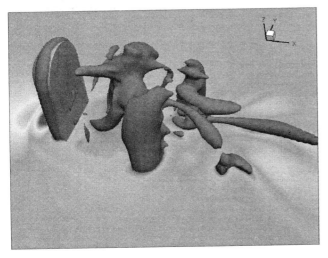

Fig. 2   Pressure iso-surfaces ($c_p = -0.28$) returned by the DES approach.

Boussinesq-viscosity models have proven insufficient to correctly predict complex flow situations, attention is drawn to a more reliable, local-linear realizable (LLR) $k - \omega$ model.[4,5] Although this work aims to advocate the use of such methods, details of the specific modelling framework are beyond the scope of the present paper.

INVESTIGATED CONFIGURATION

The investigated configuration focusses upon a surface-mounted generic car side mirror at $Re = 5.2 \times 10^5$, based on a free stream velocity of $U = 39m/s$, where experiments and predictions are reported by Siegert[6] and Hoeld[7] et al. Figure 1 illustrates the experimental setup which was carried out in the FKFS aeroacoustic wind tunnel at the University of Stuttgart. The mirror consists of a half-cylinder with D=L=0.2m diameter and length, blunted by a quarter sphere. The mirror was mounted on a flat plate with 8D width and $L_{exp} = 12D$ length. The rear face of the mirror was centrally located at 4.5 diameters downstream of the plate's leading edge. Aerodynamically covered struts were used to host the experimental equipment and to fix the plate. To reveal the influ-

ence of the size of the plate on the radiated noise, the length of the plate was extended to $L_{ext} = 16.5D$ in the present investigation (referred to as extendend region in the following).

The flow field is characterised by 3D, unsteady separated flow. The noise generation is driven by the interaction between the shedding vortices and the plate. The involved shedding primarily consists of a contribution in z-direction from the cylindrical part, impacting on the plate between one and two diameters downstream of the rear face, and a second vortex, shedding from the crest of the quarter sphere, that penetrates onto the plate at three to four diameters downstream of the rear face (cf. Figure 2). Figure 8 illustrates the footprint of the vortex structure on the plate by means of the surface rms-values of the fluctuating pressure. Assuming the Strouhal number of the cylinder vortex to follow the standard value $Str \approx 0.2$, a first dominant frequency is estimated by $f = Str \times U/D \approx 40$ Hz.

As depicted by Figure 3, a total of 34 pressure sensors for time averaged measurements have been employed on the obstacle. Instantaneous pressure signals were obtained from additional 23 piezo-electric sensors. The propagation of sound is validated against 15 microphones, 11 of them located in an envelope of 2.5 diameters from the mirror (cf. Figure 4).

Since the use of an additional transition strip device did significantly augment the generated sound, no transition strip was used in the experiments. Oil-flow visualisation revealed that flow is clearly supercritical, with transition occuring approximately 0.15 diameters upstream of rear-face edge. In view of the difficulties associated with a detailed transition control, the turbulence-closure model was active in all boundary layers. Due to the low Mach number (M=0.11), the flow field is considered to be incompressible throughout the noise-generation analysis.

NUMERICAL PROCEDURE

The flow solver ELAN3[17] consists of an implicit pressure-based Finite-Volume Navier-Stokes procedure employing semi-structured grids. The algorithm is based on the strong conservation form of the momentum equations within general body-fitted coordinates and employs a fully co-located storage arrangement. Diffusion terms are approximated using second-order central differences, whereas advective fluxes are approximated by either centered or upwind-biased, high-order bounded (monotonic) schemes. All high-order schemes are applied in scalar form by means of a deferred correction procedure. Transient terms are approximated by fully implicit, second-order accurate finite differences. The odd-even decoupling problem of the cell-centered scheme is supressed with a fourth-order artificial-dissipation pressure term in the continuity equation based on the apparent-

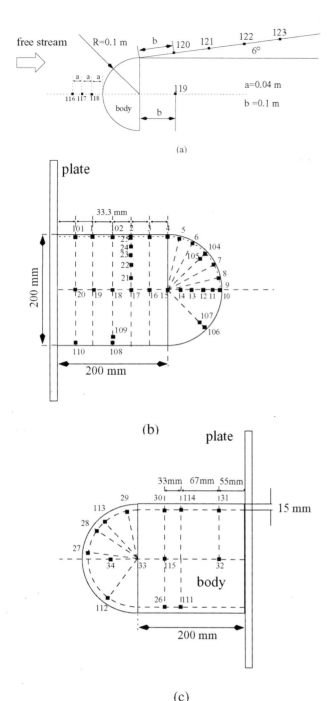

(a)

(b)

(c)

Fig. 3 Pressure sensor locations; a) top, b) front, c) rear view (Höld[7] et al.).

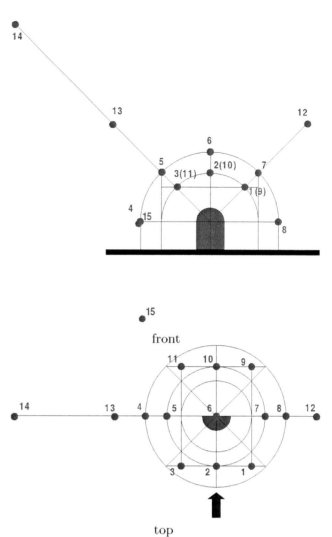

Fig. 4 Microphone positions employed for the assessment of the acoustic results (Siegert[6] et al.).

pressure/viscosity principle. For each time step, the solution is iterated to convergence using a pressure–correction approach. Furthermore, the solver is parallelized, where the performance has been quantified to roughly 60 MFLOPs per PE on a CRAY T3E-900.

Computational Grid & Boundary Conditions

The computational mesh is based on a structured-grid multi-block arrangement involving 38 blocks with a total of 2.5×10^6 grid points. Figure 5 displays a portion of the surface grid. The first cell spacing normal to the wall is about $\Delta n = 3 \times 10^{-4}$ which results in

$0.5 < Y^+ < 60$. Normal to the wall, the stretching ratio is about 1.4, which is more than the usual recommendation.[18] The circumferential resolution of the cylinder surface is $\Delta s = 0.033 \times D$ on average, the height of the cylinder is discretized by $\Delta z = 0.016 \times D$. The computational domain covers only the flat-plate area, the height of the domain is $H = 11.5 \times D$. Inlet conditions pertain to low turbulence-intensity ($\nu_t = 5\nu$, $Tu = 0.5\%$) flow, featuring zero boundary-layer thickness. Outlet conditions are non-reflective. The adopted turbulent wall-boundary condition follows the universal adaptive approach described by Rung,[19] which is insensitive to the near-wall resolution properties of the grid. As can be seen in Figure 5, the resolution of the wake regime is clearly sub-optimal, here the computational mesh should ideally consist of cubic cells. Moreover, the fine grid area should follow the footprint of the vortices illustrated by Figure 8. Supplementary, a more continuous resolution of the spanwise and circumferential part of the half cylinder is desirable.

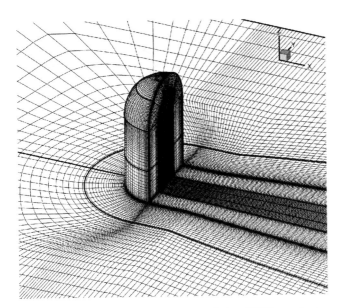

Fig. 5 Employed surface grid of the CFD analysis.

Transient Discretisation

Two time steps, $\Delta t = 0.0195 \times T = 10^{-4} s$ (coarse) and $\Delta t = 0.0039 \times T = 2 \cdot 10^{-5} s$ (fine) have been investigated in conjunction with DES. The URANS simulations are restricted to the coarse time step. Generally, the adopted numerical procedure requires 9-12 time steps for an accurate representation of harmonic disturbances. Hence, the resolved frequencies are limited to approximately $f_{\max} = 800\text{-}1000$ Hz for the coarse time step and $f_{\max} = 4000\text{-}5000$ Hz for the fine time step.

In order to speed up the flow-development process, the computation is initialised by a steady RANS approach. Before starting to record the time history, the inital transient is removed based on $T_{\text{initial}} = 15\,T$ time units. Due to the limited computational resources, all simulations were carried out over $T_{\text{total}} = 50\,T$. This admittedly short total simulation time has a major impact on the quality of the results in the low-frequency regime. Assuming the statistics to converge after 100 time units, the lowest, statistically resolved frequencies of the present simulations are $f_{\min} \approx 40 Hz$.

The acoustic analogy solver applies a retarded-time algorithm.[20] The part of the CFD grid associated with the rigid surfaces of plate and mirror provides the spatial discretisation of the surface. For fixed observer position $\underline{x}$ and time t the integrands in equation (2) are evaluated for each surface element. Since these integrands have to be evaluated at the retarded time $\tau = t - r/c$, the determination of this emission time is required for each element. CFD provides the unsteady surface pressure only at discrete times; furthermore, the pressure's time derivative appears inside the integrals, hence interpolation and numerical derivation in time is required to calculate the integrands.

In case of the investigated configuration, the surface grid consists of 36630 elements with an area of

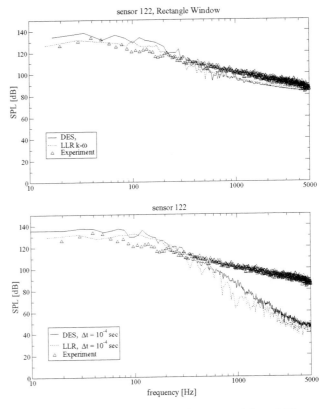

Fig. 6 Sound pressure levels at position 122 returned by CFD.

$A = 5.42\,m^2$. Thus the average edge length of surface elements is $\Delta l = 1.2\,cm$. Interpolation and numerical derivation are of third and second order respectively.

Computational Effort

The computational effort of the present study is primarily caused by the unsteady CFD approach. Calculations were done on a massively parallel LINUX Cluster (Kernel 2.4.9) using 38 processors (INTEL PIII 850Mhz, 256MB RAM). The performance was quantified to approximately 5 (coarse) time steps/hour, which yields turn-around times of 6 weeks for the coarse time step and 30 weeks for the fine time step. Hence, the computational expenses – 25000 (coarse) - 120000 (fine) CPUh – are still considerable, bearing in mind the simplicity of the configuration.

RESULTS

Data Evaluation

To compare the experimental data with the results of the numerical simulations, the sound pressure level (SPL) $20 \log(\hat{p}/p_0)$ based on a reference pressure of $p_0 = 20\,\mu\text{Pa}$ is calculated. For improved statistical properties, the SPL was obtained by averaging over Discrete Fourier Transforms (DFT) of 4 data-segments of equal size, which overlap by one half of their length. The Hanning window avoids the overestimation of the SPL at large frequencies that appears when non-periodic data is transformed by DFT. This

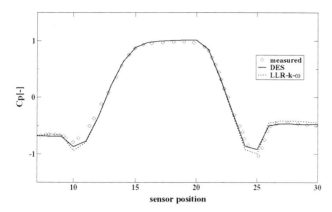

Fig. 7 Comparison of predicted and measured time-mean pressure coefficient.

effect is illustrated in Figure 6, which shows the estimated sound pressure level at position 122 obtained without the application of a Window Function (upper part) and with the application of the Hanning Window (lower part). The agreement between experimental and numerical results in the upper part is only the result of an inconsistent application of the Fourier Transform. Keeping in mind that the numerical simulation applying the coarse time step can only resolve frequencies up to $f_{max} \approx 800-1000$ Hz, the obtained agreement at higher frequencies $f > 1000$ Hz is misleading.

CFD Analysis

All results presented were carried out with the coarse time step $\Delta t = 10^{-4}s$ unless otherwise stated.

Figure 7 illustrates the performance of the CFD procedure by means of the predicted time-mean pressure coefficient. The sensor positions are taken from Figures 3b and 3c. The agreement between the predicted and measured data is reasonable, thus the remainder of this subsection is confined to the comparison of transient data. Strictly speaking, the underlying simple near-wall Boussinesq-viscosity models are not able to render transient boundary-layer phenomena, e.g. the decoupling of Reynolds stresses and mean strain often observed in oscillating boundary-layers. Since the governing scales of the flow's gross characteristics exceed the boundary-layer scales in many aeroacoustic applications, the boundary-layer can nonetheless be modelled by means of URANS without significant performance losses.

Figure 8 illustrates the predicted p'_{rms} values obtained from the URANS simulations. The comparison reveals that the URANS results are afflicted by a reduction of transient motion in the near wake regime. The club-shaped structures are less pronounced and the high-intensity regime is shifted downstream when compared with DES results.

A particular benefit of the adopted URANS closure emerges from the supression of premature transition due to irrotational strain in the vicinity of the stagna-

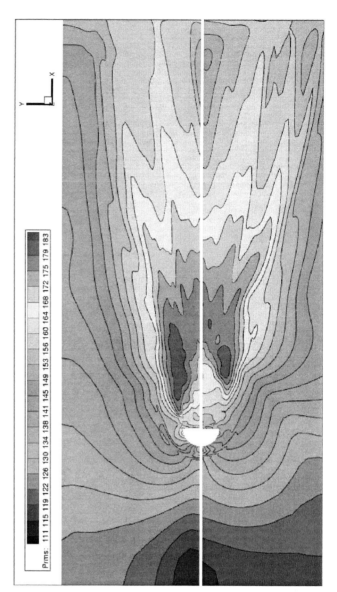

Fig. 8 Surface values of p'_{rms} returned by DES approach (left) and URANS approach (right).

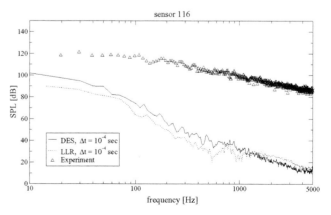

Fig. 9 Sound pressure levels at position 116 returned by CFD.

1510

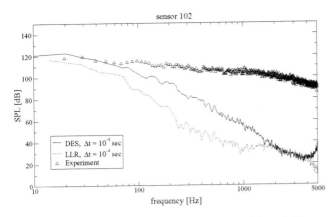

Fig. 10 Sound pressure levels at position 102 returned by CFD.

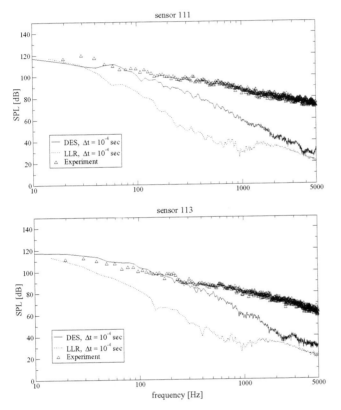

Fig. 11 Sound pressure levels at positions 111 and 113 returned by CFD.

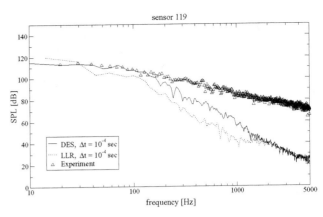

Fig. 12 Sound pressure levels at position 119 returned by CFD.

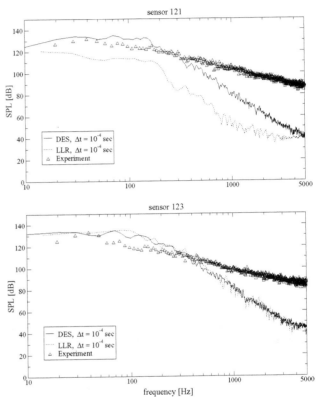

Fig. 13 Sound pressure levels at positions 121 and 123 returned by CFD.

tion zone. The latter is clearly observed by the lack of augmentation of p'_{rms} upstream of the mirror.

Results obtained for the most upstream location 116 on the plate are depicted by Figure 9. All simulations fail to predict the measured SPL by approximately 25 dB even at low frequencies, indicating that the upstream portion of the mesh is far to coarse to render the benefits of the DES approach. Moreover, disturbances initiated by the leading edge of the plate are not considered in the present simulations.

When attention is drawn to measurement position 102 located on the cylinder surface upstream of the rear face, the predicted results significantly improve (cf. Figure 10). Although the simulations still

underpredict the SPL at high frequencies, they return a fair amount of accuracy for lower frequencies. The results gained by the employed URANS are about 20 dB lower than those by the DES for a wide range of frequencies. One should bear in mind, that the upstream grid is sub-optimal in conjunction with DES.

A similar picture emerges for the rear face stations 111 and 113, which are displayed in Figure 11. The deviations between predictions and experiments pertaining to the low-frequency range in position 111 are attributed to the short total-simulation time T_{total}, which should cause less difficulties in the near-crest location 113. Figure 12 illustrates the predictive accuracy returned for station 119, centrally located on

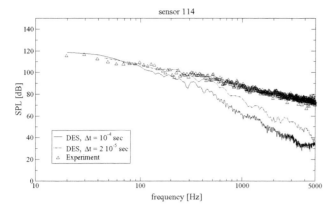

Fig. 14 Sound pressure levels at position 114 returned by CFD.

the plate at 0.5 diameters aft of the cylinder. Results obtained for station 119 confirm the above mentioned findings.

The most interesting picture emerges from Figure 13, which focusses upon stations 121 and 123, located one and two diameters downstream of the mirror's side edge, respectively. At position 121, the SPL derived by the URANS simulation is much lower compared to the experimental data. The DES results are about 20 dB above the URANS values and the comparison with the measured SPL reveals an overestimation by 10-15 dB for frequencies up to $f = 350$ Hz for this position. The picture changes completely for positions further downstream, as is shown for position 122 and 123 (cf. Figures 6, lower part, and 13). A clear difference between the two modelling practises for the coarse time step is no longer visible. This can be explained by the contours of the plate surface pressure as shown in Figure 8, where the high-intensity regime is slightly shifted downstream in URANS results. At position 123, all simulations predict the sound pressure level too high by about 10-20 dB for frequencies between $f = 50-500$ Hz.

A better resolution of the time dependency by a smaller time step $\Delta t = 2 \cdot 10^{-5}$s shows no significant influence on the obtained sound pressure level in general (e.g. Figure 13, position 121). At some positions (Figure 14), however, a slight improvement of the SPL can be observed, which in this case may be due to a finer grid resolution around this position.

Acoustic Analysis

Figure 15 compares the measured sound pressure levels at various microphone positions with results provided by the FWH procedure, which has been applied to the extended plate (L_{ext}) unless otherwise stated.

The numerical results fail to predict lower frequencies $f < 30$ Hz. This deviation is attributed to the short simulation time T_{total} and to the contribution of background noise to the measured data in the wind tunnel experiments, especially at low frequencies.[7]

The sharp decline of the predicted SPL for frequen-

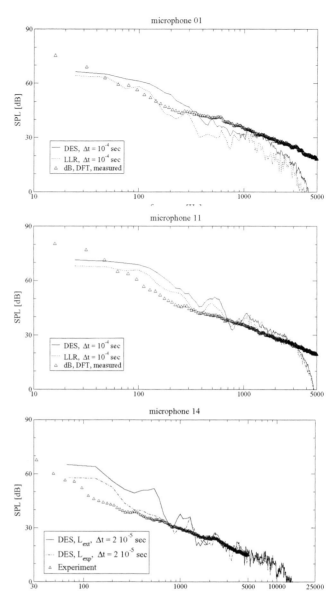

Fig. 15 Sound pressure levels at microphones 1, 11 and 14 returned by the FWH procedure.

cies beyond $f = 2000$ Hz for the coarse time step is reasonable, as these exceed the limit of resolved frequencies of the procedures applied for timewise interpolation and derivation. A similar behaviour emerges for the fine time step at higher frequencies (e.g. microphone 14).

All results overestimate the SPL for frequencies between $f = 60-800$ Hz by about 10-15 dB. This may be attributed to the overestimation of the surface SPL in regions with the strongest acoustic sources (cf. Figure 13, position 123) by up to 20 dB for all simulations. Moreover, the results in Figure 15 were derived for the extended plate (L_{ext}), which contributes to the SPL as an additional acoustic source region.

To investigate the influence of the plate length on the microphone SPL, the radiated sound was also calculated by the FWH procedure with the plate length

(L_{exp}) used in experiments. Figure 16 compares the results for various microphone positions calculated from the extended (L_{ext}) and the experimental (L_{exp}) source region. Here, the calculated sound pressure levels are based on DES results, but a similar behaviour was found for the URANS and DES (fine time step) simulations as well (cf. Figure 15, microphone 14).

Due to the spatial proximity, the prediction at microphone 4 is predominantly influenced by the high-intensity regime, therefore the effect of the truncation is negligible here. In addition, the scalar product $\hat{r} \cdot \underline{n}$ appearing in all pressure-based source terms, equation (2), reaches its minimum for this microphone, owing to its low position above the plate.

An increased dependence on the truncation is seen in the results for microphone 10, which is located higher above the plate than microphone 4, although closer to the high-intensity regime. Thus, this region constitutes the main source of noise and the SPL is lowered only by 2-6 dB for frequencies under $f = 700$ Hz.

The effect intensifies at microphone 14, which is located relatively far away from the high-intensity regime and the extended region, respectively, and high above the plate. Thus it has no special dependence on one of these regions and the truncation's effect becomes clearly visible. The SPL is about 5-15 dB lower, which leads to a better agreement with the experimental results. In general the URANS returns lower sound pressure levels than the DES for all microphone positions, which is consistent with the lower surface SPL obtained by the URANS simulation.

CONCLUSIONS

The present investigation compares the predictive prospects of two turbulence modelling practices, i.e. DES and URANS, with regard to the noise generation simulations. Both approaches run at equal cost. Although, the present URANS results show a similar behaviour as formerly reported investigations of Hoeld et al.[7] and Siegert et al.,[6] the predicted flow field still overestimates the contribution of periodic, 2D, low-frequency structures at the expense of random, three-dimensional unsteadiness. Accordingly, the sound-field predictions are biased towards low-frequency, tonal noise. In contrast, the DES simulations are able to predict the higher frequency sources with reasonable amounts of accuracy. Existing deficiencies of the DES are mainly attributed to an insufficient numerical grid. An encouraging feature of the present investigations is the superiority of the DES approach even in conjunction with sub-optimal standard RANS meshes. The application of time step refinement enhances the resolution properties of the DES.

In conjunction with URANS, the quality of the acoustic prognosis is much better than expected. Generally, DES and URANS based predictions return similar far-field results. Significant predictive differences

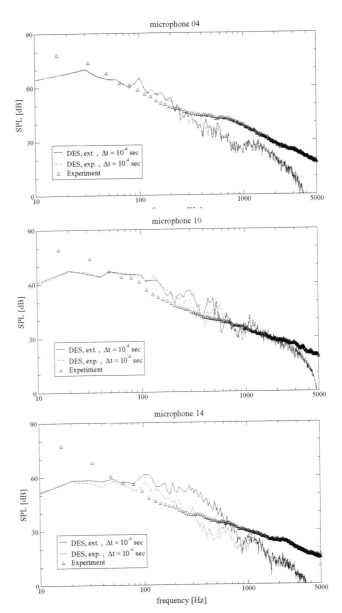

Fig. 16 Sound pressure levels at microphones 4, 10 and 14 returned by the FWH procedure.

are observed in lateral and downstream locations, where DES based results outperform URANS based sound predictions by 5-10 dB in the high-frequency regime (Str ≥ 2).

Future work will be devoted to further of local grid refinement, the impact of the approximation of advective fluxes and the consideration of the volume source in the FWH equation.

ACKNOWLEDGEMENT

This research was partially funded by the German National Science Foundation (Deutsche Forschungsgemeinschaft, DFG) and the joint DaimlerChrysler/Bombardier Transportation advanced technology-development project AIRTRANS.

References

[1]Spalart, P., "Strategies for Turbulence Modelling and Simulation," *Engineering Turbulence Modelling and Experiments 4*, Elsevier, Amsterdam, 1999, pp. 3–17.

[2]Shur, M., Spalart, P., Strelets, M., and Travin, A., "Detached–eddy Simulation of an Airfoil at High Angle of Attack," *Engineering Turbulence Modelling and Experiments 4*, Elsevier, Amsterdam, 1999, pp. 669–678.

[3]Travin, A., Shur, M., Strelets, M., and Spalart, P., "Detached-Eddy Simulations Past a Circular Cylinder," *Flow, Turbulence and Combustion*, Vol. 63, 2000, pp. 293–313.

[4]Rung, T. and Thiele, F., "Computational Modelling of Complex Boundary-Layer Flows," *9th Int. Symp. on Transport Phenomena in Thermal-Fluid Engineering, Singapore*, 1996.

[5]Schatz, M. and Thiele, F., "Numerical Study of High-Lift Flow with Separation Control by Periodic Excitation," *AIAA Paper 2001-0296*, 2001.

[6]Siegert, R., Schwartz, V., and Reichenberger, J., "Numerical Simulation of Aeroacoustic Sound generated by Generic Bodies Placed on a Plate II," *AIAA Paper 99-1895*, 1999.

[7]Höld, R., Brenneis, A., Eberle, A., Siegert, R., and Schwartz, V., "Numerical Simulation of Aeroacoustic Sound generated by Generic Bodies Placed on a Plate I," *AIAA Paper 99-1896*, 1999.

[8]Lighthill, M., "On Sound Generated Aerodynamically, I: General Theory," *Proceedings of the Royal Society London*, Vol. A221, 1952, pp. 564–587.

[9]Ffowcs Williams, J. and Hawkings, D., "Sound Generated by Turbulence and Surfaces in Arbitrary Motion," *Philosophical Transactions of the Royal Society*, Vol. A264, 1969, pp. 321–342.

[10]Farassat, F., "Theory of Noise Generation from Moving Bodies with Application to Helicopter Rotors," Tech. Rep. TR-451, NASA, 1975.

[11]Farassat, F., "Linear Acoustic Formulas for Calculation of Rotating Blade Noise," *AIAA Journal*, Vol. 19, No. 9, 1981, pp. 1122–1130.

[12]Strelets, M., "Detached Eddy Simulation of Massively Separated Flows," *AIAA Paper 01-0879*, 2001.

[13]Spalart, P. and Allmaras, S., "A One-Equation Turbulence Model for Aerodynamic Flows," *AIAA Paper 92-0439*, 1992.

[14]Kato, M. and Launder, B. E., "The Modelling of Turbulent Flow around Stationary and Vibrating Square Cylinders," *Proc. of 9th Symp. on Turb. Shear Flows*, Kyoto, Japan, 1993, pp. 10.4.1–10.4.6.

[15]Schmidt, S., Lübcke, H., Rung, T., and Thiele, F., "Comparison of LES and RANS in bluff–body flows," *Journal of Wind Engineering and Industrial Aerodynamics*, 2001.

[16]Durbin, P., "Separated Flow Computations with the $k - \varepsilon - v^2$ Model," *AIAA Journal*, Vol. 33 (4), 1995, pp. 659–664.

[17]Xue, L., *Entwicklung eines effizienten parallelen Lösungsalgorithmus zur dreidimensionalen Simulation komplexer turbulenter Strömungen*, Ph.D. thesis, Technische Universität Berlin, 1998.

[18]Spalart, P., "Young-Person's Guide to Detachached-Eddy Simulation Grids," Tech. Rep. CR-2001-210132, NASA, 2001.

[19]Rung, T., "Formulierung universeller Wandrandbedingungen für Transportgleichungsturbulenzmodelle," Institutsbericht 2–99, Hermann–Föttinger–Institut, Technische Universität Berlin, 1999.

[20]Brentner, K., "Numerical Algorithms for Acoustic Integrals - the Devil is in the Details," *AIAA Paper 96-1706*, 1996.

SIMULATION AND DESIGN OF AUTOMOBILE SUNROOF BUFFETING NOISE CONTROL

Kenneth J. Karbon
General Motors Corporation, Warren, MI, USA

Rajneesh Singh
Altair Engineering Inc, Troy, MI, USA

ABSTRACT

This paper presents the success story of an application of Computational Fluid Dynamics (CFD) analysis for automotive sunroof buffeting simulation and noise control design. Computational analyses of flow over an open sunroof of a car are performed to study the buffeting phenomenon and to determine the buffeting noise magnitude and frequency. Computations are performed for sunroofs with two types of buffeting noise control mechanisms. Numerical predictions are compared with the wind tunnel measurements. It is shown that CFD analysis has great potential for sunroof design and development

INTRODUCTION

Wind rush and wind buffeting noise are among the dominant automotive noise sources. Sunroof buffeting is a flow excited resonance phenomenon that usually occurs at low speeds (30-40mph)[1]. The coupling of the acoustic frequency of the passenger compartment to the periodic instability in the shear layer off the vehicle roof results in the production of high amplitude sound levels. It involves break up of the shear layer into discrete vortices, convection of the vortices with the flow, interaction of the vortices with the downstream edge of sunroof opening and feedback of acoustic disturbance through the vehicle compartment[2,3]. This inherently unsteady flow phenomenon exhibits complex flow physics and poses several challenges for numerical simulations.

Two of the important geometric parameters for the sunroof-buffeting phenomenon are the volume of the passenger compartment and the length of the sunroof opening. Other geometric parameters include the roof curvature and windshield slope. The significance of these parameters is not yet well known. There are many analytical expressions available to estimate the vortex shedding frequency of the shear layer. One such formula[1] for turbulent boundary layers is given by:

$$F = \tfrac{1}{3}(N-\tfrac{1}{4}) \ U/L, \ N=1,2,3,\ldots$$

Where U is the free stream velocity, L is the length of the sunroof opening, N is the number of vortices present across the opening. N=2 is generally observed for a typical sunroof on an automobile. No such formula exists for estimation of the noise magnitude in the passenger compartment.

CAE tools are playing an increasingly significant role in the design and development of new automotive vehicles. Building a hardware model is a relatively time consuming process. CAE analysis can be used to identify and improve the performance attributes at a much earlier stage in the design process. CFD analysis for wind noise prediction is one such area that has potential to contribute towards significant reduction in the hardware testing and thus reducing the design time for a vehicle.

The primary outputs required from the CFD analysis are the buffeting frequency and the peak noise magnitude at the buffeting frequency. PAM-FLOW software has been used for sunroof buffeting analysis at GM for the past few years. Numerical predictions are in very good agreement with the wind-tunnel measurements[4]. This paper presents the contribution of numerical analyses to the design of sunroof-buffeting noise control mechanisms.

There are many methods for suppressing the sunroof buffeting. Two of the methods used in the automotive sunroof industry are:

1. **Deflector at the front of the sunroof opening**: The wind deflectors on the front edge of the sunroof opening have been found to be very effective in suppressing the resonance. They deflect the flow such that the vortices pass over the rear edge of the opening. The interaction of the vortex with the downstream edge of the sunroof is thus weaker and therefore less noisy. Introducing notches in the deflector can reduce noise even further. The notches prevent the formation of spanwise-correlated vortices in the shear layer and thus reduce their strength. The deflectors with notches create more noise in the higher frequency bands, but such penalty is often acceptable because it is less annoying than the low frequency throbbing of sunroof buffeting.

2. **Glass comfort position**: Another fix to reduce the buffeting noise is the use of so-called comfort positions for the sunroof. In this case, the retracted sunroof glass covers part of the opening. It has been observed that the vorticies grows in strength as they convect downstream. By keeping the sunroof partially closed, vortices interact with the sunroof glass before reaching the rear edge of the opening.

Analysis of both of these methods is presented in this paper. The numerical predictions of the noise magnitude and buffeting frequency from PAM-FLOW are compared with the experimental measurements.

<u>**COMPUTATIONAL MODEL**</u>

The computational model consists of car in a rectangular box to mimic the experimental setup of noise measurements in a wind tunnel. A full car model with a realistic representation of the interior passenger compartment is used. However, accurate simulation of acoustics properties of the car interior is not attempted. All surfaces in the model and tunnel walls are acoustically rigid. Complex details of the interior like instrument panel, steering wheel are ignored. Figure 1 shows a view of the passenger compartment. Under-hood components are not included in the model. Underbody is approximated using flat panels to reduce the model complexity. All surfaces are patched by a triangular element unstructured mesh. The model is assembled in the pre-processor of the PAM-FLOW package.

Figure 1: Interior view of the passenger compartment.

A good quality mesh is a prerequisite for any accurate numerical simulation. Unstructured tetrahedral mesh for the model is generated using the PAM-GEN, a grid generating software of the PAM-FLOW package. Accurate resolution of shear layer shedding off the roof edge is important to simulate sunroof buffeting. Six layers of boundary layers are used on all the surfaces. The thickness of the first layer is about 2mm. The mesh size on the surfaces near the sunroof opening is 10mm. Surface element size on other parts of the car range from 15mm to 30 mm. The mesh size in the region near sunroof opening is controlled using the volume source lines. Figure 2 shows a view of surface mesh near the sunroof opening. The total model size is about 6 million elements.

The CFD simulations are performed using the software PAM-FLOW. PAM-FLOW is a 3-dimensional simulation code for solving Navier-Stokes equations. The spatial discretization is accomplished via finite element techniques on unstructured grids. Galerkin weighted residual method on linear elements is used. For time discretization, implicit pressure projection scheme is used for incompressible flow solutions. However, the convection term is computed explicitly using the Roe flux splitting scheme with fourth order diffusion. The Laplacian operators obtained for the pressure and velocity correction step are solved using a Preconditioned Conjugate Gradient (PCG) algorithm. The time step is computed from the Courant-Friedrich-Levy (CFL) criteria based on the velocity since the sound speed is infinite in the incompressible flow. PAM-FLOW is a fully vectorized and parallelized and can be run in shared (SMP) or distributed (DMP) mode.

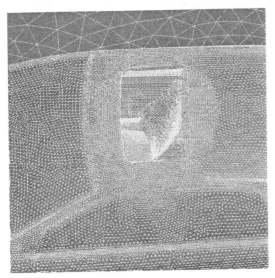

Figure 2: Surface mesh near the sunroof opening.

RESULTS AND DISCUSSION

This section describes the results of the CFD simulation of sunroof buffeting for a typical sunroof and for two different types of noise control mechanisms. Important characteristics of sunroof buffeting are described by examining the typical pressure time-history at the driver location. The pressure time-history is used to determine the frequency spectrum of the noise by performing Fourier transformation.

Computational Parameters

Computational parameters are obtained by extensive study[5] to ensure mesh-independent solution. Incompressible, transient analysis is performed at 50kph speed. Fixed velocity boundary conditions are enforced on the car surface. Tangential velocity boundary conditions are used for the wind tunnel walls. A boundary layer is not modeled on the wind tunnel walls, as it is not expected to be critical for sunroof buffeting phenomenon. A far-field condition with a secondary condition of static pressure is applied on the wind tunnel exit. A SGS turbulence model with default parameters is used in the analyses.

The MPI version of PAM-FLOW is used to reduce the computation time for analysis.

Calculations are performed using 16-processors on a SGI-3000 machine. The computation time for each case is about 75 hrs.

The fluid domain is initialized to the free stream conditions and the computations are started with a fixed CFL number of 0.5. Initial transients are damped in about 0.5 sec of simulation. Thereafter, the simulation is carried out with a constant time step for acoustic post-processing. The noise spectrum at the driver's ear is obtained by Fourier transformation of the static pressure time-history at this location.

Typical Pressure Time-history and Frequency Spectrum of Sunroof-buffeting

Unsteady pressure at the driver's ear location determines the sunroof buffeting noise. Figure 3 shows a part of the typical pressure time-history at 50 kph speed. The time-history shows a dominance of a fundamental mode coinciding with the resonance frequency. Each cycle in the pressure time history corresponds to a passage of vortex from the upstream edge of the sunroof opening to the downstream edge. The minimum pressure in the passenger cabin occurs when the vortex interacts with the rear edge of the sunroof.

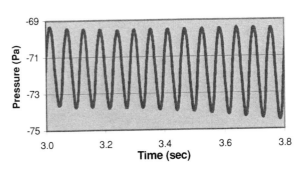

Figure 3: Typical sunroof buffeting pressure time-history at the driver ear location.

Figure 4a shows the frequency spectrum of sunroof buffeting noise predicted by the CFD analysis for a typical sunroof on a car at 50kph. The length of the sunroof opening for this case was 0.428m. The estimate for the buffeting frequency using the formula shown earlier is 21.3 Hz. It can be seen from the plot that the CFD prediction agrees well with the analytical results. The spectrum also shows peaks at higher frequencies corresponding to the higher modes of passenger compartment.

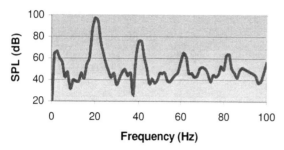

Figure 4a: Frequency spectrum of sunroof buffeting noise from the CFD analysis.

Figure 4b shows the frequency spectrum of sunroof buffeting noise measured in the wind tunnel for the same car as in the Figure 4a. It can be seen from the plot that the first mode is quite clear in the spectrum but the higher modes are well damped. The magnitude of the first mode for CFD prediction is in excellent agreement with the wind tunnel measurements. Discrepancies in the higher frequency range can be partly attributed to the differences in the hardware model in the wind tunnel and the computational model used in the analysis. The interior of the car in the CFD model does not simulate the sound absorption properties of the real car, which could cause damping of higher frequencies in the wind tunnel measurements.

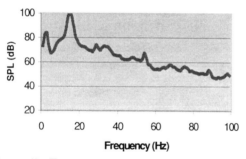

Figure 4b: Frequency spectrum of sunroof buffeting noise from the wind tunnel measurement.

Example 1: Design of Wind Deflector for Noise Control

In this example, CFD analysis is used to design a wind deflector for sunroof buffeting noise suppression. Figure 5 shows a view of three sunroofs cases. The baseline design showed significant sunroof buffeting noise. CFD analysis was used in conjunction with wind tunnel tests to design the deflectors. Two deflector designs were considered. In the first design, a straight edge deflector, referred as Deflector-A, of 30mm thickness was used to deflect the shear layer to prevent the vortices hitting the rear edge of the sunroof opening. In the second design, 10 notches were introduced in the Deflector-A. This design is referred in this paper as Deflector-B.

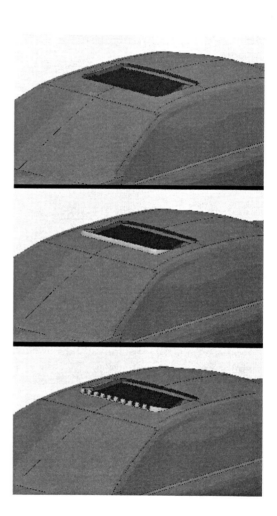

Figure 5: View of car roof wind deflector designs, (top: Baseline, middle: Deflector-A, bottom: Deflector-B).

Figure 6 shows the plot of noise amplitude of the dominant mode in the frequency spectrum. The wind tunnel tests show that the baseline design has noise amplitude of more than 98 dB and therefore corrective measures are required to reduce the acoustic annoyance in the passenger compartment. The addition of Deflector-A (straight edge deflector) reduces the noise magnitude by about 5dB. Using Deflector-B reduces this magnitude even further by about 2dB.

Comparison of the CFD predictions to the wind tunnel measurements shows that the numerical predictions are in good agreement with the experimental results. The computed results show a consistent under prediction of noise amplitude. However, the trend of noise increments is predicted quite accurately. This information is invaluable in evaluating various deflector designs without constructing the time-consuming hardware components.

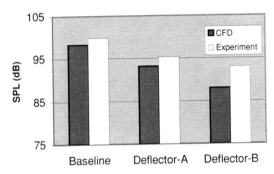

Figure 6: Peak noise amplitude for sunroof buffeting for various designs at 50kph.

Figure 7 shows a comparison of the frequency of the peak noise amplitude for the three cases. The plot shows that CFD predictions differ from the wind tunnel measurements by less than 1Hz. It is also interesting to note from the figure that Deflector-A results in the peak magnitude at slightly higher frequency while the Deflector-B has resonance at a lower frequency. The CFD predictions also capture this trend excellently.

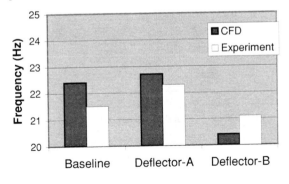

Figure 7: Frequency of the peak noise amplitude for sunroof buffeting for various designs at 50kph.

Example 2: Comfort Position for Noise Control

This section describes an application of CFD methods to evaluate the effects of comfort stop position on sunroof buffeting. Figure 8 shows a view of sunroofs for the two cases. The picture with the sunroof glass shows the glass in the fully open position. In the fully open position, sunroof glass partly covers the opening, thus reducing the opening length from 0.57m to 0.34m. The reduced opening length allows the vortices to interact with the glass before reaching the rear edge of the opening.

.

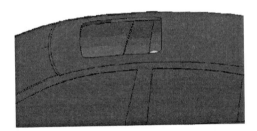

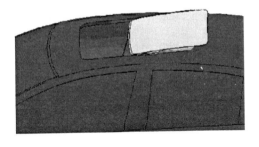

Figure 8: View of the sunroof opening with and without the sunroof glass.

Figure 9 shows the plot of noise magnitude of the dominant mode in the frequency spectrum for the two cases. The CFD predicted magnitude is smaller than the wind tunnel measurements, just like the first example. The use of retracted glass as a comfort stop helps in totally eliminating the buffeting phenomenon. The noise magnitude of 80dB or less in the frequency range showed here is acoustically insignificant.

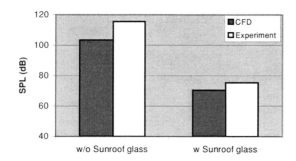

Figure 9: Peak noise amplitude for sunroof buffeting for various designs at 50kph.

CONCLUSIONS

PAM-FLOW CFD software is used to simulate the sunroof-buffeting phenomenon. The characteristics of the pressure time-history and frequency spectrum of the buffeting noise are described. Noise is computed for two sunroofs designs with noise control mechanisms. In the first case, a wind deflector is used to reduce the buffeting noise while in the second case a comfort position stop is used. Both cases compared well against the wind tunnel measurements. The results show that CFD can be used to aid the acoustic design of sunroofs for automotive vehicles. Furthermore, the influence of various geometric parameters of a vehicle can be studied to understand the phenomenon and avoid sunroof buffeting altogether.

ACKNOWLEDGEMENT

The authors would like to thank James C. Zunich and David Horgan from the Noise and Vibration Center at General Motors for providing the data of wind tunnel experiments.

REFERENCES

1. Ota, D.K., Chakravarthy, S.R., Becker, T. and Sturzenegger, T., ``Computational Study of Resonance Suppression of Open Sunroofs'', Journal of Fluids Engineering, Vol 116, pp 877-882, Dec. 1994.
2. Nelson, P.A., Halliwell, N.A., and Doak, P.E., ``Fluid Dynamics of Flow Excited Resonance, Part I: Experiment'', Journal of Sound and Vibration, Vol 78(1), pp 15-38, 1981.
3. Nelson, P.A., Halliwell, N.A., and Doak, P.E., ``Fluid Dynamics of Flow Excited Resonance, Part II: Flow Acoustic Interaction'', Journal of Sound and Vibration, Vol 91(3), pp 375-402, 1983.
4. Karbon, K. and Kumarasamy, S., ``Computational Aeroacoustics Applications in Automotive Design'', First MIT Conference on Computational Solid and Fluid Mechanics, MIT, June 2001.
5. Singh, R, ``Sunroof Buffeting Simulations Using PAM-FLOW'', Ameripam-2001, PAM-FLOW User's Conference, Detroit, Nov. 2001.
6. PAM-FLOW 2000, User's manual. ESI Group, www.esi-group.com, 2001.

AIAA 2002-2551

AERO-VIBRO-ACOUSTICS: PROBLEM STATEMENT AND METHODS FOR SIMULATION-BASED DESIGN SOLUTION

P.G. Bremner, Vibro-Acoustic Sciences, Inc, San Diego, CA

J.F. Wilby, Wilby Associates, Calabasas, CA

Abstract

This paper defines the field of "aero-vibro-acoustics" as the transmission of noise through a structure when the exterior source is specifically an aerodynamic or hydrodynamic environment. Important applications of current interest are identified and discussed briefly. They include a wide range of situations including low speed, separated flow associated with "wind noise" in automobiles, aircraft interior noise from turbulent boundary layer excitation, and launch vehicle vibration and fairing interior noise due to transonic and supersonic boundary layer and shockwave excitation. Three methods are introduced to assist in the solution of aero-vibro-acoustic problems. The methods are (1) statistical energy analysis (SEA), (2) experimental characterization of flow-induced noise sources from wind tunnel or other tests, and (3) computational aeroacoustics (CAA). Current technical problems are identified and potential solutions discussed. It is suggested that all three methods need to be applied in an integrated manner to address aero-vibro-acoustic design for applications such as wind noise inside automobiles.

Introduction

The field of "aero-vibro-acoustics" is defined as the transmission of noise through a structure, when the exterior source is an aerodynamic or hydrodynamic environment. This paper focuses on physics-based simulation methods that facilitate engineering design for control of interior noise. The design problem has two parts. The first part is simulation of the exterior flow, as influenced by design parameters such as aerodynamic shape and flow control. The second part is simulation of the transmission of exterior surface pressures to an interior sound field, as influenced by shape and physical properties of the intervening structure. In particular, this paper uses the sound transmission physics of the second part to better define the requirements on wind tunnel testing and computational aero-acoustics, which are currently being used for the first part of the problem.

Aerodynamic and hydrodynamic noise transmission has elements in common with the room acoustics problem of "sound transmission loss" in which the exterior source is assumed to be a diffuse acoustic field. A good description is provided by Fahy[1]. One important observation is that while the structure's vibration response to acoustical excitation is dominated by its resonant modes, low frequency sound transmission to the interior is controlled by the acoustically "forced" response of non-resonant modes.

Mathur & Bremner[2] have shown that airplane interior noise transmission can be predicted for high speed boundary layer noise excitation. An empirical model of the boundary layer surface pressure cross spectrum is convolved with each structural mode to estimate the resonant vibration response. The resulting sound radiation to the interior was based on room acoustics theory[1]. At the cruise conditions (Mach 0.8), the high levels of aerodynamic excitation at the convection wavenumber couple well with the resonant modes of the structure[3] so that non-resonant transmission could be neglected. Neither resonant nor non-resonant response couples well with the interior acoustics.

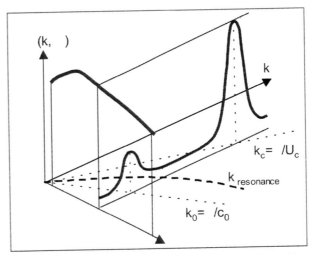

Figure 1. Wavenumber-frequency (k-ω) diagram for surface pressure spectrum (k,ω) of a sub-sonic flow; showing convective k_c and acoustic k_0 energy components and typical resonance wavenumber for a thin panel.

The problems associated with low speed flows ($M \ll 1.0$) are more difficult, particularly when there is separated flow over irregularly shaped bodies. Typically, flow Mach numbers for automobiles and submerged vehicles are 0.1 and 0.01, respectively. Boundary layer convected wavenumbers $k_c = \omega/U_c$ are up to two orders of magnitude greater than corresponding acoustical and structural wavenumbers, as indicated in Figure 1. Low speed flows were investigated first for underwater applications such as flow noise on sonar domes[4].

Hwang & Hambric[5] have shown that, under these conditions, the structural resonances present such a strong spatial filter to the excitation that only the very small amplitude, low wavenumber components of the pressure wavenumber-frequency spectrum $\Phi(k, \omega)$ need to be used to predict the structure's vibration response. The spatial filter or coupling characteristic between the surface pressure cross spectrum $\Phi(k, \omega)$ and a structure resonant mode $\Psi_{mn}(k_m, k_n)$ is sometimes called the modal joint acceptance. The main problem is to estimate the low wavenumber cross spectrum components of the flow excitation – well below the dominant hydrodynamic convection wavenumber disturbance. Hwang & Hambric show the efficacy of selected empirical models for their specific boundary layer flow condition.

Automotive Wind Noise Application

Other applications of low speed turbulent boundary layer excitation are encountered when trying to predict the noise radiated to the interior of an automobile, especially under excitation by highly separated subsonic flow. The case of aerodynamic or "wind" noise inside an automobile is a of particular current interest. George, Carr & Callister[6] conducted some of the first work in this field, but initial predictions were disappointing.

Strumolo[7] has been more successful in predicting wind noise transmission across the driver side glass. He used four different empirical models for the exterior pressure cross-spectrum – for A-pillar vortex, re-attached flow, turbulent boundary layer and mirror separation bubble flow regions – to predict resonant vibration of the side glass and the directly-radiated sound pressure level. Results are dependent on a number of empirical factors – up to four flow cross-spectrum estimates $\Phi_{1-4}(k, \omega)$, side glass modal damping $\eta_{glass}(\omega)$ and assumptions about the acoustic transmission loss through seals $TL_{seals}(\omega)$.

Coney[8,9] conducted wind tunnel measurements of the exterior pressure spectrum and the transfer functions between pressure and vibration, for each of the panel surfaces of a full automobile. However, Coney was unable to predict interior sound pressure level (SPL) to the same accuracy as Strumolo, using these measurements. The transfer function model under-predicts the measured interior SPL. Based on the data presented, the current authors noted that the Coney model also substantially under-predicts panel vibration at acoustic critical frequency[1]. Bremner[10] concluded that these trends were evidence of an exterior acoustic source present in the boundary layer pressure spectrum. Since the acoustic source was not specifically extracted from measurements, it was effectively omitted from Coney's noise transfer path model.

The need to identify the acoustic component of the exterior pressure cross spectrum - and the need to include exterior-to-interior acoustic energy transmission paths - is the main topic of this paper. It will be shown that these essential noise transmission mechanisms put very demanding requirements on both wind tunnel testing and computational aero-acoustics methods that might be used in aerodynamic design to control interior noise from low speed separated flow excitation.

Cross-spectrum Model for Low Speed Separated Flow

It is postulated that most low speed boundary layer flow fields, attached or separated, will have an acoustic energy component. Acoustic theory is derived mathematically from the Navier-Stokes equation of fluid dynamics under the assumption of small amplitude (linear), inviscid and irrotational flow disturbance. Turbulent boundary layer flow, on the other hand, is characterized by viscous shear induced by flow interaction with a boundary surface, which induces the statistically random generation of rotational eddies in a complex 3-dimensional Navier-Stokes flow field.

It is argued that the acoustic field component of a boundary layer pressure spectrum represents the natural propagation of pressure disturbances away from each instantaneous and localized eddy - at a sufficient distance from the localized eddy, where the pressure has decayed to the small amplitude acoustics range. This acoustic component – although small in amplitude compared to the pressures created by the convecting turbulence eddies – can be vitally important to the sound transmission characteristics or aero-vibro-acoustics problems.

It follows that the cross spectrum model for low-speed boundary layer flow needs to be modeled by the sum of two uncorrelated source components. The two components are the convected turbulence source $\Phi_c(k,\omega)$ and the acoustic source $\Phi_0(k,\omega)$ source. Thus,

$$\Phi_p(k,\omega) = \Phi_c(k,\omega) + \Phi_0(k,\omega) \qquad (1)$$

where k is wavenumber (rad/m) and ω is frequency (rad/sec). Each source component needs to be described by a surface pressure cross-spectrum. For convenience, the form of the cross spectrum is generally assumed to be separable in frequency and spatial domains. For a homogeneous source, the frequency content is described by the space-averaged auto-spectrum $\Phi_p(\omega)$. The degree of phase correlation between pressure loads at any two points – and the phase (apparent wavenumber) relationship of the correlated part - is typically described by a spatial correlation function, transformed to the frequency domain[2].

The convected turbulence pressure cross spectrum model typically takes the form:

$$\Phi_c(x, x'; \omega) = \Phi_c(\omega) e^{-c_x k_c |\Delta x| + j b_x k_c \Delta x} e^{-c_y k_c |\Delta y| + j b_y k_c \Delta y}$$

$$(2)$$

where $k_c = \omega/U_c$ is the convection wavenumber; c_x, c_y are the spatial coherence decay coefficients in x and y directions; b_x and b_y are wavenumber factors; and $\Delta x = (x-x')$ and $\Delta y = (y-y')$.

The acoustic pressure cross spectrum that is induced by boundary layer turbulence also needs a spatial correlation description. We postulate here that a diffuse field[11] is a reasonable approximation for low Mach number flows, on the basis that the turbulent eddies are effectively random acoustic sources in space and time, and that any convection effects on the acoustic pressure are negligible. The acoustic pressure cross spectrum will therefore take the form:

$$\Phi(x, x'; \omega) = \Phi_0(\omega) \sin(k_0 r)/k_0 r \qquad (3)$$

where $\Phi_0(\omega)$ is the auto-spectrum of space-averaged acoustic pressure and $r = |x - x'|$.

As shown schematically in Figure 2, the experimental or numerical separation of Φ_0 and Φ_c will require wavenumber decomposition of the total boundary layer pressure on the surface.

DeJong, Bharj & Lee[12], recently provided evidence of an acoustic source contribution in automotive wind noise This is shown in Figure 3, which contains wind tunnel measurements and predictions. They estimated that the turbulent boundary layer pressures are 25 to 35 dB higher in level than are the corresponding acoustic components.

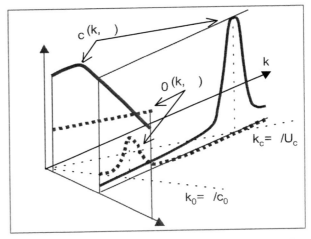

Figure 2. Wavenumber-frequency $(k\text{-}\omega)$ diagram for surface pressure spectrum of a sub-sonic, separated flow; showing turbulence spectrum Φ_c (solid) and acoustic spectrum Φ_0 (dotted) components.

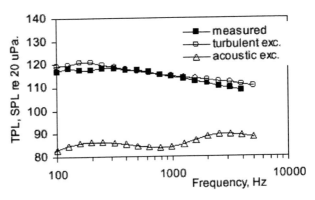

Figure 3. Turbulence and acoustic pressure components compared with measured total surface pressure, on side glass at 130 km/h in wind tunnel. Reproduced from [12].

Noise Transmission Modeling Methods

The coupling between the pressure field and the mode shapes of the responding structure can be written as[13,14,15]

$$\Phi_{pmn}(\omega) = \iint_k \Phi_p(k,\omega) |S_{mn}(k)|^2 \, dk \qquad (4)$$

where the mode shape function is defined as

$$S_{mn}(k) = \iint_A \Psi_{mn}(x) e^{-jk \cdot x} dx \qquad (5)$$

$\Phi_p(k,\omega)$ is the wavenumber-frequency pressure spectrum for the excitation field, dk denotes $dk_1 dk_2$ and dx denotes $dx_1 dx_2$. The structural mode shapes are denoted by $\psi_{mn}(\underset{\sim}{x})$ and A is the area of the structure.

Figure 4 contains typical wavenumber spectra for the modes of a panel (simply-supported or clamped boundary conditions) and turbulent boundary layer excitation, at a given frequency[5]. These spectra represent the components of the integrand of Eq. (4). The product of the spectra would result in a spectrum with two major peaks corresponding to the main modal peak and the turbulent boundary layer peak. At aerodynamic coincidence, the two peaks would overlap and the coupling would be at an overall maximum.

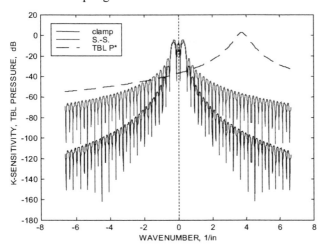

Figure 4. Wavenumber analysis of a typical panel vibration mode with clamped (blue) and simply-supported (red) boundary conditions, superimposed on turbulent boundary layer wavenumber spectrum. Reproduced from [5]

$\Phi_{mn}(\omega)$ can be related to the joint acceptance function in frequency analysis by the relationship[13]

$$j_{mn}^2(\omega) = \frac{U_c^2}{\omega^2} \frac{\Phi_{mn}(\omega)}{\Phi_p(\omega)} \qquad (6)$$

where $\Phi_p(\omega)$ is the excitation pressure spectral density and U_c the pressure field convection velocity. It is assumed that the boundary layer pressure field is temporally stationary and spatially homogeneous. Then the pressure field can be expressed as a cross correlation function that decays with spatial and time separation and convected with the flow, as indicated in Eq. (2).

The velocity spectral density of the structure is then

$$\Phi_v(\omega) = \sum_{m,n} \frac{\Phi_{pmn}(\omega)}{|Z_{mn}(\omega)|^2} \qquad (7)$$

where $Z_{mn}(\omega)$ is the mechanical impedance of the structure.

The radiation efficiency in terms of wavenumber can be given by[4]

$$\sigma_{mn} = \frac{1}{4\pi^2 A} \iint_{k<k_o} |S_{mn}(\underset{\sim}{k})|^2 \left[1 - \left(\frac{k}{k_o} \right)^2 \right]^{-0.5} d\underset{\sim}{k}$$
$$(8)$$

where $k_o = \omega / c_o$

Graham[14] has analyzed the response of rectangular plates to turbulent boundary layer excitation, using empirical and analytical representations of the turbulent boundary layer pressure field by Corcos, Efimtsov, Smol'yakov & Tkachenko, Ffowcs Williams, and Chase. His results indicate that, for structural and boundary layer parameters typical of aircraft in cruise, the response occurs in resonant, acoustically inefficient plate modes whose contributions dominate acoustic radiation whether or not they are strongly driven by the boundary layer. When the modes are strongly driven by the boundary layer, the excitation levels are determined by the "convective peak" of the wavenumber-frequency spectrum, which is where most of the fluctuating energy lies, and the radiated sound is sensitive to details of the shape and location of the peak. When the modes are weakly driven by the boundary layer, the sub-convective region of the wavenumber-frequency spectrum is important and differences between models at low wavenumbers lead to corresponding discrepancies in radiated sound predictions.

For the automotive wind noise application, the flow speed is considerably slower and more separated than the aircraft boundary layer case. Strumolo[7] estimates the sound power transmitted to the interior acoustic space using

$$\Pi_{\Delta\omega}^{rad} = \rho_0 c_0 A \langle \sigma_{rad} \rangle_{\Delta\omega} \int_{\Delta\omega} \Phi_v(\omega) d\omega \qquad (9)$$

where $\langle \sigma_{mn} \rangle_{\Delta\omega}$ is the modal radiation efficiency averaged over the modes which are resonant in the analysis frequency band. This effectively assumes that all of the sound power is radiated by the resonant vibration modes in the structure. However, it is well known in room acoustics[1] that the non-resonant (mass-controlled) modes can provide an additional sound power transmission path, typically at low frequencies, where the mass-controlled impedance of these modes is very low.

Bremner[16] has previously expanded the foregoing modal formulation to explicitly include the resonant and non-resonant contributions to transmitted sound. The total sound power radiated to the interior is

$$\Pi_{\Delta\omega}^{rad} \propto \rho_0 c_0 A \int_{\Delta\omega} d\omega \sum_{mn} \frac{\omega^2 \Phi_0(\omega) j_{mn}^2(\omega) \sigma_{mn}(\omega)}{\mu_{mn} |Y_{mn}(\omega)|^2}$$
(10)

The resonant versus non-resonant contributions can be separated in the modal summation. Neglecting stiffness-controlled modes[16] and dropping the frequency dependence notation, the total power can be partitioned into:

$$\Pi_{\Delta\omega}^{rad} \propto \rho_0 c_0 A \int_{\Delta\omega} d\omega \left\{ \sum_{\omega_{mn}\in\Delta\omega} \frac{\omega^2 \Phi \sigma_{mn}^2(\omega)}{\mu_{mn} |Y_{mn}|^2} + \sum_{\omega_{mn}<\Delta\omega} \frac{\Phi \sigma_{mn}^2(\omega)}{\mu_{mn}} \right\}$$
(11)

The product $j_{mn}^2(\omega)\sigma_{mn}(\omega)$ in Eq. (10) is replaced by $\sigma_{mn}^2(\omega)$ in Eq. (11), because the joint acceptance is proportional to radiation efficiency when the excitation is a diffuse acoustic field.

The term on the left of Eq. (11) is the power radiated by the resonant modes (ω_{mn}) and the term on the right is the power transmitted by the mass-controlled modes ($\omega_{mn}<\omega$). For automotive glass panels and a diffuse acoustic excitation field, the non-resonant modes provide the dominant transmission path below 2,000 Hz, and the resonant modes provide the dominant path above 2,000 Hz (Figure 5).

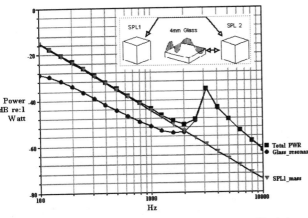

Figure 5. Components of sound power transmitted by 4mm glass panel under acoustic excitation – total power (blue); resonant (red) and non-resonant (green).

For the case of low speed, highly separated flow – such as wind noise – the exterior pressure spectrum is the sum of a high energy turbulence spectrum $\Phi_c(k_c, \omega)$ in Eq. (2) and a lower level, uncorrelated diffuse acoustic spectrum $\Phi_0(k_0, \omega)$. The total sound power radiated to the interior of the automobile can, therefore, be expanded, using Eq. (11), into four terms:

$$\Pi_{\Delta\omega}^{rad} \propto \rho_0 c_0 A \int_{\Delta\omega} d\omega \left\{ \sum_{\omega_{mn}\in\Delta\omega} \frac{\omega^2 \Phi_0 \sigma_{mn}^2(\omega_{mn})}{\mu_{mn} |Y_{mn}|^2} + \frac{\omega^2 \Phi_c j_{mn}^2 \sigma_{mn}(\omega_{mn})}{\mu_{mn} |Y_{mn}|^2} \right. $$
$$\left. + \sum_{\omega_{mn}<\Delta\omega} \frac{\Phi_0 \sigma_{mn}^2(\omega)}{\mu_{mn}} + \frac{\Phi_c j_{mn}^2(\omega)\sigma_{mn}(\omega)}{\mu_{mn}} \right\}$$
(12)

The first two terms in Eq. (12) are the power radiated by the resonant modes, as driven by the acoustic, Φ_0, and turbulence, Φ_c, spectral components, respectively. Each power component is the product of two modal coupling terms; each such term is a product in wavenumber space. Their relative contribution to total power is illustrated graphically (not to scale) in Figure 6. The two diagrams on the right hand side of Figure 6 represent the product of the turbulent boundary layer excitation and the acoustic radiation, whereas the diagram on the left hand side represents both acoustic excitation and acoustic radiation. The high-energy turbulence excitation only weakly drives the panel resonances, so that quite low levels of acoustic excitation may transmit a similar amount of sound power – especially for acoustically "fast" modes ($k_{mn} \approx k_0$).

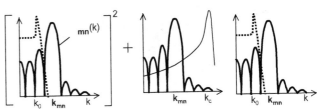

Figure 6. Wavenumber diagram for the resonant mode coupling – the first two integral terms in Eq. (12)

The last two terms in Eq. (12) are the power radiated by the non-resonant modes, as driven by the acoustic Φ_0 and turbulence Φ_c spectrum components, respectively. Their relative contribution to total power is illustrated graphically (not to scale) in Figure 7. The left term is the acoustic mass-law that will transmit a significant amount of acoustic power Φ_0 – because a number of the non-resonant modes will always be acoustically "fast" ($k_{mn} \approx k_0$). However, the high-energy turbulence excitation is so weakly coupled to non-resonant modes that its power contribution can usually be neglected.

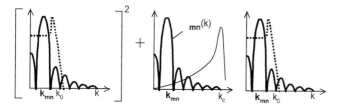

Figure 7. Wavenumber diagram for the non-resonant mode coupling – the second two integral terms in Eq. (12)

Statistical Energy Analysis

The statistical energy analysis (SEA) method as described by Lyon & DeJong[17] is well suited to modeling the energy transmission mechanisms in aero-vibro-acoustics. Price & Crocker[18] have shown how SEA can be used to accurately model the sound transmission loss problems of room acoustics. SEA models in commercial code AutoSEA2[19] (Figures 8 & 9) include explicit representations of both the resonant and the non-resonant (mass law) components of the transmission phenomenon.

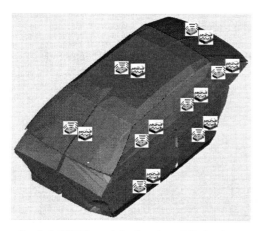

Figure 8. AutoSEA2 model of automobile body showing panel and interior sub-structuring. Flow excitation is a combination of separated turbulence and acoustic sources

DeJong, Bharj & Lee[12] applied this SEA approach to a full scale automobile exposed to flow in a wind tunnel and obtained the results shown in Figure 10. The predicted sound levels are in close agreement with measurements and the predicted sound levels due to acoustic excitation are dominant at high frequencies.

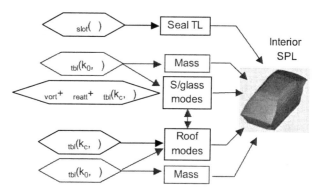

Figure 9. Noise transmission paths captured by SEA model

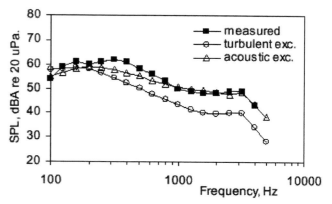

Figure 10. Interior SPL predicted by SEA model with combined turbulence source (circles) & acoustic source (triangles) compared with measurement. Reproduced from [12]

Flow Field Cross-spectrum Estimation Methods

There are three methods – empirical, test and numerical CFD. Empirical is based on observation from the latter two. Current progress and requirements defined by physics of the noise transmission process are reviewed for each of these.

Wind Tunnel Testing

Pressure spectra beneath attached and separated turbulent boundary layers have been measured in a number of situations including wind and water tunnels, on buoyant bodies and in flight, but attention was directed mainly toward the convective frequency components[4]. The measurements are dominated by convective components and do not provide information as a function of wavenumber. Interest in the low wavenumber or acoustic components in the turbulent boundary layer pressure field was directed initially towards underwater applications, but measurements have been conducted in both water and air.

A variety of measurement techniques have been tried, including one- and two-dimensional arrays of transducers, vibrating panels and membranes[4,20]. Figure 11 shows several linear arrays of microphones on an automobile for test in a wind tunnel[8].

Figure 11. A sample microphone array measurement set-up for wind tunnel testing. Reproduced from [8]

The wavenumber-frequency spectrum can be defined in terms of either the cross correlation function $R_p\left(\underline{x},\tau\right)$ or the cross spectrum $\Phi_p\left(\underline{x},\omega\right)$ using the Fourier transform relationships

$$\Phi_p\left(\underline{k},\omega\right)=\iiint_{\underline{x},\tau}R_p\left(\underline{x},\tau\right)e^{-j\left(\underline{k}.\underline{x}-\omega\tau\right)}d\underline{x}d\tau \quad (13)$$

or

$$\Phi_p\left(\underline{k},\omega\right)=\iint_{\underline{x}}\Phi_p\left(\underline{x},\omega\right)e^{-j\underline{k}.\underline{x}}d\underline{x} \quad (14)$$

The functions $R_p\left(\underline{x},\tau\right)$ and $\Phi_p\left(\underline{x},\omega\right)$ can be measured directly. However, the transducer array has to be designed carefully with the correct separation distance between adjacent transducers to achieve the desired spatial resolution for the Fourier transformation. The separation distance will depend on the wavenumber and flow speed, with the larger distances being associated with the lower wavenumbers. Also, it may be necessary to use more than one array of transducers with different separation distances between the transducers, so that the desired range of wavenumbers can be included[20].

In order to obtain reliable frequency spectra, it is necessary to ensure that background acoustic levels do not contaminate the results, particularly for attached turbulent boundary layers where the boundary layer

fluctuating pressures are relatively low. The problem is more severe in the measurement of wavenumber–frequency spectra, as shown schematically in Figure 12. The contribution of low wavenumber components to the pressure spectrum is much lower in level than that of the convected component. Thus, any background noise levels in the test facility could mask the low wavenumber components. The problem is overcome, at least to some extent, by making measurements in wind tunnels that are designed to have low noise levels in the test section. Another factor to be considered is the potential for the structure of the test vehicle to be excited by the turbulent flow and radiate sound that contaminates the results at low wavenumber[20].

There is a wide range in the measured spectral levels at low wavenumbers, the variation in the data being of the order of $\pm15\text{dB}$[21], but, as there have not been any control experiments, it has not been determined whether the variability is dependent on the facility or the measurement technique, or a combination of both. This variability in the experimental results is probably one cause of the wide range of empirical and analytical models at low wavenumbers[14].

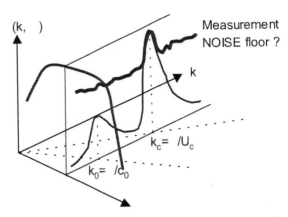

Figure 12. Schematic illustrating how measurement noise may obscure the important low wavenumber components of a low speed boundary layer pressure cross-spectrum.

Definition of the wavenumber-frequency spectrum for the boundary layer is more difficult when the pressure field is inhomogeneous, as in areas of separated flow where the pressure level, convection velocity and correlation decay vary rapidly with location. This occurs, for example, on the driver's side window of an automobile[7,9]. The pragmatic approach used in the past has been to apply some form of averaging of the pressure field, in terms of pressure level, convection velocity and correlation decay. However, there is a need for a more-formalized approach.

Computational Aero-Acoustics (CAA)

Proven codes for computational fluid dynamics (CFD) can typically capture the macro characteristics of boundary layer flow. They can reproduce separation at discontinuities and ensuing vortices and re-attachment bubbles. However, these codes have only recently been applied to problems of aero-vibro-acoustics. Unsteady codes using a Reynolds-averaged Navier Stokes (RANS) approximation for small scale turbulence have exhibited mixed success. Provided the mesh is small and the discrete time integration step size is small, these codes reduce to the wave equation and yield acoustic propagation solutions. Khourrami et al.[22] successfully used a RANS code to simulate a 50kHz acoustic whistle which was measured on a forward wing slat in low speed flow (M=0.2) at a high angle of attack. The CFD solution showed that the whistle was created by a small periodic vortex shed from a square trailing edge of the wing slat. The pressure contours in Figure 13 clearly indicate that – in the localized region where the mesh size is small enough - the acoustic wave propagation has been captured.

Figure 13. Acoustic field induced by trailing edge vortex street, simulated by high resolution RANS code. Reproduced from [22]

However, Hold et al.[23] found that their RANS code was less reliable at predicting surface pressure spectrum due to the highly–separated turbulent wake shed from a side-mirror-like obstacle in flow over a flat plate. It was concluded that the RANS code could reproduce periodic flow phenomenon but the Reynolds averaging approximation could not reproduce the unsteady pressure at mid- to high frequencies, corresponding to small scale, random turbulence interactions.

In more recent work, Siegert and Orellano[24] – working in conjunction with Technical University of Berlin – have successfully validated a large eddy simulation (LES) code on this application. The pressure spectrum results shown in Figure 14 are in very good agreement with test. However, wavenumber analyses of these

pressure spectrum predictions have not been published. It is not clear how well the LES code captures the low wavenumber and acoustic components of the pressure spectrum and therefore it is still uncertain how well the panel vibration response and sound transmission can be simulated.

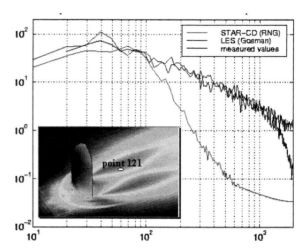

Figure 14. Surface pressure versus frequency spectrum in the wake of a mirror-like flow disturbance, comparing RANS code (red); LES code (blue) and measurement (black). Reproduced from [24].

An alternative approach is offered by the kinematic gas lattice simulation method which was evaluated by Leep-Appolini & Strumolo[25] . Their study investigated the full aero-vibro-acoustics problem of wind noise generation and transmission to the interior of three different automobile body shapes with windscreen rake angles of 55, 63 and 71 degrees. The lattice gas CFD simulations were compared with full scale wind tunnel measurements and sound measurements at the driver's ear position, inside the three body shapes.

Computed surface pressure maps demonstrate good qualitative agreement with test but there seem to be problems correctly predicting the re-attached flow line. These errors are more obvious in surface pressure spectrum predictions, with errors up to 20 dB in the expected re-attached flow zone. What is at first surprising is that these simulated surface pressure spectra were used in conjunction with Strumolo's SEA-based Wind Noise Modeler[7] to predict interior SPL at the driver's ear, with remarkable accuracy, as shown in Figure 15.

However, a wavenumber analysis of either the predicted or the measured surface pressure spectrum is not reported. It is not clear how well the gas lattice CFD code predicts the low wavenumber and acoustic components of the pressure spectrum. It is possible that these $_0$ components are correctly predicted – even though the turbulence pressure spectrum Φ_c components are not correctly simulated. That would help explain how the total exterior pressure spectrum $\Phi_p = \Phi_c + \Phi_0$ could be in error, but the SEA-based interior SPL prediction is still correct.

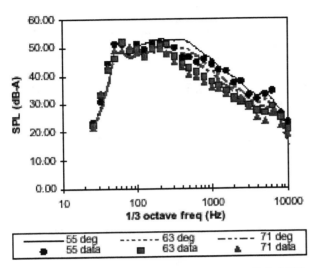

Figure 15. Comparison of experimental and predicted SPL spectra at driver's ear. Lines indicate the predicted spectra and the filled markers indicate the experimental data. Reproduced from [25].

In other fields – such as helicopter rotor noise and aircraft airframe noise – rigorous computational aeroacoustics (CAA) solutions involve up to a three-step process. CFD codes are used to define the local turbulence flow field; the Fowcs Williams-Hawking equation is used to identify effective acoustic sources in the turbulent flow region (by analogy to monopoles, dipoles and quadrupoles) and finally the acoustic radiation is solved with a boundary element-type acoustic code. This process is necessary for the prediction of exterior sound fields generated by turbulent or disturbed flow. It is not strictly necessary for problems of aero-vibro-acoustics – where we seek to recover the turbulent and acoustic pressures on a surface. However, the Fowcs Williams-Hawking acoustic analogy may well have useful application to reducing the complexity of CFD solutions – in future – for problems of aero-vibro-acoustics.

As for wind tunnel measurements, the challenge is to determine the low wavenumber turbulence and acoustic components of the flow field. This presents problems of numerical signal-to-noise ratio (see Figure 16) which need to be carefully considered in the design of a CFD solution algorithm. Wind tunnel measurements and analyses by DeJong et al.[12] – shown in Figure 3 –

indicate that the acoustic wavenumber energy is 25-35 dB lower than the turbulence pressure.

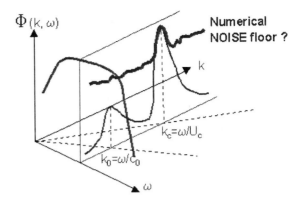

Figure 16. Schematic illustrating how numerical noise may obscure the important low wavenumber components of a low speed boundary layer pressure cross-spectrum.

Integrated Solution

It is suggested that all three methods - empirical, test and numerical CFD - need to be applied in an integrated manner to address aero-vibro-acoustic design for applications such as wind noise inside automobiles. CFD and wind tunnel testing might best be used to define empirical source models in terms of design parameters. In the automobile wind noise case, the parameters might be windshield rake angle, side glass curvature, A-pillar fairing step size, road speed and incident wind angle.

As a starting point, wavenumber analysis of surface pressures should be conducted for simple boundary layer and separated flow experiments. Candidate experiments are shown in Figure 17.

Wave number analysis of measured surface pressures and panel vibration response would be most useful in validating CFD and structural-acoustic codes. Measurement of acoustic intensity radiated into a sufficiently large anechoic acoustic cavity beneath the panel would be suitable for validating the SEA-based model for wind noise transmission.

In this manner, the correct flow pressure spectrum physics and sound transmission physics are captured. Then, the most cost-effective combination of wind tunnel and CFD tests of parametrically-varied aerodynamic shapes can be used to define empirical models for the aerodynamic source. Used in conjunction with SEA, there is the potential for a true "design" solution for problems of aero-vibro-acoustics.

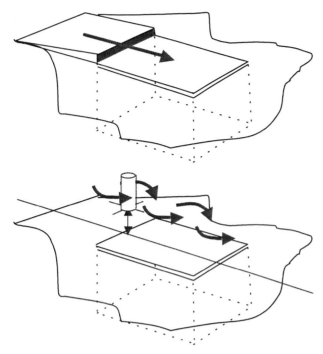

Figure 17. Suggested aero-vibro-acoustic experiments; (top) - separated flow on a plate due to an upstream step; (bottom) – turbulent wake flow field above the surface of a plate.

Conclusions

Low wavenumber and acoustic components in pressure fields beneath low speed turbulent boundary layers can play a significant role in determining noise transmission through a structure exposed to the flow. Existing analytical modeling techniques, particularly statistical energy analysis, are capable of predicting the noise transmission, provided that there are reliable methods of describing the low wavenumber components of the excitation. Past attempts to determine the low wavenumber components of a turbulent boundary layer (attached or separated) have resulted in a wide range of empirical and analytical models. This aspect of the simulation process still requires a definitive solution.

References

1. F. J. Fahy, *Sound and Structural Vibration: Radiation, Transmission & Response,* Academic Press, 1985

2. B. N. Tran, G. P. Mathur & P. G. Bremner, "Modal Energy Analysis of Aircraft Sidewall Response to Acoustic Fields", <u>Proceedings of Inter-noise 95</u>, Newport Beach

3. J. F. Wilby & F. L. Gloyna, "Vibration Measurements of an Airplane Fuselage Structure: I. Turbulent Boundary Layer Excitation", <u>J. Sound Vib</u>, <u>23</u>, 443-366, 1972.

4. W. M. Blake, *Mechanics of Flow-Induced Sound*, 2 volumes, Academic Press, London 1986

5. Y. F. Hwang & S. A. Hambric, "A Numerical technique for Computation of Flow-induced Vibration and Noise", Paper No. 4pSA2, 142nd Meeting of Acoustical Society of America, Ft. Lauderdale, December 2001

6. A. R. George, J. F .Carr & J. R. Callister, "Recent Advances in Understanding Automobile Aerodynamic Noise", Paper No. CEAS/AIAA-95-004, Proc. First Joint CEAS/AIAA Aeroacoustics Conference, Munich, Germany,1995

7. G. S. Strumolo, "The Wind Noise Modeller," SAE Paper 971921, 1997.

8. W. B. Coney, et al., "Characterization of the Wind Noise Loading of a Production Automobile Greenhouse Surfaces", <u>AD-Vol. 53-1, Fluid-Structure Interaction, Aeroelasticity, Flow Induced Vibration and Noise</u>, ASME, November 1997.

9. W. B. Coney, et al., "A Semi-Empirical Approach for Modeling Greenhouse Surface Noise", SAE Paper No. 1999-01-1811.

10. P. G. Bremner, "Simulation-based Design Method for Automotive Wind Noise", Vibro-Acoustic Sciences Inc. Technical Presentation to General Motors NVC, March 2000

11. B. J. Cron, & C. H. Sherman, "Spatial-Correlation Functions for Various Noise Models", <u>J. Acoust. Soc. Am.</u>, <u>34</u>, No.11, 1962

12. R. G. DeJong, T. S. Bharj, & J. J. Lee, "Vehicle Wind Noise Analysis Using a SEA Model with Measured Source Levels", Paper No. 2001-01-1629, <u>Proc. SAE Noise & Vibration Conf</u>, Traverse City, May 2001.

13. Y. F. Hwang & G. Maidanik, "A Wavenumber Analysis of the Coupling of a Structural Mode and Flow Turbulence", <u>J. Sound Vib.</u>, <u>142</u>, 135-152, 1990.

14. W. R. Graham, "A Comparison of Models for the Wavenumber-Frequency Spectrum of Turbulent Boundary-Layer Pressures", Paper No. CEAS/AIAA-95-097, First Joint CEAS/AIAA Aeroacoustics Conference, Munich, Germany, 1995.

15. G. P. Mathur, P. H. Denke, C. L. Chin, & B. N. Tran, "Wavenumber-Frequency Response of a Panel Excited by Turbulent Boundary Layer Pressure Field", Paper No. CEAS/AIAA-95-096, First Joint CEAS/AIAA Aeroacoustics Conference, Munich, Germany, 1995.

16. P. G. Bremner, "Finite Element based Vibro-Acoustics of Panel Systems", Proc. Conf. On Finite Element Methods in Engng., Melbourne, Australia August 1987.

17. R. H. Lyon & R. G. DeJong, *Theory and Application of Statistical Energy Analysis*, Butterworth-Heinemann, 1995.

18. A. J. Price & M. J. Crocker, "Sound Transmission through Double Panels using Statistical Energy Analysis", J. Acoust. Soc. Am., 47, 683-693, 1970

19. P. G. Bremner, T. E. Burton, & A. C. Cunningham, "AutoSEA2 – Evolution of Statistical Energy Analysis into a Mainstream Design Evaluation Tool", Proc. 1999 ASME DETC, Sept. 1999, Las Vegas, NV, 1999.

20. C. H. Sherman, S. H. Ko, & B. G. Buehler, "Measurement of the Turbulent Boundary Layer Wave-Vector Spectrum", J. Acoust. Soc. Am., 88, 386-390, 1990.

21. L. D. Pope, "Low-Wavenumber Constant of Turbulent Boundary Layer Pressure Fluctuations", Shock & Vibration Digest, 8, 3-10, 1976.

22. M. R. Khorrami, M. E. Berkman, M. Choudhari, B. A. Singer, D. P. Lockard & K. S. Brentner, "Unsteady Flow Computations of a Slat with a Blunt Trailing Edge", Paper No. AIAA-99-1805, Proc. 5th AIAA/CEAS Aeroacoustics Conference, Bellevue WA, May 1999.

23. R. Hold, A Brenneis, A, Eberle, V. Schwarz & R. Siegert, "Numerical Simulation of Aeroacoustic Sound Generated by Generic Bodires Placed on a Plate, Part 1 – Prediction of Aeroacoustic Sources", Paper No. AIAA-99-1896, Proc. 5th AIAA/CEAS Aeroacoustics Conference, Bellevue WA, May 1999.

24. Orellano, A. "On Aerodynamic Noise Prediction – Method Assessment (CFD part)", Bombardier Transportation presentation to 10th European StarCD Users Conference, London November 2001

25. Leep-Apolloni, L., Strumolo G.S. and Gulker, W. "Wind Noise Spectral Predictions Using a Lattice-based Method", Paper No. 1999-01-1810, Proc. SAE 1999 Noise & Vibration Conf., Traverse City MI, May 1999

26. Brentner, K.S. and Farassat, F. "Analytical Comparison of the Acoustic Analogy and Kirchoff Formulation for Moving Surfaces" AIAA Journal, 36, 1379-1386, 1998.

Two-Point Correlations and Acoustic Measurements of High-Speed Axisymmetric Jets

Michael J. Doty[*] and Dennis K. McLaughlin[†]

Department of Aerospace Engineering

The Pennsylvania State University

University Park, PA 16802

Abstract

This paper describes a series of acoustic and flowfield measurements of $M = 0.9$ and $M = 1.5$ axisymmetric jets using helium/air mixture jets to simulate the properties of heated jets. A summary of current acoustic results compared to existing heated jet data indicates the level of accuracy of the simulation technique. In addition, mean flow measurements of helium/air mixture jets exhibit trends similar to heated jets in terms of axial velocity profiles and shear layer thickness growth rates. A particular focus of the current work is the use of optical deflectometry to obtain two-point space-time correlations of density gradient fluctuations in the dominant noise production region of the jet. Results indicate distinct cross-correlations for the air jet cases, but less pronounced levels of correlation in helium/air mixture jet cases.

1. Introduction

The past decade has seen commercial aircraft noise become an increasing global concern both environmentally and economically. With recent community pressures, military aircraft noise near training facilities is also becoming an important issue. High-speed jet noise remains a significant contributor to overall aircraft noise of both commercial and military aircraft. As the jet noise community strives for more effective noise reduction strategies and better predictive capabilities, an improved understanding of the predominant noise sources in high-speed jets is important.

As a means of understanding jet noise sources, researchers have focused efforts on obtaining accurate measurements of jet turbulence properties. Davies et al.[1] used pairs of hot-wires and Bradshaw et al.[2] used crosswires to obtain two-point velocity correlations. Chu[3] and Harper-Bourne[4], among others have also contributed two-point correlation measurements using hot-wire instrumentation. More recently, Bridges and Podboy[5] used a pair of two-component hot-wire probes to obtain two-point velocity correlations with the advantage of updated acquisition technology and data storage capacity. The turbulence statistics provided by these studies have been important in expanding the capabilities of jet noise prediction schemes. However, the focus of these studies was limited to lower Mach number flows (typically $M = 0.7$ and below) due to hot-wire breakage problems at higher Mach numbers. Furthermore, the previously mentioned studies focused on cold jets due to the many difficulties of using hot-wires in heated flows. As interest in high-speed jet noise modeling continues to grow, there is a need for further jet turbulence data, particularly at higher Mach number and higher temperature jet flows. Because hot-wires are typically of limited value in such harsh conditions, other measurement techniques must be investigated.

The current study addresses this lack of data by using a measurement technique known as optical deflectometry to obtain two-point space-time correlation measurements in high-speed jets. The optical deflectometer is an adaptation of a crossed-beam laser system first introduced by Fisher and Krause[6]. The current system employs a quantitative schlieren technique similar to that used by McIntyre[7] to investigate turbulent mixing layers. The system is further described later in this work and more details can be found in Doty and McLaughlin[8] and Doty[9].

Another important aspect of the Penn State research program has been the use of helium/air mixture jets as a low cost alternative to heated jets. The lower density and higher velocity of a heated jet, as compared to an unheated or "cold" jet, can be simulated using a gas with a lower density and higher acoustic

---

[*] Graduate Student, Member AIAA
[†] Prof. and Head of Aerospace Engineering, Associate Fellow AIAA

velocity than air. While this technique has been used by previous researchers[10-14], the precise validity of such simulations has only recently been the subject of investigation[15,16]. Furthermore, the accuracy of the simulation in terms of representing flowfield properties is not well documented.

The current work presents a brief update of acoustic results comparing helium/air mixture jets to existing heated jet data. Flowfield measurements of pure air and helium/air mixture jets are then described. Specifically, mean velocity profile measurements and optical deflectometry measurements of two-point space-time density fluctuations are presented. Mach 0.9 and Mach 1.5 axisymmetric jets of one-half inch diameter are tested in both cold and heat-simulated conditions.

2. Experimental Procedures

2.1 Facility Description

The high-speed jet noise facility shown in Figure 1 includes a 2.07 MPa (300 psig) compressed air supply and pressurized helium cylinders. The upstream plenum is conditioned with turbulence management screens. A convergent-divergent, contoured $M = 1.5$ nozzle ($D = 12.7$ mm, 0.5 in) was used for the supersonic experiments, and a similar convergent nozzle of the same exit diameter was used for the subsonic experiments. It should be noted that after each helium/air mixture experiment (average run time approximately 15 seconds) pure air was run for several seconds to prevent an excess build-up of helium.

2.2 Instrumentation

An array of three to four condenser microphones was used for the acoustic measurements. The microphones are a mixture of those manufactured by Brüel and Kjær (B&K) (3.175 mm / 0.125 in microphones, Model 4138) and Larson Davis (6.35 mm / 0.25 in microphones, Model 2520). All microphone calibrations were performed with a B&K acoustic calibrator (Model 4231).

The microphones were placed in an arc centered at a position 63.5 mm ($x/D = 5$) downstream of the 12.7 mm nozzle exit and at a radius of 1.27 m ($R/D = 100$) in the plane of the jet nozzle as shown in Figure 2. The arc was centered at five diameters downstream of the nozzle exit because this location typically marks the end of the jet potential core, the location that is known to be the dominant noise production region of the jet. All measurements were made at angles between 20° and 90° from the jet axis. When comparing to other researchers' experiments,

previous data were scaled to the same non-dimensional radius as the current experiments (based on the $1/R^2$ dependence of intensity). Furthermore, trigonometric calculations led to slight additional changes in radius and microphone angle due to centering of previous researchers' experiments at the jet nozzle exit rather than at the end of the potential core.

Mean flow measurements in the jet plume were accomplished using a Validyne pressure transducer in conjunction with a 0.25 mm (0.01 in) Pitot probe mounted on a thin wedge. The probe was placed on a three-axis traverse system with one axis possessing a computer-controlled interface. This allowed for synchronous probe traversing and data acquisition, thereby reducing facility run time and helium usage. A second Validyne pressure transducer was used to measure the stagnation pressure at the nozzle and thus provided a measure of the jet exit velocity.

The optical deflectometer system shown in Figure 3 uses a high intensity continuous white light source driven at 72 W to produce a parallel beam approximately 15.2 cm (6 in) in diameter that illuminates the predominant noise source region of the jet. The light source can also be replaced with a stroboscope for schlieren visualization purposes. The beam is refocused to a small diameter that is partially intercepted by a knife edge and then projected through a 50/50 beamsplitter such that two identical images of equal intensity are projected as shown in Figure 3. These images are projected onto separate photomultiplier tubes (TSI Model 9162) that convert light intensity to voltage in real time. Located at the center of each photomultiplier tube is a pinhole aperture of 0.5 mm (0.02 in) diameter. The photomultiplier tubes are each supported on two-axis traverse systems that allow precise positioning of the sensing volumes at specific transverse and axial locations within the jet plume. Two images are used rather than one such that very small probe (i.e. pinhole aperture) separation distances are possible.

As noted in Doty and McLaughlin[8], the optical deflectometer is a valuable tool because it can be implemented in a relatively straightforward manner and provides capability for obtaining time-resolved data at multiple points in a high-speed flowfield. Furthermore, no seeding particles are required. Alternatively, there are limitations in using optical deflectometry. First, the quantity measured in two-point correlations is a fluctuating density gradient, not a fluctuating velocity, which is a more conventional turbulent property. Nonetheless, reasonable assumptions can be made to relate these quantities. A second limitation is that the light beam integrates density gradient fluctuations over the length that it travels, rather than focusing at a point. For this reason, measurements are concentrated at or near the edge of the jet shear layer so as not to penetrate significant portions of the jet. Focusing techniques might be possible to address this problem in future developments[17]. Finally it should be noted that, when measuring helium/air mixture jets, the index of refraction of helium is slightly different than that of heated air at the same conditions due to molecular composition. However, it is believed this effect is minor compared to the other factors to be discussed.

2.3 Presentation of Data

All acoustic results in the current study have been corrected for atmospheric attenuation based on the work of Bass *et al.*[18,19] In addition, microphone corrections were applied based on manufacturer's specifications. For the presentation of spectral information, all third-octave spectra were converted to narrowband, and all spectra were scaled to the same 1 Hz frequency bandwidth. Furthermore, the abscissa of each spectrum was non-dimensionalized by the characteristic frequency, f_c:

$$f_c = \frac{U_j}{D} \qquad (1)$$

to form the Strouhal number, St:

$$St = \frac{f}{f_c} . \qquad (2)$$

Similarly, the turbulence correlation data, except when compared to the previous data of Davies *et al.*[1], were plotted as a function of the non-dimensional time delay:

$$^* = \times f_c \qquad (3)$$

in which the dimensional time is multiplied by the characteristic frequency f_c.

The mean velocity profile results for the helium/air mixture jets require information about the local helium concentration within the jet plume. Given a known helium concentration at the nozzle exit and assuming zero helium concentration in the ambient environment, an expression for helium concentration based solely on velocity was developed. This approach is similar to the Crocco-Busemann relation involving temperature and velocity and is described in detail in Kinzie[20]. Thermal diffusion is neglected because of the

unheated nature of the jet. Furthermore, the viscous and species diffusion are assumed to be of the same magnitude, a reasonable assumption for the turbulent length scales relevant to aeroacoustics. The resulting relationship is then

$$= \frac{j}{U_j} \, u, \qquad (4)$$

where and u represent the local helium concentration and jet velocity, respectively, and the $_j$ and U_j terms refer to jet exit values. The equation is solved iteratively at each location within the jet plume.

3. Experimental Results

3.1 Flow Parameters

A summary of the flow conditions used for all the experiments is shown in Table 1. It should be noted that all helium/air mixture experiments are matched to the density ratio $_j / _a$ of the simulated heated jet condition. As described in Doty and McLaughlin[15,16], it is not possible to exactly match both the acoustic velocity ratio a_j / a_a and the density ratio $_j / _a$ of the helium/air jet to the desired conditions of a heated jet. However, the measurements[15,16] have shown that the choice of matching parameter is of minor importance for subsonic jets and nearly imperceptible in the $M = 1.5$ jet acoustics.

In this table note that the supersonic conditions referred to as $M = 1.5$ throughout this work for convenience are typically at a slightly lower Mach number. This is to account to for the boundary layer while still maintaining perfectly expanded flow. The Mach number increases slightly with increasing helium concentration to maintain perfect expansion.

M	T_j / T_a (Sim. *)	Helium Conc. % mass	U_j (m/s)	U_j / a_a	$_j / _a$	f_c (Hz)	Re
0.9	0.86	0	287	0.83	1.14	22,610	298,200
0.9	1.0*	2.8	315	0.91	0.95	24,800	270,300
0.9	1.4*	10.9	381	1.10	0.70	30,000	224,100
0.9	1.7*	17.0	420	1.22	0.58	30,070	209,100
0.9	2.3*	29.4	507	1.45	0.42	39,450	174,200
1.45	0.70	0	420	1.22	1.39	33,070	630,100
1.46	1.0*	8.1	517	1.57	0.96	40,710	534,400
1.47	1.25*	15.2	592	1.72	0.79	46,610	483,600
1.47	1.56*	23.9	667	1.94	0.61	52,520	434,000

Table 1 Detailed parameters for acoustic and turbulence experiments.

3.2 Acoustic Comparisons

Before presenting the helium/air mixture flowfield results it is important to review the acoustic results showing the level of matching with existing heated jet data[21-26]. Figure 4 shows directivity comparisons between $M = 0.9$ cold jets and three increasing temperature ratio conditions scaled from the location mentioned previously (100 R/D from the approximate end of the potential core). Results indicate the helium/air mixture jets agree with previous measurements within $\pm$ 2 dB for almost all angular positions.

Figure 5 shows similar data for the $M = 1.5$ jet with a cold jet case and three increasing temperature ratio conditions. Again, the level of agreement with previous data is typically within $\pm$ 2 dB. However, larger discrepancies of 3-4 dB exist at the 40° and 50° measurement locations for the simulated temperature ratios $T_j/T_a^* = 1.00$ and $T_j/T_a^* = 1.25$. The higher levels for the helium/air mixture jets are seen consistently at these conditions raising speculation that perhaps the effects of Mach wave emission are seen at lower velocities for the helium/air mixture jet than for the heated jet. However, this phenomenon is still under investigation. Finally, note that these data represent an improvement of previous supersonic data presented by Doty and McLaughlin[16] due to the use of the 3.175 mm microphones exclusively for the present study.

Comparisons of $M = 0.9$ helium/air mixture and heated jet spectra are shown in Figure 6a for the 90° location where convective amplification is avoided. The simulated temperature ratio of $T_j/T_a^* = 2.3$ represents the largest concentration of helium tested for $M = 0.9$ jets in this study. Figure 6b shows a similar comparison for the $M = 1.5$ case, again at the highest level of helium addition. In both instances the spectral shapes and levels compare well with the heated results. Note that the data of Norum[25] have been corrected for atmospheric attenuation for a more accurate comparison.

3.3 Mean Flowfield Results

The nondimensional centerline velocity distributions for both a pure air jet and a helium/air mixture jet at $M = 0.9$ are shown in Figure 7a. Figure 7b shows analogous data for the $M = 1.5$ jet. The remainder of the helium/air mixture results presented in this study are at the helium concentration levels shown in this figure unless otherwise noted. In both instances, the helium/air mixture jet shows an increased centerline velocity decay rate and a shorter potential core length. These trends are consistent with heated jet measurements of Lau[27] and Seiner et al.[28] and suggest

increased shear layer thickness in the internal shear region bordering the potential core.

An example of a radial velocity profile is shown in Figure 8 for $M = 0.9$ jets. While the centerline velocity profiles indicate increased shear layer thicknesses bordering the potential core, the radial velocity profiles do not show a noticeable increase in jet spreading rate with the addition of helium. In fact, Lau[27] found a slight decrease in jet spreading rate with increasing temperature which he rationalized as a rotation of the shear layer toward the jet axis upon heating.

Schlieren visualizations of the $M = 0.9$ and $M = 1.5$ jets convey a somewhat different picture of jet spreading. Figure 9 shows the rather dramatic difference in visual shear layer thickness between the pure air and helium/air mixture jet which will become important in the discussion of optical deflectometry results. A comparable difference is seen in the $M = 1.5$ jets of Figure 10.

Thus, while the visual shear layer thickness shows appreciable increase in growth with the addition of helium, the shear layer thickness based on velocity profile shows no evidence of an increase. In fact, Figure 11 shows a comparison of velocity, vorticity, and visual shear layer thicknesses for both Mach number cases. The $M = 0.9$ case shows a more dramatic difference in visual thickness with helium addition than does the $M = 1.5$ case. While the sensitivity of the schlieren visualization system definitely effects the visual thickness, it is interesting to note that for the $M = 0.9$ helium addition case the ratios of thickness parameters roughly follow those described by Papamoschou and Roshko[29] in which $= 0.5$ $_{vis}$ and $_{pit} = 0.72$ $_{vis}$. Note that , $_{vis}$, and $_{pit}$ represent the vorticity thickness, visual thickness, and Pitot (velocity) thickness, respectively.

From Figure 11 it is also possible to see a slight decrease in the rate of growth of vorticity thickness with the addition of helium at both $M = 0.9$ and $M = 1.5$. This trend agrees with the observations of Lau[27] for heated jets previously discussed. Therefore, the trends in mean velocity of a heated jet along the centerline and in the radial direction seem to be well-represented by the helium/air mixture jet.

3.4 Optical Deflectometry Results

The results in this section include initial results presented in Doty and McLaughlin[8] as well as further experiments and analysis. In Figure 12 the cross-correlation results obtained with the optical deflectometer are compared directly with hot-wire two-point correlations made in an unheated $M = 0.45$ jet by

Davies *et al.*[1] The deflectometer results are for a $M = 0.9$ unheated jet and thus are scaled to account for the velocity difference as well as nozzle size difference between the two experiments. The level of agreement with these data is strong evidence that correlations of density gradient fluctuations are roughly equivalent to velocity correlations.

The bulk of deflectometry data is shown in Figures 13 and 14. Figure 13a shows two-point cross-correlations of signal fluctuations for a $M = 0.9$ pure air jet at various probe separation distances in the dominant noise production region of the jet. The stationary probe is located on the jet lip line at $x/D = 4.0$ while the other probe moves incrementally along the lip line to $x/D = 5.5$. Figure 13b shows the associated autospectra and cross-spectrum for the case of zero separation distance between probes. The peak near $St = 0.4$ is indicative of the presence of large-scale turbulent structures. Coherence levels between probe signals in this case is typically above 0.95. Figure 13c and 13d show analogous data for the $M = 1.5$ pure air jet. In Figure 13c the two-point cross-correlations show a steeper decay versus non-dimensional time than did the $M = 0.9$ case. Furthermore, in Figure 13d the auto and cross-spectra display a broader peak (than in the $M = 0.9$ case) near $St = 0.5$.

Figure 14 is arranged in the same manner as Figure 13. The only exception is that both the $M = 0.9$ and $M = 1.5$ cases are helium/air mixture jets. Immediately the differences between these results and those of Figure 13 are apparent. First there are significantly lower levels of correlation at all non-zero separation distances for both Mach number cases. In addition the auto and cross-spectra show no signs of large-scale structure in the form of a peak at $St = 0.4 - 0.5$. Rather the spectra continue to increase in energy down to the high pass filter frequency. Not surprisingly then, the data show much less correlation.

Because this result is unexpected, a series of diagnostic experiments have been conducted. It is believed the lack of correlation for the helium/air mixture jets could be, in part, attributed to a limitation of the optical deflectometry system. Judging from the vastly different schlieren visualizations, the deflectometer could have difficulty discerning the large-scale structure in the helium/air mixture jets from the remainder of the thick visual shear layer thickness dominated by smaller scales. Nonetheless, comparisons are made to Laser Doppler Velocimetry (LDV) correlation measurements in a heated jet by Lau[30] some time ago. Figure 15 shows cross-correlation values at = 0, first for an isothermal $M = 0.9$ jet from Lau compared to the current pure air $M = 0.9$ case.

Although the measurement locations are not exactly the same, there is general agreement in Figure 15a. Figure 15b then shows a similar comparison for a $M = 0.9$ heated jet. Lau's results and the current results again show similar trends. Based on the results of Lau[30], decorrelation of turbulent structure in a heated jet is expected.

Despite the lower levels of correlations for the helium/air mixture jets, reasonably accurate convection velocity measurements were made at $x/D = 4.0 - 5.5$ along the jet lip line for both pure air and helium/air mixture jets using phase angle results from the spectral analysis. Results are shown in Table 2. The convection velocity for the $M = 0.9$ case was approximately the same for both the pure air and helium/air jet cases. Thus, U_c /U_j was lower for the helium/air jet. For the $M = 1.5$ case, the convection velocity was higher for the jet with helium; however, U_c /U_j was still lower. Overall, lower U_c /U_j values are measured for helium/air mixture jets, similar to the trend predicted for heated non-axisymmetric jets by Morris and Bhat[31].

	U_j (m/s)	U_c (m/s)	U_c/U_j	U_c/a_a
$M = 0.9$, Pure air	287	211	0.74	0.61
$M = 0.9$, $T_j/T_a^* = 1.70$	427	202	0.47	0.59
$M = 1.45$, Pure air	418	303	0.73	0.88
$M = 1.47$, $T_j/T_a^* = 1.25$	588	346	0.59	1.01

Table 2 Convection velocity calculations.

4. Concluding Remarks

This paper summarizes acoustic directivity patterns and spectra at $M = 0.9$ and $M = 1.5$ indicating the level of accuracy of applying helium/air mixtures to simulate heated jet aeroacoustics. Mean flowfield measurements at $M = 0.9$ and $M = 1.5$ exhibit shorter potential core lengths and slight decreases in vorticity thickness growth rate for the helium/air mixture jets as compared to the pure air jets. These results are consistent with trends seen in heated jets, indicating the capability of helium/air mixture jets to represent mean aerodynamic properties of heated jets as well.

Optical deflectometry measurements for the pure air jet cases show distinct cross-correlation peaks and evidence of large-scale structures. However, helium/air mixture jets demonstrated considerably smaller levels of correlation and little spectral evidence of distinct large-scale structures. The thick visual shear layer dominated by smaller scales may inhibit the visualization and measurement of the large scales. Nevertheless, limited heated jet data using an LDV system[30] also indicated decorrelation with increasing temperature. Finally, measured convection velocities indicated a decrease in U_c/U_j with the addition of helium.

Acknowledgements

This research has been supported by NASA Langley Research Center through a Graduate Student Researcher's Program Fellowship monitored by Mr. Tom Norum, Dr. Russ Thomas, and Dr. Kevin Kinzie. The authors would also like to acknowledge Dr. P. J. Morris for his assistance with this work. In addition, the authors would like to thank Mr. Vincent Tesson and Mr. Vincent Vielfaure for their assistance with experiments and Mr. Judson Rupert and Mr. Shawn Brechbill for facility support.

References

[1] Davies, P. O. A. L., Fisher, M. J., and Barratt, M. J., "The Characteristics of the Turbulence in the Mixing Region of a Round Jet," *Journal of Fluid Mechanics*, **15**, 1962 pp.337-367.

[2] Bradshaw, P., Ferriss, D. H., and Johnson, R. F., "Turbulence in the Noise-Producing Region of a Circular Jet," *Journal of Fluid Mechanics*, **19**, 1963, pp. 591-624.

[3] Chu, Wing T., "Turbulence Measurements Relevant to Jet Noise," UTIAS Report No. 119, November 1966.

[4] Harper-Bourne, M., "Jet Near-Field Noise Prediction," AIAA Paper 99-27825.

[5] Bridges, J. and Podboy, G.G., "Measurements of Two-Point Velocity Correlations in a Round Jet with Application to Jet Noise," AIAA Paper 99-1966, 5th AIAA/CEAS Aeroacoustics Conference, Seattle, WA., 1999.

[6] Fisher, M. J. and Krause, F. R., "The Crossed-Beam Correlation Technique," *Journal of Fluid Mechanics*, **28**, 1967, pp. 705-717.

[7] McIntyre, S., "Optical Experiments on Axisymmetric Compressible Mixing Layers," PhD Thesis, The Pennsylvania State University, 1994.

[8] Doty, M. J. and McLaughlin, D. K., "Two-Point Correlations of Density Gradient Fluctuations in High Speed Jets Using Optical Deflectometry," AIAA Paper 2002-0367, 40th AIAA Aerospace Sciences Meeting Exhibit, Reno, NV, 2002.

[9] Doty, M. J., "An Experimental Investigation of the Aeroacoustic Properties of High-Speed Helium/Air Mixture Axisymmetric Jets," Ph. D. Thesis, The Pennsylvania State University, 2002.

[10] Chan, Y. Y. and Westley, R., "Directional Acoustic Radiation Generated by Spatial Jet Instability," *CASI Transactions*, Vol. 6, 1973, pp. 36-41.

[11] Smith, D.J., and Johannessen, MN. H., "The Effects of Density on Subsonic Jet Noise." IUTAM Symposium on Aero and Hydro-Acoustics, Lyon, July 1985.

[12] McLaughlin, D. K., Barron, W. D., and Vaddempudi, A. R., "Acoustic Properties of Supersonic Helium/Air Jets at Low Reynolds Number," (DGLR)/AIAA Paper 92-02-047, 14th Aeroacoustics Conference, Aachen, Germany, 1992.

[13] Papamoschou, D., "Mach Wave Elimination in Supersonic Jets," *AIAA Journal*, Vol. 35, No. 10, October 1997, pp. 1604-1611.

[14] Kinzie, K. W. and McLaughlin, D. K., "Measurements of Supersonic Helium/Air Mixture Jets," *AIAA Journal*, Vol. 37, No. 11, 1999, pp. 1363-1369.

[15] Doty, M. J. and McLaughlin, D. K., "Experiments on Helium/Air Mixture Jets at High Subsonic Speeds," AIAA Paper 2000-2019, 6th AIAA/CEAS Aeroacoustics Conference, Lahaina, Hawaii, 2000.

[16] Doty, M. J. and McLaughlin, D. K., "Supersonic Helium/Air Mixture Jets With Comparison to Heated Jet Experiments," AIAA Paper 2001-2186, 7th AIAA/CEAS Aeroacoustics Conference, Maastricht, Netherlands, 2001.

[17] Alvi, F. S., Settles, G. S., and Weinstein, L. M., "A Sharp Focusing Schlieren Optical Deflectometer," AIAA Paper 93-0629, 1993.

[18] Bass, H. E., Sutherland, L. C., Blackstock, D. T., and Hester, D. M., "Atmospheric Absorption of Sound: Further Developments," *Journal of the Acoustical Society of America*, Vol. 97, No. 1, 1995, pp. 680-683.

[19] Bass, H. E., Sutherland, L. C., Blackstock, D. T., and Hester, D. M. "Erratum: Atmospheric Absorption of Sound: Further Developments," *Journal of the Acoustical Society of America*, Vol. 99, No. 2, 1996, p. 1259.

[20] Kinzie, K. W., "Aeroacoustic Properties of Moderate Reynolds Number Elliptic and Rectangular Supersonic Jets," PhD Thesis, The Pennsylvania State University, 1995.

[21] Tanna, H. K., Dean, P. D., and Burrin, R. H., "The Generation and Radiation of Supersonic Jet Noise, Volume III Turbulent Mixing Noise Data," Air Force Aero-Propulsion Laboratory, Technical Report AFAPL-TR-76-65, September 1976.

[22] Burrin, R. H., Lush, P. A., and Wynne, G. A., "The Generation and Radiation of Supersonic Jet Noise, Volume V Appendix I," Air Force Aero-Propulsion Laboratory, Technical Report AFAPL-TR-72, July 1972.

[23] Seiner, J. M. and Ponton, M. K., "Aeroacoustic Data for High Reynolds Number Supersonic Axisymmetric Jets," NASA Tech. Memo 86296, January 1985.

[24] Viswanathan, K. "Assessment of Jet Noise Theory/Prediction Methods," Proceedings of the Jet Noise Workshop, NASA / CP 2001-211152, Part 2, Ohio Aerospace Institute, Cleveland, OH, November 2001.

[25] Norum, T., NASA Langley Research Center, Jet Noise Laboratory, unpublished data, 1999.

[26] Yu, J. C., and Dosanjh, D. S., "Noise Field of a Supersonic Mach 1.5 Cold Model Jet," *The Journal of the Acoustical Society of America*, Vol. 51, No. 5, 1972, pp. 1400-1410.

[27] Lau, J. C., "Effects of Exit Mach Number and Temperature on Mean-Flow and Turbulence Characteristics in Round Jets," *Journal of Fluid Mechanics*, Vol. 105, 1981, pp. 193-218.

[28] Seiner, J. M., Ponton, M. K., Jansen, B. J., and Lagen, N. T., "The Effects of Temperature on Supersonic Jet Noise Emission," (DGLR)/AIAA Paper 92-02-046, 14th Aeroacoustics Conference, Aachen, Germany.

[29] Papamoschou, D. and Roshko, A., "The compressible Turbulent Shear Layer: An Experimental Study," *Journal of Fluid Mechanics*, Vol. 197, 1988, pp. 453-477.

[30] Lau, J. C., "Laser Velocimeter Correlation Measurements in Subsonic and Supersonic Jets," *Journal of Sound and Vibration*, Vol. 70, 1980, pp. 85-101.

[31] Morris, P.J. and Bhat, T. R. S., "Supersonic Elliptic Jet Noise," AIAA Paper 93-4409, 15th Aeroacoustics Conference, Long Beach, CA.

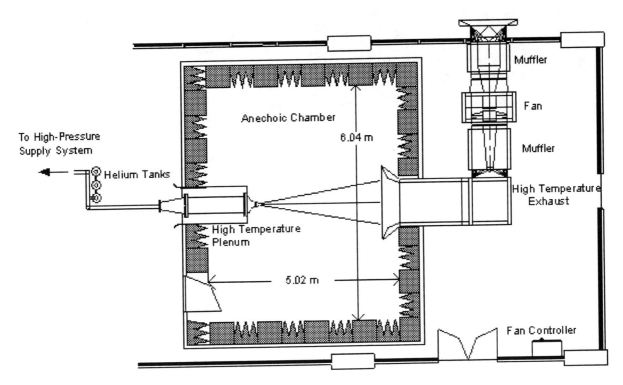

Figure 1 Schematic of high-speed jet noise facility.

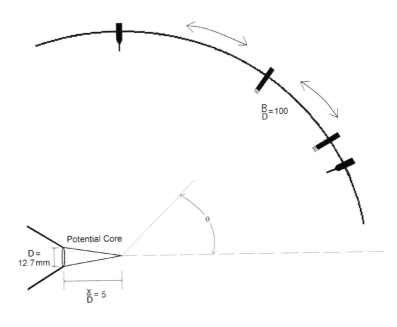

Figure 2 Schematic of microphone set-up.

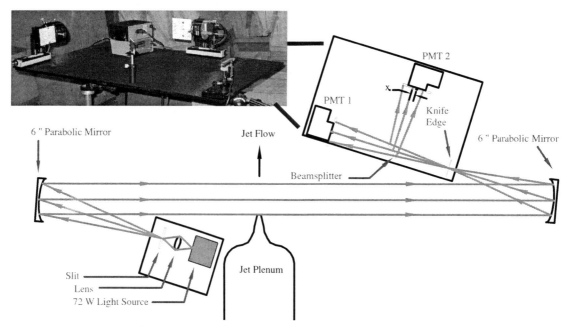

Figure 3 Schematic of optical deflectometry set-up.

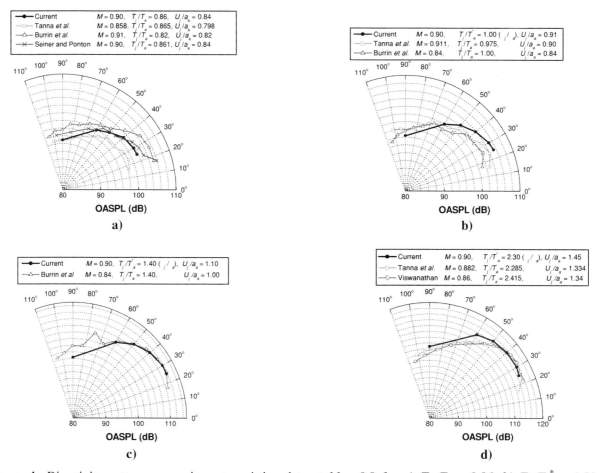

Figure 4 Directivity pattern comparisons to existing data at $M = 0.9$ for **a)** $T_j/T_a = 0.86$, **b)** $T_j/T_a^* = 1.00$, **c)** $T_j/T_a^* = 1.40$, and **d)** $T_j/T_a^* = 2.30$.

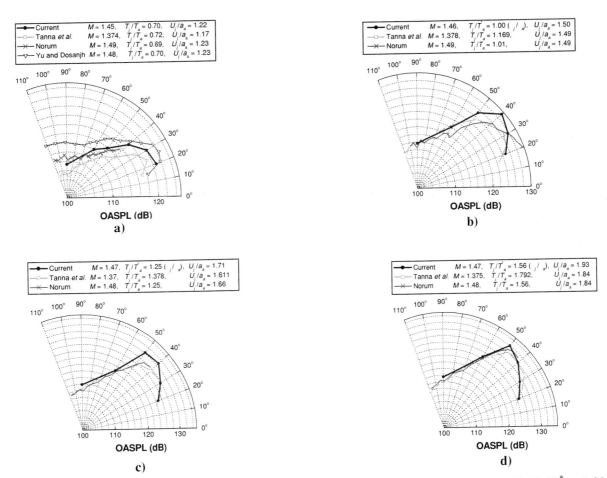

Figure 5 Directivity pattern comparisons to existing data at $M = 1.5$ for **a)** $T_j/T_a = 0.70$, **b)** $T_j/T_a^* = 1.00$, **c)** $T_j/T_a^* = 1.25$, and **d)** $T_j/T_a^* = 1.56$.

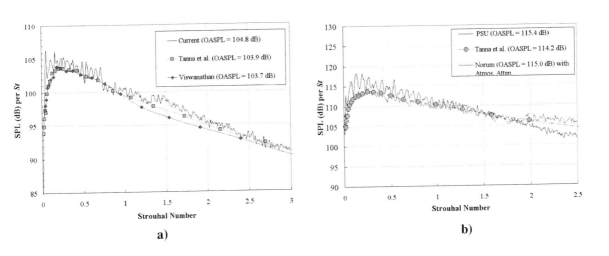

Figure 6 Spectral comparisons to existing data at 90° for **a)** $M = 0.9$, $T_j/T_a^* = 2.30$ and b) $M = 1.5$ $T_j/T_a^* = 1.56$.

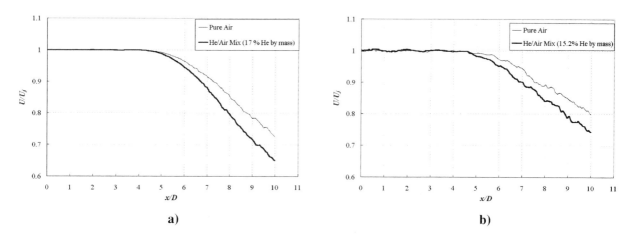

Figure 7 Axial velocity distributions for **a)** $M = 0.9$, (pure air and $T_j/T_a^* = 1.70$) and b) $M = 1.5$, (pure air and $T_j/T_a^* = 1.25$).

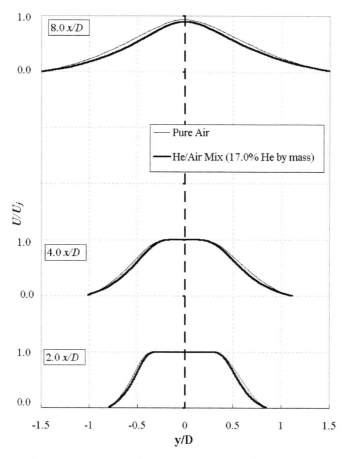

Figure 8 Radial velocity distributions for a $M = 0.9$ jet (pure air and $T_j/T_a^* = 1.70$).

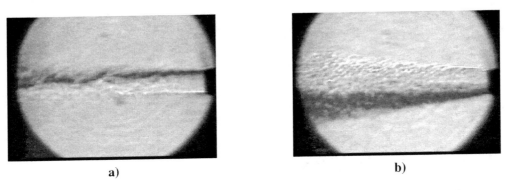

Figure 9 Schlieren images of $M = 0.9$ **a)** pure air jet and **b)** helium/air mixture jet.

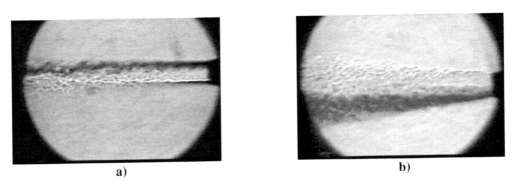

Figure 10 Schlieren images of $M = 1.5$ **a)** pure air jet and **b)** helium/air mixture jet.

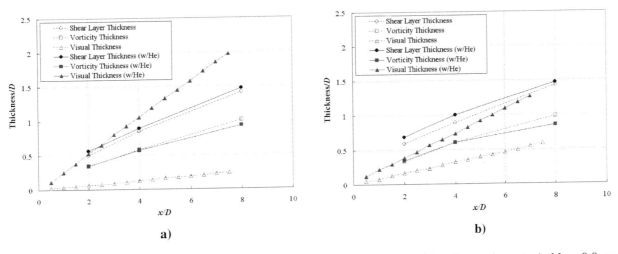

Figure 11 Comparison of thickness parameters for pure air and helium/air mixture jets at **a)** $M = 0.9$ and **b)** $M = 1.5$.

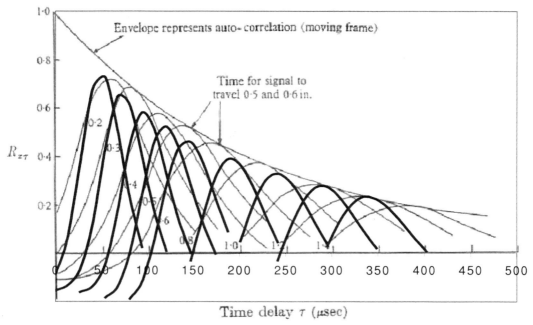

Figure 12 Comparison of deflectometry measurements at $M = 0.9$ (cold jet) and hot-wire measurements from Davies *et al.*[1] at $M = 0.45$ (cold jet) (started at $x/D = 1.5$ along the lip line, time axis scaled to account for unmatched M and D).

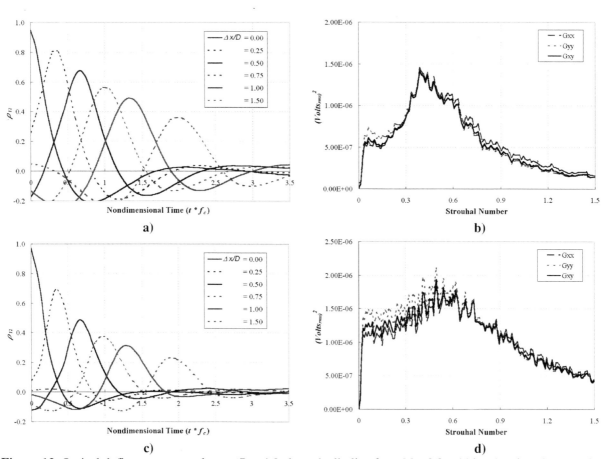

Figure 13 Optical deflectometry results at $x/D = 4.0$ along the lip line for a $M = 0.9$ cold jet showing **a)** space-time correlations and **b)** spectra at zero probe separation distance with analogous plots for a $M = 1.5$ cold jet **c)** and **d)**.

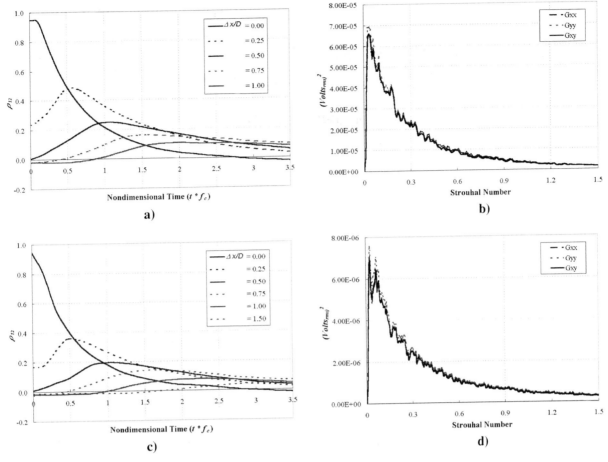

Figure 14 Optical deflectometry results at $x/D = 4.0$ along the lip line for a $M = 0.9$ helium/air mixture jet showing **a**) space-time correlations and **b**) spectra at zero probe separation distance with analogous plots for a $M = 1.5$ helium/air mixture jet **c**) and **d**).

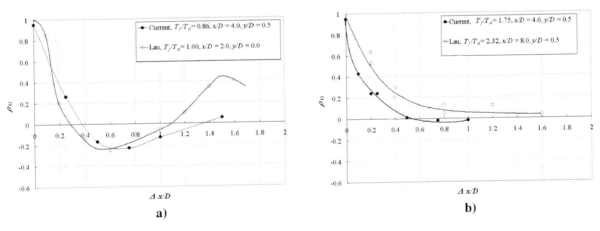

Figure 15 Cross-correlation values at zero time delay for a $M = 0.9$ **a**) pure air jet, $x/D = 4.0$, $y/D = 0.5$ compared to Lau[30] – isothermal jet, $x/D = 2.0$, $y/D = 0.0$ and **b**) $T_j/T_a^* = 1.70$, $x/D = 4.0$, $y/D = 0.5$ compared to Lau[30] – $T_j/T_a = 2.32$, $x/D = 8.0$, $y/D = 0.5$.

A COMPUTATIONAL AND EXPERIMENTAL INVESTIGATION OF SERRATED COAXIAL NOZZLES

Gary J. Page[*], James J. McGuirk[#], Mamdud Hossain[‡], Nicola J. Hughes[§] , Miles T. Trumper[‡‡]

Department of Aeronautical and Automotive Engineering, Loughborough University,

Loughborough, Leicestershire. LE11 3TU

United Kingdom

Abstract

Serrations on the nozzles of high bypass ratio turbo-fan engines are a promising technique to reduce jet noise. A study is carried out using both experimental laser measurements and computational Reynolds averaged predictions to help understand the fluid mechanics which may lead to a reduction in jet noise. Serrations are present on both primary (core) and secondary (bypass) nozzles and these are set at a zero angle to the aerodynamic flow lines. Results are presented for mean and fluctuating axial velocities up to seven primary nozzle diameters downstream. Experiments indicate that serrations give a reduction in peak turbulence intensity in the bypass/freestream shear layer which may be a mechanism to reduce jet noise. CFD gives good agreement with experiment for mean velocity, but is poor for fluctuating velocities. Initial tests with a hexahedral mesh indicate that these give better agreement with experiment as compared to the tetrahedral meshes used in the current work.

Introduction

Jet noise is an important component of the noise emission of civil turbofan aircraft. Even for high bypass ratio engines, jet noise is the most prominent source at the full power take off condition.

Nozzle designs are actively being sought which may result in significant jet noise reductions for high bypass ratio, separate jet exhaust configurations. A novel approach by which this might be achieved is to modify the complex coaxial jet flow development downstream of the nozzles by means of trailing edge

Figure 1. Boeing 777 Rolls-Royce Trent 800 full scale flight test

serrations (or 'chevrons'). Model-scale exhaust tests have measured substantial noise reductions under both static and flight-simulation conditions[1]. Whilst designs for these serrated nozzles have been flight tested[2], it is not clear as to the physical mechanisms by which noise reduction is achieved.

The aim of this work is to undertake a fundamental study, initially using high quality laser doppler velocimetry measurements and Reynolds Averaged Navier-Stokes CFD predictions, to explore the fluid dynamic changes introduced by the serrations. This knowledge will provide a basis for extending existing semi-empirical noise predictions[3,4] to reflect correctly the influence of geometric features such as serrations.

For low to medium bypass ratio engines, internal mixing of the core and bypass streams using a forced mixer offers significant jet noise reductions. Forced

[*]Lecturer G.J.Page@lboro.ac.uk
[#]Professor of Aerodynamics
[‡]Research Associate
[§]Research Associate, [‡‡] MEng student

lobed mixers have been extensively studied both experimentally[5] and computationally[6]. The lobes direct hot core flow outwards into the bypass, and cool bypass flow downwards into the core, strong vortical structures are created which enhances mixing in the initial portion before reaching the jet exit plane. At high bypass ratios, however, the noise benefit of internal mixing is small due to both the high flow area ratio and the high velocity ratio. In addition, a long bypass cowl has significant weight and drag penalty.

In the context of single stream jets, small tabs on the nozzle lip, perpendicular to the flow, have been used to give enhanced mixing of the initial shear layer[7]. However, the protrusion of the tab is likely to give undesirable thrust loss and an increase in high frequency noise.

Nozzle serrations are a more subtle approach with low protrusion into the flow and consequently thrust losses are kept to an acceptable level. Nevertheless, a significant distortion of the shear layer is introduced and their impact on noise emission from a coaxial jet can be dramatic.

Kenzakowski et al.[8] showed CFD predictions of the experimental configurations used in the noise tests[1]. Both chevron and delta tabs were considered, but only on the core nozzle since the experimental tests had concluded that bypass serrations were less effective at reducing noise. The chevron geometry was relatively severe, with alternating chevrons deflected up and down by 3° from the nominal core streamlines - this gave a strong distortion of the core/bypass shear layer with lobe like structures that 'pinch off' downstream. However, the authors comment that the fan/freestream mixing layer is still the dominant turbulent region (due to the small velocity difference between core and bypass) and the overall fan/freestream shear layer growth is not significantly altered by the presence of the chevrons (on the core).

Thomas et al.[9] also included the influence of the nacelle pylon in their predictions, using the same chevron geometry as Kenzakowski et al. Orientation of the chevrons relative to the pylon was found to have a significant effect on the lobe development created by the chevrons near the pylon.

Both these computational studies show how the turbulence kinetic energy field is affected by the presence of chevrons, but no experimental turbulence field data was available for comparison. It is also assumed that noise reduction is purely a result of the injected vorticity from the chevrons increasing core and bypass flow mixing.

Page et al.[10] showed how a standard Reynolds averaged CFD method is capable of giving good agreement with experimental mean *and* fluctuating data for a 'clean' coaxial jet configuration[11]. If this capability is also true for serrated nozzles then such a technique would be a useful tool in improving noise prediction models.

The present work uses non-intrusive laser doppler velocimetry to obtain both mean and fluctuating data for clean and serrated coaxial configurations and compares these to RANS CFD predictions using a k-ε turbulence model on an unstructured tetrahedral mesh.

Methodology

Experimental

Experimental measurements were carried out in a water-tunnel facility designed specifically for near-field jet-mixing problems[7]. The tunnel is of recirculating design, has a working section 1.125m long, 0.37m wide and 0.3m high, which was made of Perspex to allow ample optical access. For measurements on co-axial nozzles, the primary and secondary jet nozzles are fed from separately pumped flow circuits with flow rates monitored by rotameters. It is also possible to provide a third co-flowing parallel stream outside of the jet nozzles to simulate a flight stream. Turbulence management units are provided in the supply ducts feeding both jet flows in order to provide as uniform an exit profile as possible, and low turbulence levels at the nozzle exit. The tertiary co-flow is also used to create a low velocity stream (typically around 5% of the primary jet velocity) in order to stabilise the flow in the furthest downstream region of the water tunnel; measurements with and without co-flow showed this had little effect on the jet development. Figure 2 shows a schematic of the water tunnel.

A Dantec LDA system was used to provide mean velocity and turbulence data. The system used a 5W argon-ion laser, with the light separated into blue and green wavelengths (488nm and 514nm) within a transmitter box. A Bragg cell was used to provide a 40MHz shift to the beams to eliminate fringe bias and remove directional ambiguity. The beams were transmitted to a two dimensional probe via optical fibres. The multi-mode fibres were also capable of transmitting the reflected light scattered from seeding particles in the flow to photo multipliers, since the probe also incorporated its own receiving optics. Each photo multiplier contained a narrow band filter for its own specific colour. Mean and turbulence intensity of two velocity components could be obtained by processing each colour independently using standard Dantec

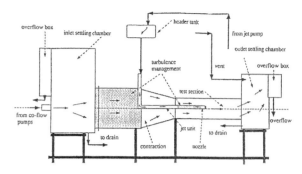

Figure 2. Water tunnel facility

BSA processors. Cross coupling of the signals within the acquisition software enabled the evaluation of the Reynolds shear stress. The use of a large beam expander increased the size of the transmitted beams, but decreased the beam 'waist', thereby enabling a reduction in the size of the interference pattern contained within the measurement volume.

For flow visualisation purposes, a Laser Induced Fluorescence (LIF) technique was used. Fluorescein dye was added in dilute quantity to either the primary or secondary jet stream. The dye was injected far upstream, so that it was fully mixed at nozzle exit. A second 5W argon-ion laser mounted on a moveable table was used as a light source. The beam was passed through a Dantec 80x20 light sheet probe containing a cylindrical lens to create a light sheet (thickness 2.5mm); this was shone through the lower surface of the water tunnel. The light sheet could be oriented either parallel or perpendicular to the jet axis. When dye-containing-water flowed through the light sheet, it fluoresced a green colour and the instantaneous cross section of the jet could be clearly seen. This allowed the effect of the serrations to be easily visualised and confirmed they had a major influence on the nozzle shear layers, with significant distortions of the nominally circular jet shape. The flow visualisation pictures were also used to guide the locations of longitudinal and transverse measurement planes for the detailed LDV measurements. Figure 3 shows the LIF set-up and Fig. 4 an example of a typical flow visualisation. The test conditions for this picture were a velocity ratio (primary/secondary) of 0.7, with plain inner and serrated outer nozzles. The jet cross-section was captured at a downstream distance of 1 primary nozzle diameter, with dye added just to the outer sec-

Figure 3. Laser Induced Fluorescence configuration

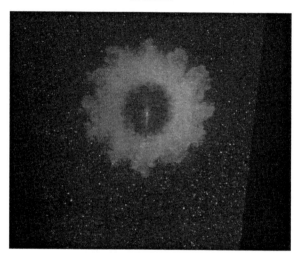

Figure 4. Typical LIF visualization - plain primary, serrated secondary

ondary flow. The individual inward and outward movements of the jet shear layer caused by the streamwise vortex emanating from the serrations is clearly visible.

Computational

The CFD methodology solves the compressible Reynolds Averaged Navier Stokes equations and uses a k-ε model coupled with wall-functions for turbulence closure. The algorithm uses an edge based data structure and can handle combinations of tetrahedral, hexahedral, prism and pyramid elements.

A median dual finite volume formulation is adopted. Spatial discretisation is based upon central differencing of the flux vector with a smoothing flux based upon one dimensional characteristic variables. This is effectively an upwind difference scheme based upon the characteristic variables of the system and is formally second order accurate. Viscous fluxes are computed by interpolating nodal gradients to edges, with a modification so that the components of the gradient aligned with the edge are replaced with a simple difference along the edge.

An explicit Runge-Kutta scheme is used to advance the solution in time towards the steady state with preconditioning and multigrid for convergence acceleration. In addition a low speed preconditioner is employed to allow this density-based method to compute very low speed flows. Further details may be found in Moinier and Giles[12] and Moinier[13], and its application to a lobed mixer geometry in Salman et al.[14]

The nozzle geometry was created parametrically within the SolidEdge CAD package, and this was imported into the ICEM Tetra grid generation system. Although previous work has discovered potential errors in turbulent mixing predictions due to the adoption of tetrahedral meshes[14] (as compared to hexahedral meshes), it was felt that the geometrical flexibility and ease of mesh adaption of tetrahedral meshes would be of great benefit to this type of flow problem.

Results

Geometry

The geometry used is representative of a separate flow nozzle with an external plug, and an area ratio (secondary to primary) of five. Clean and serrated primary and secondary nozzles were available allowing four different configurations to be studied. This paper reports the clean primary and secondary nozzles (datum configuration) and serrated primary and secondary nozzle (serrated configuration) only. The serrations are geometrically somewhat different from chevrons previously reported in the literature. Effectively, the triangular tip of the chevron has been 'squared off' as has the triangular cut -out (see Fig. 5).

Figure 6 shows the serrated nozzle geometry and the coordinate system adopted. The origin is placed along the nozzle centreline at the axial position of the

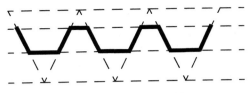

a) current serrations

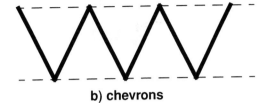

b) chevrons

Figure 5. Trailing edge treatments

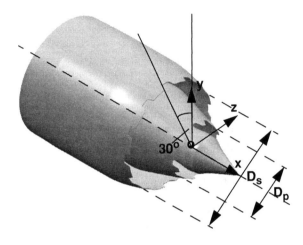

Figure 6. Serrated nozzle geometry and nomenclature

primary nozzle lip. Results will be presented with distances non-dimensionalised by the primary diameter (D_p) and velocities non-dimensionalised by the secondary exit velocity (V_s). Results shown here are for the ratio of secondary to primary velocity (λ) equal to 0.7, Table 1 shows the primary and secondary dimensions and flow conditions.

	Nozzle diameter (mm)	Velocity (ms^{-1})	CFD turbulence intensity	CFD turbulence length scale
Primary (p)	58	2.15	10% of V_p	0.1 x primary inlet channel height
Secondary (s)	116	1.5	10% of V_s	0.1 x secondary inlet channel height
Tertiary (t)	-	0.1	10% of V_t	set to give low turbulent viscosity

Table 1: Flow conditions for velocity ratio λ=0.7

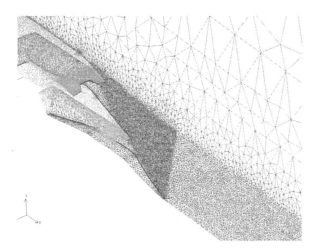

Figure 7. Serrated nozzle mixed prismatic and tetrahedral mesh

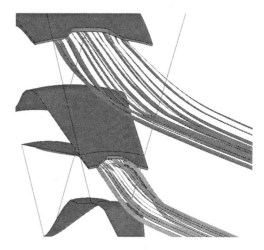

Figure 8. CFD stream ribbons for serrated nozzle

The size of the nozzle in the experimental facility meant that the furthest downstream experimental location was at 12 primary diameters, whilst the CFD domain was continued until 31 primary diameters.

Longitudinal LDA traverses were taken in the x-y plane and axial slices were taken in the y-z plane at various downstream stations.

The CFD meshes contained triangular prisms to resolve the boundary layers on the nozzle walls with tetrahedra in the remainder of the domain. The mesh was designed to cluster a large number of cells in the regions of the jet shear layers. The smallest volumes were approximately 1mm in size. Due to symmetry, only a $30°$ sector was modelled. Figure 7 shows the mesh for the serrated configuration and consists of 215 000 tetrahedra and 45 000 prisms which resulted in 412 000 nodes and 2.7 million edges.

Mean Velocity

Computed stream ribbons are shown in Fig. 8; these are placed just inside the primary and secondary nozzle lips. The primary flow deflects outwards as it travels though the cut-out region of the serration. This results in a distorted shear layer, but little evidence of a strong vortical flow nature. The flow near the cut-out of the secondary serration is less distorted and in fact the predictions show that the outer co-flow is penetrating inwards. As will be seen later, this phenomena is not found in the experiments.

Figure 9 shows axial velocity contours for the datum nozzle. It is noticeable that the wake region due to the bullet is stronger in the CFD predictions. It is believed that this is due to a poor geometric definition of the bullet in the solid model used for grid generation. A qualitative comparison of axial velocity is

shown in Fig. 10, apart from the bullet wake region, in general good agreement is found.

Comparing the datum results with the serrated nozzle axial velocities (Fig. 11 and Fig. 12) shows that the bullet wake region is stronger in both experiment and CFD. The experiment also indicates that the axial velocity near the exit of the primary nozzle is significantly reduced (this effect is present, but is weaker in the CFD). The consequence of these two effects is that the potential core velocity is reduced. Qualitative comparison in Fig. 12 also shows reasonable agreement but the reduction (in comparison to datum) of jet velocity downstream is underpredicted.

Turbulent Fluctuations

Of interest to noise prediction models is the turbulence intensity in the shear layers. Results are shown for the RMS of axial turbulent fluctuations for the datum (Fig. 13 and Fig. 14) and serrated (Fig. 15 and Fig. 16) nozzles, in the plane through the centre of the cut-out. The most important observation is that the experiments indicate that downstream in the secondary/co-flow shear layer, the turbulent fluctuations are significantly reduced. Since this shear layer is considered to be the dominant noise producing source for this type of coaxial jet, this reduction in turbulence intensity could be the mechanism by which noise reduction is observed. As a consequence of the flow gradients around the serrations, turbulent fluctuations are slightly increased in the early development of the primary/secondary shear layer. As the turbulent eddies are small in this region, this is likely to increase high frequency noise.

The CFD results clearly under predict the turbulent axial fluctuations. Previous work showed that this type of RANS k-ε approach is capable of reasonable

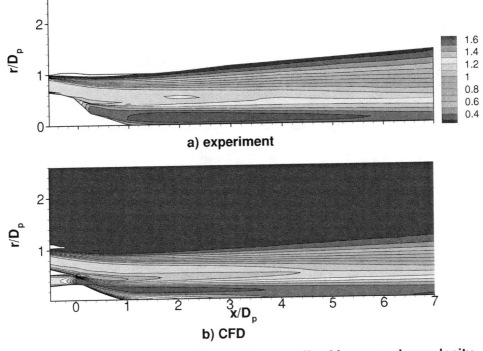

a) experiment

b) CFD

Figure 9. Datum nozzle, axial velocity normalised by secondary velocity

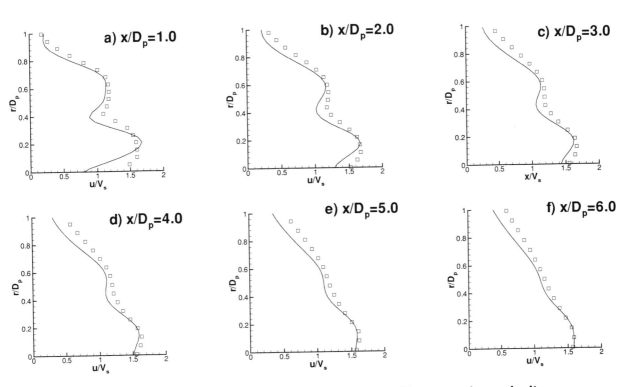

Figure 10. Datum nozzle, axial velocity normalised by secondary velocity
— CFD; ☐ experiment

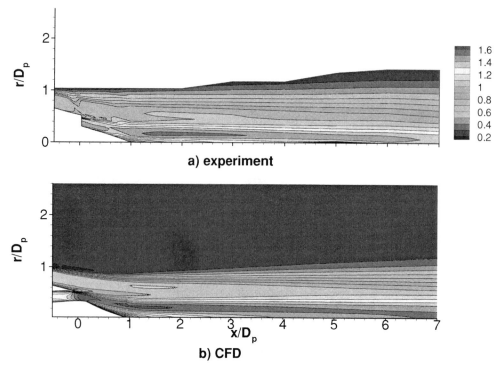

a) experiment

b) CFD

Figure 11. Serrated nozzle, axial velocity normalised by secondary velocity

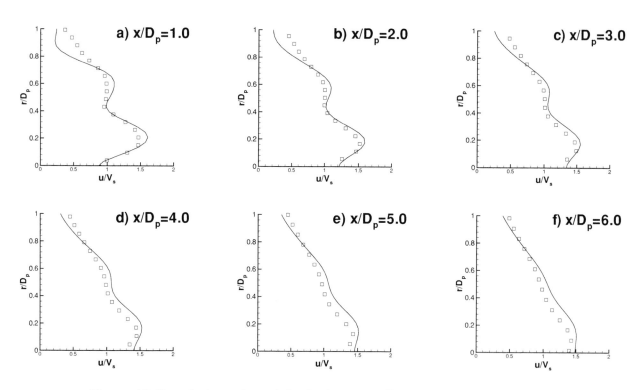

Figure 12. Serrated nozzle, axial velocity normalised by secondary velocity
— CFD; ❑ experiment

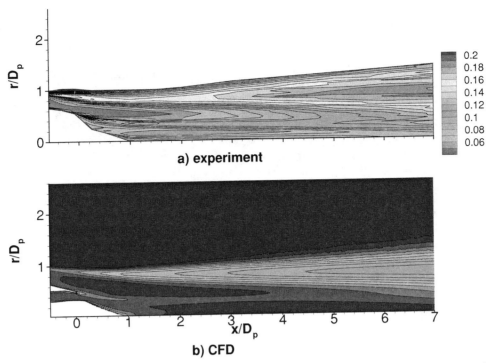

a) experiment

b) CFD

Figure 13. Datum nozzle, RMS fluctuating axial velocity normalised by secondary velocity

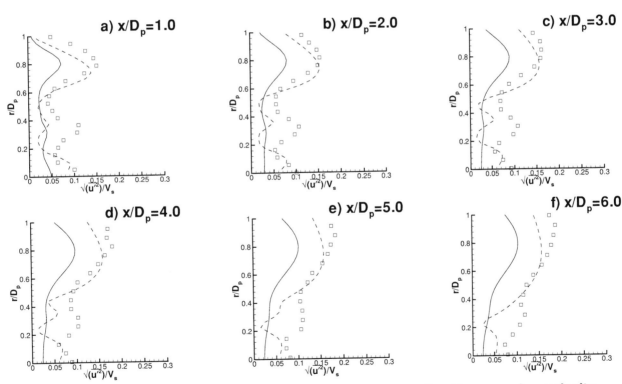

Figure 14. Datum nozzle, RMS fluctuating axial velocity normalised by secondary velocity
— CFD tetrahedra; --- CFD hexahedra; ▯ experiment

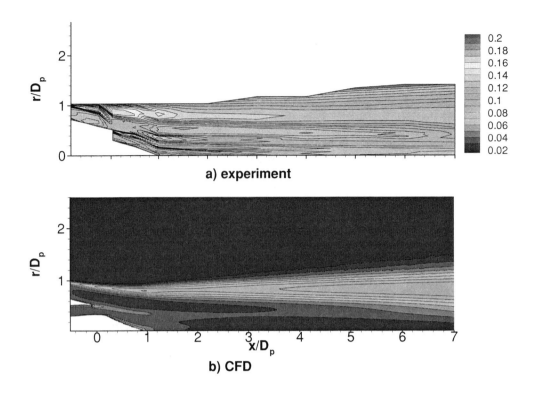

a) experiment

b) CFD

Figure 15. Serrated nozzle, RMS fluctuating axial velocity normalised by secondary velocity

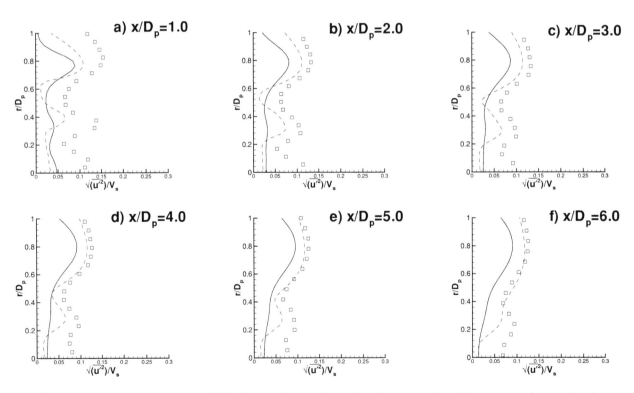

Figure 16. Serrated nozzle, RMS fluctuating axial velocity normalised by secondary velocity
— CFD tetrahedra; --- CFD hexahedra; ❏ experiment

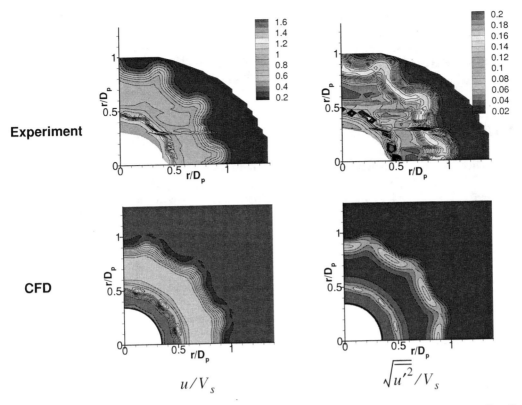

Experiment

CFD

$$u/V_s \qquad\qquad \sqrt{\overline{u'^2}}/V_s$$

Figure 17. Comparison of mean and fluctuating axial velocity at x/D_p=0.03

predictions of normal stresses in coaxial jets[10]. However, in the current work unstructured tetrahedral meshes have been adopted (as compared to structured hexahedral meshes used previously); there is some evidence that discretization error on tetrahedral meshes can give underprediction of normal stresses[6]. Preliminary calculations have been carried out using a structured hexahedral mesh and these results are shown as a dashed line in Fig. 14 and Fig. 16. Clearly the fluctuating axial velocity is in much better agreement with experiment, and importantly is able to predict the reduction in turbulence fluctuations downstream caused by the presence of the serration

Finally, an axial slice just downstream of the primary nozzle exit is shown in Fig. 17. Whilst the shape of the mean velocity contours looks similar, careful inspection of the secondary/co-flow shear layer confirms that the experiment has flow in the secondary cut-out moving radially outwards, whilst in the CFD it is moving inwards. It is believed that the horizontal wiggles apparent in both experimental plots is an artifact of the experimental facility. Whilst many tests were carried out to determine the cause of this anomaly this has proved elusive.

Conclusions

Results have been shown for experimental measurements and computational predictions for both clean and serrated coaxial nozzle configurations relevant to high bypass ratio turbofan engines. The serrations were present on both primary (core) and secondary (bypass) flows and were set at zero angle to the aerodynamic flow lines.

The main observations are:

1. The serrations distorted the jet shear layers, but did not cause a strong vortical type flow.
2. The presence of serrations reduced the axial velocity in the primary potential core.
3. In the experiments, the serrations significantly reduced the peak turbulent fluctuations in the secondary / co-flow shear layer. It is believed that this may be a mechanism to reduce jet noise.
4. The CFD were in good agreement with experiment for the mean axial velocity, but was poor for the turbulent fluctuating axial velocity. The latter appeared to be linked to numerical issues associated with tetrahedral meshes, and improvement was found by the use of hexahedral meshes.

Further work will concentrate on increasing the fidelity of the CFD predictions by using hexahedral meshes and more refined tetrahedral meshes. This should allow RANS CFD methods to be coupled to semi-empirical noise prediction techniques in order that the effect of serrations can be taken into account.

Acknowledgements

The computational portion of this work was funded through EPSRC grant GR/M84985 in conjunction with Rolls-Royce Plc and QinetiQ. The experimental work on serrated nozzles has been separately funded by Rolls-Royce Plc and QinietiQ. The authors are particularly grateful for the guidance given by Paul Strange (RR) and Craig Mead (QinetiQ).

References

[1] N.H. Saiyed, J.E. Bridges, K.L. Mikkelsen, "Acoustics and thrust of separate-flow exhaust nozzles with mixing devices for high-bypass-ratio engines", AIAA Paper 2000-1961, AIAA/CEAS, 21st AIAA Aeroacoustics Conference) Lahaina, HI, 12-14 June 2000.

[2] Nesbitt, E., Elkoby, T.R., Bhat, T.R.S., Strange, P.J.R. and Mead, C., "Correlating model-scale and full-scale test results of dual flow nozzle jets," AIAA Paper no AIAA-2002-2487, 8th AIAA/ CEAS Aeroacoustics Conference, Breckinridge, CO, 17-19 June 2002.

[3] Fisher, M.J., Preston, G.A. and Bryce, W.D., "A Modelling of the Noise from Simple Coaxial Jets, Part I: with Unheated Primary Flow," *Journal of Sound and Vibration*, Vol. 209, 1998, pp385-403.

[4] Fisher, M.J., Preston, G.A. and Mead, C.J., "A Modelling of the Noise from Simple Coaxial Jets, Part I: with Heated Primary Flow," *Journal of Sound and Vibration*, Vol. 209, 1998, pp405-417

[5] McCormick, D.C. and Bennett J.C. Jr., "Vortical and Turbulent Structure of a Lobed Mixer Free Shear Layers," *AIAA Journal*, Vol. 32, no. 9, pp1852-1859, 1994.

[6] Salman, H., McGuirk, J.J. and Page G.J., "A Numerical Study of Vortex Interactions in Lobed Mixer Flow Fields," AIAA Paper 99-3409, 30th AIAA Fluid Dynamics Conference, Norfolk, VA, July 1999.

[7] Behrouzi, P. and McGuirk, J.J., "Experimental Studies of Tab Geometry Effects on Mixing Enhancement of an Axisymmetric Jet," *JSME International Journal*, Series B, Vol. 41, 1998, pp908-917.

[8] Kenzakowski, D.C., Shipman, J., Dash, S.M., Bridges, J.E. and Saiyed, N., "Turbulence model study of laboratory jets with mixing enhancements for noise reduction," AIAA Paper 2000-0219, AIAA 38th Aerospace Sciences Meeting and Exhibit, Reno, NV, 10-12 June, 2000.

[9] Thomas, R.H., Kinzie, K.W. and Pao, S.P., "Computational analysis of a pylon-chevron core nozzle interaction," AIAA Paper 2001-2185, 7th AIAA/ CEAS Aeroacoustics Conference, Maastricht, The Netherlands, 28-30 May 2001.

[10] G.J. Page, J.J. McGuirk, P. Behrouzi, M. Hossain, M.J. Fisher, "A CFD Coupled Acoustics Approach for the Prediction of Coaxial Jet Noise,' NATO RTO-AVT Symposium on Ageing Mechanisms and Control, Part A - Developments in Aero- and Hydro-Acoustics, Manchester, UK, 8-11 Oct. 2001

[11] Ko, N.W.M and Kwan, A.S.H, "The Initial Region of Subsonic Co-axial Jets," *Journal of Fluid Mechanics*, Vol. 73, 1976.

[12] Moinier, P. and Giles, M.B., "Preconditioned Euler and Navier-Stokes Calculations on Unstructured Grids," 6th ICFD Conference on Numerical Methods for Fluid Dynamics,Oxford, UK, 1998

[13] Moinier, P. "Algorithm developments for an unstructured viscous flow solver," PhD thesis, University of Oxford, UK, Trinity Term 1999.

[14] H.Salman, J.J.McGuirk, G.J.Page and P.Moinier, "The Influence of Unstructured Mesh Type on the Prediction of Convoluted Shear Layers," ECCO-MAS 2000, Barcelona, 11-14 September 2000

EXPERIMENTS AND ANALYSES OF DISTRIBUTED EXHAUST NOZZLES

Kevin W. Kinzie[*]
NASA Langley Research Center, MS 166
Hampton, VA 23681

David B. Schein and W. David Solomon, Jr.[**]
Northrop Grumman Integrated Systems
El Segundo, CA 90245-2804

Abstract

Experimental and analytical aeroacoustic properties of several distributed exhaust nozzle (DEN) designs are presented. Significant differences between the designs are observed and correlated back to CFD flowfield predictions. Up to 20 dB of noise reduction on a spectral basis and 10 dB on an overall sound pressure level basis are demonstrated from the DEN designs compared to a round reference nozzle. The most successful DEN designs acoustically show a predicted thrust loss of approximately 10% compared to the reference nozzle. Characteristics of the individual mini-jet nozzles that comprise the DEN such as jet-jet shielding and coalescence are shown to play a major role in the noise signature.

Introduction

Jet noise continues to be a dominant aircraft noise source that limits operations of current aircraft and hinders the design of future aircraft. While techniques aimed at changing the engine cycle or those implementing mixing enhancement devices are incrementally improving the community noise situation, revolutionary improvements in conventional engine/airframe systems are required to meet NASA's perceived noise reduction goal of 20 dB in 25 years. One such concept with potential to make significant progress toward the 25-year goal is the distributed exhaust nozzle (DEN).

Noise suppression from the DEN concept results from a favorable shift in the spectral shape of the radiated jet noise. The smaller jets that comprise the distributed exhaust nozzle radiate noise at higher frequencies than larger single or dual flow exhaust nozzles. Atmospheric attenuation increases nearly exponentially with increasing frequency, and spectral noise components contribute less and less to the EPNL

noise metric as the frequency increases above 4 kHz. In fact, noise at frequencies higher than 10 kHz is not even included in the calculation of EPNL. In addition to shifting the noise signature toward more favorable high frequencies, the small jets mix with the ambient air and reduce the speed and temperature of the jet plume to lower levels that, in turn, reduce the radiated low frequency noise.

Traditionally, distributed exhaust nozzle concepts have been studied from the perspective of replacing conventional engine exhaust nozzles with another configuration composed of many small tubes, chutes, or spokes. However, this inevitably leads to high levels of base drag due to the aft facing area required to distribute the exhaust. NASA Langley Research Center is conducting research aimed at studying the distributed exhaust concept from an integrated exhaust/airframe system perspective where the propulsion system is integrated into the airframe and the small exhaust nozzles are distributed over large portions of the wing surface area. An integrated distributed exhaust propulsion system has further potential for noise reduction since additional noise suppression will be realized through shielding of engine noise away from the community by the airframe design.

In 2000, NASA teamed with Northrop Grumman Corporation (NGC) to design and test a horizontal slot nozzle[1] concept in the Low Speed Aeroacoustic Wind Tunnel (LSAWT), shown in Figure 1. While the LSAWT DEN configuration provided only minimal noise suppression, the agreement between computational fluid dynamics (CFD) predictions and thrust and flow field measurements was sufficient to justify continued application of NGC's CFD design approach in pursuit of more aggressive noise reduction. CFD has subsequently been used to

---

[*] Senior Member, AIAA
[**] Member, AIAA

design three new DEN nozzles for testing in the LaRC Small Anechoic Jet Facility (SAJF).

Two of the designs reported here are variations of ones considered for the previous LSAWT test[1]. Due to the cost and complexity of fabrication, the horizontal slot design was chosen for that test even though it had less potential for noise reduction than other designs. In order to investigate more aggressive acoustic designs, a simpler approach was chosen for the current test by fabricating the DEN models using a stereolithography process. While this restricts the flow temperature to less than 150° F, it provides a means of inexpensively screening designs.

The third design was a smaller version of the horizontal slot design[1]. Even though the horizontal slot design does not provide significant noise reduction, testing the smaller stereolithography model provided a link back to the larger scale, hot-flow model test. While the SAJF horizontal slot data are not reported here, the acoustic characteristics including spectral content and relative levels compared to the round reference nozzle were similar to those found in the larger LSAWT design. This gives confidence that the trends and observations of the two new DEN designs can also be expected as the model size increases and hot flow is used.

Nozzle Descriptions

For this work, the two new SAJF DEN designs were analyzed, tested and compared to a round reference nozzle with similar mass flow. The DEN designs were refined using CFD in an attempt to optimize aero-performance and mixing characteristics that affect noise radiation. As expected, compromises are required between these two generally opposing requirements. The first DEN design is shown in Figure 2 and will be referred to as the DROPS design because the exit holes are shaped like teardrops. Figure 3 shows the second DEN design and will be referred to as the slanted pseudo-slot (SPS) design. It is similar to the design of the slotted nozzle, also designed by Northrop Grumman, described in Gaeta, et al[2, 3] except that for the current design the exit passages are not continuous slots, but rather an array of rectangular nozzles that give the appearance of slots. In addition, the spanwise spacing of the rows for the current SPS design is further apart than that tested by Gaeta, et al[2, 3]. For the current design, the spacing is 5.5 times the slot width and for the Gaeta, et al.[2, 3] design the spacing is 3.5 times the slot width. The round reference nozzle was constructed of stainless steel while the two DEN designs were constructed using a stereolithography technique.

Figure 4 shows a sketch describing the coordinate system used for this work. An azimuthal angle of $\phi = 0°$ is the horizontal plane of symmetry as the nozzles are shown and an azimuthal angle of $\phi = 90°$ is the vertical plan of symmetry as shown. Therefore, for a measurement angle of $\phi = 0°$, the furthest row of mini-nozzles is shielded from the microphones by the closer rows. For a measurement angle of $\phi = 90°$, the microphones are directed at all the mini-nozzle rows equally. Polar directivity angles are designated by θ and are measured from the jet inlet axis with $\theta = 180°$ being aligned directly on the jet axis in the downstream direction.

The round reference nozzle had a 2-inch diameter for a total exit area of 3.14 in[2]. Several CFD iterations were performed to size the distributed exhaust nozzles such that they had approximately the same mass flow as the round nozzle. This resulted in the SPS design having an exit area of 3.32 in[2] and the DROPS design having an exit area of 3.25 in[2]. The individual mini-nozzles for the SPS design each had an area of approximately 0.030 in[2] and a single mini-nozzle for the DROPS design had an area of approximately 0.032 in[2].

Experimental Approach

The nozzles were tested in NASA Langley's Small Anechoic Jet Facility (SAJF). An eight-element microphone array on an approximate 7 foot sideline was used to measure radiated noise. Because of the size of the chamber and of the nozzles, acoustic measurements were only made in the aft quadrant from polar angles of $\theta = 90°$ to $\theta = 155°$. Narrowband data up to 100 kHz were acquired with ¼" B&K 4139 microphones and post-processed to standard 1/3 octave bands. The data were then extrapolated to a 12 foot arc centered at the nozzle exit and corrected to standard day reference conditions using the Shields and Bass atmospheric attenuation model[4].

A range of nozzle pressure ratio (NPR) conditions were measured starting from NPR = 1.45 and ending with NPR = 2.20. For all pressure conditions, the flow total temperature was held at 120° F. The flow temperature was limited to relatively cool conditions by the plastic stereolithography models. This paper focuses on the NPR = 1.72 condition since most of the CFD was run for this case, which also corresponds to the fully mixed take-off pressure ratio for the cycle conditions tested previously for the horizontal slot DEN design[1]. Four azimuthal planes were measured corresponding to $\phi = 0°$, 30°, 60°, and 90°. Only the $\phi = 0°$ and $\phi = 90°$ planes are reported in this paper as the intermediate angles did not provide significant additional insight.

CFD Analysis

CFD simulations were run on the reference nozzle and both DEN designs using Northrop Grumman's Generalized Compressible Navier-Stokes (GCNS) code[5]. Full quadrant solutions were obtained for the reference nozzle and the SPS design. The DROPS design was analyzed using 3D strip analysis with periodic boundary conditions due to time constraints. The CFD was performed at nozzle pressure ratios of 1.45, 1.72, and 2.20. However, the most detailed analysis was performed at NPR = 1.72. The total temperature for all CFD runs was 120° F.

Figure 5 shows predicted velocity contours through the hole spanwise centers for the reference nozzle and the DEN designs. The DEN designs show a dramatic increase in mixing that results in a plume with significantly lower flow velocity than the round reference nozzle. This is in contrast to the horizontal slot DEN design[1] that showed very little reduction in plume velocity compared to the reference nozzle. Figure 6 shows predicted turbulence intensity contours for the same cross sections. Again, there is a significant reduction in turbulence intensity for the DEN designs compared to the reference nozzle.

The CFD predictions show that for both of these DEN designs, the individual mini-exhaust jets maintain their identity for a significant distance before they begin to coalesce back into a larger jet plume. This is a critical factor in order for acoustic suppression to be realized from any distributed exhaust design. CFD predictions and experimental measurements of the horizontal slot DEN design[1] showed that without enough separation of the mini-jets, they will coalesce into a large plume with a noise signature more characteristic of the single large jet rather than many small jets. The CFD flowfield solutions for the current DEN designs show much greater potential for noise reduction based on jet-to-jet mixing and overall plume characteristics. The acoustic measurements presented in the next section confirm this assessment.

For the design nozzle pressure ratio of 1.72, the discharge coefficient of the SPS nozzle was 0.93 while the discharge coefficient of the DROPS nozzle was 0.95. The thrust coefficient of both the SPS and DROPS nozzles was approximately 0.89. The CFD showed a slight improvement in thrust performance (0.91) as the NPR increased to 2.20. In addition, preliminary computations also indicate a performance increase at forward flight speeds. Experimental measurements of aero-performance quantities were not made, however, earlier work demonstrated that the GCNS code is very reliable in computing these types of flows[1].

Caution should be used when comparing acoustic data from nozzles with different thrust characteristics. An aircraft system requires a specific level of thrust so a nozzle with lower thrust must either be oversized or operated at a higher pressure ratio to generate the same amount of thrust as one with better propulsive efficiency. Either of these options will increase the noise so it can be misleading to only consider noise suppression without considering the associated performance penalty. As a point of future reference, oversizing the DEN designs discussed here so that they would produce the same thrust as the round reference nozzle would result in an elevation of the DEN SPL levels shown in this paper by approximately 0.5 dB.

While the thrust loss of these DEN specimens may be unacceptable for conventional aircraft designs, the distributed exhaust concept lends itself very well toward more revolutionary aircraft designs where the small exhaust holes can be integrated into the wing surface. Such an installation could recover some of the lost performance through upper surface blowing lift enhancement. A full aircraft system mission study is required to adequately assess the acceptable thrust loss compared to the noise suppression provided by the distributed exhaust design.

Acoustic Measurements

Figures 7 and 8 show overall sound pressure level (OASPL) directivity data for the round reference nozzle compared to the DROPS and SPS nozzles at a nozzle pressure ratio of 1.72. Azimuthal variations of $\phi = 0°$ and $\phi = 90°$ are shown for the DEN designs. Both nozzles provide greatest noise suppression at the aft most angles where jet noise is typically the loudest. The $\phi = 0°$ orientation of the DROPS nozzle is nearly 10 dB quieter than the round reference nozzle at the aft most measurement angles. The DROPS nozzle shows a consistent noise benefit relative to the reference nozzle through the whole measurement range. The SPS nozzle does not achieve suppression until midway into the aft quadrant. For each DEN, there is a loud and a quiet azimuthal orientation with the $\phi = 0°$ orientation being 2 –3 dB quieter than $\phi = 90°$. Effects that contribute to the difference between azimuthal planes will be discussed shortly.

Spectra from the two DEN designs compared to the round reference nozzle at NPR = 1.72 are shown in Figures 9 through 12. Figures 9 and 10 show the DROPS and SPS for both azimuthal angles close to the peak noise polar angle of $\theta = 150°$. Figures 11 and 12 show the DROPS and SPS, respectively, for both azimuthal angles and a polar angle of $\theta = 90°$. From these spectra, it is clear that the DEN models are in fact shifting the noise to higher frequencies as designed. Significant noise reduction up to 20 dB is observed for some frequency bands compared to the round reference nozzle, which has a noise peak an order of magnitude lower in frequency than the DEN models. Consistent with the OASPL plots, the DROPS nozzle provides more noise reduction than the SPS nozzle. It is hypothesized that the DROPS nozzle provides greater separation between the mini-jets and provides more overall mixing that results in greater noise reduction.

Note that at an azimuthal orientation of $\phi = 90°$, particularly at a polar angle of $\theta = 90°$, there is a low frequency local maximum in the DEN spectrum that does not occur in the $\phi = 0°$ azimuthal orientation. Both DEN designs show a low frequency peak around 1000 Hz. This characteristic spectral "hump" is also observed in the slanted slot DEN reported in Gaeta, et al[2, 3] in the same frequency range found here.

The distinct azimuthal directivity pattern of the 1000 Hz noise hump is characteristic of a dipole source with a *cos (φ)* directivity pattern. The similarity of the hump between the SPS, DROPS, and slanted slot design also implies that a common design characteristic may be causing this noise. Gaeta, et al[2] present strong evidence tying this noise to a turbulent boundary layer – trailing edge source related to the nozzles' closeout geometry. This hypothesis could be confirmed by altering the trailing edge in a way that would alter the source coherence. However, such modifications were not made during this test series. Additional analysis of the data collected from the SPS and DROPS nozzles will be performed using to establish that velocity scaling (V^5) and directivity pattern characteristics are typical of a trailing edge noise source. Noise source prediction tools[7] used to isolate airfoil noise sources during analysis of the earlier horizontal slot nozzle data[1] will be applied, to further investigate the source of the 1000 Hz noise peak.

It is highly likely that this noise source is characteristic of these specific designs and could be removed in future designs or in integrated configurations. The resultant acoustic characteristics would thus be even more attractive than what has been shown here. Based on comparing the spectra from the two azimuthal planes in Figures 9 through 12, this hump is the primary factor in the 2 to 3 dB OASPL difference between the two azimuthal planes shown in Figures 7 and 8, especially toward the sideline polar angles. Therefore, reducing the trailing edge noise source would lower the $\phi = 90°$ azimuthal plane noise to nearly what is measured in the quieter $\phi = 0°$ azimuthal plane.

Figures 13 and 14 show plots of the noise difference between the DROPS and SPS nozzles and the reference nozzle at three different pressure ratios for

azimuthal angle $\phi = 0°$ and polar angle of $\theta = 150°$. Negative SPL values represent noise reduction while positive values indicate frequency bands louder than the round reference nozzle. Again, it is observed that the DROPS nozzle typically provides more noise reduction than the SPS nozzle. Not only does the DROPS nozzle provide more noise reduction at low frequencies, it generates less noise at high frequencies. Both nozzles provide the greatest noise reduction in the frequency range of 1 to 2 kHz, with increased noise reduction as the NPR increases. At high frequencies where excess noise is generated compared to the round reference nozzle, the two DEN designs show opposite trends. For the DROPS design, more noise is generated as NPR increases. For the SPS design, less excess noise is generated as NPR increases.

It is worthy to note that all of the acoustic trends observed here are generally consistent with those for the slanted slot DEN reported by Gaeta, et al[2, 3]. One notable difference is that the SPS nozzle reported here provides more noise reduction than the first generation slanted slot nozzle, especially at subsonic pressure ratios. The enhanced noise reduction is likely due to the previously mentioned increased spanwise spacing between the slots which allows better mixing characteristics for the SPS design compared to the slotted design tested by Gaeta, et al[2, 3].

In contrast to the horizontal slot DEN design tested previously[1], both current designs provide significant noise reduction. As mentioned earlier, it is clear from the CFD that the current designs achieve much better mixing by maintaining the individual mini-jets for a longer distance before they coalesce back into a larger plume. This separation is very important in achieving the low frequency noise reduction observed here and to shift the peak acoustic frequency to higher values. However, we also note that there is an aero-performance penalty associated with achieving the jet-jet separation and enhanced noise reduction. One of the long-term goals for DEN research is to minimize this penalty while improving or maintaining noise reduction.

Pre-test expectations for DEN acoustic performance have for earlier efforts been based on qualitative assessments of graphical CFD predictions. These assessments have been based on an understanding of Lighthill's jet noise analogy, relying on visual comparisons of velocity, turbulence intensity (like those shown in Figures 5 and 6), and turbulence length scale contours to those for the reference nozzle. Ideally, a computational aeroacoustics (CAA) model would be used in combination with CFD to predict the jet noise from new designs. Since this capability is not yet in place, a first order, non-rigorous, estimating method was derived from Lighthill's equation for jet noise and dimensional analysis. The development of this "noise parameter" is documented in the SAJF model design report[5]. Lighthill's equation for far-field acoustic pressure perturbation (above ambient) in the absence of surfaces is, in time derivative form:

$$\overline{p}(\underline{x},t) - p_\infty = \frac{x_i x_j}{4\pi c_\infty^2 |\underline{x}-\underline{y}|^3} \int_V \left[\frac{\partial^2 \overline{T_{ij}(\underline{y},\tau)}}{\partial t^2} \right] d\underline{y} \quad (1)$$

where $\overline{T_{ij}} = \rho\overline{U_i U_j}$ is the approximate applied stress field, ignoring viscous stresses and compressibility effects, $\underline{y}$ is the distance from a reference point (e.g. the nozzle exit) to the source point, $\underline{x}$ is the distance to the far field observation point (the x_i representing its components), c_∞ is the ambient sound speed, and τ is the retarded time. Integration is over all significant source volume. Writing $U_k = U_k + u_k'$, the sum of a mean and fluctuation, respectively, we have $U_i U_j = U_i U_j + U_i u_j' + U_j u_i' + u_i' u_j'$. The first term is independent of time, and the fourth term is of higher order than the second and third terms, which are symmetric, so we have $\overline{T_{ij}} = 2\rho\overline{U_j u_i}$. Assuming constant density, the equation for acoustic pressure $p'(\underline{x},t) = \overline{p}(\underline{x},t) - p_\infty$ is now:

$$p'(\underline{x},t) = \frac{\rho x_i x_j}{2\pi c_\infty^2 |\underline{x}-\underline{y}|^3} \int_V \frac{\partial^2}{\partial t^2} \left[U_j(\underline{y})u_i'(\underline{y},t-\frac{x}{c_\infty}) \right] d\underline{y} \quad (2)$$

To first order, dimensional analysis[8] gives $\partial^2/\partial t^2 \sim 1/t_{char} \sim u'^2/L^2$ where t_{char} is the characteristic time, taken as the turbulent eddy turnover time, u' is the velocity fluctuation, and L is the turbulence length scale. Note that U_j is dominated by the component in the streamwise direction, and u_i' is of the same order for each direction, so that $u_1'^2 \approx u_2'^2 \approx u_3'^2$. A simplified expression for use in qualitative comparison of the RMS acoustic pressure pressure squared for each set of CFD flow fields is then:

$$p'^2 \sim \frac{\rho^2 V^2}{4\pi^2 c_\infty^4 L^4 r^2} \left[u_1'^4(\underline{y})U_1^2(\underline{y})u_1'^2(\underline{y}) \right] \quad (3)$$

On a decibel scale, Equation (3) can be written,

$$10\log_{10}(p'^2) \sim K + 10\log_{10}\left[u_1'^6(\underline{y})U_1^2(\underline{y}) \right] \quad (4)$$

For the purpose of this first order quantitative comparison, we refer to the second term on the right side of Equation 4, $10\log_{10}(u_1'^6 U_1^2)$, as the "noise parameter." This expression (which considers the axial component of turbulence only) omits factors representing effects of the turbulence length scale and source volume.

The noise parameter was computed throughout the NPR = 1.72 flow fields using CFD output for both current and earlier DEN designs. To provide a foundation for the usefulness of these calculations, CFD solutions obtained for the previously tested horizontal slot nozzle[1] and its 2D reference nozzle were used to compute their respective noise parameter fields, also for NPR = 1.72. The noise parameter contour results are shown in Figure 15. Each picture represents a section cut through the nozzle's spanwise center. The parameter is normalized by the jet exit velocity, U_j, of the respective reference nozzle. Diagrams A and B show calculations for the previously tested 2D reference and horizontal slot configurations, respectively. Note that there is not a significant difference between the characteristics of the two fields, except that the "loudest" area (red / orange contour) extends somewhat farther downstream in the case of the 2D reference. This observation is consistent with measured data from the LSAWT test that, as mentioned earlier, produced only minimal noise reduction at low frequencies from the horizontal slots. Diagrams C, D, and E show simulation results for the subject round reference nozzle, the DROPS DEN geometry, and the SPS DEN geometry, respectively. For these cases there is a dramatic reduction in the noise parameter for each of the distributed nozzles, with the largest values in the downstream DEN plumes reduced by about 15 dB from those of the reference. This value appears reasonable considering the data shown earlier.

However, caution must be used in making predictions of noise performance using this simple parameter for a number of reasons, including: a) the parameter includes only axial turbulence fluctuations and is therefore most valid for noise radiation at $\theta = 0°$ and $\theta = 180°$, b) calculations are made point-by-point, with no source-volume integration, and c) turbulence length scale and volume are omitted, but could be included as a separate factor. Despite these simplifications, the noise parameter defined here and illustrated in Figure 15 appears to provide a first-order indication of DEN acoustic performance relative to a conventional reference nozzle.

Jet-Jet Noise Shielding Study

Characteristic to the DEN technology is a significant reduction in low frequency noise accompanied by an increase in the high frequency components of noise. For these size nozzles, the crossover point between noise suppression and the high frequency excess noise generated compared to the round reference ranges between 6 kHz and 10 kHz. The peak frequency for both DEN designs is in the range of 15 kHz. This crossover point is problematic when it comes to projecting the scale model DEN to full size. Typically, Strouhal number scaling using a scale factor related to the nozzle exit area is applied that shifts model scale frequency in proportion to the geometric scale factor. If a single factor is used to scale the model-scale DEN acoustic spectra then the high frequency cross-over would cause the DEN models to be much louder than the round reference nozzle and these frequencies would dominate the sound field on a perceived noise level (PNL) basis. However, the model scale DEN designs have two length scales. One is associated with the mini-nozzles, which are close to the actual size they would be full scale, and the other is associated with the overall nozzle exit area which is much smaller than what it would be full size. Consequently, the lower frequency energy that is generated by the coalesced jet plume should scale to even lower frequency, but the higher frequency energy generated by the individual mini-jets would not shift frequency. In addition, jet-jet acoustic shielding by the arrays of nozzles will be a significant noise reduction effect that may increase with DEN model size. Thus, a full-scale DEN may provide even more suppression on a PNL basis than observed here.

The acoustic shielding effect has been investigated thoroughly in several twin-jet studies[9, 10, 11], but only recently for DEN designs[2, 3]. Our objective here was to obtain nozzle array acoustic shielding data that might aid in scaling at least part of the DEN acoustic spectrum for larger (greater flow area) nozzle systems. It is important to note that the DEN models tested here are considered to be small, full-scale sections of a larger nozzle system (i.e. the mini-nozzles in a full size system will be the same size as tested here, there will just be a lot more of them).

To quantify the shielding effect for the current SPS design, data were acquired from modified configurations realized by successively blocking (internally) neighboring slots on both the top and bottom array. First slot #7 was blocked and data acquired, then #6 and #7 were blocked, etc. until only the #1 slot was flowing. For each of these test points, mass flow was adjusted to maintain the desired value of NPR. In this way, the acoustic effect of adding each individual subsequent slot flow could be measured. The nozzle's azimuthal orientation was $\phi = 0°$ for all shielding runs. Data obtained for NPR = 1.72 are presented here in Figures 16 through 18.

Measured one-third-octave band spectra for the $\theta = 150°$ directivity angle are shown in Figure 16. For all bands above about 2000 Hz the spread between spectra is less than 4 dB, and data for the two slots through six slots cases are nearly indistinguishable demonstrating that once two of the slots are flowing, adding additional slot flow did not appreciably increase the noise in the high frequency range. The slight increase when the seventh slot is open is likely due to model edge entrainment. The larger spread in the low frequency data is an indication of downstream coalescence of the individual exhaust plumes generating excess noise. However, this appears to occur primarily in moving from one to two slots.

Using linear acoustic theory, the change in SPL obtained by operating fewer than seven slots can be estimated. The noise reduction relative to the seven-slot case expected from N flowing slots, independent of mixing and shielding effects, is given by $10log(N/7)$. This quantity is calculated for each test case in Table 1. As an example, if only 1 slot is flowing with no interaction effects between the slots, Table 1 shows that the resulting SPL would be approximately 8.45 dB lower than if all seven slots were flowing.

To more easily evaluate the effects of jet shielding and plume coalescence on the measured spectra, data for each test point were normalized as follows. The appropriate value from Table 1 was added to each spectrum shown in Figure 16, to correct SPL levels for the number of flowing slots. Next, the spectrum levels measured for all seven slots flowing was subtracted from each of these spectra. Therefore, for a system of completely independent jets, these normalizations would result in 0 dB spectra at all frequencies. The spectra generated in this way corresponding to those of Figure 16 are shown in Figure 17. For a given data point, net negative SPL spectral values represent frequencies for which shielding of jet noise by neighboring slots occurs. Net positive SPL values indicate frequencies for which merging of mini-jets results in excess mixing noise. Data presented in Figure 17 show that for $\theta = 150°$, there is a large acoustic shielding effect for mid to high frequencies, while at low frequencies, downstream coalescence of the mini-plumes generates extra low frequency noise. As noted above, most of this appears to occur in going from the one-slot to two-slot geometry.

Normalized data for the NPR = 1.72, $\theta = 90°$ measurements are shown in Figure 18. High frequency shielding benefits, while reduced somewhat from the $\theta = 150°$ case, are 2 to 4 dB and still significant. There is, however, no indication of a low frequency penalty due to jet coalescence at this sideline radiation angle. It is significant to note that while the term shielding is used here, the differences observed between the sideline and aft polar angles imply that the individual jets may not be truly shielding in the strictest sense of the term such that individual jets are blocking, or shielding, the radiated acoustic energy from its neighbors. Rather, it is likely that reflection and refraction through the individual jet layers within the plume is the source of the large amount of "shielding" observed in the aft angles. This kind of effect would be smaller at the sideline angles compared to the aft angles, which is what is observed here. Additionally, for hot jet flow where the density gradient between jet columns is more significant than found here, the beneficial effects may increase.

Spectral data analyzed in this way will provide guidance on nozzle geometry improvements resulting in even greater noise reduction for future DEN designs. Variable slot spacing, for instance, may provide a means of realizing the benefits of jet-jet acoustic shielding while eliminating some of the excess low frequency noise due to jet coalescence.

Conclusion

The data presented here from the DEN designs show a great deal of promise for this technology. Noise reductions up to 20 dB on a spectral basis and 10 dB on an overall basis were demonstrated. While the thrust performance penalty is still relatively high, it is approaching levels that could be tolerable in future revolutionary design aircraft systems that integrate the propulsion system into the airframe. It is clear that specific details of a particular DEN design can greatly influence the aeroacoustic properties. Phenomena such as jet-jet mixing, shielding, and coalescence all play a significant role in the resulting noise reduction. Testing and analyses such as those presented here will be required to make distributed exhaust technology viable for an aircraft system. Future system and technology studies at NASA will further explore distributed exhaust nozzles as a candidate for contributing to the 20 dB perceived noise reduction enterprise goal.

Acknowledgements

Northrop Grumman performed this work under contract NAS1-02046 funded by the Propulsion Airframe Aeroacoustics subtask of NASA's Quiet Aircraft Technology Program. The authors would like to thank Sang Lee and Meaza Teshome of the NASA Langley Jet Noise Laboratory for their invaluable assistance collecting and processing the acoustic data. The authors would also like to thank Northrop Grumman's Ed Hobart and Gary Carr for their assistance with construction of the stereolithography DEN models and Brian Hallam for timely stress analysis. In addition, Krish Ahuja and Rick Gaeta of Georgia Tech provided helpful insight while comparing the slanted slot DEN results to those reported here.

References

[1] Kinzie, K. W., Brown, M. C., Schein, D. B., and Solomon, Jr., W. D., "Measurements and Predictions for a Distributed Exhaust Nozzle," AIAA Paper No. 2001-2236 presented at the 7th AIAA / CEAS Aeroacoustics Conference, Maastricht, The Netherlands, May, 2001.

[2] Gaeta, R. J., Ahuja, K. K., Schein, D. B., and Solomon, Jr., W. D., "Large Jet-Noise Reductions Through Distributed Exhausts," AIAA Paper No. 2002-2456 presented at the 8th AIAA / CEAS Aeroacoustics Conference, Breckenridge, Colorado, June, 2002.

[3] Ahuja, K.K., Gaeta, R.J., Hellman, B, Schein, D.B., and Solomon, Jr., W.D., "Distributed Exhaust Nozzles for Jet Noise Reduction," GRTI Report A6221/2001-1, Final Report for NASA Contract NAG3-2352, 2001.

[4] Shields, F. D. and Bass, H. E., "A Study of Atmospheric Absorption of High Frequency Noise and Application to Fractional Octave Bands of Noise," NASA Contractor Report 2760, 1976

[5] Malone, M. B., "Turbulence Model Evaluation for Free Shear Dominated Flows," AIAA Paper No. 96-2038 presented at the 27th AIAA Fluid Dynamics Conference, New Orleans, Louisiana, June, 1996.

[6] Solomon Jr., W. D. and Schein, D. B. "SAJF Distributed Exhaust Nozzle Model Design and Fabrication," NASA Contract No. NAS1-99068 Task 5 Final Technical Report, 2001.

[7] Brooks, T. F., Pope, D. S., and Marcolini, M. A., "Airfoil Self-Noise and Prediction," NASA Reference Publication 1218, 1989.

[8] Huang, W.J., "Numerical Solution of Aerosound from an Airfoil Using k-ε Turbulence Model," AIAA 96-0754, January 1996.

[9] Simonich, J. C., Amiet, R. K., and Schlinker, R. H., "Jet Shielding of Jet Noise," NASA Contractor Report 3966, 1986

[10] Kantola, R. A., "Shielding Aspects of Heated Twin Jet Noise," AIAA Paper No., 77-1288 presented at the 4th AIAA Aeroacoustics Conference, October, 1977.

[11] Wlezien, R. W., Rogers, C. B., Yamamoto, K. J., and Wang, B., "The Effectiveness of Acoustic Shielding for HSCT Nozzle Configurations," AIAA Paper No. 91-3280 presented at the 9th AIAA Applied Aerodynamics Conference, September, 1991.

Table 1. Expected SPL reduction compared to seven slot case if specified number of slots are flowing; 10log(N/7).

No. Slots	Delta dB
6	-0.67
5	-1.46
4	-2.43
3	-3.68
2	-5.44
1	-8.45

Figure 1. Horizontal slot DEN tested in the NASA LSAWT in 2000.

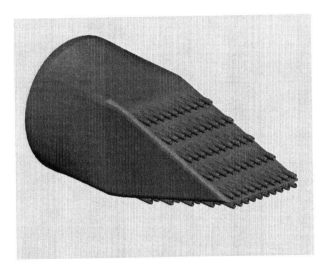

Figure 2. DROPS DEN design tested in NASA SAJF in 2002.

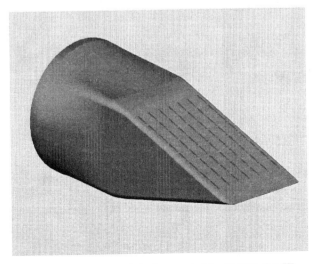

Figure 3. SPS DEN design tested in NASA SAJF in 2002.

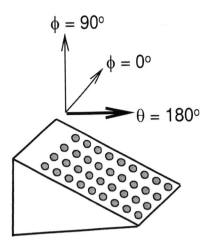

Figure 4. Sketch of nozzle coordinate system and azimuthal orientation planes.

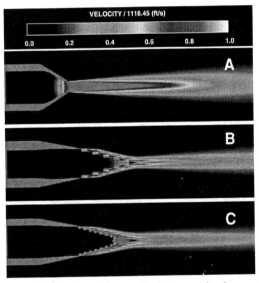

Figure 5. Centerplane velocity magnitude contours for (a) round reference nozzle, (b) DROPS, (c) SPS.

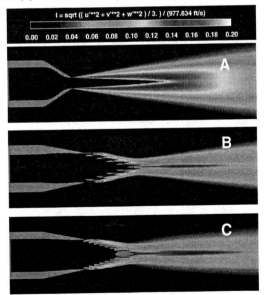

Figure 6. Centerplane turbulence intensity contours for (a) round reference nozzle, (b) DROPS, (c) SPS.

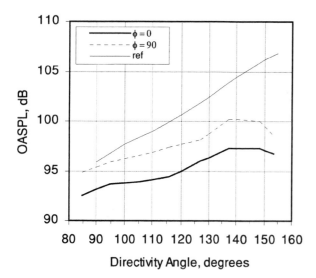

Figure 7. OASPL for DROPS nozzle and reference nozzle at NPR = 1.72.

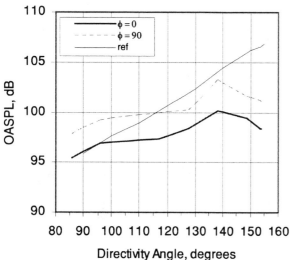

Figure 8. OASPL for SPS nozzle and reference nozzle at NPR = 1.72.

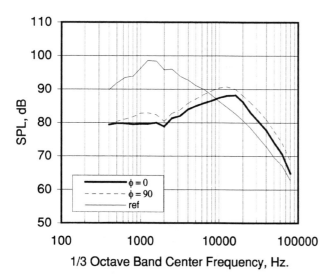

Figure 9. Spectra for DROPS nozzle and reference nozzle at NPR=1.72, θ = 150°.

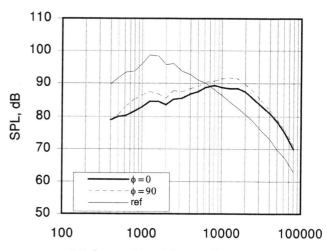

Figure 10. Spectra for SPS nozzle and reference nozzle at NPR = 1.72, θ = 150°.

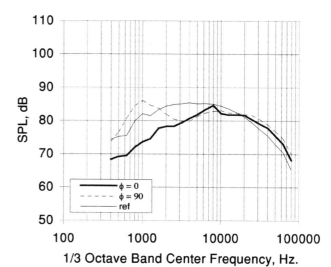

Figure 11. Spectra for DROPS nozzle and reference nozzle at NPR=1.72, θ = 90°.

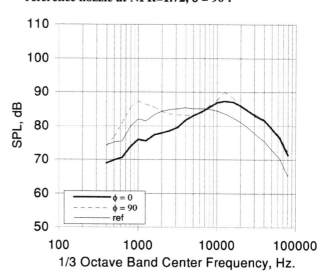

Figure 12. Spectra for SPS nozzle and reference nozzle at NPR=1.72, θ = 90°.

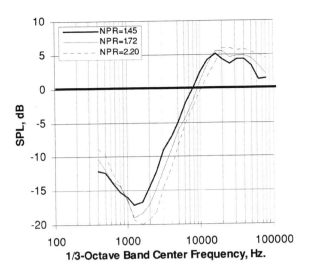

Figure 13. Difference between DROPS nozzle and reference nozzle at φ = 0°, θ = 150°.

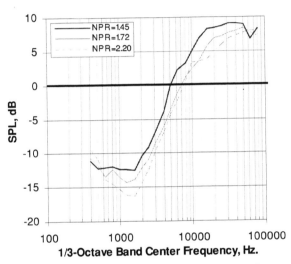

Figure 14. Difference between SPS nozzle and reference nozzle at φ = 0°, θ = 150°.

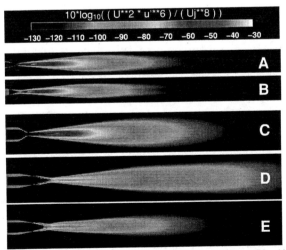

Figure 15. Noise Parameter Comparison, NPR=1.72: A) 2D Ref. (LSAWT), B) Horiz. Slot (LSAWT), C) Ref., D) DROPS, E) SPS

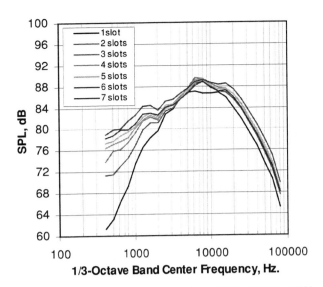

Figure 16. SPS noise shielding data, NPR=1.72, θ=150°.

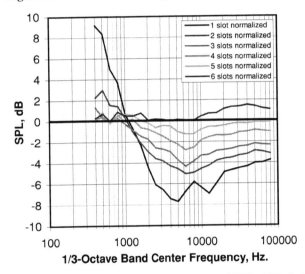

Figure 17. SPS normalized shielding data, NPR=1.72, θ=150°.

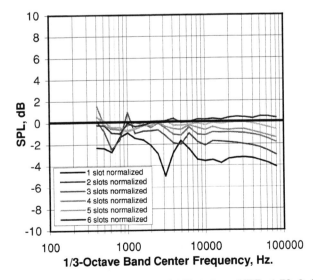

Figure 18. SPS normalized shielding data, NPR=1.72, θ=90°.

NOISE SUPPRESSION IN MODERATE-SPEED MULTISTREAM JETS

Dimitri Papamoschou *

University of California, Irvine, Irvine, California 92697-3975

This paper presents an exploratory study of alternative jet noise suppression methods for commercial turbofan engines. The basic principle is reduction of the convective Mach number of flow instabilities that produce intense downward-radiated sound. This is possible through a combination of two factors: mixing enhancement of the core stream and thickening of the bypass stream on the underside of the jet. In an initially coaxial jet, these two effects are achieved either by offsetting the nozzles or by deflecting the bypass stream**. The latter option, accomplished by installing vanes in the annular exhaust of the bypass flow, proved acoustically superior. Subscale tests of jets approximating the exhaust conditions of CFM56 and JT8D engines showed that, in both cases, the vanes produced significant suppression of downward directed noise. For the CFM56, the peak overall sound pressure level (OASPL) was suppressed by 5 dB and the effective perceived noise level (EPNL) was reduced by 2 dB. For the JT8D, peak OASPL and EPNL were both reduced by 4 dB relative to the ideal fully-mixed exhaust.

Nomenclature

a	=	speed of sound at jet exit or in freestream
$\bar{a}$	=	speed of sound associated with $\bar{u}$
D	=	diameter
$\dot{m}$	=	mass flow rate
M	=	Mach number at jet exit or in freestream
$\bar{u}$	=	peak mean velocity at given axial location
U	=	velocity at jet exit or in freestream
U_c	=	convective velocity
α	=	geometric angle of attack
γ	=	climb angle
θ	=	polar angle relative to jet centerline
ρ	=	density
ϕ	=	azimuth angle relative to vertical plane

Subscripts

p	=	primary (core) exhaust
s	=	secondary (bypass) exhaust
∞	=	flight conditions

---

*Professor, Associate Fellow AIAA

** Noise suppression via deflection of the bypass and/or core streams is proprietary to the University of California. U.S. Patent Pending.

Abbreviations

BPR	=	Bypass Ratio = $\dot{m}_s/\dot{m}_p$
EPNL	=	Effective Perceived Noise Level
OASPL	=	Overall Sound Pressure Level
PNL	=	Perceived Noise Level
SPL	=	Sound Pressure Level

Introduction

Aircraft noise is an issue of enormous environmental, financial, and technological impact. There are two main sources of noise in today's commercial aircraft engines: fan/compressor noise and jet noise. Jet noise itself is composed of turbulent mixing noise and, in the case of imperfectly expanded jets, shock noise [1]. Turbulent mixing is by far the biggest problem and is extremely difficult to control. The most celebrated formula for turbulent mixing noise is the scaling law

$$\overline{p'^2} \sim U_j^n \qquad (1)$$

It comes from dimensional analysis of the solution to Lighthill's acoustic analogy [2, 3]. The left hand side is the sound intensity, U_j is the jet velocity, and $n = 8$ for low-speed jets and approaches 3 for very-high-speed jets. This formula is the cornerstone of jet noise reduction efforts over the last half-century: reduction of jet speed using exhaust mixers or by increasing the engine bypass ratio.

Turbulent mixing is governed by the velocity difference across the mixing region, rather than by the absolute velocity. A more complete version of Eq. 1, therefore, should be

$$\overline{p'^2} \sim (U_j - U_\infty)^n \tag{2}$$

where U_∞ is the velocity of the medium surrounding the jet flow. This formula must be used with caution. It is valid only for *shear-layer-type* mixing between the jet and the surrounding medium. It does not apply to *wake-type* mixing that occurs in the vicinity of the nozzle due to the finite thicknesses of the nozzle lip and of the exit boundary layers. In fact, wake-generated noise will worsen with increasing U_∞. Experiments on hot jets in forward flight [4] confirm the validity of Eq. 2 for noise radiating in the rear arc, which is produced by large turbulent eddies. Noise emitted laterally or in the forward arc, generated mainly from fine-scale turbulence, was not attenuated by the flight effect. The reasons for the lack of attenuation are not clear and have been the subject of debate; it is possible this type of noise is influenced by wake effects near the nozzle exit. Figure 1 shows a representative plot of the directivity of OASPL for a hot jet in static and flight conditions [4]. The reduction in peak OASPL is substantial, about 6 decibels.

In coaxial jets, as created by separate-flow turbofan engines, the primary (core) jet is initially surrounded by the secondary (bypass) stream which acts as a moving medium. Given that the velocity ratio of these two flows is typically $U_s/U_p = 0.7$, one would expect dramatic reductions in the noise emitted by the core stream. As will be shown later, this is not the case. In the coaxial exhaust of typical engines, the secondary stream becomes fully mixed well upstream of the end of the primary potential core. As a result, a substantial part of the core noise source region is not covered by the secondary flow. Some noise reduction certainly occurs, but not near the levels one would have expected from Eq. 2.

Equation 2 nevertheless offers a strong incentive to explore alternative methods for noise reduction. Is it possible to reduce the *relative* velocity in the noise-emitting region of the core jet, while maintaining the same absolute core velocity? In other words, can we create a "forward-flight effect" without a huge secondary flow? In an aircraft engine, the exhaust velocities, Mach numbers, and mass flow rates are largely fixed by the engine cycle – one has little freedom in altering them. What can change, however, is the nozzle configuration. Recent work on dual-stream, high-speed jets has shown that substantial noise reduction is achievable by reshaping the nozzle from coaxial to eccentric [5]. Downward-directed Mach wave emission was reduced by the combination of two factors: (a) shortening of the primary potential core (relative to the coaxial case); and (b) thickening of the secondary flow in the downward direction [6]. The resulting synergism allowed the secondary stream to "shield" effectively the noise source region of the primary jet. In broader terms, these experiments suggest that, in a dual-stream jet, shaping of exhaust flow away from traditional configurations has the potential for significant noise reduction.

Questions remain, however, regarding the physical mechanisms and general use of this approach. Why was the primary potential core shortened? Does this technique extend to lower-speed jets where Mach wave radiation is not as intense? And, are there alternatives to the eccentric arrangement? These issues are addressed here through a combination of empirical modeling and exploratory experimentals. First, the concept of "relative velocity" is quantified better in terms of the convective Mach number M_c of the flow instability. Second, preliminary models are constructed for the axial distribution of M_c. Third, experiments on a variety of nozzle configurations clarify important physical mechanisms and identify promising configurations for noise reduction. The study then applies those configurations to sub-scale tests simulating the exhaust conditions of two widely-used engines, the General Electric CFM56 and the Pratt & Whitney JT8D. The experiments were conducted in UCI's Jet Aeroacoustics Facility (Fig. 2) which has been described extensively in prior publications [5, 7]. All sound measurements presented here are in the acoustic far field. Estimates of perceived noise level (PNL) use the flight path shown in Fig. 3. Details on the PNL estimation can be found in Ref. [7].

Convective Mach Number M_c

The large-scale turbulent structures of the jet shear layers can be viewed, at a conceptual level, as instability waves traveling with a convective speed U_c. Letting $\eta(x, t)$ represent the vortex sheet between the jet and a quiescent ambient, the simplest wave representation is of the form

$$\eta(x,t) = Ae^{i(x-U_c t)} \qquad (3)$$

where a wavenumber of unity has been chosen for simplicity. With the amplitude A constant, the instability radiates sound to the far field when the convective Mach number

$$M_c = \frac{U_c}{a_\infty} > 1 \qquad (4)$$

The next level of realism is to consider the non-parallel (growing) nature of the mean flow. In that case, linear stability theory shows that a disturbance at fixed frequency amplifies and then decays with axial distance. Instead of a simple wave, we are now dealing with a wave packet

$$\eta(x,t) = A(x)e^{i(x-U_c t)} \qquad (5)$$

As has been shown by numerous past investigations[1, 8, 9, 10], the amplitude modulation $A(x)$ changes dramatically the sound radiated by the instability. This is readily apparent when writing $\eta(x,t)$ in Fourier space,

$$\eta(x,t) = \frac{1}{2\pi} \int_{-\infty}^{\infty} \hat{A}(k-1)e^{ik\left(x-\frac{U_c}{k}\right)}dk \qquad (6)$$

The wave packet is a superposition of individual simple waves each with wavenumber k, amplitude $\hat{A}(k-1)dk/(2\pi)$, and phase speed U_c/k. The phase Mach number of each individual wave is

$$m_c = \frac{U_c/k}{a_\infty} = \frac{M_c}{k} \qquad (7)$$

Figure 4 plots m_c versus k for $M_c = 0.5$. Also plotted is a sketch of a generic $\hat{A}(k-1)$. Instabilities with $|k| < M_c$ are supersonic and radiate to the far field; those with $|k| > M_c$ are subsonic and decay exponentially with distance away from the jet axis. The energy contained in the radiating sound field is governed by the integral of $\hat{A}(k-1)$ from $-M_c$ to M_c. This example shows that subsonic instability waves can radiate sound to the far field if they are amplitude modulated. One can view this as a form of Mach wave radiation, although it is much weaker than its supersonic counterpart. Nevertheless, Mach waves carry sound to the far field so this source of noise can be very important in moderate-speed jets.

Clearly, as M_c declines there is less energy contained in the radiated sound field. This motivates the noise reduction approach presented here. Is it possible to reduce M_c at constant exit flow conditions? The following sections address this question.

Effect of Nozzle Geometry on $M_c(x)$

A large number of experiments confirm that most of the large-scale turbulent mixing noise comes from the region around the end of the potential core [11, 12, 13, 14]. Any scheme to reduce noise via reduction of the convective Mach number M_c must take this fact into account. This leads to a more specific definition of the noise reduction approach proposed here: *make M_c at the end of the potential core as low subsonic as possible.*

In a jet with fixed exit flow conditions, reduction of M_c entails one or both of the following basic methods: (a) controlling U_c; (b) controlling the medium surrounding the instability wave. The former requires some form of excitation that can change U_c not only at the nozzle exit but five to twenty diameters downstream, depending on the length of the potential core. There is no experimental evidence that this is possible in realistic flows. The latter scheme is more plausible as it involves manipulation of a secondary stream. Today all commercial aircraft engines have a secondary stream - the bypass flow.

In a dual-stream jet, there are two convective Mach numbers that influence noise emission: one for the primary instability with respect to the secondary stream,

$$M_{c_p}(x) = \frac{U_{c_p}(x) - \bar{u}_s(x)}{\bar{a}_s(x)} \qquad (8)$$

and the other for the secondary instability with respect to the ambient,

$$M_{c_s}(x) = \frac{U_{c_s}(x) - U_\infty}{a_\infty} \qquad (9)$$

In non-axisymmetric arrangements there is also an azimuthal dependence of the mean flow variables. Which one of the two convective Mach numbers is more important depends on the volume and intensity of noise sources associated with each distribution. For low secondary mass flow rate (low bypass ratio) M_{c_p} is expected to govern noise emission. For very large secondary mass flow rates M_{c_s} could become equally or more important. As will be shown next, in coaxial engine exhausts the primary (core) flow has a much longer potential core that does the secondary (bypass) flow. The end of the potential core is associated with very strong turbulent fluctuations. It is possible, therefore, that M_{c_p} is influential even for large bypass ratios. For this reason, more weight is given here on M_{c_p} than on M_{c_s}.

Direct measurements of turbulent structure convection in jets and shear layers [15, 16], coupled with surveys of the mean flow in coaxial and eccentric jets [6], offer preliminary empirical tools for the prediction of $M_{c_p}(x)$ and $M_{c_s}(x)$. This prediction should be viewed as more qualitative than quantitative as it is based on limited number of data and on models whose accuracy is on the order of 10%. However, it is expected to capture fundamental trends needed to illustrate the philosophy of the approach. Appendices A and B summarize the models.

Figure 5 shows predictions of $M_{c_p}(x)$ and $M_{c_s}(x)$ in a static jet with CFM56 exit conditions (Table 1). The convective Mach number of the core jet alone, plotted in Fig. 5a, is 0.85 at the jet exit and starts declining where the potential core ends, $x/D_p=5.5$. For the coaxial jet, Fig. 5b, M_{c_p} drops to 0.18 at the jet exit but starts rising past the end of the secondary potential core and reaches a maximum of 0.45 at the end of the primary potential core, $x/D_p=16$. Note the dramatic elongation of the primary core with addition of the annular bypass flow. Offsetting the nozzles to an eccentric geometry, Fig. 5c, shortens the primary core to $x/D_p=9$ and doubles the length of the secondary core on the underside of the jet. As a result, M_{c_p} on the underside of the jet never exceeds 0.22. The eccentric jet, therefore, is expected to be quieter in the downward direction than the coaxial jet.

It is important to realize that static conditions are not representative of the conditions under which noise from an airplane is monitored. Forward flight has significant influence on the distribution of convective Mach numbers, particularly on $M_{c_s}(x)$. For this reason, Figure 6 plots the M_c distributions for the CFM56 case with $M_\infty = 0.3$. Compared to the static case, M_{c_s} is reduced from 0.6 to 0.35. This should translate into a very substantial reduction of noise emitted by the bypass flow. Offsetting the nozzles reduces the peak value of $M_{c_p}(x)$ from 0.38 to 0.20. Given that the secondary flow is now much quieter, offsetting the nozzles may produce a stronger benefit at forward flight than at static conditions.

Figure 7 shows convective Mach number predictions for a lower-bypass engine, the JT8D-219 (Table 2). This is a mixed-flow engine that potentially could be modified to a separate-flow configuration. The peak M_{c_p}s of the perfectly-mixed exhaust and of the coaxial exhaust are roughly the same, around 0.9. Offsetting the nozzles reduces the peak M_{c_p} to 0.6.

Past experiments [5, 7], and those presented later in this paper, confirm that the eccentric exhaust is quieter than the coaxial exhaust. See Figs. 8a and 8b for the generic coaxial and eccentric nozzle shapes. As mentioned earlier, a key mechanism is the shortening of the potential core (mixing enhancement) of the primary flow. Enhanced mixing was thought to be caused by exposure of part of the primary stream to the ambient, hence creation of a larger velocity differential across the shear layer on the upper side of the jet.

This motivated a potential refinement to the eccentric nozzle, the arcuate nozzle shown in Fig. 8c. It was designed to have a very smooth transition from a full annulus at the nozzle entrance to 2/3 (240-deg.) annulus at the nozzle exit. The flow lines at the nozzle exit were parallel. The arcuate nozzle was tested against coaxial and eccentric nozzles having the same primary and secondary exit cross sectional areas.

Figure 9 shows far-field spectra of sound from jets issued from coaxial, eccentric, and arcuate nozzles. All exit flow conditions were identical. While the eccentric nozzle reduced noise, the arcuate nozzle produced negligible noise reduction at low frequencies and very small reduction at high frequency. It became evident that the eccentric nozzle creates effects not present in the arcuate nozzle and that the aforementioned reason for enhanced mixing was wrong or incomplete. Although this development was initially disappointing, it shed some light on the fluid mechanics of the eccentric nozzle and spawned alternative configurations that probably would not have been considered otherwise.

The failure of the parallel-flow, arcuate nozzle to reduce noise suggests strongly that the eccentric nozzle produces flow deflections that help promote mixing of the primary flow. A speculative drawing of the streamline shapes exiting the eccentric nozzle is presented in Fig. 10. A stagnation region is formed at the closed portion of the meniscus-shaped secondary flow passage. Streamlines in that region deflect to exit the nozzle and create locally skewed mixing layers between the primary and secondary flows. Past theoretical and experimental studies have shown that increasing the skew angle can result in very significant increase in mixing [17, 18].

Deflection of Bypass Stream

The last observation triggered investigation of methods to control the mixing layer skew angle and simultaneously deflect the bypass stream. It was also desired to maintain the overall configuration coaxial, simplifying the task of potentially implementing these methods on aircraft engines. This section overviews two such configurations. The first one involved placing a wedge in the annular bypass nozzle, essentially creating an arcuate nozzle but with non-parallel flow in the vicinity of the wedge. The second one involved installation of vanes in the bypass stream to deflect the bypass flow downward.

The wedge configuration is shown in Fig. 11. Experimentation with a variety of wedge shapes and sizes showed that the wedge angle was the most critical parameter. At the same base dimension, wedges with large angles reduced downward-emitted noise appreciably while those with small angle produced little reduction. This finding is in accord with the negligible noise reduction produced by the arcuate nozzle (Fig. 8c). Figure 12 compares spectra produced by a clean coaxial nozzle, a coaxial nozzle with wedge inserted in the bypass flow, and an eccentric nozzle. In the direction of peak noise emission, the wedge and the eccentricity produced roughly the same acoustic benefit. It appears, therefore, that streamline deflection is a critical aspect of noise reduction. In other polar directions, the wedge nozzle was moderately inferior to the eccentric one. As a result, the overall noise benefit of the wedge configuration (in terms of OASPL and PNL) was somewhat smaller than that of the eccentric nozzle. This observation is based on a limited number of experiments so one should be careful not to generalize prematurely. The wedge configuration in fact produces substantial reduction in the peak sideline noise (at azimuth angles up to 90°), a feature that will be exploited in future studies.

Figure 13 shows an exemplary drawing of the approach using vanes in the exhaust of the bypass stream. It is believed that this deflection scheme achieves two goals simultaneously: create skewed mixing layers in the vicinity of the nozzle exit and direct most of the bypass stream to the lower side of the jet so that it shields the end of the potential core. Figure 14 shows spark schlieren images that tend to support this hypothesis. The clean coaxial jet spreads very slowly. Insertion of vanes enhances mixing considerably and thickens the bypass stream on the underside of the jet. The deflectors

produced superior noise reduction compared to the wedge and eccentricity methods. Applied to an engine, they could be actively deflected or deployed, confining any thrust losses to the takeoff and landing segments only. The next section concentrates on experiments using this approach.

Subscale Simulation of Two Engines

Subscale jet experiments, using helium-air mixtures, simulated the exhaust conditions of two engines: the General Electric CFM56 and the Pratt & Whitney JT8D-219. See Fig. 2 for an overview of the experimental setup. Both engines produce static thrust in the 20,000-lb class. Estimates of perceived noise level assumed a flight path (Fig. 3) with a takeoff roll of 1300 m followed by a straight climb at $\gamma = 12°$ and at a geometric angle of attack $\alpha = 6°$. The experiments compared the acoustics of the following exhaust configurations: clean coaxial; coaxial with deflectors; eccentric; and, in the case of the JT8D, fully-mixed. Tables 1 and 2 summarize the flow conditions, nozzle configurations, and aerodynamic force predictions for each simulated engine.

Figure 15 shows a picture of the CFM56 nozzle with deflectors attached. The core nozzle had a plug that approximated the configuration of this engine found on many aircraft. The outer wall of the core nozzle extended past the exit of the bypass nozzle. Four vanes, made of thin metal sheet, were attached on the outer wall of the core nozzle immediately past the exit of the bypass nozzle. With $\phi = 0$ indicating the downward vertical direction, the vanes were placed at azimuth angles $\phi = \pm 70°$ and $\pm 110°$. The vane angle of attack was approximately 10°. The size of each vane was 4 mm in chord by 3 mm in width. The width was slightly smaller than the annulus thickness of the bypass duct.

The forces on the vanes were calculated from basic aerodynamic relations [19]. Each vane was treated as a wing with aspect ratio equal to twice the width divided by the chord length. The two-dimensional lift slope was assumed to be 0.1/deg and the parasite drag coefficient was assumed to be 0.01. Because of the small aspect ratio, the three-dimensional lift slope is quite small (around 0.04 /deg), allowing deflections up to about 25° without exceeding a lift coefficient of 1.0. It is expected, therefore, that the vanes are not stalled even at such high geometric angle of attack.

Figure 16 shows spectra in the direction of peak emission for the CFM56 cases. In the low- to mid-frequency range, the eccentric nozzle reduced the SPL by 3 dB and the nozzle with vanes reduced the SPL by 5 dB. Figure 17 shows the directivity of OASPL. There is significant reduction of OASPL at the shallow angles. The maximum level of OASPL was reduced by 3 dB in the eccentric case and by 5 dB in the vane case. For higher angles, CFM56-ECC displays a moderate noise increase while CFM56-4V10e practically coincides with the coaxial clean case. The advantage of CFM56-4V10e is also evident in the PNL comparison of Fig. 18. The effective perceived noise level (EPNL) was reduced by 2.0 dB in CFM56-4V10e versus 0.6 dB in CFM56-ECC.

The nozzle of the JT8D-2V20i configuration is pictured in Fig. 19. Here the bypass duct extended past the end of the core duct. Two vanes were installed inside the bypass duct immediately downstream of the lip of the core nozzle. The vanes were installed at $\phi = \pm 90°$ and at an angle of attack of 20°. Their dimensions were 3 mm in width by 4 mm in chord. The width was about 95% of the bypass annulus thickness, so the vanes did not intrude into the core stream. Figure 20 compares the peak-emission spectra of JT8D-COAX, JT8D-ECC, and JT8D-2V20i. Both the eccentricity and the vanes reduce noise significantly, but the vanes are clearly superior. At the moderate frequency range of 200-500 Hz (full-scale), the vanes produced a 3-4 dB benefit relative to the eccentric nozzle. Noise in the upward direction was roughly equal to that of clean coaxial exhaust, as shown in Fig. 21. This is different from the eccentric case in which upward-directed noise matches that of the isolated core jet, which is considerably louder than the coaxial jet [5]. The fact that the jet does not get much noisier in the upward direction should mitigate concerns about intense upward-directed sound reflecting from aircraft surfaces or atmospheric gradients towards the ground.

Comparisons of OASPL, plotted in Fig. 22, include the above cases and the fully-mixed exhaust. The vanes produce the largest reduction in peak OASPL. Both the eccentric exhaust and the exhaust with vanes are quieter than the mixed-flow exhaust. In terms of perceived noise, the exhaust with vanes is again superior, as shown in the PNL time history of Fig. 23. EPNL was reduced by 5.5 dB relative to the coaxial case and by 3.8 dB relative to the mixed-flow case. Note that, in this experiment, the mixed-flow exhaust is idealized. The actual mixed-flow exhaust has non-uniformities and carries noise form the internal mixer. The benefit of the separate-flow exhaust with vanes, relative to the mixed exhaust, is thus expected to be better than that shown here.

Practical Implementation Issues

Application of bypass deflectors to an aircraft engine is conceptually straight-forward as it does not involve major changes in the powerplant design. In fact, for an initially mixed-flow engine like the JT8D this method might bring simplicity by getting rid of the internal mixer. The vanes could be rotated to a certain angle of attack during the noise-sensitive segments of flight and placed at zero angle otherwise. This will confine thrust losses to the takeoff/landing phases only. Alternatively, the vanes could be deployed during takeoff/landing and then stowed flush with the nacelle surface, creating an even cleaner flow path. If a small thrust loss, on the order of one percent or less, can be tolerated for the entire mission of the airplane, the deflectors could be fixed, thereby simplifying nacelle design.

Placement of deflectors outside the bypass duct (Fig. 15) should not impact the engine cycle are as the deflectors would not change the effective cross-sectional area of the bypass nozzle. If the deflectors are placed inside the bypass duct, some adjustment to the engine cycle may be required. It is in fact possible to use the vanes both for deflecting the bypass stream and for controlling the exit area of the bypass nozzle. The latter may help reduce broadband shock noise that occurs at cruise when the bypass stream is underexpanded.

For an aircraft with wing-mounted engines, the lift force on the vanes (which for the current experiments is estimated at 3-5% of engine thrust) should have negligible impact on longitudinal trim as the axial location of the engines is near the axial location of the center of gravity. In a configuration with rear-mounted engines, vane lift will have a small effect on trim. An approximate analysis of longitudinal stability for a DC9/MD80-type airplane shows that a vane lift equal to 5% of engine thrust can be counteracted with one degree of stabilizer trim or 3° of elevator deflection.

Concluding Remarks

The OASPL plots of Figs. 1, 17, and 22 bear a resemblance which is not believed to be coincidental.

The combination of skewed mixing and concentration of the bypass stream to the underside of the jet appears to produce a "forward flight effect" in addition to the one that occurs naturally in a coaxial jet. More precisely, based on the preliminary empirical models described earlier in the paper, the aforementioned methods reduce the convective Mach numbers of instabilities that cause downward-radiated noise. Of the configurations examined so far, the vanes in the bypass duct are superior to the other configurations in reducing downward noise. As mentioned earlier, the wedge configuration (Fig. 11) shows good potential for reducing sideline noise. The vane and wedge arrangements should be seen as specific embodiments of a general approach for deflecting the bypass stream sideward and downward while maintaining an coaxial exhaust structure.

The examples shown in this paper are two of several deflector arrangements that have been tried in the recent past. All of them reduce noise when used in the spirit of Fig. 13. The investigation to date has not been very systematic and the vane design and installation have been rather crude. What is clear from the experiments is that the results are quite sensitive on the placement and geometry of the vanes. There is great potential, therefore, for optimization and improvements through a systematic study of a large parameter space that includes deflector geometry, deflector placement, and nozzle geometry. This should be accompanied by a thorough investigation of the flow physics of each configuration.

Special Notice

The method and apparatus of noise suppression via deflection of the bypass and/or core streams is proprietary to the University of California. U.S. Patent Pending.

Acknowledgments

The support by NASA Glenn Research Center is gratefully acknowledged (Grant NAG-3-2345 monitored by Dr. Khairul B. Zaman). Ms. Erin Abbey is thanked for her work on nozzle design.

Appendix A: Mean Flow Relations

This section presents a summary of relations for predicting basic features of the mean flow field of dual-stream jets. For further details the reader should consult Ref. [6]. The relations use the "classical" formula for the growth rate of a fully-turbulent, planar shear layer,

$$\delta'(\mathcal{R}, \mathcal{S}, M_{c,\text{sym}}) = 0.14 \frac{(1-\mathcal{R})(1+\sqrt{\mathcal{S}})}{1+\mathcal{R}\sqrt{\mathcal{S}}} \times$$
$$[0.23 + 0.77 \exp(-3.5 M_{c,\text{sym}}^2)] \quad (10)$$

where $\mathcal{R}$ is the velocity ratio, $\mathcal{S}$ is the density ratio, and $M_{c,\text{sym}}$ is the symmetric convective Mach number. For coaxial jets, the basic idea is that the length of the primary potential core core, $L_{p,\text{COAX}}$, lies somewhere between the potential core length of the single jet, L_{SINGLE}, and the potential core length of the coflowing jet, $L_{\text{COFLOWING}}$, by an amount dependent on the length of the secondary potential core, $L_{s,\text{COAX}}$. For the single jet,

$$\frac{L_{\text{SINGLE}}}{D_p} = \left\{ \delta'\left(0, \frac{\rho_\infty}{\rho_p}, \frac{U_p}{a_p + a_\infty}\right) \right\}^{-1} \quad (11)$$

For the coflowing jet (a jet submerged in a very large secondary flow),

$$\frac{L_{\text{COFLOWING}}}{D_p} = \left\{ \delta'\left(\frac{U_s}{U_p}, \frac{\rho_s}{\rho_p}, \frac{U_p + U_s}{a_p + a_s}\right) \right\}^{-1} \quad (12)$$

The length of the secondary potential core is

$$\frac{L_{s,\text{COAX}}}{D_p} = 2.8 \frac{H}{D_p} \left[\frac{L_{\text{COFLOWING}}/D_p}{\delta_s' L_{\text{COFLOWING}}/D_p + 1}\right] \quad (13)$$

where

$$\delta_s' = \delta'\left(\frac{U_\infty}{U_p}, \frac{\rho_\infty}{\rho_s}, \frac{U_s - U_\infty}{a_s + a_\infty}\right) \quad (14)$$

and H is the exit thickness of the secondary stream.

The length of the primary core of the coaxial jet is

$$\frac{L_{p,\text{COAX}}}{L_{\text{SINGLE}}} = 1 + \tanh\left(2.8 \frac{L_{s,\text{COAX}}}{L_{\text{COFLOWING}}}\right) \times$$
$$\left(\frac{L_{\text{COFLOWING}} - L_{\text{SINGLE}}}{L_{\text{SINGLE}}}\right) \quad (15)$$

For the eccentric jet, the length of the primary core is

$$L_{p,\text{ECC}} = L_{\text{SINGLE}} + 0.3(L_{p,\text{COAX}} - L_{\text{SINGLE}}) \quad (16)$$

and the length of the secondary core on the underside of the jet is

$$L_{s,\text{ECC}} = 2 L_{s,\text{COAX}} \quad (17)$$

For both coaxial and eccentric cases, the peak mean velocity $\overline{u}(x)$ past the end of the primary potential core decays according to

$$\frac{d(U_p/\overline{u}_p)}{d(x/D_m)} = 0.1 \qquad (18)$$

where

$$D_m = D_p\sqrt{1+\mathrm{BPR}} \qquad (19)$$

is the mass-flow-rate equivalent diameter. The peak mean velocity of the secondary stream past the end of the secondary potential core decays according to

$$\frac{d(U_s/\overline{u}_s)}{d(x/H)} = 0.1 \qquad (20)$$

Equations 10-20 allow evaluation of the axial distributions of the peak mean velocity for the primary and secondary flows. The corresponding values of speed of sound and Mach number are obtained by assuming that the mean total temperature obeys the Crocco-Busemann relation

$$\overline{T}_0(x) = \frac{\overline{T}_{0_2}\overline{u}_1 - \overline{T}_{0_1}\overline{u}_2}{\overline{u}_1 - \overline{u}_2} + \frac{\overline{T}_{0_1} - \overline{T}_{0_2}}{\overline{u}_1 - \overline{u}_2}\overline{u}(x) \qquad (21)$$

where subscripts 1 and 2 represent the end conditions of each axial distribution.

Appendix B: Convective Mach number

Prediction of the convective Mach number is based on the empirical formulae proposed by Murakami & Papamoschou [16]. Considering a shear layer between a fast stream (1) and a slow stream (2), the convective Mach number of eddies relative to the slow stream is

$$M_c = M_{c,\mathrm{sym}} + \frac{d}{\sqrt{1+(\overline{a}_2/\overline{a}_1)^2}} \qquad (22)$$

where

$$M_{c,\mathrm{sym}} = \frac{\overline{u}_1 - \overline{u}_2}{\overline{a}_1 + \overline{a}_2}, \qquad (23)$$

and

$$d = \begin{cases} 1.25\ln M_{c,\mathrm{sym}} + 1.11 & , M_{c,\mathrm{sym}} > 0.41 \\ 0 & , M_{c,\mathrm{sym}} \leq 0.41 \end{cases} \qquad (24)$$

References

[1] Tam, C.K.W., and Chen, P., "Turbulent Mixing Noise from Supersonic Jets," *AIAA Journal*, Vol. 32, No. 9, 1994, pp. 1774-1780.

[2] Lighthill, M.J., "On Sound Generated Aerodynamically: I. General Theory" *Proceedings of the Royal Society of London Series A*," Vol. 211, 1952, pp. 564-581.

[3] Lighthill, M.J., "On Sound Generated Aerodynamically: II. Turbulence as a Source of Sound," *Proceedings of the Royal Society of London Series A*," Vol. 222, 1954, pp. 1-32.

[4] Hoch, R.G. and Berthelot, M., "Use of the Bertin Aerotrain for the Investigation of Flight Effects on Aircraft Engine Exhaust Noise," *Journal of Sound and Vibration*, Vol. 54, No. 2, 1977, pp. 153-172.

[5] Papamoschou, D. and Debiasi, M., "Directional Suppression of Noise from a High-Speed Jet," *AIAA Journal*, Vol. 39, No. 3, 2001, pp. 380-387.

[6] Murakami, E., and Papamoschou, D. "Mean Flow Development of Dual-Stream Compressible Jets," *AIAA Journal*, Vol. 40, No. 6, 2002, pp. 1131-1138.

[7] Papamoschou, D. and Debiasi, M., "Mach Wave Elimination Appied to Turbofan Engines," AIAA-2002-0368.

[8] Crighton, D.G. and Huerre, P., "Shear-Layer Pressure Fluctuations and Superdirective Acoustic Sources," *Journal of Fluid Mechanics*, Vol. 220, 1990, pp. 355-368.

[9] Avital, E.J., Sandham, N.D, and Luo, K.H., "Mach Wave Radiation in Mixing Layers. Part I: Analysis of the Sound Field," *Theoretical and Computational Fluid Dynamics*, Vol. 12, 1998, pp. 73-90.

[10] Tam, C.K.W., "Jet Noise: Since 1952," *Theoretical and Computational Fluid Dynamics*," Vol. 10, 1998, pp. 393-405.

[11] Panda, J. and Zaman, K.B.M.Q., "Density Fluctuation in Asymmetric Nozzle Plumes and Correlation with Far Field Noise," AIAA-2001-0378.

[12] Panda J. and Seasholtz, R.G. "Experimental Investigation of Density Fluctuations in High-Speed Jets and Correlation with Generated Noise *Journal of Fluid Mechanics,* vol.450, Jan. 2002, pp.97-130.

[13] Hileman, J. and Samimy, M. "Turbulence Structures and the Acoustic Far Field of a Mach 1.3 Jet," *AIAA Journal,* Vol.39, No.9, 2001, pp.1716-27.

[14] Narayanan, S., Barber, T.J., and Polak, D.R., "High Subsonic Jet Experiments: Turbulence and Noise Generation Studies," *AIAA Journal,* Vol. 40, No. 3, 2002, pp. 430-437.

[15] Papamoschou, D. and Bunyajitradulya, A.,"Evolution of Large Eddies in Compressible Shear Layers," *Physics of Fluids,* Vol. 9, No. 3, 1997, pp. 756-765.

[16] Murakami, E. and Papamoschou, D., "Eddy Convection in Supersonic Coaxial Jets," *AIAA Journal,* Vol. 38, No.4, 2000, pp. 628-635.

[17] Ganyu, L. and Lele, S.K. "Inviscid Instability of Skewed Compressible Mixing Layer, " *Journal of Fluid Mechanics,* Vol. 249, 1993, pp. 441-463.

[18] Fric, T.E., "Skewed Shear-Layer Mixing Within a Duct," *AIAA Journal,* Vol.34, No.4, 1996, pp.847-9.

[19] Shevell, R.S., "Fundamentals of Flight," Prentice Hall, 1989.

Table 1: CFM56 Cases (BPR=4.8)

Test	Configuration	D_p^* (mm)	U_p (m/s)	M_p	D_s (mm)	U_s (m/s)	M_s	F_x^{**}	F_y^{**}
CFM56-BASE	Coaxial (clean)	10.0	480	0.90	23.4	330	0.96	0.0%	0.0%
CFM56-ECC	Eccentric	10.0	480	0.90	23.4	330	0.96	Unknown	Unknown
CFM56-4V10e	Coaxial with four vanes inclined 10°, ext. to bypass duct	10.0	480	0.90	23.4	330	0.96	0.8%	3.8%

* This is the effective (area-based) diameter of the primary nozzle. Actual dimensions are 14.4 mm ID with a 10-mm plug.

* F_x and F_y are estimates of the axial and transverse forces, respectively, caused by the nozzle modifications. They are presented in percent of total thrust.

Table 2: JT8D-219 Cases (BPR=1.7)

Test	Configuration	D_p (mm)	U_p (m/s)	M_p	D_s (mm)	U_s (m/s)	M_s	F_x^{**}	F_y^{**}
JT8D-COAX	Coaxial (clean)	14.4	580	1.06	21.6	370	1.05	0.0%	0.0%
JT8D-MIX	Fully mixed	14.4	460	1.05	-	-	-	0.0%	0.0%
JT8D-ECC	Eccentric	14.4	580	1.06	21.6	370	1.05	Unknown	Unknown
JT8D-2V20i	Coaxial with two vanes inclined 20°, int. to bypass duct	14.4	580	1.06	21.6	370	1.05	1.3%	5.0%

** F_x and F_y are estimates of the axial and transverse forces, respectively, caused by the nozzle modifications. They are presented in percent of total thrust.

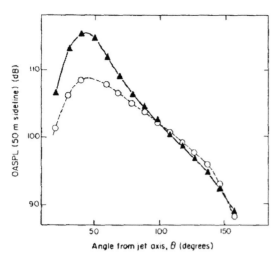

Fig.1 Overall sound pressure level versus emission angle for a single jet at static conditions (solid symbols) and in forward flight (open symbols). Jet Mach number was near sonic, jet speed was 550 m/s, and flight speed was 82 m/s. From Ref. [4].

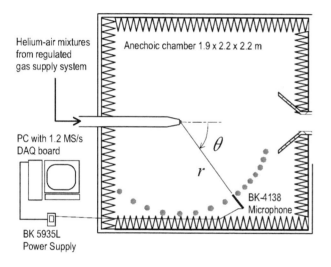

Fig.2 UCI Jet Aeroacouctics Facility.

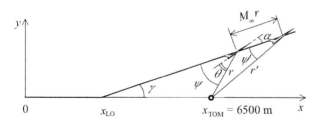

Fig.3 Flight path used for estimating perceived noise level.

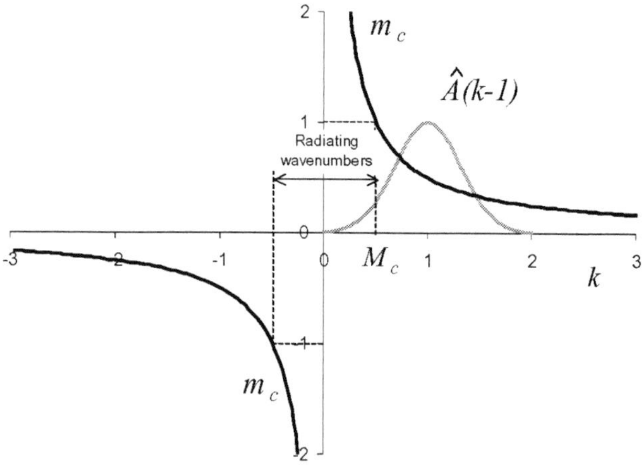

Fig.4 Phase Mach number versus wavenumber for $M_c = 0.5$.

(a)

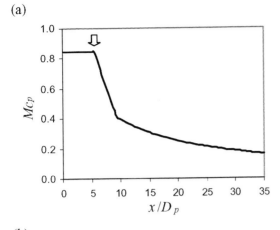

(b)

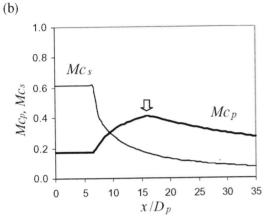

(c)

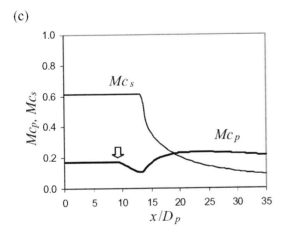

Fig.5 Estimates of convective Mach number distributions for the CFM56 exit flow at static conditions. (a) Core stream alone; (b) coaxial exhaust; (c) underside of eccentric exhaust. Arrow indicates end of primary potential core.

(a)

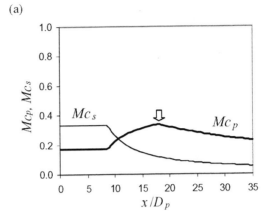

(b)

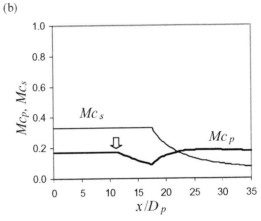

Fig.6 Estimates of convective Mach number distributions for the CFM56 exit flow in forward flight ($M_\infty = 0.3$). (a) Coaxial exhaust; (b) underside of eccentric exhaust. Arrow indicates end of primary potential core.

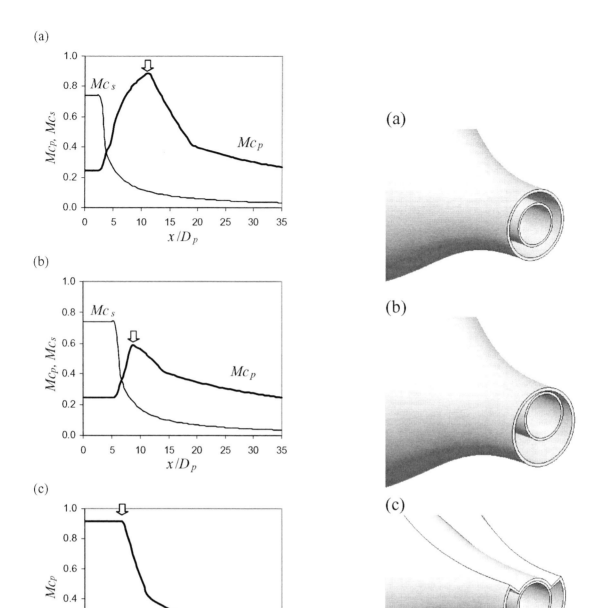

Fig.7 Estimates of convective Mach number distributions for the JT8D exit flow at static conditions. (a) Coaxial exhaust; (b) underside of eccentric exhaust; (c) fully-mixed exhaust. Arrow indicates end of primary potential core.

Fig.8 Exhaust geometry of (a) coaxial; (b) eccentric; and (c) arcuate nozzles.

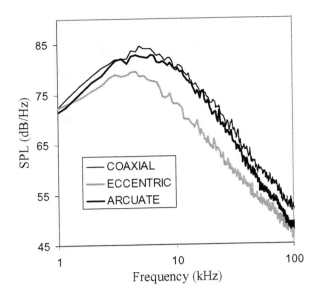

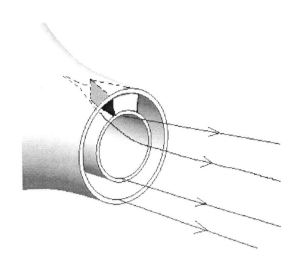

Fig.11 Coaxial nozzle with wedge inserted in the bypass annulus.

Fig.9 Spectra in the downward direction of peak emission for coaxial, eccentric, and arcuate nozzles. $U_p = 600$ m/s, $U_s = 360$ m/s, and BPR=2.5.

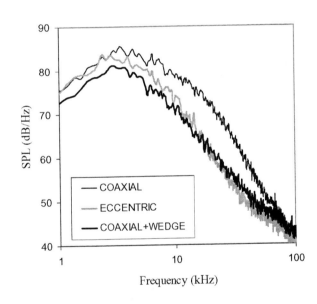

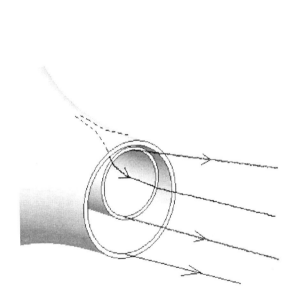

Fig.10 Conjecture on the streamline paths in the eccentric nozzle exhaust.

Fig.12 Spectra in the downward direction of peak emission for jets issuing from coaxial, coaxial with wedge, and eccentric nozzles. $U_p = 520$ m/s, $U_s = 330$ m/s, and BPR=2.5.

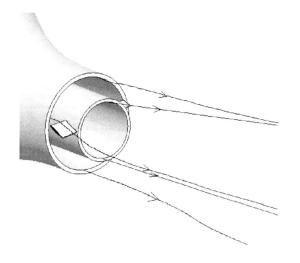

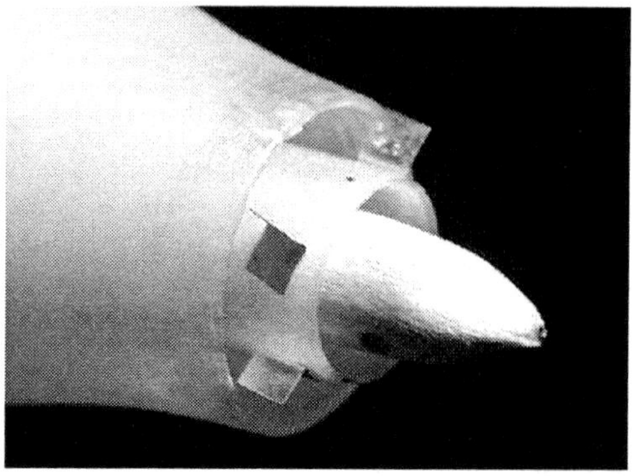

Fig.13 Coaxial nozzle with deflector vanes installed in the bypass exhaust.

Fig.15 Picture of CFM56-4V10e nozzle.

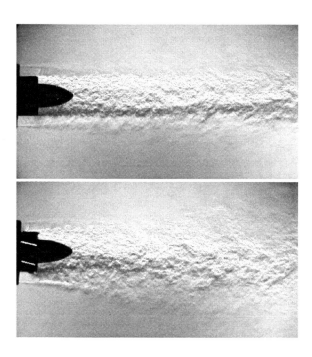

Fig.14 Schlieren images of CFM56 exhaust flow. Upper: clean coaxial nozzle. Lower: coaxial nozzle with four vanes installed immediately downstream of the bypass duct.

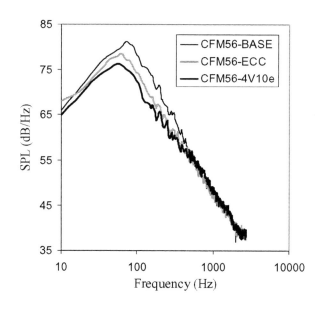

Fig.16 Spectra in the downward direction of peak emission, $\theta = 25°$, for the CFM56 coaxial, eccentric and vane configurations. The spectra were scale-up to full-size engine.

1582

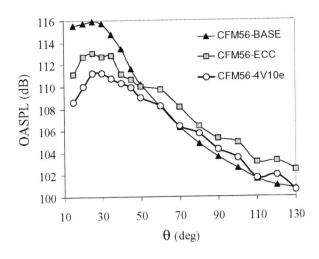

Fig.17 Downward directivity of OASPL for the CFM56 cases.

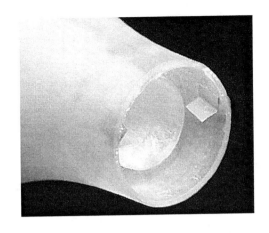

Fig.19 Picture of JT8D-2V20i nozzle.

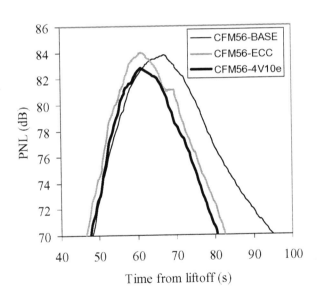

Fig.18 Time history of PNL for the CFM56 cases. EPNL (dB): 86.2 for BASE; 85.4 for ECC; and 84.2 for 4V10e.

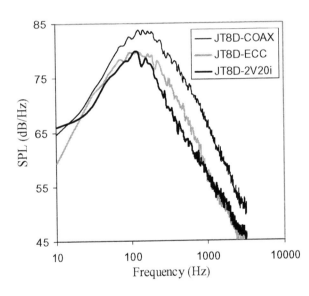

Fig.20 Spectra in the downward direction of peak emission, $\theta = 40°$, for the JT8D coaxial, eccentric, and vane configurations. The spectra were scale-up to full-size engine.

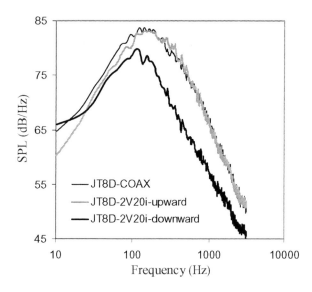

Fig.21 Spectra in the upward and downward directions of peak emission for the JT8D coaxial and vane configurations. The spectra were scale-up to full-size engine.

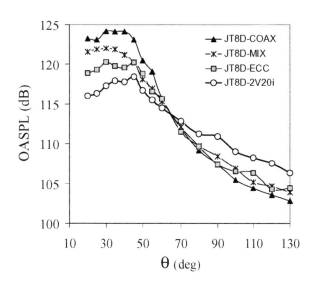

Fig.22 Downward directivity of OASPL for the JT8D cases.

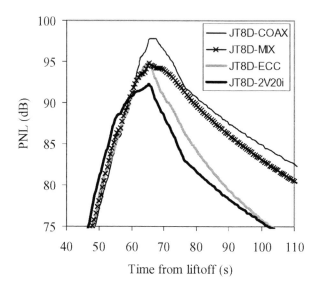

Fig.23 Time history of PNL for the JT8D cases. EPNL (dB): 98.9 for COAX; 97.2 for MIX; 94.9 for ECC; and 93.4 for 2V20i.

Experimental Investigation of Jet Noise and Core Noise Using a Small Gas Turbine Engine

Vincent Tesson*, Michael J. Doty[†] and Dennis K. McLaughlin[‡]

Department of Aerospace Engineering

The Pennsylvania State University

University Park, PA 16802

Abstract

A small gas turbine engine is used to produce a laboratory size hot air jet with which to make both flowfield and acoustic measurements. The experimental results are compared to those obtained from a simulated heated jet using a helium/air mixture jet in the same facility. For accurate acoustic comparisons, the total noise generated by the turbojet engine is decomposed into components of jet noise and core noise, and only the pure jet noise contribution is studied in detail. Directivity and spectral comparisons of both jets yield very good agreement (within 2 dB). An investigation of the jet produced by the turbojet engine using mean flow measurements and a unique deflectometry technique indicates higher turbulence levels than those in free air heated jets.

1. Introduction

As stricter federal noise regulations are implemented at commercial airports all around the world, the level of noise generated by commercial aircraft becomes a more important issue. The predominant impact of aircraft noise to surrounding communities occurs mainly during the phases of take-off and landing. Exhaust jet noise is the dominant source of sound at take-off. A better understanding of the contribution of jet mixing noise in the overall noise generated by aircraft engines is required. In addition, a characterization of the flow field of the exhaust nozzle is required. If successful, noise reduction strategies are to be expected.

The experimental component of the Penn State jet noise program encompasses a combination of acoustic and flowfield measurements of high speed (subsonic and supersonic) jets. The overall goals are to develop a more complete understanding of the jet noise generation processes as well as provide extended data for evaluation of developing analysis and computational procedures. Since jet temperature is such an important parameter in high speed jet noise, our laboratory has been developing a jet heating capability. As an interim low cost approach, mixtures of room temperature helium and air have been employed to simulate the heated air conditions. After extensive comparison with data in the open literature of high speed heated jets, the simulation that substitutes helium-air mixtures for hot jets has been shown to reproduce the acoustic fields quite accurately. The overall project goals led us to apply a newly developed optical deflectometer to measure the two-point space-time correlations of density gradient fluctuations in the dominant noise generation regions of the jet. Since this instrument has not been used (in this application) elsewhere, no density gradient correlation data are available. The absence of high speed heated jet correlation data sought for comparison, and the need of more subsonic heated jet acoustic data, led to the present experimental study.

The primary purpose of this study was to employ a small gas turbine engine to produce a laboratory size hot air jet with which to make both flowfield (mean flow and two-point space-time correlations) and acoustic measurements. Both sets of measurement are compared with data acquired with conventional free air jets and simulated heated jets by Doty[1]. It is important to note that the present hot jet is produced by a small turbomachine with characteristics similar to a conventionally sized turbojet engine. This can be interpreted as a positive feature since the main purpose of understanding the mechanism of jet noise generation and radiation to the far field is to be applied to future efforts of aircraft engine noise reduction.

The experiments with the turbojet engine were conducted at conditions that could be closely matched by selected conditions of the simulated heated jet

---

* Graduate Student, Member AIAA

[†] Graduate Student, Member AIAA

[‡] Prof. And Head of Aerospace Engineering, Associate Fellow AIAA

experiments of Doty[1]. However, higher levels of acoustic radiation to the far field were expected from the turbojet engine, due mainly to the superposition of core noise onto the pure jet mixing noise. Core noise usually refers to noise associated with combustion of the air-fuel mixture as well as noise due to the interaction of the flow with internal surfaces and passages (mainly the compressor and the turbine). Ho et al.[2], and later Mahan and Karchmer[3] characterized the combustion noise as being limited to very low frequencies 100-500 Hz with a typical spectral shape whose peak frequency is at 400 Hz. Interaction noise adds to combustion noise over a wide range of frequency and results in the broadband increase of sound levels. An additional acoustic component from the compressor and the turbine is expected in the form of tones corresponding to the multiple harmonics of their blade passage frequencies. The jet noise itself is expected to be higher due to higher levels of turbulence following the flow through the turbomachinery. In order to extract the real contribution of jet mixing noise from the measured total jet engine noise, a method to decompose the jet noise and core noise was needed. Two point correlation techniques consisting of correlating measurements from a pressure probe located inside the engine core with far field acoustic measurements have produced interesting results (Karchmer[4]). Krejsa[5] and Guedel et al.[6] have implemented an improvement with a three-signal coherence technique. And lately, Siller et al.[7] employed a microphone array focused at the nozzle exit correlated to a probe inside the combustion chamber to investigate the respective level of jet noise and core noise produced by a turbojet engine. However, a non-intrusive method of separation of jet noise from core noise developed by Parthasarathy et al.[8] is implemented in the present work, not requiring any modification of the turbojet engine. A detailed description of the method is presented further in this paper.

For the present work, acoustic measurements were conducted in the anechoic chamber with two operating conditions of the turbojet engine producing jet exit conditions of Mach 0.5, T_j/T_a=2.65 and Mach 0.7, T_j/T_a=2.94. After decomposition into core noise and pure jet noise, the data of the M=0.7 case are compared directly to the measurements of Doty[1] made in a helium-air mixture jet using the identical instrumentation and experimental procedures.

Mean-flow measurements transverse to the jet axis were performed at 2, 4, 6 and 8 jet diameters downstream the exit nozzle. In addition axial measurements were conducted along the centerline of the jet, yielding a reasonably complete mapping of the velocity and Mach number distributions of the engine exhaust jet.

Two-point space-time density gradient correlation measurements of the jet were performed by optical deflectometry. Assuming that density gradient fluctuations are coupled to velocity fluctuations, this quantitative schlieren technique is a measure of the level of turbulence of the jet flow. The measurements at two points closely situated in the jet were possible, whose correlation allowed the evaluation of the convection velocity and rate of the decorrelation of the turbulent eddies.

2. Experimental procedure

2.1 Facility Description

The small gas turbine engine used for the current experiments is a simple turbojet engine (reference SOPHIA J-850) built by *Sophia Precision Corporation*, Japan. Usually used as a propulsion system for small airplane models, its external diameter is 10.6 cm and its length is 33 cm. The engine, shown in Figure 1, has an exit nozzle diameter of 3.5 mm (1.375 in.). It is fueled with a mixture of jet fuel (A1 fuel) and white gasoline (Coleman fuel), with proportions depending on the desired flammability of the mixture.

By controlling the fuel injection rate, the gas turbine engine can be operated with a wide range of jet exhaust velocity and temperature. Its maximum rotational speed is 130,000 RPM (full throttle) and the speed is continuously adjustable from 60% to 100% of this value. The jet generated is of Mach number between 0.2 and 0.7, and of temperature between 520 K (480 ºF) and 930 K (1200 ºF) in cruise condition and for times long enough to conduct experiments. Further specifications are presented in Table 1.

Dimensions	106mm x 330mm (4.2" x 13.0")
Total Weight	1.4 kg (3.1 lbs)
Thrust	8.5 kg (18.71 lbs)
Power Weight Ratio	6.07 kgf/kg
Intake Air Volume	9 kg at 130,00 RPM
Compression Ratio	2.7
Fuel	JP-4, White Gas, Coleman Fuel/Jet A-1
Max fuel Consumption	270cc/min.
Number of compressor blades	10
Number of turbine blades	11

Table 1 Specifications of the small gas turbine engine.

The turbojet engine is operated in the High Speed Jet Noise facility of The Pennsylvania State University. Of dimensions 4.27 m × 5.18 m × 2.74 m, the chamber is anechoic down to 125 Hz. It is equipped with an exhaust fan drawing approximately 30,000 cfm at 20 feet per second from the chamber to the outside alleyway. The use of the fan ensures minimal temperature increase during the time of an experiment (typically 4 to 6 minutes) by exhausting the hot jet and the fuel fumes generated by the turbojet engine. The duct is acoustically treated and isolates the chamber from the ventilation fan noise. Microphone measurements showed that the fan perturbs noise levels in the experimental area by less than 0.5 dB.

The turbojet engine is placed directly downstream of a flow conditioning section consisting of a 1.5 meter-long plenum. The plenum is open at one end to the ambient air and at the other end connected to the engine front end (intake). The plenum conditions the flow upstream the engine and suppresses the turbulence. (The inlet flow passes through a perforated plate and two fine-mesh screens inside the plenum before it reaches the inlet section of the engine.) The plenum also suppresses the noise radiating upstream the turbojet engine. Therefore, only the side and rear-arc components of the jet engine noise are measured.

2.2 Instrumentation

The acoustic measurements are conducted with an array of four microphones manufactured by Larson & Davis. All four are 6.35 mm (¼ inch) microphones (Model 2520). The microphone calibration is performed with a Brüel & Kjær acoustic calibrator (Model 4231). The microphones are mounted on a circular boom of radius 1.75 m (68.75 in., R/D=50) centered at 17.5 cm (6.875 in., x/D=5) downstream of the 35 mm (1.375 in.) diameter nozzle exit. The microphone boom is centered at 5 diameters downstream because this is the region of dominant noise production of the jet (corresponding to the end of the jet potential core). The microphone measurements are made at angles between 30 and 120 degrees from the jet axis (Figure 2).

The probe used to perform flow measurements downstream of the turbojet nozzle is a United Sensor Corporation custom-made probe. This versatile stainless steel Pitot-static probe is equipped with a built-in thermocouple for measuring total temperature as well as total and static pressures at the same point in the fluid stream. The thermocouple has a K-type calibration, and the pressure probe is connected to a Validyne pressure transducer. The probe is mounted on a mobile apparatus composed of vertical and axial motorized stages coupled with a digital read-out. The radial motorized stage is computer-controlled. The flow conditions at any point within 1.8 jet diameters in the radial direction and between 2 and 8 jet diameters in the axial direction downstream the turbojet can be surveyed with one cycle of the stage.

The optical deflectometer system is similar to the one used by Doty[1, 9]. A combination of a 72 Watt white light source, a slit and a converging lens produce a parallel beam of approximately 15 cm in diameter between two parabolic mirrors. The parallel beam illuminates a portion of the jet and is then refocused to the acquisition optics. The acquisition optics are composed of a knife-edge cutoff that filters the optical information contained in the light beam (focused to a point) by passing only the upward light deflections that are above a certain absolute strength. The remaining beam is separated into two components by a 50/50 beam splitter, each projected on a different photomultiplier through a pinhole. Both photomultipliers are mounted on two-axis traverse systems for precise positioning. This technique allows the virtual study of two points closely situated in the jet plume since the interrogated points are actually located in identical but separate images.

2.3 Data acquisition

For the acoustic measurements, the data acquisition was performed with a high-speed acquisition interface card. The data were digitally recorded and processed on a computer equipped with the software Labview 5.0.1 by National Instruments. Acquiring 102400 points and using 100 averages, it yields spectral information from 0 to 75 kHz with a resolution of 73 Hz. A microphone correction is applied based on manufacturer's specifications. All sound pressure levels are corrected to take into account the atmospheric attenuation of high frequency noise, based on the work of Bass et al.[10]. Finally, the appropriate geometrical corrections are applied to compare present data to previous researcher's acoustics data taken at the jet exit nozzle rather than at the end of the potential core. The results are plotted in terms of Strouhal number given by $St = \dfrac{f}{fc}$ where f_c is the characteristic frequency of the jet $fc = \dfrac{Uj}{D}$. All spectra are converted to 1 Hz frequency bandwidth spectra. To proceed to accurate comparisons, all spectra are further scaled to SPL per f_c^{-1} by multiplying the ordinates by f_c.

The flow field data acquisition was performed with the same high-speed acquisition interface card at a rate of 50 scans per second.

The optical deflectometry correlation data are plotted in terms of the non-dimensional time delay $* = \times fc$.

3. Separation of core noise and jet noise

In the particular situation of static engine tests, the sources of core noise, the engine and the observer are nearly at rest with respect to each other. In addition the internal noise in the engine is "tunneled" to the exhaust nozzle where it radiates from a "compact" location. The frequencies of the radiated core noise are therefore preserved unchanged at any point of the far field. Unlike core noise sources, jet noise sources are non-compact as the strong turbulence extends 5 to 8 jet diameters downstream of the nozzle exit. In addition the jet noise sources are in motion and thus the radiated jet noise undergoes large Doppler frequency shifts. As a consequence, Parthasarathy et al.[8] suggested that the radiated field of core noise is coherent over different angular directions in contrast to jet noise that has very little coherence over widely separated directions. It is thus proposed that the cross-correlation between sound pressures from two microphones separated by a wide angle would essentially represent the auto-correlation of core noise radiated to the far field. Parthasarathy et al.[8] presented a method for separating the mean square pressures of jet noise and core noise that yields the respective overall sound pressure level in the far field at any angle to the jet axis. The extension of this method to spectral components is more relevant because of the importance of the spectra in jet noise measurement and analysis. The following system is obtained for the spectral densities of the total engine noise S, the jet noise Sj and the core noise Sc at all frequencies and two different angles θ_1 and θ_2:

$$S(\theta_1, \omega) = Sj(\theta_1, \omega) + Sc(\theta_1, \omega)$$

$$S(\theta_2, \omega) = Sj(\theta_2, \omega) + Sc(\theta_2, \omega)$$

$$= (\alpha)Sj(\theta_1, \omega) + (\beta)Sc(\theta_1, \omega)$$

$$(\theta_1, \theta_2, \omega) = \sqrt{(\beta)}Sc(\theta_1, \omega)$$

where $(\theta_1, \theta_2, \omega)$ is the cross-spectrum of sound pressures at θ_1 and θ_2. The two ratios

$$(\alpha) = \frac{Sj(\theta_2, \omega)}{Sj(\theta_1, \omega)} \quad \text{(pure jet noise directivity ratio)}$$

and $(\beta) = \dfrac{Sc(\theta_2, \omega)}{Sc(\theta_1, \omega)}$ are introduced to simplify the resolution. This system of 3 equations has 7 unknowns. Additionally three quantities $S(\theta_1, \omega)$, $S(\theta_2, \omega)$ and $(\theta_1, \theta_2, \omega)$ can be measured by spectral analysis and cross-spectral analysis of two microphones signals (at θ_1 and θ_2). Thus there are fewer equations than unknown quantities. At this point the ratio of spectral level of pure jet noise at two observation locations is inserted into the equation set from the established database, SAE Aerospace Recommended Practice, ARP 876 [11]. Using the measured quantities $S(\theta_1, \omega)$, $S(\theta_2, \omega)$ and $(\theta_1, \theta_2, \omega)$ and the ratio (α) from the SAE data, the system is solved and yields the spectral densities of core noise and jet noise, achieving separation over all frequencies.

4. Experimental results

4.1 Experimental parameters

The flow conditions used for acoustic, mean-flow and optical deflectometry experiments described in the present section are summarized in Table 2.

	Conditions	Description	M	T_j/T_a	U_j/a_a
Acoustic measurements	{1}	Turbojet engine	0.69	2.94	1.18
	{2}	Turbojet engine	0.5	2.67	0.82
	{3}	Simulated heated jet	0.69	2.94	1.26
Mean-flow measurements	{4}	Turbojet engine	~0.69	2.23	1.02
	{5}	Simulated heated jet	0.69	2.49	1.15
Optical deflectometry	{6}	Turbojet engine	0.69	2.94	1.18
	{7}	Simulated heated jet	0.69	2.49	1.15

Table 2 Detailed jet parameters of current experiments.

For each set of experiments, an effort has been made to achieve a close-match of the flow conditions between the turbojet engine and the simulated heated jet using helium-air mixture (Doty[1]). Because the fuel injection rate is the only adjustable parameter on the turbojet engine, the Mach number, the static temperature ratio (T_j/T_a) and the velocity ratio (U_j/a_a) cannot be modified independently. On the other hand, the simulated static temperature ratio and the Mach number of the simulated heated jet are independently adjustable.

4.2 Overall and directivity acoustic results

As part of the comparison to simulated heated jet experiments by Doty[1], the jet noise contribution of the turbojet engine needed to be extracted from the total noise generated by the turbojet. The separation method of Parthasarathy et al.[8] was performed on the SPL spectral data recorded at various angular positions from the jet axis on a radius of 50 jet diameters centered at 5 diameters downstream the turbojet engine exit nozzle. As shown in Table 2, two conditions of the turbojet engine produced exhaust jets of M=0.69 (conditions {1}) and M=0.5 (conditions {2}). Table 3 summarizes the overall sound pressure levels measured at M=0.69

at 5 different angular positions, as well as the evaluated levels of core noise and jet noise.

	Turbojet engine, conditions {1}				Simulated heated jet (Doty), conditions {3}
	(1)	**(2)**	**(3)**	**(4)=(1)-(3)**	**(5)**
Angle from jet axis (degrees)	Measured total engine noise (OASPL, dB)	Core noise obtained by separation method (OASPL, dB)	Jet noise obtained by separation method (OASPL, dB)	OASPL increase due to core noise (dB)	Jet noise (OASPL, dB)
30	117.58	104.86	117.34	+ 0.24	119.10
40	118.87	107.57	118.53	+ 0.33	118.16
60	117.87	114.94	114.78	+ 3.09	114.18
90	112.11	110.93	105.88	+ 6.23	105.67
120	106.97	100.45	105.87	+ 1.09	103.84

Table 3 Measured and calculated overall sound pressure levels.

Table 3 also presents the evaluated increase in overall sound pressure levels due to core noise (column (4)). For comparison purposes, the overall levels measured from the simulated heated (helium-air mixture) jet with similar jet parameters (conditions {3}) are presented in the last column of the table.

Shown in Figure 3 is the directivity of the core noise and jet noise obtained by the separation method for the M=0.69 case. A non-spherical pattern is observed for core noise, the maximum noise emission being at 60 degrees from the jet axis with a typical deviation of about 10 dB from the maximum value. For the interested reader, the results are in good agreement with the past studies of Mahan and Karchmer[3]. The directivity plot for the pure jet noise has a maximum emission direction around 30-40 degrees from the jet axis. The directivity plot of the M=0.5 case is shown in Figure 4 and illustrates more spherical patterns that are typical of lower jet exhaust velocities.

The overall level data of pure jet mixing noise produced by the turbojet engine agree with Doty's[1] simulated heated jet noise measurements within less than 2 db as shown in columns (3) and (5) of Table 3. The results are identical within 0.6 dB for median angles between 40 and 90 degrees from the jet axis.

4.3 Spectral comparison with simulated heated jet

A series of spectra showing the separation of core noise and jet noise of the turbojet engine total noise radiation to the far field is shown in Figure 5. They are the results of microphone measurements at 30, 40, 60 and 90 degrees at M=0.69 conditions (conditions {1}) decomposed with the separation method. In addition to total noise, core noise and jet noise, the SAE jet noise spectrum is superposed for the purpose of checking the validity of the jet noise directivity ratio used in the separation method. It is clear that the dominant source of jet engine noise at small angles from the jet axis is pure jet mixing noise. As the angle of measurement is increased, the core noise contribution becomes a greater fraction of the total noise with a predominantly low-frequency peak, around St=0.2. It represents the main source of noise at the sideline (90 degrees). Tones of about 20 dB corresponding to the different harmonics of the compressor and turbine blade passage frequencies clearly appear. Notice one of the limitations of the separation method: the tones are still present in jet noise after separation. This is likely due to the imperfections in the acoustic decomposition method of Parthasarathy et al.[8].

Figure 6 shows a series of comparisons of the turbojet engine jet noise spectra obtained in Figure 5 with the pure jet mixing noise measured in the simulated heated (helium-air mixture) jet at the M=0.69, $T_j/T_a=2.94$, conditions {3}. SPL levels for the heated jet have been non-dimensionalized to account for the different nozzle size and jet exhaust velocity. The spectra are limited to Strouhal number below 2.2, the use of ¼ inch microphones giving inaccurate measurements above this number for jets of such high characteristic frequency (typically 34,000). The agreement between both spectra is very good in all directions. It is a strong evidence of the accuracy of using helium-air mixture jet to simulate the acoustics of a heated jet. It also validates the separation method of jet noise and core noise developed by Parthasarathy et al.[8] and adapted in this paper, and the investigation of jet noise using a small gas turbine engine.

4.4 Mean flow measurement results

Figure 7 shows the radial Mach number profiles of the small gas turbine engine jet for M~0.69 at the downstream positions x/D=2, 4, 6 and 8. It shows that the mean flow changes from a profile with a central region of uniform Mach number to a Gaussian-like profile between 2 and 4 jet diameters downstream. The centerline Mach number presents a fast decay rate as the measurement is performed further downstream. This atypical feature is highlighted after comparison to the radial Mach number profiles of helium/air simulated heated jet obtained by Doty[1, 12], shown in Figure 8.

The same difference is observed when comparing the velocity radial profiles of the jet produced by the turbojet (Tj/Ta=2.9) and that of Doty simulation of a heated jet (Tj/Ta=2.49) at the same conditions M~0.69 (Figure 9). Here, the velocity was non-dimensionalized by the jet exhaust velocity. Again, the turbojet engine jet has a somewhat faster centerline velocity decay rate when compared with the simulated heated jet.

To confirm that the potential core (i.e. the region of the jet where the velocity distribution is uniform and equal to the jet exhaust velocity) is shorter than the typical value greater than x/D=4 for conventional free hot jets at same conditions, the centerline non-dimensional velocity profile of the turbojet engine is presented in Figure 10, in comparison with that of Doty's[12] simulation of a heated jet. It is apparent that the potential core of the turbojet engine ends between 3.5 and 4 jet diameters downstream the exit nozzle (where U=0.95Uj) and that the decay of centerline velocity is faster than that of the simulated heated jet. Furthermore Figure 9 shows a larger spreading of the turbojet engine jet, a feature that is confirmed by the velocity thickness comparison shown in Figure 11.

As expected, the levels of turbulence that take place in a turbojet engine jet are higher than those of a conventional free hot jet. Higher mixing rates make the potential core shorter and the jet spreading rate higher.

4.5 Optical deflectometry results

Figure 12 shows the positions of the sensors within the turbojet engine jet (M=0.69, conditions {6}) for the deflectometry measurements. The first set of experiments was conducted at x/D=2, with sensor separations between 0 and 1 jet exit diameters in the axial direction along the lip line. The two-point cross-correlations of the signal fluctuations are shown in Figure 13 in terms of the non-dimensional time delay $* = \times fc$. By calculating the ratio of the probes separation by the time delay between the peaks of the cross-correlation functions, convection velocities of the turbulence patterns were found to be 215 m/s ($\pm$ 30 m/s), 89% of the jet exit velocity. In Figure 14 are the cross-spectra from the photodetectors. Note that the peak is centered at St=0.1, unlike cold jets whose cross-spectra peak is at St=0.4-0.5 (Doty[9]).

The second set of experiments was conducted at x/D=4 with sensors separations between 0 and 0.75 jet exit diameters along an angle corresponding to the spreading of the jet outer shear layer and compared to similar experiments performed on the simulated heated (helium-air mixture) jet at the same relative locations. The jets had almost identical Mach number and velocity ratios (conditions {7}). Figure 15 produces a comparison of two-point cross-correlations of both jets. The decay of the engine jet cross-correlations is much steeper, suggesting that the turbulence is much more disordered and quickly becomes incoherent as it moves downstream. This characteristic of the jet produced by the turbojet engine is also highlighted by the comparison of the cross-spectra obtained for both jets (figure 16). Again the decay rate of the peak values of the cross-spectra is much greater for the turbojet engine. It thus confirms the expectations of higher and more disordered turbulence from a jet generated by the small gas turbine engine. (Note that probe separation distances of part a) of Figures 15 and 16 are not exactly the same as those of part b) of the figures.)

For further understanding of the turbulent behavior of the turbojet engine jet, calculations yield a convection velocity of 78 m/s ($\pm$ 8 m/s) for the data of Figure 15 a). Comparison of the calculated convection velocities with the exhaust jet velocity data obtained in mean-flow measurements yields respective ratios of 0.56 (x/D=2, at lip line) and 0.2 (x/D=4, along spreading angle).

5. Summary and conclusions

Detailed acoustic measurements conducted in the High Speed Jet Noise facility of The Pennsylvania State University indicate that the use of a small gas turbine engine is appropriate to investigate jet aeroacoustics. The acoustic data measured from the small gas turbine engine were processed to set aside core noise. The remaining component of pure jet noise of the total noise produced by the turbojet engine was used to evaluate the accuracy of applying helium/air mixtures to simulate heated jet aeroacoustics. Comparisons of both jets illustrate very good agreement of the directivity patterns and the spectral data (within 2 dB).

Both deflectometry and mean flow measurements demonstrate higher levels of turbulence in the jet produced by the turbojet engine, in comparison to a conventional free air jet fed from compressed gas storage tanks. It results in a shorter potential core and a larger spreading angle of the jet, which is perhaps not expected.

Acknowledgements

The authors would like to acknowledge Dr P.J. Morris and Dr C. Camci for their assistance with this work. The authors would also like to thank Mr. Shawn Brechbill and Mr. Judsen Ruppert for their technical assistance and design work.

References

[1] Doty, M. J., "An Experimental Investigation of the Aeroacoustic Properties of High-Speed, Helium/Air Mixture Axisymmetric Jets," PhD Thesis, The Pennsylvania State University, University Park, PA, 2002.

[2] Ho, P. Y. and Doyle, V. L., "Combustion Noise Prediction Update," AIAA Paper 79-0588, AIAA 5th Aeroacoustics Conference, Seattle, WA, March 1979.

[3] Mahan, R. J. and Karchmer A., "Combustion and Core Noise," *Aeroacoustics of Flight Vehicles: Theory and Practice*, NASA Reference Publication 1258, Vol. 1, WRDC Technical Report 90-3052, 1991.

[4] Karchmer, A. M., "Turbofan Engine Core Noise Source Diagnostics," National Conference on Noise Control Engineering, NOISE-CON, State College, Pennsylvania, June 1987.

[5] Krejsa, E. A., "New Technique for the Direct Measurement of Core Noise from Aircraft Engines," AIAA Paper 81-1587, AIAA/SAE/ASME 17th Joint Propulsion Conference, Colorado Springs, CO, July 1981.

[6] Guedel, A. and Farrando, A., "Experimental Study of Turboshaft Engine Core Noise," *Journal of Aircraft*, vol.23, Oct. 86, p763-767.

[7] Siller, H. A., Arnold, F. and Michel, U., "Investigation of Aero-Engine Core-Noise Using a Phased Microphone Array," AIAA Paper 20001-2269, 7th AIAA/CEAS Aeroacoustics Conference, Maastricht, The Netherlands, May 2001.

[8] Parthasarathy, S. P., Cuffel, R. F. and Massier, P. F., "Separation of Core Noise and Jet Noise," AIAA Paper 79-0589, 5th Aeroacoustics Conference, Seattle, Washington, March 1979.

[9] Doty, M. J. and McLaughlin, D. K., "Two-Point Correlations of Density Gradient Fluctuations in High Speed Jets Using Optical Deflectometry," AIAA Paper 2002-0367, 40th AIAA Aerospace Sciences Meeting & Exhibit, Reno, NV, January 2002.

[10] Bass, H. E., Sutherland, L. C., Blackstock, D. T. and Hester, D. M., "Atmospheric Absorption of Sound: Further Developments," *Journal of the Acoustical Society of America*, Vol. 97, No. 1, 1995, pp.680-683.

[11] SAE, Aerospace Recommended Practice, ARP 876, Rev. D, Issued 1978-03, Revised 1994-01.

[12] Doty, M. J. and McLaughlin, D. K., "Two-Point Correlations and Acoustic Measurements of High-Speed Axisymmetric Jets," AIAA Paper 2002-2553, 8th AIAA/CEAS Aeroacoustics Conference, Breckenridge, CO, June 2002.

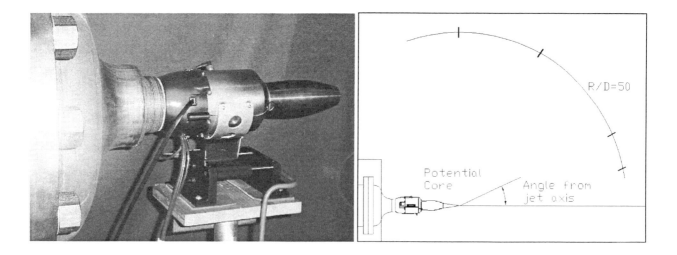

Figure 1 Sophia small gas turbine engine.

Figure 2 Microphone set-up.

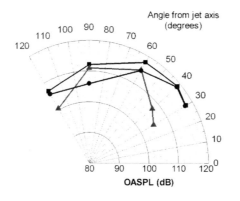

Figure 3 Directivity pattern of jet engine noise (obtained by Parthasarathy separation method), M=0.69.

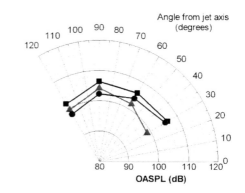

Figure 4 Directivity pattern of jet engine noise (obtained by Parthasarathy separation method), M=0.5.

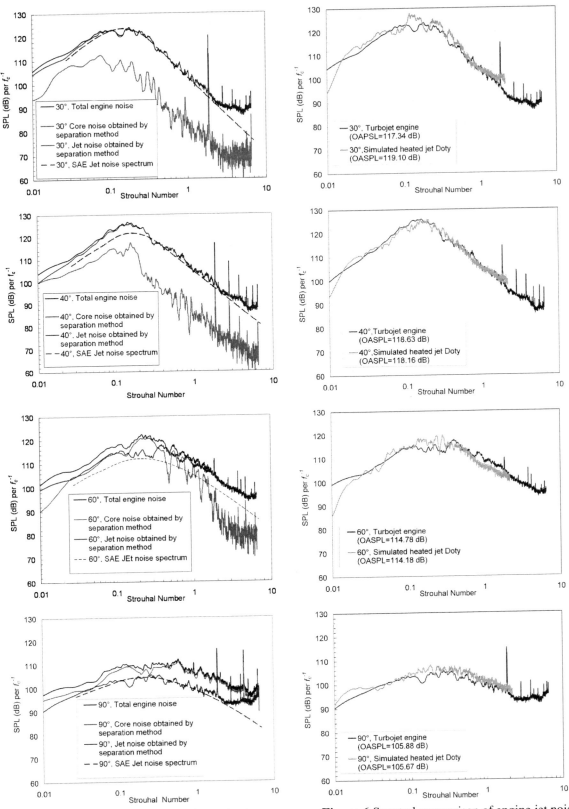

Figure 5 Spectral separation of engine noise into core noise and jet noise, at 30, 40, 60 and 90 degrees from jet axis, M=0.69.

Figure 6 Spectral comparison of engine jet noise obtained by separation method with pure mixing jet noise from simulated heated jet (Doty). M=0.69, T_j/T_a=2.94.

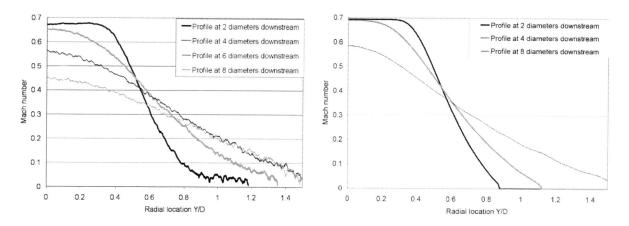

Figure 7 Radial Mach number profiles of turbojet engine at 2, 4, 6 and 8 jet diameters downstream, M~0.69.

Figure 8 Radial Mach number profiles of the simulated heated jet at 2, 4 and 8 jet diameters downstream, M=0.69.

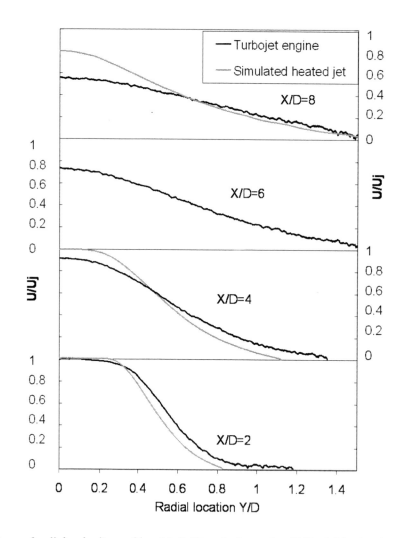

Figure 9 Comparison of radial velocity profiles. M~0.69, turbojet engine T_j/T_a=2.23, simulated heated jet T_j/T_a=2.49.

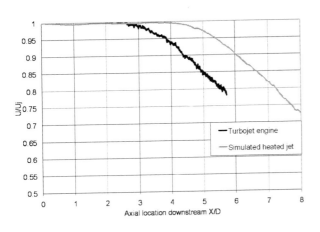

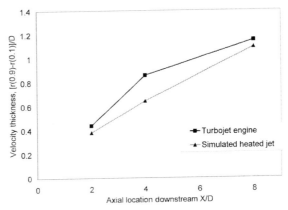

Figure 10 Comparison of centerline velocity profile, M~0.69.

Figure 11 Comparison of velocity thickness, M~0.69.

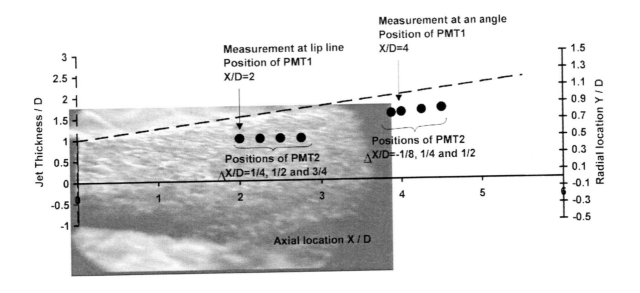

Figure 12 Optical deflectometry measurements. First set: Photomultiplier 1 at x/D=2, photomultiplier 2 mobile downstream along the lip line. Second set: PMT 1 at x/D=4, PMT 2 mobile upstream and downstream at an angle equal to the jet spreading angle.

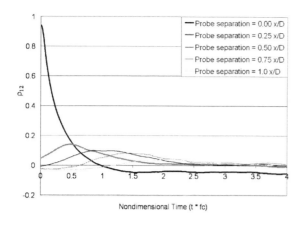

Figure 13 Space-time two-point correlations at various probe separation at x/D=2 along the lip line, of engine jet M=0.69.

Figure 14 Cross-spectra at various probe separation at x/D=2 along the lip line, of engine jet M=0.69.

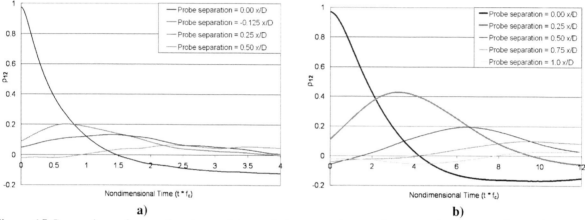

a)

b)

Figure 15 Comparison of space-time two-point correlations at various probe separation at an angle equal to the jet spreading angle, x/D=4 **a)** Turbojet engine M=0.69, T_j/T_a=2.94 **b)** Simulated heated jet M=0.69, T_j/T_a=2.49.

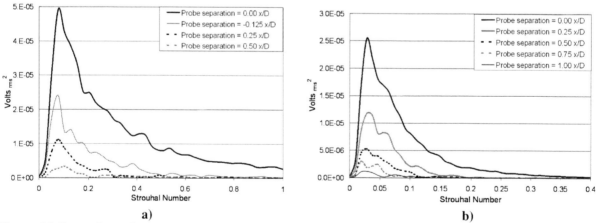

a)

b)

Figure 16 Comparison of cross-spectra at various probe separation at an angle equal to the jet spreading angle, x/D=4 **a)** Turbojet engine M=0.69, T_j/T_a=2.94 **b)** Simulated heated jet M=0.69, T_j/T_a=2.49.

AIAA 2002-2559

SCATTERING OF ACOUSTIC AND VORTICITY DISTURBANCES BY AN UNLOADED ANNULAR CASCADE IN A SWIRLING FLOW

Amr A. Ali *
University of Notre Dame,
Notre Dame, IN 46556, USA

Oliver V. Atassi †
Pratt & Whitney
East Hartford, CT 06108, USA

Hafiz M. Atassi ‡
University of Notre Dame,
Notre Dame, IN 46556, USA

This paper is concerned with studying the scattering of acoustic and vortical disturbances by an unloaded annular cascade in a mean swirling flow. Mathematical formulation, boundary conditions, and upstream disturbance representation are discussed. Results are validated by comparison with lifting surface methods for uniform flows and with the narrow annulus limit for swirling flows. The effects of hub to tip ratio, swirl, twist, reduced frequency, and upstream disturbance are studied.

INTRODUCTION

The scattering of acoustic and vortical disturbances by a row of blades is an important source of noise and unsteady aerodynamic forces in turbofan engines. This scattering depends on the blade geometry and the mean flow profile. Downstream of the fan and upstream of the guide vane blades the flow is not uniform but has a swirling motion. The swirl produces centrifugal and Coriolis forces causing a force imbalance which deflects the fluid motion and couples the vortical, entropic and acoustic modes.[1]

The two dimensional approximation was first considered in modeling the unsteady aerodynamics of annular cascades of airfoils. In this approximation, the cascade is unrolled into a linear cascade of infinite number of blades which is the limiting case for an annular cascade when the annulus is narrow. In such case, the centrifugal and Coriolis forces resulting from the swirling motion are neglected and the upstream mean flow is assumed uniform.

For a flat plate unloaded linear cascade, the un-

steady velocity field can be split into a known purely convected incident vortical disturbance and a scattered potential disturbance. The potential disturbance is produced in response to the incident vortical disturbance due to the coupling at the blade surface. In this case, the problem is formulated in terms of a singular integral equation,[2],[3] Numerical solutions were obtained for the unsteady pressure distribution on the blades,[4],[5] and the acoustic radiation upstream and downstream.[6],[7]

For a loaded linear cascade in an inviscid potential flow, the velocity field still can be split into vortical and potential disturbances. However, the vortical disturbances are no longer purely convected but undergo significant distortion as they are carried downstream by the mean flow. The potential disturbances are governed by a non-constant coefficients convected wave equation,[8],[9],[10] Explicit expression for vortical disturbances in a potential mean flow was obtained in[11] after modifying the splitting technique to avoid singularity on the blades. Based on this expression, a numerical solution has been obtained for the problem of unsteady disturbances interacting with loaded two-dimensional airfoils,[12] and cascades,[13],[14]

The three dimensional geometry of the annular duct was considered by Namba[15] and Schulten[16] where a

*Visiting Assistant Professor, Member AIAA
†Research Engineer, Member AIAA
‡Viola D. Hank Professor, Fellow AIAA.

singularity method which accounts for the spanwise nonuniformity of the incident disturbance was developed. However, such methods cannot account for the effects of nonuniform mean flow. A linearized Euler analysis was also developed by Montgomery and Verdon.[17] They assumed the gust to be simply convected by the mean flow and neglect the changes in amplitude and phase of the incoming disturbance caused by the mean flow. These changes turned out to be significant as shown by Golubev and Atassi[18] and Elhadidi et. al.[19] where they analyzed the evolution of unsteady incident disturbances in a swirling mean flow in an annular duct. More recently a model was developed for the interaction of unsteady incident disturbance in a swirling mean motion with an annular cascade of unloaded blades.[20] The incident disturbances are modeled using a combined eigenmode analysis with initial-value problem solutions. Numerical solutions were obtained for the unsteady blade pressure in the rotor-wake/stator interaction problem.

Representation of upstream disturbances is a challenging issue for swirling flows because of the coupling between the pressure, vorticity, and entropy. For subsonic flows, some acoustic information has to come from the solution inside the computational domain. As a result, the upstream disturbance can not be specified arbitrarily. The upstream disturbance should not have any component that propagate opposite to flow direction. Consequently, an exact analytic representation of the upstream disturbance requires prior knowledge of how to separate disturbances into in-going part and outgoing part. For uniform flow this knowledge is available because pressure, vorticity, and entropy are uncoupled and the information propagating out of the computational domain is related solely to pressure waves.

A normal mode analysis [21,22] showed that the mean swirl significantly modifies the acoustic and vortical spectral composition of the flow. This affects the propagation and the number of modes cut-on in the duct. This analysis showed that the coupling between pressure and vorticity for the vortical disturbances (moving with speeds of the order of the flow speed) is very small such that the pressure associated with vortical disturbances is much smaller than the pressure associated with the acoustic disturbances and can be neglected. However, the coupling between pressure and vorticity for the acoustic modes is very strong if the mean flow is rotational, implying that the vorticity associated with acoustic modes is significant. Based on the normal mode analysis, the authors[23] have derived nonreflecting boundary conditions for 'acoustic' and 'vortical' waves propagating in a duct with a swirling flow. These boundary conditions have been implemented in an explicit scheme for the propagation of 'acoustic' and 'vorticity' waves.

The present work analyzes and quantifies the effect of the swirling motion on the scattering of acoustic and vortical disturbances by a row of unloaded blades. the problem of vortical and acoustic disturbances scattering by a blade row in a swirling flow is numerically formulated using the primitive variables. The numerical calculations are validated versus the solutions of the lifting surface theories of Namba[24] and Schulten[16] for uniform flows and the narrow annulus approximation for swirling flows. The effect of swirl, blade twist, hub to tip ratio, and upstream disturbance on the scattering process is then investigated.

Mathematical Formulation

We consider a non-viscous, non-heat-conducting fluid and use the Euler Equations as the governing equations. The flow quantities are then expanded as follows

$$\mathbf{U}(\mathbf{x},t) = \mathbf{U}_0(\mathbf{x}) + \mathbf{u}(\mathbf{x},t), \qquad (1)$$
$$p(\mathbf{x},t) = p_0(\mathbf{x}) + p'(\mathbf{x},t), \qquad (2)$$
$$\rho(\mathbf{x},t) = \rho_0(\mathbf{x}) + \rho'(\mathbf{x},t), \qquad (3)$$

where $\mathbf{x}$ represents the position vector, $\mathbf{U}_o$, p_o, ρ_o are the steady mean velocity, pressure, and density, respectively. The corresponding unsteady perturbation quantities, $\mathbf{u}$, p', ρ' are such that $|\mathbf{u}(\mathbf{x},t)| \ll |\mathbf{U}_0(\mathbf{x})|$, $|p'(\mathbf{x},t)| \ll p_0(\mathbf{x})$ and $|\rho'(\mathbf{x},t)| \ll \rho_0(\mathbf{x})$.

The mean flow is assumed axisymmetric and of the form,

$$\mathbf{U}(\mathbf{x}) = U_x(r)\mathbf{e}_x + U_\theta(r)\mathbf{e}_\theta, \qquad (4)$$

where U_x and U_θ are the mean velocity components in the axial and circumferential directions, respectively. $\mathbf{e}_x$ and $\mathbf{e}_\theta$ represent unit vectors in the axial and circumferential directions, respectively. The mean flow is, in general, vortical with vorticity given by,

$$\vec{\zeta} = \nabla \times \mathbf{U} = \frac{1}{r}\frac{d(rU_\theta)}{dr}\mathbf{e}_x - \frac{dU_x}{dr}\mathbf{e}_\theta. \qquad (5)$$

For simplicity, we model the swirling mean flow component as a combination of a rigid body rotation and a free vortex,

$$U_\theta = \Omega r + \frac{\Gamma}{r}. \qquad (6)$$

This model can be defined by the two constant parameters Ω and Γ. We further assume the flow to be isentropic with a uniform enthalpy from hub to tip. In this case, the axial component of velocity is given by

$$U_x^2 = U_o^2 - 2[\Omega^2(r^2 - r_m^2) + 2\Omega\Gamma\ln(\frac{r}{r_m})], \qquad (7)$$

where U_o is the axial velocity at the mean radius of the duct r_m. It is convenient for presenting the numerical results to define the axial and swirl velocities in terms of the Mach numbers at the mean radius $M_0 = U_0/c_{om}$, $M_\Omega = (\Omega r_m)/c_{om}$ and $M_\Gamma = \Gamma/(r_m c_{om})$, where c_{om} is the speed of sound at r_m. We nondimensionalize lengths with respect to the mean radius r_m, and define the reduced frequency as $\tilde{\omega} = \frac{\omega r_m}{c_{om}}$.

We assume time-harmonic disturbances of the form $e^{-i\omega t}$. Since the numerical scheme used for our computations is explicit, we retain the time derivative terms in the equations with the understanding that they will vanish for large time. The linearized Euler equations can be written as follows,

$$\left([I]\left(\frac{\partial}{\partial t} - i\omega\right) + [A_x]\frac{\partial}{\partial x} + [B_\theta]\frac{1}{r}\frac{\partial}{\partial \theta} \right.$$
$$\left. + [C_r]\frac{\partial}{\partial r} + [D]\right)\mathbf{Y} = 0, \qquad (8)$$

where

$$\mathbf{Y} = \begin{bmatrix} \rho' \\ u_x \\ u_\theta \\ u_r \end{bmatrix}, \qquad (9)$$

$$[A_x] = \begin{bmatrix} U_x & \rho_o & 0 & 0 \\ \frac{c_o^2}{\rho_o} & U_x & 0 & 0 \\ 0 & 0 & U_x & 0 \\ 0 & 0 & 0 & U_x \end{bmatrix}, \qquad (10)$$

$$[B_\theta] = \begin{bmatrix} U_\theta & 0 & \rho_o & 0 \\ 0 & U_\theta & 0 & 0 \\ \frac{c_o^2}{\rho_o} & 0 & U_\theta & 0 \\ 0 & 0 & 0 & U_\theta \end{bmatrix}, \qquad (11)$$

$$[C_r] = \begin{bmatrix} 0 & 0 & 0 & \rho_o \\ 0 & 0 & 0 & 0 \\ 0 & 0 & 0 & 0 \\ \frac{c_o^2}{\rho_o} & 0 & 0 & 0 \end{bmatrix}, \qquad (12)$$

and

$$[D] = \begin{bmatrix} 0 & 0 & 0 & \frac{d\rho_o}{dr} + \frac{\rho_o}{r} \\ 0 & 0 & 0 & \frac{dU_x}{dr} \\ 0 & 0 & 0 & \frac{U_\theta}{r} + \frac{dU_\theta}{dr} \\ \frac{d}{dr}\left(\frac{c_o^2}{\rho_o}\right) & 0 & \frac{-2U_\theta}{r} & 0 \end{bmatrix}, \qquad (13)$$

where $[I]$ is the unit matrix and u_x, u_θ, and u_r are the components of the disturbance velocity $\mathbf{u}$ in the axial, circumferential, and radial directions, respectively. Since the flow is isentropic, the unsteady pressure is related to the unsteady density by, $p' = c_o^2\rho'$.

The above equations are solved using the second order accurate Lax Wendroff scheme in the passage between two unloaded blades for an incoming upstream disturbance. The blades are placed in the middle third of the computational domain along the circumferential boundaries. The two circumferential boundaries are stream surfaces. Computations are performed using the curvilinear coordinates (ξ, η, ζ) representing the

characteristics of the mean flow,

$$\xi = x, \qquad (14)$$
$$\eta = r, \qquad (15)$$
$$\zeta = \theta - \frac{xU_\theta}{rU_x}. \qquad (16)$$

Nonreflecting boundary conditions are imposed at the duct inlet and exit. These boundary conditions, explained briefly below, were derived and tested for acoustic and vortical disturbances in[23]. The impermeability condition is imposed at the hub and tip radii and on the blades' surfaces.

Upstream Disturbance Representation

Without loss of generality, the upstream disturbance can be written in the form,

$$\mathbf{u_I}(r,\theta) = \sum_{m'=-\infty}^{\infty} \hat{\mathbf{u}}_{m'}(r)e^{i(m'\theta-\omega t)}, \qquad (17)$$

$$\rho'_I(r,\theta) = \sum_{m'=-\infty}^{\infty} \hat{\rho}_{m'}(r)e^{i(m'\theta-\omega t)}, \qquad (18)$$

where m' is an integer. For rotor/stator interaction, the dominant terms in (17) and (18) will be such that $m' = pB$ and $\omega = pB\Omega$ where p is an integer representing the harmonic order of the blade passing frequency, B is the number of rotor blades, and Ω is the shaft angular speed. One of the above Fourier modes is considered at a time. This Fourier component approaches the stator and interacts with the vanes producing unsteady forces on the vanes' surfaces and radiating sound in the farfield.

The upstream disturbances, $\mathbf{u_I}$ and ρ'_I, must satisfy the continuity and momentum equations. For subsonic flows, these disturbances can not be imposed arbitrarily. In the present analysis we prescribe the disturbances in the following way. The normal mode analysis[22] shows that the pressure associated with vortical disturbances is several orders of magnitude less than that associated with acoustic disturbances. Thus neglecting the pressure associated with the vortical disturbances, we write

$$\hat{\rho} = \hat{\rho}^{(a)}, \qquad (19)$$
$$\hat{\mathbf{u}} = \hat{\mathbf{u}}^{(a)} + \hat{\mathbf{u}}^{(v)}. \qquad (20)$$

In the above equations the subscript m' has been dropped. The superscripts (a) and (v) refer to the acoustic and vortical parts, respectively. The acoustic part is defined entirely in terms of the normal modes,

$$\rho'^{(a)}(r,\theta,x) = \sum_{n=0}^{\infty}\sum_{m=-\infty}^{\infty} a_{mn}\mathcal{P}_{mn}(r)e^{i(k_{mn}x+m\theta)}, \quad (21)$$

$$\mathbf{u_I}^{(a)}(r,\theta,x) = \sum_{n=0}^{\infty}\sum_{m=-\infty}^{\infty} a_{mn}\mathbf{u}_{mn}(r)e^{i(k_{mn}x+m\theta)}, \quad (22)$$

where, k_{mn} is the axial wave number corresponding to the density and the velocity eigenfunctions, $\mathcal{P}_{mn}$ and $\mathbf{u}_{mn}$ of the acoustic mode (mn), respectively.

The vortical part is assumed of the form,

$$\hat{\mathbf{u}}^{(v)} = \mathbf{a}(r)e^{ih(r)}. \tag{23}$$

The exponent allows radial variations in phase. The components of the vector $\mathbf{a}$ can not be specified arbitrarily for subsonic flows. To derive the condition that must be satisfied by $\hat{\mathbf{u}}^{(v)}$, we assume that the pressure (density) associated with the vortical disturbances is very small as shown by the normal mode analysis and neglect the ρ' and $\frac{\partial \rho'}{\partial x}$ terms in the continuity and momentum equations. Combining the continuity and the x-momentum equation to eliminate $\frac{\partial u_x}{\partial x}$, we get,

$$i\alpha\hat{u}_x + \frac{im'}{r}\hat{u}_\theta + (\frac{1}{r} + \frac{1}{\rho_o}\frac{d\rho_o}{dr} - \frac{1}{U_x}\frac{dU_x}{dr})\hat{u}_r + \frac{d\hat{u}_r}{dr} = 0, \tag{24}$$

where,

$$\alpha = \frac{\omega}{U_x} - \frac{m'U_\theta}{rU_x}. \tag{25}$$

In terms of the $\mathbf{a}$ components, the above condition becomes,

$$i\alpha a_x + \frac{im'}{r}a_\theta + (\frac{1}{r} + \frac{1}{\rho_o}\frac{d\rho_o}{dr} + i\frac{dh}{dr} - \frac{1}{U_x}\frac{dU_x}{dr})a_r + \frac{da_r}{dr} = 0. \tag{26}$$

This condition reduces to the divergence-free condition in the two-dimensional theory.

To facilitate comparison with the two-dimensional theory we take the upstream vortical velocity component normal to the streamlines in the $x - \theta$ plane equal to a constant $a_{(u)}$ from hub to tip. In order to satisfy (26), we take,

$$a_r = f(r), \tag{27}$$

$$a_\theta = \left(\frac{-iU_\theta}{\omega U_x}\frac{dU_x}{dr} - \frac{U_\theta}{\omega}\frac{dh}{dr} + \frac{iU_\theta}{\omega}(\frac{1}{r} + \frac{1}{\rho_o}\frac{d\rho_o}{dr})\right)a_r$$
$$+ \left(\frac{U\alpha}{\omega} + \frac{iU_\theta}{\omega}\frac{da_r}{dr}\right)a_{(u)}, \tag{28}$$

and the axial component is given by condition (26). $U = \sqrt{U_x^2 + U_\theta^2}$ and $f(r)$ is an arbitrary function that satisfies the impermeability condition at the hub and the tip. The phase $h(r)$ is given by,

$$h(r) = \alpha x_o + k_r(r - r_h), \tag{29}$$

where x_o is the x coordinate at the location of the inflow boundary, α is defined by (25) and represent the phase at the inflow boundary in the $2 - D$ theory, and k_r is a constant given by,

$$k_r = \frac{\pi n'}{r_t - r_h}, \tag{30}$$

where n' is an integer.

Quasi-Periodic Condition

A quasi-periodic condition is applied in the θ direction,

$$\mathbf{Y}(x, \theta_e, r) = \mathbf{Y}(x, 0, r)e^{i\sigma}. \tag{31}$$

where $\sigma = m'\theta_e$, $\theta_e = \frac{2\pi}{V}$, and V is the number of blades (vanes) in the row. All variables upstream of the blades must satisfy this condition. This condition is equally applied to the density and the velocity component normal to the wakes downstream of the blades (vanes).

Thus the propagating acoustic waves must satisfy the condition,

$$m\theta_e = m'\theta_e - 2q\pi, \tag{32}$$

where q is an integer. For a rotor/stator interaction, $m' = pB$ and hence we arrive at the Tyler and Sofrin[25] condition,

$$m = pB - qV. \tag{33}$$

Nonreflecting Boundary Conditions

Away from the blade row the farfield behavior of the scattered unsteady disturbances is governed by the eigenmode analysis given in[21]. To satisfy the causality condition that energy from the source must propagate out of the computational domain, we segregate the modes propagating downstream and denote them with a $(+)$ sign and the modes propagating upstream and denote them with a $(-)$ sign. Thus we express the unsteady density in the farfield as follows,

$$\rho'^{\pm}(r, \theta, x) = \sum_{n=0}^{\infty} \sum_{m \in S_m^{\pm}} c_{mn}^{\pm} \mathcal{P}_{mn}^{\pm}(r)e^{i(k_{mn}^{\pm}x + m\theta)}, \tag{34}$$

where $k_{mn}^{\pm}$ are the axial wave numbers corresponding to the density eigenfunctions $\mathcal{P}_{mn}^{\pm}(r)$. $S_{mn}^{\pm}$ are the sets of all possible values of m.

For computational purpose we truncate the series of equation (34) to $\tilde{M}$ circumferential modes and $\tilde{N}$ radial modes,

$$\rho'^{\pm}(r, \theta, x) = \sum_{n=0}^{\tilde{N}} \sum_{m \in \tilde{S}_m^{\pm}} c_{mn}^{\pm} \mathcal{P}_{mn}^{\pm}(r)e^{i(k_{mn}^{\pm}x + m\theta)}, \tag{35}$$

where $\tilde{S}_m^{\pm}$ are finite subsets of $S_m^{\pm}$.

Applying expansion (35) at two adjacent planes at the boundary, the unknown coefficients c_{mn} can be eliminated yielding a nonreflecting boundary condition.

Numerically, let ρ'_{ij} be the value of ρ' at the grid point (i,j) at the exit boundary corresponding to $x = x_N$, where i is the index along the radial direction and j is the index along the circumferential direction,

$$\rho'_{ij} = \sum_{n=0}^{\tilde{N}} \sum_{m \in \tilde{S}_m^{+}} c_{mn}^{+} \mathcal{P}_{mn}^{+}(r_i)e^{i(k_{mn}^{+}x_N + m\theta_j)}. \tag{36}$$

This can be cast in matrix form,

$$\mathbf{P}_N = [C_N]\mathbf{c}, \tag{37}$$

where the elements of the vector $\mathbf{P}_N$ are the unsteady density of the different grid points at the exit plane at $x = x_N$. The elements of the vector $\mathbf{c}$ are the coefficients c_{mn}^+, and the elements of the matrix $[C_N]$ are the values of the normal modes $\mathcal{P}_{mn}^+(r_i)e^{i(k_{mn}^+ x_N + m\theta_j)}$ at (i,j). Note that the number of modes used in the expansion may be smaller than the number of grid points of the computational domain.

Similarly, we can write the solution at the previous axial cross-section located at $x = x_{N-1}$ as,

$$\mathbf{P}_{N-1} = [C_{N-1}]\mathbf{c}. \tag{38}$$

Solving the previous equation for $\mathbf{c}$,

$$\mathbf{c} = [C_{N-1}]^{-1}\mathbf{P}_{N-1}, \tag{39}$$

and substituting in equation (37), we get,

$$\mathbf{P}_N = [C_N][C_{N-1}]^{-1}\mathbf{P}_{N-1}. \tag{40}$$

Equation (40) is the exit boundary condition we use to complete the definition of the boundary-value problem. Note that (40) is not local, i.e., the density at the point $\rho'(N, i_o, j_o)$ depends on the value of density at all the grid points of the previous cross section $(N-1, i, j)$. No boundary condition is required for the velocity at the outflow boundary. The velocity information should be provided from the solution inside the computational domain.

The formulation of the inflow condition will be similar to that of the exit condition except that the density associated with incoming acoustic waves will be subtracted from the total density prior to the application of the inflow conditions,

$$(\mathbf{P} - \mathbf{P}_I)_1 = [C_1][C_2]^{-1}(\mathbf{P} - \mathbf{P}_I)_2. \tag{41}$$

where the elements of the vector $\mathbf{P}_I$ represent the density of the incident acoustic disturbance, the subscript 1 refers to the axial inlet plane, and the subscript 2 refers to the axial plane adjacent to the inlet plane.

The above boundary condition has been tested for acoustic and vortical propagation in a duct with a swirling flow.[23]

Results

We first validate our calculations versus the lifting surface theory for a uniform flow and versus the two-dimensional theory or the narrow annulus limit for a swirling flow. We then carry out the calculations for a swirling flow in a full annulus and study the effects of swirl, blade twist, hub to tip ratio, reduced frequency, and upstream disturbance distribution on the unsteady aerodynamic forces and the radiated acoustics. We will consider the scattering of both vortical

and acoustic waves. We define the sectional lift coefficient as,

$$c_L'(r) = \frac{L'}{\rho_o U a_{(u)} c}, \tag{42}$$

where L' is the force per unit span and c is the chord length. ρ_o, U, $a_{(u)}$, c are evaluated at the radial location of the considered section. The acoustic coefficients are calculated so that the maximum value of pressure eigenfunctions are equal to unity and the pressure is normalized by $\rho_{om}c_{om}a_{um}$ where ρ_{om}, c_{om}, a_{um} are the values of the mean density, the mean speed of sound, and the upwash at the mean radius, respectively. Our calculation are carried out with the coordinates centered at the mid-chord of one of the blades (vanes).

However, for our comparison with the solution of the benchmark problem of Hanson[26] in the next section, we use the same normalization proposed in that benchmark problem.

Validation versus Uniform flows

To validate our numerical scheme we consider the case proposed by Hanson[26] as a CAA benchmark problem. In this problem, an annular cascade of 24 flat plate stator vanes is placed in a parallel annulus duct. The mean flow is axial and uniform. A gust is introduced at the inlet of the duct. The gust is of the form given in equation (23) with a circumferential component,

$$\hat{u}_\theta(r) = 0.1 U e^{i(pB\Omega x/U + 2\pi n q'(r-r_h)/(r_t-r_h))}, \tag{43}$$

where U is the axial flow speed, Ω is the rotor angular velocity, and $B = 16$ is the number of rotor blades. The blade passing frequency (BPF) fundamental, $p = 1$ was considered. The reduced frequency $\bar{\omega} = pB\Omega r_m/c_{om}$ is constant over the span and equals to 9.396 and the hub-tip ratio is 0.5. We consider four cases with different wake phase variations, $q' = 0, 1, 2,$ and 3. Comparison is made with the existing lifting surface results of Namba[24] and Schulten.[16]

We first compare the aerodynamic results obtained from Schulten's lifting surface code against our numerical scheme for a case with significant radial phase variation, $q' = 1$, in the vortical disturbance. Figure(1) shows the real and imaginary parts of the unsteady pressure jump along the blade chord for $q' = 1$ at different spanwise locations (10%, 50%, and 90% span). The results are in good agreement with those obtained by Schulten. Figure(2) shows the real and imaginary parts of the unsteady pressure jump across the blade span for $q' = 1$ at different chordwise locations (10%, 20%, 50%, and 90% chord). The results agree well with Schulten's results. Slight differences exist at the hub and the tip. Note the unsteady pressure jump shows significant variation from the hub to the tip.

For the acoustic results, the complex coefficients c_{mn} defined by (34) are compared to those obtained

q'	m	n	Namba	Schulten	Current Computations
0	-8	0	1.1780×10^{-2}	1.1745×10^{-2}	1.3332×10^{-2}
0	-8	1	1.9301×10^{-2}	1.9064×10^{-2}	1.8358×10^{-2}
1	-8	0	1.6870×10^{-3}	4.1793×10^{-3}	3.9596×10^{-3}
1	-8	1	1.3088×10^{-2}	2.2913×10^{-2}	2.0612×10^{-2}
2	-8	0	8.9005×10^{-4}	9.4530×10^{-4}	1.0867×10^{-3}
2	-8	1	4.8305×10^{-3}	3.8368×10^{-3}	4.4787×10^{-3}
3	-8	0	5.8400×10^{-4}	6.5845×10^{-4}	7.1097×10^{-4}
3	-8	1	3.0332×10^{-3}	2.6001×10^{-3}	2.9529×10^{-3}

Table 1 Comparison of the absolute values of the upstream coefficients c_{mn} with the lifting surface theories.

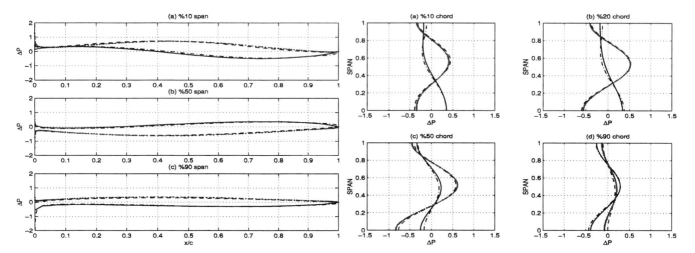

Fig. 1 Unsteady pressure jump along the blade chord for $q' = 1$ at different spanwise locations. Current computations (real part (-), imaginary part(- -)) are compared to those of Schulten (real part (-.-), imaginary part (..))

Fig. 2 Unsteady pressure jump along the blade span for $q' = 1$ at different chordwise locations. Current computations (real part (-), imaginary part(- -)) are compared to those of Schulten (real part (-.-), imaginary part (..))

by Namba and Schulten for the upstream and downstream propagating modes. The normal mode analysis shows that for the present case, there are two propagating modes upstream and two propagating modes downstream. They correspond to modes (-8,0) and (-8,1). The absolute values of the coefficients $c_{-8,0}$ and $c_{-8,1}$ are shown in Table (1) for the upstream propagating modes and in Table (2) for the downstream propagating modes. More detailed comparison is given in[27].

Validation versus Swirling Flows in the Narrow Annulus Limit

We compare our three-dimensional computations to the two-dimensional approximation obtained using the integral formulation given in[7]. We consider a rotor/stator interaction problem with $B = 16$ and $V = 24$ and a mean flow of total Mach number of 0.5 and a stagger angle of 45° ($U_x = U_\theta = 0.3536$). The c/r_m ratio is 0.3491. For the three-dimensional calculation we take $r_h/r_t = 0.98$. The 3-D results are compared to the 2-D calculations in Fig. (3) for the lift coefficient and in Fig. (4) for the absolute value

of the acoustic coefficient $c_{-8,0}$, for reduced frequencies of π, 4.5, 4.7, 2π, 3π, and 4π using a grid of $\{n_x \times n_\theta \times n_r\} = \{81 \times 15 \times 7\}$. The results are in good agreement. The maximum differences between 2-D and 3-D calculations occur as expected near the first acoustic mode cut-on frequency 4.655. The large difference seen in the upstream acoustic coefficient for $\omega = 4.7$ is due to the fact that this frequency is very close to the cut-on frequency.

Effect of Hub-Tip Ratio

The effect of hub-tip ratio is studied for hub-tip ratios of 0.6, 0.6667, 0.7391, 0.8182, and 0.9048, for a rotor/stator interaction problem with $B = 16$ and $V = 24$ and a mean flow of $M_o = 0.3536$, $M_\Omega = 0.1$, $M_\Gamma = 0.1$. The c/r_m ratio at the mean radius is 0.3491, $\tilde{\omega} = 3\pi$, and a grid of $\{n_x \times n_\theta \times n_r\} = \{161 \times 21 \times 21\}$ is used.

Figure (5) compares the absolute value of the unsteady lift coefficient along the span for the different hub-tip ratios. The figure shows significant effect of the hub-tip ratio. For the largest two ratios, variations in the lift coefficient along the span is small.

q'	m	n	Namba	Schulten	Current Computations
0	-8	0	1.7144×10^{-2}	1.4972×10^{-2}	1.8328×10^{-2}
0	-8	1	1.8946×10^{-2}	1.7850×10^{-2}	1.8413×10^{-2}
1	-8	0	1.0155×10^{-2}	9.9075×10^{-3}	1.0863×10^{-2}
1	-8	1	2.7500×10^{-2}	2.4696×10^{-2}	2.5465×10^{-2}
2	-8	0	3.3653×10^{-3}	3.0988×10^{-3}	3.6577×10^{-3}
2	-8	1	6.0722×10^{-3}	6.6977×10^{-3}	6.1183×10^{-3}
3	-8	0	2.0496×10^{-3}	1.9710×10^{-3}	2.3436×10^{-3}
3	-8	1	3.7287×10^{-3}	4.2455×10^{-3}	3.9937×10^{-3}

Table 2 Comparison of the absolute values of the downstream coefficients c_{mn} with the lifting surface theories.

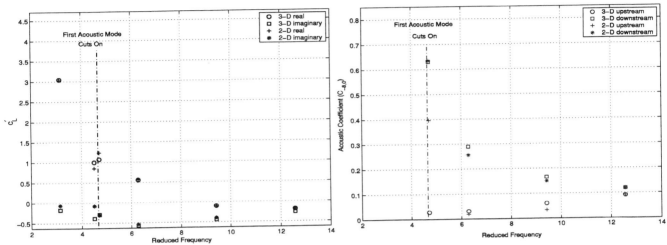

Fig. 3 Comparison of the lift coefficient between 3-D and 2-D calculations in the narrow annulus limit. $M = 0.5$ and stagger= 45°.

Fig. 4 Comparison of the upstream and downstream acoustic coefficient $c_{-8,0}$ between 3-D and 2-D calculations in the narrow annulus limit. $M = 0.5$ and stagger= 45°.

These variations become significant as the ratio decreases. For $r_h/r_t = 0.6$ and 0.6667, two propagating acoustic modes exist. For the other three values of r_h/r_t only one mode propagates. This explains the difference in the trend of the results between the two cases of $r_h/r_t = 0.6$ and 0.6667 and the other cases.

The magnitude of the upstream and downstream acoustic coefficients for the different hub-tip ratios are compared in Fig. (6). The downstream acoustic coefficient of the first radial mode ($n = 0$) increases as the hub-tip ratio decreases until the second mode cuts on. Both downstream and upstream coefficients of the second acoustic mode increase as the hub-tip ratio decreases.

Effect of Swirl and Twist

We consider four different mean flows with the same total Mach number of 0.4062 at the mean radius. The first mean flow is uniform and the other three flows are swirling flows. The three swirling flows have the same axial and swirl Mach numbers of 0.3536 and 0.2, respectively, at the mean radius. The first swirl is a free vortex of $M_\Gamma = 0.2$, the second swirl is a rigid body rotation of $M_\Omega = 0.2$, and the third swirl is a combination of free vortex and rigid body rotation,

$M_\Gamma = 0.1$ and $M_\Omega = 0.1$. The axial and circumferential mean velocities, and the stagger distributions for the four mean flows are shown in figures (7), (8), and (9), respectively. The c/r_m ratio at the mean radius is 0.3491, $\tilde{\omega} = 3\pi$, $B = 16$, $V = 24$, $r_h/r_t = 0.6$ and a grid of $\{n_x \times n_\theta \times n_r\} = \{161 \times 21 \times 21\}$ is used.

Figure (10) compares the absolute value of the unsteady lift coefficient along the span for the different mean flows. The figure shows significant difference in the value and variation trend between the uniform flow case and the swirling flow cases indicating that the swirl effect is significant. The differences in the lift coefficient of the three swirling flows are not significant indicating that the effect of the stagger distribution is small.

The magnitude of the upstream and downstream acoustic coefficients for the different mean flows are compared in Table (3). For the uniform flow, only one propagating acoustic mode exists, while two propagating modes exist for the three swirling flows. The table shows that the upstream acoustic coefficients are much smaller in the swirling flows than in the uniform flow. It also shows that the swirl model has a significant effect on both upstream and downstream acoustic

| | $M_o = 0.4062$ | $M_o = 0.3536$ | $M_o = 0.3536$ | $M_o = 0.3536$ |
| | $M_\Omega = 0$ | $M_\Omega = 0$ | $M_\Omega = 0.2$ | $M_\Omega = 0.1$ |
	$M_\Gamma = 0$	$M_\Gamma = 0.2$	$M_\Gamma = 0$	$M_\Gamma = 0.1$
First Downstream Mode	0.2015	0.1610	0.1375	0.1349
Second Downstream Mode	Cut off	0.07869	0.2140	0.1698
First Upstream Mode	0.1363	0.0143	0.0313	0.0195
Second Upstream Mode	Cut off	0.0370	0.0763	0.0586

Table 3 Absolute values of the upstream and downstream acoustic coefficients c_{mn}. $r_h/r_t = 0.6$ and $\tilde{\omega} = 3\pi$.

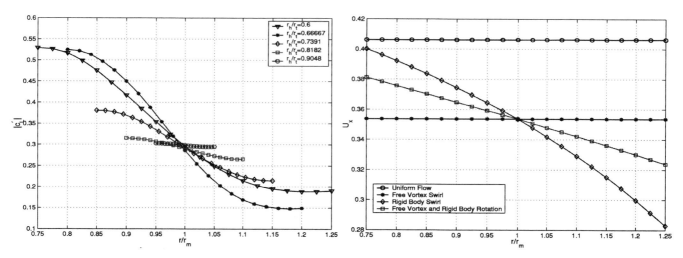

Fig. 5 Comparison of the lift coefficient for different hub-tip ratios. $M_o = 0.3536$, $M_\Omega = 0.1$, $M_\Gamma = 0.1$ and $\tilde{\omega} = 3\pi$.

Fig. 7 Axial flow component for the different mean flows with $r_h/r_t = 0.6$.

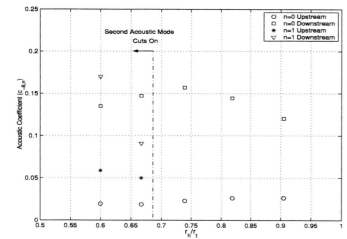

Fig. 6 Comparison of the upstream and downstream acoustic coefficients for different hub-tip ratios. $M_o = 0.3536$, $M_\Omega = 0.1$, $M_\Gamma = 0.1$ and $\tilde{\omega} = 3\pi$.

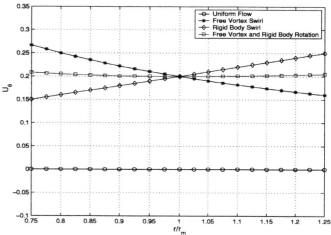

Fig. 8 Swirl component for the different mean flows with $r_h/r_t = 0.6$.

$\{161 \times 21 \times 21\}$ is used.

Figure (11) compares the absolute value of the unsteady lift coefficient along the span for different values of the reduced frequency. If we exclude 2π (the first frequency considered after the first acoustic mode cuts on), the figure shows that the lift coefficient decreases systematically as the frequency decreases.

The magnitude of the upstream and downstream acoustic coefficients for the different reduced frequen-

coefficients.

Reduced Frequency Effect

The effect of the reduced frequency on the unsteady lift coefficient and acoustic coefficients is studied for a mean flow of $M_o = 0.3536$, $M_\Omega = 0.1$, and $M_\Gamma = 0.1$, $r_h/r_t = 0.6667$, c/r_m at the mean radius is 0.3491, $\tilde{\omega} = 3\pi$, $B = 16$, $V = 24$, and a grid of $\{n_x \times n_\theta \times n_r\} =$

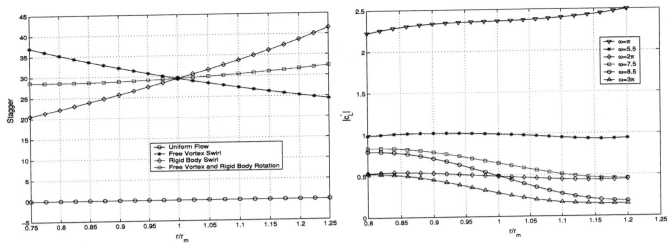

Fig. 9 Stagger distribution for the different mean flows with $r_h/r_t = 0.6$.

Fig. 11 Comparison of the lift coefficient for different reduced frequencies. $M_o = 0.3536$, $M_\Omega = 0.1$, $M_\Gamma = 0.1$ and $r_h/r_t = 0.6667$.

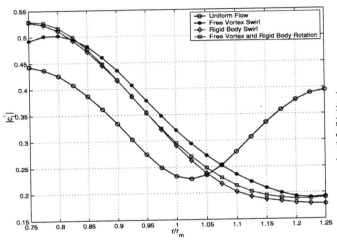

Fig. 10 Comparison of the lift coefficient for different mean flows. $r_h/r_t = 0.6$ and $\tilde\omega = 3\pi$.

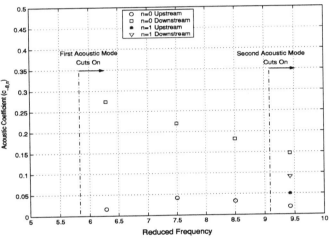

Fig. 12 Comparison of the upstream and downstream acoustic coefficients for different reduced frequencies. $M_o = 0.3536$, $M_\Omega = 0.1$, $M_\Gamma = 0.1$ and $r_h/r_t = 0.6667$.

cies are compared in Fig. (12). Note that the downstream acoustic coefficient of the first radial mode decreases as the reduced frequency increases. This behavior is smooth and not affected by the cut-on of the second mode as was the case for the narrow annulus limit.

Three-dimensional Upstream Disturbance

To investigate the effect of the gust three dimensionality, we consider two cases in the first case we have a two dimensional gust with $a_r = 0$ and the second case with $a_r = sin(\pi(r - r_h)/(r_t - r_h))$ for a mean flow of $M_o = 0.3536$, $M_\Omega = 0.1$, and $M_\Gamma = 0.1$, $r_h/r_t = 0.6667$, c/r_m at the mean radius is 0.3491, $\tilde\omega = 3\pi$, $B = 16$, $V = 24$, and a grid of $\{n_x \times n_\theta \times n_r\} = \{161 \times 21 \times 21\}$ is used.

Figure (13) compares the absolute value of the unsteady lift coefficient along the span for the two cases. The lift coefficient is higher when $a_r = 0$, especially near the tip. The magnitude of the upstream and

downstream acoustic coefficients for the two cases are compared in Table (4). The acoustic coefficients decrease significantly for both upstream and downstream modes for a_r different from zero.

Acoustic Upstream Disturbance

We consider now the scattering of an incident acoustic mode of $m = -8$ and $n = 0$ and compare that to the scattering of a vortical disturbance. We take the upwash component to be the same at the mean radius and equal to 1. for both disturbances. For the vortical disturbance this upwash is constant along the radius but for the acoustic mode it changes slightly (about 10%). This upwash corresponds to an acoustic mode with a coefficient $c_{-8,0} = 1.18$. In the two cases, $M_o = 0.3536$, $M_\Omega = 0.1$, $M_\Gamma = 0.1$, $r_h/r_t = 0.6667$, $c/r_m = 0.3491$ at the mean radius, $\tilde\omega = 3\pi$, and a grid

	2-D Upstream Disturbance	3-D Upstream Disturbance
First Downstream Mode	0.1471	0.1094
Second Downstream Mode	0.0908	0.0.0617
First Upstream Mode	0.0185	0.0143
Second Upstream Mode	0.0498	0.0418

Table 4 Absolute values of the upstream and downstream acoustic coefficients c_{mn} for 2-D and 3-D upstream disturbances.

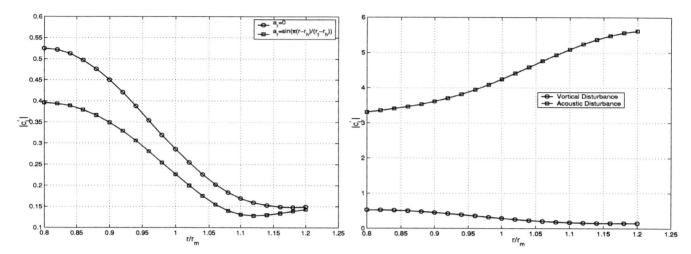

Fig. 13 Comparison of the lift coefficient for 2-D and 3-D upstream disturbances. $M_o = 0.3536$, $M_\Omega = 0.1$, $M_\Gamma = 0.1$, $r_h/r_t = 0.6667$, and $\tilde{\omega} = 3\pi$.

Fig. 14 Comparison of the lift coefficient for acoustic and vortical upstream disturbances. $M_o = 0.3536$, $M_\Omega = 0.1$, $M_\Gamma = 0.1$, $r_h/r_t = 0.6667$, and $\tilde{\omega} = 3\pi$.

of $\{n_x \times n_\theta \times n_r\} = \{161 \times 21 \times 21\}$ is used. The vortical disturbance has $a_r = 0$ and $n' = 0$.

Figure (14) compares the absolute value of the unsteady lift coefficient along the span for the two cases. The lift coefficient is much higher for the acoustic disturbance. This may be explained by the fact that the wavelength of the acoustic wave in the x-direction is much larger than that of the vortical wave. This causes phase cancellation along the blade in the case of vortical disturbance, thus reducing the lift coefficient compared to the case of upstream acoustic disturbance.

The magnitude of the upstream and downstream acoustic coefficients for the two cases are compared in Table (5). The acoustic coefficients are much higher in the case of acoustic disturbance especially for the first acoustic mode. This is because the incident acoustic wave has already a coefficient of 1.18. The incident acoustic wave is scattered upstream and downstream, however, the part scattered upstream is small.

Conclusions

The problem of scattering of vortical and acoustic waves by an annular blade cascade in a swirling flow is formulated. The numerical calculations has been validated for uniform flows by comparison with lifting surface theories and for swirling flows with narrow annulus 2-D solution. The effect of hub-tip ratios, swirl, twist, frequency, and upstream disturbance have been examined.

Acknowledgments

This research was partially supported by United Technologies Pratt & Whitney under NASA Glenn contract AST NAS 3-27727 with Dennis Huff as project manager, and Office of Naval Research grant No. N00014-00-1-0130 with L. Patrick Purtell as program manager. H. M. Atassi would like to thank the Ohio Aerospace Institute Aeroacoustic Consortium for its support.

References

[1]Kerrobrock, J. L., "Small Disturbances in Turbomachine Annuli with Swirl," *AIAA Journal*, Vol. 15, 1977, pp. 794–803.

[2]Kaji, S. and Okazaki, T., "Propagation of Sound Waves Through a Blade Row. II. Analysis based on the Acceleration Potential Method," *Journal of Sound and Vibration*, Vol. 11, 1970, pp. 355–375.

[3]Goldstein, M., *Aeroacoustics*, Mcgraw-Hill International Book Company, 1976.

[4]Smith, S. N., "Discrete Frequency Sound Generation in Axial Flows of Turbomachines," 1971, CUED/A-Turbo/TR29.

[5]Ventres, C. S., "A Computer Program to Calculate Cascade 2D Kernel," 1980, NASA Technical Memorandum.

[6]Kaji, S. and Okazaki, T., "Generation of Sound by Rotor-Stator Interaction," *Journal of Sound and Vibration*, Vol. 13, 1970, pp. 281–307.

[7]Hamad, G. and Atassi, H. M., "Sound Generation in a Cascade by 3D Disturbance Convected in a Subsonic Flow,"

	Vortical Upstream Disturbance	Acoustic Upstream Disturbance
First Downstream Mode	0.1471	0.8608
Second Downstream Mode	0.0908	0.1458
First Upstream Mode	0.0185	0.0718
Second Upstream Mode	0.0498	0.0775

Table 5 Absolute values of the upstream and downstream acoustic coefficients c_{mn} for acoustic and vortical upstream disturbances.

AIAA 81-2046, 7th Aeroacoustic Conference, Palo Alto, CA, 1981.

[8] Goldstein, M. E. and Atassi, H. M., "A Complete Second-Order Theory for the Unsteady Flow About an Airfoil Due to a Periodic Gust," *Journal of Fluid Mechanics*, Vol. 74, 1976, pp. 741–765.

[9] Goldstein, M. E., "Unsteady Vortical and Entropic Distortions of Potential Flows Round Arbitrary Obstacles," *Journal of Fluid Mechanics*, Vol. 89, 1978, pp. 433–468.

[10] Atassi, H. M., *Unsteady Aerodynamics of Vortical flows: early and recent developments. In Aerodynamics and Aeroacoustics*, ed. Fung, K.-Y., World Scientific, 1994, pp. 121–172.

[11] Atassi, H. M. and Grzedzinski, J., "Unsteady Disturbances of Streaming Motions Around Bodies," *Journal of Fluid Mechanics*, Vol. 209, 1989, pp. 385–403.

[12] Scott, J. R. and Atassi, H. M., "A Finite-Difference Frequency Domain Numerical Scheme for the Solution of the Gust Response Problem," *Journal of Computational Physics*, Vol. 119, 1995, pp. 75–93.

[13] Hall, K. C. and Verdon, J. M., "Gust Response Analysis for Cascades Operating in Nonuniform Mean Flows," *AIAA Journal*, Vol. 29, No. 9, 1991, pp. 1463–1471.

[14] Fang, J. and Atassi, H., *Compressible Flows with Vortical Disturbances Around a Cascade of Loaded Airfoils. In Unsteady Aerodynamics, Aeroacoustics, and Aeroelasticity of Turbomachines and Propellers*, Ed. Atassi, H. M., 1993, pp. 149–176, Springer-Verlag.

[15] Namba, M., "Three-Dimensional Flow," 1987, In Unsteady Turbomachinery Aerodynamics, AGARD-AG-298.

[16] Schulten, J. B. H. M., "Sound Generated by Rotor Wakes Interacting with a Leaned Vane Stator," *AIAA Journal*, Vol. 20, 1982, pp. 1352–1358.

[17] Montgomery, M. D. and Verdon, J. M., "A Three-Dimensional Linearized Unsteady Euler Analysis for Turbomachinery Blade Rows," 1997, NASA CR-4770.

[18] Golubev, V. V. and Atassi, H. M., "Unsteady Swirling Flows in Annular Cascades. Part I. Evolution of Incident Disturbances," *AIAA*, Vol. 38, 2000, pp. 1142–1149.

[19] Elhadidi, B. M., Atassi, H. M., Envia, E., and Podboy, G., "Evolution of Rotor Wake in Swirling Flow," 2000, To be presented in the 6th AIAA/CEAS Aeroacoustics Conference at Maui, Hawaii.

[20] Golubev, V. V. and Atassi, H. M., "Interaction of Unsteady Swirling Flows with Annular Cascades. Part II. Aerodynamic Blade Response," To appear in AIAA Journal.

[21] Ali, A. A., Atassi, O. V., and Atassi, H. M., "Acoustic Eigenmodes in a Coannular Duct with a General Swirling Flow," *AIAA 2000-1954, 6th AIAA/CEAS Aeroacoustics Conference at Maui, Hawai*, 2000.

[22] Ali, A. A., *Aeroacoustics and stability of Swirling Flow*, Ph.D. thesis, University of Notre Dame, 2001.

[23] Ali, A. A., Atassi, O. V., and Atassi, H. M., "Derivation and Implementation of Inflow/Outflow Conditions for Aeroacoustic problems with Swirling Flows," *AIAA 2001-2173, 7th AIAA/CEAS Aeroacoustics Conference at Maastricht, The Netherlands*, 2001.

[24] Namba, M., "Three-Dimensional Analysis of Blade Force and Sound Generation for an Annular Cascade in Distorted Flows," *Journal of Sound and Vibration*, Vol. 50, 1977, pp. 479–508.

[25] Tyler, J. M. and Sofrin, T. G., "Axial flow compressor noise studies," *SAE Transactions*, Vol. 70, 1962, pp. 309–332.

[26] Hanson, D. B., "Fan Stator with Harmonic Excitation by Rotor Wake," 1999, Third CAA Workshop on Benchmark Problems, Category 4.

[27] Atassi, O. V. and Ali, A. A., "Inflow/Outflow Conditions for Time-Harmonic Internal Aeroacoustic Problems," *Journal of Computational Acoustics*, Vol. 10, No. 2, 2002.

HIGH FREQUENCY SOUND RADIATION FROM AN ANNULAR CASCADE IN SWIRLING FLOWS

Basman Elhadidi * and **Hafiz M. Atassi** †

Department of Aerospace and Mechanical Engineering
University of Notre Dame, Notre Dame, IN 46556, USA

Abstract

A model is presented for the interaction of high frequency unsteady three-dimensional incident disturbances with an annular cascade of unloaded blades in swirling flows. Results for the unsteady blade loading and the far-field acoustic pressure are validated by comparison with two-dimensional linear cascade theory in the narrow annulus limit. Numerical results indicate that the dependence of the vortical part of the unsteady flow on the acoustic part becomes weaker as the reduced frequency increases as predicted by asymptotic analysis. Computations indicate that full three-dimensional solutions are essential at high frequency. A detailed study leads to the conclusion that the unsteady lift and acoustic pressure are highly dependent on the meanflow swirl, both at low and high frequencies. High frequency calculations indicate that the spanwise variation of the swirl angle (blade twist) has significant effects on the spanwise unsteady lift distribution and propagating acoustic pressure. Spanwise modulation of the incident gust reduces the unsteady lift considerably.

Introduction

One of the primary noise sources for modern high by-pass engines is the interaction of unsteady rotor wake with downstream stator vanes. The impinging wakes produce fluctuating aerodynamic forces along the blade surface and, as a result of this interaction process, sound is radiated in the duct.

Turbomachinery blades have complicated geometries which give rise to several interference effects. Simplified models are developed to examine the different geometrical characteristics of modern high by-pass engines. The early models considered linear cascades of flat plate airfoils that took into account the blade interference effects.[1] Numerical codes were then developed to solve the governing integral equations and directly give the unsteady blade pressure and the duct propagating modes.[2,3] For high-frequency, Peake[4] and Glegg[5] used the Weiner-Hopf technique to solve the integral equation. Fang and Atassi[6] and Hall and Verdon[7] developed numerical models to account for the effect of blade loading. Three-dimensional theories were developed by Namba and Schulten,[8] using a boundary integral method. Full numerical models were recently developed by Montgomery and Verdon[9] and by Wilson.[10]

In the present paper, we develop a computationally efficient model which fully accounts for the effects of meanflow swirl in an annular cascade. The results presented in this paper are limited to unloaded blades and harmonic excitations. They cover a broad range of frequencies, $\omega_{rm} = \frac{\omega r_m}{c_o}$, up to 15.

Inflow/outflow conditions have an important effect on the numerical solution. Exact non-reflecting boundary conditions were developed by Fang and Atassi[6] for the two-dimensional cascade, Atassi[11] for three-dimensional cascades with uniform flow, Golubev and Atassi[12] and Ali et.al.[13] for swirling flows. The technique used here is similar to the method developed by Ali et.al.[13]

This work is a step towards the modeling of a three-dimensional high-frequency gust interacting with a cascade taking into account blade loading, twist and lean. The formulation is based on unsteady velocity splitting.[1] This formulation has shown better numerical efficiency compared to primitive variable formulations, which is essential for broadband noise calculations.

First we present the mathematical formulation of the problem and introduce exact non-reflecting boundary conditions at inflow/outflow. Then we

*Research Assistant, Fellow, Center of Applied Mathematics, AIAA Member

†Viola D. Hank Professor, Fellow AIAA

briefly outline the numerical discretization scheme, and follow with a set of parametric studies and results.

Mathematical formulation

Governing equations

The flow variables, velocity $\vec{V}$, pressure p, density ρ and entropy s, are considered to be the sum of their mean values $\vec{U}_o$, p_o, ρ_o, s_o and their disturbances $\vec{u}'$, p', ρ' and s'. We further assume that the meanflow is given by,

$$\vec{U}_o = U_x(r)\vec{e}_x + U_\theta(r)\vec{e}_\theta,$$

where U_x and U_θ are the axial and swirl meanflow components. The linearized Euler equations can be solved by the primitive variable approach, or by an approach based on the velocity splitting.[1] Traditionally for potential meanflow, the unsteady velocity may be split into vortical, entropic and potential components.[14] The pressure is only associated with the potential ϕ, and the vorticity is associated with the vortical component $\vec{u}^R$. For general meanflows the equations for $\vec{u}^R$, and ϕ are coupled. A normal mode analysis by Golubev and Atassi[15] for swirling flows indicated that the coupling between ϕ and $\vec{u}^R$ is weak at high frequencies. This leads to a high frequency model which neglected the coupling for the vortical velocity to first order.[12] In the present paper we cast the equations using the velocity decomposition. Writing the unsteady velocity disturbance $\vec{u}'$, as the sum of a vortical component $\vec{u}^R$, an entropy component $\frac{s'}{2c_p}\vec{U}_o$ and a potential component $\nabla\phi$,

$$\vec{u}'(x,r,\theta,t) = \vec{u}^R + \frac{s'}{2c_p}\vec{U}_o + \nabla\phi. \quad (1)$$

The linearized Euler equations reduces to,

$$\frac{D_o\vec{u}^R}{Dt} + \vec{u}^R \cdot \nabla\vec{U}_o =$$
$$\nabla\phi \times \vec{\zeta} - \frac{D_o\phi}{Dt}\frac{\nabla s_o}{c_p} - \frac{\vec{U}_o}{2c_p}\frac{D_o s'}{Dt}, \quad (2)$$

$$\frac{D_o}{Dt}\left(\frac{1}{c_o^2}\frac{D_o\phi}{Dt}\right) - \frac{1}{\rho_o}\nabla\cdot(\rho_o\nabla\phi) =$$
$$\frac{1}{\rho_o}\nabla\cdot\left(\rho_o\vec{u}^{(R)}\right) + \frac{\vec{U}_o \cdot \nabla s'}{2c_p} - \frac{1}{c_p}\frac{D_o s'}{Dt}, \quad (3)$$

$$\frac{D_o s'}{Dt} + \left(\vec{u}^R + \nabla\phi + \frac{s'}{2c_p}\vec{U}_o\right)\cdot\nabla s_o = 0, \quad (4)$$

where $\vec{\zeta}$ is the meanflow vorticity and c_o is the speed of sound. $\frac{D_o}{Dt} = \frac{\partial}{\partial t} + \vec{U}_o \cdot \nabla$ is the material derivative associated with the meanflow. The pressure is defined as,

$$p' = -\rho_o\frac{D\phi}{Dt}. \quad (5)$$

Meanflow model

For simplicity we assume in the present paper that the meanflow is inviscid, isentropic and has constant enthalpy across blade span. We also define the swirl component of the mean velocity as a combination of a solid body rotation (Ωr), and a free vortex $(\frac{\Gamma}{r})$,

$$M_\theta(r) = \Omega r + \frac{\Gamma}{r}.$$

Applying the Crocco's equation, it may be shown that the corresponding axial Mach number satisfies,

$$M_x^2(r) = M_{xm}^2 - 2\left[\Omega^2\left(r^2 - 1\right) + 2\Omega\Gamma\log r\right].$$

Where M_{xm} is the axial Mach number at the mean radius.

Initial conditions

For isentropic flows, the unsteady velocity disturbance $\vec{u}'$ is given by,

$$\vec{u}'(x,r,\theta,t) = \vec{u}^R + \nabla\phi.$$

This disturbance velocity has both acoustic and convected disturbances coupled together. For the convected component, it may be shown that for high frequency, $\omega >> 1$,

$$\vec{u}^R(x,r,\theta,t) = \int_\omega \sum_{m'=-\infty}^{\infty} \vec{A}_{m'}(x,r)e^{i\varphi}d\omega,$$

$$\phi(x,r,\theta,t) = \int_\omega \sum_{m'=-\infty}^{\infty} i\frac{\vec{A}_{m'}\cdot\nabla\varphi}{|\nabla\varphi|^2}e^{i\varphi}d\omega,$$

where,

$$\varphi = \alpha x + m'\theta - \omega t,$$
$$\alpha = \frac{\omega - \frac{m'M_\theta}{r}}{M_x}.$$

$\vec{A}_{m'}(x,r)$ represents the decomposed convected vortical component in the Fourier frequency domain, for a particular azimuthal mode m'. The corresponding convected velocity for a given mode is given by,

$$\vec{u}'_{m'} = \left(\vec{A}_{m'} - \frac{\vec{A}_{m'}\cdot\nabla\varphi}{|\nabla\varphi|^2}\nabla\varphi\right)e^{i\varphi}. \quad (6)$$

Any incident gust, $\vec{u}'_I$ can be represented in the form,

$$\vec{u}'_I(x_I, r, \theta, t) = \int_\omega \sum_{m'=-\infty}^{\infty} \vec{a}_{m'}(r) e^{i\varphi} d\omega, \qquad (7)$$

$\vec{a}_{m'}(r)$ represents the decomposed gust in the Fourier frequency domain. x_I is the incident gust location, and αx_I is included in the phase to facilitate comparison with other computational codes. For the rotor-stator interaction problem, $m' = pB$, p is an integer, B is the number of rotor blades. $\omega = pB\Omega$, where Ω represents the shaft rotational speed. For this study, only the first blade passing frequency is considered, i.e., $p = 1$. From equations (6,7) we find that,

$$\vec{a}_{m'}(r) = \vec{A}_{m'}(x_I, r) - \frac{\vec{A}_{m'} \cdot \nabla\varphi}{|\nabla\varphi|^2} \nabla\varphi.$$

In this study, for simplicity $\vec{a}_{m'}(r)$ was chosen as,

$$\vec{a}_{m'} = \frac{M(r)}{r\omega} (-m', 0, \alpha r) e^{ik_r^{(n')}\tilde{r}},$$
$$k_r^{(n')} = \frac{-2\pi n'}{r_{tip} - r_{hub}},$$
$$\tilde{r} = r - r_{hub}.$$

$M(r)$ is the resultant Mach number at r. $k_r^{(n')}$ is included to facilitate comparison with theories developed for uniform upstream meanflow. For this choice of incident disturbance $\vec{A}_{m'}(x_I, r) = \vec{a}_{m'}(r)$.

Boundary conditions

Three types of boundary conditions exist. At the hub and tip radii, and blade surfaces we have solid surfaces, along which we apply the impermeability conditions,

$$\vec{u}' \cdot \vec{n} = 0.$$

The computational domain is limited to a single blade passage by two surfaces as shown in figure (1). Along the free surfaces (upstream and downstream of blade section), we impose the quasi-periodicity conditions for p' and $\vec{u}' \cdot \vec{n}$,

$$p'(x, r, \vartheta) = p'(x, r, 0)e^{i\sigma},$$
$$\vec{u}'(x, r, \vartheta) \cdot \vec{n} = \vec{u}'(x, r, 0) \cdot \vec{n}e^{i\sigma}.$$

$\vartheta = \frac{2\pi}{V}$ is the angular blade spacing, V is the number of vane blades. For rotor-stator interaction problems the inter blade phase angle $\sigma =$ $\frac{2pB\pi}{V}$. The inter blade phase angle accounts for the quasi-periodicity of the propagating waves. The inflow/outflow boundary conditions are the non-reflecting boundary conditions that will be discussed in details. Figure (1) shows the computational domain used in this problem.

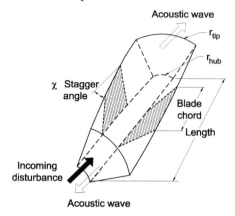

Fig. 1   Schematic of the computational domain.

Non-reflecting boundary conditions

Upstream and downstream of a blade row, the far-field behavior of the scattered pressure field can be expressed by the eigenmode analysis presented by Golubev and Atassi[15] and Ali et.al.[16] The pressure may be expanded in terms of the eigenfunctions,

$$p'(x, r, \theta) = \sum_{m \in S_m^\pm} \sum_{n=0}^{\infty} c_{mn}^\pm \mathcal{P}_{mn}^\pm(r) e^{i(k_{mn}^\pm x + m\theta)},$$

where n and m are the radial and azimuthal mode numbers. S_m is the set of all values of m. For rotor-stator interaction, m is given by the Tyler-Sofrin condition, $m = pB - qV$, q is an integer. The positive/negative signs refer to downstream/upstream propagating waves. k_{mn} and $\mathcal{P}_{mn}$ are the axial wave number and corresponding eigenfunction of the mode mn.

According to the causality principle, only outgoing waves are permitted at the inlet/outlet sections. The correct propagating modes are selected according to the group velocity. The downstream pressure can be expressed as,

$$p'(x, r, \theta) = \sum_{m \in S_m} \sum_{n=0}^{\infty} c_{mn} \mathcal{P}_{mn}(r) e^{i(k_{mn}x + m\theta)}.$$

Numerically, a fixed number of eigenmodes can be used at the inflow and outflow, and the pressure is expressed as,

$$p'(x,r,\theta) = \sum_{m \in S_m} \sum_{n=1}^{N_R} c_{mn} \mathcal{P}_{mn}(r) e^{i(k_{mn}x + m\theta)}, \quad (8)$$

where the summation m is truncated to N_θ terms. N_R, N_θ are the radial and tangential number of grid points used in the computation. In the case of uniform flow, the basis functions, $\mathcal{P}$, are complete and orthogonal and the coefficients c_{mn} can be easily obtained by taking the inner product,

$$c_{mn} = \langle p'(x,r,\theta), r\mathcal{P}_{mn}(r) e^{i(k_{mn}x + m\theta)} \rangle.$$

However, for swirling flows the eigenmodes $\mathcal{P}_{mn}$ are not orthogonal. First transform the modes to an orthonormal set using the Gram-Schmit procedure and then take the inner product.

Assuming that the outgoing waves are governed by equation (8), we seek a relationship between the values of p at the outlet, x_2, to those in the interior domain, x_1, of the form,

$$p'(x_2, r, \theta) = \mathcal{M}p'(x_1, r, \theta), \quad (9)$$

where $\mathcal{M}$ is a mapping function. This mapping function can be easily built by evaluating the coefficients c_{mn} at x_1, and substituting this expression into equation (8) evaluated at x_2.

It is important to note that this mapping function can be used both at the inlet and outlet sections. However, at the inlet section, it is numerically efficient to use a mapping function based on the acoustic part of ϕ. Using equation (5), the basis function for potential Φ_{mn}, can be related to the basis function of pressure $\mathcal{P}_{mn}$,

$$\Phi_{mn} = \frac{i\mathcal{P}_{mn}}{\rho_o \left(-\omega + U_x k_{mn} + \frac{U_\theta}{r}m\right)}.$$

The mapping function based on the potential *can not* be used at the outflow section, because the potential is not continuous along the wake boundary.

Normalization

The normalization is based on the reference density and speed of sound at the mean radius, ρ_{om}, c_{om}. The pressure difference is normalized by $\rho_{om}c_{om}^2$. The basis functions for the expansions needed in the non-reflecting boundary conditions are normalized such that the maximum value of each mode is unity. The length scales are normalized with respect to the

mean radius, and the reduced frequency ω_{rm} is normalized with respect to mean radius and speed of sound. The unsteady sectional lift coefficient is defined as,

$$c_{l'} = \frac{\int_0^c \Delta p' d\xi}{\rho_o c_o a_n c},$$

where ξ is the tangential coordinate along the blade chord, a_n is the normal component of the initial disturbance to the blade. For the initial distribution presented in this paper, $a_n/c_o = 1$.

Numerical procedure

The eigenmodes needed for the non-reflecting boundary conditions are obtained by a mixed spectral/shooting algorithm provided by Ali et.al.[16] To perform the integration needed for the inner product, a piecewise continuous solution is assumed between the grid points.

The system of equations (2,3) are solved iteratively. First equation (2) is solved using the initial conditions for the gust, neglecting the right hand side. Then equation (3) is solved. These two steps are called iteration 1. Iteration 2 will begin by calculating the right hand side of equation (2) from the previous values of ϕ, followed by solving (3). This procedure is repeated until the changes in both the vortical and potential velocities satisfy the convergence criteria.

The problem is solved along the meanflow streamlines in the physical domain, and is transformed to a uniform grid in the computational domain by applying the transformation, $x = \xi, r = \zeta, \theta = \eta - \frac{U_\theta x}{U_x}$. The vortical wave propagation, equation (2), is solved using a fourth order Runge Kutta scheme. The wave equation (3) is solved using a second order finite difference scheme. The quasi periodicity condition is fourth order accurate. Applying second order differencing resulted in wave dissipation and loss of phase. However, the associated cost of having the fourth order accurate differencing is large, increasing the matrix bandwidth two orders of magnitude. The algebraic system of equations is solved using an iterative BiConjugate Gradient Stabilized technique and incomplete LU factorization included in PETSc.[17]

The model is computationally efficient and results for a single frequency can be obtained in minutes on a single processor SunBlade 1000 computer for the narrow annulus limit, and around an hour for the full annulus case. The computational cost can be further reduced using parallel processing for broadband calculations. For the aeroacoustics benchmark problem[18] (uniform meanflow), Elhadidi and Atassi,[19] performed extensive grid convergence tests and comparison with the results of Namba and Schulten.[8] The comparison of the unsteady lift, acoustic pressure and unsteady pressure difference was excellent.

Results

Two cases are tested and shown in this section, the narrow annulus limit and full annulus. The narrow annulus limit is used to validate the numerical scheme. The full annulus is used to examine the solver convergence properties, and three-dimensional rotor-stator interaction effects. Table (1) presents the geometrical and grid data for both problems.

Tip radius r_{tip}	1.0
Hub radius r_{hub} (narrow annulus)	0.98
Hub radius r_{hub} (full annulus)	0.75
Number of vanes V	24
Number of blades B	16
Chord (c)	$\frac{2\pi}{V}$
Domain length (L)	$3c$
Computation grid (narrow annulus)	$N_r = 7, N_\theta = 31, N_x = 181$
Computation grid (full annulus)	$N_r = 35, N_\theta = 31, N_x = 181$

Table 1   Geometrical and grid data

Narrow annulus limit

For comparison with a linear cascade, we use an integral equation based code, LINC.[3] To replicate the two dimensional limit case, the ratio $\frac{r_{tip}}{r_{hub}} \to 1$. For this comparison the axial and swirl Mach numbers were chosen to have a stagger angle equal to 45°, $M_x = 0.36, M_\theta = 0.36$. For this meanflow, there is no velocity variation in the span direction, and the system of equations (2,3) becomes uncoupled. Figures (2-4) present the comparison of the unsteady pressure difference between LINC and our solution for reduced frequencies, $\omega_{rm} = 0.5\pi, 4.5\pi, 6.5\pi$. For $\omega_{rm} = 0.5$ there are no propagating modes, for $\omega_{rm} = 4.5$ there is one propagating mode, and for $\omega_{rm} = 6.5\pi$ there are two propagating modes. As it is seen from the figures the comparison of the unsteady pressure difference is excellent for all frequencies. A comparison for both the unsteady lift (real and imaginary parts) and acoustic pressure is

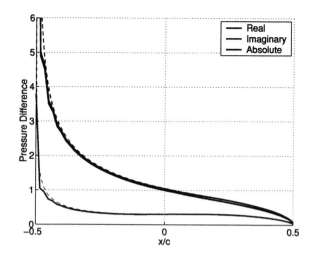

Fig. 2   Comparison between LINC and computed pressure difference, $\omega_{rm} = 0.5\pi$.

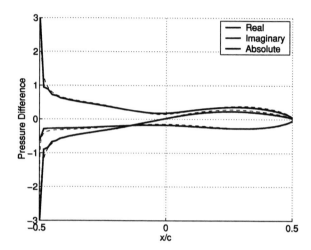

Fig. 3   Comparison between LINC and computed pressure difference, $\omega_{rm} = 4.5\pi$.

presented in figures (5,6). These figures show good comparison of the unsteady lift, downstream and upstream acoustic pressure with LINC.

Full annulus

Convergence characteristics

Computational efficiency is important particularly for broadband calculations. The coupling of equations (2-3) increases the computational time requirements. In what follows we examine the number of iterations needed, N_c, for the system to converge to the required solution. High frequency analysis indicates that the right hand side of equation (2) may be small and could be neglected. During each coupling equation (3) must be solved either by an iterative or

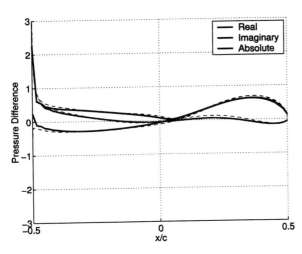

Fig. 4 **Comparison between LINC and computed pressure difference, $\omega_{rm} = 6.5\pi$.**

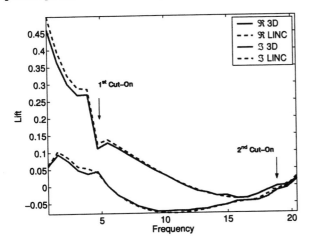

Fig. 5 **Comparison of unsteady lift.**

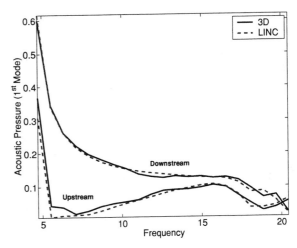

Fig. 6 **Comparison of upstream and downstream acoustic pressure.**

direct solver. In this scheme an iterative solver was chosen because, (i) it is much faster than any direct solver for three-dimensional problems, (ii) it can always use the solutions of the previous coupling as a first guess in the new coupling iteration. To test the convergence and solver properties, a test was run with a stagger angle equal to 45° at the mean radius, with $M_{xm} = 0.36$, $M_\theta = 0.18r + \frac{0.18}{r}$. Four tests were done at reduced frequencies, $\omega_{rm} = \pi, 2.5\pi, 6\pi, 8.5\pi$. Figure (7), presents both the number of coupling iterations (number of bars for each case), and the number of solver iterations, N_s needed by the solver in each coupling (vertical axis). Two key results may be drawn from this figure. First, the number of coupling iterations decreases as the frequency increases, in fact for $\omega_{rm} = 8.5\pi$, the first coupling takes over 95% of the total computer time. Second the total

computer time increases as the reduced frequency increases. This however, may be addressed separately by choosing better iterative or parallel solvers.

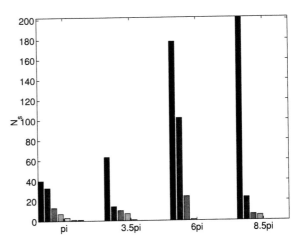

Fig. 7 **Solver convergence properties**

A close examination of equation (2) reveals that the left hand side of is $\mathcal{O}(\omega)$, and the right hand side is of $\mathcal{O}(1)$. This means that it may be possible to neglect the right hand side of equation (2) for high frequency calculations. Figures (8), compares the absolute pressure difference between the final solution and the first two iterations at the mean radius for a reduced frequency $\omega_{rm} = 3.5\pi$. As seen from the figure, there is hardly any difference in the computed pressure difference. The results are equally good at the tip and hub regions as shown in figure (9) for the tip section.

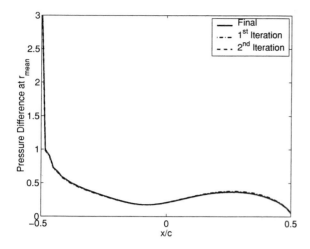

Fig. 8 Comparison the pressure difference between first two iteration and final solution at mean radius, $\omega_{rm} = 3.5\pi$.

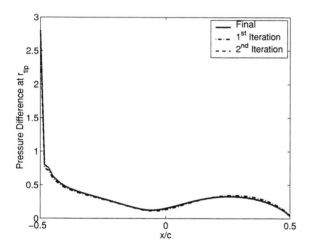

Fig. 9 Comparison the pressure difference between first two iteration and final solution at tip radius, $\omega_{rm} = 3.5\pi$.

Comparison with strip theory

One could consider a large annulus as a superposition of several narrow annuli, this is know as strip theory. This approximation is commonly used for meanflow computation of the steady and unsteady blade aerodynamics and its validity is examined here. A comparison of the sectional lift coefficient between three-dimensional calculations and that of strip theory is shown in figure (10) for a reduced frequency $\omega_{rm} = 3.5\pi$. There are marked differences in the spanwise lift distribution, which have previously been analyzed for the case of uniform meanflow.[19] The discrepancy results from the different number of propagating modes, which are discrete and different

at each radius in strip theory, while being continuous and uniform along the duct annulus in the three-dimensional solution. This effect is a high frequency effect, because the higher the reduced frequency the greater the discrepancy between the number of cut-on modes in both the duct and strip theory.[19,20]

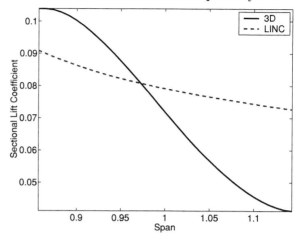

Fig. 10 Comparison of sectional lift coefficient with LINC

Effect of swirl

In this study, the effect of increasing the blade stagger angle is examined. In this comparison the axial meanflow and the swirl meanflow at the mean radius are related together by specifying the stagger angle, χ, and the resultant Mach number M,

$$\tan\chi = \frac{M_{\theta m}}{M_{xm}},$$

$$M = \sqrt{M_{xm}^2 + M_\theta^2}.$$

For all cases the Mach number was fixed at 0.5 at the mean radius. Figure (11) presents the unsteady lift for four different cases with stagger angles, $\chi = 0^o, 15^o, 30^o, 45^o$. As seen from the figure the unsteady lift differs at high frequencies. At the low frequency a discrepancy is seen for the stagger angle $\chi = 45^o$ from the rest. This discrepancy may be explained with the aid of figure (12). For $\chi = 45^o$, the acoustic pressure cuts-on at a lower frequency than others, resulting in the reduction of unsteady lift. Figures (12-13) present the absolute values of the downstream acoustic pressure. Two observations are made from these figures. The number of propagating modes and the sound pressure are strongly dependent on the stagger angle (swirl magnitude) and frequency.

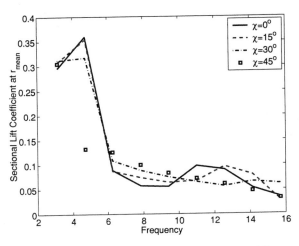

Fig. 11 Comparison of unsteady lift for different swirl configurations

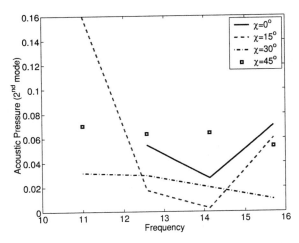

Fig. 13 Comparison of downstream propagating sound intensity for different swirl configurations

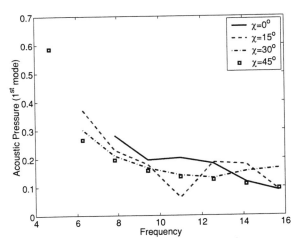

Fig. 12 Comparison of downstream propagating sound intensity for different swirl configurations

Effect of blade twist

Blade twist is used to modify the incident angle of attack to prevent flow separation and engine surge. An analysis is presented here to analyze the effect of twist on the unsteady lift and propagating sound pressure. For this study, the meanflow distribution was chosen as, $M_{xm} = 0.36$, $M_\theta = 0.36r\gamma + \frac{0.36}{r}(1 - \gamma)$, where γ took values of $0, 0.25, 0.5$. This distribution resulted in blade twists approximately equal to $-8.2^o, 0^o, 8.3^o$, where the blade twist is defined as the difference of stagger angles between tip and hub radii. Figure (14-16) compare the unsteady sectional lift distribution at the hub, mean and tip radii for all blades. As it is clearly seen there are differences in the lift except at the mean radius, where the stagger angle is constant for all three cases. The spanwise

sectional lift distribution is seen in figure (17) at a reduced frequency $\omega_{rm} = 3\pi$.

Figures (18-19) present the value of the sound pressure for the first and second modes. For the first mode the differences are negligible, for the second mode the differences become pronounced and significant. From figure (19), it is apparent that as the twist deviates from 0°, the acoustic pressure increases, specially with positive twist. This effect only occurs at high frequency, indicating that blade twist may lead to higher sound propagation.

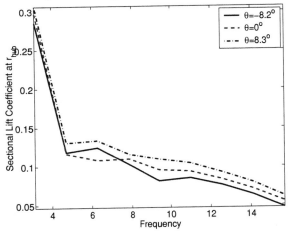

Fig. 14 Comparison of unsteady lift at hub radius

Effect of incident gust modulation

In this section, the effect of having $n' \neq 0$ is studied. In all the previous results the value of $n' = 0$, which is a measure of the three-dimensionality of the disturbance. For this study the meanflow is given by,

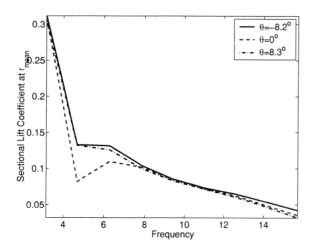

Fig. 15 Comparison of unsteady lift at mean radius

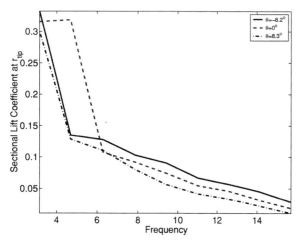

Fig. 16 Comparison of unsteady lift at tip radius

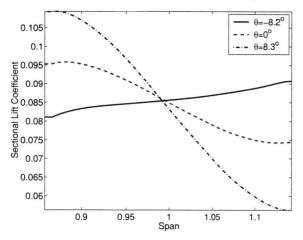

Fig. 17 Comparison of unsteady lift along span, $\omega_{rm} = 3\pi$

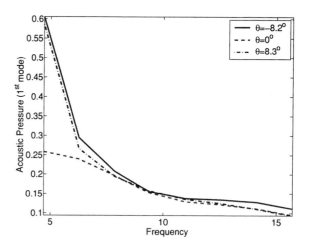

Fig. 18 Comparison of downstream propagating sound intensity for different twist configurations

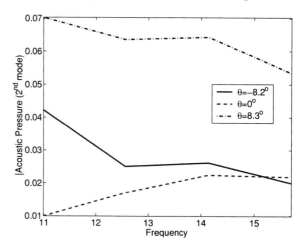

Fig. 19 Comparison of downstream propagating sound intensity for different twist configurations

$M_{xm} = 0.36, M_{\theta} = 0.18r + \frac{0.18}{r}$. Figure (20) shows the effect of increasing n' on the unsteady lift at the mean radius. The reduction of lift is expected as known from the results presented by Atassi.[1]

Figures (21-22) present the values of the downstream acoustic pressure. The first modes decay considerably for $n' \neq 0$, however the second mode has much higher amplitude, for $n' = 1$, at high reduced frequencies. This amplification indicates that the gust spanwise mode energizes the corresponding spanwise acoustic mode, and for $n' = 1$, this coincides with the second mode.

Conclusion

A model is developed for the interaction of incident vortical waves with an annular cascade with

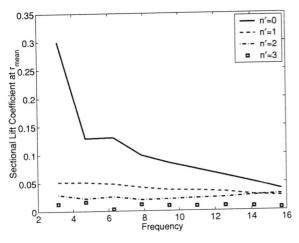

Fig. 20   Comparison of unsteady lift for different n'

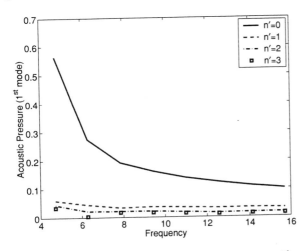

Fig. 21   Comparison of downstream propagating sound intensity for different n'

mean swirling flow. The model uses the high frequency approximation to define the incident gust as it evolves in a swirling flow. Exact non-reflecting inflow/outflow conditions are applied at the inlet and exit boundaries, respectively. Numerical results show no reflection of the acoustic modes at the inflow/outflow, indicating that the boundary conditions are fully transparent to any outgoing acoustic waves.

The numerical scheme is efficient for problems with high reduced frequency, and the computational efficiency depends solely on the efficiency of the algebraic solver for the wave equation.

Little or no dispersion is encountered at the blade leading edge, even though, a singularity exits. Comparison with the linear strip theory (narrow annulus

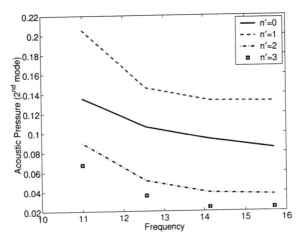

Fig. 22   Comparison of downstream propagating sound intensity for different n'

limit) for the unsteady lift distribution and acoustic pressure is excellent.

The coupling between the vortical and pressure modes is weak, and becomes weaker as the reduced frequency increases. This is seen from the computations, that indicate that less coupling iterations are needed between the wave equation and the vorticity evolution equations.

Comparison of results with strip theory indicates that the full three-dimensional calculations are essential for predicting both the correct unsteady blade loading and the number of propagating acoustic modes. Strip theory can be used only for low frequencies, and for small tip to hub ratios.

Since the blades considered in the present analysis have zero loading, the stagger angle is equal to the meanflow swirl angle. The results indicate that the swirl angle has a significant effect on the unsteady blade loading and the number and intensity of the propagating modes. The variation of the swirl angle along the span is identical here to the blade twist. For high frequency modes, the intensity of the acoustic modes strongly increases with the twist.

Spanwise modulation of the incident disturbances (higher radial mode number n') greatly reduce the unsteady blade lift and the acoustic sound propagation. This may be enhanced in practice by lean and sweep, to increase the number of wake cross-overs along the span. However, higher order propagating acoustic modes may become more dominant. This is a high frequency effects that needs careful examination.

Improving the solver characteristics for the wave equation will guarantee an efficient technique for calculating both broadband and tonal response for the gust interaction problem.

Acknowledgment

This research is partially supported by the Office of Naval Research Grant No. N00014-00-1-0130 and monitored by Dr.L.Patrick Purtell. B. Elhadidi would like to thank the Notre Dame Center of Applied Mathematics for its support. H.M.Atassi would like to thank the Ohio Aerospace Institute Aeroacoustics Consortium for its support.

References

[1] Atassi, H.M., *Unsteady Aerodynamics and Vortical Flows: Early and Recent Developments*, Aerodynamics and Aeroacoustics, Editor K.Y.Fung, Chapter 4, World Scientific, p. 121-171, 1994.

[2] Smith, S.N., *Discrete Frequency Sound Generation in Axial Flow Machines*, Aeronautical Council *R&M* 3709, 1973.

[3] Atassi, H. and Hammad, G., *Sound Generated in a Cascade by Three-Dimensional Disturbances convected in a Subsonic Flow*, 7th AIAA Aeroacoustics conference, AIAA-81-2046, 1981.

[4] Peake, N., *The Interaction Between a High Frequency Gust and a Blade Row*, Journal of Fluid Mechanics, Vol. 241, p.261-289, 1993.

[5] Glegg, S., *The Response of a swept Blade Row To a Three-Dimensional Gust*, Journal of Sound and Vibration, Vol. 227, p.29-64, 1999.

[6] Fang, J., and Atassi, H., *Compressible Flows with Vortical Disturbances Around a Cascade of Loaded Airfoils*, Proceedings of the 6th International Symposium on Unsteady Aerodynamics, Aeroacoustics and Aeroelasticity of Turbomachines and Propellers, September 15-19, 1991.

[7] Verdon, J.M., and Hall, K.C., *Development of a Linearized Aerodynamic Analysis for Cascade Gust Response Predictions*, NASA Contractor Report 4308, July 1990.

[8] Namba, M. and Schulten J., *Numerical Results of Lifting Surface Theory, Category 4 Benchmark Problem* 3rd *CAA Workshop*, NLR-TP-2000-013, 31st January 2000.

[9] Montgomery, M.D. and Verdon, J.M., *A Three-Dimensional Linearized Unsteady Euler Analysis for Turbomachinery Blade Rows*, NASA CR-4770, 1997.

[10] Wilson, A.G., *Application of CFD to Wake/Aerofoil Interaction Noise-A Flat Plate Validation Case*, 7th AIAA/CEAS Aeroacoustics Conference, AIAA2001-2135, May 2001, Netherlands.

[11] Atassi, O., *Inflow/Outflow Conditions for Time Harmonic Internal Aeroacoustic Problems*, AIAA 99-0482, 37th AIAA Aerospace Sciences Meeting and Exhibit, Jan.11-14, Reno, NV, 1999.

[12] Golubev, V. and Atassi, H., *Interaction of Unsteady Swirling Flows with Annular Cascades. Part II. Aerodynamic Blade Response*, AIAA Journal, Vol. 38, No. 7, p.1150-1158, July 2000.

[13] Ali, A., Atassi, O. and Atassi, H., *Derivation and Implementation of Inflow/Outflow Conditions for Aeroacoustic Problems with Swirling Flows*, To appear in 7th AIAA/CEAS Aeroacoustics Conference, Amsterdam.

[14] Goldstein, M.E., *Aeroacoustics*, McGraw-Hill International Book Company, 1976.

[15] Golubev, V. and Atassi, H., *Acoustic-Vorticity Waves in Swirling Flows*, Journal of Sound and Vibration, Vol. 209, p.203-222, 1998.

[16] Ali, A., Atassi, H., Atassi, O., *Acoustic Eigenmodes in a Coannular Duct with a General Swirling Flow*, 6th AIAA/CEAS Aeroacoustics Conference and Exhibit, AIAA 2000-1954.

[17] Balay, S., Gropp, W., McInnes, L., Barry, S., *PETSc Users Manual*, ANL-95/11-Revision 2.1.0, Argonne National Laboratory, 2000.

[18] Third Computational Aeroacoustics (CAA) workshop on Benchmark Problems. NASA/CP-2000-209790. June 2000.

[19] Elhadidi, B, and Atassi, H. *Sound Generation and Scattering from Radial Vanes in Uniform Flow*, Seventh International Conference of Fluid Dynamics and Propulsion, Sharm El-Sheikh, 19-21 December 2001.

[20] Majumdar, S.J, and Peake, N. *Three-Dimensional Effects in Cascade-Gust Interaction*, Wave Motion, Vol.23, p. 321-337, 1996.

BUZZ-SAW NOISE SPECTRA AND DIRECTIVITY
FROM FLYOVER TESTS

H.A. Siller * and U. Michel [†]

German Aerospace Center (DLR), Institute of Propulsion Technology
Müller-Breslau-Str. 8, 10623 Berlin, Germany

A fly-over noise test with an Airbus A319 was conducted jointly by DLR and Lufthansa with support from Airbus and Snecma. The signals of a large array of 238 electret microphones were recorded. In a first test, the noise emission of each engine was studied by running the other engine with flight-idle power. De-dopplerised narrow-band frequency spectra averaged over a large number of microphones were used. Alternatively, the noise emission from the inlet of each engine was evaluated with both engines at take-off power with the aid of a phased microphone array focused on each moving engine inlet. The results show as expected that buzz-saw noise is mainly radiated in the forward arc. The peaks at multiples of the shaft frequency can easily be identified in the de-dopplerised narrow-band spectra. The directivity of a number of frequency components is evaluated. The characteristics of buzz-saw noise are seen to vary between individual engines and even, for the same engine, between different fly-overs. The resulting directivities also indicate that mode scattering has a large influence on the radiated buzz-saw noise field.

Introduction

The present paper is a by-product of a flight-test that was jointly carried out by DLR and Lufthansa with support of Airbus and Snecma. The test flights with an Airbus A319 were performed on October 9th and 10th 2001. The Airbus A319 is equipped with CFM56-5A5 engines which are a low-thrust version in the CFM56-5A family with a bypass ratio of 6.2 and a dual stream nozzle. The experiment was aimed at testing the effects of modifications to the airframe and to one of the engines on the noise emission of the aircraft. The modifications of the engine consisted of taping the casing liner immediately in front of the rotor, a proposal by Snecma, and of replacing the core nozzle by a serrated nozzle designed by DLR and manufactured by Lufthansa Technik. Another objective was to acquire noise data for the validation of semi-empirical prediction schemes for airframe noise sources, for which first results are reported by Pott-Pollenske et al.[1] The influence of the engine modifications on the noise emission will be reported later.

Apart from these intentions, the resulting data showed interesting results with respect to buzz-saw noise, an aeroacoustic problem of practically all modern aero-engines with high bypass ratios.

The test set-up on the ground included a large phased array of microphones consisting of 238 relatively cheap electret microphones for the localisation of the noise sources on the flying aircraft. These microphones were also used to determine the de-dopplerised narrow-band frequency spectra for a range of emission angles. These spectra revealed

*henri.siller@dlr.de, phone : +49 30 310006-57, fax : -39
[†]ulf.michel@dlr.de, phone : +49 30 310006-26, fax : -39

Fig. 1   Microphone array installed on the test site

the large contribution of buzz-saw noise in the forward arc (i.e. for emission angles $\theta < 90°$).

"Buzz" consists of tones at multiples of the shaft frequency f_s of the fan. Origins of these tones are a series of nonuniform shock waves and expansion fans that develop upstream of the fan rotor whenever the relative rotor tip Mach number is larger than one.

The mechanism of buzz-saw noise was first investigated and reported in the 1970s. A recent comprehensive description can be found in McAlpine & Fisher[2] together with a new numerical prediction method. The problem is studied there with the assumption of a uniform flow in a hard-walled circular cylindrical duct. Under these conditions, the pressure field in front of the rotor is stationary in the rotor frame of reference and can be decomposed into azimuthal Fourier components of order m which rotate together with the rotor. As a result, each component will

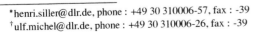

radiate sound from the inlet with a frequency of $f_m = m \, f_s$ if the component can propagate in the duct.

Aero-engines are fitted with liners. The influence of lining was studied by McAlpine & Fisher.[3] Since the effectiveness of lining depends primarily on frequency and flow speed, certain buzz-saw noise components are more attenuated than others, a result that is shown to depend on the flow speed in the inlet.[3]

The situation in aero-engines differs from the assumptions made by McAlpine & Fisher.[2,3] The first difference is the presence of liner splices which permits the manufacture and installation of the liner in sections. The consequence of these splices is that the rotating pressure field in the inlet is no longer stationary in the rotor frame of reference. The acoustic influence can be determined with the theory of Tyler & Sofrin[4] and yields scattered modes. As a result the buzz component emitted at a frequency of $f_m = m \, f_s$ will contain duct modes of many orders $m + ks$, where s is the number of (assumed to be uniformly spaced) splices and $k = \ldots, -1, 0, 1, \ldots$ is an integer.

The situation in an aero-engine in flight is further complicated by the nonuniform flow in the inlet due to the flow angle between the engine axis and the flight stream and/or the inlet droop. In this case the shock system in front of the rotor blades is modulated during each rotation. The result is an increase of buzz-saw noise which can be noticed by passengers in the front rows of an aircraft when the aircraft rotates at the end of the take-off run. This increase is caused by additional modes of order $m + l$ for each frequency $f_m = m \, f_s$, where $l = \ldots, -1, 0, 1, \ldots$.

Any experimental investigation of buzz-saw noise requires a narrow-band analysis with a band-width equal to a small fraction of the shaft rotation frequency. This can be performed quite easily on a static test bed with a fan model or a real aero-engine. The effects of fan speed, blade geometry, inlet acoustic liner design, etc., can be studied.

However, the effect of inlet flow angle and the influence of flight speed can not easily be tested on static test beds and requires fly-over tests for its investigation. The situation is much more difficult in the fly-over case because the frequencies observed on the ground are Doppler-shifted and change considerably during a fly-over. A de-dopplerisation of the microphone data has to be performed which requires a precise knowledge of the aircrafts position as a function of time.

No studies with de-dopplerised narrow-band spectra of buzz-saw noise in flight are known to the authors. It is shown in this report how this can be done. The experimental set-up and the data processing are described first followed by a presentation of some experimental results.

Experimental set-up

New 256 channel data-acquisition hardware developed at DLR was used for the first time in this measurement campaign. It features analogue-to-digital converters with a resolution of 24 bits and a measured signal-to-noise ratio of 108 dB, making the self-noise of the microphone capsules the limiting factor. The analogue signal cable length is minimised by positioning the analogue-to-digital converters close to the microphones, while the long cables connecting the array microphones to the data acquisition computer carry only digital signals. The large dynamic range makes it unnecessary to use microphone amplifiers. This and the digital transmission of the signals reduces signal distortion, system costs, and complexity. The computer stores the data into memory and subsequently writes it to hard disk. Currently, the maximum sampling rate is 78 kHz, independent of the number of up to 256 channels used, and the recording time is only limited by the memory size of the computer.

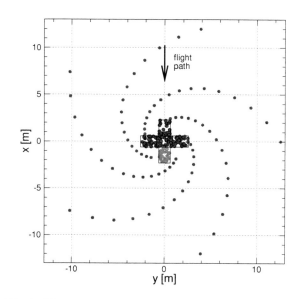

Fig. 2 Microphone array with 78 microphones in spiral arms and 160 microphones in 5 plates

The microphones used were Sennheiser KE4 electret capsules. They were arranged into a large microphone array with a diameter of 25 meters (see figure 2) consisting of two sub-arrays of different shapes. A large array consisted of 78 microphones located on 5 logarithmic spirals. 5 microphones were located on a circle. The diameters of the circles decreased with a factor $10^{-1/20} = 0.891$. It is possible to keep the beam-width for one-third-octave bands constant by reducing the array size by two radial steps with a resulting diameter ratio of 0.794 for neighbouring frequency bands. The beam-width can also be adjusted for different fly-over altitudes in steps of 11% by changing the diameter of the largest circle used. (See discussion on beam pattern in Piet et al.[5])

The microphones were mounted with grazing incidence on 1 m by 2 m moisture resistant wooden plates laid out on the grass of the test site as shown in figure 1. The microphones were connected to cabinets containing 32 analogue-to-digital converters. The positions of the cabinets were chosen such that the cables carrying analogue signals were as short as possible. All 32 digitised microphone signals are transmitted to the computer via a single CAT 5 shielded twisted pair computer network cable.

A second array with 160 microphones consisting of five pre-fabricated plates was placed in the centre of the spiral. The latter array was designed and built for an investigation of the noise from the wake vortices of aircraft. The plates were equipped with 32 flush mounted microphones each and had built-in analogue-to-digital converters. A cover of acoustic foam reduced the influence of wind noise.

The aircraft altitude, airspeed, engine data, GPS position, aircraft cockpit time, and computed wind vector were recorded in steps of one second using an on-board system. The GPS (not DGPS) position was recorded with an uncertainty of one half of a second. Therefore, the position information as a function of time of the aircraft could only be used as a hint for the data reduction. Additional ground based equipment was used for more precise estimates. The aircraft ground speed was determined by two line cameras positioned before and after the array on the flight path with a known distance. The altitude of the fly-over was determined by an array of three laser distance meters separated by 15 m perpendicular to the flight path. These distance meters scanned for a target with a frequency of 500 Hz and created a trigger signal when they acquired a target during a fly-over. The analogue signals of the line cameras and the trigger pulses of the distance meters were recorded together with the microphone signals. In addition, colleagues from DLR Braunschweig (Institute of Aerodynamics and Fluid Technology) determined the fly-over altitude with a photographic method.[1]

Data processing

The original data, sampled at 38095 Hz, are first re-sampled with a multiple of the engine's shaft frequency f_s,

$$f_{res} = f_s \frac{2048}{6}$$

for the position of a moving engine inlet on the aircraft. See Piet et al.[5] for details of the de-dopplerisation procedure. This ensures that buzz related peaks appear at integer multiples of the shaft frequency at every 6th line in the discrete frequency spectrum.

A time series of 12288 samples is then used for the further frequency analysis using a Fast Fourier Transform for 11 time segments with 2048 samples with an overlap of 0.5, windowed with a Hanning function. The length of the time series corresponds to an averaging time of 0.3 s. For a typical fly-over with a ground speed of 80 m/s and an altitude of 200 m, the aircraft moved about 25 m in 0.3 s. The greatest change of the emission angle during this length of time is $\Delta\theta = \pm 3.7°$; it occurs when the aircraft is directly over the array at $\theta = 90°$.

The data are processed using two different methods:

- **De-dopplerised frequency spectra** require the computation of the power-spectral density of an unspecified number of de-dopplerised microphone signals followed by an averaging over these microphones.

- **Focused frequency spectra** require a beam-forming algorithm consisting of an averaging in the time domain of the de-dopplerised time series of the microphones in a phased array and subsequent computation of the power-spectral density of the resulting averaged time series.

The 160 microphone signals from the five plates were used for the computation of de-dopplerised frequency spectra because the signals were free of wind noise.

The 78 microphone spiral-arm array was used for the calculation of focused frequency spectra using a delay-and-sum beam-forming approach.[6] The array processing procedure for moving sources with application to aircraft fly-over measurements and its limitations are described in detail by Piet et al.[5]

In order to achieve optimal de-dopplerisation, the DLR data-reduction software had to be extended to include the influence of the average wind vector.

Experimental results

Directivity of buzz-saw noise

In order to investigate the sound characteristics of both engines individually, fly-overs were performed with one engine running at 93 % NLC and the other in flight idle. For one of these flights, figure 3 shows the evolution of the narrow-band spectra of the unmodified engine as a function of the emission angle θ. Ten instances of the sound-pressure level for emission angles $45° \leq \theta \leq 90°$ rel. to the flight direction are shown in one plot offset relative to each other by 10 dB, starting from the spectrum for $\theta = 90°$ at the bottom. Data that would allow for the study of smaller emission angles was not acquired. The frequency axis is scaled with the engine shaft frequency so that the peaks in the spectra can be associated with the engine order. The

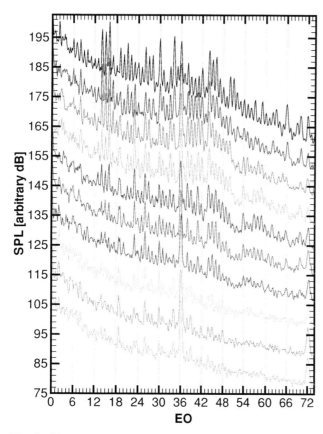

Fig. 3 Flyover with the unmodified engine at 93 % NLC and the modified in flight idle; de-dopplerised narrow band spectra for increments of $\Delta\theta = 5°$ shifted by 10 dB each from bottom ($\theta = 90°$) to top ($\theta = 45°$). SPL is defined with the same arbitrary reference in all figures.

blade-passing frequency is at EO = 36, its first harmonic at EO = 72, and buzz tones show at integer multiples of the engine order. The sound pressure levels are normalised to a distance of one meter.

However, the de-dopplerised spectra are affected by all noise sources of the aircraft. Peaks that do not scale with the engine order are not buzz-related, e.g. the peak at EO ≈ 18.5 that first appears at $\theta = 70°$, until it stands out alone at $\theta = 90°$. A map of the sound sources obtained from focusing the spiral array on the aircraft shows that this peak results from the inlet of the right engine that is running in flight-idle (see figure 4).

Figure 3 shows that buzz-saw noise is mainly radiated in the forward arc. The intensity of buzz-saw noise decreases from $\theta = 45°$, the smallest values of θ that could be evaluated, until $\theta = 80°$, where most buzz-related peaks have decayed considerably.

The directivity of the radiated noise is different for the buzz related peaks (at multiples of rotor shaft frequency) and for the blade passing frequency and its harmonics. Figure 5 shows that the maximum at the blade passing fre-

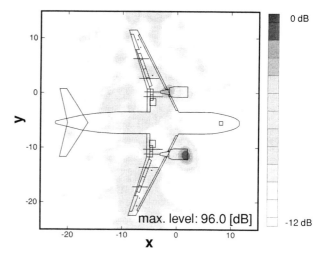

Fig. 4 Sound source map of the narrow band around 1365 Hz (EO=18.5) for $\theta = 85°$; left (upper) engine: 93 % NLC, right (lower) engine in flight idle

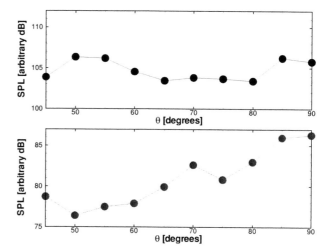

Fig. 5 Directivity of BPF and 2 BPF for the data shown in figure 3

quency (EO = 36) occurs at $\theta = 85°$, with another weaker local maximum at $\theta = 50°$. The strong appearance of the blade passing frequency in the far field cannot be explained as a buzz-saw noise component but indicates strong interaction noise between the non-uniform flow field in the inlet and the rotor. The rotor-stator interaction noise of this engine is cut off at the blade passing frequency . The first harmonic of the blade passing frequency has a maximum at $\theta = 90°$ (see figure 5).

The Doppler-amplification in the forward arc is not removed in any of the figures. A proper correction would reduce the levels in the forward arc. Also, no correction due to attenuation in the atmosphere was applied. This would increase the levels in the forward arc, especially at higher frequencies.

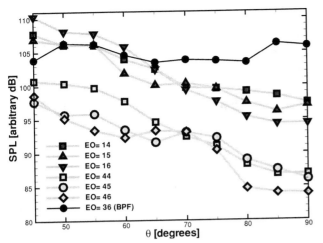

Fig. 6 Directivity of EO peaks 14 to 16 and 44 to 46 for the data shown in figure 3

The strongest buzz-saw noise peaks in figure 3 occur at engine orders 14, 15, and 16. Above the blade passing frequency, there is another group of three neighbouring strong peaks at engine orders 44 to 46. Figure 6 shows the directivity of these peaks in comparison with the blade-passing frequency. At $\theta = 45°$, the peaks at engine orders 14-16 have higher levels than the blade passing frequency. These buzz related peaks show a strong decrease between $45° \leq \theta \leq 70°$, followed by a weaker decrease up to 90°. Smaller angles than $\theta = 45°$ could not be analysed due to the late start of recording.

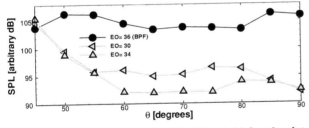

Fig. 7 Directivity of peaks for EO 30 and 34 for the data shown in figure 3

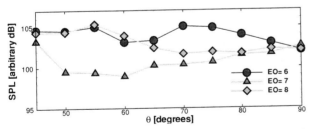

Fig. 8 Directivity of EO 6 and 8 peaks for the data shown in figure 3

The peaks at engine orders 30 and 34 (see figure 7) show a different behaviour: while they show higher levels than the blade passing frequency at $\theta = 45°$, they decrease rapidly by 10 dB between $\theta = 45°$ and $\theta = 55°$.

The directivities are more uniform for engine orders between 6 and 8 as shown in figure 8.

Influence of mode scattering

According to the theory for uniform mean flow and uniform acoustic wall impedance, one would expect that each buzz component would have a distinctive peak in the directivity at a certain emission angle. The peak angle of a radial duct mode would be expected close to the phase-normal angle of the propagating wave. The first few engine orders are cut-off according to this theory. The lowest cut-on mode for a hard-walled circular cylindrical duct should peak close to $\theta = 90°$ and this peak should move to smaller angles for increasing frequencies.

In contrast to this theory, the measured directivities generally show a smooth variation with emission angle which can only be explained if the radiation for each engine order consists of several azimuthal modes. This is most likely related to the scattering of buzz-saw noise in the engine inlet by the liner splices and the non-uniform inflow as described in the introduction. In this case, the casing liner immediately in front of the fan rotor consists of 6 pieces with 6 wide splices, while the inlet liner has 3 splices.

Comparison of different fly-overs

During the measurement campaign, four fly-overs were performed with only the left (unmodified) engine providing thrust and the right (modified) engine running in flight-idle. Table 1 lists parameters for these fly-overs and shows that the fly-overs were performed at reasonably comparable conditions. Fly-overs L-1 to L-3 were flown consecutively, while L-4 was performed after the aircraft had landed and taken off again providing the chance of different blade stagger angles.

fly-over	ground speed	alti-tude	glide angle	pitch	N1	acceleration
	[m/s]	[m]	[deg]	[deg]	[Hz]	[m/s²]
L-1	88.9	203	0	3	73.6	0.6
L-2	94.3	204	0	3	73.6	0.4
L-3	92.4	204	0	3	73.6	0.7
L-4	93.2	206	0	3	74.0	0.5

Table 1 Overview of single-engine flights (fan spool of left engine running at $N_1 = 93\%$ NLC, right engine in flight idle)

Corresponding measurements were also made with the modified right engine and will be reported in a forthcoming paper.

Figure 9 shows the power-spectral density at an emission angle of $\theta = 50°$ for the fly-overs listed in table 1. Although there is some variation between different fly-overs, the over-all sound characteristic of the engine remains fairly similar.

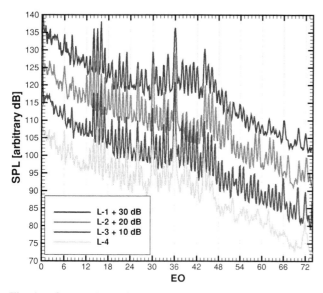

Fig. 9   Comparison of spectra at $\theta = 50°$ for single-engine fly-overs listed in table 1; the spectra are offset by 10 dB each

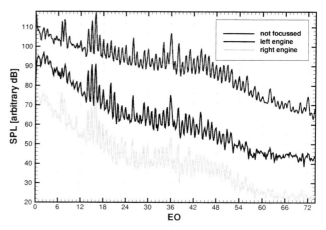

Fig. 10   Comparison of averaged de-dopplerised spectrum (top) with spectra from the spiral array focused on the left and right (bottom) engine inlets; take-off at 88% NLC; $\theta = 55°$; the spectra are offset by 10 dB each

Comparison of the two engines

The modifications to the airframe and engine were removed for testing the standard aircraft on the second day of the campaign. The single engine fly-overs were not repeated, assuming that the engines were identical.

The test method used for the single-engine fly-overs could not be used for a comparison of individual engine characteristics since the spectra would contain noise contributions from both engines. The two engines had to be compared in the take-off configuration with both engines running at a speed of 88% NLC. The fly-over altitude was $h = 362$ m compared to only $h = 203$ m for the single engine tests. In order to separate the noise contribution of the two engines, the phased array was focused on the two engine inlets. Narrow-band spectra were computed from the focused signals.

Figure 10 shows a comparison of the spectra from the two engine inlets together with the unfocused de-dopplerised spectrum obtained from the 160 microphones in the central plates of the array. The angle of $\theta = 55°$ was the smallest emission angle that could be evaluated for the fly-overs in take-off configuration. The distributions of the buzz peaks and their strengths differ for both engines, however not more than between individual flights with the same engine. The peaks near engine orders 7 and 8 are caused by tones generated at cavities underneath both wings. Because of the relatively low frequencies ($f \approx 516$ Hz and 580 Hz) and great height of the fly-over, these tones are not well suppressed by the phased array.

The spectra in figure 10 cannot be compared with those in the previous figures because the engines were run at different speed and the focusing results in a more rapid decrease of the levels with increasing frequencies.

Contribution of buzz tones to the total noise level

The contribution of buzz-saw noise to the total noise level shall be estimated now by comparing the A-weighted sound-pressure level of the original spectra with the spectra obtained by reducing the sound-pressure levels of the buzz peaks to the lower limit in the adjacent frequency bands. Figure 11 shows the result of such a calculation for an emission angle of $\theta = 45°$, where the buzz-saw noise has its maximum. If buzz-saw noise could be removed completely, the sound pressure level would be reduced by 4.4 dB(A) at this angle. However, the sound reduction potential in terms of EPNdB is much lower since buzz-saw noise occurs only in the forward arc and jet noise still dominates in the rear arc.

Conclusions

It can be concluded that fly-over noise tests are feasible for the investigation of buzz-saw noise. The influence of acoustic liner improvements or of any other changes to the engine inlet on buzz-saw noise can be tested in flight. A successful data reduction is only possible with a perfect de-dopplerisation of the microphone data and this requires an exact knowledge of the locations of the engine inlets as a function of time. The wind vector has to be considered in the de-dopplerisation process, although it suffices to use a constant wind vector for the whole distance between aircraft and microphones.

The results presented in this paper verify the observation that aero-engines in flight radiate buzz-saw noise mainly in the forward arc. The directivity of each radiated buzz

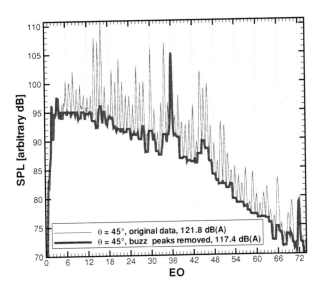

Fig. 11 Original spectrum and lower limit of a hypothetical buzz-free spectrum for θ = 45°

component can be investigated separately. The levels of most buzz components decrease rapidly between θ = 45° and θ = 70°. The directivity patterns of individual buzz tones change with frequency. They do not feature narrow peaks for a certain angle, a result that indicates that the radiated buzz-saw noise components are not dominated by a single mode, but are the result of an acoustic scattering by the splices in the acoustic liners and the non-uniform mean flow in the inlet.

The test procedure described in this report would be capable of studying the effect of a splice-less liner on the radiation pattern of each buzz component.

The contribution of the buzz tones to the total noise level can be estimated by reducing the levels of the buzz tones in the narrow-band spectra to the level of adjacent broadband level. This procedure shows that engine noise would be reduced by up to 4.4 dB(A) if buzz-saw noise could be eliminated. However, this reduction would only be achieved near the peak radiation angle of buzz-saw noise which is located at 45 degrees relative to the flight direction or smaller angles.

Acknowledgments

The tests were initiated by Dr. Frank Walle of Lufthansa and Prof. Heinrich Weyer of DLR in an effort to identify the noise reduction potential of the A319/A320/A321 fleet through retro-fits and to support the aircraft noise research at DLR. DLR and Snecma proposed the modifications which were designed with support and approval of Airbus. Lufthansa Technik manufactured and installed the devices and prepared the paperwork for approval by the German Federal Aviation Authority (Luftfahrt-Bundesamt) for measuring flights.

The efforts and motivation of all participants are appreciated who made it possible to carry out the flights only four months after the decision was made. Out of the many participants, Dr. Gerd Saueressig and Dr. Andreas Waibel of Lufthansa shall be mentioned as they had the immense task of organising the test campaign. The aircraft was flown with remarkable precision by the management pilots Raimund Müller, Jürgen Schadt, and Siegfried Wegeleben after practicing the procedures in a flight simulator.

The efforts of Airbus and Snecma in supporting the tests are also very much appreciated. The valuable discussions with Hervé Batard of Airbus concerning the scattering of buzz tones in the inlet are acknowledged.

It may be mentioned that the test was performed one month after the attacks of September 11, 2001 in spite of the dramatic financial situation of the airline industry. This shows how important noise reduction efforts are considered by Lufthansa.

References

[1]Pott-Pollenske, M., Dobrzynski, W., Buchholz, H., Gehlhar, B., and Walle, F., "Validation of a Semi-Empirical Airframe Noise Prediction Method Through Dedicated A319 Flyover Noise Measurements," AIAA Paper 2002-2470, 2002, 8th AIAA/CEAS Aeroacoustics Conference, Breckenridge, Co, June 17-19, 2002.

[2]McAlpine, A. and Fisher, M. J., "On the prediction of "buzz-saw" noise in aero-engine inlet ducts," J. Sound Vib., Vol. 248, No. 1, 2001, pp. 123–149.

[3]McAlpine, A. and Fisher, M. J., "The effect of acoustic lining on "buzz-saw" noise generated by an aero-engine," AIAA/CEAS Paper 2001-2201, 2001, 7th AIAA/CEAS Aeroacoustics Conference, Maastricht, Netherlands, May 28-30, 2001.

[4]Tyler, J. M. and Sofrin, T. G., "Axial Flow Compressor Noise Studies," Transactions of the Society of Automotive Engineers, Vol. 70, 1962, pp. 309–332.

[5]Piet, J.-F., Michel, U., and Böhning, P., "Localization of the Acoustic Sources of the A340 with a Large Phased Microphone Array During Flight Tests," AIAA Paper 2002-2506, 2002, 8th AIAA/CEAS Aeroacoustics Conference, Breckenridge, Co, June 17-19, 2002.

[6]Johnson, D. H. and Dudgeon, D. E., Array Signal Processing, Concepts and Techniques, P T R Prentice Hall, Englewood Cliffs, 1993.

INLET MODE MEASUREMENTS WITH AN INFLOW CONTROL DEVICE MICROPHONE ARRAY

Justin H. Lan[*], John W. Premo[†]
The Boeing Company
Seattle, WA 98124

Daniel L. Sutliff[‡]
SEST, Inc.
Cleveland, OH 44135

Abstract

A unique application for phased arrays is the Inflow Control Device microphone array for determining engine inlet propagating mode distributions. The proof-of-concept test was performed on the NASA Glenn 48" Active Noise Control Fan, since the modal distribution of the fan tone harmonics could be accurately measured by the rotating rake system. An array of 40 microphones was installed on the NASA Glenn Inflow Control Device. An acoustic duct propagation code, CDUCT, was used to generate the steering vector predictions, which are required for classical phased array beamforming. The steering vectors consist of the CDUCT predicted complex acoustic pressure at the microphone locations for each propagating mode. The phase-accurate microphone data is then projected in the steering vector directions in order to determine the modal distribution. The dominant circumferential modes indicated by the ICD array match those from the rotating rake. The current ICD array has more difficulty in accurately determining the radial mode distribution. The signal-to-noise also decreases in the presence of more than one dominant mode. The CDUCT calculated steering vectors are accurate for well cut-on modes. However, errors are larger for modes closer to cut-off, which can adversely affect the signal-to-noise capabilities of the ICD array. This increase in errors is consistent with the small-angle parabolic approximation used in CDUCT. It is noted that examining microphone contour plots on the ICD can provide quick and useful information about the modal distribution of the inlet noise.

[*] Research Engineer, Acoustics and Fluid Mechanics, AIAA Senior Member
[†] Research Engineer, Acoustics and Fluid Mechanics, AIAA Member
[‡] Senior Aeroacoustics Researcher, AIAA Senior Member

Nomenclature

C	steering vector matrix
C^t	complex conjugate transpose of C
m	circumferential mode number
M	number of cut-on modes
n	radial mode number
N	number of ICD microphones
PWL	mode power level, dB
PWL_{int}	power level for interaction modes, dB
PWL_{tot}	total mode power level, dB
$\bar{s}$	source mode pressure level vector, dB
$\bar{u}$	ICD microphone data vector, Pa

Introduction

Currently, there is a need to reduce engine inlet radiated noise from modern transport aircraft. This can be accomplished by reducing the noise at its source in the engine, designing more efficient passive acoustic lining systems, or possibly active noise control. Characterizing the modal content of the inlet noise can be a very important step to meeting these goals. The modal content can be used to determine the source of noise, which then provides a design guideline for reducing the noise. The modal content can also be used to validate noise source predictions and noise propagation methods, which could lead to the design of better lining systems. Furthermore, the noise source characteristics are often required for active noise control methods.

There are several different methods for inlet mode measurements including: wall-mounted transducer arrays[1,2], rotating rake[3], or an external axially traversing and rotating hoop system[4]. This paper describes a unique inlet mode measurement system that utilizes an inflow control device (ICD) structure as a transducer-mounting platform. This novel array is briefly described in References [5] and [6], and is further analyzed in this paper. An ICD is an acoustically transparent spherical-like structure that is placed in front of an engine inlet or model fan rig during static noise testing. Its purpose is to prevent the ingestion of large-scale turbulence and ground vortices that could interact with the fan and produce extraneous noise. An array of transducers is distributed along the ICD surface, and the transducer data is beamformed to produce the modal distribution of the inlet-radiated noise. The ICD array has several advantages in that it is generally less intrusive than other techniques, it is easier to implement in large full-scale engine tests, it can be permanently installed on an ICD to provide modal information for a variety of engines and inlet configurations, and it can potentially provide circumferential and radial information for tones and broadband noise. One disadvantage in the ICD phased array processing is the requirement for the computation of a large number of steering vectors[5]. These steering vectors describe an inlet mode pattern as measured at the ICD transducer locations and must be calculated for all propagating modes. The proof-of-concept test was performed at the NASA Glenn Active Noise Control Fan facility since a rotating rake mode measurement system was available for comparison. The main objective of this paper is to describe the test, and discuss the evaluation of the ICD array concept. The use of the duct propagation code, CDUCT[6], for the steering vector predictions will also be evaluated.

Experimental Apparatus

Active Noise Control Fan

The proof-of-concept test was performed on the NASA Glenn 48" Active Noise Control Fan[7] (ANCF) shown in Figure 1. The ANCF is a ducted fan used to test noise reduction concepts and for aeroacoustic code verification. The four foot diameter fan produces a tip speed of ~425 ft/sec at 1800 rpm resulting in a Blade Passing Frequency (BPF) of approximately 500 Hz. An Inflow Control Device (ICD) is used to reduce the ingested turbulence that could interact with the rotor and produce extraneous noise. A 16-bladed rotor in combination with a variable stator vane count and spacing produces the desired rotor-stator interaction modal content. Thirty stator vanes at one-chord spacing were used for the ICD array test. In addition, 10 or 15 ¼-inch diameter rods were placed in front of the rotor to produce additional modes. These combinations were chosen to provide a variety of modal structures to verify the ICD array technique. The expected interaction modes and their cut-on corrected rpm (rpmc) are shown in Table I. A mode is shown as

an ordered (m,n) pair where m represents the circumferential mode number and n represents the radial mode number.

TABLE I Modal Structure with 30 Stator Vanes and:

(a) 10 rods

BPF		2BPF	
mode	rpmc	mode	rpmc
(-4,0)	1773	(2,0)	509
		(2,1)	1118
		(2,2)	1662
		(2,3)	2195
		(-8,0)	1608

(b) 15 rods

BPF		2BPF	
mode	rpmc	mode	rpmc
(1,0)	614	(2,0)	509
(1,1)	1777	(2,1)	1118
		(2,2)	1662
		(2,3)	2195

Rotating Rake

A schematic showing the location of the rotating rake on the ANCF is presented in Figure 2. The rotating rake instrumentation system provides a complete map of the duct modal signature at BPF and 2BPF for either the inlet or exhaust duct[3]. The circumferential modes arise from a Doppler induced frequency shift due to the unique and discrete rotation rate of each m-order[8]. Radial modes are computed from a least squares data fit of the radial pressure profile using the hardwall Bessel functions as the basis functions. Rotating rake data were acquired for the entire fan speed range tested.

The modal data from the rotating rake will be presented in 3-D format. The base plane axes are the circumferential and radial modes (m and n, respectively). The vertical value axis is the power level (PWL) in the (m,n) mode. The sum of all the radial power in a circumferential mode provides the total power in that circumferential mode. PWL_{int} is the sum of all cut-on rotor-stator interaction modes. The sum of all modes provides the PWL_{tot} in the harmonic presented. The typical 3-D chart provides information as to the dominant modes present; usually those due to the rotor-stator interaction.

ICD Array

An array of 40 electret-type cylindrical microphones was distributed on the ICD. The layout consisted of four rings with 10 non-uniformly spaced microphones in each ring. This distribution is presented in Table II and graphically shown in Figure 3. The locations of the microphones were determined with a tape measure.

TABLE II Microphone ICD Array Distribution

$\Phi =$

$\Theta=90°$	$\Theta=70°$	$\Theta=50°$	$\Theta=30°$
0°	0°	0°	0°
8°	16°	16°	16°
33°	33°	41°	49°
57°	65°	74°	82°
106°	115°	115°	123°
180°	180°	180°	180°
254°	245°	245°	237°
303°	295°	286°	278°
327°	327°	319°	311°
352°	344°	344°	344°

A classical beamforming technique described in Reference [5] is used to process the ICD array data to obtain estimates of the circumferential and radial mode content on the ICD. Since the primary focus of this test is BPF and 2BPF for a comparison to the rotating rake results, the microphone time histories were synchronously acquired using a 128 points per-revolution fan shaft encoder. This synchronized data allows the relative microphone phase information to be accurately captured. Each microphone time history is averaged over 512 revolutions in order to reduce the random component of the signal, and a discrete Fourier transform is applied to obtain the microphone complex pressure at BPF and 2BPF. A model for the microphone complex pressure can be written as

$$\bar{u} = C\bar{s} \tag{1}$$

where $\bar{u}$ is the data vector consisting of the microphone complex pressures at one frequency, C is a steering vector matrix, and $\bar{s}$ is a source mode pressure level vector. The length of $\bar{u}$ is equal to the number of microphones, N. The length of the source mode pressure level vector is equal to the number of cut-on modes, M, in the duct and consists of the duct mode amplitude and phase. The steering vector matrix has the dimensions of N by M. Each column in C is the complex pressure at the microphone locations resulting from a given duct mode. The values in C are predicted by propagating each cut-on duct mode from the inlet to the ICD microphone locations using the duct propagation code CDUCT.[6]

CDUCT solves the convected Helmholtz equation with a parabolic approximation that ignores back-reflected waves, and is solved with a fast marching technique. An example CDUCT solution is shown in Figure 4, which shows the real part of pressure for a (-4,0) mode at BPF at 2200 rpm in the inlet and near the ICD surface. It is noted that any acoustic duct propagation method could potentially be used to generate the steering vector matrix. The CDUCT code was used in this test primarily for validation purposes.

Both sides of Eqn. (1) are pre-multiplied by the complex conjugate transpose of C which results in

$$C'\bar{u} = C'C\bar{s} \tag{2}$$

If the array is designed properly, then $C'C$ will be nearly orthogonal. Each column in C can be normalized such that the diagonal term in $C'C$ will be 1 and $C'C$ will be approximately equal to the identity matrix. The simplest technique for obtaining the source mode pressure level vector, $\bar{s}$, is to assume that the normalized $C'C$ matrix is exactly the identity matrix, which results in

$$\bar{s} = C'\bar{u} \tag{3}$$

When the normalized C' is used, $\bar{s}$ represents the average pressure level for each source mode on the ICD. Eqn. (3) is essentially a dot product operator where the estimate of each mode pressure level is a result of the projection of the data, $\bar{u}$, into the direction of the steering vector (each column of C). Due to the approximate nature of the assumption that $C'C$ is exactly orthogonal, the mode estimates obtained through Eqn. (3) do not conserve the mode power. Energy in a single mode will spill-over into other modes, which is analogous to the existence of sidelobes in a typical phased array application. It is noted that a singular value decomposition method or least squares method could be used to solve Eqn. (2), however it is not done here.

A plot of the normalized $C'C$ matrix on a dB scale will give an indication of the signal-to-noise ratio capabilities of the array and how well the different modes can be distinguished from each other. Figure 5 shows the orthogonality plot for BPF at 2200 rpm. The displayed value in each square is taken from the lower left corner in this "corner" contour plot. At BPF, there are 11 cut-on circumferential modes at the first radial and 3 cut-on circumferential modes at the second radial, which correspond to index numbers 1 through 11 and 12 through 14, respectively. In general, the signal-to-noise ratio is 8dB or greater except at the zeroth order circumferential mode where it becomes 6dB between the different radials. Figure 6 shows the orthogonality plot for 2BPF at 2200 rpm. At 2BPF, there are 23, 15, 9, and 5 cut-on circumferential modes at the first, second, third, and fourth radials, respectively. In general, the signal-to-noise ratio is 7dB or greater except at the zeroth order circumferential mode where it becomes 3 to 6dB between the radials.

Rotating Rake Results

The complete modal map for BPF & 2BPF at 2200 rpmc is shown on Figure 7a (10 rods) and 7b (15 rods). The interaction modes (shaded) are clearly dominant at 20-40 dB above the non-interaction modes. Almost all of the power in the harmonic is due to the interaction mode. The interaction mode PWLs are 15-25 dB above the sum of all other modes. This type of modal purity allows for the ideal discrimination of the mode patterns on the ICD for this specific test.

ICD Array Results

The modal distribution obtained from the ICD array for BPF and 2BPF at 2200 rpmc is shown in Figures 8a,b and 9a,b for the 10 and 15-rod configurations, respectively. The total mode pressure level at a circumferential mode is the log-sum of all the radial mode pressure levels in that circumferential mode. The mode pressure levels in the dB scale are referenced to 2.0×10^{-5} Pa. The strongest modes match the expected interaction modes shown in Table I and measured by the rotating rake. For the 10-rod configuration at BPF, the signal-to-noise for the (-4,0) mode is 8dB, which is much less than that obtained from the rotating rake. The 8dB does match the expected signal-to-noise which is plotted in Figure 10 as one line from the BPF orthogonality plot (Figure 5) corresponding to the (-4,0) mode. For the 10-rod configuration at 2BPF, the signal-to-noise for the total mode pressure level at m=2 is 7dB. It is noted that the relative levels between the radial modes do not match those obtained by the rotating rake. Figure 11 shows the expected signal-to-noise of 7dB from the 2BPF orthogonality plot corresponding to the (2,0) mode. The highest peaks coincide with different radial modes at m=2 and indicate that the ICD array has more trouble separating the radial modes, which could explain the difference between the rotating rake and ICD array radial mode results. The CDUCT requirement of a fake extended centerbody (shown in Figure 4) in the calculation also affects the radial mode distribution. For the (-8,0) mode at 2BPF, the signal-to noise is only 1dB which does not match the expected signal-to-noise of 9dB shown in Figure 12. It is noted that the expected signal-to-noise only accounts for the presence of a single mode. The presence of more than one dominant mode could potentially decrease the signal-to-noise, since one mode could mask important microphone information that is needed to determine the strength of the other mode. Errors in the CDUCT steering vector predictions are known to increase for modes that are closer to cut-off since CDUCT employs a small-angle parabolic approximation[6]. This error could also explain the discrepancy between the predicted and measured

signal-to-noise at (-8,0) since the CDUCT predicted steering vector might not closely match the measured ICD microphone data for the (-8,0) mode. Signal-to-noise results from the 15-rod configuration are similar.

The measured ICD microphone data can be displayed as color contour plots in order to illustrate the appearance of different modes on the ICD. The number of lobes in the real part of pressure plot (either red or blue areas) gives an indication of the circumferential mode number content in the sound field. The direction of rotation of the circumferential mode can be determined by observing the direction of the tail of the pressure lobe pattern. From forward looking aft, if the tail of the pressure lobe pattern is pointing in the counter-clockwise direction, the mode is positive (rotating in the direction of the fan rotation). If the tail of the pressure lobe pattern points in the clockwise direction, the mode is negative (illustrated in the CDUCT predicted pressure plot in Figure 4). The SPL plot can indicate the presence of a single dominant circumferential mode if there is a circular band of high level in the plot. More than one strong circumferential mode will result in an interference pattern. Figure 13a,b show the ICD contour plots for the 10-rod configuration at BPF and 2BPF, respectively. Each grid intersection corresponds to a microphone data point and the color contours are interpolated in-between points. At BPF, the expected m=-4 can be observed, though the sparseness of the microphone array prevents a perfect match with the CDUCT predicted (-4,0) pattern (Figure 4). The circular band in the SPL plot indicates a single dominant circumferential mode. At 2BPF, the expected m=2 can be observed. The expected m=-8 can not be distinguished due to the sparseness of the microphone array. However, the SPL plot does indicate the presence of more than one circumferential mode, which causes an interference pattern. Figure 14a,b show the ICD contour plots for the 15-rod configuration at BPF and 2BPF, respectively. The expected m=1 for BPF and m=2 for 2BPF are clearly observed. The strong circular bands at BPF and 2BPF in the SPL plot indicate the presence of single dominant circumferential modes.

Concluding Remarks

The indicated circumferential modes from the ICD array technique match the expected interaction modes and the measured modes from the rotating rake. The comparison of the radial mode distribution at 2BPF indicates a discrepancy between the rotating rake and ICD array. This discrepancy can be explained by the fact that the signal-to-noise capability of the current ICD array has more trouble with radial mode separation. The ICD contour plots can provide quick and useful information about the modal structure of the propagating noise. Furthermore, the ICD microphone data can be useful for validation of aeroacoustic propagation codes. The CDUCT propagation code gives accurate steering vector predictions for well cut-on modes, though errors are larger for modes closer to cut-off. This is consistent with the assumptions within the CDUCT theory. The ability of the ICD array to distinguish between two dominant modes will be further investigated. Improvements to the signal-to-noise capabilities of the ICD array technique can be obtained through the use of additional microphones, improved microphone distribution, and improved steering vector predictions. Applying the ICD array technique to determine the modal distribution of broadband noise will also be investigated.

Acknowledgement

Partial funding for this test and subsequent analysis was provided through NASA Langley Research Center under contract NAS1-97040 Task 5. The authors would also like to acknowledge Bob Dougherty's contributions as the originator and developer of the ICD array technique and for his role as the original author and developer of the CDUCT code.

References

1. Joppa, P.D., "Duct Mode Measurement of Fan Broadband Noise", Proceedings of NOISE-CON 96 Vol I, Seattle, WA, Sept. 29 – Oct. 2, 1996, pp. 127-132.
2. Rademaker, E.R., Sijtsma, P., Tester, B.J., "Mode Detection with an Optimised Array in a Model Turbofan Engine Intake at Varying Shaft Speeds", AIAA 2001-2181
3. Sutliff, D.L., Nallasamy, M., Heidelberg, L.J., Elliott, D.M., "Baseline Acoustic Levels of the NASA Active Noise Control Fan Rig", NASA TM 107214/ AIAA 96-1745, May 1996.
4. Farassat, F., Nark, D.M., Thomas, R.H., "The Detection of Radiated Modes From Ducted Fan Engines", AIAA 2001-2138.
5. Dougherty, R.P., "Phased Array Beamforming for Aeroacoustics", AIAA Professional Development Short Course, Bellevue, WA, May 8-9, 1999.
6. Lan, J.H., "Turbofan Duct Propagation Model", NASA CR-2001-211245.
7. Heidelberg, L.J., Hall, D.G., Bridges, J.E., Nallasamy, M., "A Unique Ducted Fan Test Bed for Active Noise Control and Aeroacoustics Research", NASA TM 107213/AIAA2 96-1740, May 1996.
8. Tyler, J.M., and Sofrin, T.G., "Axial Flow Compressor Noise Studies," SAE Transactions, Vol. 70, 1962, pp. 309-332.

Figure 1 Active Noise Control Fan

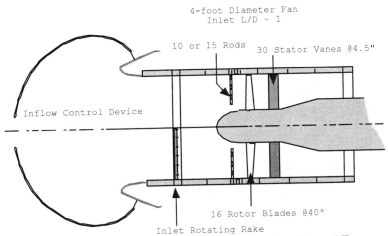

4-foot Diameter Fan
Inlet L/D ~ 1

10 or 15 Rods   30 Stator Vanes @4.5"

Inflow Control Device

16 Rotor Blades @40°

Inlet Rotating Rake

Figure 2 Schematic of Active Noise Control Fan

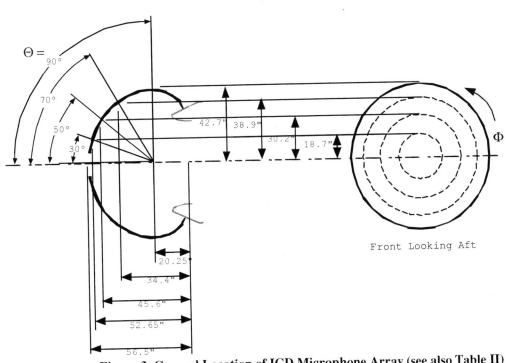

$\Theta =$ 90°

70°

50°

30°

42.7" 38.9"

30.2" 18.7"

Φ

Front Looking Aft

20.25"

34.4"

45.6"

52.65"

56.5"

Figure 3 General Location of ICD Microphone Array (see also Table II)

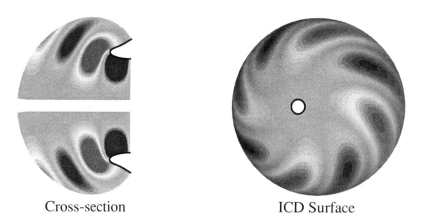

Cross-section   ICD Surface

Figure 4 CDUCT Calculated Real Part of Pressure at BPF, (-4,0) Mode, 2200 RPM

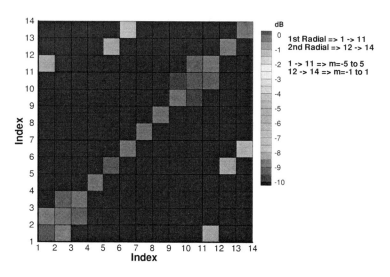

Figure 5 Orthogonality Plot at BPF, 2200 RPM

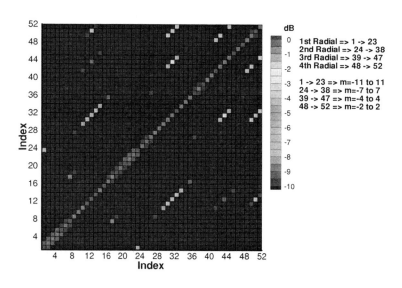

Figure 6 Orthogonality Plot for 2BPF, 2200 RPM

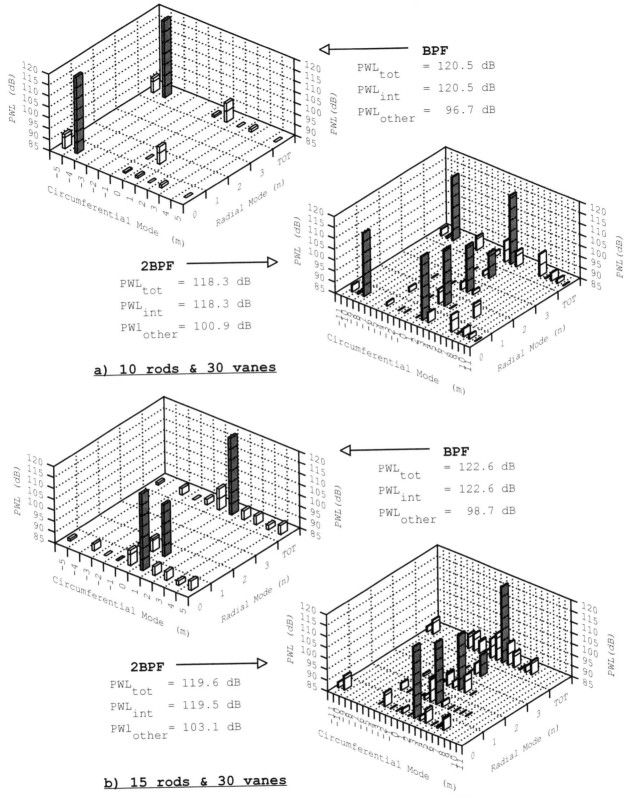

BPF

PWL_{tot} = 120.5 dB

PWL_{int} = 120.5 dB

PWL_{other} = 96.7 dB

2BPF

PWL_{tot} = 118.3 dB

PWL_{int} = 118.3 dB

PWl_{other} = 100.9 dB

a) 10 rods & 30 vanes

BPF

PWL_{tot} = 122.6 dB

PWL_{int} = 122.6 dB

PWL_{other} = 98.7 dB

2BPF

PWL_{tot} = 119.6 dB

PWL_{int} = 119.5 dB

PWl_{other} = 103.1 dB

b) 15 rods & 30 vanes

Figure 7 Complete Modal Structure at 2200 RPMC

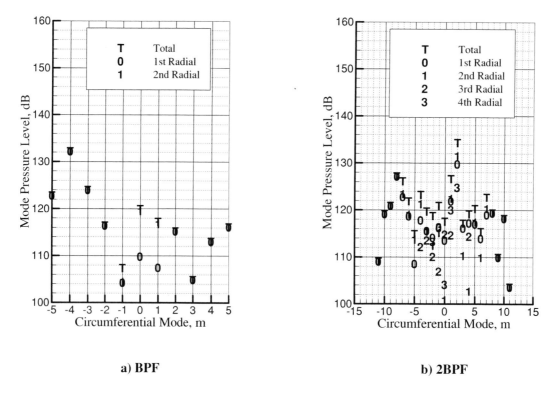

a) BPF   b) 2BPF

Figure 8 ICD Modal Distribution at 2200 RPMC, 16 Blades, 10 Rods, 30 Vanes

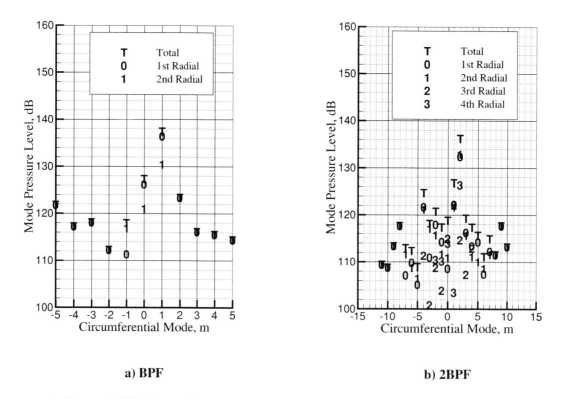

a) BPF   b) 2BPF

Figure 9 ICD Modal Distribution at 2200 RPMC, 16 Blades, 15 Rods, 30 Vanes

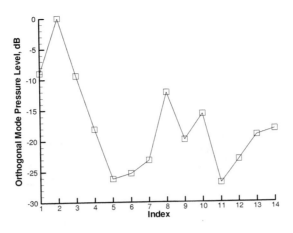

Figure 10 Expected Signal-To-Noise at BPF for (-4,0) Mode

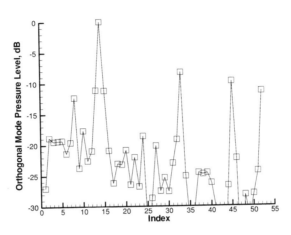

Figure 11 Expected Signal-To-Noise at 2BPF for (2,0) Mode

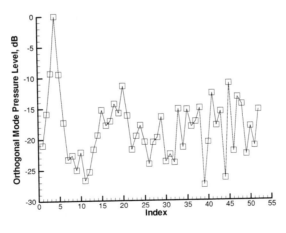

Figure 12 Expected Signal-To-Noise at 2BPF for (-8,0) Mode

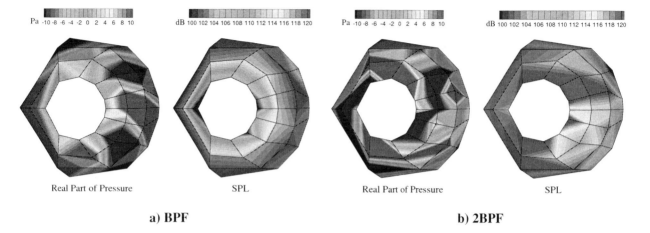

Real Part of Pressure | SPL | Real Part of Pressure | SPL

a) BPF   b) 2BPF

Figure 13 Measured ICD Microphone Data for 16 Blades, 10 Rods, 30 Vanes, 2200 RPMC

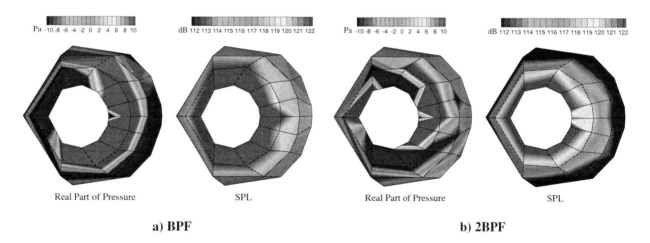

Real Part of Pressure | SPL | Real Part of Pressure | SPL

a) BPF   b) 2BPF

Figure 14 Measured ICD Microphone Data for 16 Blades, 15 Rods, 30 Vanes, 2200 RPMC

DUCT MODE MEASUREMENTS ON THE TFE731-60 FULL SCALE ENGINE

Daniel L. Sutliff[*]
SEST, Inc.
Cleveland, Ohio 44135

Kevin E. Konno[†] and Laurence J. Heidelberg[‡]
National Aeronautics and Space Administration
Glenn Research Center
Cleveland, Ohio 44135

Abstract

A continuously rotating rake with radial microphones was developed to measure the inlet and exhaust duct modes on a TFE731-60 turbofan engine. This was the first time the rotating rake technology was used on a production engine. The modal signature for the first three fan harmonics was obtained in the inlet and exhaust. Rotor-stator and rotor-strut interaction modes were measured. Total harmonic power was calculated over a range of fan speeds. Above sonic tip speed, the rotor locked mode was not strong enough to be identified, but the "buzz-saw" noise at fan sub-harmonics was identified.

Introduction

The Advanced Subsonic Technology (AST) program sponsored the Engine Validation of Noise Reduction Concepts (EVNRC). A full-scale turbofan engine, the TFE731-60 was used as a test bed for part of this program. A continuously rotating rake with radially distributed microphones was developed for use on the Honeywell TFE731-60 as an acoustic diagnostic tool. Rotating rake technology had been developed and used successfully on model scale[1] and a dedicated test bed.[2] The test was accomplished in two separate, repeated, entries during June and August 1999.

Experimental Apparatus

TFE731-60 Turbofan Engine

A TFE731-60 engine with accompanying reference inlet and nozzle was used for this test. Basic engine information is described in table 1. The TFE731-60 has 22 rotor blades and 52 stator blades. The rotor-stator interaction mode at blade passing frequency (BPF) is cut-off below sonic rotor tip speed. The engine was tested at the Honeywell engine test stand in San Tan, Arizona. A photograph of the engine on the test stand, and a schematic of the fan flow-path are shown in figure 1.

Rotating Rake

Methodology

The classic paper by Tyler and Sofrin[3] presents the theory of fan-duct mode generation and propagation. The generation of circumferential spinning modes is governed by the following equation:

$$m = sB \pm kV \qquad (1)$$

where
m = circumferential mode number
s = harmonic index
B = number of rotor blades
k = an integer (0,1,2,...)
V = number of stator vanes

The rotor locked, or rotor alone, mode (m=sB) spins at the shaft rotation speed. It is the potential field of the rotor. Separate rotor-stator and rotor-strut interaction modes also exists at the same m-order, when k=0. These modes, and higher order modes, can only propagate in a narrow annular duct if the blade tip speed which correspond to their spin rate is above Mach = 1.0. Lower order modes, which spin faster, may propagate if their spin rate results in sonic speed. The critical tip Mach number is slightly greater than 1.0 for non-narrow annular ducts. The spin rate of a circumferential mode is determined by the following equation:

$$\Omega m = sB\Omega/m \qquad (2)$$

where:
Ωm = mode rotation speed
Ω = shaft rotation speed

---

[*] Senior Aeroacoustics Researcher, Senior Member AIAA
[†] Aerospace Engineer
[‡] Aerospace Engineer, Senior Member AIAA

Each circumferential mode, m, can have one or more radial modes, n. Mode propagation is dependent on the cut-off frequency, which is unique to each (m,n) mode. This frequency is dependent on geometric parameters and the eigenvalue of a combined Bessel function that is a solution to the cylindrical wave equation. Below the cut-off frequency the mode will decay exponentially. Above cut-off, propagation occurs and acoustic power is transmitted down the duct and into the farfield. The cut-off frequency is given by:

$$f_{co} = \hat{e}c/\pi D \qquad (3)$$

where:

f_{co} = cut-off frequency
$\hat{e}$ = bessel function eigenvalue
c = speed of sound
D = duct diameter

The Bessel function eigenvalue incorporates the duct geometry effects. The cut off ratio gives the ratio of the mode frequency to its cut-off frequency.

$$\zeta = f/f_{co} = \pi s B (\Omega m) D / 60 \hat{e}c \qquad (4)$$

The rotating rake instrumentation system provides a complete map of the duct modal signature at 1BPF, 2BPF, and 3BPF (blade passing frequency) for either the inlet or the exhaust duct.[4] The resolution of circumferential modes arise from a Doppler induced frequency shift due to the unique and discrete rotation rate of each m-order imparted by the continuous rotation of the rake.[5] Radial modes are computed from a least squares data fit of the radial pressure profile using the hardwall Bessel functions as the basis functions.[6]

The modal data from the rotating rake are presented in 3-D format. The base plane axes are m- and n-order, and the vertical value axis in the PWL in the (m,n) mode. Along the wall of the m-order axis the sum of all the radials provides the power in that circumferential mode. The sum of all provides the PWL in the harmonic presented. A typical modal decomposition provides information as to the dominant modes present, usually those due to the rotor stator interaction. Of secondary interest will be other modes, which may be due to inflow distortions or other geometric disturbances.

The circumferential rotor-stator interaction modes for the first three blade passing frequencies are presented in table 2a. In addition, there are 10 downstream exhaust struts that could produce Tyler-Sofrin type interaction modes shown on table 2b.

Hardware

The rake acquires pressure data as it spins around the nacelle using a series of radially distributed pressure transducers pointing at the fan. The rake is used in two locations—the inlet and the exhaust. The inlet rake rotates around the duct centerline inside the nacelle at the throat. At the nozzle, the rake rotates at the exit plane of the bypass duct. Photographs and schematic drawings of the rakes are shown on figure 2. The rotating parts are shown in red while the stationary parts are blue. Both rakes have windscreens covering the transducers to: lower vortex shedding noise from the inlet rake; and lower interaction with the viscous wake for the exhaust rake.

The rotational speed of the rake was required to be a specific whole number fraction, i.e., 1/200 in this case, of the TFE731-60 fan shaft speed and in phase with the shaft. This means that when the fan has rotated 200 times, the rotating rake will have completed exactly one revolution in that time span within ±0.2°. This speed and phase synchronization is necessary in order to resolve the Doppler induced frequency shift of the spinning acoustic modes. Consequently, the rake requires a very accurate drive and control system. This accuracy must also be repeated over the entire test period (five to ten minutes) without build-up of phase error. The rake must follow the fan precisely even though the fan will wander in speed (5 to 10 rpm or so) throughout the test period. Consequently, the rake drive system must be slaved directly to the fan. Table 3 contains a list of rake control system performance requirements.

The inlet installation was a design challenge, since the whole rotating rake mechanism had to fit inside the Inflow Control Device (ICD). An ICD is used to eliminate the ground vortex and reduce the incoming atmospheric turbulence thus simulating in-flight noise during static testing.

Test Conditions

Rotating Rake measurements were taken over a fan speed range of approximately 6000 to 10000 rpm. Nominal data points were taken at 60, 64, 67, 75, 81, 88, and 94 percent of N1C$_{max}$. The TFE731-60 is a geared fan with a ratio of 2.0645 so that N1C max corresponds to Nf$_{max}$=10,172 rpm; V$_{tip}$=1362 fps. Approach is 64 percent N1C (V$_{tip}$=872 fps), cutback is 81 percent N1C (V$_{tip}$=1104 fps). Due to operational constraints 81 percent was not achievable; 78 percent N1C was substituted. Points at 88 percent and above represent supersonic rotor tip speeds.

Two entries, separated by a major configuration change, were tested. A major difference between the two entries was that for the first entry the engine was side mounted, allowing the engine to pitch up with increasing thrust, causing the rotating rake to no longer rotate about the engine centerline. This may have caused an inaccuracy in the inlet measurements due to positioning error, which was not quantified. For the second entry, the engine was top mounted, reducing the pitch-up with thrust considerably.

Results and Discussion

The complete mode map (circumferential and radial) for the inlet and exhaust ducts for the first blade passing harmonic at 60% N1C are shown on figure 3. The measurement noise floor is estimated to be about 95 dB. The inlet modes are dominated by the co-rotating (positive) spinning modes. This is because the contra-rotating modes are blocked by the rotor.[7] The exhaust mode distribution is more uniformly distributed between the co- and contra-rotating modes. The overall PWLs are 114.8 in the inlet, and 115.2 dB in the exhaust. While the rotor-stator interaction mode is cut-off at BPF below sonic rotor tip speed, the rotor-strut-modes are cut-on. These strut modes are identifiable, but their contribution to the overall PWL is minor as can be seen by comparing the sum of the strut mode PWL to the overall PWL.

The m-order distribution for the high speed (88 percent N1C) is shown on figure 4. (The complete mode-map is available, but the density prevented meaningful display.) At this speed, the rotor locked mode (m=22) is cut-on. The inlet shows the increase in the m=22 and the neighboring modes. Recall that the m=22 mode is actually the sum of the rotor-locked mode, the rotor-stator interaction mode (k=0), the rotor-strut interaction mode, and the rake wake interference mode. The exhaust shows a general increase in all modes with the rotor-strut interaction modes showing a modest dominance over the non Tyler-Sofrin interaction modes, or extraneous modes.

Figure 5 summarizes the strut modes and the total harmonic power levels versus %N1C for BPF. In the subsonic tip regime, the PWL is dominated by the sum of the extraneous modes. The cut-on of the m=22 modes above a sonic tip speed contributes to a 15 dB increase in the overall PWL.

Figure 6 shows the m-order distribution for 2xBPF for 60 percent N1C. The rotor-vane interaction is the m=−8. This mode is almost 10 dB higher than the other modes, though in the inlet it is considerably lower due to rotor blockage. At the 88 percent N1C, (figure 7), the inlet shows a strong m=−14 and m=+14. Though the m=+14 is a strut mode, neither mode is strongly present at other speeds. In general, the rotor-strut modes at 2BPF do not rise above the extraneous mode levels.

Figure 8 shows that at 2BPF the PWL is exhaust dominated by 5 to 10 dB. In the exhaust, the rotor-vane interaction mode is a significant contributor to the overall PWL, only 3 to 6 dB below. The second

harmonic of the rotor-locked mode (m=44) is not significant.

The two separate test entries, separated by a major configuration change, allowed for a determination of the repeatability of the mode measurement technique. Figure 9 shows the repeatability for two runs for each entry. The BPF rotor-strut-interaction modes agree to within a few dB. For the strong rotor-vane interaction mode at 2BPF, the m-order repeatability is within 1 dB. The individual radials show good repeatability with the stronger radials demonstrating closer agreement. Other speeds demonstrated similar repeatability.

The rotor-locked mode (m=22 at BPF) cuts on at 8341 rpmc. As discussed before, this mode is contaminated by the rake-wake rotor interaction. For the subsonic rotor speeds the rake-wake rotor interference which shows up at m=22 is the only mode that should be measured at m=22. Therefore it may be possible to draw a qualitative conclusion about the rotor-locked mode by comparing the levels of m=22 above and below cut-on as in figure 10a. Since the m=22 mode changes very little as the rotor-locked is cut-on it is assumed that what is being measured by the rake is mostly the interference mode, and that the rotor-locked mode is not distinguishable from the interference. For comparison, the m=22 mode measured in exhaust is shown, and the clear increase as the combined modes at m=22 is observed. (There is no rotor wake contamination with the rake in the exhaust.)

The lower shaft-orders (21,20,19...1) also contribute to the "buzz-saw" noise generated near sonic tip speed. The mode generated at each shaft-order is numerically identical, i.e., at the 20th shaft order the m=20 mode is generated. Figures 10b and 10c show m-order contribution for all shaft orders below BPF. The highest levels occur at shaft-orders 11 to 15. As a result of the eigenvalues, at the lower shaft-order/m-order (so/m) the cut-off ratio actually decreases, to the point that for so/m 13 and below the mode is classically cut-off. This is part of the reason for the mode pressure rise at so/m = 14. However, Mach number effects cause propagation of these lower shaft-order/m-orders.

Conclusions

The first Rotating Rake mode measurements were taken on a full-scale turbofan engine, the TFE731-60. The rotor-strut interaction modes at BPF were identified as the dominant modes but were to be a minor contribution to overall PWL, due to the strength of the extraneous (background) modes. Rotor transmission losses were shown to result in lower co-rotating modes in the inlet. The 2BPF rotor-vane interaction mode was clearly identified in the inlet and exhaust, and observed to dominate.

Repeatability of the measurements was shown to be excellent by comparing results from two separate test builds.

An attempt to measure the rotor-locked noise was inconclusive though some information showed the sub-harmonics ("buzz-saw") to be dominated by the shaft-orders just under 1/2 BPF.

Acknowledgments

This work was done as a part of a contract with Honeywell Engines and Systems, NAS3–97151. Rotating Rake hardware was developed by Aerospace Design Fabrication, Inc. under NAS3–27600 by George Pinkas and Ray Homyk. The reporting and analysis was under contract NAS3–00170, SEST, Inc. The contributions of Kevin Detreich, Dale Brock, and Gary Meshew at the San Tan facility were vital.

References

1. Heidelberg, L.J., and Hall, D.G., "Inlet Acoustic Mode Measurements Using a Continuously Rotating Rake," *Journal of Aircraft*, pp. 761–767, July–August 1995.
2. Heidelberg, L.J., Hall, D.G., Bridges, J.E., and Nallasamy, M., "A Unique Ducted Fan Test Bed for Active Noise Control and Aeroacoustics Research," NASA TM–107213, AIAA 96–1740, May 1996.
3. Tyler J.M., and Sofrin T.G., "Axial Flow Compressor Noise Studies," SAE Transactions, vol. 70, 1962, pp. 309–332.
4. Sutliff, D.L., Nallasamy, M., Heidelberg, L.J., and Elliott, D.M., "Baseline Acoustic Levels of the NASA Active Noise Control Fan Rig," NASA TM–107214, AIAA 96–1745, May 1996.
5. Hall, D.G., Heidelberg, L.H., and Konno, K., "Acoustic Mode Measurements in the Inlet of a Model Turbofan Using a Continuously Rotating Rake: Data Collection/Analysis Techniques." NASA TM–105936, January 1993, also AIAA 93–0599, January 1993.
6. Moore, C.J., "Measurement of Radial and Circumferential Modes in Annular and Circular Ducts," *Journal of Sound and Vibration*, vol. 62, no. 2, 1979, pp. 235–256.
7. Hanson, D.B., "Acoustic Reflection and Transmission of Rotor and Stators Including Mode and Frequency Scattering," AIAA/CEAS 97–1610, May 1997.

Table 1. TFE731-60 engine parameters

Basic Engine Weight	988 lb
Takeoff, Sea Level, Static Thrust	5000 lb
Airflow	187 lb/sec
Cruise Bypass Ratio	3.9
Cycle Pressure Ratio	22
Geared Fan Pressure Ratio	1.70

Table 2a. Rotor-stator interaction modes

Harmonic	Interaction modes
1BPF	2*
2BPF	44,–8
3BPF	66,14

*cut-off at subsonic speeds

Table 2b. Rotor-strut interaction modes

Harmonic	Interaction modes
1BPF	22,12,2,–8,–18
2BPF	44,34,24,14,4,–6,–16,–26,–36
3BPF	66,56,46,36,26,16,6, –4, –14, –24, –34, –44, –54, –64

Table 3. Rake design parameters

Maximum fan speed	10,000 rpm
Rake speed ratio	1/200
Maximum rake speed	50 rpm
Accuracy of fan-following rake speed	±0.2° of rake rotation
Test point duration	10 minutes
Number of microphones	Inlet: 14 Nozzle: 8
Max duct flow (M#)	Inlet: 0.60 Nozzle 0.85

(a) Photograph of TFE731-60 engine on Honeywell test stand

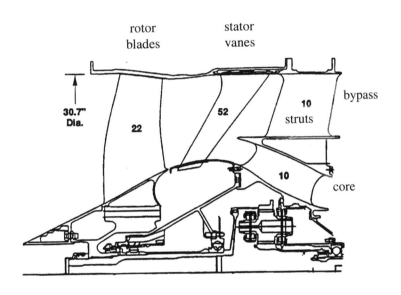

(b) Schematic of fan flow-path

Figure 1. Honeywell TFE731-60 Engine

(a) Photographs of inlet rake installed on TFE731-60 engine

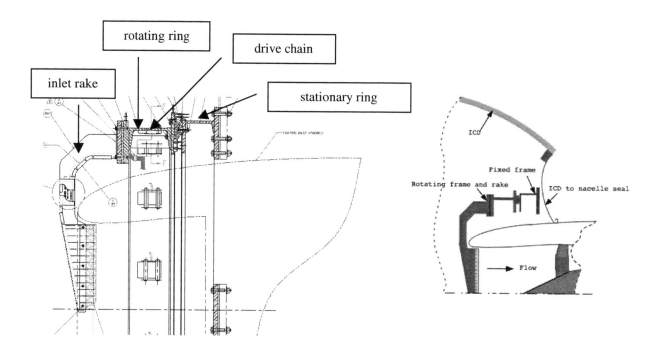

(b) Schematic side view of inlet rake assembly

Figure 2. Photographs of rakes installed on TFE731-60 engine

(c) Photographs of exhaust rake installed on TFE731-60 engine

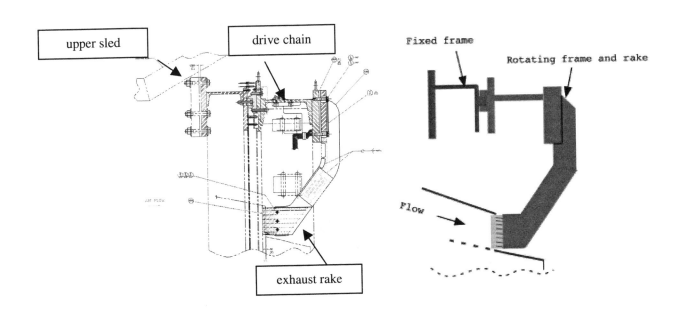

(d) Schematic side view of exhaust rake assembly

Figure 2. Photographs of rakes installed on TFE731-60 engine (concluded)

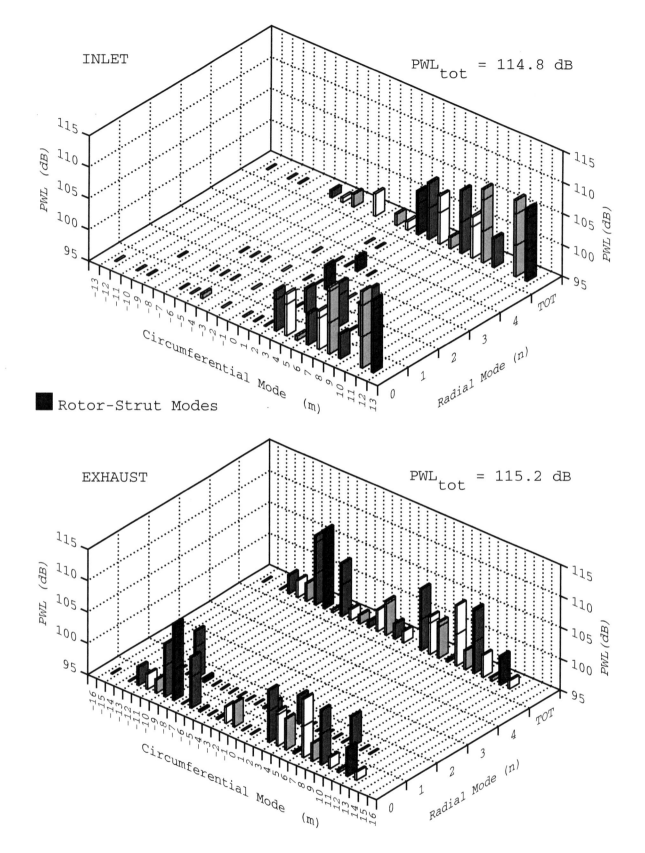

INLET

PWL_{tot} = 114.8 dB

Rotor-Strut Modes

EXHAUST

PWL_{tot} = 115.2 dB

Figure 3. Mode map for 60% N1C, 1xBPF

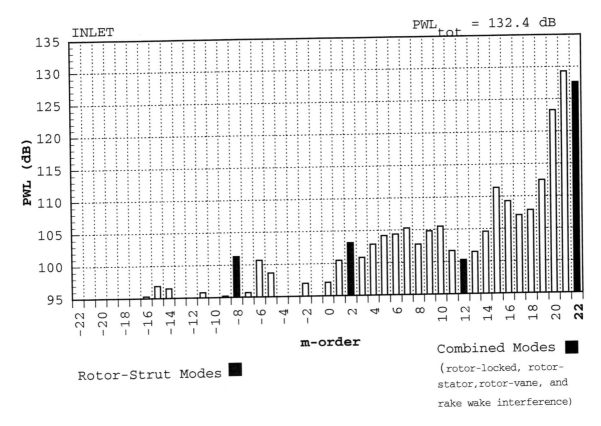

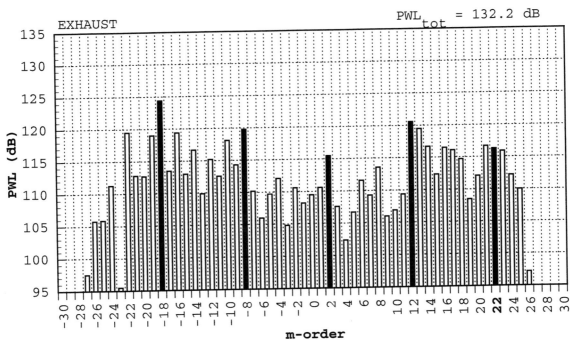

Figure 4. Mode map for 88% N1C, 1xBPF

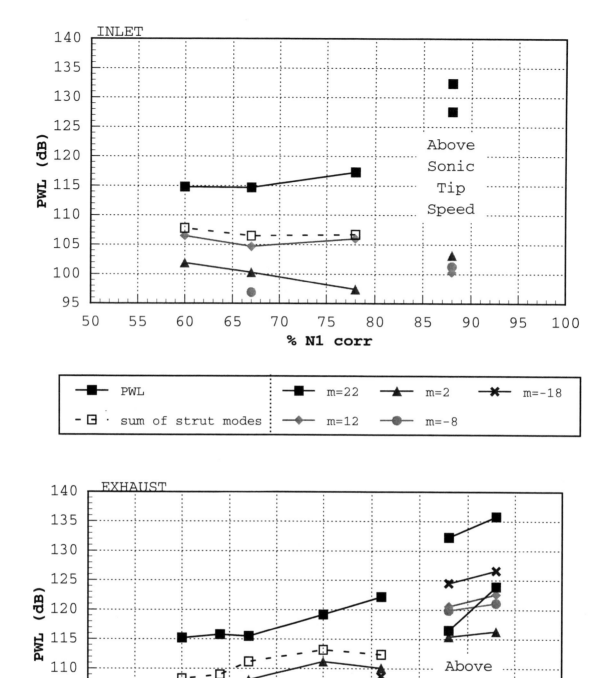

Figure 5. Total harmonic power versus corrected percent speed, 1xBPF

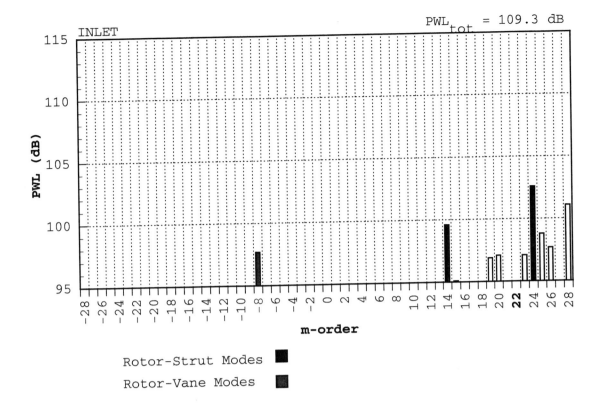

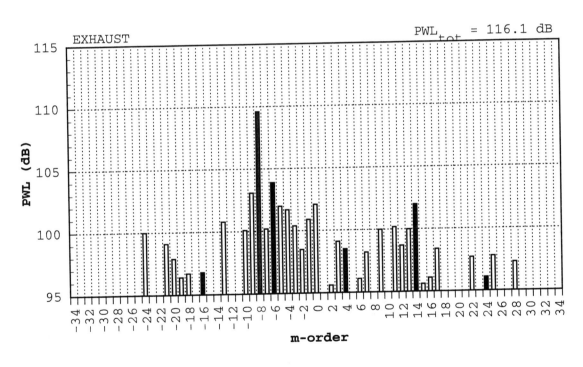

Figure 6. Mode map for 60% N1C, 2xBPF

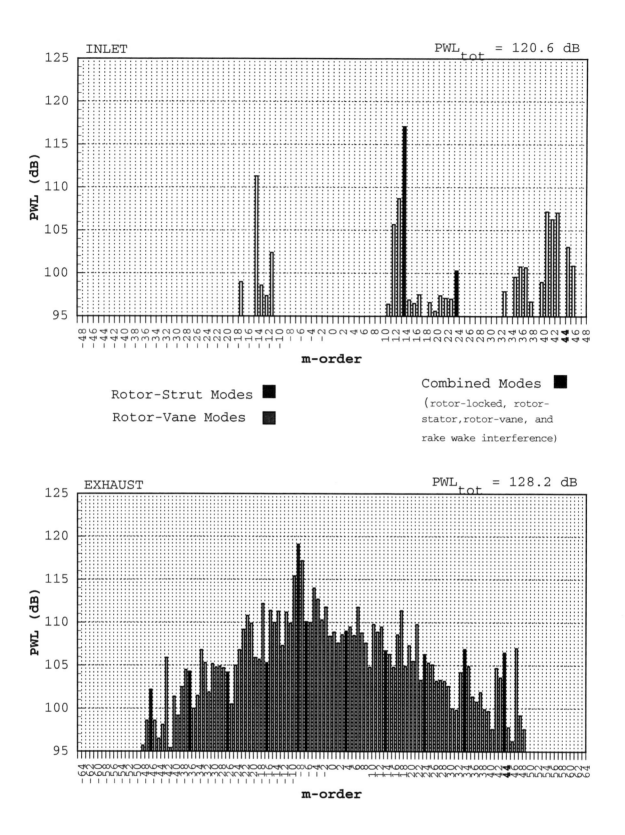

Figure 7. Mode map for 88% N1C, 2xBPF

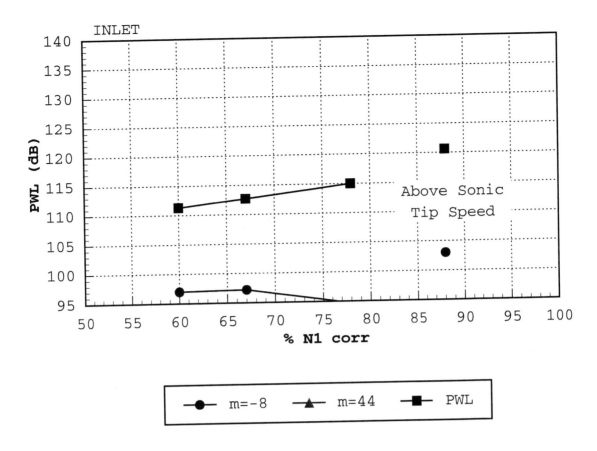

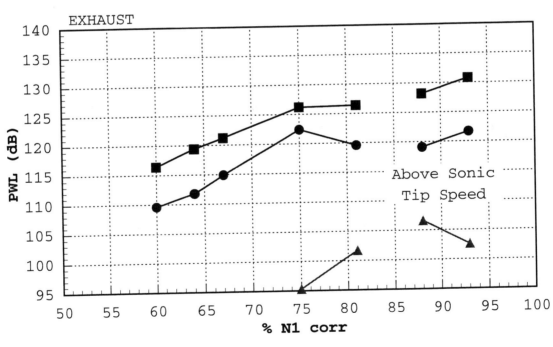

Figure 8. Total harmonic power versus N1C, 2xBPF

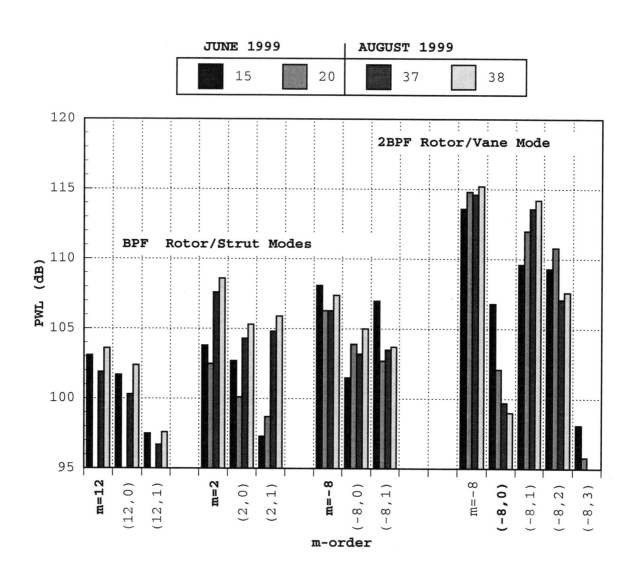

Figure 9. Repeatability of interaction modes in the exhaust (67% N1C)

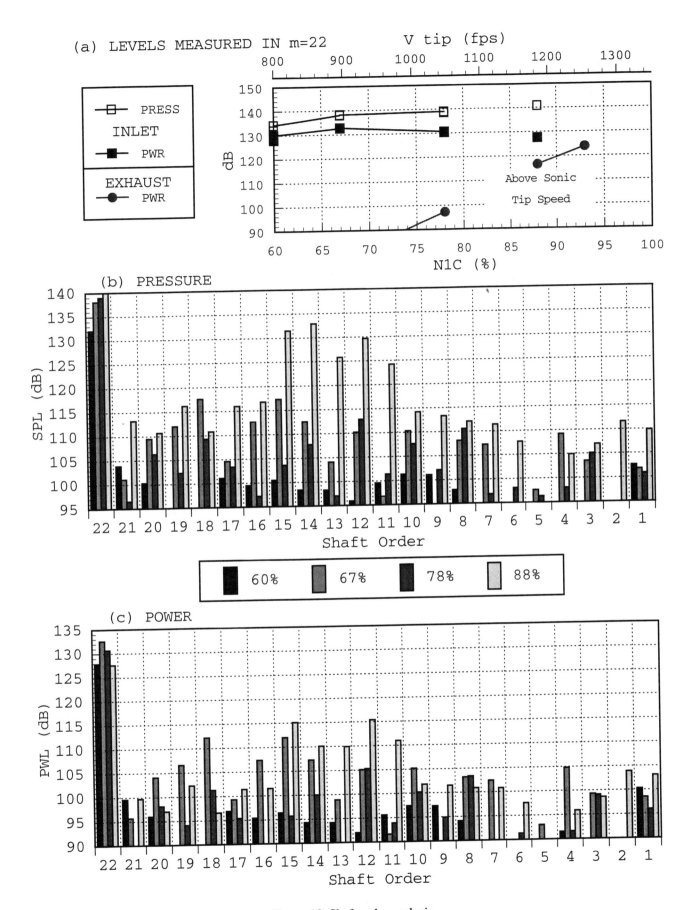

Figure 10. Shaft order analysis

AN EMPIRICAL SPECTRAL MODEL OF SURFACE-PRESSURE FLUCTUATIONS THAT INCLUDES REYNOLDS NUMBER EFFECTS

Michael Goody[*]

Naval Surface Warfare Center, Carderock Division
West Bethesda, MD 20817-5700

ABSTRACT

An empirical model of the surface pressure spectrum beneath a 2-D, zero-pressure-gradient boundary layer is presented that is based on the experimental surface pressure spectra measured by 7 research groups. The measurements cover a large range of Reynolds number, $1400 < Re_\theta < 23400$. The model is a simple function of the ratio of the time scales of the outer to inner boundary layer. It incorporates the effect of Reynolds number through the time scale ratio, and compares well to experimental data. Spectral features of the experimental data, the scaling behavior of the surface pressure spectrum, and the mean square pressure are also discussed.

NOMENCLATURE

C_f Skin friction coefficient, τ_w / Q_e

d Sensing diameter of the pressure transducer

d^+ d normalized by the viscous length scale, $= u_\tau d / \nu$

p Unsteady pressure (mean zero) due to turbulence

$\overline{p^2}$ Mean square unsteady pressure

Q_e Dynamic pressure at the boundary layer edge

U Magnitude of the flow velocity

U_C Convection velocity of p

U_e Velocity at the boundary layer edge

u_τ Friction velocity, $= (\tau_w / \rho)^{1/2}$

Re_θ Momentum Reynolds number, $= U_e \theta / \nu$

R_T Ratio of time scales of p (Equation (4))

δ Boundary layer thickness

δ^* Boundary layer displacement thickness

μ Viscosity of fluid

ν Kinematic viscosity, $= \mu / \rho$

θ Boundary layer momentum thickness

ρ Mass density of fluid

τ_w Shear stress at the wall

ω Angular frequency

Φ Spectral power density of surface pressure fluctuations such that,

$$\overline{p^2} = \int_0^\infty \Phi(\omega)\, d\omega$$

---

[*] Mechanical Engineer, Code 7250, Signatures Directorate, Member AIAA

INTRODUCTION

Boundary Layer Scaling– General

Scaling is a technique that is often used in the analysis of boundary layers. It is based on the concept of *self-similarity*, in which a function of some variable(s) retains the same shape for a wide variety of conditions. If self-similar, a dependent variable can be made non-dimensional by appropriate length, velocity, and/or pressure scales and expressed as a *universal* function of independent variable(s) that are also made non-dimensional on appropriate length, velocity, and/or pressure scales[1,2]. The function is called *universal* because it does not change for a wide variety of conditions. Blasius used self-similarity to solve the equations of motion for laminar boundary layers exactly.

The application of self-similarity to the analysis of turbulent boundary layers is more complicated. One characteristic of turbulent boundary layers is the existence of many relevant length, velocity, and pressure scales. The different boundary layer scales are related to organized motions or coherent structures[3,4] that exist in the boundary layer. Traditionally, a two-layer model has been used to scale the turbulent boundary layer[5,6]. The flow nearest the wall (known as the inner layer) has a set of length, velocity, and pressure scales associated with it. The flow away from the wall (known as the outer layer and consisting of most of the boundary layer) has a different set of length, velocity, and pressure scales associated with it.

The situation is complicated even further when the effect of Reynolds number is considered[7,8]. The Reynolds number is the ratio of inertial to viscous forces in the boundary layer. Most practical flows (i.e. the flow over airplanes and ships) have a large Reynolds number. Most laboratory flows (i.e. wind tunnels and water tunnels) have a small Reynolds number. Therefore, understanding the effect of Reynolds number is crucial when applying laboratory results to the analysis of practical flows.

Recently, Buschmann and Gad-el-Hak[9] extended the analysis of Afzal[10] to relate changes in the mean velocity profile with Reynolds number to the change in the ratio of inner to outer length scale, $u_\tau \delta / \nu$.

Although conceived independent of Buschmann and Gad-el-Hak, the present empirical model is based on a similar precept. Namely, that Reynolds number affects the surface pressure spectrum through the ratio of outer to inner time scale– the *time scale ratio*, R_T. The time scale ratio increases as the Reynolds number increases.

Scaling the Surface Pressure Spectrum

There is no universal scaling that collapses the p spectra beneath flows with different Reynolds number at all frequencies. Traditionally, the two-layer model is applied to pressure fluctuations by using different scales to collapse the p spectrum in specific frequency ranges. The high frequency end of the p spectra collapse to within measurement uncertainties when normalized using inner-layer scales– τ_w as the pressure scale and v/u_τ^2 as the time scale and the spectrum decays as ω^{-5} (Figure 1). There is general agreement in the literature on the proper pressure and time scales for the p spectrum at high frequencies. The same is not true for the p spectrum in the low and middle frequency ranges. Researchers[11,12] have shown p spectra that collapse at low frequencies using an outer-layer scaling of either τ_w or Q_e as the pressure scale and δ^*/U_e as the time scale[†]. Farabee and Casarella[13] reported that Q_e and δ^*/U_e only collapse p spectra at very low frequencies, $\omega\delta^*/U_e \leq 0.03$[‡], and that the spectrum increases as ω^2 in this frequency range, which is in agreement with the theoretical results of others[11,14]. Some researchers[13,15,16] have used τ_w as the pressure scale and δ/u_τ as the time scale to collapse p spectra at middle frequencies. Goody[17] reviewed the experimental p spectra of 6 research groups that cover a large Reynolds number range ($1400 < Re_\theta < 23400$) and showed that the spectra collapse at low and middle frequencies when τ_w is used as the pressure scale and either δ^*/U_e, δ/U_e, δ^*/u_τ, or δ/u_τ is used as the time scale.

It has been postulated[11,14,18], using arguments related to the existence of an inner scaling and an outer scaling, that an *overlap* range exists in the p spectrum beneath 2-D boundary layers at high Reynolds number. Both inner- and outer-layer scaling collapse the p spectrum in the overlap range. Theoretically[11,14,18], it is argued that the p spectrum in this frequency range decreases as ω^{-1} and is due to universal turbulent motions within the log-layer where the convection velocity of turbulent

structures approaches the local mean flow velocity. However, the measured spectral decay is closer to $\omega^{-0.7}$ to $\omega^{-0.8}$. For example, McGrath and Simpson[19] measured an $\omega^{-0.7}$ decay, Blake[20] measured an $\omega^{-0.75}$ decay, and Goody[21] measured an $\omega^{-0.8}$ decay within the overlap region. Both theoretical and experimental results show that the size/existence of the overlap frequency range increases with Reynolds number. The low Re_θ ($= 1400$) p data of Schewe[22] only tangentially approach a power law spectral decay within the overlap range

Spectral Models of the Pressure Spectrum

Howe[23] gives the following model for $\Phi(\omega)$ and attributes it to Chase[24],

$$\frac{\Phi(\omega)U_e}{\tau_w^2 \, \delta^*} = \frac{2\left(\dfrac{\omega\delta^*}{U_e}\right)^2}{\left[\left(\dfrac{\omega\delta^*}{U_e}\right)^2 + 0.0144\right]^{\frac{3}{2}}} \qquad (1)$$

Equation (1) is presently referred to as the Chase-Howe model. At low frequencies, the model spectrum is proportional to ω^2 and at higher frequencies it varies as ω^{-1}, both of which are consistent with theoretical results. However, Equation (1) does not include an ω^{-5} spectral decay, which has been measured and theoretically shown to exist at the highest frequencies. The multiplicative constant in the numerator (2) of Equation (1) is not in the equation given in Howe[23], which describes a double-sided spectrum. The constant is used here in order to make Equation (1) consistent with the definition of Φ used here (single-sided).

Equation (1) is a simplification of Chase's model[24]. The model proposed by Chase is a more comprehensive model for the wavevector-frequency p spectrum. It is by no means the only spectral model of p. Graham[25] discussed the wavevector-frequency spectral models of Corcos[26], Efimtsov[27], Smol'yakov and Tkachenko[28], Chase[24], and Ffowcs Williams[29] (as approximated by Hwang and Geib[30]) with regard to their ability to accurately predict the modal excitation of a simply-supported, thin, elastic plate by calculating the radiated sound. Other notable spectral models are those of Witting[31] and Panton and Robert[32]. The spectral models mentioned above are based on the theoretical formulations of either Lighthill[33,34] or Kraichnan[35]. Lighthill[33,34] expressed the momentum equation governing fluid flow in the form of a wave equation– known as *acoustic analogy*. Kraichnan[35] expressed p as a Poisson equation by taking the divergence of the momentum equation that governs fluid flow. Though based on theoretical formulations, each of the above spectral models still rely on empirical data at various

---

[†] Some researchers refer to the scale combination τ_w and δ^*/U_e as a *mixed* scaling.

[‡] The spectra of Farabee and Casarella are the only data set, of those discussed presently, that contains a significant number of data points in this low frequency range.

points in their development to varying degrees of sophistication.

Equation (1) was used as the starting point for the present empirical model because of its attractive mathematical form. It is able to describe the essential features of the frequency spectrum of p with limited degrees of freedom (adjustable constants). Thus, it is more closely related to the flow physics than a simple polynomial curve fit, but less complex than a more general model for the wavenumber-frequency p spectrum.

The Experimental Data

The experimental p spectra presented here are single-sided. The p spectra of Farabee and Casarella[13], Olivero-Bally et al[15], McGrath and Simpson[19], and Blake[20] were multiplied by 2 in order to be consistent with the definition of Φ used here. The data of McGrath and Simpson[19] presented here is an unpublished re-reduction of the original data that was performed by Shinpaugh and Simpson and corrected for the low frequency response ($<100\,\text{Hz}$) of their transducer.

Some relevant flow conditions for each of the data sets is given in Table 1. Each of the data sets included in the present analysis addressed the two main measurement issues concerning the p spectrum[17]. At low frequencies, the measured p spectrum can be contaminated by facility-related, background noise. The data sets included presently either used an acoustically quiet wind tunnel or employed a noise cancellation technique[36,37,38] to correct the measured p spectrum. Farabee and Casarella[13] used both, an acoustically quiet wind tunnel and a noise cancellation technique, and were able to measure the p spectrum at frequencies over an order of magnitude lower than any of the other investigations considered here, or found elsewhere in the literature. The p spectrum measured by Farabee and Casarella[13] is the only measured p spectrum that could be found in the literature that extends to frequencies that are low enough to exhibit a spectral increase proportional to ω^2.

At high frequencies, spectral levels are attenuated due to the non-zero, finite size of the pressure transducer used. Contributions to p from sources (coherent structures) that are smaller than the transducer sensing area are spatially integrated, and thereby attenuated, since they have zero mean (by definition of p)[39,40,41,42]. Typically, the transducer sensing diameter, scaled on inner-layer variables, $d^+ = u_\tau d / \nu$, is used to characterize whether the attenuation is significant. Schewe[22] reports that $d^+ < 19$ is adequate to resolve the high frequency p. Gravante et al[16] report that $12 < d^+ < 18$ is required. The transducer size for the present data sets is in the range $9 < d^+ < 80$ (Table 1). Corcos[39] provides an attenuation table, in the form

$$\frac{\Phi(\omega)_{\text{MEASURED}}}{\Phi(\omega)_{\text{TRUE}}} \quad \text{as a function of} \quad \frac{\omega r}{U_C}$$

where r is the sensing radius for a circular transducer. Others[22,43,44,45] have verified that the table provided by Corcos[39] accurately recovers the true high-frequency spectral values for $\omega r / U_C < 4$. The data sets included presently were measured using among the smallest transducers of data reported in the literature. None of the data sets included presently were corrected for high-frequency attenuation when published. Therefore, all of the data sets have been corrected for high-frequency attenuation here, using the attenuation table provided by Corcos[39] and assuming that $U_C = 0.6 U_e$.

A byproduct of the present analysis is a simple equation that is useful as a low-order estimate of how well a transducer resolves p in a given flow. Using the table provided by Corcos[39], with $U_C = 0.6 U_e$, the expression

$$\left(\frac{\omega \nu}{u_\tau^2} \right)_{\text{OF ATTENUATION}} \approx \frac{10 \times (\text{Attenuation in dB})}{d^+} \quad (2)$$

closely fits the data sets considered presently (Figure 2) for attenuation less than 3 dB (50%), which corresponds to $\omega r / U_C < 1$. Equation (2) relates a given attenuation to the inner-scaled frequency at which the measured p spectrum will be attenuated by that amount. For example, the p spectrum measured by a transducer with $d^+ = 10$ will be attenuated by approximately 1 dB at $\omega \nu / u_\tau^2 = 1$.

THE NEW MODEL EQUATION

The present empirical model of the p spectrum is a modified form of the Chase-Howe model (Equation 1). When compared to the experimental data surveyed presently, the spectral levels of the Chase-Howe model are low at low frequencies and do not decay as rapidly at high frequencies (Figure 3). In order to agree better with the experimental data, Equation (1) was modified with the following considerations in mind:

(1) A term was added to the denominator so that spectral levels decay as ω^{-5} as $\omega \to \infty$,

(2) The exponents in the denominator were changed to better agree with the *measured* p spectral behavior at middle frequencies (the overlap range),

(3) A multiplicative constant was added to the model function in order to raise the spectral levels at all frequencies so that they better agree with the experimental data, and,

(4) Accurately reflect the Reynolds number trends that exist in the data

A functional form, which incorporates the above considerations, is

$$\frac{\Phi(\omega)U_e}{\tau_w^2\,\delta} = \frac{C_2\left(\dfrac{\omega\delta}{U_e}\right)^2}{\left[\left(\dfrac{\omega\delta}{U_e}\right)^{0.75}+C_1\right]^{3.7}+\left[C_3\left(\dfrac{\omega\delta}{U_e}\right)\right]^7} \qquad (3)$$

where C_1, C_2, and/or C_3 vary with Reynolds number. Equation (3) increases as ω^2 at the lowest frequencies, decays as approximately $\omega^{-0.7}$ at middle frequencies (overlap range), and ω^{-5} at the highest frequencies. The ratio of C_1 to C_3 determines the size of the overlap range ($\omega^{-0.7}$ decay– which doesn't exist beneath low Reynolds number flows). The model parameters (C_1, C_2, and C_3) were set based on the following postulates:

(1) The p spectrum collapses to a universal curve at low frequencies when normalized using τ_w as the pressure scale and δ/U_e as the time scale, independent of Reynolds number (Figure 4). Normalizing the p spectra on Q_e only collapse the experimental data at the lowest frequencies ($\omega\delta/U_e < 0.3$; Figure 5). Only the measurements of Farabee and Casarella[13] have a significant number of data points at frequencies at which Q_e collapse the p spectra. The p spectra collapse over a larger frequency range ($\omega\delta/U_e < 10$) when normalized using τ_w. Therefore, τ_w was used in the present model as the low frequency pressure scale. The low frequency time scale uses δ rather than δ^* since the largest coherent structures are of order δ. The ratio δ/δ^* varies with Reynolds number, so δ and δ^* are not equivalent as outer-layer length scales[12]. Goody[17] showed that the time scales δ^*/U_e, δ/U_e, δ^*/u_τ, and δ/u_τ collapse experimental p spectra at low frequencies over a large range of Reynolds number ($1400 < Re_\theta < 23400$) as long as τ_w is used as the pressure scale.

(2) The p spectrum collapses to a universal curve at high frequencies when normalized using τ_w as the pressure scale and ν/u_τ^2 as the time scale, independent of Reynolds number (Figure 1), which leads to

(3) The only effect of Reynolds number on the *shape* of the p spectrum is to increase the size of the overlap range.

The first postulate set the value of C_1 and C_2. The variation of C_3 with Reynolds number was determined using the second postulate. The goal was to, in effect, express Φ as a $f(\omega\delta/U_e)$ at low frequencies and as a $f(\omega\nu/u_\tau^2)$ at the highest frequencies. This led to the ratio of the outer-layer to inner-layer time scale,

$$\frac{\left(\dfrac{\delta}{U_e}\right)}{\left(\dfrac{\nu}{u_\tau^2}\right)}=\frac{u_\tau^2\delta}{U_e\nu}=\left(\frac{u_\tau}{U_e}\right)\left(\frac{u_\tau\delta}{\nu}\right)=\left(\frac{u_\tau\delta}{\nu}\right)\sqrt{\frac{C_f}{2}}\equiv R_T \qquad (4)$$

As R_T increases, the low-frequency, outer-layer-scaled frequency range moves away from the high-frequency, inner-layer-scaled frequency range and the size of the overlap range increases. Thus, following the third postulate, it is R_T, rather than the Reynolds number, which characterizes what is commonly called "the Reynolds number effect" on the p spectrum.

The model satisfies the first two postulates quantitatively as,

$$(1)\;\left[10\log_{10}\left(\frac{\Phi(\omega)U_e}{\tau_w^2\,\delta}\right)\right]_{\text{MAX}}\approx -1.6\text{ dB} \;\;\text{at}\;\; \frac{\omega\delta}{U_e}\approx 1.4$$

$$(2)\;\left[10\log_{10}\left(\frac{\Phi(\omega)u_\tau^2}{\tau_w^2\,\nu}\right)\right]=-13.5\text{ dB} \;\;\text{at}\;\; \frac{\omega\nu}{u_\tau^2}=2$$

using the model parameters

$$\begin{aligned}C_1 &= 0.5\\ C_2 &= 3.0 \qquad (5)\\ C_3 &= 1.1\,R_T^{-0.57}\end{aligned}$$

Example comparisons of the model to experimental data are shown in Figure 6 and Figure 7.

The final form of the empirical model is

$$\frac{\Phi(\omega)U_e}{\tau_w^2\,\delta} = \frac{3.0\left(\dfrac{\omega\delta}{U_e}\right)^2}{\left[\left(\dfrac{\omega\delta}{U_e}\right)^{0.75}+0.5\right]^{3.7}+\left[C_3\left(\dfrac{\omega\delta}{U_e}\right)\right]^7} \qquad (6)$$

where $C_3 = 1.1\,R_T^{-0.57}$

with R_T as defined in Equation (4). The scaling behavior of the present model is shown in Figure 8 and Figure 9 for $10 \leq R_T \leq 2000$. Since the model strictly follows to the high-frequency, inner-layer scaling, the model offers a high degree of confidence when extrapolated to flows with a higher Reynolds number than the data sets surveyed in the present analysis.

The Mean Square Pressure

The mean square pressure may be calculated by integrating the p spectrum over all frequencies,

$$\frac{\overline{p^2}}{\tau_w^2}=\int_0^\infty\left[\frac{\Phi(\omega)U_e}{\tau_w^2\,\delta}\right]d\left(\frac{\omega\delta}{U_e}\right) \qquad (7)$$

Since each of the data sets were published without any high-frequency correction, the mean square pressure was calculated for each data set by integrating the p spectrum (Equation (7)), after correcting each using the table of Corcos[39]. The results are given in Table 3 alongside the value that was published. Correcting the p spectra for high-frequency attenuation increased $\overline{p^2}/\tau_w^2$ by as much as 17%. Table 3 also shows the value of $\overline{p^2}/\tau_w^2$ calculated by integrating the model spectrum at values of R_T which correspond to the value of R_T for each data set. The mean square pressures of the model spectra are within 11% of the value calculated by integrating the corrected data sets. Eleven percent is within a typical experimental uncertainty of a measured $\overline{p^2}/\tau_w^2$ value. The variation of $\overline{p^2}/\tau_w^2$ with R_T is shown in Figure 10. The corrected experimental data does not follow any clear trend. However, the variation of $\overline{p^2}/\tau_w^2$ of the model spectrum can be closely described by the equation,

$$\frac{\overline{p^2}}{\tau_w^2} = 0.645 + 3.8\left[\ln\left(R_T\right)\right]^2 \qquad (8)$$

The logarithmic form of Equation (8) resembles the equations proposed by Farabee and Casarella[13],

$$\frac{\overline{p^2}}{\tau_w^2} = \begin{cases} 6.5 & \left(\dfrac{u_\tau \delta}{\nu} \le 333\right) \\ 6.5 + 1.86\left[\ln\left(\dfrac{1}{333}\dfrac{u_\tau \delta}{\nu}\right)\right] & \left(\dfrac{u_\tau \delta}{\nu} > 333\right) \end{cases} \qquad (9)$$

and Olivero-Bally et al[15],

$$\frac{\overline{p^2}}{\tau_w^2} = 9.9 + 3.6\left[\ln\left(0.001\frac{u_\tau \delta}{\nu}\right)\right] \qquad (10)$$

Farabee and Casarella[13] and Olivero-Bally et al[15] use δ/u_τ as the low-frequency (outer-layer) time scale based on the premise that u_τ scales both the inner- and outer-layer velocity. The ratio of outer-layer time scale to inner-layer time scale is identical to the ratio of outer-layer to inner-layer length scales when such a formulation is used. The time scale δ/U_e is used presently since it explicitly incorporates conditions at the edge of the boundary layer, through U_e, which influence the outer-layer (low-frequency) coherent structures. While u_τ is a velocity scale of the outer-layer, u_τ scales the outer-layer only when used <u>with</u> U_e in the form of the defect law,

$$\frac{U - U_e}{u_\tau} = f\left(\frac{y}{\delta}\right) \qquad (11)$$

Therefore, it is proposed that an outer-layer (low-frequency) scaling should explicitly include some information about the flow conditions at the edge of the boundary layer.

RELATING R_T AND REYNOLDS NUMBER

The time scale, R_T, is used here to characterize what is commonly known as "the Reynolds number effect" on the p spectrum. A more accurate term is "the effect of *the range of relevant scales*". The Reynolds number has classically been used in the form

$$Re_L \equiv \frac{\rho U^2}{\mu \dfrac{U}{L}} = \frac{\text{inertial forces}}{\text{viscous forces}} = \frac{U_e L}{\nu} \qquad (12)$$

(where L is a length scale of the problem)

to determine when the viscous terms of the Navier-Stokes are not significant, in relation to the inertial terms, and can be neglected for given flow conditions. The limit $Re \to \infty$ has also been shown to be a requirement for mathematically rigorous self-similarity[2]. The term *Reynolds number* has since been commonly used with a broader, less precise meaning– that is, a measure of how turbulent a flow is, in other words, how far from laminar a flow is. Unfortunately, the mathematical definition of Reynolds number (Equation (12)) is often retained and used in conjunction with the broader meaning. Equation (12) is often too restrictive to be used in conjunction with the broader meaning.

The distinction between "the effect of Reynolds number" and "the effect of the range of relevant scales" is more than a matter of semantics. The two are fundamentally different approaches. The present analysis is a case in point– it links the physics of the p spectrum *directly* to the scales of the flow. The analysis is empirical. Any use of boundary layer scales is empirical in nature– either a scaling combination collapses the curves, or it doesn't. Whether or not the curves collapse can only be verified through experiments. The "effect of the range of relevant scales" is *related* to the Reynolds number, but the two are not the *same*. Following the "effect of the range of relevant scales" approach does not restrict a proposed metric of the boundary layer to the form

$$\text{Metric} = \frac{(\text{velocity scale})(\text{length scale})}{\nu} \qquad (13)$$

For example, R_T, which is used presently.

Since the Reynolds number is more commonly used than R_T to describe a boundary layer, it is useful to show how the two are related. Assuming that the velocity profile can be approximated as

$$\frac{U}{U_e} = \left(\frac{y}{\delta}\right)^{\frac{1}{7}} \qquad (14)$$

and using Blasius' empirical equation for the resistance coefficient in pipe-flow, in the forms

$$C_f = 0.045\left(\frac{\nu}{U_e\delta}\right)^{\frac{1}{4}} \qquad (15)$$

$$\frac{\delta}{x} = 0.37\left(\frac{\nu}{U_e x}\right)^{\frac{1}{5}} \qquad (16)$$

It can be shown that

$$R_T = 0.129\left(\frac{U_e\theta}{\nu}\right)^{\frac{3}{4}} \qquad (17)$$

$$R_T = 0.0107\left(\frac{U_e x}{\nu}\right)^{\frac{3}{5}} \qquad (18)$$

Figure 11 shows that Equation (17) agrees well with experimental data, however, there is better agreement when the constant is slightly changed to

$$R_T = 0.11\left(\frac{U_e\theta}{\nu}\right)^{\frac{3}{4}} \qquad (19)$$

It is noted that Equations (15) and (16) are only strictly valid for low Reynolds number flat-plate boundary layers. However, they are sufficient to qualitatively show how R_T varies with Reynolds. Careful examination of Table 3 shows that as Re_θ of the data increases from 5000–6000, R_T decreases. This discrepancy is because R_T incorporates more information about the boundary layer than Re_θ. Qualitatively, the range, $10 < R_T < 2000$, corresponds to $408 < Re_\theta < 478,000$.

CONCLUSIONS

An empirical spectral model of p has been presented that is similar, in functional form, to the Chase-Howe model and uses the time scale ratio of the boundary layer as a parameter. The model is based on the observed scaling behavior of surface pressure spectra that have been measured by 7 research groups and cover a large range of Reynolds number, $1400 < Re_\theta < 23400$. It is proposed that "the effect of Reynolds number" is more aptly described as "the effect of the range of relevant scales". "The effect of the range of relevant scales" is incorporated into the new model based on the postulate that the only effect of the range of relevant scales is to increase the size of the overlap frequency range. The model can be confidently extrapolated to higher Reynolds number flows since it strictly follows the Reynolds number independent, high-frequency, inner-layer scaling. The p spectral levels and mean square pressure predicted by the model compare well to experimental data.

ACKNOWLEDGEMENTS

This work was sponsored by the Office of Naval Research– Dr. L. P. Purtell, program monitor.

REFERENCES

[1] Schetz, J.A., 1993, *Boundary Layer Analysis*, Prentice-Hall.

[2] Tennekes, H. and Lumley, J.L., 1972, *A First Course in Turbulence*, MIT Press.

[3] Hussain, A.K.M.F., 1986, "Coherent Structures and Turbulence," *Journal of Fluid Mechanics*, Vol. 173, pp. 303-356.

[4] Robinson, S.K., 1991, "Coherent Motions in the Turbulent Boundary Layer," *Annual Review of Fluid Mechanics*, Vol. 23, pp. 601-639.

[5] Panton, R.L., 1990, "Scaling Turbulent Wall Layers," Journal of Fluids Engineering, Vol. 112, pp. 425-432.

[6] Panton, R.L., 2000, "Some Issues Concerning Wall Turbulence," http://www.me.utexas.edu/~panton/.

[7] Gad-el-Hak, M. and Bandyopadhyay, P.R., 1994, "Reynolds Number Effects in Wall-Bounded Turbulent Flows, " *Applied Mechanics Reviews*, Vol. 47, No. 8, pp. 307-365.

[8] DeGraaff, D.B. and Eaton, J.K., 2000, "Reynolds-number Scaling of the Flat-plate Turbulent Boundary Layer," *Journal of Fluid Mechanics*, Vol. 422, pp. 319-346.

[9] Buschmann, M.H and Gad-el-Hak, M., 2001, "The Logarithmic Law In Turbulent Boundary Layers: The Debate Continues," Paper CEF-22, *ASME: Proceedings ICFDP7*, 19-21 Dec 2001.

[10] Afzal, N., 1976, "Millikan's Argument at Moderately Large Reynolds Numbers," *Physics of Fluids*, Vol. 19, pp. 600-602.

[11] Blake, W.K., 1986, *Mechanics of Flow-Induced Sound and Vibration*, Academic Press.

[12] Keith, W.L., Hurdis, D.A., and Abraham, B.M., 1992, "A Comparison of Turbulent Boundary Layer Wall-Pressure Spectra," *Journal of Fluids Engineering*, Vol. 114, pp. 338-347.

[13] Farabee, T.M. and Casarella, M.J., 1991, "Spectral Features of Wall Pressure Fluctuations Beneath Turbulent Boundary Layers," *Physics of Fluids A*, Vol. 3, pp. 2410-2420.

[14] Bradshaw, P., 1967, "'Inactive' Motion and Pressure Fluctuations in Turbulent Boundary Layers," *Journal of Fluid Mechanics*, Vol. 30, pp. 241-258.

[15] Olivero-Bally, P., Forestier, B.B., Focquenoy, E., and Olivero, P., 1993, "Wall-Pressure Fluctuations in Natural and Manipulated Turbulent Boundary Layers in Air and Water," *ASME FED-Vol. 168, Flow Noise Modeling, Measurement, and Control*, pp. 63-74.

[16] Gravante, S.P., Naquib, A.M., Wark, C.E., and Nagib, H.M., 1998, "Characterization of the Pressure Fluctuations Under a Fully Developed Turbulent Boundary Layer," *AIAA Journal*, Vol. 36, pp. 1808-1816.

[17] Goody, M.C., 1999, "An Experimental Investigation of Pressure Fluctuations in Three-Dimensional Turbulent Boundary Layers," Ph.D. Dissertation, *VPI & SU*, Blacksburg, VA. http://scholar.lib.vt.edu/theses/available/etd-120399-144042/

[18] Panton, R.L. and Linebarger, J.H., 1974, "Wall Pressure Spectra Calculations for Equilibrium Boundary Layers," *Journal of Fluid Mechanics*, Vol. 65, pp. 261-287.

[19] McGrath, B.E. and Simpson, R.L., 1987, "Some Features of Surface Pressure Fluctuations in Turbulent Boundary Layers with Zero and Favorable Pressure Gradients," *NASA CR-4051*.

[20] Blake, W.K., 1970, "Turbulent Boundary-Layer Wall-Pressure Fluctuations on Smooth and Rough Walls," *Journal of Fluid Mechanics*, Vol. 44, pp. 637.

[21] Goody, M.C and Simpson, R.L., 1999, "Surface Pressure Fluctuations Beneath Two- and Three-Dimensional Turbulent Boundary Layers," *AIAA Journal*, Vol. 38, No. 10, pp. 1822-1831.

[22] Schewe, G., 1983, "On the Structure and Resolution of Wall-Pressure Fluctuations Associated with Turbulent Boundary-Layer Flow," *Journal of Fluid Mechanics*, Vol. 134, pp. 311-328.

[23] Howe, M.S., 1998, *Acoustics of Fluid-Structure Interactions*, Cambridge University Press, p. 208.

[24] Chase, D.M., 1980, "Modeling the Wavevector-Frequency Spectrum of Turbulent Boundary Layer Wall Pressure," *Journal of Sound and Vibration*, Vol. 70, No. 1, pp. 29-67.

[25] Graham, W.R., 1997, "A Comparison of Models for the Wavevector-Frequency Spectrum of Turbulent Boundary Layer Pressures," *Journal of Sound and Vibration*, Vol. 206, pp. 541-565.

[26] Corcos, G.M., 1964, "The Structure of the Turbulent Pressure Field in Boundary-Layer Flows," *Journal of Fluid Mechanics*, Vol. 18, pp. 353-378.

[27] Efimtsov, B.M., 1982, "Characteristics of the Field of Turbulent Wall Pressure Fluctuations at Large Reynolds Numbers," *Soviet Physics—Acoustics*, Vol. 28, No. 4, pp. 289-292.

[28] Smol'yakov, A.V. and Tkachenko, V.M., 1991, "Model of a Field of Pseudosonic Turbulent Wall Pressures and Experimental data," *Soviet Physics—Acoustics*, Vol. 37, No. 6, pp. 627-631.

[29] Ffowcs Williams, J.E., 1982, "Boundary-Layer Pressures and the Corcos Model: A Development to Incorporate Low Wavenumber Constraints," *Journal of Fluid Mechanics*, Vol. 125, pp. 9-25.

[30] Hwang, Y.F. and Geib, F.E., 1984, "Estimation of the Wavevector-Frequency Spectrum of Turbulent Boundary Layer Wall Pressure by Multiple Linear Regression," *Journal of Vibration, Acoustics, Stress and reliability in Design*, Vol. 106, pp. 334-342.

[31] Witting, J.M., 1986, "A Spectral Model of Pressure Fluctuations at a Rigid Wall Bounding an Incompressible Fluid, Based on Turbulent Structures in the Boundary Layer," *Noise Control Engineering Journal*, Vol. 26, pp. 28-43.

[32] Panton, R.L. and Robert, G., 1994, "The Wavenumber-Phase Velocity Representation for the Turbulent Wall-Pressure Spectrum," *Journal of Fluids Engineering*, Vol. 116, pp. 447-483.

[33] Lighthill, M.J., 1952, "On Sound Generated Aerodynamically: I. General Theory," *Proceedings of the Royal Society of London. Series A*, Vol. 211, pp. 564-587.

[34] Lighthill, M.J., 1954, "On Sound Generated Aerodynamically: II. Turbulence as a Source of Sound," *Proceedings of the Royal Society of London. Series A*, Vol. 222, pp. 1-32.

[35] Kraichnan, R.H., 1956, "Pressure Fluctuations in Turbulent Flow over a Flat Plate," *Journal of the Acoustical Society of America*, Vol. 28, No. 3, pp. 378-390.

[36] Helal, H.M., Casarella, M.J., and Farabee, T.M., 1989, "An Application of Noise Cancellation Techniques to the Measurement of Wall Pressure Fluctuations in a Wind Tunnel," *ASME Winter Annual Meeting*, NCA Vol. 5, Report No. H00563, pp. 49-59.

[37] Agarwal, N.K. and Simpson, R.L., 1989, "A New Technique for Obtaining the Turbulent Pressure Spectrum from the Surface Pressure Spectrum," *Journal of Sound and Vibration*, Vol. 135, pp. 346-350.

[38] Naquib, A.M., Gravante, S.P., and Wark, C.E., 1989, "Extraction of Turbulent Wall-Pressure Time-Series using an Optimal Filtering Scheme," *Experiments in Fluids*, Vol. 22, pp. 14-22.

[39] Corcos, G.M., 1963, "Resolution of Pressure in Turbulence," *Journal of the Acoustical Society of America*, Vol. 35, No. 2, pp. 192-199.

[40] Willmarth, W.W. and Roos, F.W., 1965, "Resolution and Structure of the Wall Pressure Field Beneath a Turbulent Boundary Layer," *Journal of Fluid Mechanics*, Vol. 22, pp. 81-94.

[41] White, P.H., 1967, "Effect of Transducer Size, Shape, and Surface Sensitivity on the Measurement of Boundary Layer Pressures," *Journal of the Acoustical Society of America*, Vol. 41, No. 5, pp. 1358-1363.

[42] Chase, D.M., 1969, "Turbulent-Boundary-Layer Pressure Fluctuations and Wavenumber Filtering by Nonuniform Spatial Averaging," *Journal of the Acoustical Society of America*, Vol. 46, No. 5, pp. 1350-1365.

[43] Gilchrist, R.B. and Strawderman, W.A., 1965, "Experimental Hydrophone-Size Correction Factor for Boundary-Layer Pressure Fluctuations," *Journal of the Acoustical Society of America*, Vol. 38, pp. 298-302.

[44] Geib, F.E., 1969, "Measurements on the Effect of Transducer Size on the Resolution of Boundary-Layer Pressure Fluctuations," *Journal of the Acoustical Society of America*, Vol. 46, No. 1, pp. 253-261.

[45] Lueptow, R.M., 1995, "Transducer Resolution and the Turbulent Wall Pressure Spectrum," *Journal of the Acoustical Society of America*, Vol. 97, No. 1, pp. 370-378.

Reference	Data Set	Fluid	BL Scale Ratios		Measurement Issues			
			Time (R_T)	Pressure (C_f)	Low Frequency	High Frequency		
						d^+	3 dB attenuation	
							$\omega\delta/U_e$	$\omega v/u_\tau^2$
Blake[20]	BL 8210	Air	94.71	0.00293	AWT	43	65.1	0.69
	BL 10200		104.12	0.00274		51	61.7	0.59
	BL 13200		120.70	0.00245		63	61.2	0.51
	BL 17000		138.02	0.00218		78	60.1	0.44
Farabee and Casarella[13]	FC 3386	Air	47.11	0.00325	AWT NC	33	39.8	0.85
	FC 4487		60.02	0.00306		44	39.1	0.65
	FC 6025		76.18	0.00287		57	39.7	0.52
Gravante et al[16]	GR 4972	Air	63.12	0.00273	NC	12	159	2.52
	GR 6241		73.23	0.00264		12	191	2.61
	GR 7076		87.69	0.00278		12	223	2.54
Goody and Simpson[21]	GS 7300	Air	81.99	0.00262	NC	29	88.2	1.08
	GS 23400		274.02	0.00217		31	303	1.11
McGrath and Simpson[19]	MS 7010	Air	86.44	0.00280	NC	27	97.4	1.11
	MS 18820		186.04	0.00226		36	179	0.95
Olivero-Bally et al[15]	OB 4261	Air	65.92	0.00323	NC	10	194	2.92
	OB 5586		80.53	0.00300		9	258	3.17
	OB 8700	H_2O	192.91	0.00322	NC	30	187	0.95
	OB 21400		371.56	0.00253		80	149	0.40
Schewe[22]	SCH 1400	Air	24.69	0.00395	AWT	19	33.8	1.37

AWT = Acoustic Wind Tunnel Used;   NC = Noise Cancellation Employed

Table 1. Some relevant experimental parameters for each of the data sets. Each data set name is constructed using a unique letter combination that denotes the reference, and a number that corresponds to the Re_θ of the data set. The 3 dB attenuation points were calculated using the attenuated power table of Corcos[39] and assuming that $U_C = 0.6U_e$.

| Reference | Data Set | Measurement Range | | Spectral Features | | | |
| | | $\omega\delta/U_e$ | $\omega v/u_\tau^2$ | $[\Phi(\omega)U_e/\tau_w^2\delta]_{MAX}$ | | $[\Phi(\omega)u_\tau^2/\tau_w^2 v]$(dB), $\omega v/u_\tau^2=1$ | |
				dB	$\omega\delta/U_e$	Published	Corrected
Blake[20]	BL 8210	1.1 − 156	0.0011 − 2.2	-4	1.5 − 4.0	-6.6	-1.8
	BL 10200	0.42 − 172	0.0041 − 1.7	-3	1.5 − 3.0	-5.1	0.7
	BL 13200	0.41 − 139	0.0034 − 1.2	-1	2.0	-5.1	2.1
	BL 17000	0.38 − 22	0.0027 − 0.2	-2	1.0 − 4.0		
Farabee & Casarella[13]	FC 3386	0.012 − 116	0.00026 − 2.5	-3	1.0 − 3.0	-2.7	1.0
	FC 4487	0.0078 − 139	0.00013 − 2.3	-3	1.0 − 3.0	-1.7	3.4
	FC 6025	0.0076 − 152	0.00010 − 2.0	-2	1.0 − 3.0	-4.1	2.8
Gravante et al[16]	GR 4972	0.74 − 185	0.012 − 2.9	-2	2.0 − 4.0	0.3	1.4
	GR 6241	1.09 − 208	0.015 − 2.8	-2	1.5 − 5.0	-1.5	-0.4
	GR 7076	0.96 − 251	0.011 − 2.9	-2	2.0 − 5.0	-3.3	-2.2
Goody & Simpson[21]	GS 7300	0.90 − 177	0.0011 − 2.2			-1.4	1.4
	GS 23400	0.93 − 525	0.0034 − 1.9			1.9	4.6
McGrath & Simpson[19]	MS 7010	0.13 − 115	0.0015 − 1.3	0	0.5 − 0.7	-2.7	0.0
	MS 18820	0.20 − 159	0.0011 − 0.85	1	0.5 − 0.8		
Olivero-Bally et al[15]	OB 4261	2.4 − 100	0.036 − 1.5			2.5	3.5
	OB 5586	1.2 − 115	0.014 − 1.4	0	1.5 − 4.0	1.6	2.5
	OB 8700	0.79 − 157	0.0041 − 0.81	0	2.0 − 4.0		
	OB 21400	1.4 − 176	0.0038 − 0.47	-1	1.5 − 4.0		
Schewe[22]	SCH 1400	0.56 − 37	0.0023 − 1.5	-2	1.0 − 4.0	2.6	4.7

Table 2. Selected spectral features of each of the data sets. Missing entries indicate that the spectral feature could not be ascertained from the data set. The "corrected" dB level (last column) was calculated using the attenuated power table of Corcos[39] and assuming that $U_C = 0.6U_e$.

Data Set	Re_θ	R_T	$\overline{p^2}/\tau_w^2$				
			Published	Corrected	Difference[†]	Model	Difference[‡]
SCH 1400	1400	24.69	6.7	9.9	9.8 %	7.5	-6.9 %
FC 3386	3386	47.11	9.7	10.7	2.3 %	10.9	0.6 %
OB 4261	4261	65.92	9.1	18.7	17 %	12.0	-11 %
FC 4487	4487	60.02	10.1	13.8	7.6 %	12.3	-2.8 %
GR 4972	4972	63.12	9.0	10.7	4.2 %	12.4	3.7 %
OB 5586	5586	80.53		20.7		13.7	-10 %
FC 6025	6025	76.18	10.8	17.3	12 %	14.0	-5.2 %
GR 6241	6241	73.23	9.0	10.6	4.0 %	13.2	5.5 %
MS 7010	7010	86.44	12.7	13.0	0.6 %	14.5	2.6 %
GR 7076	7076	87.69	8.2	10.3	5.7 %	14.4	8.3 %
GS 7300	7300	81.99	11.8	13.6	3.4 %	13.9	0.6 %
BL 8210	8210	94.71	13.0	11.4	-3.2 %	15.3	7.2 %
OB 8700	8700	192.9	14.2	19.0	7.2 %	19.6	0.8 %
BL 10200	10200	104.1	13.0	13.6	1.1 %	15.7	3.6 %
BL 13200	13200	120.7	13.0	21.8	13 %	17.1	-6.1 %
BL 17000	17000	138.0	13.0	10.0	-6.5 %	10.0	0 %
MS 18820	18820	186.0	13.5	17.4	6.4 %	19.5	2.8 %
OB 21400	21400	371.6	14.4	20.9	9.2 %	23.0	2.4 %
GS 23400	23400	274.0	18.7	21.7	3.7 %	22.1	0.4 %

[†] The percent difference between the Corrected and Reported value

[‡] The percent difference between the Model and Corrected value

Table 3. The mean square pressure normalized by the wall shear stress for each data set compared to the value computed by integrating the model p spectrum. The "corrected" value was computed by integrating the experimental p spectra after correcting each for high-frequency attenuation due to finite transducer size using the table provided by Corcos[39] with $U_C = 0.6U_e$.

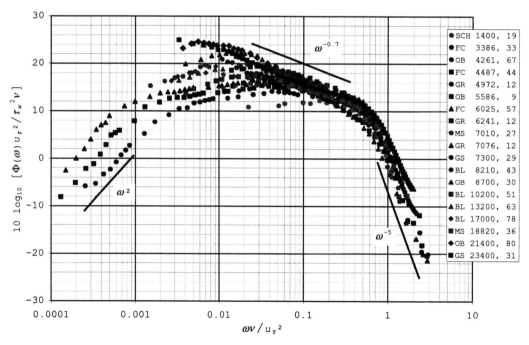

Figure 1. Experimental p spectra normalized by inner variables– τ_w as the pressure scale and v/u_τ^2 as the time scale. Each data set name is constructed using a unique letter combination that denotes the reference (see Table 1) and a number that corresponds to the Re_θ of the data set. The second number in the legend is the d^+ of the transducer used to measure the data set. The p spectra are corrected for high-frequency attenuation due to finite transducer size using the table provided by Corcos[39] with $U_C = 0.6U_e$.

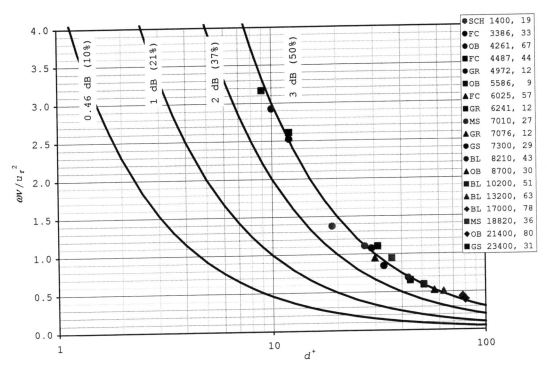

Figure 2. The inner-scaled frequency, $\omega v/u_\tau^2$, at which the measured p spectrum is attenuated as a function of d^+. The solid black lines denote the indicated amount of attenuation (Equation (2)). The experimental data is only shown for 3 dB attenuation. The agreement between Equation (2) and the data is similar for the other attenuation curves. Each data set name is constructed using a unique letter combination that denotes the reference (see Table 1) and a number that corresponds to the Re_θ of the data set. The 2nd number in the legend is the d^+ of the transducer used to measure the data set.

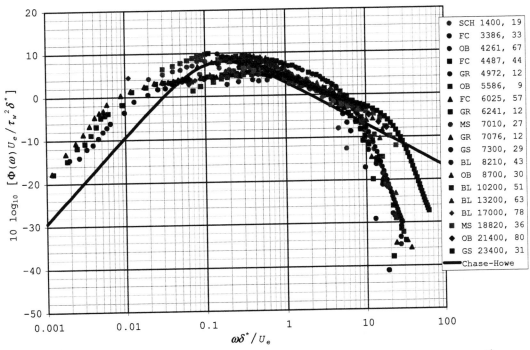

Figure 3. Experimental p spectra normalized by outer variables– τ_w as the pressure scale and δ^*/U_e as the time scale. Each data set name is constructed using a unique letter combination that denotes the reference (see Table 1) and a number that corresponds to the Re_θ of the data set. The second number in the legend is the d^+ of the transducer used to measure the data set. The p spectra plotted here are as they were published– no correction has been applied.

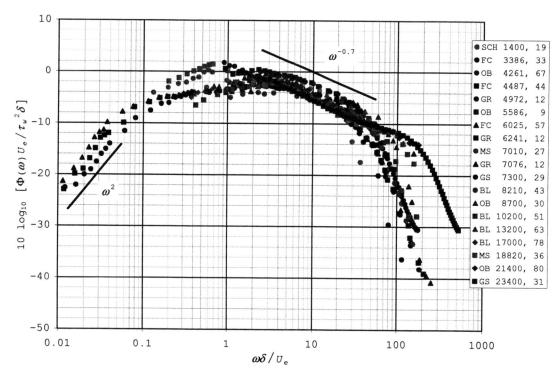

Figure 4. Experimental p spectra normalized by outer variables– τ_w as the pressure scale and δ/U_e as the time scale. Each data set name consists of a unique letter combination that denotes the reference (see Table 1) and a number that corresponds to the Re_θ of the data set. The second number in the legend is the d^+ of the transducer used to measure the data set. The p spectra are corrected for high-frequency attenuation due to finite transducer size using the table provided by Corcos[39] with $U_C = 0.6U_e$.

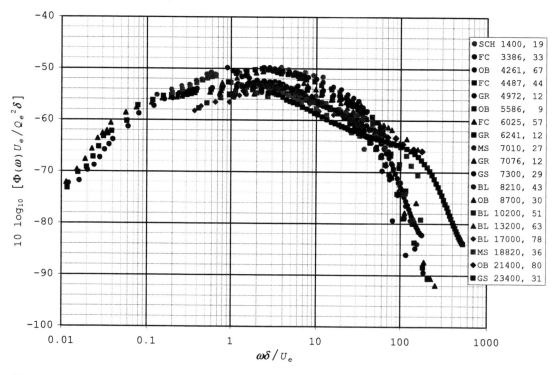

Figure 5. Experimental p spectra normalized by outer variables– Q_e as the pressure scale and δ/U_e as the time scale. Each data set name is constructed using a unique letter combination that denotes the reference (see Table 1) and a number that corresponds to the Re_θ of the data set. The second number in the legend is the d^+ of the transducer used to measure the data set. The p spectra are corrected for high-frequency attenuation due to finite transducer size using the table provided by Corcos[39] with $U_C = 0.6U_e$.

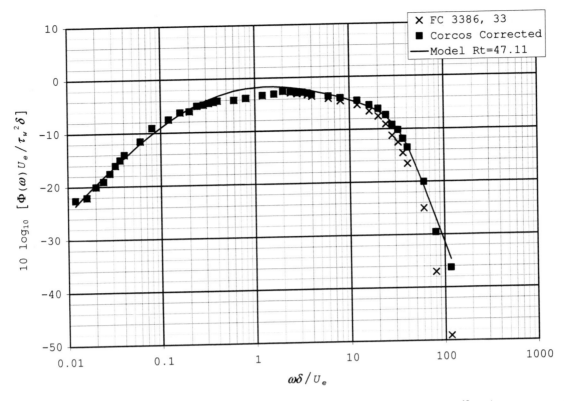

Figure 6. A comparison of the present model with the data of Farabee and Casarella[13]: $d^+ = 33$, $Re_\theta = 3386$, $R_T = 47.11$.

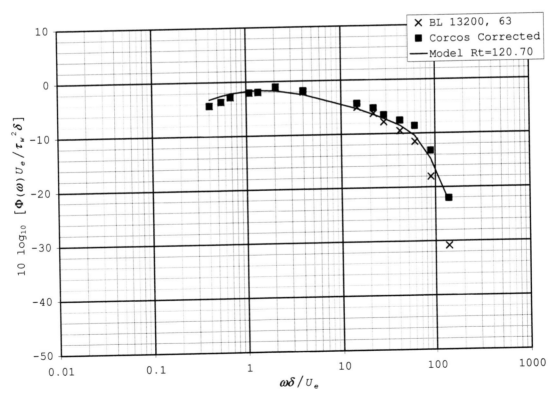

Figure 7. A comparison of the present model with the data of Blake[20]: $d^+ = 63$, $Re_\theta = 13200$, $R_T = 120.7$.

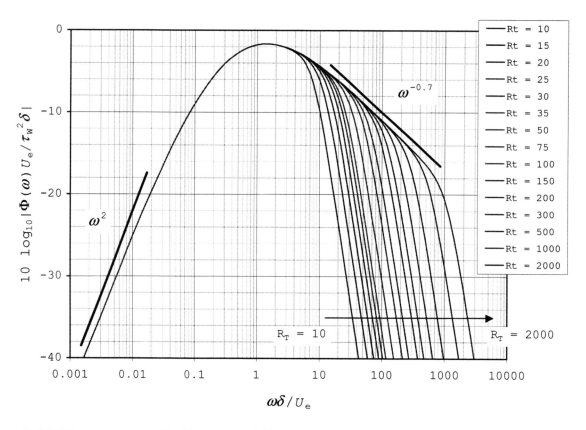

Figure 8. Model p spectra normalized by outer variables– τ_w as the pressure scale and δ/U_e as the time scale.

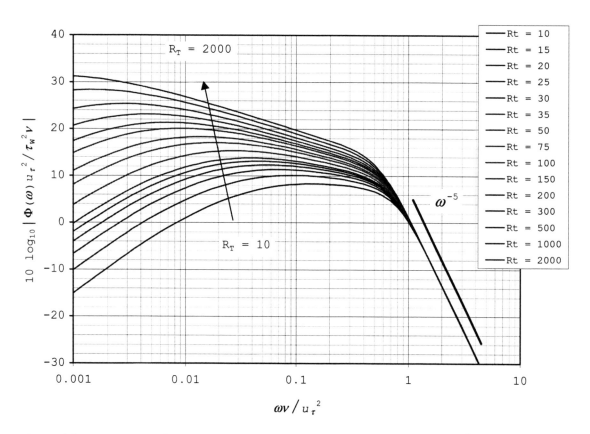

Figure 9. Model p spectra normalized by inner variables– τ_w as the pressure scale and ν/u_τ^2 as the time scale.

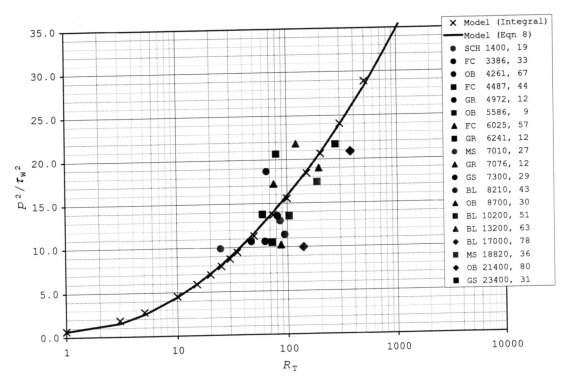

Figure 10. The mean square pressure normalized by the wall shear stress for each data set compared to the value computed by integrating the model p spectrum. The value for each data set was computed by integrating the experimental p spectra after correcting for high-frequency attenuation due to finite transducer size using the table provided by Corcos[39] with $U_C = 0.6 U_e$. Each data set name consists of a unique letter combination that denotes the reference (see Table 1) and a number that corresponds to the Re_θ of the data set.

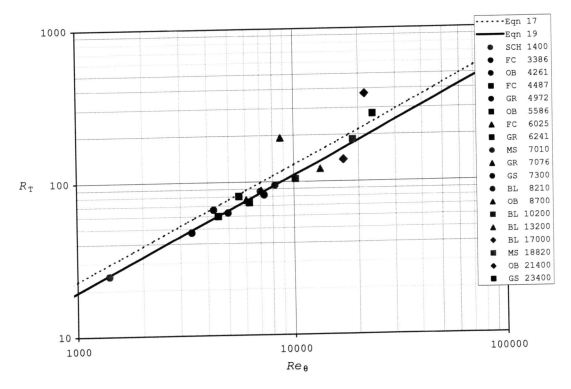

Figure 11. The time scale ratio, R_T, as a function of Re_θ for the experimental data sets.

PHASE SYNCHRONIZATION AND DESYNCHRONIZATION OF STRUCTURAL RESPONSE INDUCED BY TURBULENT AND EXTERNAL SOUND

Lucio Maestrello[*]

NASA Langley Research Center
Hampton, VA 23681-2199

Abstract

Acoustic and turbulent boundary layer flow loadings over a flexible structure are used to study the spatial-temporal dynamics of the response of the structure. The stability of the spatial synchronization and desynchronization by an active external force is investigated with an array of coupled transducers on the structure. In the synchronous state, the structural phase is locked, which leads to the formation of spatial patterns while the amplitude peaks exhibit chaotic behaviors. Large amplitude, spatially symmetric loading is superimposed on broadband, but in the desynchronized state, the spectrum broadens and the phase space is lost. The resulting pattern bears a striking resemblance to phase turbulence. The transition is achieved by using a low power external actuator to trigger broadband behaviors from the knowledge of the external acoustic load inducing synchronization. The changes are made favorably and efficiently to alter the frequency distribution of power, not the total power level. Before synchronization effects are seen, the panel response to the turbulent boundary layer loading is discontinuously spatiotemporally correlated. The stability develops from different competing wavelengths; the spatial scale is significantly shorter than when forced with the superimposed external sound. When the external sound level decreases and the synchronized phases are lost, changes in the character of the spectra can be linked to the occurrence of spatial phase transition. These changes can develop broadband response. Synchronized responses of fuselage structure panels have been observed in subsonic and supersonic aircraft; results from two flights tests are discussed.

---

[*]Senior Research Scientist, Aerodynamics, Aerothermodynamics, and Acoustics Competency, Associate Fellow AIAA.

1. Background

The interaction of two unrelated nonlinear signals, surface pressure from turbulent boundary layer flow and external high intensity tonal sound, can induce synchronization of the response of a flexible structure. As a result, large amplitude, spatially symmetric loading is superimposed on broadband loading. The history of synchronization goes back to Huygens 1673[1] in his observation of two pendulum clocks. Synchronization which occurs in nonlinear self-sustained oscillators driven by an external periodic force coupled with each other is described by Anishchenko et al.[2] In the early 1990s, the work of Pecora and Carroll[3] stimulated interest in the synchronization of chaotic systems. Since then, it has become an active field of research over a range of disciplines including engineering, physics, chemistry, biology, medicine, astronomy.[3–8] Over the last decade applications have been developed in communication systems where the message is masked by chaos.[9] Heagy et al.[5] and Rosenblum et al.[6] have focused on the instabilities of the synchronous state, which turn out to be very useful for practical applications in nonlinear dynamics. The opposite of phase synchronization is phase desynchronization that is the known physical phenomena in engineering of systems that undergo structural changes due to changes in the degrees of freedom or symmetry and are also used in the study of DNA helix.[2]

The phenomenon of *phase synchronization of coupled chaotic systems* is presently a topic of great interest.[2,5,6] Periodic systems are usually called synchronized if either their phase or frequencies are locked.[10] We demonstrate synchronization from two dissimilar nonlinear chaotic inputs—turbulent boundary layer and exterior tonal sound—when globally coupled to the structure. We show that this behavior is due to synchronization of the phase of the input while the amplitude remains uncorrelated in most cases;[6] we have found also some cases of frequency synchronization.[11]

As a result, the structure becomes highly loaded and coupled to both exterior and interior pressures; the response indicates the presence of harmonics and subharmonics superimposed on broadband.[12,13,14] In the absence of exterior acoustic forcing, the response of the structure possesses spatiotemporal behavior and shorter spatial scale due to coupling with exterior turbulent boundary layer loading.[15,16] Synchronization of sound with turbulent and laminar boundary layers also occurs as an interference problem in wind tunnel experiments; this has been a difficult problem.

This paper also describes desynchronized response, which is a result of phase transition designed to redistribute the power into broadband by using a low power actuator to control the response. An alternative method was proposed by Zheng et al.[17,18,19] The control approach allows us to select and manipulate the outcome of synchronized response from a fixed space point and to estimate the transient time that the trajectories take to converge into the desynchronized state. Non-feedback control is used to perform changes in the system response. This method has been applied in various fields, such as chemical reaction, neuron chaos, electronic systems.[20,21,22] They have been extended to control high-dimensional systems and applied to other situations such as the synchronization of chaotic systems and the control of spatial systems. Spatial phase synchronization is perceived as increasing aircraft interior noise and structural fatigue, whereas desynchronization has a rather general meaning such as suppressing synchronization when harmful while producing chaos when useful. The time series analysis provides tools to identify dynamical systems from the measured data. The present experiment provides two examples of different structures and external forcing to describe the stability of synchronous oscillation and to demonstrate its applicability.

The first part of this experiment relates to the spatiotemporal dynamics over multidomain regions of space when the panel is forced by turbulent boundary layer. The interactions among these regions lead to spatiotemporal chaos. The second part relates to single-domain response due to synchronization of the turbulent boundary layer with external tonal sound. The third part is on transition from synchronous to asynchronous phase response by forcing the panels with an external force actuator. With knowledge of the initial forcing condition, the response can be manipulated with a very small amount of power to trigger the tonal response into broadband. This paper begins with instrumentation

and signal processing in Sec. 2. Sec. 3 describes the panel response experiment. Analysis and interpretation is discussed in Sec. 4.

2. Instrumentation and Signal Processing

The apparatus is an open circuit wind tunnel which has been described at length in previous papers.[12] The present experiment is conducted on two aluminum aircraft structures of different sizes mounted on the wind tunnel sidewall opposite the anechoic wall, where the acoustic source is located, and is designed to study boundary layer and sound interaction problems. Panel A consists of two flat sections joined by a tear stopper mounted on a rigid baffle (Fig. 1) with measurements along the centerline of the downstream section. Two sections are necessary to allow wave transmission from one to the other. Each section is 0.65 m long, 0.20 m wide, 0.001 m thick, and the tear stopper is 0.0125 m wide, 0.0128 m thick. Panel B is a curved fuselage structure made in six sections with one longitudinal and two lateral tear stoppers equally spaced (Fig. 2). Measurements are made on the lower center section of the panel. Each section is 1.019 m long, 0.305 m wide, and 0.109 cm thick, with a radius of curvature of 2.529 m. The boundaries of the panel with tear stoppers and frame are smooth with a radius of curvature of 0.04 m to minimize the amplitude of reflected waves at the boundaries. The geometry of the tear stoppers on panel B is a departure from the standard blunt discontinuity used in aircraft and on panel A. The Reynolds number per meter Re/m is 2.85×10^5, velocity freestream U_e is 46 m/s, and boundary layer thickness is 0.060 m. The acoustic field is created by four 120-W speakers on the anechoic side with a power level of 138 dB. The forcing frequency of the speakers is set to $f_1 = 475$ Hz for panel A, and $f_1 = 1075$, $f_2 = 1212$, and $f_3 = 1362$ Hz for panel B. Miniature pressure transducers measure the wall pressure fluctuations. The flow velocity is measured by a hot wire anemometer, and the vibration response is measured by miniature accelerometers. The active controller is a feed-forward, open-loop system[23] freely suspended and mounted at the center of the panel. Accelerometer signals provide the output signal from the panel motion. An accelerometer is also placed at the shaker-panel interface. Data are analyzed to evaluate the response and used to identify nonlinearity.[23] The study of the dynamical property, Hilbert transform, is used in signal processing. This approach gives the instantaneous phase and amplitude for the signal, which is a complex function of time.[7,2]

3. Response of Panels

We investigated a scheme for modulating the structural fundamental and formation of harmonic and subharmonic frequencies, as well as for demodulating the response into broadband chaos. Chaos response is a desirable feature in the present application. The first part of the experiment relates the spatiotemporal dynamics over the multidomain region of space when the panel is forced by the turbulent boundary layer. The interaction among these regions leads to spatiotemporal chaos. The second part relates to single-domain response due to synchronization of the turbulent boundary layer and tonal sound loadings, using mono- and three-incommensurate frequency forcing. The third part is on transition from synchronous to asynchronous phase response. As a result, the spectrum broadens by driving the panels with an external force actuator at the initial sound-forcing conditions. The question whether the experiment can be regarded as a representation of in-flight aircraft structural response by exploring the nonlinear dynamics is discussed in Sec. 3.6 where flight test data in subsonic and supersonic aircraft are analyzed.

3.1. Response Due to Turbulent Boundary Layer Loading

Discrete time measurements of the response are made at different spatial locations using a one-dimensional array of accelerometers along a panel centerline. With an appropriate dc bias, one observes the time-dependent propagation and the spatial extent of the nonpropagating waves and the formation of the spatial structure of the surface when forced by the turbulent boundary layer. The continuous change of domain response is an example of spatiotemporal chaos. The pattern is described in terms of amplitude, time, and space along the centerline of the panel and bears a striking resemblance to spatiotemporal chaos turbulence. Data show wide unpredictable ranges of pattern formations with unrepeatable occurrences that coexist and evolve in space-time. Results also show that the spatial scales of the propagating disturbances are less than the boundary layer thickness $\delta(y)$ and much less than the length of the panel. Space-time response indicates reduction in amplitude with distance downstream due to the suppression of the growth of the higher frequency components. The spatial and temporal responses of the panel wave are not separable, the spatial evolution can affect the temporal behavior and vice versa.

The acceleration responses $g(x,t)$ and the phase $dg(x,t)/dt$ versus $g(x,t)$ over the time interval $\Delta t = 0.04$ sec along the panel centerline of panel A, at four equally spaced locations $x = 0.00624, 0.1248, 0.1822, 0.2196$ m are shown in Figs. 3a and 3b. The vibrating motion is induced by the fluid-elastic coupling of the turbulent shear layer. The data indicate distinct propagating wave patterns as well as nonpropagating ones emitting disturbance very slowly with time. The nonpropagating pattern coexists over a larger portion of time before switching into propagating patterns again by superimposition. The propagation disturbances have velocity less than the boundary layer freestream velocity. The result contradicts time-averaged space-time correlation measurements which show continuous well-behaved convection patterns.

3.2. Spatial Phase Synchronization Induced by Turbulent Boundary Layer and Sound Forcing

Synchronized response of a typical aircraft panel structure results from the interaction between an external tonal sound and a turbulent boundary layer forcing a structure. The degree to which the panel oscillations adjust to a synchronous response depend on the degree to which the forcing adjusts to the panel motion.

Phase synchronization is associated with spatial ordering of the phase induced by turbulent boundary layer $\phi_1(t)$ with external sound phase $\phi_2(t)$ on the structure. As a result, the phase difference is

$$\phi_{n,m}(t) = n\,\phi_1(t) - m\,\phi_2(t) = \text{Constant}$$

where ϕ_1 and ϕ_2 are phases, n and m are integers, and $\phi_{m,n}$ is the generalized phase difference. This condition is valid for quasi-periodic oscillations only with two incommensurate frequencies. The second type corresponds to phase locking described by Rosenblum et al.[6] in coupled chaotic system as

$$|n\,\phi_1(t) - m\,\phi_2(t)| < \text{Constant}$$

the amplitudes of the two systems may be completely uncorrelated, that is, linearly independent. Note that for the determination of synchronous states it is irrelevant whether the amplitudes of both inputs are different. Alternatively one can use the concept of frequency synchronization if the weaker condition[11]

$$\Gamma_{n,m}(t) = <n\phi_1(t) - m\phi_2(t)> = 0$$

is satisfied; $< >$ denotes time average.

Experimentally, the phase due to the interaction of the flow and external sound slips. Reconstructing the phase synchronization from experimental data has a limit, since the total phase is made up of coherent, average, and random fluctuating parts as indicated by Anishchenko et al.[2] and Pikovsky et al.[7] The experimental phase synchronization is characterized by a sharp peak response, whereas the asynchronous response spreads over a broadband at nearly equal power. Synchronization is a function of the coupling strength because of particular instability driven by long acoustic wavelength on the turbulent boundary layer forcing the structure.

The flow speed and tonal sound are kept low in the beginning. As time progresses, the flow and acoustic loading are gradually increased until the panel reaches a transition into a synchronized response. During the transition, the response remains synchronized for a certain period of time, becomes unsynchronized, and then becomes synchronized again. After further increases in tonal level, the response becomes nearly continuous to permanently synchronized. At fixed forcing frequencies as the flow velocity increases to the constant value, the formation of harmonics and subharmonics of the driving frequency and the phase locking on the panel superimposed on the broadband turbulent boundary layer loading are observed. The synchronized spatial pattern is attributed to high acoustic loading and to the spatial scale of the tonal sound relationship to the spatial scale of the convected turbulent boundary layer flow.

3.3. Monofrequency Forcing Turbulent Boundary Layer—Panel A

Measurements for panel A are made in real time at three equally spaced locations along the centerline. The high amplitude tonal sound on turbulent boundary layer at frequency $f_1 = 475$ Hz leads to a spatial phase synchronization response. The synchronized phase is characterized by many closely spaced peaks resulting from the modulation in the phase and time domains. The combination of the acoustic and turbulent pressure fluctuations gives rise to the time series of the acceleration response $g(x,t)$ representing the motion of the surface. The corresponding computed power spectral density $G(x,T)$ and the total phase $dg(x,t)/dt$ versus $g(x,t)$ are shown in Figs. 4a and 4b. The figures describe the main feature of the dynamics. The response seems to consist of harmonic waves coupled with random fluctuating amplitude and bandwidth. Data from selected locations show that their motions are temporally chaotic but spatially periodic.

An increase in synchronization response, that is, a measurement of phase coherence, is regarded as a state of increased acoustic loading that will induce coupling with the turbulent flow; thus, the response of the structure is affected. The phase space measured over finite time is also nearly periodic with superimposed irregular modulations, concentrated over bandwidths, whereas outside the phase difference, changes are nearly continuous and averaged approximately over 2π. The phase spreading is due to the lack of phase synchronization leading toward phase turbulence. The synchronized spectrum is broadband with superimposed sharp periodic peaks indicating dominant frequencies. The windows of chaos are apparent between synchronized peaks. The broadening of the peak bandwidth can be thought of as an amplitude modulation of the spectrum of an otherwise periodic response. As a result the power spectra plots contain superimposed peaks and bandwidth modulation; this leads to the conclusion that the panel surface maintains periodic response with oscillating peak amplitude and bandwidth from location to location. The intensity distribution decreases with harmonic order irregularity, perhaps because of phase-amplitude-frequency mismatch between harmonic bands due to depletion of nonlinearity. Spatial symmetry imposes stringent conditions on the dynamics response of the structure; when symmetry is slightly broken because of an increase in external sound level, one observes complicated quasi-periodic behavior. The spectrum of the response leads to the conclusion that the panel surface maintains periodic response with oscillating peak amplitude and bandwidth from location to location.

The results exhibit spatial phase synchronization, which has not been studied theoretically. The plots (Fig. 4) are obtained from the short time signal processes of the time series data; the phase and spectra peaks, due to temporal superposition of events, contain coherent, average, and random fluctuation parts as interpreted by Pikovsky et al.[7] The chaotic peak and bandwidth modulations create a complex phase. Different ways have been used to define the phase in signal analysis. The problem is discussed in Sec. 4.

3.4. Multiple Frequencies Forcing Turbulent Boundary Layer—Panel B

Measurements of the panel response are made simultaneously at four equally spaced points along the centerline of the bottom center panel (Fig. 2). Figs. 5a and 5b show the acceleration response $g(x,t)$ of the time series over the time interval t and the computed power spectral density $G(f,T)$. The tonal sound is superimposed on the turbulent boundary layer broadband response generated of three incommensurate frequencies $f_1 = 1075$, $f_2 = 1212$, and $f_3 = 1362$ Hz. The time series is made up by wave packet response. The modulations in the series have been previously observed[23,24] to be the result of frequency locking due to the intermix periodic and nonperiodic phases and frequencies.[23] A particular feature of the power spectra is the appearance of incommensurate frequencies mixed with harmonics and subharmonics. As a result, differences in response between locations are mainly on the association of the harmonics and subharmonics transient due to unstable-unstable fluid and acoustic forcing.[22] The two inputs, the turbulent boundary layer and sound, are coupled; synchronization in their dynamical variables has occurred because of coupling strength induced by their unstable pair of inputs. Observations from different data runs have indicated the occurrence of a nonuniqueness spatial-temporal response between runs. An example, the plots in Fig. 5, indicates a temporal shift between the top two locations (interpreted convective effects), whereas at the bottom two locations it is weakly correlated and frozen in space.

3.5. Phase Desynchronization Induced by External Forcing

The desynchronization of a synchronous response is a changed power distribution from peak level to broadband level using active external forcing. A small shaker attached to the panel provides the external force.

Control of a dynamic system, via phase transition, has to be associated with improved performance to be of value in aircraft applications. Control of the peak spectral density of a synchronized response is a loss of synchronization, which gives rise to multiscaling and phase turbulence. The changes of the phase from partially synchronized to synchronized are shown in Figs. 6a and 6b for panel A at location $x = 0.02331$ m. The spectra also reduced to broadband level, via partially synchronized into desynchronized state, are shown in Figs. 6c and 6d compared with the synchronized response. The initial tonal forcing triggers changes in the response redistributing the energy of the fundamental and harmonics into broadband. In this experiment, the property of the initial forcing relates to frequency, amplitude, and phase of the fundamental tones at each fixed-point measurement on the panel.[12,27,22,28] The broadband spectra of the panel response has lower amplitude than the synchronized

spectra; the change in response is obtained without significant change in total response power. The spectra peak level reduces about 15-dB power on the average. The integrated spectra level indicates that a small amount of energy is lost in the process because of the broadband redistribution. The resulting response is made up of a large number of unstable orbits, similar to the response when the structure is forced by turbulent boundary layer alone. The initial tonal forcing was found to be an effective trigger of changes in the redistributing energy favorably and efficiently.[27] The stability of the fundamentals and harmonics, as well as incommensurable frequencies, not shown, play a large role on the active control dynamics. The enhanced stability seems to be the breakup of large spatial domain of the synchronized response into smaller space domain. The synchronized control responses, originated from different runs, cannot be duplicated experimentally. Spatial domain is large enough that the boundary spatial effects can be neglected when the response is synchronized. The breakup of the synchronized domain leads to a progressive collapse of the spatial domain. The spatially synchronized perturbations have larger amplitude than the asynchronous spatiotemporal perturbations.

3.6. Flight Test Measurements

Synchronized responses from measurements on selected airplane fuselage structure panels in subsonic and supersonic flights are discussed.

3.6.1. Subsonic flight. The data analyzed on a Boeing MD-90 (derivative of DC-9) fuselage panel were recorded at Mach number 0.80 and an altitude of 10,000 m, by Mathur et al.[29] The response of the accelerometer 41, located 8 m downstream on the right side of the fuselage, was analyzed. The analysis is from the time series using short-time signal processing. The series indicates the occurrence of sharp periodic peaks intermixed with nonperiodic ones. The peaks and bandwidth oscillate because of the nonstationarity of the input. The time series, the computed spectrum, and phase responses are shown in Figs. 7a, 7b, and 7c. Periodic peaks at approximately a 263-Hz interval dominate the response; the amplitude levels exceed the broadband level by 10-dB power. Note that few peaks dominate the response, due to turbulent boundary layer loading alone, because the measurement location is remote from engine noise and wing interference. The phase indicates convection; the disturbances propagate along the direction of flow. The panel response is not synchronized, as in the previous experiments in

Secs. 3.3, 3.4, and 3.5. The peak frequency loadings are associated with both incommensurate and commensurate frequencies; the dominant peaks are periodic. Because the initial forcing was established to be the origin of the response state, control can be applied to the original orbits, which can yield an improved performance or steady state. A single low power activator on the panel may control the peak periodicity loading that propagates over the entire surface[27,30]. Since 1971, from measurements on a Boeing 727[31] at Mach number 0.85, only a few modes were known to dominate the response and interior noise level toward the front part of the fuselage; this is consistent with present measurements.

3.6.2. Supersonic flight.

The data analyzed on a panel structure of a Tu-144LL supersonic transport was recorded at Mach number 1.95 and an altitude of 17,000 m and reported by Rizzi et al.[32] The data are from an accelerometer above the wing and window on the right side of the fuselage, location 10.15. The data were analyzed from the time series; the computed power spectrum and phase responses are shown in Figs. 8a, 8b, and 8c. The three plots indicate nonperiodic, nonstationary behaviors, well-defined spectra peaks, and the phase indicative of convection waves on the panel surface propagating along the direction of flow.[33] With regard to the time history plots, successive time records indicate portions which are solely characterized by turbulent boundary layer loading (Fig. 8d) and other portions can be characterized by superposition of moving shock on turbulent boundary layer (Fig. 8e). The superposition of shocks with turbulent boundary layer can induce a synchronized response.[4,6,7] The results are not surprising, because the pressure above the wing is known to have nonuniform distribution, due to compression-expansion waves temporally super-imposed on turbulent boundary layer.

4. Analysis and Interpretation of Experimental Data

A prediction of the evolution of the driven system based on data from the response is possible because any time series measured at the response may be viewed as a time series from the combined systems, drive and response, and may, thus, be used to reconstruct and predict the dynamics of drive and response.[22] For small coupling, the response of the panel structure undergoes a transition from synchronized state to a chaotic state or spatially disordered phase. These phases indicate that the synchronous state is self-sustained.

4.1. Panel Response Spectrum

Consider the motion of n points on a nonlinear flexible panel at $x = x_1, x_2,..., x_n$, subject to the loading by the pressure fluctuation $p_T(x_i,t)$ in the turbulent boundary layer and an external periodic acoustic excitation $p_A(x_i,t)$ at $x = x_i$ (Fig. 9). As a simple model, assume that the motion of the point x_i is governed by a nonlinear differential equation,

$$\ddot{u}_i(t) + \mu\, \dot{u}_i(t) + r_i(w_i) = p_i(t) + q_i(t) \quad (i = 1,2,...,n) \quad (1)$$

where u_i is panel displacement; r_i is nonlinear elastic restoring force, which, for large separation of points, has no interaction with other points; $p_i(t) = p_T(x_i,t)$ and $q_i(t) = p_A(x_i,t)$ where $i = 1, 2,..., n$, and μ is the damping coefficient. For a fixed point x_i, by dropping the index i, equation (1) can be rewritten as

$$\ddot{u}(t) + \mu\, \dot{u} + r(u) = p(t) + q(t) \quad (2)$$

Here, the turbulent pressure $p(t)$ is a random function of t and the acoustic pressure $q(t)$ is given by

$$q(t) = A\cos\theta(t) \quad (3)$$

where the phase $\theta(t) = \omega t + \theta_0$, the amplitude A and the frequencies ω are positive constants, and θ_0 is the initial phase. As commonly assumed, for a nonlinear beam, the nonlinear restoring force $r(u)$ is close to a cubic function. For a nonlinear beam, Homes et al.[28,34] gives

$$r(u) = k^2 u - \alpha u^3 + \mathrm{O}(u^4) \quad (k > 0,\ \alpha > 0) \quad (4)$$

where the term of $\mathrm{O}(u)^4$ and higher will be neglected.

In view of Equations (3) and (4), Equation (2) yields

$$\ddot{u} + \mu\, \dot{u} + k^2 u - \alpha u^3 = A\cos(\omega t + \theta_0) + p(t) \quad (5)$$

Suppose there is no flow excitation, $p(t) = 0$. It is well-known that the simple harmonic acoustic forcing can generate harmonic response as

$$u(t) = u_A(t) = A_1\cos(\omega t + \theta_1) + A_2\cos(2\omega t + \theta_2) + ... + A_n\cos(n\omega t + \theta_n) + ...$$

Without the acoustic excitation ($A = 0$), the solution $u_T(t)$ of Equation (5) exhibits a broadband random signal. The combination of the acoustic and turbulent pressure excitations gives rise to the acceleration spectrum $G(f,T)$ of the response $u(t)$ as shown in Fig. 4a. The response consists of harmonic response embedded in the randomly fluctuating signal (without control).

4.2. Phase Synchronization

The experimental data (Fig. 4a) show that for $n = 3$, the acceleration spectra are similar for three cases at $x = x_1, x_2, x_3$ as far as the phase $\psi(t)$ of the periodic component is concerned. The results exhibit a spatial phase synchronization, which has not yet been studied theoretically. The notion of phase synchronization implies interaction between phases of two self-sustained oscillators where the amplitude can be uncorrelated, a concept introduced by Pikovsky et al.[35] At a fixed point, the phase synchronization in the presence of noise, such as Equation (5), has been investigated by several authors (Anishchenko et al.[2]). For simplicity, set $\theta_0 = 0$, and write

$$u(t) = b(t) \cos \psi(t)$$

where b and ψ are the amplitude and phase for the response signal. It is possible to obtain a first-order, coupled equation for b and ψ (Anishchenko et al.[2]). However, as a simple approximation, one can neglect the slow amplitude variations. See Pikovsky et al.[7] to get the stochastic equation for the phase difference $\phi(t) = \psi(t) - \theta(t)$ as follows:

$$\phi(t) = (\Omega - \omega) - G(\phi) + \xi(t) \qquad (6)$$

where Ω is the frequency of free oscillation for the nonlinear Equation (5), G is a 2π periodic function, and $\xi(t)$ is a random process function. Due to the random perturbation $\xi(t)$, the phase difference $\phi(t)$ is incoherent and shows random fluctuation. Therefore the total phase $\psi(t) = \theta(t) + \phi(t)$ consists of a coherent part, the average phase $<\psi(t)>$ plus a random fluctuation as shown in Fig. 4b.

The temporal oscillations over spatially selected points on the panel A were evaluated. To investigate the problem of phase synchronization one can apply the method introduced by Rosenblum et al.[6] and Pikovsky et al.[7] Using this approach, the temporal difference $\Delta\phi(t) = \phi_1(t) - \phi_2(t)$ between the instantaneous phases $\phi_1(t)$ and $\phi_2(t)$ of the coupled response can be followed. The method consists of extracting the phase of the scalar $s(t)$ and amplitude $A(t)$ via the construction of the analytic signal which is a complex function of time defined as

$$s(t) + j\bar{s}(t) \equiv A(t)\, e^{j\phi(t)} \qquad (7)$$

where

$$\bar{s}(t) + \frac{1}{\pi} \mathrm{PV} \int_{-\infty}^{\infty} \frac{s(\tau)}{t - \tau}\, dt \qquad (8)$$

denotes the Hilbert transform of $s(t)$, j is the imaginary unit, and PV means that the integral is taken in the sense of the Cauchy principal value. The instantaneous amplitude $A(t)$ and the instantaneous phase $\phi(t)$ of the signal $s(t)$ between two inputs are

$$\phi_{n,m}(t) = |n\,\phi_1(t) - m\,\phi_2(t) - \delta| < \mu \qquad (9)$$

where μ is a small parameter ($\mu < 2\pi$) and δ is average phase shift. Generally the relative phase difference remains bound to small interval μ and mean value δ during the synchronous state, Equation (9) corresponding to phase locking.[35] In our system one can expect the condition of phase synchronization to be satisfied over a finite time. The phase difference $|\phi_1 - \phi_2|$ for $\delta = 0.03$ of the unsteady acceleration response from the time series of Fig. 4a, $x = 0.1552$ m, is shown in Fig. 10. The phase difference of the lowest modes oscillates over a small angular difference; however, the tendency to destabilize can be seen as t increases. The synchronous state is again recovered as time increases.

5. Conclusions

We have described a wind tunnel experiment of spatial phase synchronization of flexible structures where the amplitude-bandwidth oscillations are chaotic and the phase synchronized. The response emerges from two nonidentical chaotic inputs, acoustic, and turbulent boundary layer loading. The response is desynchronized into broadband chaos by active forcing. A single, low power external actuator is sufficient to overcome the spatial response of synchronization; this results in a redistribution of tonal components into broadband at nearly equal power, a spatiotemporal chaotic behavior. Synchronization without external coupling is not possible; also maintaining broadband chaos from synchronization without external forcing is not possible. The conclusions are summarized as follows:

1. Reconstructing phase synchronization from experimental data that are used to identify the dynamics has limits, since the total phase is made up of coherent, average, and random fluctuating parts.

2. Phase synchronization due to small changes in system input cause large variations in response.

3. The loading and response mechanisms described are verifiable and pertain to that encountered on contemporary aircraft.

4. The power required to induce desynchronization in the present system is estimated to be 10 percent of the total but the power required to maintain it is less.

5. The controller is simple and easy to realize.

6. The results exhibit spatial phase synchronization which has not yet been studied theoretically.

7. Control of the synchronized response, from two chaotic inputs, can perhaps be extended to trigger further changes toward an initial periodic state.

References

1. Huygens, C., "Horologium Oscillatorium," Apud F. Muguet, Paris, 1673.

2. Anishchenko, V. S., Vadivasova, T. E., Postnov, D. E., and Safonova, M. A., "Synchronization of Chaos," *International Journal of Bifurcation and Chaos*, Vol. 2, No. 3, 1992, pp. 633–644.

3. Pecora, Louis M., and Carroll, Thomas L., "Synchronization in Chaotic Systems," *Physical Review Letters*, Vol. 64, No. 8, 1990, pp. 821–824.

4. Rulkov, Nikolai F., Sushchik, Mikhail M., Tsimring, Lev S., and Abarbanel, Henry D. I., "Generalized Synchronization of Chaos in Directionally Coupled Chaotic Systems," *Physical Review E*, Vol. 51, No. 2, 1995, pp. 980–994.

5. Heagy, J. F., Carroll, T. L., and Pecora, L. M., "Synchronous Chaos in Coupled Oscillator Systems," *Physical Review E*, Vol. 50, No. 3, 1994, pp. 1874–1885.

6. Rosenblum, Michael G., Pikovsky, Arkady S., and Kurths, Jürgen, "Phase Synchronization of Chaotic Oscillator," *Physical Review Letters*, Vol. 76, No. 11, 1996, pp. 1804–1807.

7. Pikovsky, Arkady S., Rosenblum, Michael G., Osipov, Grigory V., and Kurths, Jürgen, "Phase Synchronization of Chaotic Oscillators by External Driving," *Physica D*, Vol. 104, No. 3–4, 1997, pp. 219–238.

8. Hu, Gang, Zhang, Ying, Cerdeira, Hilda A., and Chen, Shigang, "From Low-Dimensional Synchronous Chaos to High-Dimensional Desynchronous Spatiotemporal Chaos in Coupled System," *Physical Review Letters*, Vol. 85, No. 16, 2000, pp. 3377–3380.

9. Terry, John R., and VanWiggeren, Gregory D., "Chaotic Communication Using Generalized Synchronization," *Chaos, Solitons & Fractals*, Vol. 12, No. 1, 2001, pp. 145–152.

10. Tass, P., Rosenblum, M. G., Weule, J., Kurths, J., Pikovsky, A., Volkmann, J., Schnitzler, A., and Freund, H.-J., "Detection of $n{:}m$ Phase Locking From Noisy Data: Application to Magnetoencephalography," *Physical Review Letters*, Vol. 81, No. 12, 1998, pp. 3291–3294.

11. Holstein-Rathlou, Niels-Hanrik, Yip, Kay-Pong, Sosnovtseva, Olga V., and Mosekilde, Erik, "Synchronization Phenomena in Nephron-Nephron Interaction," *Chaos*, Vol. 11, No. 2, 2001, pp. 417–426.

12. Maestrello, L., "Active Control of Panel Vibration Induced by Accelerated Turbulent Boundary Layer and Sound," *AIAA Journal*, Vol. 35, 1997, pp. 796–801.

13. Dowell, E. H., "*Aeroelasticity of Plate and Shells*," Noordhoff International Publishing, Leyden, 1975.

14. Reynolds, R. R., and Dowell, E. H., "Nonlinear Aeroelastic Response of Panels," AIAA Paper 93-1599-CP, 1993.

15. Chow, P. L., and Maestrello, L., "Vibration Control of a Non-Linear Elastic Panel," *International Journal of Non-Linear Mechanics*, Vol. 36, No. 4, 2001, pp. 709–718.

16. Ting, L., "Boundary Layer Over a Flat Plate in Presence of Shear Flow," *Physics of Fluids*, Vol. 3, 1960, pp. 78–81.

17. Zheng, Zhigang, Hu, Bambi, and Hu, Gang, "Collective Phase Slips and Phase Synchronizations in Coupled Oscillator Systems," *Physical Review E*, Vol. 62, No. 1, 2000, pp. 402–408.

18. Zheng, Zhigang, Hu, Gang, and Hu, Bambi, "Phase Slips and Phase Synchronization of Coupled Oscillators," *Physical Review Letters*, Vol. 81, No. 24, 1998, pp. 5318–5321.

19. Hu, Bambi, and Zheng, Zhigang, "Phase Synchronizations: Transitions From High- to Low-

Dimensional Tori Through Chaos," *International Journal of Bifurcation and Chaos*, Vol. 10, No. 10, 2000, pp. 2399–2414.

20. Jackson, E. A., "On the Control of Complex Dynamical System," *Physica D*, Vol. 50, 1991, pp. 341–366.

21. Lima, Ricardo, and Pettini, Marco, "Suppression of Chaos by Resonant Parametric Perturbations," *Physical Review A*, Vol. 41, No. 2, Jan. 1990, pp. 726–733.

22. Coombers, S., and Lord, G. J., "Desynchronization of Pulse-Coupled Integrated-and-Fire Neurons," *Physical Review E*, Vol. 55, No. 3, 1997, pp. 55–57.

23. Maestrello, L., "Controlling Vibrational Chaos of a Curved Structure," *AIAA Journal*, Vol. 39, No. 4, 2001, pp. 581–589.

24. Gao, J. Y., Narducci, L. S., Schulman, M., and Yuan, J. M., "Route to Chaos in a Bistable System With Delay," *Physical Review*, Vol. A28, No. 5, 1983, p. 2910.

25. Maza, D., Vallone, A., Mancini, H., and Boccaletti, S., "Experimental Phase Synchronization of a Chaotic Convective Flow," *Physical Review Letters*, Vol. 85, No. 26, 2000, pp. 5567–5570.

26. Yanchuk, Sergiy, Maistrenko, Yuri, Lading, Brian, and Mosekilde, Erik, "Effects of a Parameter Mismatch on the Synchronization of Two Coupled Chaotic Oscillators," *International Journal of Bifurcation and Chaos*, Vol. 10, No. 11, 2000, pp. 2629–2648.

27. Maestrello, L., "The Influence of Initial Forcing on Non-Linear Control," *Journal of Sound and Vibration*, Vol. 239, No. 4, 2001, pp. 873–883.

28. Holmes, P. J., and Whitley, D. C., "On the Attracting Set for Duffing's Equation, I: Analytical Methods for Small Force and Damping," *Partial Differential Equations and Dynamical Systems*, Edited by W. E. Fitzgibbon III, Pitman, London, 1984, pp. 211–240.

29. Mathur, G. P., Tran, B. N., and Simpson, M. A., "MD-90 Cabin Noise Diagnostics Flight Test," Rept. CRAD-9402-TR-4885, Boeing Co. (Contract NAS1-20268), Oct. 1998.

30. Maestrello, L., "Active Control by Conservation of Energy Concept," AIAA Paper 2000-2045, June 2000.

31. Bhat, W. V., and Wilby, J. F., "Interior Noise Radiation by an Aircraft Fuselage Subjected to Turbulent Boundary Layer Excitation and Evaluation of Noise Reduction Treatments," *Journal of Sound and Vibration*, Vol. 18, No. 4, 1971, pp. 449–464.

32. Rizzi, S. A., Rackl, R. G., and Andrianov, E. V., "*Flight Test Measurements From the Tu-144LL Structure/Cabin Noise Experiment*," NASA/TM-2000-209858, 2000.

33. Frendi, A., "Coupling Between a Supersonic Turbulent Boundary Layer and Flexible Structure," *AIAA Journal*, Vol. 35, No. 1, 1997, pp. 58–56.

34. Holmes, P. J., and Rand, D. A., "Phase Portraits and Bifurcations of the Nonlinear Oscillator." *International Journal of Non-Linear Mechanics*, Vol. 15, 1980, pp. 449–458.

35. Pikovsky, Arkady, Rosenblum, Michael, and Kurths, Jürgen, "Phase Synchronization in Regular and Chaotic Systems," *International Journal of Bifurcation and Chaos*, Vol. 10, No. 10, 2000, pp. 2291–2305.

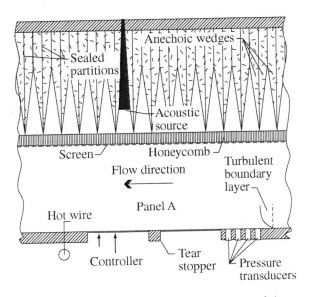

Figure 1. Wind tunnel setup with flat panel A.

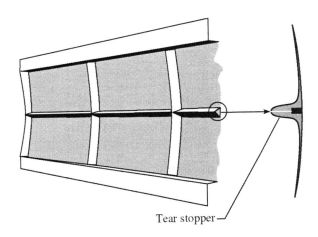

Figure 2. Curved panel B.

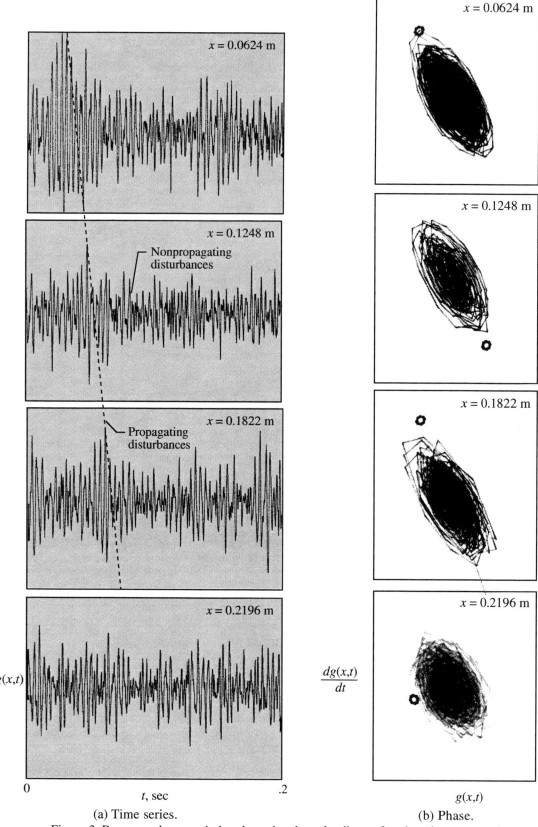

(a) Time series.

(b) Phase.

Figure 3. Response due to turbulent boundary layer loading at four locations on panel A.

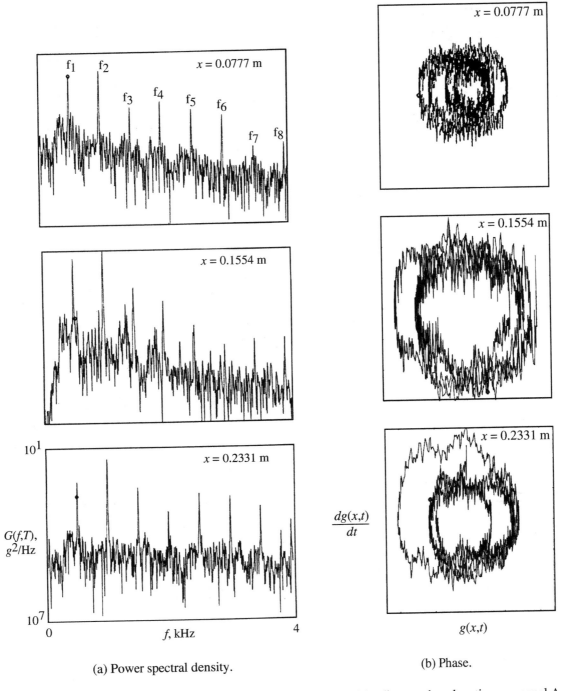

f_1 f_2

f_3 f_4

f_5 f_6

f_7 f_8

$x = 0.0777$ m

$x = 0.1554$ m

$x = 0.2331$ m

10^1

10^7

$G(f,T),$
g^2/Hz

0   f, kHz   4

$x = 0.0777$ m

$x = 0.1554$ m

$x = 0.2331$ m

$\dfrac{dg(x,t)}{dt}$

$g(x,t)$

(a) Power spectral density.

(b) Phase.

Figure 4. Response due to turbulent boundary layer and tonal sound loadings at three locations on panel A.

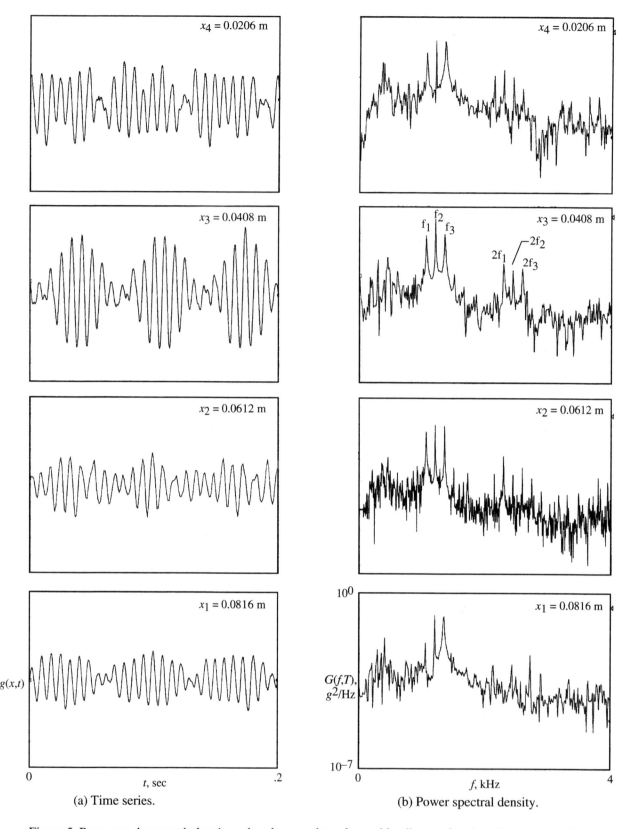

Figure 5. Response due to turbulent boundary layer and tonal sound loadings at four locations on panel B.

1678

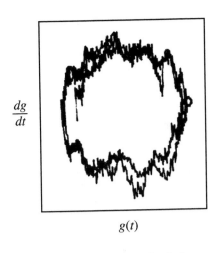

$\dfrac{dg}{dt}$

$g(t)$

(a) Partially synchronized phase.

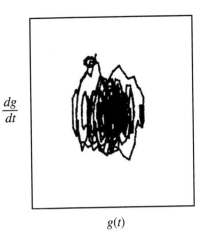

$\dfrac{dg}{dt}$

$g(t)$

(b) Desynchronized phase.

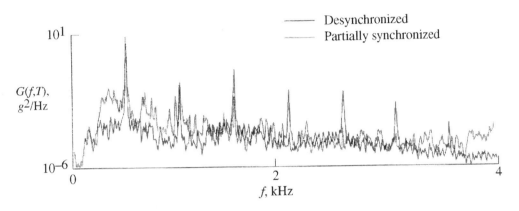

——— Desynchronized
——— Partially synchronized

10^1

$G(f,T)$, g^2/Hz

10^{-6}

0

2

4

f, kHz

(c) Power spectral density with partially synchronized and desynchronized phases.

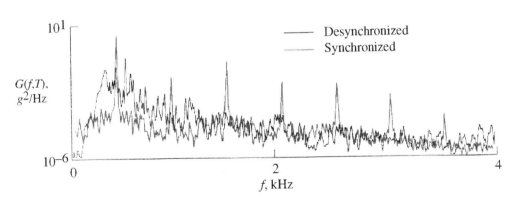

——— Desynchronized
········ Synchronized

10^1

$G(f,T)$, g^2/Hz

10^{-6}

0

2

4

f, kHz

(d) Power spectral density with synchronized and desynchronized phases.

Figure 6. Response on panel A.

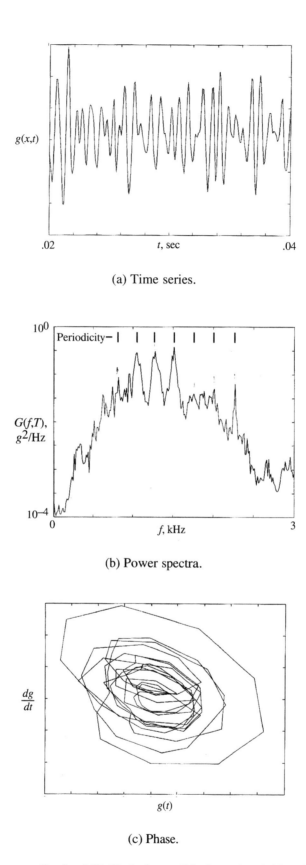

(a) Time series.

(b) Power spectra.

(c) Phase.

Figure 7. Panel response on Boeing MD-90 airplane at Mach number 0.80 and altitude of 10,000 m.

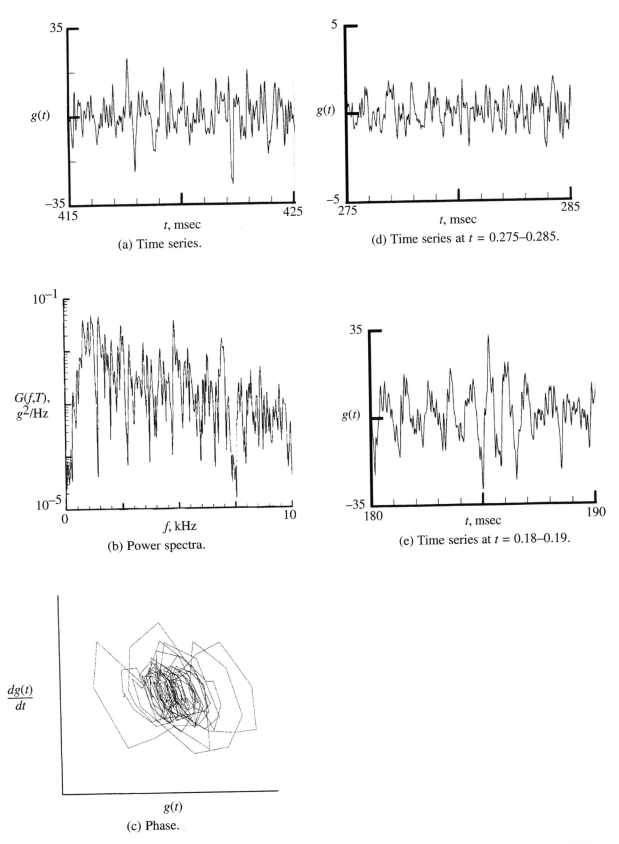

(a) Time series.

(d) Time series at $t = 0.275$–0.285.

(b) Power spectra.

(e) Time series at $t = 0.18$–0.19.

(c) Phase.

Figure 8. Panel response on Tu-144LL supersonic transport at Mach number 1.95 and altitude of 17,000 m.

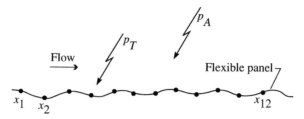

Figure 9. Analytical model.

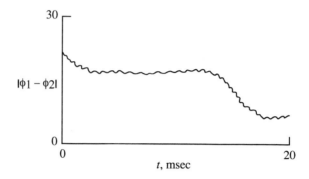

Figure 10. Phase difference of synchronous state versus time.

AERODYNAMIC NOISE PREDICTION IN INTERNAL FLOWS USING LES AND LINEAR EULER EQUATIONS

F. Crouzet,* P. Lafon,† T. Buchal,‡ D. Laurence§
EDF, Research and Development Division
1, Avenue du Général de Gaulle, 92141 Clamart Cedex, France,

Abstract

A hybrid computational method for the calculation of flow noise is presented : Large Eddy Simulation (LES) for the flow and Linearized Euler Equations (LEE) for the acoustic propagation. The source term that is introduced in the LEE is the one previously defined in the SNGR (Stochastic Noise Generation and Radiation) model. But instead of calculating this source term by means of a stochastic simulation of the fluctuating turbulent velocity field, it is directly calculated using the unsteady turbulent field given by the LES computations. This approach is applied to the case of a diaphragm in a duct. Two computations for two different upstream mean velocities are carried out. Source terms calculated on the LES grid are projected on the acoustic grid. The results are in good agreement with experimental ones.

Introduction

Some new aeroacoustic noise prediction methods rely on the computation of Euler equations associated with source terms. Two different ways are possible in order to obtain the aerodynamic fields needed for the calculation of source terms. A first possibility is to solve Reynolds Averaged Navier Stokes equations (RANS). The problem is then to generate the source term which is time dependent. A method called Stochastic Noise Generation and Radiation (SNGR) model was proposed[1,2,14] ; in this model, the space-time turbulence velocity field is reconstructed by a sum of Fourier modes using an assumed energy spectrum shape scaled by the RANS model. A second solution is to use LES methods which give the time-dependent fields of turbulent fluctuations. The calculation of the source term is then straightforward.

The present paper is devoted to the validation of the second approach : LES - source term - acoustic calculation.

Source and acoustic propagation modelling

In the framework of Lighthill's theory, standard aeroacoustic noise prediction methods rely on an analogy featuring a propagation equation associated with source terms. These formulations require time-average[4] or unsteady[3,7] flow computations, they provide acoustic far-fields but do not account for all acoustic flow interactions. More complex wave operators were derived to improve these prediction methods in the presence of complex free flows.[13] However, these classical approches need to solve an integral equation and their application to confined configurations is not straightforward because it requires the determination of near-wall adapted Green's functions.[17]

In this context, aeroacoustic noise prediction methods have been developed using Linear Euler Equations. LEE are used by :

- introducing a source term calculated from flow data[1,2,8,14]

- coupling the aerodynamic computation and the acoustic one[15]

These approaches are called hybrid methods because they consider separately the aerodynamic and acoustic modellings. On the other hand, compressible DNS and LES are able to give both turbulent and acoustic fluctuations. These approaches are still very expensive but very useful for the understanding of physics and the validation of simpler methods : Bogey et al[8] showed that the source term used in the SNGR model was the right one for LEE equations.

So the LEE system that is retained is[1,2,8,14] :

---

*Research Scientist
†Research Scientist, Member AIAA
‡Research Engineer
§Research Scientist

$$\frac{\partial \rho'}{\partial t} + u_{jo}\frac{\partial \rho'}{\partial x_j} + u'_j\frac{\partial \rho_o}{\partial x_j} + \rho_o\frac{\partial u'_j}{\partial x_j} + \rho'\frac{\partial u_{jo}}{\partial x_j} \quad = \quad 0$$

$$\frac{\partial u'_i}{\partial t} + u_{jo}\frac{\partial u'_i}{\partial x_j} + u'_j\frac{\partial u_{io}}{\partial x_j} + \frac{1}{\rho_o}\frac{\partial p'}{\partial x_i} - \frac{\rho'}{\rho_o^2}\frac{\partial p_o}{\partial x_i} \quad = \quad S_i$$

$$\frac{\partial p'}{\partial t} + u_{jo}\frac{\partial p'}{\partial x_j} + u'_j\frac{\partial p_o}{\partial x_j} + \gamma p_o\frac{\partial u'_j}{\partial x_j} + \gamma p'\frac{\partial u_{jo}}{\partial x_j} \quad = \quad 0$$
$$(1)$$

where the subscript 0 denotes the mean quantities and where the source term reads as follows:

$$S_i = -\left\{ u_{jt}\frac{\partial u_{it}}{\partial x_j} - \overline{u_{jt}\frac{\partial u_{it}}{\partial x_j}} \right\}$$

The subscript t in the source term expression denotes turbulent fluctuating quantities. It is this source term that we are going to calculate using turbulent fluctuations given by LES computations.

The case of a diaphragm in a duct

The configuration of a duct obstructed by a diaphragm has already been studied for the validation of the SNGR model in 2D[1] and in 3D[14] . In this paper, the same case is choosen to carry out the validation of the hybrid method : LES - source term - acoustic calculaltion. LES and acoustic calculations require very different conditions especially for spatial discretization. Therefore, two different grids are used : a LES grid, on which source terms are computed, and an acoustic grid, on which source terms are projected. The approach presented in this paper can be summerized by figure 1.

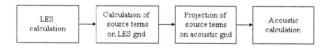

Figure 1: The hybrid method

The computational domain retained for LES calculations is presented in figure 2.

The computational domain retained for acoustic calculations, presented in figure 3, is much longer, 400 mm upstream of the diaphragm, and 1200 mm downstream, in order to obtain the far field acoustic radiation.

The LES grid is much more refined close to the diaphragm whereas the acoustic one is regular (see table 1) : a range of turbulent eddies generated by

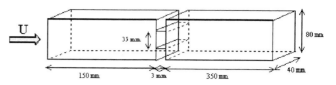

Figure 2: Aerodynamic computational domain

Figure 3: Acoustic computational domain

the shear layers needs to be well represented for the overall accuracy of the LES computation. Two cases are considered : U (mean velocity in the duct) $= 6\ ms^{-1}$ and $14\ ms^{-1}$.

LES computation

LES model

The LES computations are carrried out with the ESTET code developed by the R&D Division of Electricité de France. It solves LES equations for incompressible flow.

LES equations for imcompressible flows are obtained by filtering Naviers Stokes equations in order to keep only the large scale components of the total field. Noting $\tilde{f}$ the filtered variable associated with f, one obtains the following set of equations :

$$\frac{\partial \tilde{u}}{\partial t} + (\tilde{u}\cdot\nabla)\tilde{u} = -\frac{1}{\rho}\nabla\tilde{p} - \nabla\left(\nu\left(\nabla\tilde{u}+(\nabla\tilde{u})^t\right)\right) + \nabla\left(\tilde{T}\right)$$

$$div\left(\tilde{u}\right) = 0$$

where T is the subgrid scale (SGS) tensor defined by

$$T_{ij} = \tilde{u}_i\tilde{u}_j - \widetilde{u_i u_j}$$

The simple smagorinsky model is used to model eddy viscosity; which leads to express the SGS tensor as follows :

$$T_{ij} = -2\nu_t\tilde{S}_{ij} + \frac{1}{3}T_{kk}\delta_{ij}$$

where $\tilde{S}_{ij}$ is the filtered strain rate tensor.

$$\tilde{S}_{ij} = \frac{1}{2}\left(\frac{\partial \tilde{u}_i}{\partial x_j} + \frac{\partial \tilde{u}_j}{\partial x_i}\right)$$

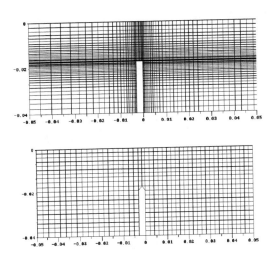

Table 1: Detail of LES grid (top) and acoustic grid (bottom)

The turbulent eddy viscosity is

$$\nu_t = \left(C_s D \tilde{\Delta} \right)^2 \sqrt{2 \tilde{S_{ij}} \tilde{S_{ij}}}$$

C_s is the smagorinsky constant, $\tilde{\Delta}$ the mean radius of a grid cell. D is the Van Driest near-wall damping function : $D = 1 - \exp\left(\frac{-y^+}{A+}\right)$.

This simple smagorinsky subgrid model is based on rather crude asumptions. However, it was shown to give reasonable results in similar studies of flow over bluff bodies and detached shear layers.

Numerical method

The ESTET code uses a conservative finite volume method. Two staggered structured grids are used to store velocities and scalars. Periodic boundary conditions are employed in the transverse direction. At the walls, the standard logarithmic wall function is imposed. Such a wall function can be used since it is not the main source of turbulence in our case.

The instaneous velocity field computed by LES is displayed in figure 4.

Figure 4: LES velocity field - longitudinal component ($U = 14\ ms^{-1}$, $t = 6.6\ 10^{-2}s$)

Acoustic computation

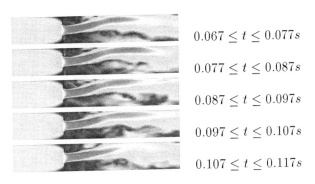

0.067 ≤ t ≤ 0.077s

0.077 ≤ t ≤ 0.087s

0.087 ≤ t ≤ 0.097s

0.097 ≤ t ≤ 0.107s

0.107 ≤ t ≤ 0.117s

Table 2: Velocity averaged on $10^{-2}s$ time periods ($U = 14\ ms^{-1}$)

The source terms

The source terms are calculated on the LES grid because it is expected that the gradients are estimated more accurately on the original grid.

Turbulent velocities are obtained by extracting the fluctuating part of the computed LES velocity field assumed to be stationary. In our case, as displayed in table 2, a detailed analysis of the computed velocity field shows a non-physical pulsed jet phenomenon, which means that the computed velocity field is not fully stationary. The oscillations are thought to be generated by non perfect outflow boundary conditions.

Such a phenomenom leads to an overestimation of the source terms since it adds a continuous component to the turbulent velocity field. Hence turbulent velocity is computed by considering a succession of quasi stationary periods. The so filtered instantaneous velocity is displayed in table 3.

Figure 5 shows an instantaneous field of the source terms computed by the method described above.

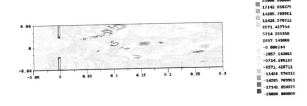

Figure 5: Source term - longitudinal component ($U = 14\ ms^{-1}$)

The source terms are then projected on the acoustic grid. Since LES grid and acoustic grid have very different spatial characteristics, one must differentiate two cases as shown in table 4:

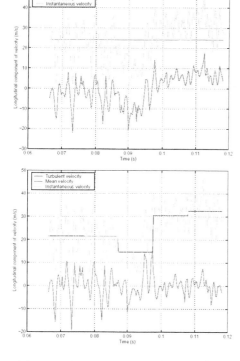

Table 3: Filtered and non filtered instantaneous velocity - longitudinal component ($U = 14\ ms^{-1}$)

- Case 1 : wherever acoustic grid is more refined than LES grid, the source terms are linearly interpolated between the two closest cells of LES grid.

- Case 2 : wherever acoustic grid is less refined than LES grid, the source terms are averaged by taking into account all the cells contained in the volume of the size of an acoustic cell.

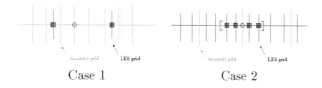

Case 1   Case 2

Table 4: Source projection on Acoustic grid

In order to limit the size of LES savings, the source terms are calculated every $2.5\,10^{-5}s$. The acoustic time step being much shorter, source terms at each acoustic time step are estimated by a linear interpolation between two successive LES outputs. The global approach is summerized in figure 6.

Numerical computations

Acoustic computations were carried out with the EOLE3D code developped by the R&D divison of

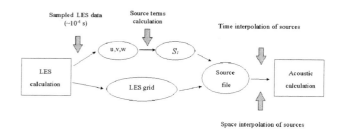

Figure 6: The global computational approach

Electricité de France. It solves the LEE equations in a structured grid using DRP (dispersion relation Preserving) scheme proposed by Tam[16] for space resolution and a fourth order Runge-Kutta sheme for time resolution. DRP scheme is a centered finite difference scheme based on a 7 point element ; its properties have been optimized to preserve dispersing relations.

The reflecting conditions are obtained by the ghost point method. They simulate a perfect reflecting condition on the inner walls of the duct. The inflow condition and the absorbing boundary condition are calculated using characteristic method. This 1-dimensional method is adapted to our confined case in which downstream and upstream acoustic wave surfaces are quite parallel to absorbing surfaces.

The purpose of the present work is to validate a hybrid method based on the computation of source terms provided by LES calculations. In this first approach, we don't aim at characterizing the interactions between acoustics and the mean flow. That is why, even if LEE are able to take into account the mean flow effects, we neglect them for the acoustic computations. It is expected that this doesn't modify the accuracy of the total radiated acoustic power.

Acoustic results

Figure 7 displays the acoustic pressure field computed by the hybrid method. One can clearly differenciate two areas : the source area characterized by high value of pressure, and the propagating area where acoustics waves lie upstream and dowstream the diaphragm.

For a 6 ms^{-1} mean velocity, acoustic waves are quite plane ones as shown in figure 8 whereas for a 14 ms^{-1} mean velocity, a transverse mode clearly appears (figure 9).

The total acoustic power is estimated by calculating the acoustic intensity radiated at both ends of the duct. Assuming the absorbing condition are perfect,

Figure 7: Elevated pressure field ($U = 6 \ ms^{-1}$)

Figure 8: Pressure field ($U = 6 \ ms^{-1}$)

and since the flow Mach numbers are very low, the total power is simply calculated by :

$$W = \int_S \overline{\vec{u}\,(t)\,p\,(t)} d\vec{S}$$

where S is the surface of both ends of the domain. The power expressed in dB is compared with experiments carried out in the CLARINETTE experimental device of the the R&D division of EDF. The computational results for the $14 \ ms^{-1}$ case matches well experimental ones (see figure 9 and 11). For the lower velocity, no experiments were available, but the computational results confirm the power 4 law identified in previous works.[1,14,17] One can note that the frequency resolution of the acoustic power spectrum presented in figure 10 is limited by the real duration of the computation.

Conclusion

This study presents a hybrid method in which acoustic sources corresponding to a given turbulent flow are directly provided by LES computation. These terms are incorporated into a linear Euler code to predict noise radiation and propagation. Source

Figure 9: Pressure field ($U = 14 \ ms^{-1}$)

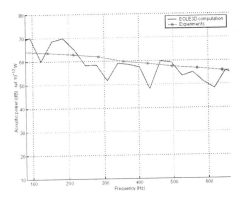

Figure 10: Acoustic power spectrum in dB ($U = 14 \ ms^{-1}$)

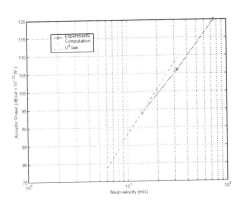

Figure 11: Acoustic power with respect to the mean flow velocity

terms are computed assuming that the turbulent velocity field is uncompressible, which is thougt to be acceptable for low mach number.

The method is very sensitive to the accuracy of aerodynamic computation : a slightly nonstationary aerodynamic field can lead to highly overestimate the source terms and therefore the generated noise. When care is taken, numerical estimates are found to be in good agreement with experimental predictions. These results confirm the expression of the source term derived in previous works[1,2,14] and validated by Bogey et al.[8]

Further studies are necessary to extend the validation of the method to a wider range of mean flow velocities and to other configurations typical of industrial applications.

Acknowledgements

This work was carried out within the framework of the PREDIT research program supported by the French Ministère de l'Education Nationale, de la Recherche et de la Technologie.

References

[1] BAILLY C., LAFON P., CANDEL S. (1996) Computation of Noise Generation and Propagation for Free and Confined Turbulent Flows. *AIAA-96-1732.*

[2] BAILLY C., JUVÉ D. (1999) A Stochastic Approach to Compute Subsonic Noise Using Linearized Euler's Equations. *AIAA-99-1872.*

[3] BASTIN F., LAFON P., CANDEL S. (1997) Computation of jet mixing noise due to coherent structures: the plane jet case. *J. Fluid Mech.* **11**, 1-40.

[4] BÉCHARA W., BAILLY C., LAFON P., CANDEL S. (1995) Application of a $k - \epsilon$ model to the prediction of noise for simple and coaxial free jets. *J. Acoust. Soc. Am.*, **97**(6), 3518-3531.

[5] BERMAN C., RAMOS J. (1989) Simultaneous computation of jet turbulence and noise. *AIAA-89-1091.*

[6] BOGEY C., BAILLY C., JUVÉ D. (2000) Large Eddy Simulation of a subsonic jet : direct calculation of its radiated sound field. *AIAA-00-2009.*

[7] BOGEY C., BAILLY C., JUVÉ D. (2001) Noise computation using Lighthill's equation with inclusion of mean flow-acoustics interactions. *AIAA-01-2255.*

[8] BOGEY C., BAILLY C., JUVÉ D. (2002) Computation of Flow Noise Using Source Terms in Linearized Euler's Equations. *AIAA Journal,* **40**(2), 235-243.

[9] COLONIUS T., FREUND J.B. (2000) Application of Lighthill's equation to a Mach 1.92 turbulent jet. *AIAA Journal,* **38**(2), 368-370.

[10] FREUND J.B. (1999) Acoustic sources in a turbulent jet : a direct numerical simulation study. *AIAA-99-1858.*

[11] LIGHTHILL M.J. 1952 On sound generated aerodynamically - I. General theory, *Proceedings of the Royal Society of London,* **A211**, 1107, 564-587.

[12] LIGHTHILL M.J. 1954 On sound generated aerodynamically - II. Turbulence as a source of sound, *Proceedings of the Royal Society of London,* **A222**, 1148, 1-32.

[13] LILLEY G.M. 1972 The generation and radiation of supersonic jet noise. Vol. IV - Theory of turbulence generated jet noise, noise radiation from upstream sources, and combustion noise. Part II: Generation of sound in a mixing region, *Air Force Aero Propulsion Laboratory,* AFAPL-TR-72-53.

[14] LONGATTE E., LAFON P., CANDEL S. (1998) Computation of Noise Generation by Turbulence in Internal Flows. *AIAA-98-2332.*

[15] MORRIS P.J., LONG L.N., SCHEIDEGGER T.E., WAND Q., PILON A.R. (1998) High speed jet simulations. *AIAA-98-2290.*

[16] TAM, C.K.W., WEBB, J.C. (1993) Dispersion -Relation-Preserving Finite Difference Schemes for Computational Acoustics. *Journal of Computational Physics,* **107**, 262-281.

[17] VAN HERPE F., CRIGHTON D.G., LAFON P. (1995) Noise generation by turbulent flow in a duct obstructed by a diaphragm. *AIAA-95-035.*

A CORRELATION LENGTH SCALE FOR THE PREDICTION OF AEROACOUSTIC RESPONSE

Denis A. Lynch III[*] and Thomas J. Mueller[†]
University of Notre Dame, Notre Dame, Indiana 46556-5684
and
William K. Blake[‡]
David Taylor Research Center, West Bethesda, Maryland 20817-5700

Abstract

Expressions to describe the correlation length scales of turbulent inflow to an aerodynamic body are derived as functions of the classic integral length scale and anisotropy correction factors. These one-point parameters are significantly easier to determine experimentally than traditional correlation scale measurement techniques, which involve multiple probes at multiple locations. As such correlation scales are necessary to properly estimate the aeroacoustic response of the body, such a technique could have substantial benefit in a wide variety of applications. The approach is applied to a recent experimental study examining the response of a stator downstream of a propeller that is itself ingesting broadband turbulence. Results suggest that the derived expressions not only accurately represent correlation length scales, but also enable the accurate prediction of the acoustic output of the stator.

Nomenclature

English Symbols

C	chord length
f	temporal frequency
k	wave number vector
L_i	geometric length scale
M	Mach number
q	dynamic pressure
R_{ij}	correlation function between turbulent velocity components u_i and u_j
r	separation distance between two points
$\mathcal{S}e$	aerodynamic response function (Sears function)

U	mean velocity component
u	turbulent velocity component
x	flow location (position)

Greek Symbols

α_c, β_c	anisotropy scaling factors
β	angle between acoustic source and receiver, measured with respect to dipole axis
δ	Kronecker delta function
γ^2	coherence function
Λ	classic turbulence integral length scale
$\Lambda_i\vert_j$	turbulence correlation scale of jth component of velocity in ith direction
ω	gust or event frequency ($=2\pi f$)
Φ_{ii}	auto-power spectrum in the ith direction
$\Phi_{ii}(\vec{r})$	cross-power spectrum in the ith direction (separated by distance $\vec{r}$)
$\Phi_{p_{rad}}$	radiated farfield acoustic pressure
$\phi_{ii}(\vec{r})$	non-dimensional cross-spectral density function of turbulence in the ith direction (separated by distance $\vec{r}$)
ρ_o	density of fluid

Common Superscripts, Subscripts or Symbol Modifications

i^*	complex conjugate of quantity i
$\vec{i}$	three-dimensional vector of quantity i
i_1	quantity i in the freestream direction
i_2	quantity i in the direction normal to airfoil (stator) surface
i_3	quantity i in the spanwise direction of airfoil (stator) surface
i_∞	freestream quantity

[*]Post-Doctoral Research Associate, Department of Aerospace and Mechanical Engineering

[†]Roth-Gibson Professor, Department of Aerospace and Mechanical Engineering. Associate Fellow AIAA

[‡]Chief Scientist, Hydroacoustics, C.D. Code 7051, N.S.W.C. Building 3, Room 221

1 Introduction

The relationship between broadband inflow turbulence and the aeroacoustic response of an aerodynamic body has been studied in great detail. Theoretical modeling of this response originally considered a gust interacting with a flat plate, and has grown in complexity over the years. However, the expressions still depend on several fundamental quantities, one of which is the correlation length scale of the turbulence.

In practice, this correlation length scale has often been taken as the classic integral length scale. In point of fact, while the two are related, the correlation scale has some differences, as will be illustrated in this paper. Unfortunately, this correlation scale is much more challenging to determine experimentally, as it requires two-point measurements at an infinite number of probe separation distances. It is therefore advantageous to derive an expression for this correlation length scale in terms of quantities that are more easily determined, such as the classic integral length scale.

This paper describes the theoretical derivation of such a relationship. The equations derived will then be applied to an experimental study, with the predictive capability of the theoretical relationships being analyzed. The benefit of these efforts is manifested in the accurate prediction of correlation scales used in the modeling of a body's aeroacoustic response with a minimal amount of additional time-consuming, costly measurements.

2 Derivation of Integral Correlation Length Scales

The aeroacoustic response of an airfoil responding to an unsteady gust has been well-documented. The majority of this work is built directly on the pioneering efforts of von Kármán and Sears[1] and Sears.[2] In effect, the acoustic output generated by the airfoil may be accurately estimated from characteristics of the turbulent flowfield driving the response of the airfoil using derived theoretical expressions. A full explanation of this derivation is not provided here for brevity, but is given in Chapter 11 of Blake.[3] The governing equation for the acoustic output of an airfoil, $\Phi_{p_{rad}}$, assuming a compact source, is

$$\frac{\Phi_{p_{rad}}(\omega)}{q_\infty{}^2 M_\infty{}^2} = \sin^2\beta \left(\frac{\overline{u_2{}^2}}{U_\infty{}^2}\right)\left(\frac{L_3}{r}\right)^2\left(\frac{\omega C}{2U_\infty}\right)^2$$

$$\times \quad \phi_{22}(\omega)\frac{2\Lambda_3(\omega)|_2}{L_3}\left|Se\left(\frac{\omega C}{2U_\infty}\right)\right|^2 \quad (1)$$

Here, almost all of these terms represent quantities that may be obtained through detailed but feasible measure-

ments. The freestream dynamic pressure, Mach number, and velocity (q_∞, M_∞, and U_∞, respectively) are easily determined. The angle β, or angle between the acoustic measurement position and chord of the airfoil, is defined in the experimental setup. The quantities $\overline{u_2{}^2}$ and $\phi_{22}(\omega)$ represent the mean square turbulence and normalized turbulence spectrum in the x_2 (normal to the airfoil) direction (the coordinate system for all discussion in this paper is defined in Section 2.1). The frequency in question is represented by ω, and Se represents the classic Sears function.

The final two terms, L_3 and $\Lambda_3|_2$, represent contributions to the acoustic output of the system as a function of spanwise dependence. L_3 actually defines the span of the airfoil or airfoil section being considered, while $\Lambda_3|_2$ is the spanwise correlation length of the gust velocity. In other words, this term speaks to how correlated the response of the airfoil is in the spanwise direction. If the spanwise correlation is large, then the acoustic output from the unsteady pressure response of adjacent airfoil sections will sum in the farfield. Likewise, if the spanwise correlation is small, then the unsteady pressure field of adjacent airfoil sections will be unrelated, greatly reducing the radiated acoustic output. It is clear that an important factor in the prediction of the unsteady pressure response, and therefore the farfield acoustic response, of a propeller blade or stator vane is the spanwise correlation of the gust velocity, $\Lambda_3|_2$.

The definition and use of this necessary length scale is not new. Beyond the presentation mentioned above taken from Blake,[3] this length scale is also defined and used in works by Amiet,[4] Wygnanski,[5] and Glegg.[6] It has been examined recently in much closer detail by Devenport et al.[7, 8] and Glegg et al.[9] In papers such as these, the length scales in question were usually determined in one of three basic ways. First, scales could be determined using an exhaustive array of two-point velocity correlation measurements. Second, the length scales could be estimated using some physical scale of the turbulence (such as the half-width or momentum thickness of the wake of the turbulence generating body). The final method assumes a curve shape for the turbulence spectra and adjusts the unknown but desired length scales and intensity levels to obtain a best fit of the one-point spectra measurements to the assumed shape. The difference in this paper is the goal to express the correlation length scale using one-point flowfield measurements and using equations based on the classic integral length scale.

An integral correlation length scale is defined such

that

$$\Lambda_i(\omega)|_j = \int\limits_0^\infty \phi_{jj}(r_i, \omega) dr_i. \qquad (2)$$

The term $\Lambda_j(\omega)|_i$ can be read as "the correlation in the r_j-direction of the ith-component of velocity." It should be noted that a special case of this correlation length scale is the classic turbulence integral length scale. That is, $\phi_{jj}(r_i, \omega)$ is simply the Fourier transform of the correlation function $R_{jj}(r_i, t)$. If the time scale t is dropped and $i = j$, then the resulting equation is

$$\Lambda_j = \int\limits_0^\infty R_{jj}(r_j) dr_j. \qquad (3)$$

To be precise, Λ_1 (defined using Equation 3 with $j = 1$) is the turbulence integral scale of isotropic turbulence. This scale defines turbulence energy spectra. Other correlation length scales, as defined in the more general Equation 2, are *frequency dependent* correlation lengths, and are derived from specific integral "cuts" through the three-dimensional wave number energy spectrum. For the current consideration, analysis is kept in the frequency domain with the frequency dependence preserved, as in the more general definition of Equation 2.

2.1 Extractions from Turbulence Modeling

In order to complete the model for the spanwise correlation of the gust velocity, a number of assumptions are made regarding the inflow turbulence. While many of these assumptions simply do not hold for many complex flowfields, it provides a baseline for the development of the theory. Corrections will be introduced as necessary.

First, a coordinate system is defined. Here, x_1 corresponds to the streamwise direction, x_2 to the cross-stream direction normal to the aerodynamic body in question, and x_3 the cross-stream direction along the span of the aerodynamic body. The flow is aligned such that the primary direction is the same as the mean convection velocity, U_c. Therefore

$$\begin{aligned}
\vec{U} &= \{U_c, 0, 0\} &\longrightarrow& \quad \vec{U} \cdot \vec{k} = U_1 k_1 = U_c k_1 \\
\vec{r} &= \{r_1, r_2, r_3\} &\longrightarrow& \quad \vec{U} \cdot \vec{r} = U_1 r_1 = U_c r_1 \quad (4)
\end{aligned}$$

From this, the convective wave number is defined as $k_1 = k_c = \omega/U_c$.

Next, the flow is assumed quasi-isotropic in the energy sense. The isotropic assumption means that the turbulent energy has no preferred direction and is homogeneous. However, even in cases where the flow has both preferred direction and inhomogeneities, the flow

may still show some signs of isotropy.[10] Therefore, this assumption of isotropy in the energy sense is made. Expressed mathematically, this can be written

$$\overline{u_1^2} = \overline{u_2^2} = \overline{u_3^2} = \overline{u^2}, \qquad (5)$$

where the directions are as defined above.

A related assumption which comes from this assumption of quasi-isotropy in the energy sense is that the respective energy densities are also equal. It is further assumed that the energy densities are properly non-dimensionalized such that

$$\int\limits_{-\infty}^\infty \Phi_{ii}(\omega) d\omega = 1, \qquad i = 1, 2, 3. \qquad (6)$$

In the case of isotropic turbulence, a correlation function between velocity components u_i and u_j is defined as

$$R_{ij}(\vec{r}) = R_{ij}\left(\sqrt{r_1^2 + r_2^2 + r_3^2}\right). \qquad (7)$$

While the turbulence is defined as isotropic in the energy sense, it certainly not so in the spatial sense. To model this anisotropy, stretching scale factors are introduced in the definition of $\vec{r}$ such that the magnitude is expressed

$$|\vec{r}|^2 = r^2 = r_1^2 + \left(\frac{r_2}{\beta_c}\right)^2 + \left(\frac{r_3}{\alpha_c}\right)^2, \qquad (8)$$

where α_c and β_c represent stretching parameters. These stretching parameters have been used in previous efforts to account for anisotropy in the flow.[11] Including these parameters, the energy density as a function of wave number can be expressed as

$$\begin{aligned}
\Phi_{ij}(\vec{k}) &= \frac{1}{(2\pi)^3} \iiint\limits_{-\infty}^\infty R_{ij}(\vec{r}) e^{i\vec{k}\cdot\vec{r}} d^3\vec{r} \\
&= \frac{1}{(2\pi)^3} \iiint\limits_{-\infty}^\infty R_{ij}\left(\sqrt{r_1^2 + \left(\frac{r_2}{\beta_c}\right)^2 + \left(\frac{r_3}{\alpha_c}\right)^2}\right) \\
&\quad \times e^{i\vec{k}\cdot\vec{r}} d^3\vec{r} \\
&= \frac{\alpha_c \beta_c}{(2\pi)^3} \iiint\limits_{-\infty}^\infty R_{ij}\left(\sqrt{r_1^2 + \left(\frac{r_2}{\beta_c}\right)^2 + \left(\frac{r_3}{\alpha_c}\right)^2}\right) \\
&\quad \times e^{i\left(k_1 r_1 + k_2 \beta_c \frac{r_2}{\beta_c} + k_3 \alpha_c \frac{r_3}{\alpha_c}\right)} dr_1 d\frac{r_2}{\beta_c} d\frac{r_3}{\alpha_c} \\
&= \frac{\alpha_c \beta_c}{(2\pi)^3} \iiint\limits_{-\infty}^\infty R_{ij}(\breve{r}) e^{i\breve{k}\cdot\breve{r}} d^3\breve{r} \\
\Phi_{ij}(\vec{k}) &= \alpha_c \beta_c \Phi_{ij}(\breve{k}), \qquad (9)
\end{aligned}$$

where $\vec{\mathbf{k}} = \{k_1, k_2\beta_c, k_3\alpha_c\}$ and

$$k_1 = \text{vector aligned with flow direction;}$$
$$k_2 = \text{vertical cross-stream direction}$$
$$\text{(the "gust" direction); and}$$
$$k_3 = \text{spanwise cross-stream direction.}$$

This allows $\Phi_{ij}(\vec{\mathbf{k}})$ to be modeled using isotropic turbulence models. From Hinze,[12] the two-sided wave number spectra are given as

$$\Phi_{ii}(\vec{\mathbf{k}}) = \frac{2\Lambda^3}{\pi^2} \frac{\mathbf{k}^2 - \mathbf{k}_i{}^2}{(1 + \mathbf{k}^2\Lambda^2)^3}, \qquad (10)$$

where $i = 1, 2, 3$, Λ is the classic integral scale turbulence parameter and

$$\begin{aligned} \mathbf{k}^2 &= \mathbf{k}_1{}^2 + \mathbf{k}_2{}^2 + \mathbf{k}_3{}^2 \\ &= k_1{}^2 + (\beta_c k_2)^2 + (\alpha_c k_3)^2. \end{aligned} \qquad (11)$$

The combination of Equation 9 with Equation 10 gives, after some simplification, expressions for the energy density of velocity in all three primary directions as a function of wave numbers k_i, the classic integral length scale Λ, and stretching parameters α_c and β_c:

$$\Phi_{11}(\vec{k}) = \frac{C_1 \left[(k_2\beta_c)^2 + (k_3\alpha_c)^2 \right] \Lambda^2}{\left[1 + \left(k_1{}^2 + (k_2\beta_c)^2 + (k_3\alpha_c)^2 \right) \Lambda^2 \right]^3} \qquad (12)$$

$$\Phi_{22}(\vec{k}) = \frac{C_1 \left[k_1{}^2 + (k_3\alpha_c)^2 \right] \Lambda^2}{\left[1 + \left(k_1{}^2 + (k_2\beta_c)^2 + (k_3\alpha_c)^2 \right) \Lambda^2 \right]^3} \qquad (13)$$

$$\Phi_{33}(\vec{k}) = \frac{C_1 \left[k_1{}^2 + (k_2\beta_c)^2 \right] \Lambda^2}{\left[1 + \left(k_1{}^2 + (k_2\beta_c)^2 + (k_3\alpha_c)^2 \right) \Lambda^2 \right]^3} \qquad (14)$$

where

$$C_1 = \alpha_c\beta_c \frac{2\Lambda^3}{\pi^2}. \qquad (15)$$

Now that the energy density can be expressed in this fashion, attention turns to the definition of the correlation lengths in question. Note that while related, these are *not* the same as the integral length scale, as discussed earlier.

In measurements involving two sensors, a cross-spectral density function involving a spanwise separation can be defined as

$$\Phi_{ii}(r_1 = 0, r_2 = 0, r_3; \omega) = <u_i(\vec{r} + \vec{x}; \omega)u_i{}^*(\vec{x}; \omega)>, \qquad (16)$$

where the asterisk denotes the complex conjugate. The auto-spectral density can be defined in the special case where $r_3 \to 0$, namely

$$\begin{aligned} \Phi_{ii}(\omega) &= <u_i(\vec{x}; \omega)u_i{}^*(\vec{x}; \omega)> \\ &= \Phi_{ii}(r_1 = 0, r_2 = 0, r_3 = 0; \omega). \end{aligned} \qquad (17)$$

Further, the cross-spectral density function of a given spanwise separation may be non-dimensionalized using the auto-spectral density,

$$\phi_{ii}(r_3; \omega) = \frac{\Phi_{ii}(r_1 = r_2 = 0, r_3; \omega)}{\Phi_{ii}(\omega)}, \qquad (18)$$

where $\phi_{ii}(r_3 = 0; \omega) = 1$ and $\phi_{ii}(r_3 \to \infty; \omega) < 1$. Typically, ϕ_{ii} is a complex quantity.

An important distinction needs to be emphasized at this point. Figure 1 shows the difference between two commonly measured scales. Figure 1a depicts the spanwise correlation of the streamwise, or u_1, velocity. This is the most commonly measured correlation length in traditional turbulence measurements. However, the important correlation length in terms of the acoustic production from an airfoil or propeller, as explained in Section 2, is the spanwise correlation of the normal gust, or u_2, component of velocity. These two components are not the same, even in the case of isotropic turbulence.

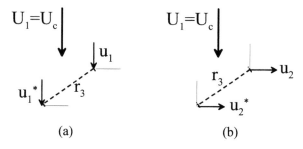

Figure 1: Schematic Comparing a) Spanwise Correlation of Streamwise Velocity, u_1, and b) Spanwise Correlation of Gust Velocity, u_2

From Equation 2, the spanwise correlation lengths in question are now defined as

$$2\Lambda_3(\omega)|_1 = \int_{-\infty}^{\infty} \phi_{11}(r_3; \omega)dr_3, \qquad (19)$$

$$2\Lambda_3(\omega)|_2 = \int_{-\infty}^{\infty} \phi_{22}(r_3; \omega)dr_3. \qquad (20)$$

In the strictest sense, these correlation lengths may be found by finding $\Phi_{ii}(r_3, \omega)$ for an infinite set of separation distances r_3, then integrating the non-dimensionalized spectral density. Obviously, this is inconvenient, and so a simplified expression is sought, one that will also allow for quasi-isotropic flows, to predict these length scales. Again, for the purposes of the unsteady response of an airfoil or propeller blade, the length scale defined in Equation 20 is the critical term.

2.2 Integral Correlation Length Scales as Functions of Turbulence Integral Length Scale

Sections 2.2.1 through 2.2.3 use the relations defined above in order to derive closed-form expressions for relevant correlation scales as functions of frequency and turbulence integral length scale. Section 2.2.1 includes a detailed derivation of the expression for spanwise correlation length of the streamwise velocity component. Since the analysis is similar, the derivation for spanwise correlation length of the normal velocity component (Section 2.2.2) is not as detailed. Section 2.2.3 defines relationships between these scales, as well as presents, without derivation, the corresponding correlation length scales in the normal direction.

2.2.1 Spanwise Correlation Length of the Streamwise Velocity Component

As the spanwise correlation of the streamwise component is the most commonly measured of these correlation lengths, it is proper to consider it first. From Equation 19,

$$2\Lambda_3(\omega)|_1 = \int_{-\infty}^{\infty} \phi_{11}(r_3; \omega) dr_3$$

$$= \frac{1}{\Phi_{11}(\omega)} \int_{-\infty}^{\infty} \Phi_{11}(r_1 = r_2 = 0, r_3; \omega) dr_3 \quad (21)$$

By definition, $\Phi_{ij}(\vec{r}; \omega)$ can be written, without loss of generality,

$$\Phi_{ij}(\vec{r}; \omega) = \iiint_{-\infty}^{\infty} \Phi_{ij}(\vec{k}; \omega) e^{i\vec{k}\cdot\vec{r}} d^3\vec{k}$$

$$\Phi_{ij}(\vec{r}; \omega) = \iiint_{-\infty}^{\infty} \Phi_{ij}(\vec{k}; \omega) \delta(\omega - \vec{U}\cdot\vec{k}) e^{i\vec{k}\cdot\vec{r}} d^3\vec{k},$$

where δ is defined as the Kronecker delta function. Integrating over U_1, as that relates only to the convection

velocity U_c, gives

$$\Phi_{ij}(\vec{r}; \omega) = \frac{1}{U_c} \iint_{-\infty}^{\infty} \Phi_{ij}(\vec{k}') e^{i\vec{k}'\cdot\vec{r}} dk_2 dk_3, \quad (22)$$

where $\vec{k}' = \{k_c, k_2, k_3\}$ since $k_1 = k_c = \omega/U_c$ is the convective wave number, a natural result of considering the turbulence field frozen. There is no separation in the normal direction, so $r_2 = 0$, giving

$$\Phi_{ij}(\vec{r}; \omega) = \frac{1}{U_c} \iint_{-\infty}^{\infty} \Phi_{ij}(\vec{k}') e^{ik_3 r_3} dk_2 dk_3. \quad (23)$$

Substitution of Equation 23 into Equation 21 gives

$$\Phi_{11}(\omega)2\Lambda_3(\omega)|_1 = \frac{1}{U_c} \iint_{-\infty}^{\infty} \Phi_{11}(k_c, k_2, k_3)$$

$$\times \left\{ \int_{-\infty}^{\infty} e^{ik_3 r_3} dr_3 \right\} dk_2 dk_3. \quad (24)$$

Integration over r_3 gives a result of $2\pi\delta(k_3)$, where δ is the Kronecker delta function. Therefore, the resulting double integral has a non-zero value only in the case of $k_3 = 0$. The expression can be written

$$\Phi_{11}(\omega)2\Lambda_3(\omega)|_1 = \frac{2\pi}{U_c} \int_{-\infty}^{\infty} \Phi_{11}(k_c, k_2, k_3 = 0) dk_2.$$

$$(25)$$

Equation 12 gives an expression for $\Phi_{11}(\vec{k})$. Substitution and simplification (for example, setting $k_3 = 0$) gives

$$\Phi_{11}(\omega)2\Lambda_3(\omega)|_1 = \frac{2\pi}{U_c} \frac{2\alpha_c\Lambda^2}{\pi^2}$$

$$\times \int_{-\infty}^{\infty} \frac{[\beta_c k_2 \Lambda]^2 \, d(\beta_c k_2 \Lambda)}{[1 + (k_1\Lambda)^2 + (\beta_c k_2 \Lambda)^2]^3}. \quad (26)$$

From Gradshteyn and Ryzhik,[13]

$$\int_0^{\infty} \frac{x^2 dx}{(ax^2 + c)^3} = \frac{\pi}{16(ac)^{3/2}}, \quad (27)$$

so combining Equations 26 and 27 gives

$$\Phi_{11}(\omega)2\Lambda_3(\omega)|_1 = \frac{2\pi}{U_c} \frac{2\alpha_c\Lambda^2}{\pi^2} \frac{\pi}{8} \frac{1}{[1 + (k_c\Lambda)^2]^{3/2}}$$

$$= \frac{\Lambda^2\alpha_c}{2U_c} \frac{1}{[1 + (k_c\Lambda)^2]^{3/2}}. \quad (28)$$

1693

Now, an expression for $\Phi_{11}(\omega)$ can be determined by integrating over all three wave number domains. Employing the simplification of Equation 22 and expression for $\Phi_{11}(\vec{k})$ of Equation 12,

$$
\begin{aligned}
\Phi_{11}(\omega) &= \frac{1}{U_c} \iint\limits_{-\infty}^{\infty} \Phi_{11}(k_c, k_2, k_3) dk_2 dk_3 \\
&= \frac{1}{U_c} \frac{2\Lambda^3}{\pi^2} \alpha_c \beta_c \\
&\times \iint\limits_{-\infty}^{\infty} \frac{[(k_2\beta_c)^2 + (k_3\alpha_c)^2]\Lambda^2 dk_2\, dk_3}{[1 + (k_c^2 + (k_2\beta_c)^2 + (k_3\alpha_c)^2)\Lambda^2]^3} \\
&= \frac{1}{U_c} \frac{2\Lambda}{\pi^2} \iint\limits_{-\infty}^{\infty} \Big[[(k_2\beta_c)^2 + (k_3\alpha_c)^2]\, \Lambda^2 \\
&\times \frac{d(k_2\beta_c\Lambda)\, d(k_3\alpha_c\Lambda)}{\left[1 + \left(k_c^2 + (k_2\beta_c)^2 + (k_3\alpha_c)^2\right)\Lambda^2\right]^3} \Big]
\end{aligned} \tag{29}
$$

It can be shown that

$$
\iint\limits_{-\infty}^{\infty} \frac{(x^2 + y^2)\, dx\, dy}{[C^2 + x^2 + y^2]^3} = \frac{\pi}{2C^2}, \tag{30}
$$

giving the final form of $\Phi_{11}(\omega)$ as

$$
\begin{aligned}
\Phi_{11}(\omega) &= \frac{1}{U_c} \frac{2\Lambda}{\pi^2} \frac{\pi}{2\left(1 + (k_c\Lambda)^2\right)} \\
&= \frac{\Lambda}{\pi U_c} \frac{1}{1 + (k_c\Lambda)^2}.
\end{aligned} \tag{31}
$$

It should be noted that this expression is the same as the two-sided wave number spectrum for isotropic turbulence in the streamwise direction as defined in Hinze.[12]

Finally, Equations 28 and 31 may be combined to give a ratio of the spanwise correlation scale of streamwise velocity to the traditional integral length scale, namely

$$
\frac{\Lambda_3(\omega)|_1}{\Lambda} = \frac{\pi\alpha_c}{4} \frac{1}{[1 + (k_c\Lambda)^2]^{1/2}}. \tag{32}
$$

This equation represents an important result in this experimental effort. The correlation scale, which is obtained by integrating the normalized u_1 cross-spectral density over the separation variable r_3, may be predicted simply by measuring the traditional integral length scale and accounting for anisotropy between the k_1 and k_3 directions using the term α_c. While this correlation scale is commonly measured,[10] it is *not* the correlation scale needed to predict the unsteady surface pressure and farfield acoustic response of an airfoil or propeller in a turbulent field.

2.2.2 Spanwise Correlation Length of the Normal Velocity Component

Attention is now turned to developing a prediction for the spanwise correlation length of the normal, or "gust" component of velocity, used in the prediction of the aeroacoustic response of an airfoil (see Equation 1). Again, it can be measured by integrating the non-dimensional cross-spectral density over the separation variable r_3. From Equation 20 and the arguments used for Equation 21,

$$
2\Lambda_3(\omega)|_2 = \frac{1}{\Phi_{22}(\omega)} \int\limits_{-\infty}^{\infty} \Phi_{22}(r_1 = r_2 = 0, r_3; \omega) dr_3 \tag{33}
$$

Hinze[12] shows that $\Phi_{22}(\omega)$ can also be expressed in terms of the classic turbulence length scale, Λ. This expression can be written as

$$
\Phi_{22}(\omega) = \frac{\Lambda}{2\pi U_c} \frac{1 + 3(k_c\Lambda)^2}{(1 + (k_c\Lambda)^2)^2}, \tag{34}
$$

leaving only the numerator of Equation 33 to be determined. Using the same arguments as outlined in Equations 22 through 25 of Section 2.2.1, k_3 is set to zero and, after substitution of Equation 13,

$$
\begin{aligned}
\Phi_{22}(\omega)2\Lambda_3(\omega)|_2 &= \frac{4}{\pi U_c} \alpha_c \Lambda^2 (k_c\Lambda)^2 \\
&\times \int\limits_{-\infty}^{\infty} \frac{d(k_2\beta_c\Lambda)}{[1 + (k_c\Lambda)^2 + (k_2\beta_c\Lambda)^2]^3} \tag{35}
\end{aligned}
$$

Again, Gradshteyn and Ryzhik[13] show that

$$
\int\limits_{-\infty}^{\infty} \frac{dx}{[ax^2 + c]^3} = \frac{3\pi}{16c^2\sqrt{ac}}. \tag{36}
$$

Substitution gives

$$
\Phi_{11}(\omega)2\Lambda_3(\omega)|_2 = \frac{3\Lambda^2\alpha_c(k_c\Lambda)^2}{2U_c} \frac{1}{[1 + (k_c\Lambda)^2]^{5/2}} \tag{37}
$$

Finally, combining Equations 34 and 37 gives a similar ratio as found before, namely

$$
\frac{\Lambda_3(\omega)|_2}{\Lambda} = \frac{3\pi\alpha_c}{2} \frac{(k_c\Lambda)^2}{[1 + (k_c\Lambda)^2]^{1/2}(1 + 3(k_c\Lambda)^2)} \tag{38}
$$

In this sense, the correlation length needed for predicting the acoustic output of the system may be estimated simply by measuring the classic turbulence length scale and employing a convective wave number. Experimental examination of this result can be made by measuring this length scale in the traditional sense.

2.2.3 Additional Correlation Scale Relationships

Again, $\Lambda_3(\omega)|_2$ represents the correlation scale of the normal velocity in the spanwise direction, and is key in predicting the unsteady pressure and farfield acoustic output of an airfoil or propeller. As $\Lambda_3(\omega)|_1$ is often measured experimentally or estimated, a relationship between the two scales is also useful:

$$\frac{\Lambda_3(\omega)|_2}{\Lambda_3(\omega)|_1} = \frac{\Lambda_3(\omega)|_2}{\Lambda} \times \frac{\Lambda}{\Lambda_3(\omega)|_1}$$
$$= \frac{6(k_c\Lambda)^2}{[1 + 3(k_c\Lambda)^2]} \quad (39)$$

For completeness (although not used in this investigation), similar correlation lengths in the normal direction may be found for these same velocity components. Using the notation defined above,

$$\frac{\Lambda_2(\omega)|_1}{\Lambda} = \frac{\pi\beta_c}{4}\frac{1}{[1 + (k_c\Lambda)^2]^{1/2}}, \quad (40)$$

$$\frac{\Lambda_2(\omega)|_2}{\Lambda} = \frac{3\pi\beta_c}{2}\frac{(k_c\Lambda)^2}{[1 + (k_c\Lambda)^2]^{1/2}(1 + 3(k_c\Lambda)^2)} \quad (41)$$

3 Experimental Setup

A series of experiments were completed in order to examine the effectiveness of this predictive tool. All experiments were performed in the Anechoic Wind Tunnel (AWT) at the Hessert Center for Aerospace Research at the University of Notre Dame. The AWT was constructed in the early 1990s as part of the development of the Hessert Center for Aerospace Research. The anechoic chamber has a working space 6.1m (20ft) wide by 7.9m (26ft) long by 2.4m (8ft) high with 55.9cm (22in.) fiberglass sound absorbing wedges on all six sides. This wedge configuration provides a low frequency cutoff of about 100 Hz. Above the cutoff frequency, the wedges have a coefficient of energy absorption at normal incidence of 0.99 or greater. A low turbulence subsonic free-jet test section wind tunnel has been developed to fit into this anechoic chamber for aerodynamic and sound pressure level measurements generated from propellers, fans, pumps, airfoil configurations, etc. The cross-sectional area of the test region is 0.37m² (4ft²) with a maximum velocity of about 30.5 m/s (100 ft/s). A complete description of the tunnel's individual components and important characteristics is presented in Mueller et al.[14, 15]

The examination of correlation length scale was one component of a larger study to examine the unsteady response of stator vanes located downstream of a propeller that was ingesting broadband turbulence.[16, 17] While a detailed discussion of the critical results of this study are beyond the scope of the current paper, the effort focused on distinguishing between different contributions to the turbulent flowfield that then interacted with the downstream stator. These contributions included the upstream turbulence ingested and modified by the propeller, the propeller wake, and propeller blade tip vortices. Independent of the sources involved, flowfield measurements, using an X-wire, defined the turbulence spectra that generated the aeroacoustic response of the stator vane. The spectra described in this paper represent a circumferential average, corresponding to the flowfield "seen" by the stator vanes.

A photograph of the propeller/stator system integrated in the AWT is provided in Figure 2. Freestream velocity travels through an upstream turbulence generation grid. This flow travels downstream through the propeller plane, where the grid-generated turbulence is modified by the movement of the propeller. In addition to this modification of the flow, the wake of the propeller changes the flow characteristics. These influences convect downstream and over a flat plate airfoil, an idealized stator. The unsteady surface pressure (and thus the farfield acoustics) generated over the stator is the result of the unsteady flow seen by the airfoil. The coordinate system for this survey was a standard Cartesian system using primary directions of the flow and airfoil as reference points. For example, the primary (axial) flow direction in the system is represented by x_1. This also represents the chordwise direction of the stator when it is arranged at 0° angle of attack relative to the direction of the freestream flow upstream of the influence of the propeller. Likewise, the normal and spanwise direction of the stator in this orientation are also primary reference directions (x_2 and x_3, respectively). Note that this coordinate system is consistent with the theoretical arguments presented in Section 2.

The propeller plane was located 0.61m (2ft.) downstream of the turbulence generation grids, as the flow has been meticulously examined in this location for both turbulence grid conditions (with and without the presence of an upstream grid). Extensive studies[10, 16] have shown that the grid-generated turbulence approaches isotropy in this plane. Key flow characteristics for cases with and without an upstream grid are presented in Table 1.

An appropriate length scale associated with the positioning of the stator is the maximum chord length of the rotor or propeller blade. At a distance of one chord length, the influence of the unsteady pressure field from either the rotor or stator on its compliment can be ignored.[3, 18, 19] Therefore, positioning of the stator

Figure 2: Propeller/Stator Test Rig
Mounted in Anechoic Wind Tunnel

Table 1: Key Characteristics of
Turbulence Generation Grid

Grid Name	Clean Flow	3in. Grid
Mesh Size, cm (in.)	N/A	7.62 (3.0)
Rod Diameter, cm (in.)	N/A	0.953 (0.375)
Grid Solidity	0	0.33
RMS Turbulence Velocity, m/s (ft/s)	0.02 (0.07)	0.79 (2.60)
RMS Turbulence Intensity	0.15%	6.2%

Table 2: Summary of Experimental
Operating Conditions

Freestream Velocity, m/s (ft/s)		12.7 (41.7)
Stator Chord Reynolds Number		5.4×10^4
BPF for Four-Bladed Propeller	Unloaded	162Hz
	Loaded	200Hz
BPF for Ten-Bladed Propeller	Unloaded	480Hz
	Loaded	550Hz
BPF for Twenty-Bladed Propeller	Unloaded	960Hz
	Loaded	1,100Hz

showing excellent matching of the x_1 component, suggested cross-contamination effects were minimal. For the velocity measurements, the downstream stators were removed so the X-wire probe could be placed at the streamwise location corresponding to the leading edge of the stator. This turbulence characteristics at this point represent the turbulence driving the aeroacoustic response of the stator.

All measurement points involved 625 ensembles of 4096 samples taken at a sampling frequency of 8000Hz. The locations of the measurements are explained in the schematic in Figure 3, representing the measurement positions downstream of the four-bladed propeller. The chord length of the ten- and twenty-bladed propeller was only 2.54cm (1in.), so the streamwise position of these measurements were much closer to the trailing edge of the respective propellers. All measurements took place beneath the propeller dynamometer and assumed to be equal at matching locations on the top of the dynamometer (the location of the second stator vane). Geometrical interference from the propeller dynamometer dictated a minimum radial distance from the center of the dynamometer hub. Therefore, measurements were made in 1.27cm (0.5in.) increments starting at a radial distance of 3.18cm (1.25in.) from the center of the dynamometer hub and continuing out to a distance of 15.9cm (6.25in.) from the center of the dynamometer hub. The outermost distances of each set were considered the "freestream" condition, as there was no evidence of propeller influence that these locations.

Twin X-wires were used in the determination of spanwise turbulence correlation length scale. The experimental method for determination of this correlation length scale is to take two velocity probes and measure the cross-correlation between the two. Integrating this cross-correlation from zero separation to a distance in which the correlation goes to zero gives the value for the correlation length scale. However, this was not done in the current investigation. These repeated correlation measurements for the range of separations needed would in-

downstream of the rotor was based on this scaling. In the study, three different propellers, composed of four, ten, and twenty blades, respectively, were used in order to examine the effect of blade spacing. The length scale of the four-bladed propeller is significantly larger than that of the ten- and twenty-bladed propeller due to chord length differences.

A brief summary of operating conditions is given in Table 2. Operating conditions were selected to take advantage of prior experiments within the same facility.[10, 16]

Velocity measurements were taken using an X-wire anemometry probe. The X-wire anemometry probe is, through proper calibration, able to measure two components of the velocity vector simultaneously. By phase-lock triggering data acquisition and manually rotating the probe $90°$ in the probe holder, all three components of the vector could be determined. Careful checking of the measurements in both the x_1-x_2 and x_1-x_3 planes,

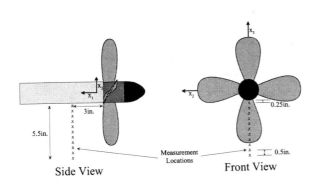

Figure 3: Schematic of Velocity Measurement Locations (Four-Bladed Propeller Locations Shown)

volve a significant amount of measurement and processing time. Multiply this time by the test matrix, which considers multiple points downstream of three different propellers, each operating at two different test conditions (corresponding to loaded and unloaded blades) for different upstream flow conditions (as manifested in the selection of the upstream grid), and the time involved would prevent the completion of other efforts more central to the current research effort.

Rather than spend an inordinate amount of time focusing on this effort, an idea from Wojno[10] was incorporated into the current study. From Corcos[20] and Dryden,[21] an assumption of exponential spatial decay is assumed for the correlation of the turbulence. That is,

$$g(r_i) \approx e^{-\frac{r_i}{\Lambda_i}}, \qquad (42)$$

where $g(r_i)$ is the non-dimensional lateral velocity correlation function, r_i is the spatial separation distance in the specified direction, and Λ_i is the correlation length scale. In terms of the actual experimental procedure, the equation can be rewritten as

$$
\sqrt{\gamma^2(f, r_i)} \equiv \left[\frac{\Phi_{u_{2_1} u_{2_2}}(f, r_i) \Phi^*_{u_{2_1} u_{2_2}}(f, r_i)}{\Phi_{u_{2_1} u_{2_1}}(f) \Phi_{u_{2_2} u_{2_2}}(f)} \right]^{\frac{1}{2}}
$$
$$
= g(r_i)
$$
$$
\approx e^{-\frac{|r_i|}{\Lambda_3|_2}}, \qquad (43)
$$

where γ^2 is the coherence function defined in terms of the turbulence cross-spectra and auto-spectra, Φ_{ij} and Φ_{ii}, respectively. In the above equation, the primary subscript denotes a velocity direction (in this case, the normal or x_2-direction) and the secondary subscript denotes a probe number (1 or 2). In this way, the correlation length scale, which is frequency dependent, may be determined by measuring the coherence between two probes at a defined separation r_i (in this case, $i = 3$ for

a spanwise separation), then solving for $\Lambda_3|_2$. Wojno found that in assuming this functional form, cases for a range of probe separations collapse to a uniform curve.

A similar analysis was performed in the current study. The effectiveness of such an assumption, as well as a more thorough analysis of the derivation presented in Section 2, are presented in Section 4.

4 Experimental Results

The analysis and results described in this section were completed for the entire test matrix described in Section 3. That is, the analysis was completed at all measurement locations downstream of all propellers at both loading conditions for each propeller. The results presented below are typical, but focus on only two measurement points in one propeller/loading condition, emphasizing analysis of the techniques rather than a discussion of all results in the matrix. A more thorough discussion is presented in Lynch.[16] The points considered for this discussion were measurements downstream of the four-bladed propeller in the "unloaded" condition ($J = 1.4$), located downstream of the 3in. turbulence generation grid. One point was located 7.0cm (2.75in.) from the hub center, while the other was 15.9cm (6.25in.) from the hub center. These represent cases of the turbulence being a contribution from propeller and upstream sources and upstream sources only, respectively. They are labeled as "Propeller and Upstream Turbulence" and "Upstream Turbulence Only" locations, respectively, in the following graphs.

In order to efficiently measure this correlation length scale, an exponential spatial decay model was assumed for the correlation of the turbulence. This mirrors the techniques employed by Corcos,[20] Dryden,[21] and Wojno,[10] and is explained in Section 3. This employs a coherence measurement between two probes separated by a distance r (see Equation 43). The square root of coherence is plotted as a function of frequency for a range of separation distances in Figure 4. Note that the separation distances required between the two probes are quite small, increasing the difficulty in the measurements. A benefit to the technique presented in this paper is that all necessary measurements are single-point, thereby requiring only one probe.

Returning to Figure 4, the effectiveness of the Corcos model would be reflected in the collapse of coherence measurements to a single curve in the calculation of correlation length. However, even at small separation distances, the coherence between probes quickly falls to zero, especially for small scales of turbulence (reflected in higher frequencies). Bendat and Piersol[22] and

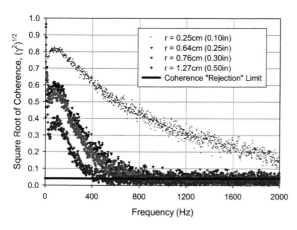

Figure 4: Square Root of Coherence as a Function of Frequency ("Upstream Turbulence Only" Location)

Wojno[10] conclude that the resolution of the coherence measurements can be described as

$$\Delta \sqrt{\gamma^2} \sim \frac{1}{\sqrt{N}}, \qquad (44)$$

where N is the number of ensembles taken (625 for these tests). This gives a $\Delta \sqrt{\gamma^2}$, or resolution, of 0.04. Therefore, if the square root of the coherence is less than that value, it is statistically zero and removed from consideration. This is reflected in the coherence "rejection" line shown in Figure 4.

The results of application of this technique are shown in Figure 5. While the cleanest, most informative data is represented by the smallest separation, the curves from all separations considered collapse to a uniform curve in the calculation of length scale.

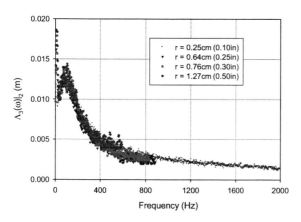

Figure 5: Experimental Estimation of Correlation Length Scale $\Lambda_3|_2$ Using Corcos Model for Spatial Correlation Decay ("Upstream Turbulence Only" Location)

There now exists some measure of merit for the predicted correlation length scale expression given in Equation 38. The first case considered is that position representative of turbulence contributions from only the upstream grid. Wojno[10] showed that this grid-generated turbulence reaches a nearly isotropic state at the propeller plane, and Lynch[16] concluded that there is no quantifiable influence from the propeller at this measurement location. As such, it represents the "simplest" case for the model. Figure 6 compares the experimental data set formed by the combination of separation distances depicted in Figure 5 with function generated using Equation 38. With isotropy, $\alpha_c \sim 1$ and the key parameter is Λ, which was calculated as 1.8cm (0.70in.). Results are plotted as a function of non-dimensional wave number, requiring a conversion to the spatial domain using a frozen-field assumption (recall from Section 2.1 that $k_1 = k_c$). As is clearly seen, the prediction based only on integral length scale is in excellent agreement with experimental data. In fact, when considering Figures 4 through 6, the most significant departures between the prediction and experimental results comes from the experimental data contributed by the largest separation between probes, where coherence values are small. For the better data sets associated with smaller separations, the agreement is excellent.

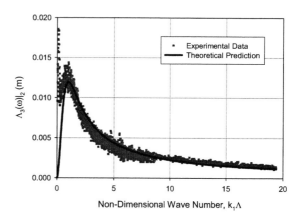

Figure 6: Comparison of Experimentally Estimated and Predicted Correlation Scale $\Lambda_3|_2$ ("Upstream Turbulence Only" Location)

The turbulent flowfield is much more complex in the region influenced by the propeller. The details are beyond the scope of this paper (but are discussed in detail in Lynch[16]). Basically, the flowfield over most of the region influenced by the propeller (away from hub and tip effects) is the result of superposition of contributions from (1) propeller wakes and (2) ingested turbulence which is modified by the propeller. Models developed in Lynch[16] capture the relative levels of these contributions, but in terms of the response of the downstream stator, the total turbulence is the quantity of interest. Still, there are a number of important results from the modeling of contributions that could effect correlation length scale. The broadband contribution of the propeller wake dominates only at high frequencies. However, at low frequencies, the propeller geometry works to suppress the largest scales of ingested turbulence. The result is a smaller turbulence integral length scale, which should manifest itself in a corresponding decrease in spanwise correlation scale (assuming the two are indeed related). Further, it is unrealistic to assume that the turbulence is still accurately represented with an isotropic assumption.

The same analysis as the "upstream turbulence only" case was used on a point influenced by the presence of a propeller. The only changes in the analysis were the artificial removal of tonal peaks in the spectrum associated with wakes passing the sensor at harmonics of blade passage frequency (BPF), and the consideration of anisotropy as it relates to the correction factor, α_c. The results are shown in Figure 7. Again, while not specifically shown in this case, the most significant disagreement between theory and experimental data occurred with the experimental data contribution of the largest probe separation. Note that the values of the length scale reflect the expected decrease caused by a decrease in integral length scale.

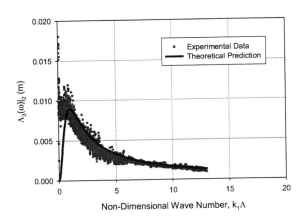

Figure 7: Comparison of Experimentally Estimated and Predicted Correlation Scale $\Lambda_3|_2$ ("Propeller and Upstream Turbulence" Location)

As the predicted scales closely reflect those experimentally estimated, attention now turns to the effectiveness of the formula presented in Equation 1 to predict the acoustic contribution of the stator. The effective modeling of correlation length scale is highly encouraging as a tool to now be used to predict the acoustic output of

the system.

Again focusing the consideration to the broadband turbulence field responsible for the unsteady response of the stator, the stator pair pictured in Figure 2 can be divided into two primary sections. These sections are the areas affected by unmodified grid-generated turbulence and those affected by propeller-modified turbulence. Analysis of the propeller-modified turbulence field suggests that, with proper non-dimensionalization by local values of variables such as RMS turbulence intensity and freestream velocity, the propeller-modified field could be represented by the measurements at one point.[16] That is, the non-dimensionalized turbulence quantities downstream of the propeller were basically uniform in terms of the broadband turbulence (with the exception of the regions near the hub and near the passing tip vortices). Therefore, the prediction of the acoustic output from the stators could be made using one point which represents grid-generated turbulence, and one point which represents propeller-modified turbulence. These two models would then be applied over the length of the stator to which each turbulence field applied (the term L_3 in Equation 1). As Scharpf[23] noted that the stream tube changes for the four-bladed propeller were negligible, it was decided that the simple geometry provided a satisfactory approximation for these lengths of influence. Specifically, the length of interest for the propeller-modified turbulence was equal to the diameter of the given propeller (minus the diameter of the dynamometer hub), while the length of interest for the unmodified grid-generated turbulence was the difference between the tunnel width and the propeller diameter.

Application of the appropriate lengths and length scales gives a prediction for the acoustic output of the stator. One immediate comparison can be made if the prediction is summed with the measured acoustic output of the propeller, then comparing that curve to that of the propeller/stator combination. Figure 8 shows such a comparison, with the "propeller only" curve showing the baseline to which the stator output prediction is added. Again, the purpose of this effort is not the prediction of the acoustic output of the propeller, which has been developed in prior efforts at the University of Notre Dame.[24, 25, 26, 27] Over the entire frequency range of interest, the theoretical curve accurately predicts the measured value, including the peaks associated with the BPF harmonics. The only large discrepancy occurs between 900-1100Hz, a region shown to be dominated by stator trailing edge noise, which is not included in the theoretical models described here.[16] This prediction is impressive not only for the ability of the length scale estimation given in Section 2 to predict the acoustic output,

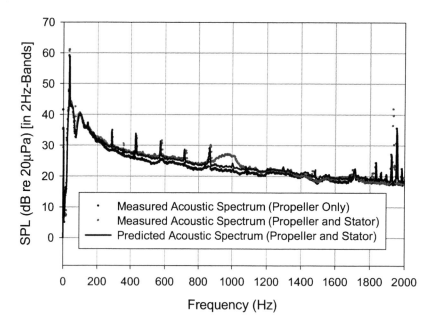

Figure 8: Comparison of Predicted and Experimentally Measured Acoustic Output of the Propeller/Stator System for Four-Bladed Propeller Behind 3in. Grid, Unloaded Case ($J = 1.4$)

but that this output prediction is based on turbulence measurements at only two locations.

5   Conclusions

This paper provides a derivation of correlation length scale as a function of classic turbulence integral length scale. The benefit of such a tool is that such a scale, traditionally determined utilizing an array of two-point correlation measurements, may be determined using relatively simple one-point measurements. Its utility is illustrated in the accurate estimation of the aeroacoustic response of a stator to a turbulent flowfield.

Acknowledgments

This research was performed at the Hessert Center for Aerospace Research, a division of the Department of Aerospace and Mechanical Engineering, at the University of Notre Dame. The work was supported by the U.S. Navy, Office of Naval Research, located in Arlington, Virginia, under contracts #N00014-99-1-0284 and #N00014-01-1-0424. The program manager was Dr. L. Patrick Purtell.

References

[1] von Kármán, T. and Sears, W. R., "Airfoil Theory for Non-Uniform Motion," *Journal of the Aeronautical Sciences*, Vol. 5, No. 10, August 1938, pp. 379–390.

[2] Sears, W. R., "Some Aspects of Non-Stationary Airfoil Theory and its Practical Application," *Journal of the Aeronautical Sciences*, Vol. 8, No. 3, January 1941, pp. 104–108.

[3] Blake, W. K., *Mechanics of Flow Induced Sound and Vibration*, John Wiley and Sons, Inc., New York, NY, 1986.

[4] Amiet, R. K., "Acoustic Radiation from an Airfoil in a Turbulent Stream," *Journal of Sound and Vibration*, Vol. 41, No. 4, 1975, pp. 407–420.

[5] Wygnanski, I. et al., "On the Large-Scale Structures in Two-Dimensional Small-Deficit, Turbulent Wakes," *Journal of Fluid Mechanics*, Vol. 168, 1986, pp. 31–71.

[6] Glegg, S., "Prediction of Blade Wake Interaction Noise Based on a Turbulent Vortex Model," *AIAA Journal*, Vol. 29, No. 10, October 1991, pp. 1545–1551.

[7] Devenport, W. J. et al., "Wave Number Frequency Spectra of a Lifting Wake for Broadband Noise Prediction," *AIAA Journal*, Vol. 36, No. 6, June 1998, pp. 881–887.

[8] Devenport, W. J. et al., "Two-Point Descriptions of Wake Turbulence with Application to Noise Prediction," *AIAA Journal*, Vol. 39, No. 12, December 2001, pp. 2302–2307.

[9] Glegg, S. et al., "Broadband Helicopter Noise Generated by Blade Wake Interactions," *Journal of the American Helicopter Society*, Vol. 44, No. 4, October 1999, pp. 293–301.

[10] Wojno, J. P., *An Experimental Investigation of the Aeroacoustic Response of a Ten-Bladed Rotor Ingesting Grid-Generated Turbulence*, Ph.D. thesis, University of Notre Dame, 1999.

[11] Panton, R. L. and Linebarger, J. H., "Wall Pressure Spectra Calculations for Equilibrium Boundary Layers," *Journal of Fluid Mechanics*, Vol. 65, No. 2, 1974, pp. 261–287.

[12] Hinze, J. O., *Turbulence*, McGraw–Hill, New York, NY, 1975.

[13] Gradshteyn, I. S. and Ryzhik, I. M., *Table of Integrals, Series, and Products*, Academic Press, New York, NY, 1980.

[14] Mueller, T. J. et al., "The Design of a Low-Noise, Low-Turbulence Wind Tunnel for Acoustic Measurements," *Proceedings of the 17th AIAA Ground Testing Conference*, No. 92-3883, American Institute of Aeronautics and Astronautics, 1992.

[15] Mueller, T. J. et al., "A New Low Speed Wind Tunnel for Acoustic Measurements," *Proceedings of the European Forum on Wind Tunnels and Wind Tunnel Test Techniques*, Royal Aeronautical Society, 1992.

[16] Lynch, III, D. A., *An Experimental Investigation of the Unsteady Response of a Stator Located Downstream of a Propeller Ingesting Broadband Turbulence*, Ph.D. thesis, University of Notre Dame, 2001.

[17] Lynch, III, D. A. et al., "Aeroacoustic Response of an Airfoil Downstream of a Propeller Ingesting Broadband Turbulence," *Proceedings of the 7th AIAA/CEAS Aeroacoustics Conference*, No. AIAA 2001-2240, American Institute of Aeronautics and Astronautics, May 2001.

[18] Kaji, S. and Okazaki, T., "Generation of Sound by Rotor-Stator Interaction," *Journal of Sound and Vibration*, Vol. 13, No. 3, 1970, pp. 281–307.

[19] Falk, E. A., *An Experimental Investigation of Aerodynamic Forcing in the F109 Turbofan Engine Compressor*, Ph.D. thesis, University of Notre Dame, 2000.

[20] Corcos, G. M., "The Structure of the Turbulent Pressure Field in Boundary-Layer Flows," *Journal of Fluid Mechanics*, Vol. 18, 1964, pp. 353–378.

[21] Dryden, H. L., "Turbulence Investigations at the National Bureau of Standards," *Proceedings of the 5th International Congress of Applied Mathematics*, 1938.

[22] Bendat, J. S. and Piersol, A. G., *Random Data: Analysis and Measurement Procedures*, John Wiley and Sons, Inc., New York, NY, 2000.

[23] Scharpf, D. F., *An Experimental Investigation of the Sources of Propeller Noise Due to Turbulence Ingestion*, Ph.D. thesis, University of Notre Dame, 1993.

[24] Minniti, III, R. J. et al., "Inferring Propeller Inflow and Radiation from Near-Field Response, Part 1: Analytic Development," *AIAA Journal*, Vol. 39, No. 6, June 2001, pp. 1030–1036.

[25] Minniti, III, R. J. et al., "Inferring Propeller Inflow and Radiation from Near-Field Response, Part 2: Empirical Application," *AIAA Journal*, Vol. 39, No. 6, June 2001, pp. 1037–1046.

[26] Wojno, J. P. et al., "Rotor Turbulence Ingestion Noise, Part I: Experimental Characterization of Grid-Generated Turbulence," *AIAA Journal*, Vol. 40, No. 1, January 2002, pp. 16–25.

[27] Wojno, J. P. et al., "Rotor Turbulence Ingestion Noise, Part II: Rotor Aeroacoustic Response," *AIAA Journal*, Vol. 40, No. 1, January 2002, pp. 26–32.

AIAA 2002-2570

THERMOACOUSTIC PROPERTIES
OF CAN ANNULAR COMBUSTORS

Sven Bethke, Werner Krebs, Patrick Flohr, Bernd Prade

SIEMENS AG Power Generation
Wiesenstraße 35
D 45473 Mülheim an der Ruhr, Germany

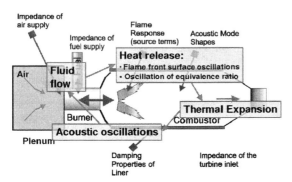

Fig. 1: Thermoacoustic feedback cycle.

Abstract

The development of low NO_x and high performance gas turbines requires detailed knowledge of the phenomenon of thermoacoustic combustion oscillations. Prediction of thermoacoustic instabilities already in the phase of engine design becomes increasingly important. To determine the complicated relationship and interaction between acoustics and thermal heat release, the thermoacoustic feedback cycle has to be investigated and broken down into its elementary tasks. One major task is the acoustic modal analysis which is treated here. A detailed 3-D finite element analysis of a can annular combustor design is performed. First, a single can configuration is investigated. The influence of the boundary condition at the head end plate on the modes of acoustic pressure distribution is investigated. The acoustic boundary condition at the burner outlet are represented by the burner impedance. It is shown by the analysis that correct impedance boundary condition is crucial for the modal analysis of a can annular system. Further refinements of this model due

to e.g. adaptions to different gas flow velocities or slightly modified burner designs do not have significant effects. Subsequently extended acoustic equations are used to take into account the steady state flow velocity of the gas. But this affects the modes of the acoustic pressure distribution only marginally as far as the FE model only includes the combustion chamber. In this case the crucial regions through the burner as well as through the termination at the exit of the combustion chamber were supplied by impedance boundary conditions. The simulation of a combustion chamber including inlet guide vanes and exhaust discharge shows that the Ma-number through these narrow gaps has indeed strong effects on the acoustic properties. To study potential can–can interaction a finite element of a multiple can configuration was performed. A FE analysis of a can annular combustor configuration shows that the axial modes found from the single can FE models are only a small fraction of possible eigenfrequencies. Due to the interconnections through the cross flame tubes and through the manifold upstream the turbine vanes several additional eigenfrequencies are possible.

1. Introduction

The primary goal of current gas turbine development is to increase turbine inlet temperature and lower NO_x-emissions. Due to high power densities these low NO_x and high performance combustion systems for gas turbines, unfortunately, are prone to produce thermoacoustic combustion instabilities and combustion driven vibrations. These oscillations are determined by a feedback cycle between effects of fluid flow, heat release, thermal expansion and acoustic oscillations (cf. Fig. 1) already described by Rayleigh and may be excited unrestively until severe engine failures will occur. Therefore, prediction of thermoacoustic instabilities already in the phase of engine design becomes increasingly important to take countermeasures to supress these instabilities and extend the operational envelope of gas turbines.

In order to develop measures preventing thermoacoustic instabilities the complicated relationship and interaction between acoustics and thermal heat release have to be considered. Figure

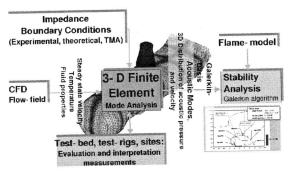

Fig. 2: Thermoacoustic stability analysis.

2 illustrates the interrelations between the tasks which are dealt by the stability analysis. Modes of acoustic pressure distribution and eigenfrequencies are strongly coupled to the stability analysis, because knowledge of the acoustic system's eigenfrequencies is a precondition for using the Galerkin algorithm (see Krebs et al.[1]). The 3-D Finite Element mode analysis and the subsequent stability analysis are the main tasks of the thermoacoustic evaluation process.

The acoustic behavior of the combustion chamber on its own already shows complex interdependicies between boundary conditions at burner exit, outlet of combustion chamber, and liner, and furthermore acoustic properties of gas as well as steady state flow velocity.

Can annular designs of combustion chambers are widely-used in stationary gas-turbine design. Especially inside these can combustors acoustics strongly depend on boundary conditions at both ends: at inlet downstream burner exit as well as at exit of combustion chamber upstream turbine.

3-D finite element simulations of acoustic properties of a can annular combustor were performed. The finite element model described in section 4 includes the whole combustion chamber starting at the head end plate and ending upstream the turbine inlet. First (section 5), the effect of the impedance of the burner is analyzed, taking into account influencing factors including gas flow rate and type of burner. The burner

impedance is derived experimentally (see section 3). Secondly, the importance of the acoustic boundary condition at the exit of the combustion chamber was evaluated. The effect of this boundary condition is of particular importance because the acoustic termination used in test rigs usually differs from that at the exit of the actual set-up in the engine. A vane simulation section to simulate the acoustic termination due to the vanes of the turbine was considered and analysed by the finite element model in section 6. Additionally, the consequence of the influence of steady state flow field on the solution is explored.

Finally, in section 7, an arrangement of interconnected cans in can annular combustors is acoustically evaluated. The effect of the can-can interconnection through cross flame tubes and the annular manifold upstream turbine vanes is determined by 3-D acoustic finite element simulations taking into account detailed impedance boundary conditions as described above.

2. Theory

The fluid used here is composed of fuel gas, air and exhaust. This fluid is frictionless and it is assumed to observe the equation of state for perfect gases:

$$p = \varrho \cdot R \cdot T \qquad (1)$$

where p ambient pressure
      R   specific gas constant
      T absolute temperature
      ϱ fluid density

The speed of sound a_0 usually is a real value. For perfect gases a_0 is:

$$a_0 = \sqrt{\kappa \cdot R \cdot T} \qquad (2)$$

where κ ratio of heat capacities

Fluid flow of perfect gas is characterized by only time t, position — e.g. x, y, z —, ambient pressure p, density ϱ, temperature T, and velocity v_x, v_y, v_z. The variables are linked by the equation of continuity:

$$\frac{\partial \varrho}{\partial t} + \nabla \cdot (\varrho \, \vec{v}) = 0 \qquad (3)$$

where $\vec{v}$ (v_x, v_y, v_z), vector of velocities

      ∇ Nabla-operator: $\frac{\partial}{\partial x}\vec{i} + \frac{\partial}{\partial y}\vec{j} + \frac{\partial}{\partial z}\vec{k}$

      $\vec{i}, \vec{j}, \vec{k}$ Unit vectors in x, y, z-direction and by conservation of momentum:

$$\varrho \frac{D\vec{v}}{Dt} + \nabla p = 0 \; . \qquad (4)$$

where $\frac{Dq}{Dt}$ $\quad \frac{\partial q}{\partial t} + v_x \frac{\partial q}{\partial x} + v_y \frac{\partial q}{\partial y} + v_z \frac{\partial q}{\partial z}$ total derivative on any quantity q

If the flow is assumed to be irrotational, the vector of velocities can be expressed in terms of a velocity potential Φ:

$$\vec{v} = \nabla \Phi \; . \qquad (5)$$

In acoustic problems a small perturbation is superimposed to the distribution of the steady state flow. Hence, the velocity potential Φ is consisting of the potential Φ_0 of the steady state flow and an acoustic portion Φ':

$$\Phi = \Phi_0 + \Phi' \; . \qquad (6)$$

The solution for the potential of the acoustic velocity Φ' is:

$$\Phi' = \alpha \, \Phi'_A \, e^{j\omega t} \; . \qquad (7)$$

where Φ'_A $\quad$ amplitude of time-harmonic acoustic potential
ω $\quad$ angular frequency
α $\quad$ $\alpha \ll 1$

Assuming irrotational and barotropic flow — i.e. ϱ is a function of pressure only — the equations of continuity and conservation of momentum results in the nonlinear, unsteady flow equation as described by Coyette[2] and finally leads to an algebraic system of equations to solve for the steady state flow:

$$\mathbf{K}_0 \cdot \vec{\Phi}_0 = \mathbf{C}_0 \cdot \vec{\Psi}_{on} \; , \qquad (8)$$

where $\mathbf{K}_0$ $\quad$ Stiffness matrix
$\mathbf{C}_0$ $\quad$ Coupling matrix
$\vec{\Phi}_o$ $\quad$ vector of nodal potentials
$\vec{\Psi}_{on}$ $\quad$ vector of normal gradients of the velocity potential along boundary

Just as the steady state flow the amplitudes of the acoustic potential are derived from a set of nodal values $\vec{\Phi}'_A$. The direct response frequency analysis then solves the following system of equations for the selected frequencies ω:

$$\left[\mathbf{K}_A + j\omega \mathbf{D}_A - \omega^2 \mathbf{M}_A \right] \cdot \vec{\Phi}'_A = \mathbf{C}_A \cdot \vec{\Psi}_{An} \; . \qquad (9)$$

where $\mathbf{K}_A$ $\quad$ Stiffness matrix
$\mathbf{D}_A$ $\quad$ Damping matrix
$\mathbf{C}_A$ $\quad$ Coupling matrix
$\mathbf{M}_A$ $\quad$ Mass matrix

$\vec{\Phi}'_A$ $\quad$ Vector of nodal acoustic potentials
$\vec{\Psi}_{An}$ $\quad$ Vector of normal gradients of acoustic velocity potential

The steady state flow velocity affects $\mathbf{K}_A$, $\mathbf{D}_A$ and $\mathbf{C}_A$ as described by Coyette[2]. In the particular case of zero steady state flow velocity these expression is reduced to the usual acoustic task.

The following results will use normalized non-dimensional frequency f/f_0. Using characteristic length l_0 and average speed of sound a the characteristic time $\tau_0 = l_0/a_0$ and frequency $f_0 = 1/\tau_0$ are defined. The characteristic length l_0 is the acousticly relevant axial length of the can combustion chamber.

3. Boundary Conditions, Impedances

The absorbent acoustic boundaries at both ends of the FE-model are simulated imposing boundary conditions of complex normal admittance or impedance. Admittance A_n is defined as the complex ratio of velocity over pressure whereas, vice versa, the reciprocal value is the impedance Z_n:

$$A_n = \frac{v_n}{p} \text{ and } Z_n = \frac{p}{v_n} \; . \qquad (10)$$

where A_n $\quad$ normal admittance
Z_n $\quad$ normal impedance
v_n $\quad$ normal acoustic velocity related to boundary
p $\quad$ acoustic pressure

The material is only locally reacting and only the normal component of the acoustic particle velocity is taken into acount — bulk absorbing materials can be applied by complex sound speed. The normals of elements in the FE-model follow special conventions regarding their directions. This affects signs of boundary conditions applied on those elements. Within the FE-model normals to element faces are always pointing outwards from the acoustic domain, therefore, the admittance boundary condition is defined as the ratio:

$$A_n = $$
$$\frac{\text{velocity in the direction of the element normal}}{\text{acoustic pressure}}$$
$$= \frac{\text{velocity in the outward direction}}{\text{acoustic pressure}} \qquad (11)$$

The reflection coefficient R is defined by a forward traveling wave p^+ which normally impinges at an

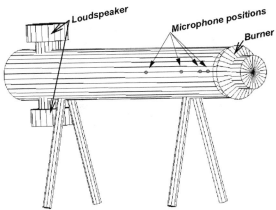

Fig. 3: Experimental set-up for measurement of burner impedance.

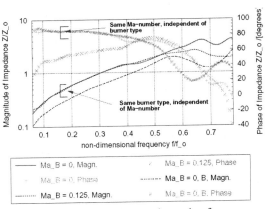

Fig. 4: Experimental results for burner impedance Z/Z_0: Effect of steady state flow through burner and type of burner (comparison to burner type B).

interface and by the reflected wave p^-. The wave is partly reflected and partly transmitted, i.e. acoustic energy is absorbed. Using the assumption that field variables acoustic pressure p and velocity v are varying time harmonically:

$$p(x,t) = \hat{P}(x) \cdot \mathrm{e}^{j\omega t} \quad \text{and} \quad (12)$$

$$v(x,t) = \hat{V}(x) \cdot \mathrm{e}^{j\omega t} \; , \quad (13)$$

where x \quad coordinate

the reflection coefficient R respective the transmission coefficient T are defined by:

$$R = \frac{\hat{P}^-}{\hat{P}^+} \quad \text{and} \quad T = \frac{\hat{P}^{tr}}{\hat{P}^+} \; . \quad (14)$$

The impedance, e.g. of the turbine's guide vanes, can be derived according to e.g. Blackstock[3] via the impedance Z at any point in the acoustic domain:

$$Z(d) = \frac{\hat{P}(d)}{\hat{V}(d)} = Z_0 \cdot \frac{\mathrm{e}^{jkd} + R\,\mathrm{e}^{-jkd}}{\mathrm{e}^{jkd} - R\,\mathrm{e}^{-jkd}} \; . \quad (15)$$

where $k =$ \quad ω/a_0, wave number

$d =$ \quad $l - x$, distance from the exit boundary condition.

$Z_0 =$ \quad $\varrho_0 \cdot a_0$, characteristic impedance

Particularly, for $d = 0$, $Z(d = 0)$ is the impedance of the turbine's guide vanes Z_n. Equation (15) solved for R results in:

$$R = \frac{Z_n - Z_0}{Z_n + Z_0} \; . \quad (16)$$

3.1. Burner: Impedance Measurement

The complex burner impedance Z_b defines the upstream end of the combustion chamber and

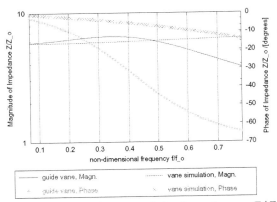

Fig. 5: Theoretical approach for impedances Z/Z_0 of guide vanes and vane simulating cylinders at exit of combustion chamber (Mach-numbers: Ma_{VSS} resp. $\mathrm{Ma}_{Vane} = 0.8$)

represents the acoustic properties of the flowpath upstream the burner exit. This impedance was quantified experimentally in an atmospheric test-rig without combustion. The method of transfer functions using two microphones was used (cf. Munjal[4]). The experimental set-up is shown in Fig. 3. A plane field of sound-waves was produced by loudspeakers downstream the burner. The acoustic pressure was measured at different axial positions by two microphones. The measured transfer function between microphones gives the impedance of the burner exit plane. The tests were performed under no-flow conditions as well as at various levels of steady state flow discharged through the burner. The positions of microphones were selected so that effects of turbulent fluctuations and flow noise on pressure signal were minimized.

3.2. Burner: Measured Impedance

The experimental results for burner impedances with and without steady state flow through the burner are shown in figure 4 (see Krebs et al.[5]). The figure shows magnitude and phase of the burner impedance for the cases of stagnant fluid ($Ma_B = 0$) and flow through the burner ($Ma_B = 0.125$). The magnitude is normalized by the characteristic impedance $Z_0 = \varrho_0 \cdot a_0$ of the medium.

The acoustic velocity at the burner exit precedes the acoustic pressure by roughly a quarter wave — i.e. the phase of the impedance is about 90 degrees — over a wide range of frequencies. This behavior generally appears at a pressure release termination with perfect reflection. Increasing the steady state flow through the burner reduces the phase of the impedance. This is accompanied by a decrease of the magnitude of the reflection coefficient R. The magnitude of the impedance increases with rising frequencies since at higher frequencies the amplitude of the acoustic velocity decreases. The Mach-number inside the burner affects the magnitude of the impedance only negligible.

Furthermore, figure 4 shows that the type of burner potentially effects both, magnitude as well as phase of impedances, dependent on the range of frequencies. The two burner designs are different regarding flow passage and insertion of a perforated plate. In this particular case the phase is not affected for lower frequencies whereas at higher frequencies the phase is affected by the set-up of the burner and the magnitude is shifted slightly over the whole range of frequencies considered.

3.3. Combustion chamber exit: Impedance

At the exit of the combustion chamber the guide vanes of the turbine form the acoustic boundary condition. In the case of combustion chambers in test-rigs the set-up of the exit boundary varies depending on the operating conditions of the facility. According to test conditions the acoustic exit boundary is simulated by several designs, e.g. pressure release termination, rows or arrays of cylinders, etc., which are to a greater or lesser extend qualified for the simulation of effects of high Mach-number flow through the guide vanes of the turbine on acoustics. Figure 5 shows results of a basic theoretical approach to calculate acoustic boundary conditions at the exit of the combustion chamber. The impedance of the turbine's guide vanes and a vane simulating array

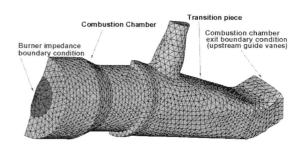

Fig. 6: FE model of one single can combustion chamber.

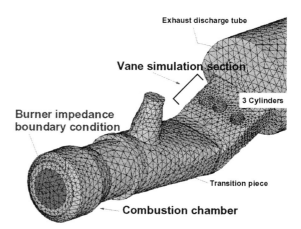

Fig. 7: FE model of one single can combustion chamber of test-rig set-u, including vane simulation section.

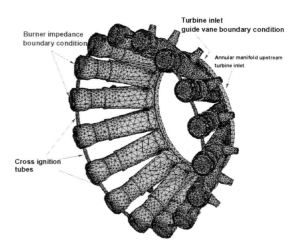

Fig. 8: FE model of a can annular combustor.

of cylinders are simulated and compared. Obviously, different acoustic properties are plausible because unequal fluid flow conditions exist downstream of these obstacles. Compared to the fluid flow behind the vanes, the cylinders are generating much more vortices which affect the reflection of the exit boundary condition.

4. FE Model

Three FE models are used to investigate the thermoacoustic properties and the behavior of the can annular combustor and perform 3-D finite element acoustic mode analyses as a prerequisite for an integrated stability analysis.

The first model shown by figure 6 includes the whole combustion chamber including the transition piece. The FE domain spans from the head end plate to the exit of the transition piece upstream the turbine inlet. At these boundaries absorbing boundary conditions are applied. This FE model is suitable to investigate effects of different impedances due to, e.g. variation of Mach-number through the burner (see section 3.2). The second FE model represents the basic features of typical test-rig set-ups. The model in figure 7 includes the whole combustion chamber, the vane simulation section and the exhaust discharge tube. The vane simulation section is composed of three cylinders simulating the guiding vanes such as commonly used in test-rigs. The exhaust discharge tube is terminated by a non-reflecting boundary condition. This model is used to determine the impedance of the cross-sectional area upstream the vane simulation section and its dependency from the Mach-number through this section. At the head end plate an absorbent boundary condition is applied as described in section 3.2.

The last model is a can annular combustor made up of sixteen separate can-type combustion chambers (see figure 8). Single cans are interconnected through cross flame tubes and an annular manifold upstream the turbine inlet. An impedance as described in section 3.2 is applied to the surfaces related to the head end plate. The boundary condition at the annular manifold upstream the turbine is defined by an impedance according to section 3.3.

5. Finite Element Modal Analysis

The acoustic finite element analysis is done by solving equations 8 and 9. The finite element procedure determines the steady state response of the acoustic medium on a forced excitation as a function of the particular frequency ω of the driver unit. The vibrating panel boundary condition is applied to excite waves within the fluid. When the frequency is approaching an eigenfrequency of the acoustic system, the acoustic pressure is

at its maximum similar to the well-known forced harmonic oscillator. Because the frequency has to be varied over the whole range of interest — using appropriate frequency increments — to detect these peaks of acoustic pressure, this steady state frequency response approach is more expensive than the direct solution of a real-valued eigenvalue problem.

The main focus of this paper is on the determination of can combustors eigenfrequencies and mode shapes only, hence, it is not intended to model absolute values of acoustic pressure amplitudes.

It is usefull to compare the results taking into account absorbent boundary conditions at the inlet and at the exit of the combustion chamber with the eigenmodes of the combustors if rigid acoustic boundaries, i.e. $Z_{b/VSS} \to \infty$, are applied at both ends of the combustion chamber. It is supposed that the boundary conditions have noticeable influence on the eigenmodes, because the acoustic behavior of can combustors is mainly dominated by axial acoustic modes, whose pressure distribution is bounded to the ancillary conditions at both ends.

The mode shapes at the first nine eigenfrequencies are shown by figure 9. The first three

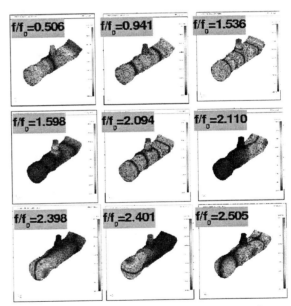

Fig. 9: Acoustic pressure distribution if rigid termination applied at all boundaries.

eigenfrequencies are axial modes at $f/f_0 = 0.506$, 0.941, and 1.536. The fourth axial mode is at $f/f_0 = 2.094$. The first azimuthal mode is formed in the combustion chamber at higher frequencies at $f/f_0 = 2.398$. The higher the frequency

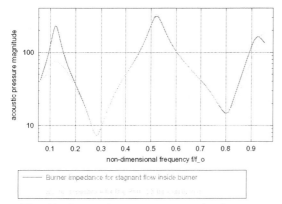

Fig. 10: Acoustic pressure magnitude versus
non-dimensional frequency f/f_0:
Comparison of results from burner impedance
for stagnant flow and for $Ma_B = 0.125$.

correspond to the first and second axial mode of
the rigid terminated combustion chamber shown
by figure 9. The mode shapes of the acoustic
pressure distribution for all three frequencies are
shown by figure 11.

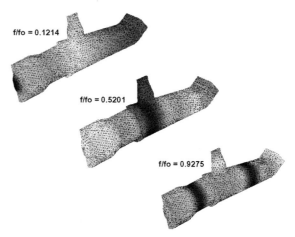

Fig. 11: Acoustic pressure distribution if
burner impedance for stagnant flow
applied to head end plate.

the more mixed modes occur. In the range of
higher frequencies above $f/f_0 \geq 1.8$ the eigenfrequencies are closely together, so that it will
be hard to identify a correlation between these
numerically determined eigenfrequencies and experimental data.

The estimation of influences on impedances
are important to assess the degree of accuracy
that is needed for defining reliable boundary conditions. The sensitivity of eigenfrequencies calculated by the FE analysis on e.g. fluid velocity
through burner or design and set-up of burner are
important tasks for defining realistic but sufficient
standards for preparation of impedance data.

5.1. Effect of Mach-number Ma_B

Absorbent boundary conditions for two cases
of burner Mach-numbers Ma_B were applied to
the surface area at the head end plate of the FE
model according to figure 6. The first instance
assumes that stagnant fluid stands in the burner,
i.e. $Ma_B = 0$. The impedance specified at the head
end plate is taken from section 3.2 (cf. figure 4).
The exit face of the transition piece is terminated
by impedances for turbine guide vanes according
to section 3.3.

Figure 10 shows the acoustic pressure magnitude versus the non-dimensional frequency f/f_0.
Three peaks between $f/f_0 = 0.1$ and 1 ($f/f_0 =
0.1214$, 0.5201 and 0.9275) are existing on the
solid line of figure 10. The first peak represents a "bulk" mode whose closing ends on both
sides are determined by the respective impedances
$Z = p/v_n$. This mode corresponds to the zero'th
mode that occurs at $f/f_0 = 0$ for rigid termination at both ends. The other two axial modes

Section 3.2 pointed out that steady state flow
through the burner most notably affects the phase
of the impedance. But, as shown by figure 10, this
affects the eigenfrequencies only marginally. The
peaks of the dashed line are occuring almost at
the same frequencies than those described above.
At low frequencies, apparently, the amplitude of
the acoustic pressure is changed due to different
phase between burner impedances for stagnant
and $Ma_B = 0.125$ flow conditions. Note that the
fuel/air mass flow is only taken into account by
the impedance of the burner. No effect of steady
state flow on equation 9 is considered here, but
only the usual acoustic equation is solved.

The FE analysis is predominantly affected by
basically applying an impedance at the head end
plate instead of using rigid ($Z \to \infty$) terminating
boundary conditions. Further detailing of these
impedances with regard only to particular flow
conditions inside the burner results in secondary
effects.

5.2. Effect of Burner

Beside the question on the effect of steady
state flow, the burner design is another important task whose influence on the formation of
acoustic pressure mode shapes has to be investigated. In addition to the burner type A used
so far in this paper, a second type B of burner

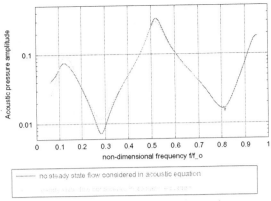

Fig. 14: Acoustic pressure magnitude versus
non-dimensional frequency f/f_0:
Comparison of results from FE analysis
with and without provision for steady state flow
in acoustic equations.

was measured with regard to burner impedance as discussed in section 3.2. A comparison of results from impedance measurements at stagnant fluid conditions was already shown in figure 4. A comparison of curves of acoustic pressure magnitude versus frequency is plotted in figure 12. The

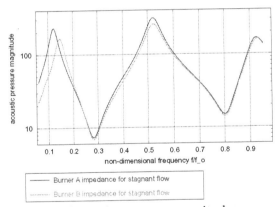

Fig. 12: Acoustic pressure magnitude versus
non-dimensional frequency f/f_0:
Comparison of results from burner impedance
for two different burner designs.

slight shift of the first peak from the "bulk" mode towards $f/f_0 = 0.1474$ reflects the lower magnitude of the impedance, whereas both axial modes were nearly unaffected by the assumed differences in burner design. The mode shapes of acoustic pressure are in principle similar to those shown in figure 11, thus images of these shapes are omitted.

5.3. Effect of Steady State Flow on Solution of Acoustic Equations

The FE models so far do not include the effect of the steady state flow on the acoustic properties as implemented in the FE code by use of equation 9 as described in section 2. First the steady state flow field is solved using equation 8. The resulting field of steady state flow velocities is reproduced in figure 13. The effect of flow velocity

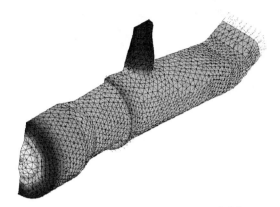

Fig. 13: Steady state flow velocity field.

on eigenfrequencies is shown by comparison to results described in section 5.1 where this effect was neglected (cf. figure 14). The comparison of both curves, again, shows only an effect that is negligible. This conclusion results from the fact that the Mach-number inside the combustion chamber is much less than 0.1, and, — because the effect of Mach-number is depending on $k/(1 \pm \text{Ma})$ — to gain an effect, the Mach-number should be in the range of 0.1 to 1. Nevertheless, if the flow passages through the burner or the passage through the turbine vanes — respectively the vane simulation section — is added to the FE model, the effect of steady state flow velocity on the aoustics must not be neglected, because much higher Mach-number will appear just at the boundaries of the combustion chamber.

6. Vane Simulation Section

The model shown by figure 7 is used to investigate the acoustic properties of the vane simulating cylinders commonly used in test-rig set-ups. The influence of the Mach-number of the fluid flow through the cylinders on the reflection of the acoustic waves is considered. The field of steady state fluid velocities is determined by solving equation 8. Three different cases are considered. Beside the baseline case of no steady state flow, two Mach-numbers — $\text{Ma}_{VSS} = 0.47$

and 0.8 — of the flow between the cylinders forming the vane simulation section are used. Figure 15 shows an image of the flow velocity field

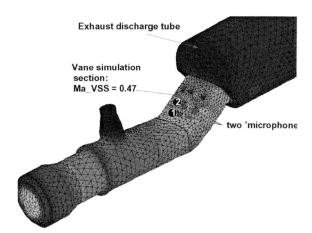

Fig. 15: Steady state flow velocity field through the vane simulation section ($\mathrm{Ma}_{VSS} = 0.47$).

for a Mach-number Ma_{VSS} of 0.47 through the vane simulation section. Inside the combustion chamber as well as through the exhaust discharge tube the Mach-number is $\mathrm{Ma} \ll 1$, and, therefore, the influence of the steady state velocity field on the acoustic behavior is negligible. However, at the flow passage through the vane simulating cylinders the Mach-number reaches values of 0.47 (respective 0.8) and here the influence of this steady state flow must be taken into account.

At the exit of the exhaust discharge tube a non-reflecting boundary is assumed, i.e. the reflection factor R is zero. At this surface the characteristic impedance of the fluid $Z_0 = \varrho_0 \cdot a_0$ is applied. Transmitted parts of the waves that are excited upstream the vane simulation section near the burner were not reflected again at the exit of the exhaus discharge tube. Hence, inside this tube no standing mode of acoustic pressure distribution is formed.

To estimate the acoustic properties of the array of vane simulating cylinders two imaginary microphones are installed in the FE model upstream the row of cylinders as shown by figure 15. The reflection coefficient is calculated according to Munjal[4]:

$$ R(\omega) = \frac{H_{21}(\omega) - e^{-jk^+ \cdot (z_1 - z_2)}}{e^{+jk^- \cdot (z_1 - z_2)} - H_{21}(\omega)} \cdot e^{+j(k^+ + k^-) \cdot z_1} , \tag{17} $$

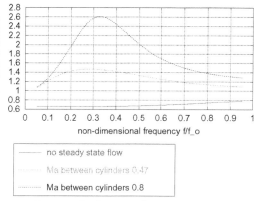

Fig. 16: Reflection factor of vane simulation section depending on Mach-number ($\mathrm{Ma}_{VSS} = 0.0$, 0.47 and 0.8).

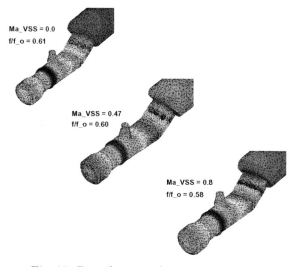

Fig. 17: Distribution of acoustic pressure for different steady state flow velocities at $f/f_0 \approx 0.6$ ($\mathrm{Ma}_{VSS} = 0.0$, 0.47 and 0.8).

where z_1, z_2 distances of microphones 1 and 2 from boundary
$\quad\quad\; k^{\pm} \quad\; k_0/(1 \pm \mathrm{Ma})$
$\quad\quad\; k_0 \quad\; = \omega/a_0$: Wavenumber

$$ H_{21} = \frac{p_2(\omega)}{p_1(\omega)} . \tag{18} $$

where p_1, p_2 complex acoustic pressures at microphones 1 and 2

This procedure is similar to the method of determining impedances from experimental data as described by section 3.1. The result for $R(\omega)$ versus the non-dimensional frequency f/f_0 is shown by figure 16. The plot shows that the high Mach-

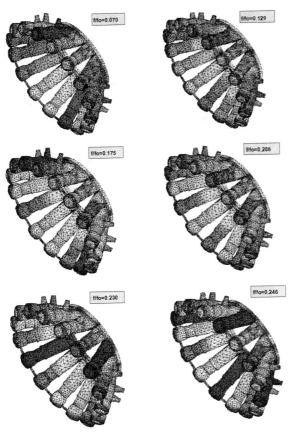

Fig. 19: Acoustic pressure distribution.

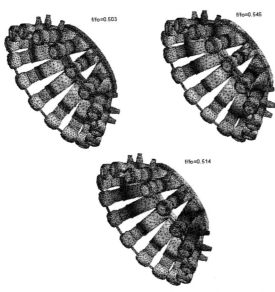

Fig. 20: Acoustic pressure distribution, cont.

number flow through the vane simulation passage at about $\mathrm{Ma}_{VSS} = 0.47$ and 0.8 has a strong effect on the reflection characteristics of this unit. For the case of stagnant flow ($\mathrm{Ma}_{VSS} = 0$) the reflection coefficient is between 0.6 and 0.8. The

high Mach-number flow condition at the narrow gap through the passage of the cylinders affects efficiently the acoustic behavior as shown by figure 16 and the reflection factor is more than unity (cf. Munjal[4]). A comparison of the mode shapes of acoustic pressure distributions at $f/f_0 \approx 0.6$ are shown in figure 17. Plotting the acoustic pressure amplitude near the burner versus the non-dimensional frequency f/f_0 (cf. figure 18) shows

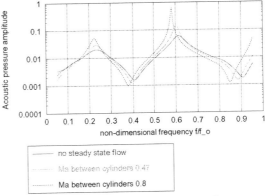

Fig. 18: Acoustic pressure magnitude versus non-dimensional frequency f/f_0: Comparison of results from FE analysis of test-rig set-up for stagnant fluid and $\mathrm{Ma}_{VSS} = 0.47$ and 0.8.

the eigenfrequencies of the system at $f/f_0 \approx 0.236$ and 0.614 for the case of no fluid flow through the array of cylinders. These frequencies are much higher than those calculated in section 5.1 (cf. figures 10 and 11) because the termination due to the flow area change without flow results in an acoustic pressure distribution whose crest is much more upstream the obstacle than the result with high Mach-number flow as pointed up by figure 17. Increasing the Mach-number through the vane simulation section shifts the eigenfrequencies towards the results calculated in section 5.1.

7. Can-annular Combustion Chamber

The last important task is the evaluation of the interconnections between multiple cans in a can annular combustor. Due to limited resources usually only one single can is tested at the test-facility. The direct transfer of the experimental acoustic results to the real engine implies that one single can is not acoustically interconnected to its neighbors in the can annular combustor set-up, too. A rough numerical finite element analysis using the model described by figure 8 shows that several additional eigenfrequencies are occurring due to the interconnection between the cans through cross flame tubes and through the manifold upstream the guide vanes of the turbine. The modes of the acoustic pressure distribution related to the first six eigenmodes are compiled in figure 19. Compared to the stand-alone can combustion chamber additional modes occur, where the pressure distribution spreads out over the whole annulus and several cans. All eigenfrequencies related to the modes in figure 19 are far below than the eigenfrequencies shown in figure 9. In contrast to these modes all modes in figure 19 are azimuthal modes. An axial mode at $f/f_0 = 0.503$ in the can annular combustor is shown in figure 20. This mode correlates to figure 9. Very close to this pure axial mode several mixed modes occur as shown by figure 20.

8. Conclusion

For the basic understanding and as a prerequisite for the thermoacoustic stability analysis the acoustic finite element analysis of combustion systems is of major importance. Because of limited resources the calculational domain has to be bounded by ancillary conditions. These boundary conditions determine the degree of accuracy and reality of the FE analysis.

First, the implication of defining boundaries on the FE analysis of one single, stand-alone can was investigated. The influence of applying measured burner impedances on the head end plate was evaluated. The implementation of an impedance for the burner has the most important effect. If this impedance is further suited to different gas flow velocities through the burner or slight burner design modifications the effect on the result of the FE analysis is of second order.

Subsequently, the steady state flow through the combustion chamber was taken into account. As long as the FE model only includes the combustion chamber the consideration of the gas flow affects the modes only marginally. The crucial regions through the burner and through the vanes respective vane simulation section were supplied by impedance boundary conditions. On the other hand, the simulation of the combustion chamber

including vane simulation section and the downstream exhaust discharge tube showed that the effect of the Mach-number through these narrow gaps must not be neglected. The reflection coefficient of the vane simulation section was determined from the distribution of acoustic pressure from the FE simulation and showed strong dependency on the Mach-number between the cylinders of the vane simulation section.

An important issue is the acoustic interaction between the cans in can annular combustors. A FE analysis of a can annular combustor configuration showed that beside the axial modes along the single can combustion chambers several azimuthal and mixed axial/azimuthal modes occur concerning the ring of can combustors. Hence, due to the interconnections through the cross flame tubes and through the manifold at the inlet into the turbine several additional eigenfrequencies are possible, which could not be excited by the flame during the test in a single can test-rig but have to be determined by FE analyses.

9. References

[1] Krebs, W., Walz, G., Hoffmann, S.: Thermoacoustic analysis of annular combustors. Proceedings of the 5th AIAA Aeroacoustic Conference, May 1999.

[2] Coyette, J.-P.: FLOWFEM Flow Acoustic Using Finite Elements. LMS Numerical Technologies, Technical Report, Leuwen, Belgium, 2001.

[3] Blackstock, D. T.: Fundamentals of Physical Acoustics. John Wiley & Sons, Inc., New York, 2000.

[4] Munjal, M. L.: Acoustics of Ducts and Mufflers. John Wiley & Sons, Inc., 1987.

[5] Krebs, W., Walz, G., Flohr, P., Hoffmann, S.: Modal Analysis of Annular Combustors: Effect of Burner Impedance. Proceedings of ASME Turbo Expo 2001, New Orleans, June 2001.

AIAA 2002-2571

CHARACTER OF MACH WAVE RADIATION AND CONVECTION VELOCITY ESTIMATION IN SUPERSONIC SHEAR LAYERS

Tobias Rossmann[*], M. Godfrey Mungal[†], and Ronald K. Hanson[‡]
High Temperature Gasdynamics Laboratory, Mechanical Engineering Department
Stanford University, Stanford, California 94305

The nature of acoustic radiation from mixing layers at high compressibility conditions is studied. Strong acoustic waves are generated by slow moving large-scale turbulent structures over a wide range of convective Mach numbers and density ratios. Strong waves and curved shocks associated with large disturbances are seen over a limited density ratio and compressibility range. Convection velocities are estimated by measuring the local Mach wave angle radiating from the disturbance but do not appear to follow the stream selection rule. For $M_c < 2$, the convection velocity favors the low speed velocity in all cases. Evidence of co-layer behavior at $M_c = 2.84$ is apparent from dual measured convection velocities. Behavior of curved, strong shocks in a time sequence image shows shock waves anchored to the leading edge of structures and external to the shear layer, rather than embedded as eddy shocklets.

I. INTRODUCTION

The turbulent structure dynamics of compressible shear layers affect both the mixing ability and noise production of the flowfield. While the growth rate and mixedness of the two-dimensional shear layer (Figure 1) have been widely studied, improved experimental and numerical capabilities have recently been employed to study the problem of noise generation by turbulent vortical structures. Noise generation mechanisms strengthen as compressibility levels are increased; thus, examining the creation of Mach wave radiation at high compressibility conditions is necessary for the full understanding of turbulent noise generation.

The creation of acoustic waves from turbulent zones is usually associated with the interaction of large-scale structures with the freestream velocity. The large-scale structures are known to move at a convection velocity which differs from either freestream velocity. At low compressibility conditions, the structures convect at the theoretical convection velocity derived from two-dimensional isentropic assumptions. At higher levels of compressibility, large-scale structures tend to have convection speeds much nearer those of the freestreams. This convection velocity asymmetry at high compressibility has typically been associated with laboratory frame effects (the stream selection rule) or with other instability modes becoming dominant. The interaction of the large-scale structures, moving at the convection velocity, with the freestream is generally accepted as the mechanism for noise generation in mixing layers.

As compressibility conditions are increased, a point will be reached at which the difference between the freestream velocity and the convection velocity of the large-scale structures will exceed the local speed of sound. When this occurs, the structures act as a wavy interface in supersonic flow, with Mach waves radiating from the interface[1]. If the structure penetration into the freestream is large, the resulting flow disturbance is also large, and the structures tend to act as bluff bodies in supersonic flow, with curved bow shocks surrounding them. Illustrative schematics of the two behaviors are shown in Figure 2. Few experimental planar mixing layer results have achieved high enough compressibility conditions to see these oblique waves, which are common in supersonic jet flows.

Previous experimentation explored whether the acoustic radiation from planar layers is due to this bluff body effect or due to a supersonic instability mode that

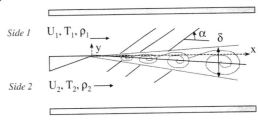

FIGURE 1 Schematic of mixing layer. Fast side refers to side 1 and is always supersonic in this study. Slow side refers to side 2 and is always subsonic in this study. δ refers to the visual thickness of the mixing layer. α is the local Mach wave angle. z is the spanwise coordinate of the mixing layer (into the page).

[*] Member, AIAA
    Current Address:
        Advanced Projects Research, Inc.
        1925 McKinley Ave, Suite B
        La Verne, CA 91750
[†] Professor, Associate Fellow AIAA
[‡] Professor, Fellow AIAA

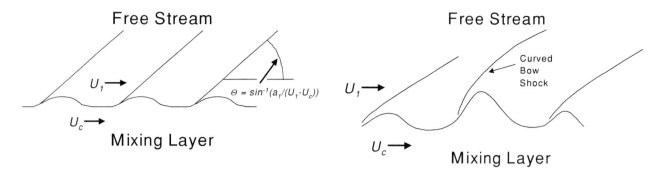

FIGURE 2 Schematics of the creation of shocks in compressible mixing layers due to slow moving structures, which protrude into the freestream. Case (a) shows a weak disturbance interface where regular Mach waves are radiated. Case (b) shows a strong disturbance where a locally curved shock is launched as the structure acts more like a bluff body in supersonic flow.

is independent of the large-scale structures. Blumen *et al.* showed that the compressible shear layer has supersonic instabilities[2] which are amplified at $M_c > 1$. Papamoschou argued that curved streamlines present in the shear layer generate waves, which coalesce into oblique shocks[3]. Barre *et al.* interpreted their results to show that compressibility inhibits entrainment and causes the creation of oblique shocks, which radiate from the shear layer[4]. He also showed that the speed of the radiating sound sources is different from the convection velocity of the large-scale structures. However, Smith and Dutton found using double-pulsed imaging that shocks emanating from the shear layer convect at the same speed as the large-scale structures[5].

In order to estimate the convection velocity of the large-scale structures using only the presence of Mach waves in the Schlieren images, the definition of the convective Mach number is used. The concept of the convective Mach number, M_c, was first developed by Bogdanoff[6] and further refined by Papamoschou and Roshko[7] to collapse the experimental growth rate data from many experiments and simulations to a single curve. Its definition can also be used to determine the convection velocity of large-scale structures simply by measuring the Mach wave angle of the radiated wave. Eqn. 1 shows the definition of the stream convective Mach number.

$$M_{c_1} = \frac{U_1 - U_c}{a_1} \text{ and } M_{c_2} = \frac{U_c - U_2}{a_2} \qquad \text{Eqn. 1}$$

If the pressure recovery in the layer is assumed to occur isentropically between two-dimensional structures, a symmetric convective Mach number can be defined based on the conditions in both freestreams (where $\gamma_1 = \gamma_2$,), Eqn. 2.

$$M_{c_1} = M_{c_2} = M_{c_{symm}} = \frac{U_1 - U_2}{a_1 + a_2}. \qquad \text{Eqn. 2}$$

Finally, if the Mach wave angles are measured, the convection velocity can be calculated if the free stream conditions are known using Eqn. 3.

$$U_1 - \frac{a_1}{\sin(\mu_1)} = U_c = \frac{a_2}{\sin(\mu_2)} + U_2 \qquad \text{Eqn. 3}$$

High convective Mach number mixing layers ($M_c > 1.5$) have also been shown numerically to exhibit multiple convection velocities, with turbulent eddies having a preference for a fast or slow velocity dependent on their position within the layer. No concrete experimental evidence for co-layer behavior has to date been seen in a compressible mixing layer, but detailed linear[8] and parabolized stability analyses[9] have indicated their existence at very high levels of compressibility or heat release.

In the present study, mixing layers are examined over a wide range of compressibilities and density ratios. Schlieren imaging of the flowfield is used to observe the character of the acoustic radiation generated by the shear layer. The local angle of the generated Mach waves are measured and used to calculate the large-scale structure convection velocity. These data are collected using a novel, shock tunnel-driven, supersonic mixing layer facility designed to generate compressibilities up to $M_c = 3$.

II. EXPERIMENTAL SETUP

The facility used for this study has been previously described in Rossmann *et al*[10]. It consists of a 2.6m driver section and a 9m driven section with an area ration $(A_4/A_1) = 2.41$ (Figure 3). The shock tunnel maximum operating pressure is 120 atm with typical test times of 2 msec. Shock speed information is gathered by the use of five piezoelectric pressure transducers mounted at 30cm intervals. Pressure data from these transducers, plus a high accuracy Kistler transducer to measure the variations in P_5, are recorded

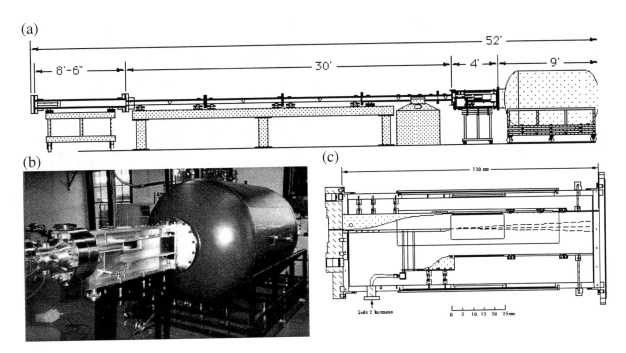

FIGURE 3 (a) Schematic of Stanford Shock Tunnel. (b) Image showing hypersonic mixing facility between shock tunnel and dump tank. (c) Schematic of mixing facility showing imaging locations, supersonic and subsonic nozzles as well as variable angle inner walls.

by a 12 bit, 8 channel Gagescope. Shock speed attenuation is ascertained by fitting the change in shock speed with distance to a second order polynomial.

The hypersonic mixing test section is shown in Figure 3b. For the fast stream, the gases from the shock tunnel reflected region are expanded in a two-dimensional nozzle block from a 0.5mm high slot (which is the nozzle throat). The slow speed stream is injected from a perforated plate and then conditioned by set of screens, perforated plates, and a 1.4:1 area contraction before meeting the fast stream at the edge of the splitter tip. The mixing layer then evolves into a 10cm W x 9cm H x 70cm viewing section with variable angle upper and lower walls. The exit of the mixing facility is joined to a 3 m³ dump tank, which is used to maintain a constant test section pressure during the test time. Various nozzle blocks are used to create fast side Mach numbers of 3.3, 3.9, and 5.2. With these nozzles, variable diaphragm pressure ratios, and easily variable low-speed side mixtures, the convective Mach number achieved in the test section is continuously variable from $M_c = 0.8$ to 2.9. Optical access is provided by opposed fused silica windows. Two piezoelectric pressure transducers mounted on each wall monitor the streamwise pressure gradient. The angles of the walls are adjusted for each run condition to minimize this pressure gradient.

A Schlieren system, used to capture growth rate and density information, is set up in a regular Z arrangement. A Xenon spark gap lamp with a 40μsec light duration is used along with a Hadland 468 framing camera, gated at 250 nsec to freeze the flow. The light is collimated and focused by a set of 30cm f/6 parabolic mirrors. A horizontal knife edge is placed at the focus, making the system sensitive to vertical density gradients. The image is captured with either a 200 mm f/4 lens or 105 mm f/2.8 lens, depending on the desired magnification, and then relayed onto the eight independent CCD arrays using a prismatic beam splitter. The intensifiers on the CCD arrays are sequentially fired with an interframe time of 4 μsec. The intensifier gate timing allows a 1 pixel blur at the maximum free stream velocity, while the interframe time allows for significant movement of structures during imaging. Synchronization of events with usable test time is achieved with via a SRS Model DG535 Pulse delay generator.

III. RESULTS AND DISCUSSION

III.1 TEST CONDITIONS

Owing to the versatility of the impulse driven mixing facility, many combinations of free stream Mach numbers and gases are used in this study. Compressibility conditions are primarily varied by altering the constituents of the low-speed stream. Stagnation conditions in the shock tunnel, and thus fast-speed stream conditions, were held constant for a substantial set of tests since tuning these conditions in the shock tunnel took several runs (hours) to complete;

changing the constituents of the injected low-speed flow was quickly accomplished. The convective Mach number is varied from 0.85 to 2.84 with density ratios from 0.2 to 2.25. Typically, using two different fast-stream Mach numbers, two different density ratio conditions are examined at a constant convective Mach number, thus allowing the examination of pure density ratio effects. The test section upper wall is set to 0 degrees while the lower wall is set in the range of to +1 to -0.5 degrees to minimize the streamwise pressure gradient.

III.2 SHOCK BEHAVIOR WITH VARYING M_c AND s

Shown in Figure 4 is a comparison of several experimental runs involving different combinations of convective Mach number and density ratio. For the low compressibility, low-density ratio case (upper left hand corner, $M_c = 1.4$, $s = 0.5$), the upper free stream contains a pattern of weak Mach waves. The same is true for the highly compressible $M_c = 2.24$ case shown to the right. No strong shocks emanating from the layer are in evidence. Rather, the Mach wave radiation is a well behaved pattern similar to that of supersonic jets. Hall *et al.* observed a similar pattern of Mach waves in the low-speed free stream of an $M_c = 0.96$ shear layer[11]. They reasoned that their strength was due to the weak disturbances radiating from the shear layer, manifesting themselves in the side-wall pressure traces.

These shocks are not the result of pressure disturbances, emanating either from the splitter tip or the nozzle, reflecting between the upper wall of the test section and the shear layer. Instead, they are caused by slowly moving large-scale structures where the difference between their velocity and the upper stream is supersonic. This was shown schematically in Figure 2a. If the structures do not protrude too far into the free stream, they will act like a wavy interface of slower convecting fluid. The velocity difference between the free stream and the convection velocity can become greater than the local speed of sound causing the flowfield to resemble a wavy wall in supersonic flow, a canonical example of linearized supersonic flow. Figure 2a resembles the shock patterns seen in the low-density ratio cases of Figure 4.

However, when the convective Mach number is increased above 1.6 and the density ratio is also high ($s > 1$), strong shocks emanating from the shear layer at a variety of angles within each image are seen (Figure 4). This shock pattern is better represented by Figure 2b. If the structures protrude significantly into the free stream, then the assumption of small, linearized disturbances in a supersonic flow no longer holds. Individual structures now act as bluff bodies, with curved bow shocks attached to their leading edges (as shown in Figure 2b).

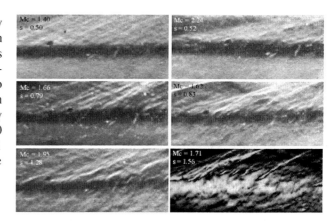

FIGURE 4 Instantaneous Schlieren images that highlight the acoustic radiation field in the upper free stream, which is caused by the interaction of the large scale structures and the supersonic flow. The lower right shows the inverted Schlieren signal from the mixing layer (yellow) and the non-inverted signal from the radiated waves (blue) so as to highlight the wave/structure interaction.

The interaction of the wave and large-scale structure is most evident in the $M_c = 1.71$ case, shown in false color in Figure 4 to enhance the contrast. Here the inverted image (which shows the mixing layer as bright) is combined with the raw image, which highlights the shock waves. Clearly, there are curved shocks that can be associated with particular structures, which has also been shown by spatially resolved imaging techniques[12]. The large-scale structures appear to have a preferred orientation with respect to the upper free stream, suggesting that the shock waves interact with the structures to elongate them in the streamwise direction. The existence of these strong local shocks appears to be associated with a certain range of both the convective Mach number and the density ratio. These curved shocks are strongest in the experimental data typically above $s = 0.7$ and $M_c = 1.5$, but tend to diminish as the compressibility is increased. Above $M_c = 2.5$, the curved shocks are much weaker for the higher density ratio cases.

As the density ratio is increased for the two-dimensional mixing layer, the convection velocity tends to favor the slow-speed stream velocity. This stream selection rule also correlates with the findings from the Schlieren images. Consequently, the existence of radiated waves into the freestream appears to be fixed with density ratio over a wide range of convective Mach numbers.

III.3 CONVECTIVE VELOCITY ESTIMATION

With multiple framing capabilities, a cross-correlation of two Schlieren images of known time separation should yield the convection velocity of large-scale structures. However, the large-scale structures must be discernable in both images in order to provide an accurate estimate of the displacement. Of the images collected in this study, very few displayed clearly observable large-scale structure, likely due to the increased three-dimensionality of the shear layer at these convective Mach numbers. Since Schlieren is a line-of-sight integrated technique, high levels of three-dimensionality will cause the signals of individual structures to be stacked on each other, resulting in a more uniform image.

For those images which did have observable structure, the correlation peaks were far too broad to support a reasonable estimate of the structure displacement. This broadening often occurs when the structure changes shape between images or the signal strength from the structure varies between images. The latter is very likely in Schlieren images of highly three-dimensional phenomena, where one element in the line-of-sight may be "brighter" in one image and then fade in another. Thus, due to both its difficulty in determining structures and poor correlations, the cross-correlation technique for convection velocity measurements was not used since structures are highly three-dimensional in mixing layers above $M_c = 1$.

Another promising method for measuring the structure speed is to measure the local angle of Mach wave radiation in the free stream. From Eqn. 3, the local Mach angle is directly related to the convection speed if the fast-stream conditions are known. Typically, there is a small distribution of Mach angles in the free stream, as long as the large-scale structures cause small disturbances. At some compressibility conditions when

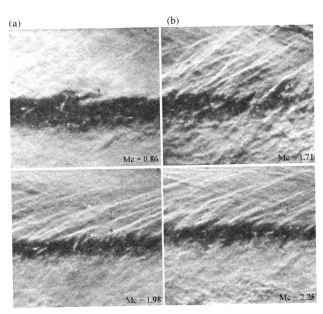

(a)   (b)

Mc = 0.86   Mc = 1.71

Mc = 1.98   Mc = 2.25

FIGURE 5 Magnified Schlieren images displaying the differing character of the acoustic radiation field with increasing convective Mach number. Imaged area is 8 x 7 cm, centered 14 cm downstream of the splitter tip.

the disturbances are large, the radiated shocks are locally curved, and the weak Mach wave limit is not necessarily reached for each wave. Figure 5 shows a magnified view of four different shear layer conditions, three of which show considerable acoustic radiation. Images (a), (c), and (d) clearly show a preferred Mach angle in the freestream. However, image (b) shows a wide variation of Mach angles as well as scalar structures which significantly protrude into the fast stream, causing bluff-body type shock patterns to form. Significant bias errors when measuring the local angle lead to large standard deviations in the convection velocity measurements for conditions like image (b) of Figure 5. Fortunately, these strongly curved shock conditions occur only over a small portion of the range of convective Mach numbers and density ratios examined in this study. This approach for convective velocity estimation was previously employed by Hall *et al* who measured both the wave angles and the phase lag between two pressure measurements on the walls of their test section, which yielded similar results[11].

Convection velocity estimation by Mach wave radiation was performed on Schlieren images where there were clear acoustic waves in the freestream. The angles of approximately 80 individual Mach waves were recorded and averaged per compressibility condition. The framing camera captures eight Schlieren images for each experimental run. Mach wave angles were measured visually with respect to the mean streamline of the shear layer (y=0) to account for the direction of motion of the large-scale structures. However, since this estimation technique is based on visual measurement of angles, the convection speed was averaged over several experimental runs at the same compressibility condition. This was done to reduce the bias errors associated with the selection of Mach waves and the measurement technique. Each convective velocity datum is the result of the measurement and averaging of approximately 160 to 320 individual waves.

Once identified, the Mach waves were labeled with a colored line. The composite image with the color identifiers was then processed with simple edge detection schemes sensitive only to the colored indicating lines. The slope (angle) of the lines was found by linear regression. This procedure automated the process of extracting the angles from the images, as long as the Mach wave locations were specified manually. The average convection speed of the structures was then computed using Eqn. 1, since the freestream conditions were known. For the compressibility range considered, the clearest acoustic waves were consistently on the fast side of the mixing layer. There were also waves in evidence in the slow-speed stream; however, these were both weaker and less abundant. Thus, all the convection velocity

FIGURE 6 Marking of Mach wave radiation in a $M_c = 1.66$, $s = 0.78$ shear layer.

measurements presented are taken from Mach waves radiating on the fast-stream side of the mixing layer.

Figure 6 shows a raw Schlieren image of a Mc = 1.66 shear layer. The Mach wave radiation is clearly visible as before. The individual Mach waves and angle measurements are laid over the original image to provide a visual sense of the variation of angles in a typical image. While the structures continue to grow and develop, the angle variance increases with downstream distance, since the larger structures protrude more into the freestream. The measured convective velocity for this case is 440 ± 50 m/sec and represents and average of over 250 individual Mach wave angle measurements. Selection bias was overcome by measuring all discernable Mach waves in the field of view. From this convection velocity, the actual convective Mach number can be computed using Eqn. 1, yielding $M_{c1} = 2.63$ and $M_{c2} = 0.83$. The empirical model developed by Papamoschou and Bunyajitradulya[13] states that the convective Mach numbers should be $M_{c1} = 0.09$, $M_{c2} = 3.3$.

The results of the convection velocity estimation technique are shown in Figure 7, as the fast- and slow-side convective Mach numbers versus the symmetric, or low compressibility, Mach number. The convection velocity for this study is nearly uniformly below the symmetric value, as the fast-stream convective Mach number is typically greater than the symmetric convective Mach number. The slow-speed convective Mach number is also plotted, under the assumption that there is a single convection velocity for large-scale structures. There is some correlation between the actual convective Mach number and that computed by Eqn. 2. In cases with discernable Mach waves on the low speed side, the convection velocity computed from those wave angles and freestream conditions matched well the measurements from the high-speed side up to $M_c = 2$.

Figure 8 displays the comparison of the high compressibility data from this study with several other convection velocity measurements. While other researchers have seen the large-scale structure convection speed demonstrate a very strong affinity for either the slow or fast freestream velocity, the data here suggest that there is little correlation between M_{c1} and M_{c2}. The convection velocity appears to scale strongly with the density ratio, as expected from the isentropic pressure recovery solution at low compressibilities. Also, the data point to convection speeds which are

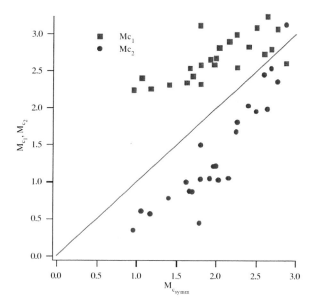

FIGURE 7 Measured convective Mach numbers plotted versus the symmetric (isentropic) convective Mach number. Data above $M_{c\_symm} = 2$ likely exhibits co-layer behavior, thus the inferred M_{c2} data from M_{c1} in this region is likely incorrect.

equal to or slower than the symmetric value. Conversely, previous experimentation would suggest that since the shear layer has both a supersonic and subsonic stream, the measured convection velocity should favor the high-speed side, thus creating strong shocks on the low-speed side of the mixing layer.

Papamoschou and Bunyajitradulya suggested that laboratory frame effects associated with the boundary layer interaction just aft of the splitter tip cause a preference for low or high convection velocities, depending on whether the mixing layer is a supersonic-subsonic or supersonic-supersonic combination[13]. This has been previously become known as the stream selection rule[14]. However, the images here suggest that at high compressibility, the opposite is true. The supersonic-subsonic conditions which prevail in this study correlate to convection speeds with an affinity for the slow-speed freestream of the mixing layer, contradicting the stream selection rule.

The main difference between this study and others shown in Figure 8 is that the previous experiments at high compressibility cases ($M_{c\_symm}>1$) were performed with very high density ratios (s>4), using helium as the fast stream gas. Therefore, the speed of sound in the lower stream is much smaller than in the upper, and shocks are more easily visualized in that stream. The high convective Mach number conditions generated in this study had density ratios of greater than 0.4 and less than 2, with the majority near s = 1. Furthermore, the images of Papamoschou and Roshko show no freestream radiation at all up to a convective Mach number of 1.4 at a density ratio of 2; however,

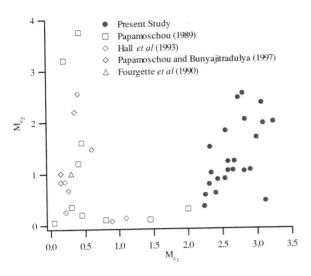

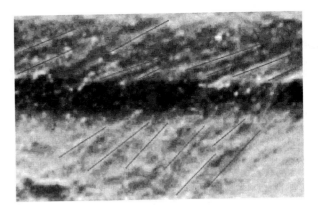

FIGURE 9 Marking of Mach wave radiation on both sides of a $M_c = 2.84$, s $= 1.38$ shear layer to investigate co-layer behavior at very high compressibility conditions.

FIGURE 8 Measured convective Mach numbers plotted with previous data by other researchers[3,11,13,20].

this could be a Schlieren sensitivity issue[7]. Finally, as the compressibility is increased above $M_c = 1.5$, other convection modes which have definite convective velocity affinities (fast and slow modes) have been shown to be important[9]. The results of this study could be dominated by slow instability modes causing shocks to be borne on only one side of the shear layer without regard for the stream selection rule. Thus, the findings here complicate the ability to predict the convection velocity of a compressible shear layer with a simple theoretical model that is based on lower compressibility results.

In order to assess co-layer behavior or multiple convection velocities within the shear layer, images were sought with shock waves clearly visible in both the upper and lower streams. Shown in Figure 9 is an instantaneous side-view Schlieren image from the $M_c = 2.84$, s $= 1.38$ shear layer condition. Shocks in both streams will occur, according to the same model used before, if the structures are supersonic with respect to the lower stream as well as the upper stream. Using the Mach wave radiation technique outlined above, the lower convection velocity is estimated to be 410 ± 70 m/sec, while the upper convection velocity is 980 ± 90 m/sec. Since the difference in the velocities is greater than the associated uncertainties with the Mach wave radiation technique, it is likely that two separate convection velocities exist in this mixing layer condition. These convection velocities would then be associated with separate fast- and slow-mode structures which would inhabit different transverse locations within the shear layer.

III.4 SHOCKLETS

Small shocks associated with turbulent eddies, which have come to be known as "eddy shocklets", have been observed in numerical simulations of turbulent mixing flows[15-17], and on a larger scale, in a counter-flowing supersonic shear layer[18]. Significant importance has been given to the role shocklets might play in redistributing kinetic energy through dilatational dissipation[18] and altering the structure convection velocity. The high compressibility conditions in the shock tunnel mixing layer facility allow for the investigation of potential shocklet behaviors at high convective Mach numbers, where numerical analyses have shown they exist.

Figure 10 shows a time history of a shock structure that looks very much like the eddy shocklet shown by Papamoschou[18] in the only other experimental evidence known to the authors. The mixing layer conditions associated with the image are $M_c = 2.0$, s $= 1.28$, which are comparable to those used by Papamoschou. In this time series, a bright bow shock, seemingly embedded in the shear layer, convects downstream as it ascends through the layer. The shock becomes less curved as it rises within the layer, implying that the scalar structure to which it is attached is accelerating downstream or its size is decreasing. It is also of interest that the structure associated with the shock is drawn into the upper free stream as a result of the turning of the flow locally by the curved shock surface.

Whether this shock structure is indeed a shocklet contained within the layer, or simply a bow shock structure attached to an eddy with a significant cross stream velocity, is unclear from a single Schlieren image. However, as has been shown previously in spatially resolved imaging experiments[12], the structures

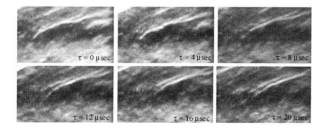

FIGURE 10. Schlieren image time sequence of a "shocklet" type behavior in a $M_c = 2.0$ mixing layer. Motion of the shock across the layer suggests that it is attached to a local eddy and not embedded inside the layer.

and shocks associated with the shear layer are highly three-dimensional. Also, though shocks may appear embedded within the layer in Schlieren images, the shocks exist only on the edge of large structures which entrain large amounts of fluid. Thus, the structures will appear in the line-of-sight integrated Schlieren technique to be deep within the layer and move within the shear layer. However, their true structure is no different from attached bow shocks, which radiate from the high-speed interface into the upper free stream.

IV. CONCLUSIONS

The images and data presented here illustrate the role and character of acoustic radiation in highly compressible shear layers. The convection velocity of large-scale structures in a compressible mixing layer flowfield was measured over a wide range of density ratios and compressibilities. The local angle of the Mach wave radiation generated by the shear layer was used to determine the local convection velocity. The derived convection velocities were found to be uniformly less than the isentropic value, in disagreement with the empirical stream selection rule for supersonic-subsonic shear layer combinations. The fast-stream convective Mach number (M_{c1}) did increase with increasing symmetric (isentropic) convective Mach number.

The nature of the acoustic radiation into the freestream was seen to vary with both density ratio and compressibility. For small s and M_c mixing layers, no radiation was present. However, when the density ratio exceeded 0.4-0.5 at $M_c \geq 1.3$, weak Mach wave radiation in the fast-stream was seen. As the compressibility and density ratio were increased, the Mach waves more closely resembled curved bow shocks as the large-scale structures protruded farther into the freestream. Above $M_c = 2.0$, the acoustic radiation resembled weak Mach waves, again moving into the fast-stream side.

Information about both eddy shocklets and co-layers was also derived from the image data. Large-scale structures maintain steady shocks on their trailing edges which can appear in line-of-sight integrated image techniques to be embedded in the shear layer. However, a time sequence of such a shock shows that it is simply a curved bow shock attached to the face of a large-scale structure. Also, two distinctly different convection velocities were measured on each side of a $M_c = 2.84$ shear layer. These convection velocities were each associated with the nearer freestream speed, possibly demonstrating the existence of co-layers at very high compressibility conditions.

V. REFERENCES

[1] Smits, A. and Dussage, J-P. (1996) *Turbulent Shear Layers in Supersonic Flow*, Springer Verlag, New York.

[2] Blumen, W., Drazin, P.G., and Billings, D.F. (1975) "Shear Layer Instability of an Inviscid Compressible Fluid. Part 2," *J. Fluid Mech.*, Vol. 71, part 2, pp. 305-316.

[3] Papamoschou, D. (1989) "Structure of the Compressible Turbulent Shear Layer," *AIAA 89-0126*, 27th Aerospace Sciences Meeting, Reno, NV.

[4] Barre, S., Quine, C., and Dussage, J-P. (1994) "Effects of Compressibility on the Structure of Supersonic Mixing Layers: Experimental Results," *J. Fluid Mech.*, Vol. 259, pp. 47-78.

[5] Smith, K.C. and Dutton, J.C. (1999) "Evolution and Convection of Large-scale Structures in Supersonic Reattaching Shear Flows," *Phys. Fluids*, Vol. 11, No. 8, pp. 2127-2138.

[6] Bogdanoff, D.W. (1983) "Compressibility Effects in Turbulent Shear Layers," *AIAA Journal*, Vol. 21, No. 6, pp. 926-927.

[7] Papamoschou, D. and Roshko, A. (1988) "The Compressible Turbulent Shear Layer: An Experimental Study," *J. Fluids Mech.*, Vol. 197, pp. 453-477.

[8] Sandham, N.D. and Reynolds, W.C. (1989) "Three-Dimensional Simulations of Large Eddies in the Compressible Mixing Layer," *J. Fluid Mech.*, Vol. 224, pp. 133-158.

[9] Day, M.J., Reynolds, W.C., and Mansour, N.N. (1998) "The Structure of the Compressible Reacting Mixing Layer: Insights from Linear Stability Analysis," *Phys. Fluids*, Vol. 10, No. 4, pp. 993-1007.

[10] Rossmann, T., Mungal, M.G., and Hanson, R.K. (1999) "A New Shock Tunnel Driven Facility for High Compressibility Mixing Layer Studies," *AIAA 99-0415*, 37th Aerospace Sciences Meeting, Reno, NV.

[11] Hall, J.L., Dimotakis, P.E., and Rosemann, H. (1993) "Experiments in Nonreacting Compressible Shear Layers," *AIAA Journal*, Vol. 31, No. 12, pp. 2247-2254.

[12] Rossmann, T., Mungal, M. G., and Hanson, R. K. (2002) "Evolution and Growth of Large Scale Structures in High Compressibility Mixing Layers," *J. of Turbulence*, Vol. 3, No. 9, pp. 1-18.

[13] Papamoschou D. and Bunyajitradulya A. (1997) "Evolution of Large Eddies in Compressible Shear Layers," *Phys. Fluids*, Vol. 9, No. 3, pp. 756-765.

[14] Dimotakis, P.E. (1991) "On the Convection Velocity of Turbulent Structures in Supersonic Shear Layers," *AIAA 91-1724*, 29th Aerospace Science Meeting, Reno, NV.

[15] Lele, S. K. (1989) "Direct Numerical Simulation of Compressible Free Shear Flows," *AIAA 89-0375*, 27th Aerospace Sciences Meeting, Reno NV.

[16] Vreman, A.W., Sandham, N.D., and Luo, K.H. (1996) "Compressible Mixing Layer Growth Rate and Turbulence Characteristics," *J. Fluid Mech.*, Vol. 320, pp. 235-258

[17] Freund, J.B., Moin, P., and Lele, S.K. (2000a) "Compressibility Effects in a Turbulent Annular Mixing Layer. Part 1. Turbulence and Growth Rate," *J Fluid Mech.*, Vol. 421, pp. 229-267

[18] Papamoschou, D. (1995) "Evidence of Shocklets in a Counterflow Supersonic Shear Layer," *Phys. Fluids*, Vol. 7, pp. 233-235.

[19] Zeman, O. (1990) "Dilatational Dissipation: The Concept and Application in Modeling Compressible Mixing Layers," *Phys. Fluids*, Vol. 2, No. 2, pp. 178-188.

[20] Fourgette, D.C., Dibble, R.W., and Mungal, M.G. (1991) "Time Evolution of the Shear Layer of a Supersonic Axisymmetric Jet," *AIAA Journal*, Vol. 29, No. 7, pp .1123 – 1130.

AIAA-2002-2572

VISUALIZATION OF AERODYNAMIC SOUND SOURCE WITH COMPACT GREEN'S FUNCTION

Akiyoshi Iida[*] and Akisato Mizuno[**]
Kogakuin University, Department of Mechanical Engineering,
2665 Nakano-machi, Hachioji-shi, Tokyo, 192-0015 JAPAN
E-mail :iida@fluid.mech.Kogakuin.ac.jp
mizuno@fluid.mech.kogakuin.ac.jp

Chisachi Kato[*]
Institute of Industrial Science, University of Tokyo
4-6-1 Komaba, Meguro-ku, Tokyo, 153-8505 JAPAN
E-mail:ckato@iis.u-tokyo.ac.jp

ABSTRACT

The objective of this investigation is to develop a method for detecting the aerodynamic sound source in a low-Mach number turbulent wake. In order to evaluate vorticity contribution for the dipole sound generation, a compact Green's function is utilized for identification of the aerodynamic sound source. The compact Green's function [1] [2] denotes the acoustic efficiency of the surface dipole caused by the interaction between the vorticity fluctuation and solid surfaces. The surface dipole sources and vorticity fluctuation are measured [3][4] in the wake of a circular cylinder with Reynolds number of 4.0×10^4. The compact Green's function model can be estimate instantaneous sound source distribution, however, this method requires the spatial derivative of vorticity fluctuations. Therefore, experimental evaluation is difficult. To evaluate the compact Green's function method, we introduce coherent output power (*COP*) in terms of surface dipole and vorticity fluctuation [4]. This method can be estimated vorticity contribution to the dipole sound generation with measurement of the coherence output power in terms of the vorticity fluctuation and the surface (dipole) pressure. This method is based on the conventional Lighthill-Curle's theory [5], which shows the aerodynamic sound is calculated with the surface pressure fluctuation. The *COP* method makes use of the coherent output power instead of the surface pressure fluctuation, it is found that the intensity of *COP* corresponds to the distribution of the dipole sound source caused by unsteady vorticity fluctuation. The estimated sound source distribution with the compact Green's function model is good agreement with that of the *COP* method.

---

*Associate Professor, ** Professor

These methods are then more directly reflect the aerodynamic aspects of the sound source estimation compared with the conventional Lighthill-Curle's theory.

The experimental result shows that the dipole sound is generated near the formation region of Karman vortices. It is therefore concluded that the separated shear layers play an important role in generating aerodynamic sound.

1. INTRODUCTION

The maximum speed of high-speed trains has been in an upward trend for several years [6]. Cooling flow rates inside air conditioners and computers are also increasing. Consequently, aerodynamic noise radiated from these products is rapidly increasing, because aerodynamic noise is proportional to the sixth power of flow velocity. Aerodynamic noise must therefore be reduced in these products. Much research has been directed at noise reduction and prediction in product development [7]-[10]. Since Mach number of the flow velocity in these products is comparatively small and the wavelength of resulting aerodynamic sound is larger than the size of these products, the radiated aerodynamic sound can be formulated by Lighthill-Curle's theory, which is generally know to be the most convenient theory currently available. Therefore, the aerodynamic sound source is conventionally investigated by using surface pressure fluctuation, which acts as a dipole source, as formulated in Lighthill-Curle's Equation. However, Lighthill-Curle's theory gives us no information about the relationship between unsteady vorticity fluctuation and aerodynamic sound. That is, it only shows aerodynamic sound is generated by surface pressure fluctuation or aerodynamic forces. We therefore cannot obtain the vortex contribution to aerodynamic sound generation by using Lighthill-Curle's theory. From the aerodynamic point of view, even in a low-

Mach-number wake, we have to consider that the relationship between vorticity fluctuation and aerodynamic sound in order to reveal the origin of 'true aerodynamic sound source'. In order to estimate the contribution of unsteady vorticity fluctuation to dipole sound generation, vorticity fluctuation of a cylinder wake was measured by using a conditional sampling method at a mean flow velocity of 15 m/s and a Reynolds number of $4.0 \sim 10^4$. We attempted to visualize the aerodynamic sound source around a circular cylinder by using the experimental results of the vorticity measurement and the compact Green's function method. The dipole sound source distribution was also estimated by using coherent output power in terms of vorticity fluctuation and resulting aerodynamic sound.

2. EXPERIMENTAL APPARATUS

2.1 Vorticity Probe

To estimate the vorticity contribution to aerodynamic sound generation, it is necessary to measure vorticity fluctuation and surface pressure fluctuation, simultaneously. However, measurement of instantaneous vorticity fluctuation in a turbulent flow field is difficult because the turbulent flow field has various size of eddies. High resolution of the vorticity probe is therefore necessary both in time and spatial domains. As a vorticity probe [4] to satisfy such conditions, a probe combining four hot-wire vorticity prove was developed as shown in Fig. 1. This probe is composed of a parallel I-type probe and an X-array probe. The parallel array probe measures velocity fluctuation in the streamwise direction. This velocity is then used to calculate cross-section gradient, $\partial u/\partial y$. The X-array probe measures the cross-stream component, which is used in Taylor's hypothesis to transform temporal derivatives into streamwise derivatives, $\partial v/\partial x$. The vorticity probe can therefore measure instantaneous spanwise vorticity, $\omega_z = (\partial u/\partial y - \partial v/\partial x)$.

The vorticity distribution of the rectangular jet was measured by using the vorticity probe and was compared with that measured by the X-array probe. The experimental result showed that measurement error of the vorticity probe is about 10% [4].

2.2 Wind Tunnel

The low-noise wind tunnel [4] was used in the experiments. It has a square test section of 500 by 500 mm and a length of 2600 mm as shown in Fig. 2. This wind tunnel has an intensity of turbulence of less than 0.2 % and a non-uniformity of the velocity distribution about 1 % or less at a flow velocity of 30 m/s. And background noise of this wind tunnel is less than 30 dB at a flow velocity of 15 m/s. Velocity and vorticity are measured by a three-dimensional traversing unit mounted on the test section.

A metallic circular cylinder with a diameter D of 40 mm and a length L of 500 mm was fixed horizontally in the test section and positioned 0.25 m from the end of the contraction nozzle. The origin of the coordinate system was located at the center of the test cylinder. And the flow direction and vertical direction correspond to the X and Y axes, respectively; therefore, the spanwise direction of the cylinder is the Z axis (as shown in Fig 2). All the distances were normalized with the diameter of the test cylinder. The experiment was done at a mean flow velocity of 15 m/s and a Reynolds number of $4.0 \sim 10^4$. And the fundamental frequency of a Karman vortex was 75 Hz.

In order to decrease blockage of the traversing unit in the test section, the upper floor of the test section moves horizontally with the traversing mechanism. The vertical support is the only part of the traverse inserted in the test section. The blockage of the traverse unit is therefore less than 3%. The vorticity fluctuation ω_z was simultaneously measured at X/D=1.25-7.00 and Y/D=-1.4-1.4 in the wake of the circular cylinder. All data were digitized by a data-acquisition system with a 12-bit A/D converter at a sampling frequency of 5 kHz. There are 21 measuring points in the X direction and 29 points in the Y-direction. And the total number of the measuring points for the wake measurement is 609 points. At each measurement point, data was collected for 20 sec.

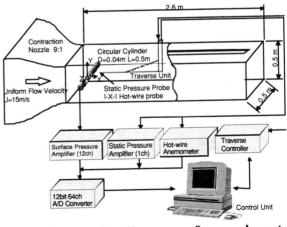

Fig.2 Schematic diagram of experimental apparatus

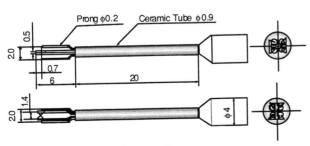

Fig.1 Vorticity probe

1723

The test cylinder had twelve pressure taps (an array of eleven taps and one reference tap) fabricated on the cylinder surface. Condenser microphones with a diameter of half an inch were embedded in the cylinder. And surface pressure fluctuation was measured through pressure taps of 1 mm diameter and about 1 mm length. Since the Helmholtz resonance frequency of the pressure tap is about 1380 Hz, gain and phase errors are respectively less than 3 dB and 5 degrees at frequencies lower than 800 Hz. Since under our experimental conditions, the dominant frequency of the pressure fluctuation lies between 50 and 300 Hz, the measurement does not influence the Helmholtz resonance.

The eleven pressure-taps are separated by 0.375 D in the spanwise direction, and spanwise distribution of surface pressure was measured at θ of 0 to 180 degrees from the forward stagnation point. The surface pressure was also recorded by the data-acquisition system simultaneously. Then, the correlation between vorticity fluctuation and surface pressure fluctuation was calculated.

If the modulation of low frequency is removed, surface pressure fluctuation at θ of 60 degrees from the forward stagnation point can be considered a sinusoidal wave with a fundamental frequency of Karman vorticity. The trigger signal for conditional sampling was therefore obtained at θ of 60 degrees. The measured data in the wake are averaged at the same phase-angle of the trigger signal.

The scale of the turbulence eddy in the streamwise direction can be evaluated by using the reciprocal of the wave number k of $U/(2\pi f)$. The streamwise scale of Karman vorticity in this study can therefore be considered to be about 30 mm. According to the upper limit of the measurable frequency of the vorticity, the smallest scale is about 2 mm. The spatial resolution of the probes is therefore sufficiently smaller than the streamwise scale of the fundamental vorticity.

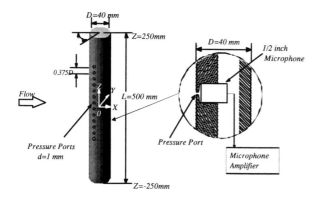

Fig.3 Test cylinder and pressure pick-up

The time required for the conditional sampling is generally long. Therefore, it is necessary to keep the conditions of the sensors. Moreover, the flow field also be constant during the experiment. In this study, measuring time was set to two hours, and the sensors were calibrated every two hours. And the averaged velocity and pressure were checked at a reference position. It takes about eight hours to measure the whole wake. The experiment was conducted two times, and was confirmed that the average velocity and intensity of turbulence did not change during the experiments.

3. BASIC EQUATION

3.1 *COP* Method

In the case of low-Mach-number wake flows, dipole source dominates resulting aerodynamic sound. Thus, aerodynamic sound can be calculated with measurement of the surface pressure fluctuation. However, we cannot examine the relationship between the unsteady vorticity fluctuation and aerodynamic sound.

From the aerodynamic point of view, we have to consider that the relationship between vorticity fluctuation and aerodynamic sound in order to reveal the origin of aerodynamic sound.

We attempt to estimate aerodynamic sound source by using a correlation measurement of unsteady-vorticity and surface-pressure fluctuation. First, we measured the coherent output power (*COP*), P_c, between the vorticity fluctuation in the wake and the surface pressure distribution. That is,

$$P_c(f)^2 = \frac{\overline{|G_{wp}(f)|^2}}{\overline{|G_w(f)||G_P(f)|}} P(f)^2, \qquad (1)$$

where G_{wp} is a cross-spectrum of vorticity and surface pressure fluctuation, and G_w is a Fourier transform of vorticity and G_p is surface pressure fluctuation. According to Lighthill-Curle's theory, aerodynamic sound can be calculated by using surface pressure fluctuation. So we replace surface pressure fluctuation with *COP* in order to estimate the vorticity contribution to aerodynamic sound as follows[4],

$$\overline{p^2(x)} = \frac{1}{16\pi^2 a^2 x^4} LL_c \overline{\left(x_i \frac{\partial f_i}{\partial t}\right)^2}, \qquad (2)$$

$$f_i = \int_0^{2\pi} n_i P_c \frac{D}{2} d\theta, \qquad (3)$$

where a denotes the speed of sound, L denotes the cylinder length, and L_c denotes coherence length of surface pressure fluctuation. Coherence length L_c is equivalent to a spanwise length along which pressure fluctuations are significantly correlated and indicates a three-dimensional structure in the wake of the circular cylinder.

The intensity of COP corresponds to a dipole sound source produced by the unsteady vorticity fluctuation. Therefore, Equations (2) and (3) show the vorticity contribution to the aerodynamic sound generation at each measurement point in the wake. In this experiment, aerodynamic sound was calculated from vorticity fluctuation at the center cross section of XY plane (Z/D=0). The aerodynamic sound depends on three dimensionality of the flow field. It is therefore necessary to measure vorticity fluctuation in the spanwise direction in the wake of the circular cylinder. It takes a long time to measure the three-dimensional structure of the wake because the number of measuring points drastically increases. And it is difficult to maintain the experimental conditions for such a long period. In this study, we estimated the three-dimensional vorticity distribution by using the spanwise coherence length previously defined by authors [3]. That is, the coherence length of a fundamental frequency is given by Equation (4),

$$\frac{L_c}{D} = \frac{511}{\sqrt{\mathrm{Re}}}. \qquad (4)$$

3.2 Compact Green's Function

The COP method is founded on Lighthill-Curle's Equation. Curle's theory is useful for aerodynamic sound prediction, however, it is not clear to reveal relationship between the vorticity and aerodynamic sound. On the other hand, Howe's equation [1] is directly estimated vorticity contribution for aerodynamic sound generation. Now, we consider that the low Mach number wake flow behind the rigid body. In this case, aerodynamic sound can be estimated with the compact body assumption. That is, the aerodynamic sound Equation can be written as follows:

$$\left\{ \frac{1}{a_0}\left(\frac{\partial}{\partial t} + \mathbf{U} \cdot \nabla\right)^2 - \nabla^2 \right\} B = div(\boldsymbol{\omega} \times \mathbf{u}), \qquad (5)$$

where,

$$B = \frac{p}{\rho_o} + \frac{1}{2}u^2. \qquad (6)$$

The right hand side of Equation (5) denotes the sound source term of wave equation.

The surface motion is regarded as incompressible, Crocco's equation is approximated as follows:

$$\frac{\partial u_i}{\partial t} + \frac{\partial B}{\partial y_i} = -(\boldsymbol{\omega} \times \mathbf{u}). \qquad (7)$$

In order to consider that the effect of rigid surface, Green's function is chosen to have vanishing normal derivative on the body surface at low Mach number flow.

$$B(x,t) = -\oint_s G(\mathbf{x}, y, t-\tau)\frac{\partial B}{\partial y_i}(y,\tau)n_j d\mathbf{S}(\mathbf{y})d\tau$$
$$+ \int G(\mathbf{x}, y, t-\tau)\frac{\partial}{\partial y_j}(\boldsymbol{\omega} \times \mathbf{u})_j(\mathbf{y},\tau)dyd\tau$$

$$(8)$$

where, n denotes outer unit normal vector on S. When the observation point is far from the source region, B can be written as follows:

$$B(x,t) = \frac{P_a}{\rho_o}, \qquad (9)$$

where, P_a denotes the far field sound pressure.

Thus, the far field pressure can be obtained from Equation (7),(8) and (9),

$$P_a = -\rho_o \int \{\boldsymbol{\omega}(\mathbf{y},\tau) \times \mathbf{u}(\mathbf{y},\tau)\} \frac{\partial}{\partial \mathbf{y}} G(\mathbf{x}, y, t-\tau)dyd\tau$$

$$(10)$$

Howe [1] introduces a compact Green's function to solve the Equation (10). Assuming that the circular cylinder is placed at low Mach number flow. The velocity potential Y_i of incompressible flow past the cylinder having unit speed in the i-direction at large distances from the surface.

The compact Green's function can be obtained [1]

$$\mathbf{G}(\mathbf{x}, \mathbf{y}, t-\tau) = \frac{\mathbf{x}_j \mathbf{Y}_j(\mathbf{y})}{4\pi a |\mathbf{x}|^2} \frac{\partial \delta}{\partial t}\bigg|_{t-|\mathbf{x}|/a}, \qquad (11)$$

where,

$$\mathbf{Y}_i = y_i\left(1 + \frac{d^2}{4\sqrt{y_1^2 + y_2^2}}\right) \quad i=1,\, 2;\ Y_3 = y_3. \qquad (12)$$

Finally, the dipole sound can be calculated by coupling source term of $(\boldsymbol{\omega} \times \mathbf{u})$ with a velocity potential Y_i, which related to a compact Green's function G, as follows:

$$P_a(\mathbf{x},t) \approx \frac{-\rho_o x_i}{4\pi a |\mathbf{x}|^2}\frac{\partial}{\partial t}\int_V (\boldsymbol{\omega} \times \mathbf{u})(y, t-|\mathbf{x}|/a) \cdot \nabla \mathbf{Y}_i dy$$

$$(13)$$

The present experiment, the aspect ratio of the circular cylinder is 12.5. Therefore, retarded time differences between the axial and radius direction. However, the measured axial coherence length is about 4 diameters [3][4]. Therefore, compact assumption can be used in the case of the present experiments.

4. RESULTS AND DISCUSSION

4.1 Flow Field Around The Circular Cylinder

The near wake of the circular cylinder measured by a conditional sampling method. Figures 4 and 5 show the velocity vector at a constant phase, ψ of =0 and 90 degrees, respectively. These figures, visualized as an observer moving downstream at 0.75U, show the separated shear layer rolls up at the formation region of Karman vortices; that is X/D=1.5 to 2.0 and Y/D=0.4. And the large-scale structure of Karman vortex is clearly observed by conditional sampling. The general tendency of these figures is similar to the precise measurement of a flying hot-wire by Cantwell et al[11]. @However, the velocity distributions just behind the circular cylinder, X/D=1.25, is influenced by the counter flow.

Vorticity distribution at a phase angle, ψ of 0 is shown in Fig. 6. The positions of the large-scale vortex estimated from the velocity vector are shown in Fig. 6 as positive and negative symbols. At X/D < 3.5, the vorticities correspond to the eddy structure.

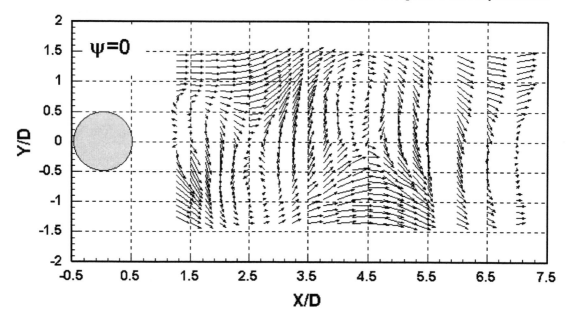

Fig.4 Velocity field at constant phase ψ = 0 as an observer moving downstream at 0.75U

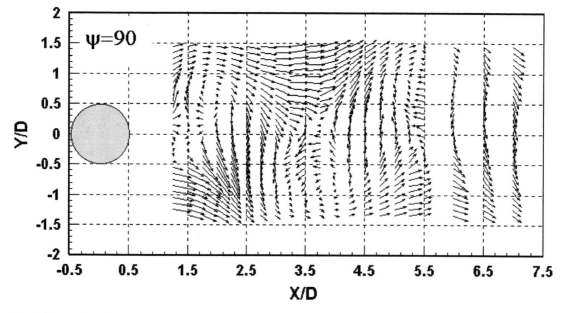

Fig.5 Velocity field at constant phase ψ = 90 as an observer moving downstream at 0.75U

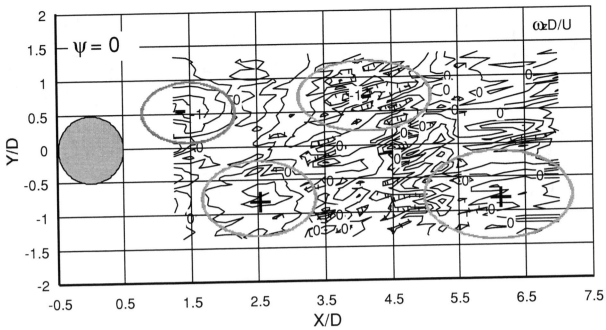

Fig.6 Contours of vorticity at constant phase ψ=0.

4.2 Aerodynamic Sound Source

Figure 9 (a) (b) shows that the velocity potential Y_1 and Y_2 of the circular cylinder. The result shows that Y_i is change just behind the cylinder. Moreover, at the fundamental frequency of the Karman vortices, the vorticity axis is parallel to the cylinder axis. Therefore, / y₂ component of gradY_i is significantly large. Thus, the dipole source may be limited near the cylinder surface.

The dipole sound source is visualized by using the compact Green's function and measured vorticity fluctuation as shown in Figure 10(a). The dipole source concentrates at X/D=1.5 and Y/D=)0.4. This region's both of gradY_1, and vortex growth rate is large. The dipole sound is therefore generated in this region. It is remarkable that the aerodynamic sound source is concentrated in a small area at Y/D=)0.4. This area does not correspond to the vorticity concentration region; that is Y/D=0.6. The aerodynamic sound source lies near the center of the cylinder but the vorticity fluctuation in near to the side of the cylinder. In this region, the alternating vortices come from both sides of the cylinder, and the separated shear layer is stretched by this vortex motion. The separated shear layer therefore rolls up at the formation region of the Karman vortices as shown in Figure 4 and 5.

At the formation region of Karman vortices, the vortex sheet rapidly accelerates to the downstream flow, as a result, the stretched shear layer at the formation region makes up about 80 % of the dipole sound. So it is concluded that the separated shear layers play an important role in generating dipole sound, and that the scale and intensity of the separated shear layer is the most important factor in controlling dipole sound generation.

The distribution of the aerodynamic sound source is also calculated by *COP* method as shown in Figure 10(b). The *COP* result of the dipole source distribution is good agreement with that of the compact Green's function model. It is revealed that the compact Green's function reflects the vorticity contribution of the dipole sound generation.

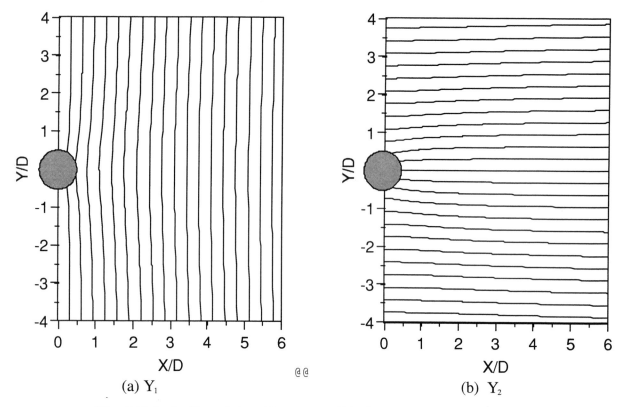

(a) Y_1 (b) Y_2

Fig. 9 Velocity Potential Y_i of incompressible flow past a circular cylinder

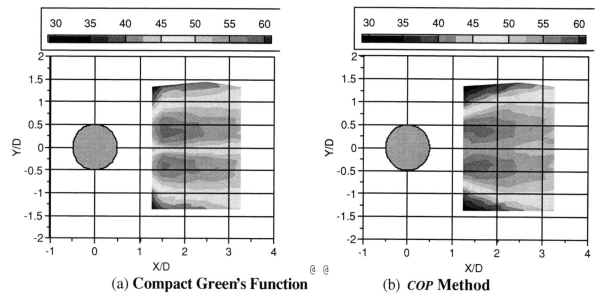

(a) **Compact Green's Function**   (b) *COP* **Method**

Fig. 10 Distribution of dipole sound source

5. SUMMARY

In order to estimate the dipole source distribution in a low Mach number wake flow, the vorticity fluctuation and the surface pressure fluctuation which act as the dipole source were measured in a wake of a circular cylinder at Reynolds number of 4.0×10^4. Since, the compact Green's function denotes the acoustic efficiency of the body shape and boundary condition of the bodies, the compact Green's function can be used for the estimation for the interaction between the vorticity fluctuation and solid surfaces. The dipole source distribution was also estimated by using the coherent output power *(COP)* in terms of vorticity fluctuation and surface pressure fluctuation. The COP corresponded to the vorticity contribution to the dipole sound generation.

The estimated sound source distribution with the compact Green's function model was good agreement with that of the *COP* method. It revealed that the compact Green's function reflected the vorticity and the surface conditions. The experimental results showed that the dipole sound is generated near the formation region of Karman vortices; that is, at X/D=1.5 to 2.0 and Y/D=±0.4 at Reynolds number of 4.0×10^4. In this region, velocity potential gradient is significantly large. Therefore, this region's acoustical efficiency is large. Moreover, at the formation region of Karman vortices, the vortex sheet rapidly accelerates to the downstream flow. As a result, the stretched shear layer at the formation region makes up about 80 % of the dipole sound. So it is concluded that the separated shear layers play an important role in generating aerodynamic sound.

The conventional, Lighthill-Curle's method gives us no information about the vorticity contribution for dipole sound generation. The compact Green's function model and *COP* method are useful to understand dipole sound generation. These methods are therefore suitable for the estimation for the relationship between the dipole sound source and vorticity fluctuation.

ACKNOWLEDGMENTS

The authors appreciate to Dr. T. Takaishi, Railway Technical Research Institute, for his many fruitful discussions about the generation mechanism of aerodynamic sound and the compact Green's function model of the dipole sound.

REFERENCES

[1] Howe, M.S., "Acoustics of fluid-structure interactions," (1998), Cambridge University Press.

[2] Takaishi, T., Sagawa, A. and Nagakura, K., "Numerical analysis of dipole sound source around high speed trains", **AIAA 2002-0923**, (2002)

[3] Iida, A., Otaguro,T, Kato, C. and Fujita,H., "Prediction of Aerodynamic Sound Spectra from a Circular Cylinder", *Proc. FLUCOME'97* **Vol.1**, (1997), 126-131.

[4] Iida, A., Otaguro, T., Kato, C. and Shimode, S., "Analysis of Aerodynamic Sound Source with Measurement of Static-Pressure Fluctuation," *JSME International Journal* Ser. B, Vol.42. No.4, (1999), 596-604

[5] Curle, N., "The Influence of Solid Boundaries upon Aerodynamic Sound," *Proc. Roy. Soc. London*, **A231**, (1955), 505.

[6] King III, W. F., A Précis of Development in the Aeroacoustics of Fast Trains, J. Sound Vibration, 193(1), (1996), p.349-358.

[7] Kato, C., Iida, A., Takano, Y., Fujita, H.and Ikegawa, M., "Numerical Prediction of Aerodynamic Noise Radiated from Low Mach Number Turbulent Wake," *AIAA* Paper **93-0145**. (1993)

[8] Kato,s C., Iida, A., Hattori, M., Inadama, S., "Numerical simulation of aerodynamic sound source in the wake of a complex objects," **AIAA 2000-142**, (2000)

[9] Tsujimoto, K., Hayashi, A., and Miyake, Y., "Identification of noise source in low Mach number flow by DNS," **AIAA 98-2366** (1998)

[10] Phillips, O. J., "The Intensity of Aeolian Tones," *J. Fluid Mech.*, **1-6**, (1956), 607-624

[11] Cantwell, B.and Coles, D., An Experimental Study of Entrainment and Transport in the Turbulent near Wake of a Circular Cylinder, *J. Fluid Mech.*, **136** (1983), 321-374.

Numerical Prediction of Airfoil Aerodynamic Noise

Eric Manoha, Catherine Herrero, Pierre Sagaut, Stéphane Redonnet

Office National d'Études et de Recherches Aérospatiales
Department of Computational Fluid Dynamics and Aeroacoustics
BP 72, 92322 Châtillon, France
eric.manoha@onera.fr

ABSTRACT

This paper describes a new step in the development of a Computational AeroAcoustics (CAA) process whose general long term objective is the numerical prediction of the aerodynamic sound radiated by the airframe of large aircraft at approach, and especially the noise generated by deployed high lift devices such as slats and flaps. The proposed 3-step hybrid process combines CFD (Computational Fluid Dynamics) techniques and acoustic numerical methods, each one being adapted to a particular domain in which specific physical fluid mechanisms are simulated solving an adequate set of equations.

In a first step, the nearfield unsteady flow is computed via a compressible three-dimensional LES (Large Eddy Simulation). In a second step, LES-computed perturbations are injected at the inner boundary of a larger domain in which the outward propagation of small perturbations over a non-uniform mean flow is simulated using LEE (linearized Euler equations). In the third and last step, the acoustic field radiated at the external boundary of the LEE domain becomes the entry data of a Kirchhoff integration which provides the noise radiated in the far field.

The critical point of the process is the coupling, via an interface, of the LES with the LEE. This process has been carefully studied using analytical fields, an acoustic point source monopole and a convected Eulerian vortex. It has been found that the correct injection of such fields requires severe conditions in terms of space resolution, conditions which are especially difficult to meet for purely vortical fields.

In a former study, the LES of the unsteady flow around a NACA0012 airfoil has formed the basis of numerical noise predictions using acoustic integral methods. In the present paper, the same LES is used as a basis for the 3-step CAA process. First results revealed the generation of non-physical noise at the boundary interface where the airfoil's turbulent wake is injected in the Euler domain. Additional tests based on the injection of an analytical vortex suggest that this problem was most probably caused by the under-resolution of the injected vortical structures. This difficulty was not solved, but by-passed by using a LES/LEE interface which did not intercept the airfoil's wake. The final result integrates the three components, including the nearfield LES, the midfield noise propagation using LEE and the farfield noise radiation using the Kirchhoff integral.

INTRODUCTION

The general context of this paper is the numerical prediction of the aerodynamic noise generated by the high lift devices - HLD, slats and flaps - of large airliners, an important contributor to the total radiated airframe noise, especially in approach configuration. It is commonly admitted that the design of new low-noise HLD concepts incorporating specific noise reduction devices, although still relying on necessary experiments, will take growing advantage of the numerical simulation in terms of lower costs and shorter delays, especially considering the spectacular continuing progress of Computational AeroAcoustics (CAA) methods.

The problem of the numerical simulation of HLD noise is still beyond the capabilities of complete Direct Numerical Simulation (DNS), so hybrid methods are used in most practical cases. Figure 1 sketches the possible numerical strategies, showing how the nearfield turbulent flow and the farfield noise are computed separately. The idea is to divide the physical space into several domains, in which specific physical mechanisms are simulated using the most adequate set of equations with the cheapest discretization strategy.

Computational Fluid Dynamics (CFD) techniques are used to simulate the nearfield flow which contains the aerodynamic noise sources. Available techniques include steady Reynolds-Averaged Navier-Stokes (RANS) computations, in conjonction with stochastic models of the wavenumber-frequency spectrum of the turbulence [1-3], unsteady RANS methods [4-5], and Large Eddy Simulation (LES) [6-9].

This local flow solution has to be coupled to an acoustic numerical technique for the prediction of farfield noise. The most practical formulations are the integral methods such as Lighthill's analogy [7] [10] (including the Ffowcs Williams-Hawkings (FW-H) equation [4, 5, 11, 12]), the Boundary Element Method (BEM) [13] and the Kirchhoff integral.

In a former study, the compressible LES of the unsteady flow around a symmetrical NACA0012 airfoil with a blunted trailing edge has formed the basis of airfoil aerodynamic noise predictions. A detailed analysis of the nearfield unsteady flow showed that the local aeroacoustic characteristics were correctly simulated, including the local acoustic field. This suggested to define a control surface around the airfoil, on which the acoustic nature of the pressure field was established. The pressure field and normal derivative on this surface where used to compute the farfield noise via a 3D Kirchhoff method. In a second step, another noise prediction based on the Ffowcs Williams-Hawkings equation was performed using the same LES data.

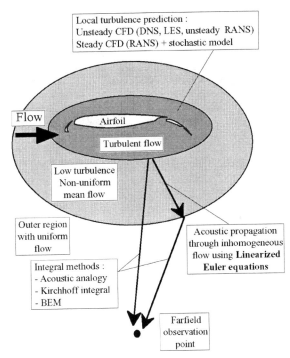

Local turbulence prediction :
Unsteady CFD (DNS, LES, unsteady RANS)
Steady CFD (RANS) + stochastic model

Flow

Airfoil

Turbulent flow

Low turbulence
Non-uniform
mean flow

Outer region
with uniform
flow

Integral methods :
- Acoustic analogy
- Kirchhoff integral
- BEM

Acoustic propagation
through inhomogeneous
flow using **Linearized
Euler equations**

Farfield
observation
point

*Figure 1 : Numerical simulation of airfoil aerodynamic noise :
possible hybrid strategies.*

Integral methods assume that, beyond a given distance from the noise sources and body surfaces, the sound propagates in a medium at rest, or moving with uniform velocity. This assumption may become a strong limitation, especially when the radiated noise results from a surface integration on a control interface which is located near solid walls, where velocity gradients are significant. In that case, only the discretized linearized Euler equations governing the acoustic propagation may account for the propagation in non-homogeneous flows. This is obtained at the price of a significant computational effort since the propagation domain must be meshed with an adequate resolution with respect to the smallest acoustic wavelength, and also because finite difference high order schemes are needed to ensure numerical accuracy and low dispersion of the propagation of acoustic waves [14]. Moreover, application to realistic geometries including airfoils need curvilinear grids [15-17] on which the use of high order schemes is not straightforward. However, the domain in which LEE are used can be strictly limited to regions where velocity gradients are significant : in most practical airframe noise problems, an external boundary can be found, beyond which the flow can be assumed uniform, so that integral methods can be used for the noise prediction at very long distance from the airframe.

The coupling of local CFD with LEE is a generic problem which has already received much attention from the CAA community. Several strategies have been proposed, depending on the type of flow data provided by CFD. Most of them rely on the formulation of a right-hand-side (RHS) "source term" which is introduced in the LEE written in a small-perturbation form. The derivation of this source is similar to the process leading to Lighthill's equation. The starting point is the Navier-Stokes equations (also in a small-perturbation form) which are reformulated to display a left-hand side (LHS) term identical to the LEE, any other terms becoming part of the RHS term which is assumed to contain the source terms responsible for noise generation. This RHS term is analyzed in order (i) to identify the principal terms contributing to the aerodynamic noise emission

and (ii) to suppress the terms that may generate unwanted non-physical noise [1, 9, 18]. In practical applications, a volume distribution of this source term is computed from the CFD results, interpolated on points belonging to the LEE grid, and then fed into the linearized equations. It should be noted that this method is particularly adequate, and probably unavoidable, when incompressible unsteady CFD is used.

The strategy proposed in the present paper is slightly different. The objective is to perform a noise prediction based on a local compressible LES coupled with LEE. In this case, the LES accurately simulates the aerodynamic noise sources and is able to provide the acoustic field generated at a very short distance, including refraction effects through the inhomogeneous unsteady flow and scattering effects on solid surfaces. Then the LES field is splitted into a perturbation field and a time-averaged non-uniform mean flow field. LES perturbations are directly injected into a LEE domain where they propagate outward through the non-uniform mean flow, naturally accounting for refraction effects in regions where mean velocity gradients are significant. The Euler domain has a radial extent of approximately one airfoil chord, since the mean flow is rather uniform beyond this limit. Consequently, the acoustic field radiated at the external boundary of the Euler domain becomes the entry data of a Kirchhoff integration which provides the noise radiated in the far field. This process is applied to an available LES computation of the flow around a NACA0012 airfoil with a blunted trailing edge.

The paper is organized as follows.

The first part briefly recalls the main features of the LES around the 3D NACA0012 airfoil with a blunted trailing edge and the noise predictions based on the Kirchhoff integration and the Ffowcs Williams Hawkings equation. Details of this flow noise prediction can be found in references [19] and [20]. It is especially emphasized how the uniform flow assumption, which is inherent to both integral methods, induces a bias in the propagation of acoustic waves. The LEE code, named E3P, which was developed for the simulation of acoustic propagation within non-homogeneous flows, is also briefly presented.

The second part is devoted to several preliminary actions that were required before to implement the E3P code in the 3-step CAA process introduced above, and to apply this process to actual LES data. These actions include (i) the derivation of a grid well suited for acoustic propagation, (ii) the description of the injection process, (iii) its validation using the analytical perturbation field generated by an acoustic monopole and (iv) tests to validate the spatial and temporal interpolations required to adapt the LES stored data to the LEE discretization requirements.

In the third part of the paper, the process of perturbation injection is applied to actual LES data. The dimensionality of the computation is firstly analyzed, then the way to split the original LES field into a mean flow field and a perturbation field is described. First result reveals strong unwanted non-physical noise generation in the region where the airfoil's wake is fed into the Euler domain, which is most probably due to the under-resolution of vortical structures in the wake. This is confirmed by additional tests in which a convected Eulerian vortex is injected in Euler grids with various refinement. This problem was not solved, but it was bypassed by using a different acoustic grid which do not intercept the airfoil's wake. The whole 3-step CAA process is finally applied to the NACA012 case.

The fourth and last part of the paper draws the main conclusions of this result, briefly presents the undergoing developments of the used LEE tool, and lists future CAA applications.

NACA0012 AIRFOIL NOISE PREDICTION
USING LES AND INTEGRAL METHOD

LES implementation

The FLU3M solver is an ONERA "in-house" industrial CFD software based on the discretization of the compressible Navier-Stokes equations on multi-block structured meshes by a cell-centered finite volume technique. General information about this solver is available in references [21-22].

LES has been recently implemented in FLU3M. The three-dimensional, Favre-filtered Navier-Stokes equations of a viscous compressible Newtonian unsteady flow are solved using a subgrid scale model of the eddy viscosity. The selective mixed scale model, developed by Sagaut and Lenormand, is used for this purpose [23-24]. A second order accurate hybrid upwind/centered implicit temporal integration is achieved, thanks to an approximate Newton method. More details about these numerical points are available in references. [25-26].

NACA0012 grid and numerical procedure

The airfoil had a $C = 0.6096$ m chord and a blunted trailing edge of thickness $H = 2.5$ mm (0.4 % of C), with reference to an airfoil noise experiment conducted at NASA in 1980 [27]. In this experiment, the airfoil had a span $S_{EXP} = 0.46$ m (or 75 % of C), whereas the LES computational domain had a spanwise extent S_{LES} representing only 3.3 % of C. The 3D grid was obtained by 33 replications in the spanwise direction, with a constant step $\Delta y = 10^{-3}C$, of a 2D curvilinear structured grid made of two domains, containing 53,354 points. The whole 3D grid contains 1.76 million points. The smallest cells are located at the TE corners, with dimensions (in wall units) $\Delta z^+ = 1.5$ in the direction normal to the wall and $\Delta x^+ = 15$ along the chord. This 2D grid extents nearly 10 chords above and below the airfoil, as well as upstream and downstream.

A no-slip condition was applied at the airfoil surface and a periodic condition was imposed in the spanwise direction. Non-reflecting characteristic boundary conditions are applied for the far field. A steady RANS computation using Baldwin-Lomax models provided an initial flow solution. In order to ensure the time-accuracy of the results, the physical time step was taken equal to 0.5 μs, meaning a sampling frequency of 2 MHz. An initial phase of 100,000 time steps was achieved, then the useful computation was performed over 130,000 time steps with a total duration of 65 ms, representing the convection of the flow over 7.5 airfoil chords. The requirements of acoustic computations led to a storage of one time sample every 100, meaning a storage sampling of 20 kHz, with a useful frequency band of 10 kHz. The total computation cost was 360 CPU hours on a NEC-SX5 computer.

The upstream flow velocity is $U_o = 69.45$ m/s (maximal velocity in the NASA experiment [27]), the Mach number is 0.205 and the Reynolds number based on U_o and C is 2.86 millions. The airfoil incidence is 5°.

Aerodynamic results showed the onset of a vortex shedding mechanism at the airfoil's trailing edge, which was confirmed by wall pressure spectra on both airfoil sides near the trailing edge (Figure 1, right side), which display a narrowband component (due to the vortex shedding) emerging out of a wideband continuum (generated by turbulent boundary layers - TBLs). They are compared (without corrections) to experimental data from [27]. Levels are slightly overestimated (3 dB), as is the vortex shedding frequency, which is explained by the excessive slenderness of the simulated TBLs, probably due to insufficient grid refinement in the transition region.

Figure 1 (left side) shows instantaneous pressure fluctuations in the LES domain, with an acoustic concentric wave pattern generated at the trailing edge, the wavelength of which corresponds to the vortex shedding mechanism. The acoustic nature of the pressure fluctuation field near the airfoil was confirmed by use of wall pressure wavenumber-frequency spectral densities, allowing to separate the convective and acoustic components in the pressure field, with their respective direction and phase velocity. Due to the strong stretching of the LES computational grid, which acts as an acoustic low-pass frequency filter, this acoustic field cannot radiate farther than a half-chord from the body. Consequently, the LES had to be relayed by an acoustic propagation method to correctly simulate the farfield noise.

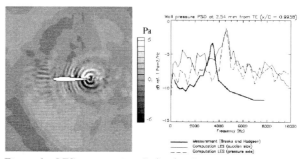

Figure 1 : LES computation. Left side : Instantaneous pressure fluctuations in the fluid. Right side : Wall pressure fluctuation spectra near the trailing edge, compared to experimental data [27].

Noise prediction based on integral methods

A 3D Kirchhoff formulation in the time domain is implemented in the ONERA's KIM code (Kirchhoff Integration Method) which was developed for helicopter rotor noise prediction [28] and jet noise prediction [29]. The formulation implemented in KIM can be found in reference [19]. A control surface enclosing the airfoil has been selected, on which it was verified that the pressure field was purely acoustic. Spanwise coherences on this control surface showed that the acoustic field was quasi-2D there, so the pressure data on the Kirchhoff surface were constructed by replication, along the S_{EXP} span of a realistic airfoil (75 % of C in [27]), of the LES data simulated in the median plane of the LES domain.

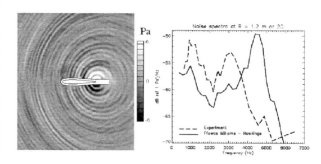

Figure 2 : Noise predictions using integral methods. Left side : Instantaneous pressure fluctuations in the fluid computed by the Kirchhoff integral. Right side : Noise spectra at two chords above the trailing edge : direct comparison of experimental data and numerical simulation using the FW-H method.

Figure 2 (left) shows a map of the acoustic pressure field computed using the Kirchhoff method. The comparison with the pressure field directly obtained from LES (Figure 1, right) clearly shows that the acoustic waves are observed at much longer distance. However, the level of the noise computed at two chords above the trailing edge was found to exceed experimental data by more than 15 dB, which was explained by an artificial overestimation of the spanwise coherence, probably induced by the limited span of the LES domain and the periodicity condition in the spanwise direction which was applied to the LES computational domain.

The spanwise integral length scale of the wall pressure fluctuations at the trailing edge were estimated from their spanwise coherence, showing that turbulent structures simulated near the wall were smaller than the 3.3%-chord span S_{LES} of the LES domain. This result suggested that the wall pressure fluctuation field could be assumed reliable, and a second noise prediction was achieved using the Ffowcs Williams-Hawkings method (dipole surface term only) from the wall pressure data computed in the LES domain (span S_{LES}.). Then the noise from a real airfoil with a span S_{EXP} was estimated by applying a factor S_{EXP}/S_{LES} on the resulting power spectral density, meaning a decorrelated summation of spanwise periodic domains.

Figure 2 (right side) compares this estimation with the noise measured in reference [27] at two chords above the trailing edge. It is interesting to notice that experimental and simulated frequency and level differ in the same way as wall pressure spectra (Figure 1), which may confirm the validity of the acoustic method.

The need for simulating the acoustic propagation in non-uniform mean flows

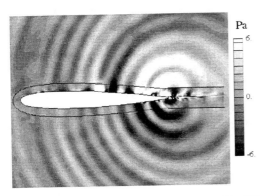

Figure 3 : Instantaneous pressure fluctuation field. LES data inside the control surface, Kirchhoff data outside.

Going back to the Kirchhoff integration, Figure 3 shows a closer view of the computed pressure fluctuation field, on which a significant discontinuity can be observed at the control surface between the LES front waves, displayed inside the surface, and the Kirchhoff front waves, displayed outside. This is particularly visible at the suction side, although the thick turbulent boundary layer tends to mask the phenomenon there. More precisely, the waves propagating in the LES domain are slightly slower than their counterpart in the Kirchhoff domain. This is explained by the assumption of a uniform velocity U_0 inherent to the Kirchhoff method, whereas the mean flow simulated via LES inside the control surface present local velocities U_e that may be significantly larger than U_0.

This is confirmed by the plot on Figure 4 showing isovalue contour of the pressure fluctuation field on the suction side. On

this view, LES data contours are plotted using solid black lines, whereas Kirchhoff data uses grey patterns. It should be noted that Kirchhoff points were arbitrarily chosen on a cartesian grid regardless their position relative to the interface : this is why Kirchhoff contours are also displayed beneath the interface. The shift between LES and Kirchhoff wave fronts is clear in the region $0.2 < x < 0.3$. This last result underlines a significant limitation of integral methods : outside a given surface or volume, they do not take into account the inhomogeneities of the mean flow.

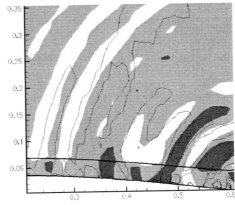

Figure 4 : Isovalue contours of instantaneous pressure fluctuation field computed via LES (black line) overlayed with Kirchhoff data (grey pattern).

This limitation may not be considered as critical in the present case, since the control surface is not so close to the airfoil, meaning that the actual mean flow outside the surface can be reasonably assumed as uniform. However, this will certainly not be the case when more complex flows will be considered. This fully justified the development of a complementary tool based on discretized LEE, which have the ability to account for acoustic propagation through local mean velocity gradients. However, since the use of LEE may become computationally very consuming, especially in complex 3D cases, it should be strictly limited to the regions where strong velocity gradients make it really necessary. In the present problem, such region could be reasonably limited to a domain extending one chord away from the airfoil. Outside this new control surface, the mean flow can be considered as rather uniform and the Kirchhoff method can be applied to provide accurate prediction of the sound at much longer distance from the airfoil.

E3P code

A code named E3P (Propagation via Euler Equations under a Small Perturbation Hypothesis) has been developed at ONERA by Redonnet [17], relying on the discretized Euler equations in a small-perturbation formulation, based on the splitting of the total field in a mean flow (subscript "o") and a perturbation field (subscript "p") :

$$[\partial_t \mathbf{u}_o + \nabla \cdot \mathbf{F}_o] + [\partial_t \mathbf{u}_p + \nabla \cdot \mathbf{F}_p] = \mathbf{q}_o + \mathbf{q}_p + \mathbf{q}_s$$

Here, the vectorial quantities $\mathbf{u}$, $\mathbf{F}$ and $\mathbf{q}$ respectively denote the unknowns, fluxes and source terms.

These equations are discretized in conservative form and can be either linearized (only first order terms are kept) or not (all linear and non-linear terms are conserved). Cartesian or curvilinear 2D/3D (monodomain) structured grids can be handled. In the space domain, the discretization uses high-order finite-difference explicit or implicit schemes. In the time domain, multi-steps schemes (Adams-Bashforth or Runge-Kutta) are implemented. Specific boundary conditions are used for solid surfaces, non-reflexive border, periodicity or perturbations injection. Non-uniform mean flows are taken into account. The characteristics of the code, as well as several test-cases of acoustic scattering on solid objets within non-uniform 2D and 3D flows, have been described in details in the reference [17].

LES/LEE COUPLING PROCESS

Acoustic grid derivation

The simulation of viscous turbulent flows via RANS or LES methods requires a high level of grid refinement near the solid walls and, on the contrary, uses strong grid stretching in the far field in order to benefit from the almost uniform flow conditions. Consequently, CFD grids are notoriously unadapted to the simulation of acoustic propagation via the LEE, which requires to be discretized on homogeneous grids with cells of rather constant size all over the domain. Figure 1 (left side) is a clear illustration of the problem. In the present case, the coupling of LES and LEE required to create a new grid for the acoustic domain. This grid was derived from the LES grid, following specific constraints (i) on the homogeneity of grid refinement, (ii) on the average cell size (with respect to the smallest wave lengths), and (iii) on intrinsic limitations of the E3P code which, for example, cannot handle multiblock structured grid.

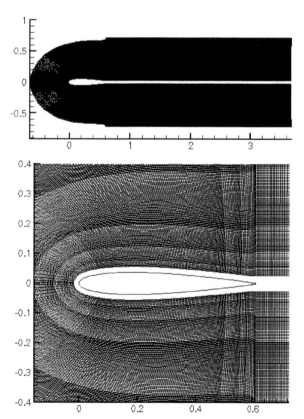

Figure 5 : Acoustic grid derived from the CFD mesh.

The interior and the exterior frontiers of the new mesh correspond, in the LES grid, to two grid lines surrounding the NACA0012 airfoil, extended by horizontal lines in the

downstream directions. This disposition was chosen to cover the largest area around the airfoil by using a single structured block. The interior border, on which LES data will be injected in the LEE domain, follows the airfoil's surface at an average distance of 1% of the chord length. This border is very close to the control surface that has been used before for direct Kirchhoff integration [19]. The outer border of the acoustic domain is approximately one chord away from the airfoil, since it was checked that the mean flow is quasi-uniform beyond this distance. Between these two frontiers, grid lines in the CFD mesh have been added or removed in order to obtain the best homogeneity in the grid refinement. In this process, many radial lines (which link the inner and the outer frontiers) were suppressed in the much refined area near the airfoil's trailing edge, and some were added in the less refined area near the airfoil's leading edge. The refining process was also applied to the C-lines surrounding the airfoil. The final grid has cells of quasi-constant size close to $\lambda_{min}/6$, for the smallest considered wave length λ_{min} (corresponding to the highest frequency of interest, say 10 kHz). This new acoustic grid involves 183 C-lines and 866 radial lines, or 158,478 points.

Data injection process

The E3P code is linked with unsteady CFD computations via an interface : a 2D (resp. 1D) interface is required for a 3D (resp. 2D) Euler calculation. The principle of the data injection process is to re-initialized the solution vector $\mathbf{u_P}$, at each time step, on a ghost point distribution outside the Euler domain, with the injected perturbation values. The number of ghost points depends on the maximum order of the used spatial scheme and spatial filter. In the present application, a sixth-order scheme (seven-point stencil) is used along with a 10th order filter (eleven-point stencil), so that the filter stencil requires 5 ghost points outside the domain, the data being finally injected on 6 points (5 ghost point plus the interface point).

One critical aspect in this process is causality : since the injection zone has a non-zero thickness (it comprises 6 lines in the present case), all ghost points are not reached at the same time by the injected data. A correct way to proceed is to pre-evaluate, at any ghost point x in the injection zone, the time $t(x)$ at which incoming data reach the point. Then, during the injection phase, each ghost point will be initialized only at time steps posterior to $t(x)$.

Before to apply it to actual LES-computed data, this data injection process has been tested using analytical data, the acoustic field generated by an harmonic point source.

Test with analytical acoustic monopole source

The acoustic field radiated in a medium at rest by a two-dimensional (cylindrical) harmonic (frequency ω) point source can be expressed using Hankel functions of first kind and order 0 : $H_1^0(x) = J_0(x) + iY_0(x)$ and 1 : $H_1^1(x) = J_1(x) + iY_1(x)$:

$$\begin{cases} \rho(r,t) = \text{Re}\{H_1^0(\omega r/c)e^{i\omega t}\} \\ p(r,t) = c^2\rho(r,t) \\ \vec{u}(r,t) = \text{Re}\{H_1^1(\omega r/c)e^{i\omega t}\}\dfrac{\vec{r}}{\|\vec{r}\|} \end{cases}$$

where J_0, J_1, Y_0, Y_1 are Bessel functions of order 0 and 1, and $\vec{r}$ is the vector joining the point source and the observer.

This analytical field is computed and injected at the inner frontier of the acoustic grid described on Figure 5. This case aims at simulating the noise generated by the vortex shedding mechanism at the trailing edge revealed by the LES computation : the point source is located at $(x, y) = (C, 0)$ (the position of the airfoil's trailing edge) and the frequency ω is chosen to stay as close as possible of the vortex shedding frequency ($f = 4.7$ kHz). The mean flow in the LEE domain is assumed to remain at rest. Figure 6 (left) shows the instanteaneous pressure field in the LEE domain after 7 time periods of the source. The reliability of the method is checked on Figure 6 (right side) by comparison between (i) the acoustic field computed by E3P and (ii) the direct analytical field at the same time step, along the $y = 0$ axis, showing a good agreement.

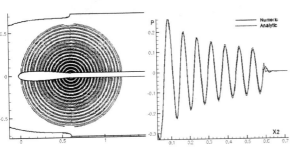

Figure 6 : Injection in the LEE domain of the acoustic field radiated by an harmonic point source. Instantaneous perturbation pressure field. Left side: Isovalue contours. Right side : Cut along the x = 0 axis, compared to analytical data.

Space interpolation

As said before, the acoustic grid was derived from the LES grid by adding (resp. suppressing) new grid lines in under- (resp. over-) resolved regions to ensure the best possible homogeneity. Consequently, LES data have to be interpolated in space so they can be injected at any new points created in the acoustic grid during the refinement process. Since such an interpolation is suspected to bias the injection process, it was tested using an analytic acoustic monopole. The source is identical as the source used on Figure 6, except that it is now centered near the airfoil's leading edge where the CFD grid is significantly under-resolved compared to the acoustic grid.

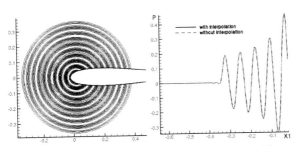

Figure 7 : Left side : pressure field isovalue contours with space interpolation. Right side: pressure field with/without interpolation :cut along the y = 0 grid line.

The pressure fields compared on Figure 7 (left) are obtained through the injection of the monopole's analytical field (i) at any point of the inner border of the LEE domain (without interpolation - solid black line) and (ii) only at the LEE points which have a counterpart in the LES domain, any other point receiving interpolated data (with interpolation - dashed grey line). The right side of Figure 7 displays a cut along the $y = 0$ axis. Boths results are almost superimposed, which shows that this space interpolation does not modifies the result.

Time interpolation

The requirements of LEE computations in terms of time sampling are of the same order as for the LES computations, which means that both codes could theoretically run with the same time step. However, this would mean (i) to let the codes run simultaneously, which is not yet operational, or (ii) to store the LES data with their original time step, which would result in a huge amount of stored data. Practically, only one LES data sample over 100 was stored in order to limit this storage volume, meaning that the time sampling of the stored data is much larger than the time step required for the Euler calculation. Consequently, a temporal interpolation of the injected data is necessary. This procedure was also tested with the same acoustic monopole as in Figure 7.

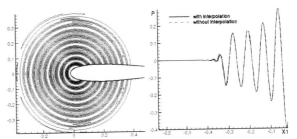

Figure 8 : Left side : pressure field isovalue contours with time interpolation. Right side: pressure field with/without interpolation :cut along the y = 0 grid line.

The pressure fields compared on Figure 8 (left) are obtained through the injection, at any point of the inner border of the LEE domain, of the monopole's analytical field (i) using the time step actually required by LEE computations (without interpolation - solid black line), and (ii) using the time step of LES stored data, and interpolating at any other LEE time step (with interpolation - dashed grey line). The right side of Figure 8, displays a cut along the $y = 0$ axis. Boths results are almost superimposed, which shows that this time interpolation does not modify the result.

LES/LEE COUPLING : NACA0012 APPLICATION

Dimensionality

Although both LES and LEE codes are intrinsically 3D, this first attempt of coupling LES and LEE was deliberately achieved in 2D, essentially due to the two-dimensional nature of the acoustic field generated by the LES, and also in order to limit the computational cost.

However, this choice raises the question of the possibility of full 3D applications of this CAA process to new complex geometries. At the present time, 3D applications are theoretically possible since each of the 3 involved codes, FLU3M (LES), E3P (LEE), and KIM (Kirchhoff) are intrinsically 3D. However, this remains technically out-of-reach due to practical limitations of the available computation resources for 3D LES and LEE (the Kirchhoff integration is less computationally demanding). For example, a LES of the unsteady flow around a NACA0012 airfoil with the same section but a realistic span (say 76 % of the chord with reference to [27]) would have required a 3D grid of about 50 millions points, and the corresponding computation using LEE for the mid field would have required a grid with similar volume. If such large grids are now handled for (advanced) steady RANS computations, they are still out-of-reach for unsteady CFD, for practical reasons of CPU time and data storage, even if LES and LEE were to be run simultaneously, which is still a computational challenge. One may argue that, for 3D airfoil configuration with constant section in the spanwise direction, the mean flow is actually 2D and the turbulent flow has constant spanwise statistical properties. This should allow to extrapolate the flow around a real-life airfoil from a CFD computation applied to a domain with a very narrow spanwise extent. This is probably correct for LES/LEE coupling process based on a source-term reconstruction from local small-scale velocity fluctuations. But when injection of acoustic waves is wanted, it has been observed that LES in narrow domains tends to overestimate the spanwise correlations at small distance from the airfoil, which renders extrapolation difficult.

Mean flow / perturbation splitting

The E3P code handles perturbations which propagate on a steady inhomogeneous flow. In our case, the mean flow was obtained at any point of the LES domain by time-averaging the unsteady data.

This process was not straightforward since it was found that the LES computation was not long enough to reach a stabilized mean flow : its average magnitude is subject to a slow drift, which has to be compared to the amplitude of turbulent fluctuations. This ratio of the drift amplitude over the turbulence amplitude is quite small in regions which are very aeroacoustically active as near the trailing edge. On the contrary, the ratio may become significant in other regions such as the leading edge, but these regions generally do not contain much flow noise sources. In order to minimize this problem, time averaging was limited to the last quarter (300 time steps) of the whole stored LES available duration (1300 time steps) to ensure that the mean flow is as stabilized as possible.

The way the mean flow is evaluated may have significant consequences on the perturbations if the latter are obtained by simply subtracting the mean flow to the original fluctuations : doing so, the drift is incorporated in the perturbations, with the consequence that the sum of the mean flow and the perturbation field is actually the original LES field but, on the other hand, perturbations do not fluctuate around a zero value. Another way to do is to evaluate, at any time step, an "instantaneous mean flow" obtained by time averaging inside a sliding window of constant duration. Then the perturbation are obtained by subtracting this instantaneous mean flow to the original LES field. Doing so, the sum of the mean flow and the perturbation field slightly differs from the original LES field but, on the other hand, it delivers perturbations which do fluctuate around zero. This last method has been adopted in the application presented below.

It should be noted that, in future LES application, this problem of slowly varying mean flow should disappear, due to a better convergence of the code.

Airfoil's wake injection : non-physical noise generation

The process of perturbation injection is now applied to actual LES data. The considered flow is the unsteady flow of the LES computation. As explained above, only the last 300 time steps (over 1300) are considered for computation of the time averaged mean flow. This mean flow is spatially interpolated on the whole acoustic grid, then the resulting perturbations are spatially and temporally interpolated at any points of the injection zone.

Figure 9 shows an instantaneous snapshot of the pressure fluctuation field at various time steps. There is an initial transitory phase in which a front wave travels from the injection zone to the outer border, then the computation stabilizes into a classical pattern of sound waves emitted near the trailing edge, a pattern very similar to that obtained with direct Kirchhoff integration (see Figure 2, left side).

On the last snapshot, strong unwanted non-physical noise is generated in the region where the airfoil's wake is injected in the Euler domain. This only happens on the suction side of the injection zone, due to the airfoil's incidence of 5°.

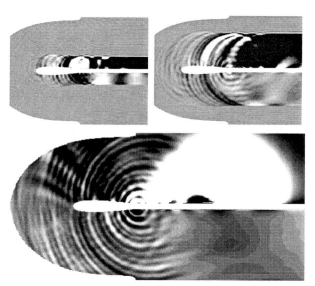

Figure 9 : Isovalue contours (range ± 2 Pa, black/white) of instantaneous pressure fluctuation field resulting from the injection of LES data into the CFD-derived acoustic grid. Initialization (top) and stabilization (bottom) with generation of non-physical noise.

In order to get a better understanding of this mechanism, additional tests of the injection process using analytical vortical fields are presented.

Analytical convected Eulerian vortex

The injected data are now the analytical perturbation field of an Eulerian vortex, convected at a uniform velocity (u_0, v_0). In cylindrical coordinates $(\vec{e}_r, \vec{e}_\theta)$, the tangential velocity, density, and pressure (perturbation) fields are given by :

$$
\begin{cases}
\vec{u}(r) = v_{max} \dfrac{r}{r_0} e^{\frac{1}{2}\left(1-\frac{r^2}{r_0^2}\right)} \vec{e}_\theta \\[2mm]
c(r) = 1 - \dfrac{(\gamma-1)}{2}\left(\dfrac{v_{max}}{c_0}\right)^2 e^{1-\frac{r^2}{r_0^2}} \\[2mm]
\rho(r) = \rho_\infty\left(c(r)^{\frac{1}{\gamma-1}} - 1\right) \qquad p(r) = p_\infty\left(c(r)^{\frac{\gamma}{\gamma-1}} - 1\right)
\end{cases}
$$

in which r denotes the distance to the centre of the vortex, v_{max} is the maximum value of the tangential velocity profile, reached at a distance $r = r_0$ from the centre of the vortex, and c_0 is the sound velocity. Figure 10 displays the radial profiles of tangential velocity $u(r)$ and pressure $p(r)$ of this vortex. The pressure profile reaches its maximum value at $r = 0$. The vorticity ω_z profile has also a cylindrical symmetry :

$$
\omega_z(r) = \frac{1}{r}\frac{\partial}{\partial r}[ru(r)] = \frac{v_{max}}{r_0}\left(2 - \frac{r^2}{r_0^2}\right) e^{\frac{1}{2}\left(1-\frac{r^2}{r_0^2}\right)}
$$

Vorticity maximum value $(\omega_z)_{max} = 2\sqrt{e}\, v_{max}/r_0$ is reached at $r = 0$. Preliminary tests using cartesian grids showed that several conditions are required for a correct injection or generation of such a rotationnal field inside a LEE domain :

- the full Euler(all terms kept) equations must be used,
- the causality must be respected : the vortical field must be progressively inserted into the layers of the interface,
- the average cell size must be about 8 times smaller than the vortex core radius r_0.

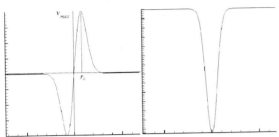

Figure 10 : Euler vortex : radial profiles of tangential velocity (left side) and pressure (right side).

Simulation of the airfoil's wake injection

The objective of this first test is to reproduce as close as possible the conditions of the injection of the airfoil's wake computed via LES presented on Figure 9. As shown on Figure 11, an analytical vortex is injected with a 5° incidence at the border of a grid extracted from the acoustic grid presented above (Figure 5) in the region where the airfoil's wake enters the LEE domain and where non-physical noise is generated. The vortex main characteristics are $r_c \approx 0.8$ mm and $v_{max} \approx 3.4$ m/s, with a resulting static pressure peak $p_{max} \approx -15$ Pa and maximum vorticity $(\omega_z)_{max} \approx 1.5 \; 10^3 \; \text{s}^{-1}$. With these values, the vortex size roughly match the airfoil wake's thickness (sum of the trailing edge bluntness and the boundary layer thicknesses) and the average spanwise vorticity ω_z computed via LES in this region ($\approx 5 \; 10^3 \; \text{s}^{-1}$). The convection velocity in the injection zone is given by the mean flow provided by averaging the LES computation over 300 instants.

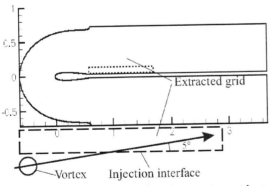

Figure 11 : Injection of an analytical vortex in a grid extracted from the CFD-derived acoustic grid.

Figure 12 shows the instantaneous velocity vector field (left side) and isovalue contours of the pressure field (right side) at several successive instants, in a domain accompanying the vortex. The first snapshot is taken when the vortex reaches the injection zone. The second one is taken when the vortex has just entered the domain, generating concentric waves of noise propagating upward, with pressure levels about 3 Pa, which is quite above the acoustic pressure actually generated by the

airfoil's trailing edge. The third and last snapshot corresponds to a latest time when the vortex has fully entered the domain : the static pressure profile ($p_{max} \approx -15$ Pa) is convected along with the vortex, but there is no more spurious noise emission. The velocity vector fields on this third snapshot shows the low resolution of the injected vortex, inducing a "square" aspect.

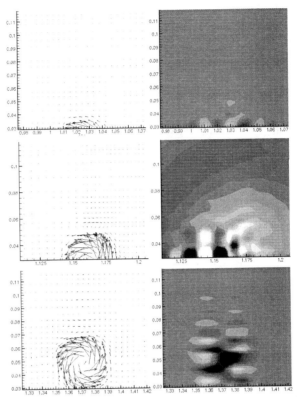

Figure 12 : Injection of an analytical vortex in a grid extracted from the CFD-derived acoustic grid, at successive instants. Left side : velocity vector field. Right side : isovalue contours of pressure field (range = 7. Pa, black/white).

Complementary test with refined grid

In this second test, a vortex with the same characteristics (r_0, v_{max}) is injected in a domain with the same outer dimensions, but with a much higher grid resolution. In this case, the average cell size is roughly 1/8th of the vortex core radius, meeting the refinement requirements exposed before. Figure 13 (A, B, C) show the velocity and pressure fields at three successive instants. The pressure contour plots display the static pressure contour convected along with the vortex (see Figure 10, right side) without radiating any unwanted noise. Figure 13 (D) shows superimposition of the velocity vector field at successive times, beginning just before the vortex enters the domain and ending when the whole vortex diameter is inside the domain. Figure 13 (E) shows isovalue contours of the instantaneous pressure field at the same instants : the pressure field created at the initial time is convected without generating spurious noise, which is confirmed by the bottom graph of Figure 13 (E) which displays pressure profiles going by the centre of each vortex at the same instants.

This last test shows that, whenever vortical structures are accurately resolved in the CFD domain, then they should be correctly injected in the Euler domain. On the contrary, the first test suggests that under-resolved rotationnal structures cannot be injected without generating non physical noise. This two tests do not provide a clear explanation of the spurious noise generation observed on Figure 9, but they suggest that the under-resolution of vortical structures plays an important role in this mechanism.

Figure 3), which did not take account of the inhomogeneities of the flow.

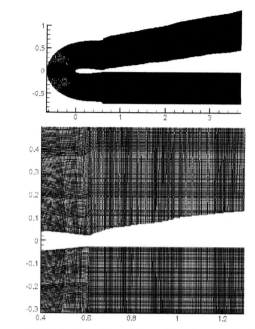

Figure 14 : Derivation of a problem-adapted acoustic grid

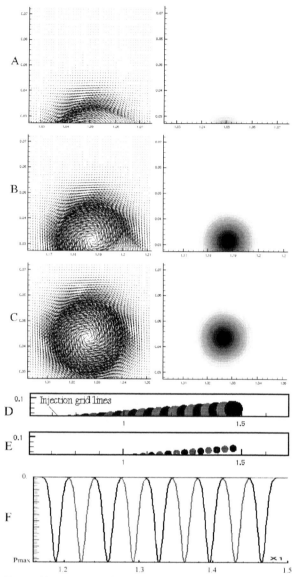

Figure 13 : Injection of an analytical vortex in a refined domain at successive instants. A, B, C : Left side : velocity vector field. Right side : isovalue contours of pressure field (range [-15, 0] Pa black/white. D : velocity vector field. E : pressure field isocontours. F : pressure field profiles going by the centre of the vortex at each instant.

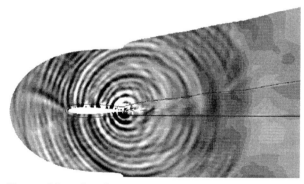

Figure 15 : Isovalue contours of instantaneous pressure fluctuation field (range ± 2. Pa, black/white) computed from (i) LES - inside the injection interface and (ii) E3P (from LES data injection) outside the injection interface.

Derivation of a problem-adapted acoustic grid

This difficulty caused by under-resolved vorticity injection has not been solved, but by-passed in the present application by constructing a new acoustic grid especially designed to prevent the airfoil's wake to cross the injection surface. Figure 14 shows how this grid was constructed via a vertical shift of radial grid lines in the upper part of the original acoustic grid. Figure 15 shows the result obtained with this new grid. In that case the coupling of LES and LEE does not give birth to spurious noise.

Figure 16 shows a closer view of Figure 15 centered on the airfoil. This view shows that there is no discontinuities at the injection interface between the LES wave fronts and the E3P wave fronts, as it was observed with the Kirchhoff method (see

Figure 16 : Same as Figure 15 (closer view).

Figure 17 compares noise spectra obtained from the E3P computation and from the Kirchhoff integration at 1/3 chord from the airfoil above the trailing edge, a near field region where the 3D Kirchhoff field can be considered as two-dimensional, allowing its direct comparison with the 2D Euler result. The two spectra are qualitatively and quantitatively rather similar.

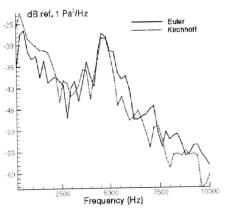

Figure 17 : Comparison between spectra obtained from E3P result and Kirchhoff result at 1/3 chord the airfoil.

Figure 18 shows the radial evolution of the pressure spectra for the three computations (LES, E3P and Kirchhoff), integrated in the frequency domain [4 kHz-6 kHz] centered on the frequency of the vortex shedding, with respect to the logarithmic vertical distance from the airfoil trailing edge. The curve in solid line corresponds to the field calculated by LES : near the airfoil ($z < 0.012$ m), the turbulent boundary layer induces very important levels. In the region 0.012 m $< z < 0.12$ m, the pressure field becomes purely acoustic and the pressure fluctuations decrease as $1/\sqrt{z}$. Then, the CFD mesh becomes too stretched, with cell size becoming larger than one quarter of the acoustic wavelength in this frequency band and the propagation is stopped. Curve in dashed line is the result of the Kirchhoff integration using the LES data on the Kirchhoff control surface. In the region $z > 0.04$ m, LES and Kirchhoff curves differ by ≈ 3 dB, which has been explained by the temporal undersampling of the available LES data (a problem that could have been simply avoided by a temporal interpolation of these LES stored data). However, one can observe that LES and Euler evolutions almost collapse in this region.

Figure 19 shows a directivity diagram obtained by computing the noise radiated (computed by Euler and Kirchhoff methods) on equally spaced points located on a circle of radius $r = 0.7$ m (about one airfoil chord) centered on the airfoil trailing edge. Both diagrams are in good agreement.

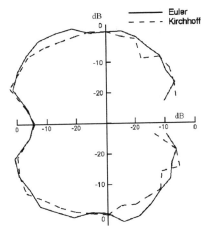

Figure 19 : Directivity diagram (dB) of radiated noise on a circle of radius about one airfoil chord centered on the trailing edge. Comparison between Euler and Kirchhoff results.

Finally, Figure 20 aims to evaluate the continuity between the pressure fields computed by LES (solid black line) and Euler – grey pattern) the control surface. This result must be compared to its counterpart obtained with Kirchhoff data and presented on Figure 4, on the acoustic waves emitted at the trailing edge are slightly slower in the LES domain (grey pattern) than their counterpart propagating in the Kirchhoff domain, especially after propagating along a half chord in the upstream direction. On Figure 20, LES and Euler wave fronts match better, since acoustic waves in the Euler domain propagate against a mean flow with correct velocity and non homogeneities. However, LES and Euler wave fronts are not completely superimposed, which probably results from the fact that, in the Euler calculation, the mean flow is an average over 300 instants, whereas the actual real flow has a slow temporal drift.

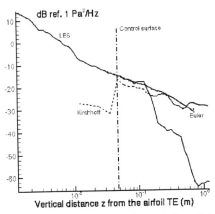

Figure 18 : Comparison between the radial evolution of the pressure spectra (integrated frequency band [4 kHz-6 kHz]) for LES, E3P, and Kirchhoff computations with respect to the vertical distance from the airfoil trailing edge.

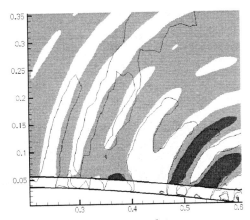

Figure 20 : Isovalue contours of instantaneous pressure fluctuation field computed via LES (solid black lines) overlayed with Euler data (grey pattern). This plot is to be compared to similar result obtained with Kirchhoff data on Figure 4.

Final result including LES, LEE and Kirchhoff integration

In this last part, the whole 3-step CAA process is applied to the NACA0012 case, including a farfield noise prediction performed by use of a Kirchhoff integration based on the pressure field and its normal derivative on the external boundary of the Euler domain.

Figure 21 shows the superimposition of pressure fluctuations field obtained from LES (below the LES/LEE interface interface), pressure fluctuations field obtained from E3P by injection of LES data on the new acoustic grid (between the two interfaces) and pressure fluctuations field obtained from Kirchhoff by integration of Euler data on the surface indicated by the highest black line (as far as this highest interface). The wave fronts are continuous from one domain to an other.

An interesting point is that acoustic waves emitted by the airfoil's leading edge are hardly visible on this figure. This phenomenon has been already observed on wall pressure wavenumber-frequency spectra computed at mid chord on the suction side [19] and confirms that the leading edge acts as a geometrical singularity on which incident acoustic waves coming from the trailing edge are scattered.

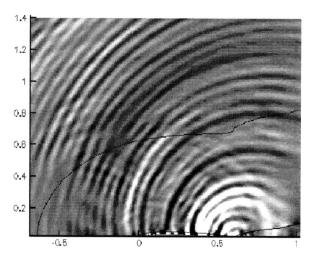

Figure 21 : Isovalue contours (range ± 3. Pa black/white) of instantaneous pressure fluctuations field computed from (i) LES data - inside the injection interface, (ii) E3P (from LES data injection) - between the injection interface and the Kirchhoff control surface, and (iii) from Kirchhoff integration - beyond the Kirchhoff control surface.

CONCLUSIONS AND UNDERGOING WORKS

This paper describes a significant step towards the development of an integrated CAA process aiming at the numerical prediction of the aerodynamic self-noise of complex 3D airfoil. This hybrid process combines three numerical methods, each one simulating specific fluid mechanisms (unsteady aerodynamics or acoustics) in a particular domain, by solving the adequate set of equations using the most economic discretization strategy : (i) a compressible LES is used to simulate the local unsteady flow around the airfoil configuration, (ii) the LEE simulate the acoustic propagation through an intermediate domain in which turbulence is not significant but mean velocity gradients are substantial, and (iii) a Kirchhoff integration provides the farfield noise.

The critical point of the method is the coupling between LES and LEE. Several authors have developed coupling process

based on the derivation of a volume RHS source term for the LEE from the unsteady flow data provided by the unsteady CFD. Unlike these authors, the present study analyses a more straightforward technique based on the direct injection of LES data at the border of the LEE domain, a process which relies on the compressibility of LES and its ability to correctly simulate the local acoustic field.

This process virtually offers the following advantages, each one with its intrinsic limitations :

(i) Unsteady CFD data storage : when the LES and LEE computation are not simultaneous, but successive, which is most often the case, the requirement of spatial storage for LES are theoretically decreased by one dimension : a surface instead of a volume for 3D applications, a linear curve instead of a surface for 2D applications. However, this advantage must be carefully evaluated : due to the high order of the used spatial filter and scheme, the injection interface must comprise up to 6 layers. This may lead to a storage amount a size comparing with a volume distribution strictly limited to the most noisy turbulent sources.

(ii) Injection of raw CFD data : one motivation of a coupling process based on data injection was the possibility to inject small perturbations directly derived from LES results (by subtracting the time-average mean flow) without additional filter or source-term reconstruction. The data injection process has been validated with analytical fields, firstly the noise radiated by an acoustic monopole, then a convected eulerian vortex. The tests revealed that analytical fields are injected without generating noticeable spurious noise as long as the conditions of causality (the analytical field must be progressively inserted into the layers of the injection interface) and grid resolution (the cell size in the LEE domain must be compatible with the length scales of injected structures) are fulfilled. The tests also demonstrated that the grid resolution condition has drastic consequences when actual CFD including vorticity data are used. This is probably because typical vortical structures in real unsteady flows are expected to cover a wide range of dimensions and are convected at low velocity, at least in the low Mach number applications encountered in the airframe noise domain : at a given frequency f, their apparent length scale U/f is small. This is why first test of injecting actual LES data in a LEE domain revealed a generation of non-physical noise in the region where the injection interface intercepts the airfoil's wake. The direct consequence is that the injection of raw LES perturbation without particular precaution on any interface of a LEE domain is far from straightforward.

This problem has not been solved but, in the present NACA0012 application, it has been by-passed by using a different LEE domain in which the injection border was re-designed to not intercept the airfoil's wake. In that case, the two-dimensional LES/LEE coupling was achieved correctly, as well as the association with the Kirchhoff integration to compute the farfield radiation. The nearfield noise spectra computed via E3P were compared with similar spectra obtained in a former study via the LES/Kirchhoff coupling technique. The Euler calculation being two-dimensional, these spectra are compared in the nearfield region (1/3 chord from the airfoil) where the Kirchhoff field can be considered as two-dimensional,. The spectra are, as expected, quite identical, but the wavefront patterns are slightly different, which is essentially due to the refraction effects through the non-uniform flow, which is not taken account in the LES/Kirchhoff method. In the case of the whole 3-step CAA process (LES/LEE/Kirchhoff), the wave fronts are more continuous from one domain to an other than with the LES/Kirchhoff technique.

It should be noted that this last result apparently do not provide substantially more qualitative nor quantitative information than former noise predictions achieved via integral methods applied on the same LES. This is certainly because the studied airfoil configuration is rather simple, although representative of many practical aeroacoustic situations : the mean flow outside the coupling interface presents relatively smooth velocity gradients, so that the uniform flow assumption inherent to integral methods is relevant in that case.

In fact this application only suggests what could be the capabilities of this CAA process in much more complex aeroacoustic mechanisms. With this viewpoint, this result can be considered as a significant progress towards the longterm development of an accurate CAA process for reliable airframe noise prediction and reduction.

However, the process do have inherent drawbacks, including a computing cost that may become prohibitive if full 3D applications are considered. This is why more conventional techniques such as integral methods will most probably remain operational for some time before LEE becomes routinely integrated in the numerical prediction of aerodynamic noise generated by complex airfoil configurations.

Despite expected difficulties, this CAA method will be applied to more sophisticated airfoil geometries in the next future. The first step, currently under progress, will be to achieve another LES of the unsteady flow around the same NACA0012 airfoil, based on a new grid constructed with the objective of a better simulation of the TBLs. The second step will be the computation, via LES, of the unsteady flow around a high lift wing with deployed slat and flap (with a constant section in the spanwise direction).

Applications of CAA computations to these complex unsteady CFD realizations will become possible through the future evolutions of the LEE code E3P. The development of this laboratory code has been stopped, and its most specific functionalities are currently being implemented in the FLU3M solver, an industrial CFD software that has been developed at ONERA for several years, which is already the framework of the LES. These functionalities are, essentially, a finite-difference high-order scheme module, along with specific filters and free field boundary conditions. The objective of this implementation is double : firstly, the simulation of acoustic propagation via the LEE will benefit from functionalities already developed in FLU3M, and especially the capability to easily handle complex multiblock grids. Secondly, unsteady CFD computations will benefit from the high-order spatial schemes, allowing to reduce the grid refinement of a given problem without altering the accuracy of the solution. This new tool will benefit to classical LES, but will also be ideally applied to emerging techniques such as Non Linear Disturbance Equations (NLDE) in which the classical splitting between the mean flow and the perturbation field is applied to the full Navier-Stokes equations.

ACKNOWLEDGEMENTS

This work was funded by the SPAé (Office of Aeronautical Programs).

BIBLIOGRAPHY

[1] Béchara W., Bailly C. and Lafon P. *"Stochastic Approach to Noise Modeling for Free Turbulent Flows"* AIAA Journal, Vol. 32, No. 3, pp.455-463, March, 1994.

[2] Bailly C., Lafon P. and Candel S. *"A Stochastic Approach To Compute Noise Generation and radiation of Free Turbulent Flows"*, CEAS-AIAA Paper 95-092, 1st AIAA-CEAS Aeroacoustics Conference, München (D), 12-15 June, 1995.

[3] Kalizin G., Kalitzin N. and Wilde, A. *"A Factorization Scheme for RANS Turbulence Models and SNGR Predictions of Trailing Edge Noise"*, AIAA Paper No. 2000-1982, 6th AIAA-CEAS Aeroacoustics Conference, Lahaina (Hawaii), 12-14 June, 2000.

[4] Singer B.A., Brentner K.S., Lockard D.P. and Lilley G.M. *"Simulation of Acoustic Scattering from a Trailing Edge"*, AIAA Paper 99-0231, 37th Aerospace Sciences Meeting and Exhibit, Reno (NV), Jan. 12-15, 1999.

[5] Singer B.A., Lockard D.P., Brentner K.S. *"Computational Aeroacoustic Analysis of Slat Trailing-Edge Flow"*, AIAA Journal, Vol. 38, No. 9, pp. 1558-1564, September, 2000.

[6] Spyropoulos E.T. and Holmes B.S. *"Computation of the airframe noise of a wing-flap configuration"*, AIAA Paper 99-1801, 5th CEAS/AIAA Aeroacoustics Conference, Seattle, USA, 10-12 May, 1999.

[7] Manoha E., Troff B. and Sagaut P. *"Trailing Edge Noise Prediction using Large Eddy Simulation and Acoustic Analogy"*, AIAA Journal, Vol. 38, No. 4, pp. 575-583, April (also AIAA Paper 98-1066), 2000.

[8] Wang M. and Moin P. *"Computation of Trailing-Edge Flow and Noise Using Large-Eddy Simulation"*, AIAA Journal, Vol. 38, No. 12, pp. 2201-2209, December, 2000.

[9] Ewert R., Meinke M. and Schröder W. *"Comparison of Source Term Formulations for a Hybrid CFD/CAA Method"*, AIAA Paper 2001-2200, 7th AIAA/CEAS Aeroacoustics Conference, Maastricht (NL), May 28-30, 2001.

[10] Lighthill M.J. *"On sound generated aerodynamically. I. General theory*, Proc. Roy. Soc. Lond., Vol. A 211, pp. 564-587. *II. Turbulence as a source of sound"*, Proc. Roy. Soc. Lond. A 222, pp. 1-32, 1952.

[11] Ffowcs Williams J.E. and Hawkings D.L. *"Sound generation by turbulence and surfaces in arbitrary motion"*, Phil. Trans. Royal Soc., Vol. A 264, pp. 321-342, 1969.

[12] Gloerfelt X., Bailly C. and Juvé D. *"Computation of the noise radiated by a subsonic cavity using direct simulation and acoustic analogy"*, AIAA Paper 2001-2226, 7th AIAA/CEAS Aeroacoustics Conference, Maastricht (NL), May 28-30, 2001.

[13] Manoha E., Elias G., Troff B. and Sagaut P. *"Towards the Use of Boundary Element Method in Computational Aeroacoustics"*, AIAA Paper 99-1980, 5th CEAS/AIAA Aeroacoustics Conference, Seattle, USA, 10-12 May, 1999.

[14] Tam C.K.W. and Webb, J.C. *"Dispersion-Relation-Preserving Finite Difference Schemes for Computational Acoustics"*, Journal of Computational Physics, Vol. 107, pp. 262-281, 1993.

[15] Grogger H.A., Delfs J.W., Lauke T.G., Lummer M. and Yin J. *"Simulation of leading-edge noise of airfoils using CAA based on body-fitted grids"*, 7th International Congress on Sound and Vibration, Garmisch-Partenkirchen, Germany, 4-7 July, 2000.

[16] Grogger H.A., Lummer M and Lauke T.G. *"Simulating the Interaction of a Three-Dimensional Vortex with Airfoils using CAA"*, AIAA Paper 2001-2137, 7th CEAS/AIAA Aeroacoustics Conference, Maastricht, The Netherlands, 28-30 May, 2001.

[17] Redonnet S., Manoha E. and Sagaut P. *"Numerical Simulation of Propagation of Small Perturbations interacting with Flows and Solid Bodies"*, AIAA Paper n° 2001-2223, 7th

CEAS/AIAA Aeroacoustics Conference, Maastricht, The Netherlands, 28-30 May, 2001.

[18] Bailly C., Lafon P. and Candel S. *"A Stochastic Approach To Compute Subsonic Noise Using Linearized Euler Equations"*, AIAA Paper 99-1872, 5th CEAS/AIAA Aeroacoustics Conference, Seattle, USA, 10-12 May, 1999.

[19] Manoha E., Delahay C., Ben Khelil S., Guillen P., Sagaut P. and Mary Y. *"Numerical prediction of the unsteady flow and radiated noise from a 3D lifting airfoil"*, AIAA Paper 2001-2133, 7th CEAS/AIAA Aeroacoustics Conference, Maastricht, The Netherlands, 28-30 May, 2001.

[20] Manoha E., Delahay C., Redonnet S., Ben Khelil S., Guillen P., Sagaut P. and Mary I. *"Numerical prediction of the unsteady flow and radiated noise from a 3D lifting airfoil"*, NATO/RTO Applied Vehicle Technology Panel, Symposium on Aging Mechanisms and Control, Development in Computational Aero- and Hydro- Acoustics, Manchester, United Kingdom, 8-11 October, 2001.

[21] Péchier M. *"Prévision numérique de l'effet Magnus pour des configurations de munitions"*, Thèse de l'Université de Poitiers, 1999.

[22] Péchier M., Guillen P. and Gayzac R. *"Magnus Effect over Finned Projectiles"*, J. of Aircraft and Rockets, 2001.

[23] Lenormand E., Sagaut P. and Ta Phuoc L. *"Large Eddy Simulations of Subsonic and Supersonic Channel Flow at Moderate Reynolds Number"*, Int. J. Numer. Meth. Fluids, Vol. 32, pp. 369-406, 2000.

[24] Lenormand E., Sagaut P., Ta Phuoc L. and Comte P. *"Subgrid-Scale Models for Large Eddy Simulations of Compressible Wall Bounded Flows"*, AIAA Journal, Vol. 38, pp. 1340-1350, 2000.

[25] Mary I. and Sagaut P. *"Large Eddy Simulation of Flow around a high lift airfoil"*, AIAA Paper 2001-2559, 15th CFD Conference, Anaheim (Ca), 11-14 June, 2001.

[26] Weber C. and Ducros, F. *"Large-Eddy and Reynolds-Averaged Navier-Stokes Simulation of Turbulent Flow over an airfoil"*, Int. J. CFD, Vol. 13, pp. 327-355, 2000.

[27] Brooks T.F. and Hodgson T.H. *"Prediction and comparison of trailing edge noise using measured surface pressures"*, Journal of Sound and Vibration, Vol. 78 (1), pp. 69-117, 1981.

[28] Rahier G. and Prieur, J. *"An Efficient Kirchhoff Integration Method for Rotor Noise Prediction Starting Indifferently from Subsonically or Supersonically Rotating Meshes"*, 53rd Annual Forum of the American Helicopter Society, Virginia Beach, VA, April-May, 1997.

[29] Seror C., Sagaut P. and Rahier G. *"Prévision du bruit de jet de l'ATSF : simulation aéroacoustique d'un jet supersonique à section rectangulaire"*, RTS ONERA n° 12/4418 DSNA/Y, Février, 2000.

A Component Based Empirical Model for Airframe Noise Prediction

Y. P. Guo & K. J. Yamamoto
Boeing Space and Communications
Huntington Beach, CA 92647

R. W. Stoker
Boeing Commercial Airplane Company
Seattle, WA 98124

This paper presents an empirical model for airframe noise prediction. The model is derived from a large database of airframe noise tests, involving various airplane models at various operating conditions. The model correlates far field noise not only to gross airplane parameters such as the dimensions of the high lift system and flight Mach number, but also to flow quantities that are physically responsible for the noise generation. For example, flap side edge noise is correlated to the strength of the vortex in the roll-up cross flow at the side edge. Noise data used in the development of the model are acquired by using phased microphone arrays, which enables the decomposition of the total noise into components, relating the noise to the individual components of the wing/high lift system. This is done by beam-forming the phased microphone array data onto the airplane, leading to source distributions on the airplane, which are then integrated over individual components and propagated to the far field to derive the noise from the components. The wing/high lift system in this prediction model is divided into six components, namely, the leading edge slat, the outboard flap side edge, the inboard flap side edge, the high-speed aileron, the wing trailing edge and a residue term. The first five components are chosen to represent the most dominant airframe noise sources and the last to account for areas not covered by the first five components. In this paper, the methodology and results of this component-based model is presented, including source identification by source strength maps, component integration to derive far field spectra, validation/calibration of the integrated spectra by conventional free field microphone data, extrapolation of small-scale model test data to full-scale conditions with Reynolds number dependent scaling laws and the correlation between noise and flow quantities. Validations of the predictions with flight test data are also given to show the accuracy of the developed prediction tool.

1. Introduction

Empirical models have long been used for airframe noise prediction (e.g. Bauer & Munson 1978; Fink 1979; Yamamoto *et al* 1995). These models usually rely on test data available and the understanding of the source mechanisms. In recent years, there has been much research effort on airframe noise with significant progresses in many aspects, including the understanding of physical sources and measurements techniques such as phased microphone array. These lead to the possibility of improved prediction tools that are more physics-based. In this paper, we present the

development of an empirical tool for airframe noise prediction. Our empirical model is based on a large acoustic database consisting of elliptic mirror data for Boeing 737, 757 and 777 and phased microphone array data for Boeing 767, DC-10 and MD-11. The elliptical mirror data are also the database used by Boeing to develop an early version of component-based prediction models (Yee *et al* 1996), while the phased array data are made available only in recent years.

One of the main advantages of using phased array measurements and elliptical mirror data, instead of the traditional free field microphone data, is that the total noise can be decomposed into subcomponents. This is feasible because the beam-forming technique used in the array data processing leads to source distributions on the aircraft. By dividing the aircraft surface into sub-regions according to the source distribution and by integrating the sources over these sub-regions, noise components from different sub-regions can be derived. This component-based approach is not practical for free field microphone data because the measurements from those microphones contain contributions from all sources, and these sources are aerodynamically inter-related to each other, making it very difficult to separate one from the other.

Once the noise components from the individual airframe parts are derived, the empirical tool development can go a step forward by correlating the noise to some controlling geometric and aerodynamic quantities, which renders the approach more physics-based and includes the cause-and-effect relation in the prediction. For each noise component, since the locations of the sources that generate the noise are identified, physical mechanisms for the noise generation can be analyzed so that the dominant noise-generating flow features are revealed. To correlate these flow features to the far field noise, a set of aerodynamic quantities is defined for each noise component. These quantities are derived from panel method calculations (or can be found by any other aero calculations such as CFD) and are correlated to the noise by a regression analysis.

Thus, the advances of the method presented here over previous empirical approaches in airframe noise prediction are twofold; it is component-based and it is more physics-based. The methodology is, however, by no means mature and standard. There are many issues to be resolved in the data processing. For example, the phased microphone array measurements give beam-forming results that are not directly related to far field noise spectra. To derive the noise spectra, beam-forming map integration is needed and the results have to be calibrated with free field microphone data. Another example is the extrapolation from small-scale model test data to full-scale configurations, which not only requires the conventional scaling in frequency and amplitude according to the size of the model, but also need Reynolds number dependent corrections, especially for models that are less than about 10 percent of full-scale configurations (Guo *et al* 1998; 2000)

In the following sections, the process of the data analysis, the identification of component sources, the derivation of the far field component noises and their correlation with flow parameters will be described in detail. The validation of the derived noise prediction tools will also be discussed and comparisons will be made with free field measurements from both small-scale and full-scale tests.

2. Sub-Component Sources

The source maps from the phased microphone array and the elliptic mirror can be used to identify major sources and hence to define sub-regions for the source integration. To illustrate this, figures 1 shows the source distribution for a 4.7% MD-11 semi-span model at 10 kHz. The test is done at NASA Ames in the 12 ft pressure wind tunnel where the phased microphone array is mounted on the wind tunnel wall (test details given in Guo *et al* 1998). The test conditions for the plot shown in figure 1 are the flow Much number $M=0.207$ and the flaps and slats respectively deployed at 35 and 20 degrees. For this example, the source map shows dominant sources at the two flap side edges. Other sources with relatively smaller amplitudes are also seen at the leading edge slat locations and the trailing edge locations of the wing/flap system away from the flap side edges.

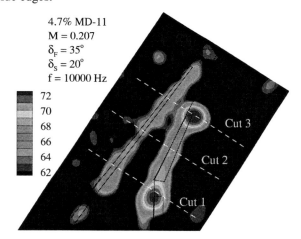

Figure 1. Example of airframe noise source distribution derived from phased microphone array measurements. The source strengths along the cuts are given in figure 2.

To further quantify the relative importance of the sources at different locations, we choose a few cuts on the source map and plot the source strengths along these cuts. The cut locations are shown in figure 1 and the source strengths along these cuts are plotted in figure 2. Cut 1 goes through the dominant source at the inboard edge of the flap. The source strength plot (the bottom diagram in figure 2) clearly shows the dominance of this source. Along this cut, the flap side edge source is at least 10 dB stronger than the background. The slat noise source is also clearly seen in this plot, which is about 6 dB lower than the flap edge source, but is still well above the background. When the cuts are taken at other locations, other sources are revealed very clearly. Cut 2 (the middle diagram in figure 2) is at the middle span location and shows both the slat source and the trailing edge source. At this location, the amplitudes of these two sources are quite comparable. The top diagram in figure 2 is the cut at the outboard flap side edge. Similarly to the inboard flap edge, the noise source along this cut is dominated by the flap side edge, though the slat source is also seen here.

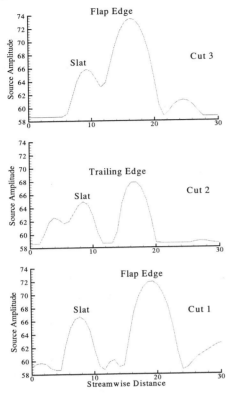

Figure 2. Source strengths along three cuts in the stream-wise direction, showing the dominant sources at the flap edges, the slats and the trailing edges.

From the source strength plots in figure 2, it is clear that the sources at the flap side edges have much higher amplitudes than those at other locations such as the slat and the trailing edge. This however does not necessarily mean that the other sources are less important. This is because though the other sources may have weaker strengths, they may have a much larger source area than the flap side edge sources which are usually very concentrated. The far field noise is determined by the integration of the source strength over the source area. Thus, a weaker source distribution with a larger source area may lead to more noise in the far field. The source strengths are also frequency dependent; the dominant sources at one frequency may become less important at other frequencies.

Based the analysis of the source maps and the source strengths at different locations, we divide the wing area into sub-regions for the component analysis. The sub-regions are used for source integration to derive far field spectra. They also correspond to sub-

components of the wing/high lift system, each of which may have different noise generation mechanisms. There are altogether six components, namely, the leading edge slat, the outboard flap edge, the inboard flap edge, the trailing edge, the high-speed aileron and a residue noise floor. An example of the definitions for the sub-regions is illustrated in figure 3 for the MD-11 data shown in figures 1 and 2. For other models, the sub-regions are similarly defined. It is appropriate to point out that this definition of sub-regions does involve a certain degree of arbitrariness, especially in the shapes and sizes of the sub-regions. For example, the high-speed aileron component is defined as a rectangular region close to the wing tip. This region actually contains some trailing edge sources. It is not further divided for the sake of simplifying the computations. The arbitrariness in the definition of the sub-regions, however, does not pose a severe limitation on the analysis for two reasons. The first is that the sub-regions are always required to cover the entire wing area so that the sum of the noise components is always equal to the total noise of the wing, though the noise components themselves may vary with different definitions of the sub-regions. The second reason is that the sub-regions are required to contain the respective dominant sources in the regions. Since the dominant sources are much stronger than other sources within each sub-region, the variations in shape and size of the sub-region definition is not very critical in the source strength integration. The integration is dominated by the major sources. It should also be noted that the locations and the sizes of the sub-regions are frequency-dependent. As frequency varies, the source characteristics also change. Thus, the decomposition of the sources should also change with frequency.

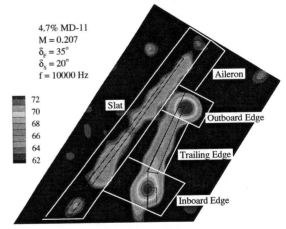

Figure 3. Example of sub-region definitions for the source strength integration to derive the noise spectra.

3. Integrated Spectra

The technique of integrating the sub-region sources is standard, involving summing all the beam-forming steering points within a sub-region and dividing the result by the calibration integral. The latter basically established the relation between the source integration and the far field spectrum. In summing the source strengths, a local maximum is identified within each sub-region at each frequency so that contributions more than 6 dB below the local maximum are ignored in the summation. This is to ensure the exclusion of side-lobes in the integration. This works well with sub-regions that contain dominant sources with well-defined local maximum. For sub-regions with no apparent dominant source, such as the residue component and the high-speed aileron component at some frequencies, the 6 dB cutoff may include some side-lobe contributions in the integration, which causes spectral build-up in the far field spectra, especially at high frequencies. This in turn may affect the total noise when the components are added. When this happens, the spectral build-up must be corrected by imposing a fall-off with frequency. The precise form of the fall-off is not critical because the components that need correction are usually not the dominant components; their contributions to the total noise are usually not significant. Some examples of the

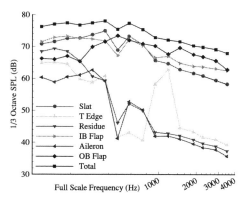

Figure 4. Example of airframe noise spectra for different components, integrated from phased array measurements.

integrated component spectra are shown in figure 4. The model and flow conditions for this figure are the same as those in figure 1. In this case, the spectral correction is needed only for the residue component.

To ensure that the spectra integrated from phase array beam-forming data accurately represent the far field noise spectra, the integrated results should be calibrated with free field microphone measurements. Some examples of comparisons between the two are given in figure 5 for the 4.7% MD-11 model, for which free field microphone data are available, obtained from

an earlier test in the NASA Ames 40-by-80 wind tunnel (Hayes *et al* 1997; Guo *et al* 1998). The comparisons are clearly favorable with quite satisfactory results for both the spectral shapes and the absolute amplitudes. Comparisons are also made for other models in our database and similar accuracy is seen in those comparisons.

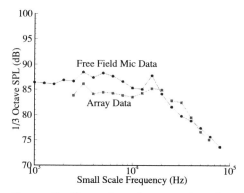

Figure 5. Comparison between free field microphone data and array integrated spectra.

Comparisons between different models can also be made, as shown in figure 6 for the models 737, 757 and 767. The plots are for the inboard flap edge source. The data for the first two models (737 and 757) are taken by the elliptic mirror while those for the 767 model are from the integrated phased microphone array. Evidently, both the spectral shapes and the absolute levels of the spectra show quite reasonable comparison, validating the method for deriving the spectra from beam-forming source maps.

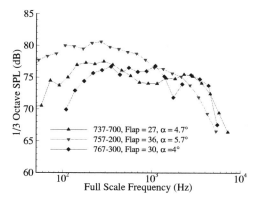

Figure 6. Comparison of the integrated spectra of the inboard flap side edge sources for different airplane models.

4. Extrapolation to Full-Scale

According to conventional procedures (e.g. Yee *et al* 1996; Allen *et al* 1997; Hayes *et al* 1997), the critical parameter in the extrapolation process is the ratio of the model dimension to that of the full-scale aircraft. This ratio is important because both frequencies and amplitudes are scaled by it. The extrapolation procedure is quite straightforward and has been previously described. Thus, it will be described here only very briefly. The process basically involves first extrapolating the measured wind tunnel data from the microphone locations to unit distance from the assumed source location. This essentially scales out the effects of spherical spreading, as well as atmospheric absorption under the test day conditions. The second step is then to scale the results at unit distance from the source from small scale to full scale, which involves scaling the frequencies down and amplitudes up, both by the model dimension ratio. The scaled data are then extrapolated to the far field, typically the certification distance of 394 feet away from the aircraft center. By doing so, the losses due to spherical spreading and atmospheric absorption at standard acoustic day conditions are accounted for.

Following this procedure, the small-scale data can be extrapolated to full-scale at certification conditions. The extrapolated results, however, do not agree well with full-scale measurements. Some examples are shown in figure 7 for the MD-11 model. The comparison between the extrapolated results and the flight data is between the green triangles and the red squares. The comparisons in this figure are reasonably good for frequencies below about 500 Hz, but shows significant discrepancies for higher frequencies. The extrapolated data significantly underestimate the fly-over data in the middle and high frequency region by as much as 10 dB. It is apparent that our limited database does not allow us to satisfactorily understand the reasons for these large discrepancies. We postulate that the small-scale of the model aircraft may cause quite

different flow behavior from that of the full-scale aircraft, as is commonly described as Reynolds number effects (Guo *et al* 1998; 2000) and corrections are needed to rectify these effects.

An attempt to derive a correction for the Reynolds number effects has been made recently (Guo *et al* 1998; 2000). In this case, we argue that the dominant length scale in the flow should be dependent on the Reynolds number, instead of the physical dimension of the model aircraft. There are many cases in which the flow is governed by a length scale dependent of the flow conditions, turbulent boundary layer flow being a typical example where the thickness of the boundary layer is determined by the local Reynolds number (Blake 1986). If this idea holds for the flow surrounding the high lift system of the aircraft, it implies that the procedure for the extrapolation from small to full scale should be modified. In particular, the length scale extrapolation should depend on the flow conditions, as well as the physical dimensions of the models. One consequence of this is a quite different frequency scaling law from that in the conventional approach described earlier in this section. The difference between the two is quite significant for models smaller than about 10% of the full-scale aircraft. For example, for the 4.7% DC10 model, the scale-down of the small-scale frequencies should be done by the factor 0.087, when the Reynolds number effects are taken account of, instead of 0.047 as in the conventional extrapolation procedures. With this correction alone, the comparison between the extrapolated data and flight data can be greatly improved. This is also demonstrated in figure 7 by the blue circles. Clearly, the comparison between small-scale data and full-scale data becomes much more satisfactory when the Reynolds number corrections are applied.

5. Correlation Analysis

The correlation analysis is done on a database consisting of a total of 233 noise data sets. The database includes many airplane models with variations in both configurations and flow conditions. Table 1 summarizes the database. For most phased array measurements, the array is located in the overhead location (90 degrees). Apart from the array and elliptical mirror data, we also have free field microphone data and flight data, which are used for calibration and validation.

With the component noise spectra derived, the next step is to correlate them to the controlling geometric and aerodynamic quantities. Geometric parameters include the dimensions of the components, such as chord length, span and thickness. There are common flow quantities for all the components, such as

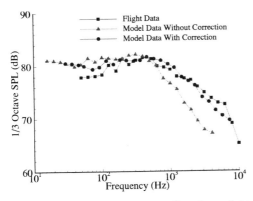

Figure 7. Extrapolation from small-scale model test data to full-scale configurations, showing the importance of Reynolds number dependent corrections.

Table 1. Model configurations and flow conditions in the acoustic database.

Airplane Model	Mach Number	AOA (Deg.)	Flap Angle (Deg.)
737-300	0.18, 0.2, 0.22, 0.24	0, 4.7, 6.7, 8.7	25, 27, 30
737-700	0.2, 0.24	0, 4, 6, 8	25, 30, 40
757	0.18, 0.2, 0.22, 0.24	0, 5.7, 7.7, 9.7	20, 25, 36
767	0.2, 0.24	0, 2, 4, 6, 8, 10, 12, 14	30
777	0.2, 0.24	0, 7.34, 9.34	30
DC-10	0.21, 0.26, 0.28	4.7	25, 35, 50
MD-11	0.26, 0.28	4.7	35, 50

the free stream flow Mach number and the model angle of attack. Each component also has unique flow quantities, which are identified by analyzing each noise source separately. For flap side edge sources, the side edge vortex strength and the cross flow velocity are two examples that are unique to these sources.

The correlation analysis is to derive relations between the far field noise spectra and the flow and geometry parameters. To this end, we assume that

$$S = S_0 F(St) D(\theta)$$
$$\times M^{b_1} C_L^{b_2} (\ell/r)^{b_3} (\sin \alpha)^{b_4} (\sin \delta)^{b_5} \cdots . \quad (5.1)$$

Here S is the noise spectrum for a particular component and S_0 is a constant. The frequency dependency of the noise is given by the normalized the spectrum $F(St)$ in terms of the Strouhal number

$$St = f\ell/U_0 \quad (5.2)$$

with f denoting the frequency, ℓ a length of the component (its thickness, say) and U_0 the free stream velocity. The directivity of the noise is given by the directivity factor $D(\theta)$, θ being the directivity angle in the fly over plane. In (5.1), the other symbols are the flow mach number $M = U_0/c$, c being the constant sound speed, angle of attack α, sectional lift coefficient of the component C_L, deployment angle of the component δ and the far field microphone distance r. These are the parameters common to all the components. For each particular component, parameters unique to that component are to be added to the general expression (5.1). In particular, the strengths of the side edge vortex and the velocity of the span-wise cross flow are added for the flap side edge noise sources, and for the slat noise sources, the vortex strengths in the cove region,

and the velocity of the flow in the gap between the slat trailing edge and the main wing are added. As indicated in the general expression (5.1), the dependencies of the noise spectra on these parameters are assumed to be of the simple form of a power law. The indices of the power laws (b_1, b_2, b_3, $\cdots$) are to be determined by the regression analysis of the database.

The aerodynamic quantities to be correlated to the far field noise include the static loading on the high lift system components (slats, flaps and ailerons). To find this, panel codes are used for all the models, which are known to give reasonably accurate lift calculations. The details of these calculations are documented in Sen *et al* (2000) and will not be repeated here. In applying the results developed here, other aero calculation method such as CFD can also be used to derive the flow parameters.

There are other quantities that are related, but not directly given by the panel code calculations. For these parameters, simple derivations are done to compute their values. One such parameter is the side edge vortex strength at flap side edges. From the definition of the side edge vortex, it is given by the jump in the wake vorticity distribution across the side edge location, namely

$$\Gamma = \gamma_2 - \gamma_1 = \Delta\gamma(\eta), \quad (5.3)$$

where Γ denotes the strength of the side edge vortex, $\gamma(\eta)$ is the wake vorticity distribution along the non-dimensional span-wise coordinate η and the subscripts 1 and 2 respectively denote the two locations right before and after the side edge (see figure 8). From aerodynamics, it is known that the wake vorticity is related to the lift by

$$L(\eta) = \rho_0 U_0 \gamma(\eta), \quad (5.4)$$

where L is the sectional lift (lift per unit span) and ρ_0 is the constant mean density. From this, the side edge vortex strength (5.3) can be related to the lift by

$$\Gamma = \Delta L(\eta)/\rho_0 U_0. \quad (5.5)$$

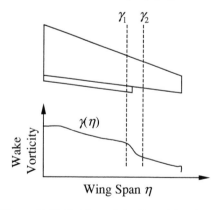

Figure 8. Definition of the flap side edge vortex.

By further making use of the definition of the sectional lift coefficient, this can be rewritten as

$$\Gamma = 2bU_0 \Delta C_L, \qquad (5.6)$$

which relates the side edge vortex strength to the semi-span b of the flap, the free stream velocity U_0 and the jump in the sectional lift coefficient across the flap side edge. The last quantity can be derived directly from the panel code calculation or any other CFD calculations.

Another flow parameter that is correlated to the noise for the flap side edge component is the velocity of the span-wise cross-flow, which needs to be estimated from the results of aero calculations. This velocity can be related to the velocity of the steady potential mean flow on the flap surface away from the side edge. From the theory of potential flows, it is known that the velocity near the flap side edge decreases away from the edge. We argue that this potential flow behavior only occurs in the immediate vicinity of the side edge, probably on the order of the local flap thickness, where the static loading difference between the upper and the lower surface is not significant. Away from the side edge region, the cross flow is driven by the loading on the flap. Thus, we assume that the cross flow velocity is maintained at V by the loading difference on the flap. In this region, the total velocity is the sum of the cross flow and the chord-wise mean flow originating from upstream. The application of the Bernoulli equation then leads to

$$p_s + \frac{\rho_0}{2}(U^2 + V^2) = p_0 + \frac{\rho_0}{2}U_0^2, \quad (5.7)$$

where U and V are the velocity on the flap surface respectively in the chord-wise and the span-wise direction, p_s and p_0 are the pressure respectively on the flap surface and at infinity and U_o is the constant free stream velocity at infinity. By making use of the definition for the pressure coefficient

$$C_p = (p_s - p_0)/(0.5\rho_0 U_0^2), \qquad (5.8)$$

the equation (5.7) can be rewritten as

$$\frac{V^2}{U_0^2} = 1 - C_p - \frac{U^2}{U_0^2}, \qquad (5.9)$$

where C_p is a function of the chord-wise coordinate. When the flap is deployed, the stream-wise flow is bent to follow the flap. Thus, we write

$$U = U_0 \cos(\alpha + \delta_F)(1 - C_p), \quad (5.10)$$

where α is the angle of attack of the main wing and δ_F is the flap deployment angle. With this substituted into (5.9), we find that

$$V = \{\sin^2(\alpha + \delta_F) + C_p \cos^2(\alpha + \delta_F)\}^{1/2}$$
$$\times (1 - C_p)^{1/2} U_0. \qquad (5.11)$$

Through this, the cross flow velocity V is related to the aerodynamic properties of the flap, as well as the geometry parameters. Note that in the limiting case of flat plate airfoils where the wing is at zero angle of attack with the flap retracted, we have $\alpha=0$ and $\delta_F =0$, which would lead to zero pressure coefficient $C_p=0$. In that case, the cross flow velocity would be identically zero, as expected. Also at any stagnation point on the flap where C_p is close to unity, both the chord-wise and the cross flow velocity become close to zero, again as expected from the definition of stagnation points. All these can be regarded as a partial validation of the estimate. Another validation can be made by noting that the velocity V is also used in the empirical correlation published by Yee *et al* (1996). In that case, a value of V for the Boeing 737 aircraft with flaps deployed at 40 degrees is given as $0.4974U_0$. By using the results above with α and δ_F respectively taken to be 5 and 40 degrees, and with a typical value of C_p taken as 0.5, we estimate that $V=0.6088U_0$ very close to that used by Yee *et al* (1996).

6. Results of Correlation Analysis

The functional dependency of the noise on the geometric and aerodynamic quantities is assumed to follow the form (5.1). The indices of the power laws (b_1, b_2, b_3, $\cdots$) are found by correlating the overall sound pressure levels (OASPL) at the overhead position (90 degrees) with these parameters by standard linear regression analysis. This leads to a set of indices for each of the components, as summarized in table 2.

Table 2. Summary of indices in equation (5.1).

	Aileron	IB Flap	OB Flap	Slat
S_0	37.3	0.65	0.86	219.8
b_1	5.8	5.3	5.3	5.6
b_2	3.36	0.05	0.05	4.45
b_3	3.46	1.78	4.12	1.15
b_4	3.46	0.0	0.0	1.03
b_5	3.36	2.02	2.02	0.0

These are the correlation parameters common to all the components. There are also parameters unique to each individual component. For example, the flap side edge noise is also related to the strength of the side edge vortex and to the velocity of the span-wise flow. For the two side edges, the results for these two parameters are given in table 3.

1749

The results given in tables 2 and 3 determine the functional dependencies of the overall sound pressure levels on the geometric and aerodynamic parameters. The frequency dependence is then found by subtracting the OASPL from the data sets and then fitting the data

Table 3. Indices for flap side edge noise.

	IB Flap	OB Flap
Γ	0.12	0.21
V	0.11	0.11

in terms of a sixth order polynomial equation. This leads to normalized spectra as a function of the Strouhal number. A general form used in the curve fitting is

$$10\log\{F(St)\} = \sum_{n=0}^{6} a_n \{\log(St)\}^n, \quad (6.1)$$

where $F(St)$ is the spectral function defined in (5.1) and the Strouhal number St is given by (5.2). To illustrate, figure 9 shows two examples of the normalized data sets for the outboard flap side edge noise and the slat noise. For both cases, the data include all the configurations and the smooth curve is the results of (6.1). It is clear from the figure that the data collapse quite well around about unity Strouhal number, but discrepancies are noticeable at both high and low Strouhal numbers. This may be an indication that more than one curve should be used to collapse the data, meaning that there may be more than one major sources for each components. For example, the slat noise may come from both the cove vortex fluctuations and the gap flow fluctuations, each contribute differently in different frequency domains. In this case, each source would correlate to different geometric and flow parameters. This decomposition in frequency is not done here, but will be pursued later.

The coefficients in the equation (6.1) are derived by linear regression analysis and are given in table 4.

Table 4. Coefficients of the normalized spectra.

	Aileron	IB Flap	OB Flap	Slat
a_0	-14.05	-13.18	-14.51	-12.73
a_1	9.02	10.03	9.20	4.05
a_2	-6.04	-9.41	-4.79	-4.30
a_3	-4.33	-6.62	-3.89	-1.85
a_4	2.11	4.10	1.32	0.19
a_5	0.57	1.42	0.41	0.22
a_6	-0.71	-1.07	-0.59	-0.40

The directivity factor $D(\theta)$ in (5.1), which is applied to the data at the overhead locations, was developed based on the analysis of free microphone data of the DC-10 scale model test. The data are shown in figure 10 in terms of overall sound pressure levels. It is clear from this figure that the OASPL directivity of the DC-10 total airframe noise (excluding landing gear noise) is relatively flat. Figure 11 further shows that the spectral shapes also have weak directivity dependency, though there are noticeable variations in the high frequency region.

To address these variations in the high frequency

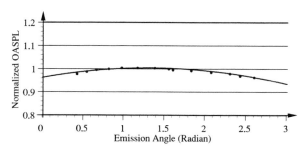

Figure 10. Directivity of normalized overall sound pressure levels of DC-10 airframe noise.

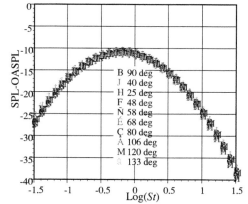

Figure 11. Directivity of normalized sound pressure levels of DC-10 airframe noise.

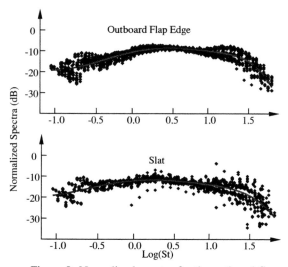

Figure 9. Normalized spectra for the outboard flap side edge and the slat sources.

region, we choose to allow slight spectral variations at each directivity angle. Thus, the curve fitting for the directivity function assumes the form

$$10\log\{D(\theta, St)\}$$
$$= d_0 + d_1 \log(St) + d_2 \{\log(St)\}^2. \quad (6.2)$$

By making use of the DC-10 flight data, the coefficients in this equation can be determined, which are listed in table 5.

Table 5. Coefficients for directivity

θ	d_0	d_1	d_2
25	-2.13	-0.56	-0.39
32	-1.16	-0.48	-0.45
39	-0.4	-0.26	-0.48
48	0.08	-0.07	-0.60
57	0.47	-0.04	-0.51
68	0.4	0.05	-0.44
80	0.34	-0.06	-0.38
90	0.0	0.0	0.0
106	-0.85	-0.07	0.16
120	-1.39	-0.14	0.16
133	-2.01	-0.72	-0.04

7. Validation of Prediction Method

To validate the predictions from the tools developed here, comparisons of the present model with flight test data are made, which are done by calculating

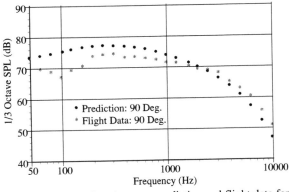

Figure 12. Comparison between prediction and flight data for Boeing 737 airframe noise at overhead position (394 ft.) with M=0.238, δ_F=40° and landing gear up.

the components and then adding all the components together to find the total noise. Two examples are shown in figures 12 and 13, both for approach configurations at aircraft noise certification conditions.

Figure 12 shows flight test data versus predictions comparison for Boeing 737 and figure 13 for DC-10. For both cases, reasonably good agreement is noted. The present model seems to capture general features of airframe noise.

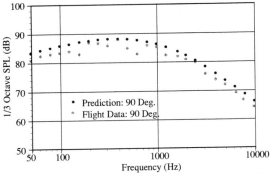

Figure 13. Comparison between prediction and flight data for DC-10 airframe noise at overhead position (394 ft.) with M=0.26, δ_F=50° and landing gear up.

8. Conclusions

In this paper, we have presented the development of a component-based empirical tool for airframe noise prediction. In comparison with previously developed empirical methods, there are many advances in the present approach. One is that the component-based approach relies on a new classification of the noise sources, which is made feasible by recent progresses in airframe noise research. For example, flap side edge noise is now commonly known as one of the dominant contributors to the total airframe noise. Thus, this component is emphasized in the prediction tool developed here, in contrast to previous models that emphasize more trailing edge noise.

Another advance in our method is that the prediction schemes for the components are derived from actual data, which is again in contrast to previous methods that divide the total noise into components but have to rely on modeling for each component. This is because recent development in phased microphone array measurements has made it feasible to find the noise sources for individual components, while for conventional measurements by free field microphones, source separation is very difficult and not practical.

The approach present here is also more physics-based. This is because the predictions are made not only from airplane gross dimensions and gross flow parameters, but also from local flow quantities that are directly responsible for noise generation. This incorporates the cause-and-effect relations of sound generation in the empirical method and represents a step forward in airframe noise prediction.

It should be pointed out that mainly due to time constraints, the advantages mentioned above are not completely achieved in the present study. For example, we postulated that slat noise is very likely related to the slat cove vortex and the gap flow between the slat trailing edge and the main wing, but we did not have time to derive the correlation between slat noise and these flow quantities. However, this is clearly not a fundamental drawback; it only indicates the on-going nature of the research.

9. Acknowledgement

A large part of the database used in this paper was collected under the NASA Advanced Subsonic Technology Program and the development of the empirical model was partially funded by NASA with R. A. Golub as technical monitor. The authors wish to thank R. A. Golub for his support.

R. Sen, B. Hardy, G. Miller and M. Donelson were involved in the work described here and made valuable contributions.

10. References

Allen C. S. & Soderman P. T. 1997 Scaling and extrapolating small-scale in-flow wind tunnel jet noise to full scale fly-over jet noise. *AIAA Paper 97-1602.*

Bauer A. B. & Munson A. G. 1978 Airframe noise of the DC-9-31. *NASA Contract Report* 3027.

Blake W. K. 1986 Mechanics of Flow-Induced Sound and Vibration. Academic Press.

Fink M. R. 1979 Airframe noise prediction method FAA-RD-77-29.

Fink M. R. 1979 Noise component method for airframe noise. *J. Aircraft* **16**(10), 659-665.

Guo Y. P., Bent P., Yamamoto K. & Joshi M. 1998 Surface pressure fluctuations on DC-10 high lift system and their correlation with far field noise. NASA Contract Report CRAD-9310-TR-4872.

Guo Y. P., Stoker B., Hardy B. A., Bent P. & Joshi M. 1998 DC-10/MD-11 acoustic test in NASA Ames 12-ft pressurized wind tunnel. NASA Contract Report CRAD-9310-TR-4894.

Guo Y. P., Hardy B. A., Bent P., Yamamoto K. & Joshi M. C. 1998 Noise characteristics of DC-10 aircraft high lift system. NASA Contract Report CRAD-9310-TR-4893.

Guo Y. P., Joshi M., Bent P. & Yamamoto K. 2000 Surface pressure fluctuations on aircraft flaps and their correlation with far field noise. *J. Fluid Mech.* **415**, 175-202.

Hayes J. A., Horne W. C., Soderman P. T. and Bent P. H. 1997 Airframe noise characteristics of a 4.7% scale DC-10 model. *AIAA Paper 97-1594.*

Sen R., Hardy B., Yamamoto K., Guo Y. P. & Miller G. 2000 Airframe noise sub-component definition and model. NASA Contract Report. NAS1-97040.

Yamamoto K. J., Donelson M. J., Huang S. C. & Joshi M. C. 1995 Airframe noise prediction evaluation. NASA Contract Report 4695.

Yee P., Underbrink J. R., Sen R., Kusunose K., Dougherty R. & Blackner A. M. 1996 Airframe noise generation and radiation. NASA Contract Report.

AIAA 2002-2575

INVESTIGATION OF THE PHYSICAL MECHANISMS OF TONAL SOUND GENERATION BY SLATS

Anurag Agarwal* and Philip J. Morris†

Department of Aerospace Engineering
The Pennsylvania State University
University Park, PA 16802, U.S.A.

The physical mechanisms for the occurrence of high-amplitude, high-frequency tonal noise generated by the flow through the gap between the slat and the main element during aircraft approach are explored using a detailed local stability analysis of the slat wake. Based on the physical characteristics of the wake, vortex shedding frequencies are predicted for different slat deployment angles. It is proposed that the observed tonal noise is due to a whistling mechanism. When the vortex shedding frequency at the slat trailing edge matches one of the transverse resonance frequencies of the gap between the slat and the main element, an intense, tonal sound field is produced. The predictions of tones and frequencies from the proposed whistling mechanism are in good agreement with experimental measurements.

1 Introduction

HIGH-LIFT devices are deployed to enable aircraft to achieve slower flying speeds that reduces the take-off and landing distances, and reduces the angle of attack near minimum speed, which prevents the wing from stalling. For a typical wing of a commercial aircraft these devices include slats ahead of the main-element and flaps behind the main-element. It is well known that a multi-element wing is better than a single-element wing in achieving the above mentioned goals. Smith[1] showed that a two-element wing is capable of generating more lift than a single-element wing for the same angle of attack. This result can be generalized to a multi-element wing.

Usually there exists a slot (gap) both between the slat and the main wing, and between the main wing and the flap. The slots aid in inducing five different yet inter-dependent phenomena that are responsible for the effectiveness of a multi-element wing in achieving a higher lift. These phenomena as explained by Smith[1] are:

The slat effect: The positive circulation on the slat induces a velocity which counteracts the high velocity near the leading edge of the main element, thus reducing the pressure peak on the suction surface of the main element. This alleviates the pressure recovery demands and hence postpones separation of the boundary layer. Although this reduces the lift on the main element, the total lift due to the two elements is still increased.

The circulation effect: The circulation on the main element induces a cross-flow near the trailing edge on the pressure side of the slat, thus increasing the slat's effective angle of attack. For the Kutta condition to be satisfied at the slat trailing edge, this cross flow has to be balanced by a increased circulation on the slat. Hence the lift due to the slat is enhanced due to the presence of the main element.

The dumping effect: The circulation of the main element also increases the tangential velocity near the slat trailing-edge. Hence, flow from the slat is discharged at a higher velocity, this reduces the pressure recovery demands on the boundary layer of the slat.

Off the surface pressure recovery: The boundary layer from a forward element is dumped at a velocity much higher than that of the free stream. The final deceleration takes place outside the boundary layer, in the wake of the slat. This is a more efficient mechanism.

Fresh boundary layer effect: Both the slat and the main element start with a fresh boundary layer and can thus withstand stronger pressure gradients.

Most of the same effects apply to the performance of flaps or multiple flaps.

The deployment of high-lift devices with slots is essential. However, such devices significantly in-

---

*Graduate Research Assistant, Student Member, AIAA
†Boeing/A. D. Welliver Professor, Fellow AIAA

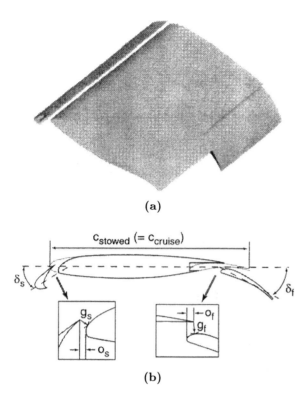

(a)

(b)

Fig. 1 Three-element high-lift system. a) Three-dimensional model, b) Cross-sectional view. (from Khorrami et al.[2])

crease the aircraft airframe noise. This is the noise generated by the non-propulsive components of the vehicle. The major components of airframe noise in an approach configuration are flap side-edge, slat, and landing gear noise. Experimental studies reveal that a high frequency tonal noise, emanating from the vicinity of the slat, may dominate the total radiated noise during approach. It may be conjectured that this tonal noise is generated due to the interaction of the fluid flow with the slat and the main element as it passes through the gap between them.

Experiments have been conducted by researchers from the NASA Langley Research Center and the Boeing Commercial Airplane Company on the three-element model shown in Fig. (1). The experiments were conducted in the NASA Langley Research Center's Low Turbulence Pressure Tunnel (LTPT). For a slat deflection of 30 deg., the measured acoustic spectrum showed a significant hump in the 40 – 50 KHz range. The frequency of the tone varied only slightly with changes in the gap height, overhang, or the flow Reynolds number (see Fig. (1(b))). However, when the slat deflection was lowered to 20 deg., the tone was not discernible.

Numerical experiments by Khorrami et al.,[2] simulated the flow around the three-element wing used in these experiments, with a fully turbulent, 2-D unsteady RANS simulation. They used a high spatial resolution to capture the finite but small thickness of the trailing edge of the slat. For a 30 deg. deflection of the slat, vortex shedding from the blunt slat trailing edge was observed, the frequency of which was in good agreement with the tone frequency that was observed in the LTPT experiment. This led Khorrami et al.[2] to conjecture that the vortex-shedding from the slat trailing edge might be responsible for the observed slat tone. When the simulations were repeated for a lower slat deflection of 20 deg., no vortex shedding was detected. Therefore, a connection between vortex shedding at the slat trailing edge and the observed slat tone provides a reasonable interpretation of the computations and experiments.

Singer et al.[3] used the unsteady results of Khorrami et al.[2] in the near-field to obtain the far-field acoustic spectrum through the application of the Ffowcs Williams and Hawkings equation. For a slat deflection of 30 deg., the radiated tone frequency in the far-field matched the vortex-shedding frequency obtained by Khorrami et al.[2] For a deflection of 20 deg., the tone was not present. This provides further support to Khorrami et al.'s[2] conjecture relating the slat trailing edge vortex shedding to the high frequency slat tone.

Storms et al.[4] conducted experiments on a three-element high-lift wing for both part- and full-span slats, in the 7 × 10 ft. wind tunnel at the NASA Ames Research Center. Acoustic spectra for both full- and part-span slats revealed a high frequency hump in the spectrum for a slat deflection angle of 26 deg. When the slat deflection was reduced to 6 degrees, the high frequency hump disappeared. This was similar to the observations of Khorrami et al.[2] Storms et al.[4] also reduced the slat gap to almost zero (almost a Kruger flap configuration), keeping the deflection angle fixed at 26 deg. This shifted the frequency peak to a slightly lower frequency, but it did not eliminate the hump altogether. However, when the small gap between the slat and the main element was taped/closed, to make sure that no fluid flowed through the gap, the hump was eliminated completely. This shows that the slat trailing edge and the gap between the slat and the main element are instrumental in the generation of the high frequency tone.

Even though these studies indicate that the high frequency tonal noise originates from a region near the slat trailing edge, and that vortex shedding at the slat trailing edge is at least partly responsible for the noise mechanism, the physics of the noise generation mechanism is still not fully understood. Tam and Pastouchenko[5] proposed that the frequency of vortex shedding at the slat trailing edge is set by a feedback loop. A vortex is first shed at the slat trailing edge, which acts as an acoustic source. The acoustic waves travel through the slat gap while being convected with the flow. They are reflected from the main element and strike the slat trailing edge. This results in another vortex being shed. The process repeats, thus setting the vortex shedding frequency. However, this acoustic resonance model cannot explain all the features of the experiments. Especially, the cases where no tone occurs. The model proposed by Tam and Pastouchenko[5] provides a viable mechanism for the selection of a particular frequency. The shear layer in their simulation starts with nearly zero thickness, as the Euler equations are solved upstream of the slat trailing edge. In addition, the slat trailing edge is assumed to have zero thickness. Thus, in the vicinity of the slat trailing edge, there are neither any incoming boundary layers, nor any thickness to the slat. It could be argued that such a thin shear layer from an infinitely thin splitter plate would be able to support any frequency associated with the Tam and Pastouchenko[5] acoustic resonance model. Thus, there is no obvious reason why resonance, and a tone at some frequency, would not occur in the 20 deg. slat deflection case.

In this paper, we propose a mechanism in the form of an aeroacoustic whistle that explains the observed high frequency tones. The normal or natural modes of the whistle are set by the transverse resonance frequencies of the gap. This is similar to the process proposed by Tam and Pastouchenko.[5] If the modes in this gap are excited by an external source at a frequency that matches one of the gap's normal modes, then high amplitude tonal noise would be produced. It is proposed that the time harmonic source excitation is provided by the vortex shedding process at the blunt slat trailing-edge. Thus, in our model, the bluntness of the slat trailing edge and the finite thickness of the slat boundary layers, as well as the gap between the slat and the main element together make an aeroacoustic whistle.

In order to predict the vortex shedding frequency and the effects of other parametric variations, the characteristics of the slat wake are analyzed with a local stability analysis. Local stability analysis is a very powerful tool capable of providing a link between the local characteristics and the global dynamics (cf. Koch;[6] Chomaz et al.[7]). Therefore, the vortex shedding frequency can be predicted only on the local characteristics of the wake. This enables us to predict the vortex shedding frequency based on the mean flow data of Khorrami et al.,[2] and compare it with the frequency observed in their numerical simulations. Local stability analysis also facilitates parametric studies like the effects of varying gap setting and compressibility effects. Also, the effect of changing wake depth or width is easily examined. It is shown that based on the local stability analysis and the proposed whistling mechanism, the predicted tone frequencies are in good agreement with the experimental measurements. It is also shown that for the slat deflection of 20 deg., the vortex shedding frequency does not match the transverse resonance frequency of the gap, thus providing a plausible explanation for the absence of the tone in the lower slat deflection case.

The rest of this paper is organized as follows. The basic equations for the local stability analysis are discussed in Sec. (2). The details of the numerical procedure for the local stability analysis: that is, the absolute instability and the dispersion relation solver, are discussed in Sec. (3). The slat-wake characteristics, based on the local stability analysis and the global frequency predictions are presented in Sec. (4). In Sec. (5), the aeroacoustic whistling mechanism is described, and comparisons are made between predicted and observed tones in the experiments. The effects of variations in the slat gap, and in the Mach and Reynolds numbers on the observed tonal frequency are described in Sec. (6)

2 Basic equations

The local stability characteristics of the slat wake are analyzed using classical linear stability analysis based on the assumption of a locally parallel mean flow. In this approach, disturbances superimposed on the basic (mean) state are described by the governing fluid flow equations (Navier-Stokes), and all nonlinear terms in the equations are neglected. Since the coefficients, which are functions of the mean state, are independent of time (t) and the streamwise coordinate (x), the disturbances are assumed to be cyclic in x and t. Therefore, any disturbance quantity may be represented as

$$\phi'(x,y,t) = \Re\left\{ \hat{\phi}(y) \exp\left[(kx - \omega t)\right] \right\} \quad (1)$$

where k and ω are the complex wavenumber and frequency respectively, and the hat (̂) represents the eigenfunction of the perturbation quantity. For an incompressible, viscous fluid flow, elimination of the disturbance quantities in favor of the disturbance streamfunction, leads to the Orr-Sommerfeld equation[8]

$$(U(y) - c) \left(\frac{\partial^2 \hat{\psi}}{\partial y^2} - k^2 \hat{\psi} \right) - \frac{\partial^2 U(y)}{\partial y^2} \hat{\psi} +$$

$$\frac{i}{kRe} \left(\frac{\partial^4 \hat{\psi}}{\partial y^4} - 2k^2 \frac{\partial^2 \hat{\psi}}{\partial y^2} + k^4 \hat{\psi} \right) = 0, \quad (2)$$

where $\hat{\psi}$ is the disturbance streamfunction, Re is the Reynolds number, and $U(y)$ is the parallel mean velocity. Equation (2) has been non-dimensionalised with a length scale given by the trailing edge thickness of the slat and a velocity scale given by the free-stream speed of sound. The boundary conditions are chosen to be

$$\hat{\psi} = \hat{\psi}' = 0 \quad \text{at } y = \text{ME and } \infty, \quad (3)$$

where ME is the location of the main element, which is treated as a solid wall. Equations (2) and (3) constitute an eigenvalue problem which relates the wavenumber to the frequency:

$$D(k, \omega) = 0. \quad (4)$$

Equation (4) is the dispersion relation and it is fundamental in the evaluation of the instabilities of the medium.

3   Local stability analysis – Numerical procedure

Two types of instabilities exist in a physical medium. If a disturbance introduced into the medium grows in time at every point in space, the instability is absolute. On the other hand, if the disturbance grows and propagates away from its point of introduction, so that at a fixed point in space the response eventually decays, the instability is convective. An absolute frequency (ω_o), which may be complex, has a zero group velocity based on the local linear dispersion relation ($d\omega_o/dk = 0$; Briggs,[9] Bers[10]). A region with absolute instability acts as an oscillator capable of supporting self-sustaining oscillations, whereas a region of convective instability acts as an amplifier of disturbances that are eventually convected downstream with the fluid flow.

Wakes with regions of reversed flow are known to have a region of absolute instability followed by a zone of convective instability (cf. Triantafyllou et al.,[11] Hannemann and Oertel,[12] Hammond and Redekopp[13]). Chomaz et al.[7] demonstrated that flows with a sufficient pocket of absolute instability can support global instabilities of the form displayed by vortex shedding. The connection between local and global instability will be elaborated later in the paper.

3.1   Absolute instability solver

If any part of the map of the real k-axis into the ω-plane, through the dispersion relation (4), lies in the upper-half ω-plane ($\omega_i(k_r) > 0$), then the medium is unstable to perturbations. It could either support absolutely or convectively unstable waves. The nature of the instability may be investigated by mapping lines parallel to the real k-axis, with progressively decreasing imaginary part into the frequency plane. This is sketched in Fig. (2). If in this process, a cusp is uncovered in the upper half ω-plane, the instability is absolute, and the absolute frequency and wavenumber are given by their respective values at the location of the cusp. The details of this procedure are discussed by Kupfer et al.[14] The advantage of this procedure is that it requires mapping from the wavenumber into the frequency domain. This is opposite to what is usually done in the approach that involves mapping from frequency into wavenumber space, and looking for saddle points in the frequency domain. Since, for wake-type velocity profiles, the dispersion relation is quadratic in ω, and transcendental in k, every k would have two images in ω, whereas a given ω might have several images in the k-space. This makes mapping from the frequency into the wavenumber plane extremely sensitive to initial conditions, especially close to the saddle point. This is because small changes in starting values can easily move the maps from one branch, onto another branch of the saddle. This makes it very difficult to converge on the saddle-point. On the other hand, mapping from the wavenumber into the frequency plane is fairly insensitive to initial conditions, and a robust algorithm is developed for the present analysis which uncovers the pinch points automatically without a tedious search through graphs to unravel saddle points.

3.2   Dispersion relation solver

A shooting method is used to solve the Orr-Sommerfeld equation for a given wavenumber k. For the high Reynolds number encountered in the present simulations, the Orr-Sommerfeld equation becomes very stiff. Using standard initial-value type shooting methods can result in a serious loss of accuracy. To overcome this problem the Orr-Sommerfeld equation is solved here using the method of compound matrices.[8,15] This method transforms the Orr-Sommerfeld equation into a system of six, first-order ordinary differential equations. These equations are solved with a fourth-order, fixed-step Runge-Kutta method. Even though, for a reasonably refined mesh, accuracy is not an issue with

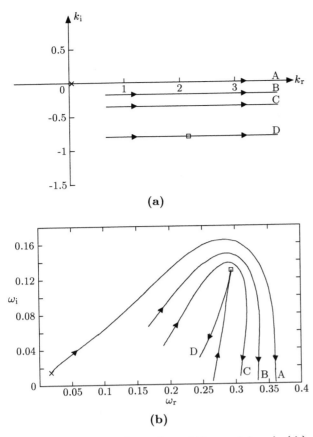

(a)

(b)

Fig. 2 **Successive lowering of the real k-axis (A) in an attempt to detect the cusp (marked □): (a) the horizontal line segments to be mapped into the ω-plane, and (b) the respective images in the ω-plane showing a cusp beneath A. (Mapping at the downstream location $dx = 44$, for the 30 deg. slat deflection case (see Fig. (5))**

this method, it is still an initial-value method, and for the present simulations, extremely good starting guesses are required for the frequency corresponding to a given wavenumber. Fortunately, for high Reynolds numbers, viscous effects are negligible, and the Rayleigh equation may be used to solve for the dispersion relation. The Rayleigh equation is given by the Orr-Sommerfeld equation (2) with $1/Re = 0$. However, the Rayleigh equation has a regular singular point at y_c given by $U(y_c) = c$. This critical point must be avoided by deforming the integration contour in the complex y-plane. Since the mean velocity profiles used for stability analysis are known only for real coordinates, an extension of their definition in the complex-plane is difficult. Therefore, the mean velocity profiles must be approximated by an appropriate functional representation to solve the Rayleigh equation. This might affect the accuracy of the solution. Fortunately, the first step in the determination of the absolute frequency involves a

mapping of the real k-axis into the ω-plane. For an unstable medium, which would be a self-excited case, y_c would lie off the real y-axis ($k \in \mathbb{R}$, $\Im[\omega] > 0$). Lin[16] showed, through a careful mathematical analysis, that for the self-excited case, integration along real y-axis yields the correct physical solution. Therefore, the Rayleigh equation may be easily solved when the real k-axis is being mapped into the ω-plane. The solution to the Rayleigh equation gives a good starting guess for the Orr-Sommerfeld solver and by analytical continuation, successively lower (imaginary) values of k can be mapped into the ω-plane until we get close to the cusp, after which an iterative scheme like the Newton-Raphson or Secant Method is used to converge to the exact cusp location.

4   Wake characteristics – Local and global dynamics

The mean flow data in the present analysis has been provided by Khorrami et al.[2] They performed unsteady two-dimensional Reynolds-averaged Navier-Stokes (RANS) calculations that were designed to match the experiments conducted in the NASA Langley LTPT, on the high lift wing sketched in Fig. (1). The simulations were performed for two slat deflection angles with respect to the main element: one at 30 deg. and the other at 20 deg.

The experimental model had a chord length, in stowed position, of 55 cm., whereas in the numerical simulations of Khorrami et al.,[2] the stowed chord length was normalized to 1 unit. Therefore, all space dimensions in the numerical simulations were scaled by a factor of 1:0.55. The thickness of the trailing edge of the slat used for the numerical simulations, for both the 30 and 20 deg. case, was $h = 7 \times 10^{-4}$ units (0.39 mm. for the experimental model).

In order to determine the local and global stability characteristics of the slat wake, mean flow profiles have been obtained along lines in the vicinity of the slat trailing edge that are perpendicular to the mean slat chord line at the slat trailing edge. It is expected that there would be a high probability of the existence of absolute instability in a wake with a large depth to width ratio. The length of the region downstream of the slat trailing edge, where the wake would have this property is expected to be of the order of the thickness of the slat trailing edge. Therefore, the lines along which the mean velocity profiles are extracted, are chosen to lie in this narrow region.

It is found that the velocities perpendicular to the

lines of data extraction (parallel to the slat trailing edge), are at least 90% greater than the velocities parallel to the extraction lines. Therefore, the mean flow is nearly parallel and the local dispersion characteristics of the medium may be obtained using a locally parallel mean flow approximation.

The mean velocity profiles at different downstream locations from the slat trailing edge, as a function of the cross-stream variable, y, are shown in Fig. (3) for the 30 deg. case and in Fig. (4) for the 20 deg case. The y-axis is normalized with the slat trailing edge thickness, h, and its origin is chosen to be at the mid-point of the slat trailing edge. The downstream distances are measured from the slat trailing edge, with a separation $dx = 6.19 \times 10^{-3}h$. Therefore, $h = 162dx$. It can be seen that compared to the 30 deg. case, the wake in the 20 deg. case changes more slowly with downstream distance and is also shallower and thicker.

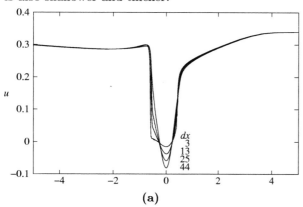

(a)

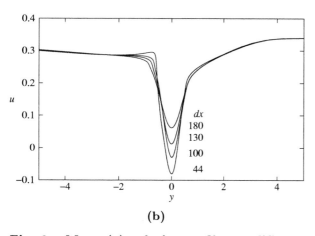

(b)

Fig. 3   Mean (u) velocity profiles at different downstream locations for the 30 deg. slat deflection case.   a) progressively more deep, b) progressively more shallow, wake.

Absolute frequencies at each downstream location in the wake are computed using the absolute instability solver described in subsection 3.1. The

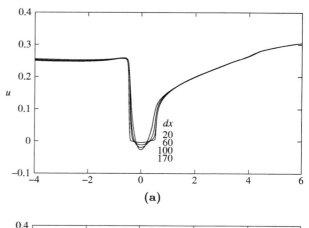

(a)

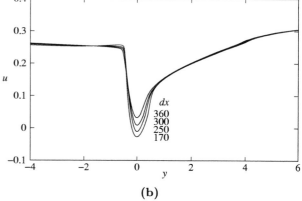

(b)

Fig. 4   Mean (u) velocity profiles at different downstream locations for the 20 deg. slat deflection case.   a) progressively more deep, b) progressively more shallow, wake.

computed results for the 30 and 20 deg. case are shown in Figs. (5) and (6) respectively. The wake is absolutely unstable in the range $x \leq 129dx$ for the 30 deg. case, and $x \leq 296dx$ for the 20 deg. case. The frequencies are normalized with the free stream speed of sound and the slat trailing edge thickness, h. It is observed that the strongest determinant of the absolute frequency is the wake depth. Increasing the depth decreases $\Re[\omega_o]$ and increases $\Im[\omega_o]$, and vice versa. There is a weaker dependence on wake width with decreases in width increasing both $\Re[\omega_o]$ and $\Im[\omega_o]$.

The presence of a global frequency, which represents the onset of global oscillations, was first predicted and related to local stability characteristics by Koch.[6]   Koch proposed that the global frequency is given by the absolute frequency at the last downstream location where the flow transitions from absolute to convective instability. Let x^{ac} be this streamwise location. Then, the global frequency is given by

$$f^{ac} = \Re[\omega_o(x^{ac})]/2\pi \qquad (5)$$

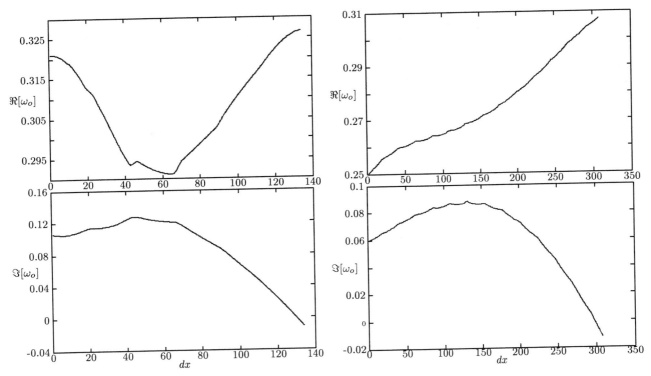

Fig. 5 The real and imaginary part of the absolute frequency for the slat wake at 30 deg. slat deflection.

Fig. 6 The real and imaginary part of the absolute frequency for the slat wake at 20 deg. slat deflection.

Based on the assumption of slow spatial variations (WKBJ approach), Chomaz et al.[7] and later Le Dizès et al.[17] showed that a finite pocket of local absolute instability in the wake region was a necessary condition for the onset of global instability. Under these circumstances, they predicted that the linear global mode is determined at the saddle point:

$$\frac{\mathrm{d}\omega_o}{\mathrm{d}x}(x_s) = 0. \tag{6}$$

The global frequency is given by the real part of the saddle-point frequency, $f^s = 2\pi^{-1}\Re[\omega_o(x_s)]$.

Pier and Huerre[18] showed that the existence of a finite region of local absolute instability was a sufficient condition for the existence of nonlinear global modes. The argued that the frequency of the nonlinear global wavemaker is set by the absolute frequency of the first streamwise location with a non-negative absolute growth rate. In present simulations, this corresponds to the first downstream location in the wake behind the slat trailing edge. That is,

$$f^I = \Re[\omega_o(x = dx)]/2\pi \tag{7}$$

The vortex shedding frequency predictions based on criteria (5), (6), and (7), together with the observed vortex shedding frequency for both the 30 and

20 deg. case are listed in Table 1 (f^{vs} is the computationally observed vortex shedding frequency). The frequencies have been scaled to their actual dimensional value.

δ_s	f^{ac}	f^s	f^I	f^{vs}
30°	46.7	42.1	46.1	45
20°	43.7	-	35.9	-

Table 1 Comparison of different global frequency criteria. (All frequencies are in KHz.)

At present, no definitive criterion exists that relates the local instability characteristics to the global dynamics. Criterion (6) is derived more formally than (5), but is based on a linear model. For flow past a flat plate with a blunt trailing edge at a Reynolds number number slightly higher than the critical value, Hammond and Redekopp[13] predicted a global frequency (non-dimensionalised with the average velocity of the streams on the two sides of the plate and the base height) of 0.1006, based on the saddle point criterion (6), whereas the numerically determined frequency was 0.1000. However, this closeness in the predicted and observed values might have been fortuitous, since this criterion does not capture some of the nonlinear effects.

Criterion (7) is based on a fully nonlinear model but is derived for a synthetic wake, one in which the

1759

presence of the solid body is neglected. Moreover, all these analyses assume a slowly varying mean flow. Nevertheless, it is clear that the global frequency must lie in the range of absolutely unstable frequencies, since convectively unstable regions cannot support self-sustained oscillations. For the 30 deg. case the predicted frequencies from all the models are in good agreement with that obtained by Khorrami et al.[2] in their numerical simulations. Indeed, every streamwise location that is absolutely unstable predicts the vortex shedding frequency fairly well.

At a slat deflection of 20 deg., Khorrami et al.[2] did not observe any vortex shedding in their RANS simulations. However, it can be seen in Fig. (6) that there is a finite pocket of absolute instability in the slat wake. In fact, the region of absolute instability is nearly twice that for the 30 deg. case. Therefore, in all probability, the slat wake for the 20 deg. deflection case should show some global oscillations. Khorrami et al.[2] report that initially in their simulations they observed some periodic flow, but the unsteady levels were weaker than the 30 deg. case and were damped by the solver. This behavior may be explained in part by the growth rate values for the 20 deg. case, which are lower than those for the 30 deg. case (Figs. (5) and (6)). However, in the NASA Langley experiments, the high frequency tone was present only in the 30 deg. case. This anomaly may be explained by an aeroacoustic whistling mechanism. The vortex shedding at the slat trailing edge acts as an acoustic source, and when the frequency of this source comes close to one of the duct (gap between the slat and the main element) modes, resonance will occur and, as a result, a high amplitude, tonal sound field is produced.

5 Aeroacoustic whistle

The natural modes of the gap can be computed from a geometrical acoustics approach. Figure (7) shows a simplified model of the gap between the slat and the main element. It is assumed that the mean flow through the gap is of a constant magnitude (u). For a source embedded in a uniform mean flow, the acoustic rays are straight lines passing through the source (for example, ray PQ in Fig. (7); cf. Whitham[19]). Note this is true only for a uniform mean flow. The wavefront at time t is a sphere of radius at centered at a downstream distance ut, a being the speed of sound. Upon hitting the main element, the ray (wave-front) will be reflected. The reflections from the main element may be evaluated simply by replacing the main element with a mirror image (P') of the source (P) about the main

element. Now both the sources, P and P', will contribute to any point within the gap. It is clear that only the ray that is traveling towards the point directly beneath the slat trailing edge (PQ), will be reflected back to the source location. From the velocity vector diagram in Fig. (7), the velocity of the wave-front in the direction of the ray is given by $c = \sqrt{a^2 - u^2}$. The reflected wave from the main element (ray $P'Q$) will again be reflected from the slat and the cycle will repeat (image of P' about the slat, and its image about the main element, and so on to infinity, thus giving infinite sources). If all these round-trips of the wavefronts are in phase, then resonance would occur. Therefore, the transverse resonance frequencies of the gap are given by

$$f^r = n\sqrt{a^2 - u^2}/2d, \quad n = 1, 2, 3, \ldots . \quad (8)$$

This is the same condition derived by Tam and Pastouchenko[5] using a slightly different argument. The duct will whistle when the vortex shedding (forcing) frequency comes close to one of the transverse resonance frequencies of the gap. Hence, high amplitude tones are expected when

$$f^{vs} = f^r, \quad (9)$$

where f^{vs} is the vortex shedding frequency.

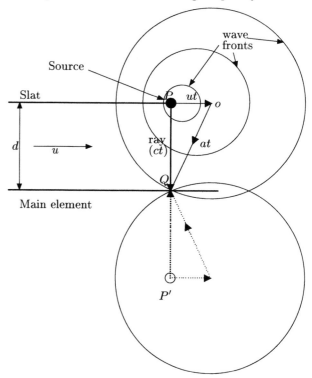

Fig. 7 Feedback process leading to resonance near the slat trailing edge.

This whistling mechanism is an extension of the feedback mechanism proposed by Tam and Pastouchenko.[5] In their formulation, Eq. (8) was viewed only as providing a feedback loop which causes vortex shedding at the slat trailing edge. Thus the number n in Eq. (8) had to be selected empirically. But, with the whistling criterion of Eq. (9) the integer n is governed by the vortex shedding frequency at the slat trailing edge, and Eq. (8) only provides the natural or normal modes of the gap.

In the NASA Langley experiment, the observed tone for a slat deflection of 30 deg., was centered around 45 KHz. From formula (8), for $u = 0.3a$, $a = 347 m/s$, $d = 1.35$ cm., the value closest to the tonal frequency is 48.7 KHz for $n = 4$. These values are a little different from those used by Tam and Pastouchenko.[5] Our values are taken from the numerical data provided by Khorrami et al.[2] (see Fig. (3)). However, minor changes in u or a have no significant effect on f^r. For this resonance frequency, the predicted vortex shedding frequencies from Fig. (5) and Table 1, nearly satisfy the whisting condition of Eq. (9). Tam and Pastouchenko[5] argue that f^r should be slightly lower than that predicted by Eq. (8), due to a time delay introduced by the boundary layer in the triggering of the shear layer instability: but, in the present model, the frequency is set by the slat near-wake, so it is not clear that a similar time delay is needed in our model. Clearly, the whistling mechanism proposed here explains the observed high frequency tone in the experiment, for the 30 deg. slat deflection case.

For the 20 deg. case, the mean velocity through the gap is slightly smaller ($u = 0.25$; see Fig. (4)). In the experiments, the gap height was nearly the same. From formula (8), $f^r = 49.76$ KHz (with $n = 4$), which is slightly higher than for the 30 deg. case. However, if there is vortex shedding at a slat deflection of 20 deg., it is expected to be at a frequency lower than the 30 deg. case. This is evident from Figs. (5) and (6), and Table 1. Also, at a 20 deg. deflection angle, the slat is aerodynamically more loaded. Therefore, the boundary layer and hence the wake thickness is expected to be greater for the 20 deg. case. This suggests that the vortex shedding frequency reduces with the reduction in the slat deflection angle. Hence, the whistling criterion of Eq. (9) would not be satisfied for the 20 deg. case. As a note of caution, it should be stressed that Fig. (6) should be used only qualitatively. The mean flow profiles used for the 20 deg. deflection case are based on a steady rather than an oscillatory flow, and the local stability analysis may not be able to provide accurate results. The low frequency region immediately behind the slat (Fig. (4(a))) is prone to most error. If there were global oscillations, the mean flow in this region would be a little deeper and thinner, instead of being almost of the thickness of the trailing edge with nearly zero velocity (Fig. (4(a))). Thus, for a stability analysis based on the mean state of an oscillatory flow, higher absolute frequencies may be expected. This also explains the absence of a saddle point (f^s) in Fig. (6) that is observed in almost all wakes that exhibit global oscillations. Hence, the values in Fig. (6) may be viewed as a lower bound for the absolute frequencies.

If Eq. (8) is thought of as a feedback process, which alone is responsible for setting the vortex shedding frequency which in turn manifests itself as the observed high-amplitude tone as proposed by Tam and Pastouchenko,[5] then a high-amplitude tone should also be observed for the 20 deg. case. This evidently is not the case, lending further support for Eq. (9) to be the criterion for the observed strong tone frequency.

6 Parametric variations

So far we have only studied the effect of slat deflection angle on the observed frequency spectrum. To further test our hypothesis, we shall discuss the following parametric variations:

6.1 Slat gap

A parametric study with varying slat gap setting has been performed. Almost no change is observed in the absolute frequencies in the wake. This would suggest that the vortex shedding frequency is almost independent of the slat gap setting, depending purely on the characteristics of the wake. Also, since our analysis has been based on the assumption of an incompressible flow, it is possible that the insensitivity to the presence of the main element (slat gap setting) may have been caused due to the neglect of compressibility effects. To this end, the local stability analyses have been repeated using the compressible Rayleigh equation. The absolute frequencies remained nearly unchanged compared with the incompressible case. This confirms the insensitivity of the vortex shedding frequency to changes in the gap height. The underlying assumption in the analysis is that the mean flow through the gap remains unchanged with varying gap settings. This assumption would be valid only if the variations in gap settings were relatively small. This result is in agreement with the observations made during the NASA Langley LTPT experiment. In the experiment, the gap and overhang settings were changed over a limited range and no appreciable shift in the high-frequency peak occurred.

6.2 Mach number

In the LTPT experiment, the free stream Mach number was increased from 0.2 to 0.3 while the slat deflection angle was kept at 30 deg. This resulted in an increase in the frequency of the observed tone. As noted by Tam and Pastouchenko,[5] a higher Mach number would reduce the thickness of the boundary layer, and reduce the time delay experienced by the acoustic waves within the boundary layer. This would increase the transverse frequency of the gap (f^r). In our opinion, a more important effect is a decreased boundary layer thickness that implies a thinner wake, and following the arguments made for slat gap settings, this would result in a higher frequency of vortex shedding. Thus, from Eq. (9), whistling would occur at a higher frequency, as observed in the experiment.

6.3 Reynolds number

Khorrami et al.[2] reported a slight decrease in the observed tonal frequency with reduction in flow Reynolds number. A reduction in Reynolds number is expected to thicken the boundary layer, and following the same arguments as in the previous two sub-sections, this would result in a decrease in both the shedding frequency and the transverse gap resonance frequency. This would explain the downshift in the observed tone frequency.

7 Conclusions

In this study, the physical characteristics of the slat wake have been analyzed through a detailed local stability analysis. Based on a locally parallel mean flow assumption, the dispersion relation given by the Orr-Sommerfeld equation has been used to obtain the absolute frequencies in the wake. It has been observed that the real part of the absolute frequency is inversely proportional to both the wake depth and thickness. Based on this local stability analysis, the predicted global, vortex shedding frequency for a 30 deg. slat deflection, is close to that observed in the numerical simulations of Khorrami et al.[2] For a slat deflection of 20 deg., the vortex shedding frequency is expected to be lower, since the slat wake is shallower and thicker compared to the 30 deg. case. However, Khorrami et al.[2] did not observe any vortex shedding for the 20 deg. case. Since the absolute growth rates are lower for the 20 deg. case, the global instabilities might have been damped by Khorrami et al.'s[2] numerical scheme.

It is proposed that the observed high frequency tone in the experiments with multi-element wings is due to a whistling mechanism. The normal modes of the whistle are given by the transverse resonance frequencies of the gap between the slat and the main element. When the vortex shedding frequency, acting as an external source, matches any one of these modes, resonance occurs and a high amplitude, tone is generated. It is conjectured that it is this noise that is observed as the high frequency hump in the experiments. For a slat deflection of 30 deg., it is shown that the whistling criterion is met. For the 20 deg. case, the vortex shedding frequency is slightly lower than for the 30 deg. case, while the transverse resonance frequency of the gap is slightly higher. Thus the whistling criterion is not satisfied in the 20 deg. case. These observations are consistent with the experimental measurements.

Acknowledgments

The authors would like to thank Drs. Khorrami, Berkman, and Choudhari for providing the data from their simulations.[2] This research is supported by NASA Langley Research Center under NASA Grant NAG1-01-009. The Technical Monitor is Dr. M. R. Khorrami.

References

[1] A. M. O. Smith, "High-Lift Aerodynamics," *Journal of Aircraft*, Vol. 12, No. 6, June 1975, pp. 501–531.

[2] M. R. Khorrami, M. E. Berkman, and M. Choudhari, "Unsteady Flow Computations of a Slat with a Blunt Trailing Edge," *AIAA Journal*, Vol. 38, No. 11, Nov. 2000, pp. 2050–2058.

[3] B. A. Singer, D. P. Lockard, and K. L. Brentner, "Computational Aeroacoustic Analysis of Slat Trailing-Edge Flow," *AIAA Journal*, Vol. 38, No. 9, Sept. 2000, pp. 1558–1564.

[4] B. L. Storms, J. C. Ross, W. C. Horne, J. A. Hayes, R. P. Dougherty, J. R. Underbrink, D. F. Scharpf, and P. J. Moriarty, "An Aeroacoustic Study of an Unswept Wing with a Three-Dimensional High-Lift System," *NASA TM-1998-112222*, Feb. 1998.

[5] C. K. W. Tam and N. Pastouchenko, "Gap Tones," *AIAA Journal*, Vol. 39, No. 8, 2001, pp. 1442–1448.

[6] W. Koch, "Local Instability Characteristics and Frequency Determination of Self-Excited Wake Flows," *Journal of Sound and Vibration*, Vol. 99, 1985, pp. 53–83.

[7] J. -M. Chomaz, P. Huerre, and L. Redekopp, "A Frequency selection Criterion in Spatially Developing Flows," *Studies in Applied Mathematics*, Vol. 84, 1991, pp. 119–144.

[8] P. G. Drazin and W. H. Reid, *Hydrodynamic Stability*, Cambridge University Press, 1981.

[9] R. J. Briggs, *Electron-Stream Interaction with Plasmas*, MIT Press, Cambridge, Mass., 1964.

[10] A. Bers, *Handbook of Plasma Physics*, Vol. 1, chap. 3.2, North-Holland Publishing Company, Amsterdam, 1983, pp. 451–517.

[11] G. Triantafyllou, M. Triantafyllou, and C. Chryssostomidis, "On the Formation of Vortex Streets behind Stationary Cylinders," *Journal of Fluid Mechanics*, Vol. 170, 1986, pp. 461–477.

[12] K. Hannemann and H. Oertel, J., "Numerical Simulation of the Absolutely and Convectively Unstable Wake," *Journal of Fluid Mechanics*, Vol. 199, 1989, pp. 55–88.

[13] D. A. Hammond and L. G. Redekopp, "Global Dynamics of Symmetric and Asymmetric Wakes," *Journal of Fluid Mechanics*, Vol. 331, 1997, pp. 231–260.

[14] K. Kupfer, A. Bers, and A. K. Ram, "The Cusp Map in the Complex-Frequency Plane for Absolute Instabilities," *Physics of Fluids*, Vol. 30, No. 10, Oct. 1987, pp. 3075–3082.

[15] B. S. Ng and W. H. Reid, "An Initial Value Method for Eigenvalue Problems Using Compound Matrices," *Journal of Computational Physics*, Vol. 30, 1979, pp. 125–136.

[16] C. C. Lin, *The Theory of Hydrodynamic stability*, Cambridge University Press, 1955.

[17] S. Le Dizès, P. Huerre, J. Chomaz, and P. Monkewitz, "Linear Global Modes in Spatially Developing Media," *Philosophical Transactions of the Royal Society of London A*, Vol. 354, 1996, pp. 169–212.

[18] B. Pier and P. Huerre, "Nonlinear Self-Sustained Structures and Fronts in Spatially Developing Wake Flows," *Journal of Fluid Mechanics*, Vol. 435, 2001, pp. 145—174.

[19] G. B. Whitham, *Linear and Nonlinear Waves*, John Wiley, 1974.

AIAA 2002-2576

ARRAY DESIGN AND PERFORMANCE FOR A LARGE SCALE AIRFRAME NOISE STUDY

Nathan J. Burnside[*]
Stephen M. Jaeger[†]
Bryan R. Reinero[‡]

AerospaceComputing Inc.
Mountain View, CA
USA

William C. Horne[§]
Paul T. Soderman[**]

NASA Ames Research Center
Moffett Field, CA
USA

ABSTRACT

Two phased microphone arrays were developed for an aeroacoustic test of a 26 % scale model of a *Boeing 777* commercial airliner. Model size and a broad frequency range of interest required that two custom arrays be used in tandem during the STAR (Subsonic Transport Aeroacoustic Research) test. A 70-microphone, 244 cm (96 in) array provided a spatial resolution of 3.4λ with moderate sidelobes under 10 kHz. A smaller 102 cm (40 in) traversing array was used to measure source directivity and provide accurate sound pressure levels with a useful range of 1 to 25 kHz and a spatial resolution of 6.5λ. The acoustic performance of both arrays was optimized using a simulated annealing method to minimize sidelobe levels and beamwidth. Both arrays used a recessed microphone Kevlar™ drumhead design to reduce microphone self-noise. Recessing the array below Kevlar™ reduces background noise by as much as 20 dB by isolating the microphones from the turbulent boundary layer. The array data must be corrected for effects of the resonance created between the array plates and the Kevlar™. Broadband speaker sources as well as airframe noise sources were used to evaluate the effectiveness of the two phased arrays. Numerous airframe noise sources and noise reduction technologies were thoroughly documented using these two custom arrays in the large-scale STAR test.

NOMENCLATURE

BW_3 3 dB beamwidth (cm)
Lp   Sound pressure dB re 20 µPa
M   Mach number

$\hat{R}$ Average cross-spectral matrix used in beamforming
λ Wavelength (cm)
θ_E Array emission angle (degrees)
θ'_E Convected array emission angle (degrees)
θ_{DA} Solid inclusion angle (degrees)
ϕ Array azimuth angle (degrees)

INTRODUCTION

NASA, in cooperation with industry partners over the past several years, has developed numerous techniques for reducing airframe noise of commercial jetliners. Much of this work has been in response to noise reduction goals set by NASA's Advanced Subsonic Technology program and the Quiet Aircraft Technology program. To better understand airframe noise mechanisms and to develop technologies to reduce these noise sources, several small and large-scale tests have been conducted.[1]

Small-scale tests have been conducted in an effort to locate and characterize noise generated by aircraft landing gear and high lift systems. Noise modification devices such as flap side edges,[2,3] porous flap tips,[4] continuous moldline technology,[5] slat cove fillers, and slat serrated trailing edges,[2] to name a few, have been evaluated in small idealized studies. While flap edges

---

[*] Research Engineer, Member AIAA
[†] Senior Research Engineer, Associate Fellow, AIAA
[‡] Student Intern, Student Member, AIAA
[§] Aerospace Engineer, Associate Fellow, AIAA
[**] Aeroacoustics Group Leader, Associate Fellow, AIAA

and slat cove gap noise sources have been recognized as significant airframe noise contributors, the landing gear has also received attention as a dominant noise source during approach.

A simplified model of a four-wheel landing gear mounted to an unswept wing was tested at Langley's LTPT Wind Tunnel to investigate the effect of gear flap interactions.[6] In addition to the tests conducted with unswept models, a few tests of swept higher-fidelity models have been performed at various facilities with phased arrays and single microphone measurements. A 4.7% *DC-10* model was tested in the NASA Ames 40 Ft- x 80- Ft Wind Tunnel (40 x 80) with favorable results for flap edge fences.[7] The same DC-10 model was tested in the NASA Ames 12 Ft. Pressure Wind Tunnel to evaluate the effects of Reynolds number variation on airframe noise sources.[8] Boeing tested a 5% scale model of a *747-400* in the DERA 5 m pressure tunnel using a phased microphone array[6] and, in coordination with the STAR test in the Ames 40 x 80, they also tested a 6.3% 777 semi-span scale model at the LSAF.[9]

Although many promising noise reduction technologies were developed and tested on small-scale models, a large-scale high-fidelity test was needed to validate work done at small-scale. To accomplish this a 26% semi-span model of a *Boeing 777* (Subsonic Transport Aeroacoustic Research model or STAR) was recently tested in the semi-anechoic 40 x 80 at NASA Ames. Several of the best noise reduction technologies developed at small-scale were tested on the STAR model.

There were few differences between the production aircraft and the STAR model, which was built to tolerances of less than 0.76 mm. The significant difference was that the model was unpowered, utilizing a flow-through nacelle in place of the engine. A second difference was that the slat brackets were not modeled exactly after the production aircraft, although they were close approximations. The model included many details not found on most wind tunnel models including high-fidelity landing gear that contained all of the intricate parts of a real landing gear assembly such as simulated hydraulic brake lines and wiring harnesses. Because of the detail and complexity of the landing gear, it was also tested as an isolated model in the Ames 7 - by 10 - Foot Wind Tunnel.[10,11]

The purpose of this paper is to discuss the design and implementation of two custom acoustic arrays used for the STAR test. Because of the intricacies and size of the model, designing a single phased array to measure levels correctly and to provide enough resolution to accurately locate potential noise sources

over the desired frequency range proved to be impractical. Design criteria as well as simulated beam responses applicable to the STAR test will be shown. Array performance will also be supported with airframe noise data acquired under a variety of test conditions.

ARRAY DESIGN

The goal of the STAR test was to validate and evaluate airframe noise reduction technologies on a large-scale test model. Through a design process, it was determined that two separate phased arrays would be needed to evaluate the noise reduction modifications. A single array, unless nested within a larger pattern cannot be optimized to: 1) accurately measure levels, 2) capture directivity, 3) and provide high spatial resolution over a broad range of frequencies. Storms et al.[2] have shown that array size is an important factor in obtaining accurate sound pressure levels. Mosher[12] also stressed the importance of understanding source type when attempting to measure overall levels. Brooks and Humphreys[13] performed a study on array size and source level with data indicating that to accurately measure source levels an array should have a solid collection angle on the order of 7°.[13] The distance between outer microphones known as array aperture also affects beamwidth and, consequently, a microphone array's spatial resolution.

A large fixed array was designed to provide a high level of spatial resolution and to produce usable results at low frequency. To determine source directivity and to measure levels more accurately, a smaller array was placed on a linear traverse. **Figure 1** shows the STAR model with the two acoustic arrays in the background.

Figure 1. The STAR model mounted in the Ames 40- by 80- Ft Wind Tunnel with the large and traversing arrays in the background.

Array Placement

Factors such as tunnel layout, model size, and desired source resolution determined the placement of the two arrays. As an array is moved away from a source its beamwidth gets larger, reducing spatial resolution. For example, it was desirable to place the arrays to maintain array azimuthal look angles of less than 45° with respect to potential noise sources. The azimuthal angle (ϕ) is defined as the angle between the array perpendicular and the line that extends from the noise source location to the array center. **Figure 2** illustrates the azimuthal angles of two sources such as the wing tip and the inboard flap inboard edge (IBIE).

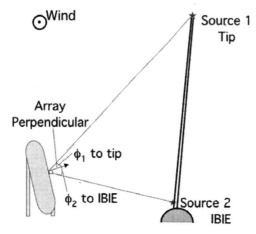

Figure 2. Array azimuthal angle, ϕ is measured from the array perpendicular to the ray path emanating from the source and extending to array center as viewed from downstream.

Because the tip of the STAR wing was 7.9 m (26 ft) from the wind tunnel floor, the traversing array was placed 5.74 m (18.8 ft) from the model. This distance, combined with a 19° array tilt favoring the wing tip, resulted in array azimuthal angles of 40° to the inboard edge of the inboard flap (IBIE) and 22° to the wing tip. For the large array a model-to-array distance of 8 m (26.25 ft) and a tilt angle of 13° created array azimuthal angles of 22° and 21° to the IBIE and wing tip, respectively.

Ideally it is desirable to place an array at a 90° emission angle from potential convected noise sources. The convected emission angle, θ'_E, as illustrated in **Figure 3** is defined as the angle between the array face and the sound path from the array center to the apparent location of the source as convected downstream. Again, because of the size of the STAR model and wing sweep, sources were distributed over a large distance in the streamwise direction. For a Mach number of 0.21, the large array was placed 295 cm (116 in) downstream of model center to achieve emission angles that bracketed 90°. With this placement the most extreme potential noise sources had emission angles of 70° to 105°.

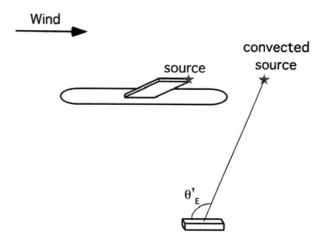

Figure 3. Convected emission angle, θ'_E for an arbitrary source.

Solid collection angle (θ_{DA}) is an important array performance parameter that is determined by array size and placement. θ_{DA} is defined as the included angle between the outermost sensors of an array as seen by a noise source. Brooks and Humphreys[13] performed a number of experiments involving integrated spectra obtained with arrays of varying collection angle. Because of the size of the STAR model, relatively large solid collection angles were expected. However, the 102 cm traversing array, placed 5.74 m from the model, created a θ_{DA} of 10.1°. The large array had a θ_{DA} of 17.3° with a pattern diameter of 244 cm and a source to array distance of 8 m.

To measure source directivity the traversing array was attached to an aerodynamic fairing mounted atop a dual-rail streamwise linear traverse. The traverse had a range of about 21 m (70 ft). During testing the small array was moved a maximum of 254 cm (100 in) upstream and 889 cm (350 in) downstream of the model pivot point. With this mobility, emission angles as low as 66° and as high as 147° were possible. To the knowledge of the authors, this was the first time a phased acoustic array was traversed in a large closed-section wind tunnel.

Microphone Self-Noise Reduction

Microphone array processing has improved dramatically in the past 10 years, but a problem that still plagues researchers is microphone self-noise. Inflow arrays experience a turbulent boundary layer over the sensors that increases microphone background noise. Two methods have been successfully used at NASA Ames to reduce microphone self-noise. One approach is to alter the diagonal of the cross-spectral matrix $\hat{R}'$ before beamforming. Off-diagonal terms of the cross-spectral matrix contain the cross-spectra between microphones. Diagonal terms of the cross-spectral matrix represent the auto-spectra of a single microphone and contain both coherent signals and incoherent noise.[12] By modifying the diagonal values with an average, calculated from off-diagonal terms, incoherent background noise is reduced.[14] Further discussion of classical frequency domain beamforming applied to aeroacoustics can be found in Mosher[12]. The second approach, developed at NASA Ames, utilizes a physical means to reduce background noise. Jaeger et al.[15] performed an extensive study to reduce this noise with a variety of schemes that recessed the microphones below the boundary layer. Recessing the microphones behind a low mass, low impedance material isolates them from the turbulent boundary layer flow. Results from a 70-element array with a 12.7 mm (1/2 in) recess behind a stretched Kevlar™ sheet showed a dramatic decrease in microphone background noise as shown in **Figure 4**.

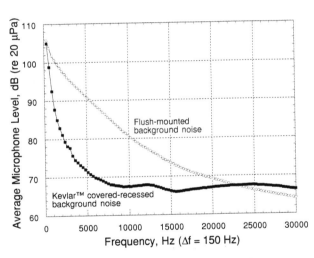

Figure 4. Average microphone sound pressure measured in the Ames 7 x 10 at Mach 0.22 with and without a Kevlar™ recessed array (from Jaeger et al.[15]).

Because of the success of several tests at NASA Ames[5,10,15] that utilized a Kevlar™ recessed array, both the large and traversing arrays were designed with a Kevlar™ screen. A unique drumhead[15] design constructed of Kevlar™, fiberglass, and aluminum was used. **Figure 5** shows a schematic of the design.

The Kevlar™ cloth was sandwiched between two fiberglass rings. Tension was applied to the cloth by

the rim as the fiberglass rings were screwed into the aluminum plate.

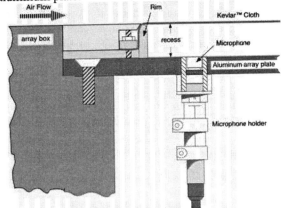

Figure 5. Kevlar™ recessed array design. Tension is applied to the Kevlar™ by stretching the cloth over the rim (from Jaeger et al.[15]).

The large array was designed with a 25.4 mm (1 in) recess and a Kevlar™ drumhead system similar to the one shown in **Figure 5**. Because Kevlar™ cloth was not available in sizes large enough to cover the 244 cm diameter array; the array was designed to have six sub groups of microphones, each with their own Kevlar™ covering as shown in **Figure 6**.

Figure 6. STAR Large Array. Six groups of microphones were used because of limited Kevlar™ size.

Although a recessed Kevlar™ covered array dramatically reduces the background noise it does not come without its challenges. Jaeger et al.[15] showed that at 25 kHz sound passing through untensioned Kevlar™ was attenuated by as much as 2 dB. A recessed array plate behind tensioned Kevlar™ however, poses another challenge because it creates resonances that attenuate and amplifies sound as a function of frequency.

To account for these effects, ongoing studies of the resonance cavity between the array plate and tensioned Kevlar™ are being conducted in the Ames anechoic chamber. Using broadband white noise, individual array microphone data have been acquired in the anechoic chamber with the Kevlar™ in place and removed. **Figure 7** shows the difference in microphone response with Kevlar™ on and off for a 25.4 mm recess. A correction procedure is currently being developed from experimental data to correct integrated array data. The initial curve fit shown in **Figure 7** uses the equation below where f is frequency, θ_E is the source emission angle, and K_{θ_n} are constants.

$$\Delta dB(f, \theta_E) = K_{\theta_{E1}} \cdot f \cdot \cos\left(f - K_{\theta_{E2}} \cdot f^2 - K_{\theta_{E3}}\right) - K_{\theta_{E4}} \cdot f^2 \quad (1)$$

Results from the 12.7 mm recess are similar with the peaks of amplification and attenuation occurring at frequencies corresponding to the smaller cavity. Data also indicates that the frequencies change with the emission angle, θ_E.

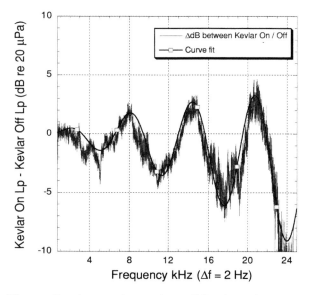

Figure 7. Attenuation and amplification of a white noise source as a function of frequency for the 25.4 mm (1 in) recessed Kevlar™ array at $\theta_E = 90°$.

Pattern Development

Both the large and the small traversing array were developed for a broadband response with minimal sidelobes. The frequency range of interest in the STAR test was 200 to 25,000 Hz. The large array was designed to provide good spatial resolution at frequencies below 10 kHz. The number of microphones and A/D digitizing cards limited each array to 70 microphones. Arrays can be optimized using simulated annealing to increase broadband array

response by reducing beamwidth and sidelobes. Reid showed that it was possible to optimize a 72-element array to perform as well as an unoptimized 100-sensor array.[16]

Microphone positions in both arrays were optimized for a narrow beamwidth and low sidelobes using a *MATLAB* based simulated annealing code.[16,17] Simulated annealing is a Monte Carlo method that optimizes the microphone locations in a manner analogous to metal annealing. When a metal is heated and then cooled slowly, atoms move from local energy minima positions into absolute minima positions.[16] Simulated annealing applied to array design, causes microphones to move from their original positions in a random direction during an iterative process. At each step, array response is calculated and compared to the response of the previous iteration. If the new pattern is an improvement it becomes the current pattern and the next iteration begins. At each step in the iterative process microphones are moved less than in the previous step. The rate at which microphone movement decreases is a user defined function and is analogous to the cooling of the molten metal.

Traversing Array

Applying the above design criteria to a 70-element, 102 cm axisymmetric pattern as shown in **Figure 8** yielded a pattern as shown in **Figure 9**. Array beampattern simulations[18] indicated that the resulting array pattern would have a spatial resolution of 6.5 λ, where λ is the acoustic wavelength. In other words, on a noise map at a given frequency, a point source would be represented as a spot with a diameter 6.5 times its wavelength.

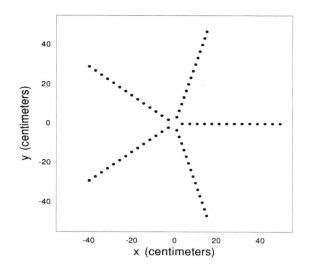

Figure 8. Axis symmetric pattern before simulated annealing.

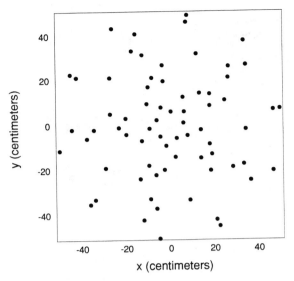

Figure 9. Traversing array pattern designed using simulated annealing.

The most important attribute of the traversing array was its broadband sidelobe levels. The highest sidelobe levels[18] at a number of frequencies were determined with a point source located 574 cm (226 in.) from array center. At 1,000 Hz these worst-case sidelobes levels were 17.5 dB below the main beam. Sidelobes increase with frequency, but at 25 kHz the worst sidelobes were still 5.4 dB below the main beam. **Figure 10** shows a simulated array response[18] at 5,100 Hz for a point source located 574 cm from the array.

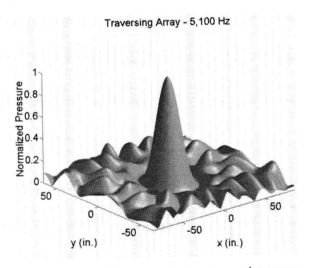

Figure 10. Traversing array response to a point source at a distance of 574 cm at 5,100 Hz. Response is $10*\log(P^2)$, where P is the RMS of the unsteady pressure. The worst-case sidelobes are 12.2 dB down.

Large Array

Design of the large array using simulated annealing was not straightforward due to the subgroupings of microphones. The large array pattern was composed of a small group of 10 center microphones, each surrounded by 5 larger groups of 12 microphones as shown in **Figure 11**. The outer groups were all identical except each was rotated 72° relative to its placement around the diameter of the large array. During the simulated annealing, microphones in the center and one outside grouping were moved to optimize array performance. However, at each step in the annealing process the entire array was evaluated for array characteristics such as beamwidth and sidelobe levels.

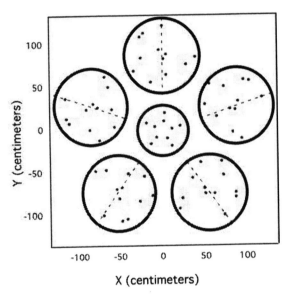

Figure 11. STAR Large array pattern. The same pattern was used for each of the outer groups of microphones.

Simulations showed that the large array had a spatial resolution of 3.4 λ, almost a factor of two better than the traversing array. Over the frequency range of interest for the large array (200 - 10,000 Hz), sidelobe levels were comparable to the traversing array. The low and high edges of the operational frequency envelope for each array were similar. At 200 Hz, worst-case sidelobes were 17.3 dB down, while the traversing array had levels of 17.4 down at 1,000 Hz. Similarly, the large array sidelobe levels increased to 4.8 dB down at 10,000 Hz while the traversing array had sidelobes 5.4 dB down at 25 kHz. For the large array sidelobes above 10 kHz quickly increased and at 15 kHz sidelobe levels exceeded the main beam. A simulated beam pattern[18] for the large array is shown in **Figure 12**.

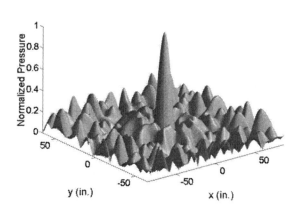

Figure 12. Simulated large array response to a source 800 cm (315 in) away at 5,100 Hz. Sidelobes are 7.5 dB down.

ARRAY RESULTS

To illustrate the performance of the two arrays, noise maps from the STAR wind tunnel test will be shown. Acoustic data taken from a speaker mounted in the landing gear cavity as well as aeroacoustic noise sources were used to evaluate array performance. The speaker was driven with pink noise with high and low pass corner frequencies of 1.5 and 20 kHz. All noise maps shown below are 432 cm by 333 cm (170 in x 131 in) with a grid resolution of 2.54 cm (1 in) and were created using the Microphone Array Phased Processing System (MAPPS) software developed at NASA Ames. A complete discussion of the development and implementation of the MAPPS processing software can be found in Watts and Mosher.[19]

Source Location

Speaker noise maps at 5,100 Hz for both the traversing and large arrays are shown in **Figure 13** and **Figure 14**. Since both noise maps show the same frequency and have 6 dB ranges relative to the peak level in the scan plane, a direct comparison in beam size can be made. Data indicated that the traversing array had a 3 dB beamwidth (BW$_3$) of 47.7 cm (18 in) at 5,100 Hz. This beamwidth translated into a spatial resolution of 6.8 λ, a deviation of 0.3 λ from the simulated value. The variation could be attributed to the elongated and distorted source caused by the downstream array angle. For the large array, a BW$_3$ of 22.9 cm (9 in) at 5,100 Hz was measured, making the spatial resolution 3.4 λ. This agrees with the simulated value for large array resolution.

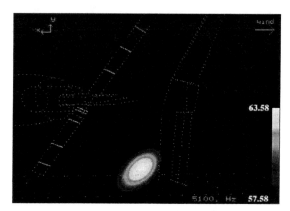

Figure 13. Traversing array noise map of speaker at 5,100 Hz and Mach 0.21(6 dB range).

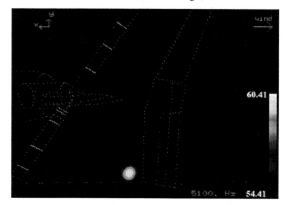

Figure 14. Large array scan of speaker at 5,100 Hz (6 dB range). Notice the improved spatial resolution of the large array.

Among the loudest components of airframe noise are the landing gear, slat and flap edges, and slat gap noise[7]. **Figure 15** shows a noise map from the large array in which all three of these noise sources can be found. This noise map was taken at M = 0.21 at 2,250 Hz with a contour range of 6 dB down from the peak in the scan.

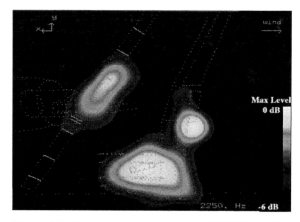

Figure 15. Large array noise map at 2,250 Hz and Mach 0.21 (6 dB range).

The high resolution of the large array at low frequencies makes these noise sources visible. Comparison of **Figure 15** with a noise map from the traversing array under the same conditions in as shown in **Figure 16,** illustrates the ability of the large array to resolve multiple sources at low frequency. The traversing array shows a single spot that includes the landing gear and inboard flap edge combined with a weaker spot occurring in the slat region.

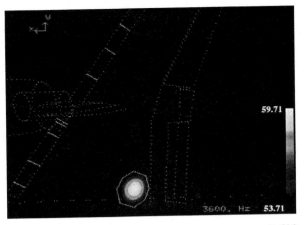

Figure 17. Integration box for large array scan at 3,600 Hz.

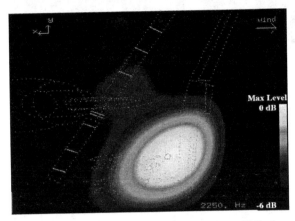

Figure 16. Traversing array at 2,250 Hz and Mach 0.21. Contours have a 6 dB range.

Amplitude Measurement

To verify that the arrays were accurately measuring sound pressure levels, a noise map was integrated using a monopole integration scheme developed by Bob Dougherty. A detailed discussion of monopole source integration can be found in Soderman et al.[20] Polygons following the 8 dB contour of a chosen source were created for each frequency, similar to the polygon shown in **Figure 17**. Energy within the boxes at each frequency was then integrated to form narrowband spectra and one third octave levels.

Traversing array integrated levels compared very well with individual microphone measurements made with no wind. **Figure 18** compares the integrated speaker results and the average array microphone spectra. The average spectrum approximates the response of a single microphone. The curves agree very well up to about 13 kHz where a difference of about 0.5 dB is found. This trend is consistent with previous work done by Brooks and Humphreys,[13] who showed that error increased as a function of frequency for a given array. Data above 20 kHz were ignored because the noise source had a low pass filter corner frequency of 20 kHz.

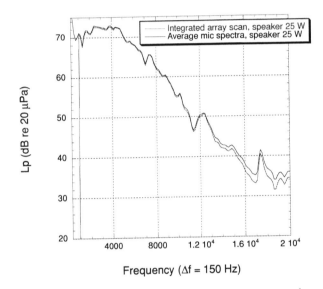

Figure 18. Speaker source measured by traversing array (no wind).

As was expected, integration of speaker noise as measured by the large array did not compare as well with a single microphone approximation as the traversing array. In the frequency range of interest for this array, below 11 kHz, errors were typically less than 0.5 dB as shown in **Figure 19**. Above 11 kHz errors were modest, typically about 1 dB.

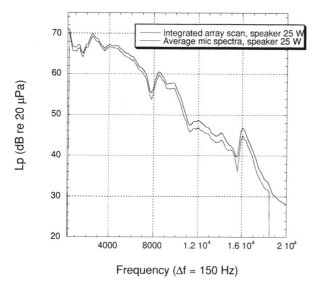

Figure 19. Large array integration for a speaker in a static tunnel.

Directivity

The traversing array made it possible to determine source directivity during the STAR test. **Figure 20**, **Figure 21**, **Figure 22**, and **Figure 23** show results of the baseline model at M = 0.18 at four traverse angles. The convected emission angles, θ'_E are referenced from the model pivot point. The 10 dB contour ranges are referenced to the peak level of the four plots after each was adjusted to account for source-to-array distance. Noise sources that exhibit directivity such as the landing gear and inboard slat, have levels that vary with array angle as shown in the four noise maps. Emission angles deviating more than a few degrees from 90, as in **Figure 20** and **Figure 23,** have elongated sources because the main lobe of the array spreads out at extreme angles.

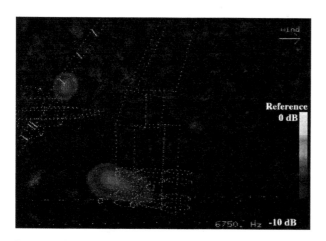

Figure 20. Traversing array scan at $\theta'_E = 58°$. Contours have a range of 10 dB.

Figure 21. Traversing array scan at $\theta'_E = 80°$.

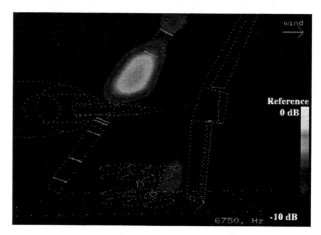

Figure 22. Traversing array scan where $\theta'_E = 115°$.

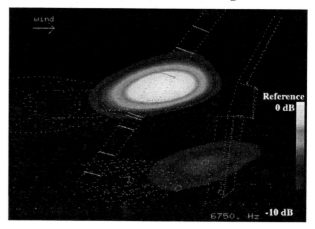

Figure 23. Traversing array scan at $\theta'_E = 133°$.

CONCLUSION

A large-scale aeroacoustic test of a *Boeing 777* model using two phased microphone arrays has been conducted at NASA Ames. Because of the broadband frequency range and the size of the model, two arrays were needed to capture source level, directivity, and location. The large and traversing arrays were optimized in tandem to achieve the desired array measurement capability over the frequency range of 200 to 25,000 Hz.

The large array provided spatial resolution of 3.4 λ up to 10 kHz allowing for source location at relatively low frequency. The traversing array had a resolution of nearly twice that of the large array but provided valuable source directivity information as well as integrated noise source levels accurate to about 0.5 dB for frequencies under 20 kHz.

Both arrays used a recessed Kevlar™ drumhead microphone self-noise reduction technique developed at NASA Ames. Use of this type of array configuration can decrease background levels by as much as 20 dB saving a great deal of money by reducing sensor count. However, use of the Kevlar™ drumhead requires that data be corrected to remove cavity resonance effects. A data correction scheme is being refined to remove the effects of the Kevlar™.

Given the broad frequency range of interest and the size of the model, both arrays performed very well. Hundreds of gigabytes of data were acquired from the two arrays. The STAR test with the two phased arrays is proving valuable high-resolution information about a host of airframe noise reduction technologies on a large-scale model.

REFERENCES

1 Macaraeg, M.G., "Fundamental Investigations of Airframe Noise," AIAA Paper 1998-2224, 4th AIAA/CEAS Aeroacoustics Conference, Toulouse, France, June 2-4, 1998.

2 Storms, B.L,, Ross, J.C., Horne, W.C., Hayes, J.A., Dougherty, R.P., Underbrink, J.R., Scharpf, D.F., and Moriarty, P.J., "An Aeroacoustic Study of an Unswept Wing with a Three-Dimensional High-Lift System," NASA TM-1998-112222, February 1998.

3 Dougherty, R.P., Scharpf, D.F., and Underbrink, J.R., "Boeing / NASA Ames Flap-Noise Test: Phased-Array Development," NASA CDRC 21-000, February 16, 1995.

4 Revell, J.D., Kuntz, H. L., Balena, F.J., Horne, W.C., Storms, B.L., and Dougherty, R.P., "Trailing-Edge Flap Noise Reduction By Porous Acoustic Treatment," AIAA Paper 1997-1646, 3rd AIAA/CEAS Aeroacoustics Conference, Atlanta, GA, May 12-14, 1997.

5 Storms, B.L., Hayes, J.A., Jaeger, S.M., Soderman, P.T., "Aeroacoustic Study of Flap-Tip Noise Reduction Using Continuous Moldline Technology," AIAA Paper 2000-1976, 6th AIAA/CEAS Aeroacoustics Conference, Lahaina, HI, June 12-14 2000.

6 Stoker, R.W., Underbrink, J. R., Neubert, G. R., "Investigations of Airframe Noise in Pressurized Wind Tunnels," AIAA Paper 2001-2107, 7th AIAA Aeroacoustics Conference, Maastricht, Netherlands, May 28-30, 2001.

7 Hayes, J.A., Horne, W.C., and Soderman, P.T., "Airframe Noise Characteristics of a 4.7 % Scale DC-10 Model," AIAA Paper 1997-1594, 3rd AIAA/CEAS Aeroacoustics Conference, Atlanta, GA, May 12-14, 1997.

8 Hayes, J.A., Horne, W.C., Jaeger, S. M., Soderman, P.T., "Measurement of Reynolds Number Effect on Airframe Noise in the 12-Foot Pressure Wind Tunnel," AIAA Paper 1999-1959, 33rd Thermophysics Conference, Norfolk, VA, June 28 – July 1, 1999.

9 Stoker, R. W., Sen, R., "An Experimental Investigation of Airframe Noise Using a Model-Scale Boeing 777," AIAA Paper 2001-0987, 39th AIAA Aerospace Sciences Meeting & Exhibit, Reno, NV, January 8-11, 2001.

10 Jaeger, S. M., Burnside, N.J., Soderman, P.T., Horne, W.C., James, K. D., "Microphone Array Measurements of a Model-scale High-fidelity Landing Gear," AIAA Paper 2002-2410, 8th AIAA/CEAS Aeroacoustics Conference, Breckenridge, CO, June 17-19, 2002.

11 Horne, W. C., James, K. D., Storms, B. L., "Flow Survey of the Wake of a Commercial Transport Main Gear," AIAA Paper 2002-2047, 8th AIAA/CEAS Aeroacoustics Conference, Breckenridge, CO, June 17-19, 2002.

12 Mosher, M., "Phased Arrays for Aeroacoustic Testing: Theoretical Development," AIAA Paper 1996-1713, 2nd AIAA/CEAS Aeroacoustics Conference, State College, PA, May 6-8, 1996.

13 Brooks, T. F., Humphreys, W. M. Jr., "Effect of Directional Array Size on Measurement of Airframe Noise Components," AIAA Paper 1999-1958, 5th AIAA Aeroacoustics Conference, Bellevue, WA, May 10-12, 1999.

14 Horne, W. C., Hayes, J. A., Jaeger, S. M., Jovic, S., "Effects of Distributed Source Coherence on the Response of Phased Acoustic Arrays," AIAA Paper 2000-1935, 6th AIAA/CEAS Aeroacoustics Conference, Lahaina, HI, June 12-14 2000.

15 Jaeger, S. M., Horne, W.C., Allen, C.S., "Effect of Surface Treatment on Array Microphone Self-Noise," AIAA Paper 2000-1937, 6th AIAA/CEAS Aeroacoustics Conference, Lahaina, HI, June 12-14 2000.

16 Reid, M. B., "Design of Optimized Arrays Using Simulated Annealing," Internal NASA Ames Research Center Document.

17 Besnard, E., Corider-Lallouet, N., Kural, O., Chen, H.P., "Design and Optimization with Advanced Simulated Annealing, " AIAA Paper 1999-0186, 37th AIAA Aerospace Sciences Meeting and Exhibit, Reno, NV, January 11-14, 1999.

18 Underbrink, J. R., "Practical Considerations in Focused Array Design for Passive Broad-Band Source Mapping Applications," Master's Thesis, Pennsylvania State University, May 1995.

19 Watts, M. E., Mosher, M., "The Microphone Array Phased Processing System (MAPPS)," AIAA Paper 1996-1714, 2nd AIAA/CEAS Aeroacoustics Conference, State College, PA, May 6-8, 1996.

20 Soderman, P. T., Kafyeke, F, Burnside, N.J., Chandrasekharan, R., Jaeger, S. M., Boudreau, J., "Airframe Noise Study of a CRJ-700 Aircraft Model in the NASA Ames 7- by 10 – Foot Wind Tunnel No. 1," AIAA Paper 2002-2406, 8th AIAA/CEAS Aeroacoustics Conference, Breckenridge, CO, June 17-19, 2002.

DENSE COMPACT RIGID OBJECT IN A TURBULENT FLOW: APPLICATION OF CURLE'S THEORY[1]

Damien J.J. Leclercq
and
Mark K. Symes

The University of Adelaide
Department of mechanical Engineering
Adelaide SA5005
Australia

Abstract

Interactions between turbulent flows and compact, hard surfaces are of considerable importance in aeroacoustics, with applications such as aircraft landing gear, high speed train pantographs, or fan noise. One main theoretical tool available to study these phenomena is the equation derived by Curle, as an extension to Lighthill's work.
Previous work found in the literature developed techniques to evaluate the applicability of Curle's equation in one of its most important simplified forms: the case of a concentrated hydrodynamic force. Discrepancies were found between experiment and theory, and discussed.
The present work aims at investigating the matter further. After a brief discussion of the applicability of Curle's equation to the case of interest, experimental results are presented, interpreted, and discussed.
The present work uses an improved and modified version of an experimental set-up that has been described in the literature, while new processing techniques are developed, in order to obtain a more thorough understanding of the physics involved. The experimental work was carried out in the reverberant blow-down facility of Adelaide University's Department of Mechanical Engineering, for Mach numbers ranging between 0.1 and 0.6, yielding results covering a broad frequency range. Over most of this frequency range, some agreement is observed between the measured radiated sound power and that predicted by Curle's equation from the measured reaction force, but some discrepancies remain to be explained and a scope for future work concludes this paper.

Introduction

This paper presents the study of the noise generated by an acoustically compact, dense object suspended in a fluctuating flow. Curle's equation, reduced to its simplest formulation for the case of a concentrated hydrodynamic force, is chosen as a reference theory, to which the experimental results are compared. Previous published attempts to experimentally verify this theory are then reviewed, and point at the necessity to further investigate the matter. An experimental arrangement is subsequently presented, and the results, obtained over a broad frequency and velocity range, are reported for several flow configurations. Although the prediction and the measurements are within 2 dB of each other over a portion of the explored region, some clear discrepancy remains to be investigated. Possible causes for this discrepancy are suggested, and additional measurements are proposed for future work.

1.   Curle's equation

Beginning with Lighthill's[1] formulation of the far field sound generated by a region of turbulent flow, Curle[2] extended the theory to include the presence of solid boundaries in contact with the turbulent flow region. Blake[3] writes Curle's equation as the sum of three terms: " the radiation from the turbulent domain (1), radiation due to the instantaneous contiguous motion with phase cancellation included (2), and radiation from a distribution of forces acting on the region (3)". The fluid density fluctuation at the time t and position $\bar{x}$ is written as:

$$4\pi c_0^2 \left(\rho(\vec{x},t) - \rho_o\right) = \underbrace{\frac{\partial^2}{\partial x_i \partial x_j} \iiint_V \frac{\left[T_{ij}\right]}{r} dV(\vec{y})}_{(1)}$$

$$\underbrace{- \iint_S \frac{l_i}{r} \left[\frac{\partial(\rho u_i)}{\partial t}\right] dS(\vec{y})}_{(2)} \qquad (1)$$

$$\underbrace{+ \frac{\partial}{\partial x_i} \iint_S \frac{l_j}{r} \left[\rho u_i u_j + \tau'_{ij} + p \delta_{ij}\right] dS(\vec{y})}_{(3)}$$

where T_{ij} is Lighthill's stress tensor:

$$T_{ij} = \rho u_i u_j + \left(p - c_0^2 \rho\right)\delta_{ij} + \tau'_{ij}, \qquad (2)$$

u is the velocity disturbance, τ'_{ij} is the viscous stress tensor, V is the volume that encompasses all regions of turbulent flow, l_i are the components of the outward normal to the bounding surface S, and [] implies evaluation at the time retarded by acoustic propagation $t-r/c$. This formulation, as well as other existing theories[4,5], takes the motion of the bounding surfaces into account.

2. Applications

2.1. Concentrated Hydrodynamic force

When applied to a concentrated hydrodynamic force, the right hand side of this equation reduces to the pressure component of the third term, related to the distribution of forces. This rearranges, for the case of a harmonic force $\overline{F_i}(t) = \mathrm{Re}\left(\left|F_i\right|e^{-i\omega t}\right)$, to the following expression for the radiated acoustic pressure:

$$p(\vec{x},t) = -ik_0 F_i \frac{x_i}{r} \frac{e^{-i(\omega t - r/c_0)}}{4\pi r} \qquad (3)$$

The radiated acoustic power is then, for a concentrated hydrodynamic force:

$$W = \iint_{\partial V} \frac{\left\langle p^2(\vec{x},t)\right\rangle}{\rho_0 c_0} dS(\vec{x})$$

$$= \frac{\pi f^2 F_i^2}{6\rho_0 c_0^3} = \frac{\pi f^2 \left\langle \left|F_i(t)\right|^2\right\rangle}{3\rho_0 c_0^3} \qquad (4)$$

The ideal case of the concentrated hydrodynamic force, where noise is generated by an imposed force, can be seen as the simplified case of a fixed rigid object in a turbulent low Mach number flow. In this case, the noise emitted from the turbulence itself is much less intense than that generated by the reaction pressures on the surface of the object. Note that the acoustically compact object with rigid surfaces, which generates the acoustic field considered here, is fixed. The surface velocity is zero, while the surface pressure is not. This is different from the oscillating sphere, where the surface pressure fluctuation is caused by the surface motion. As a result, for the same surface pressure and resulting force, the radiated acoustic power is different from that generated by an oscillating sphere, which is presented below.

2.2. Oscillating sphere

The case of the oscillating sphere is now studied using Blake's development[3] based on Curle's equation. Blake considers the sound field radiated by a sphere oscillating along the z axis with the speed U_z defined by:

$$\overline{U_z(t)} = \left|U_z\right|e^{-i\omega t}, \qquad (5)$$

Compared to the previous case, Curle's simplified equation contains another pressure term related to the direct motion induced by the sphere as well as the pressure term induced by the reaction of the fluid to the oscillating motion:

$$4\pi p(\vec{x},t) = -\iint_S \frac{l_i}{r} \left[\frac{\partial(\rho u_i)}{\partial t}\right] dS(\vec{y})$$

$$+ \frac{\partial}{\partial x_i} \iint_S \frac{l_i}{r} \left[p\right] dS(\vec{y}) \qquad (6)$$

$$= 4\pi p_u(\vec{x},t) + 4\pi p_p(\vec{x},t)$$

which holds for the case of an inviscid fluid, and when the quadrupole term associated with the Reynolds stresses can also be neglected, due to the slow motion of the sphere ($U_z/c_0 \ll 1$). Blake expresses the velocity term as:

$$p_u(\vec{x},t) = \frac{-1}{3} \rho_0 c_0 k_0^2 \overline{U_z} a^3 \cos\phi \frac{e^{-i(\omega t - k_0 r)}}{r} \qquad (7)$$

when $k_0 a \ll 1$. To evaluate the pressure term p_p, Blake uses the equation previously derived for a concentrated force :

$$p_p(\vec{x},t) = -ik_0 F_p \frac{x_i}{r} \frac{e^{-i(\omega t - r/c_0)}}{4\pi r} \qquad (8)$$

where F_p is the force applied on the fluid by the sphere. The sphere is acoustically compact, and the fluid impedance is principally mass-like. Having previously derived the added mass of the fluid to be $\frac{2}{3}\rho_0 \pi a^3$, the reaction force acting on the sphere is:

$$-\overline{F_p} = -i\omega\left(\frac{2}{3}\rho_0 \pi a^3\right)\overline{U_z}, \qquad (9)$$

which enables p_p to be written as:

$$p_p(\vec{x},t) = \frac{-1}{6}\rho_0 c_0 k_0^2 \overline{U_z} a^3 \cos\phi \frac{e^{-i(\omega t - k_0 r)}}{r} \qquad (10)$$

Finally, the total radiated pressure is:

$$p(\vec{x},t) = p_u(\vec{x},t) + p_p(\vec{x},t)$$

$$= \frac{-1}{2}\rho_0 c_0 k_0^2 \overline{U_z} a^3 \cos\phi \frac{e^{-i(\omega t - k_0 r)}}{r} \qquad (11)$$

which, in the low $k_0 a$ approximation, agrees with expressions derived by other methods[6]. For comparison purposes, this acoustic pressure is that radiated by an equivalent concentrated hydrodynamic force of amplitude $\overline{F_{eq}} = -i\omega\left(2\rho_0\pi a^3\right)\overline{U_z} = 3\overline{F_p}$, that is, three times the reaction force from the fluid on the oscillating sphere, so that the radiated acoustic power can be rewritten as:

$$W = \frac{\pi f^2}{6\rho_0 c_0^3}\left|\omega\left(2\rho_0\pi a^3\right)U_z\right|^2 \qquad (12)$$

2.3. Application to a sphere suspended in a turbulent flow

For the case of a sphere that is suspended in a turbulent flow, the low frequency far field pressure can be written as follows:

$$p(\vec{x},t) = p_u(\vec{x},t) + p_p(\vec{x},t)$$
$$= \frac{-1}{2}\rho_0 c_0 k_0^2 \overline{U_z}a^3 \cos\phi\frac{e^{-i(\omega t-k_0 r)}}{r} \qquad (13)$$
$$+ ik_0\overline{F}\cos\phi\frac{e^{-i(\omega t-k_0 r)}}{r}$$

where U_z is the vertical velocity of the sphere, and F is the force that the fluid applies to it.

If the sphere of mass m_s is suspended and moves freely, then $-i\omega m_s\overline{U_z} = \overline{F}$ at equilibrium. Hence,

$$p(\vec{x},t) = -\frac{a^3}{3}\left(\frac{3}{2}\rho_0 + \rho_s\right)c_0 k_0^2 \overline{U_z}\cos\phi\frac{e^{-i(\omega t-k_0 r)}}{r} \qquad (14)$$

where ρ_s is the density of the sphere material. Hence, for a steel sphere suspended in a turbulent air flow, the velocity-generated pressure is approximately 6000 times smaller than the force-generated pressure. In this case, the oscillating sphere theory does not apply, as the concentrated hydrodynamic force generates the acoustic field, while the fluid motion associated with the sphere displacement has a negligible effect. For the case of the oscillating sphere, this latter motion term is of prime importance. If the sphere suspension affects its motion, the mass m_s is replaced by the inertance, that is, the inverse of the frequency response between the applied force and the acceleration response. If the system is resonant with little damping, then the displacement term will rise and contribute significantly to the radiated field at resonance. The pressure term will be affected by the motion of the sphere only if the latter is comparable to the fluid flow characteristic eddy scale, which is rarely the case in applications of interest.

Hence, when the density of the radiator is much higher than that of the fluid, as is often the case, its motion can be neglected when evaluating the radiated acoustic pressure, which can then be accurately estimated from the surface pressure only.

Advantage can be taken from these conclusions in attempting to verify Curle's theory applied to a concentrated hydrodynamic force. The pressure and resulting force applied on the suspended sphere can be accurately estimated from its acceleration response, while its velocity does not affect the radiated acoustic field significantly. This advantage was used in an experimental set-up first designed and used by Bies et al.[7].

2.4. Active control application

Consider a sphere oscillating freely in a fluctuating flow, surrounded by air at rest. Acoustic waves are generated by two phenomena: the direct motion of the surrounding fluid induced by that of the sphere, and the surface pressure due to the reaction stresses between the fluid and the sphere. These result in two forces: the reaction force that the sphere applies on the moving fluid, and the reaction force that the fluid applies on the moving sphere. It is assumed here that the motion of the sphere is one or more orders of magnitude smaller than the flow fluctuation, so that both pressure terms can be simply added into the pressure term p_p, and the motion of the sphere does not significantly affect the non-acoustic fluid motion. Each contribution can be written respectively:

$$p_u(\vec{x},t) = \frac{-4\pi}{3}\rho_0 c_0 k_0^2 \overline{U_z}a^3 \frac{x_i}{r}\frac{e^{-i(\omega t-k_0 r)}}{4\pi r}, \qquad (15)$$

and

$$p_p(\vec{x},t) = -ik_0\left(F_p + F_f\right)\frac{x_i}{r}\frac{e^{-i(\omega t-r/c_0)}}{4\pi r}, \qquad (16)$$

where $-F_p = -i\omega\left(\frac{2}{3}\rho_0\pi a^3\right)U_z$ is the reaction force from the fluid opposing the sphere oscillations, and F_f is the resulting force applied by the fluctuating flow on the sphere.

The sum of these contributions can be rewritten as:

$$p = \frac{2}{3}\pi a^3\rho_0 c_0 k_0^2\left(\frac{-i}{\omega}\frac{3}{2\pi a^3\rho_0}F_f - U_z\right)\frac{x_i}{r}\frac{e^{-i(\omega t-r/c_0)}}{4\pi r} \qquad (17)$$

Hence, it is possible to minimise the noise radiated by an oscillating sphere in a fluctuating flow by minimising the right-hand side term of this equation, that is, adapt the value of U_z as a function of F_f in order to minimise the factor in brackets. It is interesting to note that cancellation of the radiated noise does not necessitate the minimisation of the surface pressure (and resulting force) or sphere motion, but requires the adaptation of the sphere oscillations to the value of the resulting force applied by the fluid flow. It is worth insisting on the fact that the above equation leading to these conclusions is based on the assumption that the amplitude of the sphere motion is much smaller than the characteristic length and velocity scales of the fluid flow. This leads to a study on active control reported by Symes et al.[8].

3.   Reported experimental attempts to validate Curle's theory

Early attempts to validate Curle's equation for the case of a concentrated hydrodynamic force were faced with difficulties that were not overcome. Clark and Ribner[9] investigated this relationship in the time domain by measuring the cross correlation between the fluctuating lift of an airfoil in a turbulent flow, and the radiated acoustic power in the direction perpendicular to its chord. This cross-correlation was then compared to that predicted from the lift auto-correlation and the use of Curle's equation. The authors obtained a prediction 2.7 dB higher than the measurements, and they attributed this discrepancy to a resonance in the model.

At roughly the same time, Heller and Widnall[10] measured the fluctuating force exerted on a spoiler from which they predicted the radiated acoustic power using Curle's equation. The measured acoustic power was found to be higher than the prediction and the discrepancy was attributed to the fact that the free-field conditions were not satisfied.

Blake[3] reports attempts to validate Curle's equation in the case of aeolian tones by Koopmann[11] and by Leehey and Hanson[12]. These authors compared predictions using a correlation length formulation, and based on correlation length and fluctuating lift measurements, to the measured sound intensity radiated by cylinders in cross-flow. The results reported by Blake show that the prediction overestimates the measurement by 0 to 3 dB for various flow speeds.

The work reported in the literature gives comparisons between the theory and the measurement at a limited number of frequencies or flow speeds, and when direct measurements are performed, the discrepancy is attributed to experimental errors. The experimental work described here was undertaken to check the applicability of Curle's equation over a broad frequency range and varying flow conditions. The procedure has been designed to allow a better evaluation of the sources of error in the experiment.

4.   Experimental Validation

The present work aims at testing Curle's equation applied to a concentrated hydrodynamic force. It is therefore necessary for the experimental set-up to measure both the force applied by the fluid and the radiated acoustic power. The experimental set-up used for the work and the measurement techniques are described. The results obtained using the rig are then reported and discussed.

4.1.   The test rig

The test rig used in the present investigation, and sketched in Figure 1, was described previously [7]. Air flows along the x direction, past an airfoil of thickness $D = 8$ mm, with an elliptic leading edge and a square trailing edge that sheds vortices, which are convected past a steel block suspended in the wake of the airfoil. The blade spanwise direction is denoted y, while the cross-flow direction is denoted z. The block dimensions are 30 x 30 x 8 mm^3, in the x, y and z directions, respectively, so that the characteristic length of the block is $l = 0.03$ m. It is suspended in its position on four taut steel wires, approximately 0.15 m long.

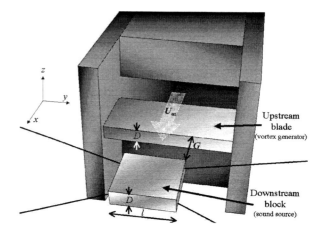

Figure 1 Sketch of the test rig

This rig was designed to create an antisymetric vortex flow around the downstream block, which results in a phase shift in the surface pressure fluctuation between the two faces of the block, thus creating a dipole acoustic source. In light of Curle's equation, such a set-up presents the main advantage of sensing the resulting force that the fluid applies to the object. Even if the fluid applies a torque on the block, the resulting rocking motion does not significantly affect the y-acceleration measurements from which the resulting force is deduced. The spacing between the upstream blade trailing edge and downstream block leading edge, noted G, can be varied between 2.3 and 6.3 D. The upstream blade is used to create the flow disturbances that interact with the downstream block to generate sound. The shed vortices are expected to impose alternate pressure pulses on either side of the block, as reported by Martin and Bies[13].

The air is supplied by pressured tanks, through a 30 x 67 mm^2 nozzle with a cross-sectional area reduction factor of 2, at flow velocities ranging from more than 200 m/s down to less than 40 m/s, as the tanks become empty. The resulting jet-like flow impinges on the upstream blade, whose leading edge is in the exit plane of the nozzle. It is equipped with pressure taps to measure the dynamic head pressure and the static pressure, in order to derive the incoming flow velocity. The flow temperature is measured with a Type T thermocouple.

The flow Reynolds number Re_D based on the blade thickness ranges between 2×10^4 and 10×10^4.

This range may be compared to the case of flow around a circular cylinder[3], where vortices with turbulent cores are shed periodically for Reynolds numbers ranging from 200 to 2×10^5.

4.2. Force measurements

The previous analysis showed that because the block has a high density compared to the ambient medium, its motion does not affect the radiated noise significantly in the present case. This small but finite motion can be used, however, to estimate the resulting force that the flow exerts on the block: the response of the suspended block is characterised by measuring the acceleration response to a hammer impact. A lightweight hammer with a piezo-electric crystal force transducer was made by the Department's electronics laboratory, and was used with a B&K 2635 charge amplifier. The hammer was calibrated with a known mass to which a reference accelerometer was attached. It has a response that is flat within ±0.4 dB between 0 and 6 kHz, at about 200 pC/N. In any case, the frequency response of the hammer is taken into account while processing the data.

A B&K 8307 accelerometer (sensitivity: 0.073 pC/ms^{-2}), inserted at the centre of the block and oriented in the z direction, measured its acceleration. The force to acceleration Frequency Response Function (FRF) relates the input force to the block acceleration response. Each FRF was averaged over 10 impacts, and the coherence obtained was above 0.99 between 200 Hz and 5 kHz. The block showed a mass-like behaviour in the frequency range of interest, and its frequency response remained flat within 1 dB in amplitude and less than 4 degrees in phase, below 6 kHz. This calibration of the system was made before and after each run, and shows a variation of less than 0.2 dB in amplitude and 0.5 degrees in phase between calibrations

The block acceleration Power Spectral Densities (PSD) measured during each run are then converted to input force PSD, by dividing them by the square of the modulus of the block calibration FRF.

4.3. Sound power measurements

The main advantage in carrying out the measurements in a reverberant room is that the radiated acoustic power level L_w can be estimated from the measured sound pressure level L_p at a few points, using the equation derived by Beranek[14] :

$$L_w = L_p + 10 \log_{10} V - 10 \log_{10} T_{60} + 10 \log_{10}(1 + S\lambda/8V) - 13.9 \text{ (dB re } 10^{-12} \text{W)} \quad (18)$$

at an ambient pressure of 1 atmosphere and a temperature of 20°C. The volume V of the room is 179.66 m^3, S = 193.20 m^2 is the total area of the reflecting surfaces, and λ is the sound wavelength. The reverberation time T_{60} was measured using a

B&K 2260 Sound Investigator for each third octave band at five locations in the room. Beranek's formula, derived for third octave spectra, had to be adapted to narrow band measurements and the measured values of T_{60} approximated as a continuous function of frequency, whose third octave levels are in agreement with the measurement. Figure 2 shows the comparison between the measurements and this function. This interpolated T_{60} was used in all subsequent processing, on the sound pressure PSD measured by three B&K microphones located at various positions in the room. The levels measured by these microphones remain within 2 dB of one another over most of the frequency range.

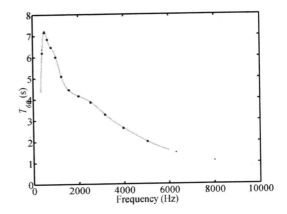

Figure 2 Measured reverberation times in each third octave frequency band, and model.

4.4. Signal processing

Signals were acquired and processed by a 16 channel B&K 2816 multi-channel analyser system sampling at a frequency of 12.8 kHz with a dynamic range higher than 80 dB. Each 800 line spectrum was averaged 50 times with a 50% overlap, which was a compromise between convergence and measurement duration, which had to be kept short because the flow speed decreases with time. These spectra were thus averaged over a duration of 3.2 s. The processed spectra were then transferred, to be processed with routines developed in Matlab where the calibrations and transducer FRFs were taken into account before further processing. All spectra presented a sharp peak at the vortex shedding frequency. The peak was tracked and its plotted value was the recorded level integrated over a 320 Hz wide band centred on the peak frequency. All levels presented in this paper are integrated in this manner.

4.5. Signal stationarity

The use of a blow-down facility raises the question of signal stationarity: as the tanks empty the flow velocity decreases and is thus not constant for each measurement. Figure 3 shows the evolution of measured flow velocity with time, as an exponential decrease over most of the range. Figure 4 shows the relative flow speed variation while the spectra are averaged 50 times, as a function of the flow speed. Because of its exponential decay, this variation remains roughly a constant fraction of the flow velocity itself, at less than 1% for velocities higher than 50 m/s, which results in a similar variation in the peak frequency. The frequency variation remains well within the band in which peak levels are measured. The flow conditions can therefore be considered stationary while each spectrum is averaged.

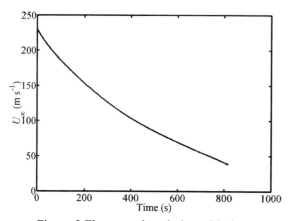

Figure 3 Flow speed evolution with time

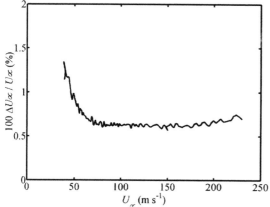

Figure 4 Relative flow speed variation during the averaging of 50 spectra

Another issue raised by the flow speed decrease is the fact that the measurements are carried out in a reverberant chamber, and that a proper evaluation of the sound power level requires enough time for the acoustic energy to build up in the room at the frequency of interest. This build-up time is directly related to the reverberation time. The tone of interest, however, decreases in frequency during the measurements, which reduces the available build-up time. In order to reduce this problem, the power levels are integrated over a finite bandwidth centred around the peak, so that the time it takes for the peak frequency to scan this bandwidth is larger than the reverberation time at the frequency of interest.

Attempts to further correct this are more likely to add uncertainty than reduce the resulting error, and this matter is not further investigated here.

5. Results

Figure 5 compares characteristic predicted and measured sound power spectra as a function of the Strouhal number $S_t = f l / U_\infty$, at flow velocities of 50, 100 and 150 m/s, for $G = 6.25D$. This figure shows that the prediction and measurements are in good agreement around the peak. The peak Strouhal number varies slightly as the flow velocity decreases, but is considered constant for the present purposes. The matter is further discussed in section 5.4.

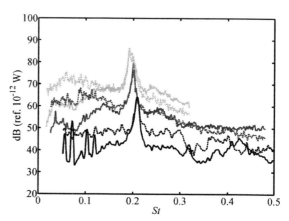

Figure 5 Measured and predicted Sound power spectra, $G = 6.3 D$, at ——**50**, ——100 and ——150 m/s. —— : Prediction ····: Measurement

5.1. Effect of separation distance on the frequency of the radiated noise

Results are presented in this paper for three typical values of the normalised separation distance G/D. The effect of this parameter on the flow and radiated noise is now studied with more flow configurations. For each value of G, the vortex shedding Strouhal number varies slightly with the velocity, as observed in Figure 5. The average Strouhal number increases with dimensionless separation G/D (Figure 6), thus indicating that the shedding frequency is not determined by the blade thickness only, because the block exerts a feedback influence on the vortex shedding process. The vortex shedding frequency for the blade alone was found to have a Strouhal number of 0.2, compared to the value of 0.21 reported in the literature for circular cylinders[3]. This means that the shed vortex pattern has a wavelength $\lambda_t = \dfrac{U_c}{U_\infty} \dfrac{D}{S_t} = 4.5\ D$, if the vortex convection velocity U_c is taken to be $0.9 U_\infty$. It can therefore be expected that the downstream block affects the vortex shedding phenomenon if it is located less than $5\ D$ downstream of the blade trailing edge. When the spacing is set at its minimal value of 2.3 D, the Strouhal number is 0.14. As the spacing increases, its value tends to that observed for the blade alone, since the interaction between the vortex shedding and the block decreases. For a spacing of 6.3 D, the presence of the block does not significantly affect the shedding frequency. This may be explained by the fact that the block increasingly prevents the vortex shedding as it approaches the blade trailing edge, to the point when the vortices are trapped in the gap, and no shedding is observed when $G/D \cong 1$.

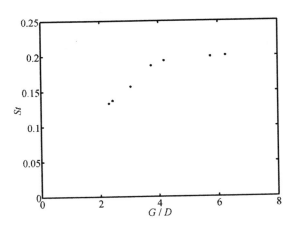

Figure 6 Evolution of the vortex shedding frequency as a function of the spacing between the upstream blade and the block

In his study of the flow and noise generated by the flow around two plates in tandem, Blazewicz[15] distinguishes three regimes for the flow in the gap between the plates: a trapped vortex regime for small gaps, a vortex street regimes for large gaps, and a transitional regime in-between, where the upper and lower shear layer generate vortex structures but do not merge with each other. At $Re_D = 15.5 \cdot 10^3$, he observed the transition regime for $2 < G/D < 3$, and the Strouhal number decreased significantly when G/D decreased below 4. It can be expected that this transition regime occurs for higher values of G/D as the Reynolds number decreases. The present observations are in good agreement with those made by Blazewicz.

5.2. Effect of separation distance on the level of the radiated noise

Figure 7 sketches the expected flow field for the case $G/D = 6.3$, with $U_c = 0.9 U_\infty$. The block surface pressure is also schematically represented. The vortex street wavelength λ_t is in this case 4.5 $D =$ 1.2 l. The resulting force on the block surface is therefore attenuated because of the spatial filtering occurring on its surface area. As the value of G/D decreases, so does the Strouhal number, and the vortex street wavelength increases, which reduces the effects of spatial filtering over the surface of the

block. For a given surface pressure fluctuation amplitude, the noise radiated then becomes more intense, which partially justifies the trend observed in Figure 9 as the ratio G/D varies. However, the spatial filtering effect is reduced because the surface pressure fluctuation is most intense close to the leading edge of the block, and decreases sharply downstream of this region, towards the trailing edge[15].

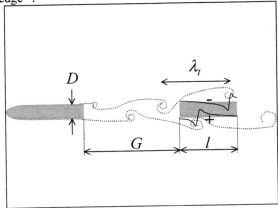

Figure 7 Sketch of the flow and surface pressure on the block with $G/D = 6.3$.

This separation distance G between the vortex shedding trailing edge and the leading edge of the block therefore affects the characteristic frequency, as well as the levels of the investigated tone.

Figure 8 shows the measured sound power spectra for separations $G/D = 2.3$, 4.2, and 6.3, respectively, as a function of flow velocity. Also represented is the power law $L_w \propto U_\infty^6$. The agreement between measurements and the sixth power law of the flow speed can be observed at high velocities ($U_\infty > 70$ ms^{-1}) for the smallest value of G/D, and at low velocities ($U_\infty < 60$ ms^{-1}) for the largest value of G/D, when the vortex shedding is the least affected by the block. This spacing has an important influence on the way the sound power evolves with flow velocity.

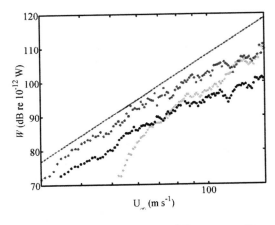

Figure 8 Sound power radiated for a separation of $G/D = \bullet$ 2.3, $\bullet$ 4.2, and $\bullet$ 6.3. The straight line represents the power law U_∞^6.

Blazewicz[15] observed that the surface pressure fluctuation on the downstream blade reached a maximum amplitude at the upper boundary of the critical regime $G/D \cong 3$, which also resulted in a maximum level of acoustic radiation. The surface pressure level decreased sharply when G decreased below $3D$, and more gently when it increased above this limit. When $G/D<1$, the flow in the gap did not contribute significantly to the surface pressure fluctuation and radiated noise. The present results show good agreement with these observations, and at any given flow speed, the sound power level is greater for $G/D=4.2$ than for $G/D=2.3$ or 6.3.

5.3. Comparison with Curle's prediction

As the flow speed decreases, the peak frequency decreases proportionally, according to the value of the Strouhal number. Sound power peak levels measured and predicted from the block acceleration at each flow velocity are represented in Figure 9 as a function of the dimensionless wavenumber kl, for three different configurations with G ranging from 2.3 to 6.3 D .

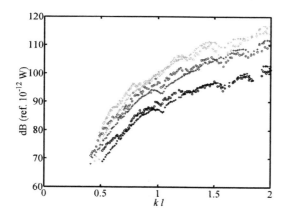

Figure 9 Measured and predicted Sound power spectra peak levels, at all flow speeds and in three configurations:
$G/D = 2.3$, 4.2, and 6.3.
+: prediction, o: measurement

For every flow configuration, the prediction curve shows roughly the same features as the measured one, except for the hump in the measured values below $kl=0.8$. The fact that a hump in the predicted sound power spectrum reflects in the measured sound power spectrum indicates that the noise radiated really is generated by the block reacting to pressure fluctuations on its horizontal faces, and that the measured phenomenon corresponds to what is expected. The hump measured in the sound power for $kl<0.8$ cannot be related to a similar feature in the prediction. It therefore seems unrelated to the pressure loading on the two main faces of the block.

Another noise radiating phenomenon, which is different from the one studied, may contribute significantly to the radiated sound. Measuring the coherence between the radiated sound and the block motion could substantiate this. Such a measurement, however, would only be meaningful in a non-reverberant environment.

Figure 9 also shows that at a given frequency, that is, at a given acoustic efficiency of the block, the radiated power increases as G/D decreases. This is partly because the surface pressure fluctuation amplitude is more intense, as it is generated by vortices that have been exposed to less viscous dissipation. Another possible reason, related to the block low-pass wavenumber filtering, was discussed in Section 5.1.

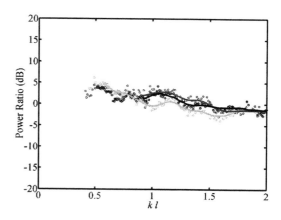

Figure 10 Power ratio estimated for the peak levels, at all flow speeds and in three configurations:
$G/D = 2.3$, — 4.2, and — 6.3.
The symbols are the measurements, and the lines their smoothed values.

Figure 10 displays the ratio between the measured peak sound power level and that estimated from the acceleration measurements, for the results presented in Figure 9. Although the points are rather scattered, the power ratio remains smaller than 2 dB for $0.8<kl<1.5$. Below this frequency range, the measured power rises sharply above the prediction, as a result of the previous observation made on the data presented in Figure 9. When $kl>1.5$, the prediction rises slowly above the measurement, mainly because the block does not behave as a compact radiator anymore, and the simplified equations presented here do not apply. The radiation efficiency decreases as the frequency increases, which explains the clear negative slope when $kl > 1$. The power ratio between the measurement and the prediction remains roughly the same when the gap length (and the shedding Strouhal number) varies, and is a function of the frequency only. At this point, it can be concluded that a systematic discrepancy exists between the theory and the measurements at the bottom end of the wavenumber range $kl<0.8$. Before questioning the applicability of Curle's equation to this experimental case, it is worth reviewing the possible sources of error in the measurements. Figure 10 shows that the discrepancy is a globally decreasing function of the frequency (or the flow velocity), and is not significantly affected by the value of G. Although this can be explained in the higher frequency range, it is expected that the power ratio reaches a plateau at zero as kl decreases to zero, and the acoustic source becomes compact.

One possible source of discrepancy is related to the use of Beranek's formula to convert the measured sound pressure level into sound power level. This approach, although practical, would be advantageously replaced by a narrow-band room calibration procedure, with a point source of known acoustic power, which could also be located near the studied source. Use of this formula adds an uncertainty that warrants further investigation when the discrepancy is less than 5 dB.

Another possible cause of discrepancy, already suggested from the data presented in Figure 9 when $kl<0.8$, is flow induced unwanted noise, which is now investigated.

5.4. Background noise

In the present case, acoustic background noise defines any acoustic pressure fluctuation that is not caused by the surface pressure fluctuation occurring on the two main faces of the block, causing its oscillation along the z-axis. For example, the noise that is generated by the blade alone, or pressure fluctuations occurring on the vertical surfaces of the block are also considered as noise, in spite of their tonal quality.

Assuming that the block does not significantly affect the noise generated by the vortex generating airfoil alone, as is the case for larger values of G/D, the background noise generated by the upstream blade can be roughly estimated by removing the block. A comparison of the sound power PSD measured with and without the block is shown in Figure 11, for U_∞=50, 100 and 150 m/s, and $G=6.25D$. As for the tone, the peak generated by the interaction between the vortex street and the block is 12 to 18 dB above the peak generated by the blade vortex shedding alone. At lower frequencies, the broad band noise in the presence of the block is not significantly higher than that measured without it. However, the signal to noise ratio around the peak of interest remains above 12 dB, which is acceptable, and it can be concluded that the noise generated by the upstream blade does not significantly perturb the sound power measurements around the vortex shedding tone.

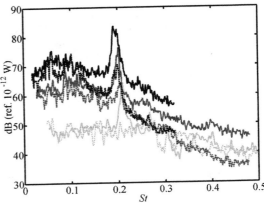

Figure 11 Background noise generated by the blade alone. Comparison between the noise generated by the blade alone and with the block. $G=6.3D$
—50, —100 and ⋯150 m/s.
— : with block ⋯: without block

In order to explain the discrepancy between the measurements and the theoretical prediction, a further understanding of the flow structure is needed. To this effect, the wall pressure is measured at the centre of the upstream blade trailing edge, using a pinhole microphone. The measured spectrum displays a peak at the same frequency as that observed on the block acceleration spectrum. If the schematic representation of Figure 7 were exact, then the trailing edge pressure sensor would be at the centre of a vortex shedding pattern, and sense a pressure fluctuation every time a vortex is shed from the trailing edge, resulting in a peak frequency that is twice that of the block acceleration. The flow pattern does therefore not correspond to what is sketched in Figure 7. This does not affect the applicability of Curle's equation, but makes the block leading edge face a potentially strong noise contributor, since the pressure fluctuation on this flow facing surface can be expected to be more intense than on the upper and lower surfaces of the block. Indeed, Figure 7 implies that this surface generates noise at a frequency that is twice that of the block's oscillation and therefore does not affect the measurements. This is contradicted by the fact that the upstream blade trailing edge wall pressure fluctuates at the same frequency as the block motion. The upstream face of the block is therefore very likely to contribute significantly to the measured sound power level at the frequency of interest. Furthermore, as noted earlier, the Strouhal number varies slightly when the flow velocity decreases below a certain threshold. This indicates the possibility of a slight variation in the flow pattern, where at low flow velocities the shed vortices strongly impinge on the block's leading edge rather than being convected past the block's horizontal surfaces when the Reynolds number is higher. The relative contribution form the block's flow facing surface would then be more important at lower flow speeds, therefore explaining the divergence between the theoretical prediction and the sound power measurements in the low frequency region. As observed earlier, a phenomenon of this type is further evidenced by the presence in the measurement of a low frequency hump that does not appear in the prediction, while the other, higher frequency features of both curves match well (Figure 9).

The noise generated by the vertical faces of the block could be estimated with another accelerometer inserted in the block along the streamwise direction, provided the motion in this direction is an accurate response to the surface pressure loading. A more adapted solution to this problem would be to measure only the sound pressure signal that is coherent with the measured block acceleration, but it cannot be implemented simply in a reverberant room. Indeed, the reverberation time is such that coherence measurements would require FFT computations on very long time series, which is not technically feasible, considering the frequency range of interest.

Alternative techniques using appropriate delays or phased microphone arrays could also be implemented, but are likely to lead to more uncertainty due to the difficulties related to the reverberant environment. Other solutions to be implemented are suggested in the conclusions below.

6. Conclusions

In order to evaluate the applicability of Curle's equation for a concentrated hydrodynamic force to an acoustically compact block in a fluctuating airflow, both the applied force and the radiated acoustic power need to be measured. The test rig used by Bies et al. [7] was found to be convenient to measure the force that a vortex wake applies to such an object. The radiated acoustic power was then estimated in a reverberant chamber based on sound pressure measurements made at three different locations. Although this technique greatly facilitates the sound power estimation, it relies on a number of hypotheses relative to such measurements and presents the major inconvenience that any unwanted noise contributions from secondary sources are also integrated in this estimation. For example, if the flow impingement on other faces of the block containing the z-axis also generates noise, the associated force fluctuation cannot be measured from the single accelerometer placed in the block along the z-axis. This very phenomenon is thought to be a possible cause for the divergence observed between the measurements and the prediction in the lower frequency range, especially on the flow-facing surface of the block.
Several solutions to this problem are envisaged:
The block can be equipped with accelerometers oriented along the two other directions x and y, and its suspension stiffness

relaxed in these directions so the corresponding forces can be estimated using the same technique. In a first step, a streamwise accelerometer could be installed as most of this suspected extraneous contribution can be assumed to come from the vertical face of the block's leading edge.

The fluctuating surface pressure can be measured on all faces of the block[16], which would then allow their relative contribution to the overall radiated sound power to be estimated. This solution is, however, limited by considerations of technical feasibility, and is made difficult because of the spatial averaging effect of the block. On one hand, the surface pressure measured by a pinhole sensor contains a broad range of wavenumbers. On the other hand, the block acts as a spatial filter and does not respond to the wall pressure fluctuations generated by the smaller scales of the flow, i.e. the high wavenumber components. Use of pinhole pressure sensors therefore requires further processing in order to extract the relevant signal only[16].

The measurements can also be performed in an anechoic room and the dipole field radiated in the direction of the measured block acceleration can be easily separated from the other noise, by measuring the sound field directivity, and with signal processing techniques to extract the sound pressure field directly related to the measured block motion. The absence of acoustic reflections allows the estimation of the coherent output power of the acoustic signal with the block acceleration as reference. This approach also clearly presents the advantage of validating the phenomena that are assumed to take place, mainly by checking the dipole nature of the sound field.

Finally, fluid flow measurements such as Particle Image Velocimetry or Laser Doppler Anemometry would also be useful to determine the actual flow structure, and estimate the validity of the assumptions made regarding the flow field. These measurements could be carried out in the reverberant chamber, and in an anechoic room, where flow measurements synchronised with pressure measurements would yield useful information on the noise generating phenomena. The use of conditional sampling techniques with synchronised measurements would enable the decomposition of the phenomena involved, in order to enhance understanding, and pinpoint the possible sources of discrepancy between the theory and the experiment.

The results presented in this paper show some agreement with the prediction based on Curle's theory, but a discrepancy of approximately 2 dB remains unaccounted for. Some possible sources of discrepancy were identified, and the next stage of this study will be carried out in an anechoic facility, with an enhanced sensing system, new data acquisition and processing techniques. This will considerably diminish the sources of extraneous noise, and allow a clear identification of noise generating phenomena of interest. This study is part of a larger program aiming at clearly identifying an aerodynamic noise generation phenomenon, obtaining a model, and implementing noise control techniques on this source. Although some work is still needed for a clear and definite description of the noise generation, the present work provides a reliable basis for active noise control implementation and testing[8,16].

Acknowledgements

This work is supported by a Large ARC Grant from the Australian Research Council.
The authors acknowledge a valuable contribution from George Osborne who made the sensing equipment that was not commercially available, and built the test rig.

[1] M.J. LIGHTHILL 1952 *Proceedings of the Royal Society, Series A* **221**, 564-587. On sound Generated Aerodynamically – I : General Theory.

[2] N. CURLE 1955 *Proceedings of the Royal Society, Series A* **231**, 505-514. The influence of solid boundaries upon aerodynamic sound.

[3] W.K. BLAKE 1986 *Mechanics of Flow Induced Sound and Vibration. Volume I.* Academic Press Inc.

[4] J.E. FFOWCS-WILLIAMS AND D.L. HAWKINGS 1969 *Phil.Trans. Roy. Soc. (London) Ser. A*, 264, 321-342. Sound generation by turbulence and surfaces in arbitrary motion.

[5] M.E. GOLDSTEIN 1976 *Aeroacoustics New York : McGraw-Hill International Book Co.* p 124.

[6] A.D. PIERCE 1989 *Acoustics : an introduction to its principles and applications.* Acoustial Society of America.

[7] D.A. BIES , J.M. PICKLES, AND D.J.J. LECLERCQ 1997 *Journal of Sound and Vibration* **204**(4), 631-634. Aerodynamic Noise Generation by a Stationary Body in a Turbulent Air Stream.

[8] M.K. SYMES, D.J.J. LECLERCQ, C.H. HANSEN 2002 *ACTIVE2002 Conference, July 2002 Southampton UK.* Sensing techniques for active control of aerodynamic noise.

[9] P.J.F. CLARK AND H.S. RIBNER 1970 *Journal of the Acoustical Society of America* **46**,3(2) 802-805. Direct Correlation of Fluctuating Lift with Radiated Sound for an Airfoil in Turbulent Flow.

[10] H.H. HELLER AND S.E. WINDNALL 1970 *Journal of the Acoustical Society of America* **47**,3(2) 924-936. Sound Radiation from Rigid Flow Spoilers Correlated with Fluctuating Forces.

[11] G.H. KOOPMANN 1969 PhD Thesis, Catholic Univ. Washington, D.C. Wind induced vibrations and their associated sound fields.

[12] P. LEEHEY AND C.E. HANSON 1971 *Journal of Sound and Vibration* **13**, 465-483. Aeolian tones associated with resonant vibration.

[13] B.T. MARTIN AND D.A. BIES 1992 *Journal of Sound and Vibration* **155**(2), 317-324. On Aerodynamic Noise Generation from Vortex Shedding in Rotating Blades.

[14] D.A. BIES, C.H. HANSEN 1996 *Engineering Noise Control* 2nd Edition, p.208

[15] A.M. BLAZEWICZ 2000 *PhD dissertation, The University of Adelaide, Department of Mechanical Engineering.* Noise Generation by interaction of vortex wakes and bluff bodies. Currently being reviewed.

[16] M.K. SYMES, D.J.J. LECLERCQ, C.H. HANSEN 2002 *ICSV9, Orlando USA, July 2002.* Surface pressure sensing for active control of aerodynamic noise.

SIMULATION OF SOUND GENERATION BY VORTICES PASSING THE TRAILING EDGE OF AIRFOILS

Markus Lummer [*], Jan W. Delfs [†], and Thomas Lauke [*]

German Aerospace Center (DLR), Lilienthalplatz 7, D-38108 Braunschweig

The interaction of vorticity with the trailing edge of airfoils is an important source of airframe noise. In order to study this process, in the present paper the interaction of a single vortex with the trailing edge of a symmetric Joukowsky airfoil under $0°$ angle of attack is calculated by the solution of nonlinear disturbance equations with a RANS mean flow in the Mach number range from 0.2 to 0.5. Nonlinearities are taken into account up to first order. The emphasis of the present study rests on the assessment of the influence of the Mach number and non-linearities on the generated sound field. It has been found that the sound intensity downstream of the profile scales approximately like M^4, which is near to the theoretical value. Taking into account non-linearities increases the sound pressure level in case of mathematically negative rotating initial vortices and decreases it in case of positive rotating ones. This should be kept in mind in the assessment of solutions obtained by the linearized Euler equations.

Introduction

The most accurate way to calculate the generation and propagation of sound in flows is the solution of the unsteady conservation laws of mass, momentum, and energy. Since this direct numerical simulation is even for simple flows an extremely expensive task, a lot of approximative methods have been proposed in order to attack real world problems. One of them is the splitting of the flow field in mean flow and turbulent and acoustic fluctuations. The mean flow is approximated by a solution of the Reynolds averaged equations (RANS), the turbulent fluctuations e.g. by an SNGR model (Stochastic Noise Generation and Radiation),[1-4] and the acoustic fluctuations by the solution of disturbance equations, e.g. the linearized Euler equations (LEE). This approach is utilized in the german SWING project (Simulation of WIng-flow Noise Generation), which shall provide the general computer code PIANO (Perturbation Investigation of Aeroacoustic NOise) for the calculation of airframe noise, especially that generated by high lift devices.

One well known mechanism of sound generation is the interaction of vorticity with airfoil trailing edges.[5-7] Therefore, in the SWING project, as one test case, the passing of single vortices over the trailing edge of airfoils is considered. As simple geometry, a symmetric Joukowsky airfoil of 10% thickness was chosen. The main objective there is to study the basic interaction process and to assess the influence of different Mach numbers and of non-linearities on the generated sound field.

A similar problem has been investigated previously by Singer et al.,[7] who calculated the generation and propagation of trailing edge noise by means of unsteady CFD calculations and solution of the Ffowcs Williams-Hawkings equation. To the large amount of analytical investigations belong the papers of Ffowcs Williams & Hall[5] and Howe.[6]

This paper is structured as follows: First, a derivation of the disturbance equations including nonlinear terms up to first order and some information upon the numerical solution procedure is given. Then some details follow of the calculation of the mean flow, a description of the computational domain and the initial conditions of the CAA calculations. Next, information about the evolution of the sound field in case of linear and nonlinear vortex interaction will be presented. Finally, the directivity and the scaling of the sound intensity with the Mach number will be discussed.

The Governing Equations

Although a RANS mean flow will be used in the solution of the disturbance equations, their derivation is demonstrated without loss of generality on the basis of the Euler equations, since viscosity effects on the sound field will be neglected.

One starts with the Euler equations for the fields of density ϱ^*, velocity $\mathbf{v}^*$ and pressure p^* for an inviscid fluid

$$\partial_t \varrho^* + \nabla \cdot \varrho^* \mathbf{v}^* = 0 \qquad (1)$$

$$\varrho^* \left(\partial_t \mathbf{v}^* + \mathbf{v}^* \cdot \nabla \mathbf{v}^* \right) + \nabla p^* = 0 \qquad (2)$$

$$\partial_t p^* + \mathbf{v}^* \cdot \nabla p^* + \gamma p^* \nabla \cdot \mathbf{v}^* = 0 \qquad (3)$$

$\gamma = c_p/c_v$ denotes the ratio of the specific heats. The pressure equation was derived from the balances of mass and energy using the equation of state for an ideal gas $p^* = (\gamma-1)\varrho^* e^*$. The equations were brought into dimensionless form with a reference length L, a reference density ϱ_∞ and a reference velocity a_∞ which was chosen to be the velocity of sound far away from the body.

*Research Engineer, Department of Technical Acoustics, Institute of Aerodynamics and Flow Technology, German Aerospace Center (DLR)

†Prof. at the TU Braunschweig, Head Technical Acoustics, Institute of Aerodynamics and Flow Technology, German Aerospace Center (DLR)

In order to derive the nonlinear disturbance equations, the flow field is split into a mean flow $\varrho_0, \mathbf{v}_0, p_0$ and disturbances $\varrho, \mathbf{v}, p$

$$\varrho^* = \varrho_0 + \varepsilon\varrho \quad , \quad \mathbf{v}^* = \mathbf{v}_0 + \varepsilon\mathbf{v} \quad , \quad p^* = p_0 + \varepsilon p \quad (4)$$

The coefficient ε is a measure for the magnitude of the disturbances. Substitution into the Euler equations yields

$$\partial_t\varrho_0 + \nabla \cdot \varrho_0\mathbf{v}_0 + \varepsilon\left[\partial_t\varrho + \nabla \cdot \varrho\mathbf{v}_0 + \nabla \cdot \varrho_0\mathbf{v}\right] + \\ + \varepsilon^2\nabla \cdot \varrho\mathbf{v} = 0 \quad (5)$$

$$(\varrho_0 + \varepsilon\varrho)(\partial_t\mathbf{v}_0 + \mathbf{v}_0 \cdot \nabla\mathbf{v}_0) + \nabla p_0 + \\ + \varepsilon\left[(\varrho_0 + \varepsilon\varrho)(\partial_t\mathbf{v} + \mathbf{v}_0 \cdot \nabla\mathbf{v} + \mathbf{v} \cdot \nabla\mathbf{v}_0 + \\ + \varepsilon\mathbf{v} \cdot \nabla\mathbf{v}) + \nabla p\right] = 0 \quad (6)$$

$$\partial_t p_0 + \mathbf{v}_0 \cdot \nabla p_0 + \gamma p_0 \cdot \nabla\mathbf{v}_0 + \\ + \varepsilon\left[\partial_t p + \mathbf{v} \cdot \nabla p_0 + \mathbf{v}_0 \cdot \nabla p + \\ + \gamma p\nabla \cdot \mathbf{v}_0 + \gamma p_0\nabla \cdot \mathbf{v}\right] + \\ + \varepsilon^2\left[\mathbf{v} \cdot \nabla p + \gamma p\nabla \cdot \mathbf{v}\right] = 0 \quad (7)$$

Now, one can determine the mean flow from the Euler equations

$$\partial_t\varrho_0 + \nabla \cdot \varrho_0\mathbf{v}_0 = 0 \quad (8)$$
$$\varrho_0\left(\partial_t\mathbf{v}_0 + \mathbf{v}_0 \cdot \nabla\mathbf{v}_0\right) + \nabla p_0 = 0 \quad (9)$$
$$\partial_t p_0 + \mathbf{v}_0 \cdot \nabla p_0 + \gamma p_0\nabla \cdot \mathbf{v}_0 = 0 \quad (10)$$

and obtains, assuming a steady mean flow, the following set of equations for the nonlinear disturbances

$$\partial_t\varrho + \nabla \cdot \varrho\mathbf{v}_0 + \nabla \cdot \varrho_0\mathbf{v} + \varepsilon\nabla \cdot \varrho\mathbf{v} = 0 \quad (11)$$

$$\partial_t\mathbf{v} + \mathbf{v}_0 \cdot \nabla\mathbf{v} + \mathbf{v} \cdot \nabla\mathbf{v}_0 + \varepsilon\mathbf{v} \cdot \nabla\mathbf{v} + \\ + \frac{\varrho\mathbf{v}_0 \cdot \nabla\mathbf{v}_0 + \nabla p}{\varrho_0 + \varepsilon\varrho} = 0 \quad (12)$$

$$\partial_t p + \mathbf{v} \cdot \nabla p_0 + \mathbf{v}_0 \cdot \nabla p + \\ + \gamma p\nabla \cdot \mathbf{v}_0 + \gamma p_0\nabla \cdot \mathbf{v} + \varepsilon\left[\mathbf{v} \cdot \nabla p + \gamma p\nabla \cdot \mathbf{v}\right] = 0 \quad (13)$$

In order to obtain a system up to $O(\varepsilon)$ one can use

$$\frac{1}{\varrho_0 + \varepsilon\varrho} \approx \frac{1}{\varrho_0}\left(1 - \varepsilon\frac{\varrho}{\varrho_0}\right) \quad (14)$$

and write the equations in the final form

$$\partial_t\varrho + (\mathbf{v}_0 + \varepsilon\mathbf{v}) \cdot \nabla\varrho + (\varrho_0 + \varepsilon\varrho)\nabla \cdot \mathbf{v} + \\ + \varrho\nabla \cdot \mathbf{v}_0 + \mathbf{v} \cdot \nabla\varrho_0 = 0 \quad (15)$$

$$\partial_t\mathbf{v} + (\mathbf{v}_0 + \varepsilon\mathbf{v}) \cdot \nabla\mathbf{v} + \mathbf{v} \cdot \nabla\mathbf{v}_0 + \\ + \left(1 - \varepsilon\frac{\varrho}{\varrho_0}\right)\frac{\varrho\mathbf{v}_0 \cdot \nabla\mathbf{v}_0 + \nabla p}{\varrho_0} = 0 \quad (16)$$

$$\partial_t p + (\mathbf{v}_0 + \varepsilon\mathbf{v}) \cdot \nabla p + \gamma(p_0 + \varepsilon p)\nabla \cdot \mathbf{v} + \\ + \mathbf{v} \cdot \nabla p_0 + \gamma p\nabla \cdot \mathbf{v}_0 = 0 \quad (17)$$

Numerical Algorithm

These equations were solved on a structured multi-block grid. Every block had curvilinear coordinates $\mathbf{x}(\xi, \eta, \zeta)$, where the continuous parameters (ξ, η, ζ) coincide with the index values of the discrete gridpoints at the nodes of the grid. The spatial derivatives were approximated by the usual 4th-order DRP-stencils.[8] Time integration was done by the standard 4th-order Runge-Kutta procedure. Inflow and outflow boundary conditions according to Tam and Webb[8] were used. The time step size in all calculations was $\Delta t = 2 \times 10^{-4}$.

Filtering

Since the utilized DRP-schemes have no dissipation, an efficient removal of spurious waves, i.e. waves which cannot be resolved on the numerical grid was necessary. The usual way to do this is to use artificial selective damping.[9] This approach is quite expensive, since additional terms have to be calculated in the differential equations. A more convenient way is to use suitable digital filters[10, 11] on the fields, periodically applied during the calculation. In the PIANO code, symmetric 6th- and 8th-order filters are implemented. In the present study, 8th-order filters were used every 25 time steps. The 6th- ($N = 3$) and 8th-order ($N = 4$) filter are defined as[10]

$$\overline{\Psi}_i = a_0\Psi_i + \sum_{j=1}^{N} a_j\left(\Psi_{i+j} + \Psi_{i-j}\right) \quad (18)$$

where the 6th-order filter coefficients are

$$a_0 = 0.6875 \, , \, a_1 = 0.46875 \, , \, a_2 = -0.1875 \, , \\ a_3 = 0.03125 \quad (19)$$

and the 8th-order ones

$$a_0 = 0.7265625 \, , \, a_1 = 0.4375 \, , \, a_2 = -0.21875 \, , \\ a_3 = 0.0625 \, , \, a_4 = -0.0078125 \quad (20)$$

$\overline{\Psi}_i$ is the filtered quantity and Ψ_i the unfiltered one. The filter is applied in the computational (ξ, η, ζ) space in the several space dimensions subsequently. No filtering was used in the first N layers normal to a wall.

Calculation of the Mean Flow

The RANS mean flow was calculated with the DLR FLOWer code.[12-14] This code solves the Navier-Stokes equations on a structured multi-block grid. Turbulence was taken into account utilizing the 2 equations k–ω model of Wilcox. The angle of attack of the profile was $\alpha = 0°$. The mean flow was calculated for the Mach numbers 0.2, 0.3, 0.4, and 0.5. Fig. 1 shows the contours of the pressure coefficient c_P and streamlines for the Mach number M = 0.2 and the Reynolds number Re $= 1.6 \times 10^6$. The Joukowsky airfoil of

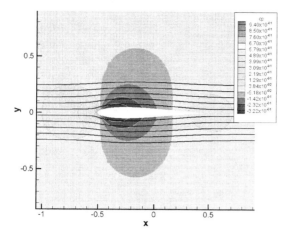

Fig. 1   The RANS mean flow for M = 0.2: Pressure coefficient c_P and streamlines.

chord length 1.0 is 10% thick and its leading and trailing edges are located on the y-axis at $x = -0.5$ and $x = +0.5$ respectively. Since it is not feasible to perform RANS calculations on CAA grids, the mean flow was transferred from the RANS grid to the CAA grid by interpolation.[15]

The Computational Grid

For the examination of the vortex trailing edge interaction it is sufficient to consider only the rear part $x > 0$ of the Joukowsky profile. The computational domain chosen was $0 < x < 1$ and $-0.5 < y < +0.5$. The density of the gridlines was increased in the boundary layers of the wing section, in the trailing edge region, and along the flow path of the vortex (cf. Fig. 2). The grid is a multi-block grid consisting of 4 blocks and a total of 34700 grid points.

The Initial Conditions

The initial disturbances of the density and pressure field were set to zero. The initial disturbance of the velocity field was obtained from a vortex of length scale r_0, which is located at the position x_0, y_0. Its stream function and velocities are

$$\Psi = r_0 V \sqrt{\frac{e}{2\ln 2}}\, e^{-\ln 2 \left(\frac{r}{r_0}\right)^2} \quad (21)$$

$$r = \sqrt{(x-x_0)^2 + (y-y_0)^2}$$

$$u = +\partial_y \Psi = -V\sqrt{2e\ln 2}\frac{y-y_0}{r_0}\, e^{-\ln 2\left(\frac{r}{r_0}\right)^2} \quad (22)$$

$$v = -\partial_x \Psi = +V\sqrt{2e\ln 2}\frac{x-x_0}{r_0}\, e^{-\ln 2\left(\frac{r}{r_0}\right)^2} \quad (23)$$

V denotes the strength of the vortex. Its absolute value is the absolute value of the largest velocity in the vortex. $V > 0$ corresponds to a vortex rotating

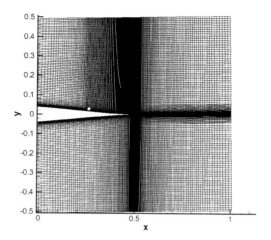

Fig. 2   The CAA grid (The small white circle at the upper surface marks the initial position of the vortex.)

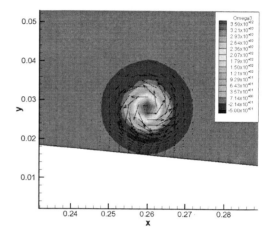

Fig. 3   The initial vortex: velocity field and vorticity for $V = +0.5$

in mathematically positive (counter-clockwise) direction. Depending on the sign of V, in the present paper is distinguished between positive or negative rotating vortices.

The length scale of the initial vortex was set to $r_0 = 5 \times 10^{-3}$ chord length. Its initial position was $x_0 = 0.26$, $y_0 = 0.028$, which means that the vortex core is outside of the boundary layer of the profile. The distance of the vortex core to the wall is about 1.2% of the chord length. Fig. 3 shows the initial velocity field of the vortex and the corresponding vorticity distribution $\omega = \partial_x v - \partial_y u$.

Since one can assume, that the disturbance velocities in the boundary layers scale roughly with the mean flow Mach number, the initial strength of the vortex, i.e. $|V|$, was chosen to be equal to the Mach number of the mean flow. Moreover, this guarantees that for different mean flow Mach numbers the same absolute value of the parameter ε denotes the same amount of non-linearity in the performed calculations.

At the wall, the initial velocity was forced to be tangential.

A total of 24 calculations were performed. For every Mach number M the vortex initial strength $V = \pm M$, and the nonlinearities $\varepsilon = 0, 0.05$, and 0.10 were examined. This corresponds to positive and negative rotating initial vortices in the linear case ($\varepsilon = 0$) and with 5% ($\varepsilon = 0.05$) and 10% ($\varepsilon = 0.10$) non-linearity.

The Sound Field in the Linear Case

In order to get an impression of the evolution of the sound field, the linear case M = 0.2, $V = +0.2$, $\varepsilon = 0$ is considered first.

It is well known that a vortex in a homogeneous mean flow produces no sound field. The vortex above is located in close vicinity of the profile and one expects by its interaction with the wall and the shear flow of the boundary layer the production of a hydrodynamic and acoustic pressure field. In order to interpret this process it is convenient to consider first a vortex in a uniform mean flow in the vicinity of a wall. By simple geometric considerations, one can conclude that a positive rotating vortex has to have a positive hydrodynamic core pressure and a negative rotating a negative one. A vortex with this matched hydrodynamic pressure field would then be convected along the wall without producing any sound waves.

Since the correct (non-radiating) pressure field corresponding to the velocity of the vortex is not known initially, the pressure and density field was initialized with 0. These initial conditions lead to the development of a strong pressure pulse just after start of the calculation. This initial bang can be seen in Fig. 4(a). In order to distinguish the pressure signal generated by the vortex trailing edge interaction from this initial artefact, it is important to locate the initial vortex sufficiently upstream from the trailing edge.

The initial pressure wave is diffracted at the trailing edge (cf. Fig 4(a)) at $t \approx 0.30$ and finally leaves the computational domain. Meanwhile, the vortex is convected downstream along the wall towards the trailing edge.

At $t \approx 1.30$ the vortex reaches the trailing edge and starts generating a sound wave (cf. Fig.4(b)). It can be seen that most of the generated sound is radiated upstream of the mean flow field (cf. Fig.4(c)). In case of a positive rotating vortex, the sign of the front of the generated sound wave is positive above the profile and negative below.

While the pressure wave leaves the computational domain, the vortex is convected further downstream and finally hits the outflow boundary (cf. Fig.4(d)). At this moment, by the imperfect outflow boundary

conditions implemented, a strong sound signal is generated and contaminates the flow field. Especially at higher Mach numbers, when the convection velocity is higher and this outflow bang occurs earlier, one has to assure that contamination of the sound signal of the vortex trailing edge interaction is avoided by a sufficient large computational domain downstream.

More appropriate boundary conditions which allow a silent outflow of vorticity are currently under investigation in the development of the PIANO code.

In case of a negative rotating initial vortex, the generated sound field changes only its sign for linear disturbances. This can easily be seen by analyzing the symmetries of the linearized Euler equations.

Influence of Mean Flow Mach Number

The sound field was calculated for the mean flow Mach numbers M = 0.2, 0.3, 0.4, and 0.5. The main effect of increasing the Mach number of the mean flow in the linear case is a more rapid interaction of the vortex with the trailing edge which results in significantly higher pressure levels.

Fig. 5 shows the pressure signal of the vortex trailing edge interaction recorded at a point 0.4 chord length above the trailing edge of the profile.

As expected, the higher the mean flow Mach number, the earlier the vortex trailing edge interaction starts and the sound wave arrives at the control point. Moreover, the convection velocity of the vortex over the trailing edge also reduces the time scale (e.g. the time difference between minimum and maximum) of the pressure wave.

Finally, one recognizes the overlinear growth of the peak values of the pressure with increasing Mach number. If one takes into account that the initial strength of the vortex was set equal to the Mach number, one concludes that the velocity of the vortex trailing edge interaction also increases the sound signal by itself.

The scaling of the sound intensity with the Mach number will be discussed in detail below.

The Sound Field in the Nonlinear Case

Taking into account nonlinearity alters the level of the generated pressure pulse significantly. The amount of nonlinearity is controlled by the value of the parameter ε.

Fig. 6 shows the pressure signals 0.4 chord length above the trailing edge for $\varepsilon = 0, 0.05$, and 0.10 as well as for positive ($V > 0$) and negative rotating ($V < 0$) initial vortices. Like already mentioned, the sign of the initial vortex strength determines the sign of the generated pressure field. The non-linearity has different effects for positive and negative rotating initial vortices. In case of positive rotating initial vortices, the pressure signal drops with increasing non-linearity, whereas in the other case the pressure signal is amplified with increasing non-linearity.

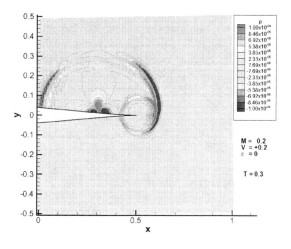

a) $t = 0.3$, propagation of initial bang

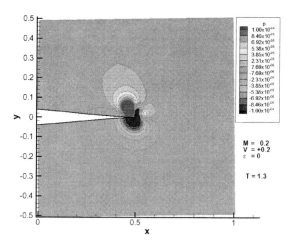

b) $t = 1.3$, start of vortex trailing edge interaction

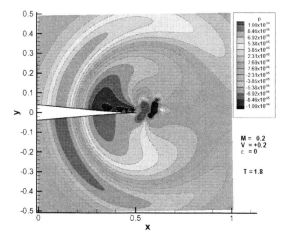

c) $t = 1.8$, propagation of sound wave

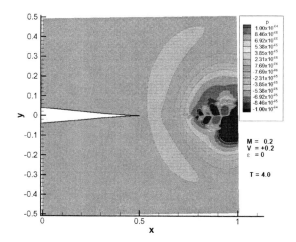

d) $t = 4.0$, numerical noise generation by outflowing vortex

Fig. 4   Pressure field

The explanation for this behavior is that taking into account non-linearity has the tendency to reduce the pressure in the vortex core by the action of centrifugal forces. In case of positive initial rotation, the positive core pressure is reduced, and in case of negative initial rotation, the negative core pressure is enlarged. This lets one expect that the individuality of the vortex is decreased in case of a positive rotating vortex and increased in case of a negative rotating one.

This clearly can be seen if one looks at the flow field of the vortex in vicinity of the trailing edge (cf. Fig. 7). Again, we consider the Mach number M = 0.2.

Fig. 7(a) shows the pressure and velocity field for the linear positive rotating vortex shortly before its interaction with the trailing edge. The position of the vortex core is at $x \lesssim 0.48$. One sees that an opposite rotating vortex with negative core pressure has devel-

oped a little bit downstream.

Fig. 7(b) shows the same situation for the nonlinear ($\varepsilon = 0.10$) positive rotating vortex. It can be seen, that the core pressure is significantly reduced. This reduced pressure in combination with smaller velocities decreases the intensity of the interaction with the trailing edge and therefore the generated sound field.

Figs. 7(c) and 7(d) show the situation for the nonlinear negative rotating vortex. It can be seen, that the negative pressure of the core is further decreased and the velocities are increased. Therefore one expects a stronger interaction with the trailing edge and a distinct stronger generated sound field than in the linear case.

Further investigation of the nonlinear pressure signals in Fig. 6 reveals with increasing non-linearity a slight shift of the first extrema towards smaller times

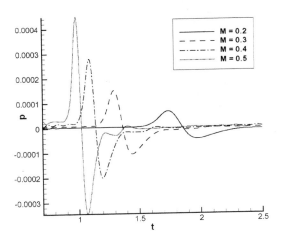

Fig. 5 Pressure history of the vortex trailing edge interaction at $(x, y) = (0.5, 0.4)$ for different Mach numbers in the linear case $\varepsilon = 0$

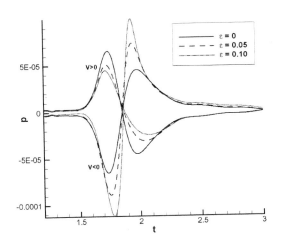

Fig. 6 Pressure history at $(x, y) = (0.5, 0.4)$ for M $= 0.2$ and different non-linearities for positive $(V > 0)$ and negative $(V < 0)$ rotating vortices

in case of $V > 0$ and to larger times in case $V < 0$. This can be explained by the influence of the induced velocity field of the mirror vortex (which is not present in the linear case), that increases the convection velocity of the positive rotating vortex and decreases that of the negative rotating one.

Directivity and Mach Number Scaling

In order to calculate the directivity of the sound field, the pressure field has to be considered in a reference frame moving with the mean flow velocity U. This situation is sketched in Fig. 8. The moving frame has the origin O^* and the polar coordinates (r, ϕ^*). The resting frame is centered in the trailing edge O and has the polar coordinates (R, ϕ). The circle C^*

stands for a wave front which is generated at $t = 0$ at the trailing edge and propagates radially in the moving frame with the velocity of sound a.

The directivity is defined as the azimuthal dependence of the intensity I of the sound field in the moving reference frame, which is proportional to $\overline{p^2}$

$$I(\phi^*) \sim \overline{p^2} = \lim_{T \to \infty} \frac{1}{2T} \int_{-T}^{T} p^2(r, \phi^*, t)dt \quad (24)$$

This definition assumes self-similar solutions in the radial direction r, i.e. solutions of the form $p(r, \phi^*, t) = P(r)Q(\phi^*, t)$. The exact evaluation of this integral would require the storage of the pressure field for every time step, which is an extremely expensive task. As an approximation, it is possible to scan the pressure field by recording pressure values $p_c = p(R, \phi, t)$ at points S along a fixed circle C around the trailing edge (cf. Fig. 8) and to apply an angle and amplitude correction on p_c. The angle correction is obtained by the geometric relation between ϕ and ϕ^* of the triangle OO^*S

$$\phi^* = \arccos\left(\cos\phi\sqrt{1 - M^2\sin^2\phi} - M\sin^2\phi\right) \quad (25)$$

where M $= U/a$ stands for the mean flow Mach number.

The amplitude correction accounts for the fact that the pressure value $p_c(R, \phi, t)$ belongs to different radial distances r of the wave, depending on ϕ. p_c has to be decreased in vicinity of the origin O^* of the pressure wave and increased away from it. A simple geometric correction is as follows: if the radial dependence of the pressure in the moving frame is $P(r) \sim r^{-n}$, the corrected pressure value is

$$p(\phi, t) = p_c(\phi, t)\left(\frac{r(\phi)}{R}\right)^n \quad (26)$$

The exponent n is obtained from the analysis of the far field behavior of two dimensional cylindrical waves and set to $n = 0.5$. The ratio r/R is obtained again from the triangle OO^*S (cf. Fig. 8)

$$\frac{r(\phi)}{R} = \frac{1}{M\cos\phi + \sqrt{1 - M^2\sin^2\phi}} \quad (27)$$

In downstream direction $(\phi = 0)$, the pressure on the circle C is therefore decreased by the factor $1/(1+M)^n$ and in upstream direction $(\phi = \pi)$ increased by the factor $1/(1 - M)^n$.

Using the pressure values on the circle C, the directivity is now approximated by

$$I(\phi^*) \sim \left(\frac{r(\phi^*)}{R}\right)^{2n} \underbrace{\lim_{T \to \infty} \frac{1}{2T} \int_{-T}^{T} p_c^2(R, \phi^*, t)dt}_{\equiv I_c(\phi^*)} \quad (28)$$

1791

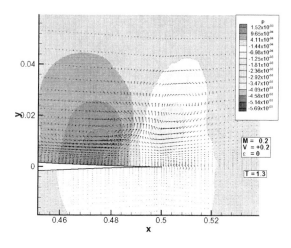

a) Linear case, positive rotating initial vortex

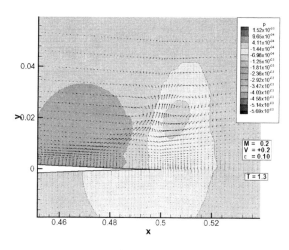

b) Nonlinear case, positive rotating initial vortex

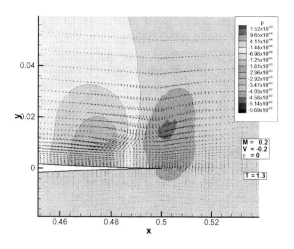

c) Linear case, negative rotating initial vortex

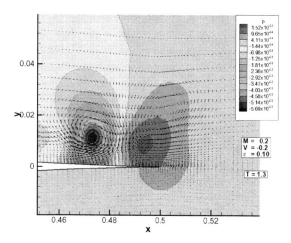

d) Nonlinear case, negative rotating initial vortex

Fig. 7 Influence of non-linearity at $t = 1.3$, **M** $= 0.2$

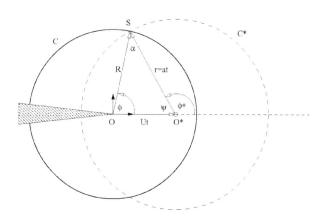

Fig. 8 The directivity in a moving frame

This formula applies to an infinite (or at least very long) signal, i.e. the interaction of a very large number of vortices with the trailing edge. In the present case, the pressure signal generated by the interaction of only one vortex with the trailing edge is considered. Therefore, one has a very short signal and the mean square value of the pressure can only be approximated by

$$I_c(\phi^*) \approx \frac{1}{\tau^*} \int_{t_0}^{t_1} p_c^2(R, \phi^*, t) dt \quad , \quad \tau^* = t_1 - t_0 \quad (29)$$

The integral has to be taken over the pressure signal of the vortex trailing edge interaction and τ^* is a measure for the time scale of the interaction. In order to determine the scaling of I with the Mach number it is convenient to consider the scaling of the integral and the scaling of the time scale τ^* separately.

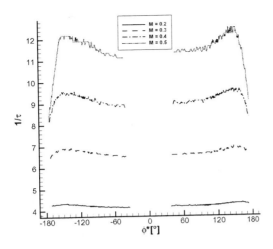

Fig. 9 The reciprocal of the interaction time $1/\tau$

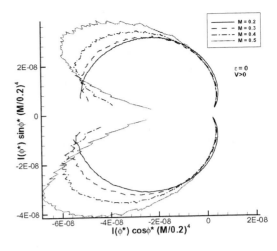

a) Linear case, positive rotating initial vortex

The integration boundaries t_0 and t_1 were determined by inspection of the time signal $p_c(t)$ (cf. Fig. 5) and chosen to be in the low pressure region sufficiently before and after the extrema of the pressure. Usually, t_0 and t_1 are functions of ϕ.

Unfortunately this gave no well defined values t_0, t_1 for the determination of the time scale τ^* of the interaction. As a resort, τ^* was replaced by the time difference τ between the two extrema of the pressure signal, i.e.

$$\tau = \left| t(p_c^{\max}) - t(p_c^{\min}) \right| \tag{30}$$

This assumes a linear relation between the time difference between the extrema of the signal and the whole interaction process, which seems to be quite reasonable. Fig. 9 shows the value of $1/\tau$ as function of ϕ^*. One observes a slightly superlinear scaling with the Mach number. Remarkable is the strong drop in the vicinity of the profile at higher Mach numbers.

Thus, the intensity is finally approximated by the expression

$$I(\phi^*) = \left(\frac{r(\phi^*)}{R} \right)^{2n} \frac{1}{\tau} \int_{t_0}^{t_1} p_c^2(R, \phi^*, t)dt \tag{31}$$

with $n = 0.5$.

Fig. 10 shows the polar plots of $I(\phi^*)$ in the linear case and for nonlinear disturbances ($\varepsilon = 0.10$) in case of negative and positive rotating initial vortices for different Mach numbers. The curves $I(\phi^*)$ were scaled according to M^4. This gives good coincidence in the linear case (Fig. 10(a)) for angles $|\phi^*| < 110°$. For nonlinear disturbances and a negative rotating initial vortex (Fig. 10(b)) the concidence of the intensity curves for M^4 scaling seems to be even a little bit better. Nonlinear disturbances combined with a positive rotating initial vortices $V > 0$ (Fig. 10(c)) show larger

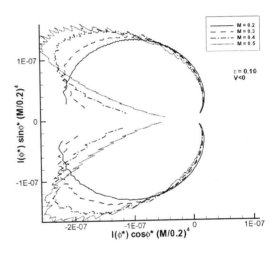

b) Nonlinear case, negative rotating initial vortex

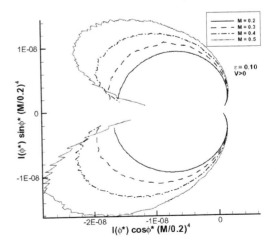

c) Nonlinear case, positive rotating initial vortex

Fig. 10 Directivity of sound intensity

discrepancies. A scaling proportional $M^{4.2}$ would give better coincidence in this case.

Larger discrepancies growing with Mach number occur in the upstream direction $|\phi^*| > 110°$. The reason for the failure of the scaling in upstream direction could be the presence of an inhomogeneous mean flow field. Especially at M = 0.5 and near the body, a strong decrease of sound intensity can be observed. This could be an effect of the boundary layers of the mean flow, which have the tendency to diffract the pressure waves away from the body. Due to the small length scale of the boundary layers, this effect is expected to be larger for the shorter wave length of the pressure waves at higher M.

From analytical considerations one expects a scaling of the far field sound intensity with M^4 in the 2-dimensional case.[7] This result is usually derived for the interaction of a turbulent boundary layer with the trailing edge of a flat plate in the limit M $\rightarrow$ 0. In light of the lot of approximations utilized for the calculation of the sound intensity, the correspondence between calculations and analytical predictions is remarkably good.

A point at issue could be the relatively small extent of the computational domain, which could hinder to reach the far field of the pressure inside its boundaries. In order to check the far field behavior of the sound field, pressure values on a circle moving with the pressure pulse have been extracted. The radial dependence of these pressure values was about $p \sim r^{-0.61}$, which is not too far away from the analytical far field behavior $p \sim r^{-0.5}$, although it is indicating some near field influence on the solution.

Summary and Conclusion

The sound generation due to the interaction of a single vortex with the trailing edge of a symmetric Joukowsky airfoil of 10% thickness has been calculated by the solution of nonlinear disturbance equations. Nonlinearities have been taken into account up to first order. The mean flow was calculated by the solution of RANS equations for 0° angle of attack. The Mach number was varied between M = 0.2 and M = 0.5.

The position of the initial vortex was on the upper part of the profile, about 0.24 chord length before the trailing edge and 0.012 chord length distance from the wall. Sound generation by positive and negative rotating initial vortices was considered. The maximum value of the scaled velocity of the initial vortex was set equal to the Mach number of the mean flow.

During its movement along the wall, the linear vortices developed a positive core pressure in case of positive rotation and a negative one in case of negative rotation.

Taking non-linearity into account reduced the pressure in the vortex core. This led to an attenuation of the positive rotating vortex, and to an intensification of the negative rotating one. This can clearly be seen in the plots of the flow field. As a result the pressure signal of the vortex trailing edge interaction was amplified for negative rotating vortices and decreased for positive rotating ones. Moreover, by induction from the mirror vortex, the convection velocity of the positive rotating vortex along the wall was slightly increased, and that of the negative rotating one slightly decreased.

The directivity of the sound intensity could be calculated only approximately from pressure values recorded on a static circle. In order to determine a scaling law, the mean square value of the pressure had to be approximated by the product of a reciprocal of a characteristic time of the interaction and an integral over the square of the pressure signal. Best scaling according to M^4 was achieved in the downstream region of the flow ($|\phi^*| < 110°$) in case of linear disturbances and nonlinear negative rotating ones. In case of nonlinear positive rotating vortices, a scaling with $M^{4.2}$ would give the best fit. These results compare quite well with the theoretical scaling law, which suggests a scaling according M^4.

Larger discrepancies have been found in upstream direction for higher mean flow Mach numbers and in vicinity of the profile. The reason for this could be the inhomogeneities of the mean flow, especially the presence of boundary layers. In conclusion a homogeneous scaling with M could not be observed for all radiation angles.

The influence of the non-linearities on the generated sound field was larger than the authors expected. However, since non-linearities can decrease and increase the sound pressure levels depending on the sign of the initial vortex disturbance, it could be possible that these opposite effects cancel in case of a turbulent boundary layer passing over the trailing edge of an airfoil. Nevertheless, CAA results obtained by the solution of the linearized Euler equations should be handled with care.

Future work will be focussed on realistic airfoil geometries with finite trailing edges and the presence of lift, including three-dimensional disturbances and far field extrapolations using integral methods.

References

[1]Bailly, C. and Juvé, D., "A stochastic approach to compute subsonic noise using linearized Euler's equations", AIAA-paper 99-1872, American Institute of Aeronautics and Astronautics, 1999.

[2]Bailly, C., Lafon, P., and Candel, S., "A stochastic approach to compute noise generation and radiation of free turbulent flows", *1st AIAA/CEAS Aeroacoustics Conference*, 1995.

[3]Bailly, C., Lafon, P., and Candel, S., "Computation of noise generation and propagation for free and confined turbulent flows", *2nd AIAA/CEAS Aeroacoustics Conference*, 1996.

[4]Kalitzin, N. and Wilde, A., "Application of the Stochastic Noise Generation and Radiation Model to Trailing Edge Noise", *Aeroacoustic Workshop in connection with the German*

research project *SWING — Proceedings*, edited by P. Költzsch and N. Kalitzin, TU Dresden, Dresden, 1999.

[5]Ffowcs Williams, J. E. and Hall, L. H., "Aerodynamic sound generation by turbulent flow in the vicinity of a scattering half plane", *Journal of Fluid Mechanics*, Vol. 40, 1970, pp. 657–670.

[6]Howe, M. S., "Trailing Edge Noise at Low Mach Numbers", *Journal of Sound and Vibration*, Vol. 225, No. 2, 1999, pp. 211–238.

[7]Singer, B. A., Brentner, K. S., Lockard, D. P., and Lilley, G. M., "Simulation of Acoustic Scattering from a Trailing edge", AIAA-paper 99-0231, American Institute of Aeronautics and Astronautics, 1999.

[8]Tam, C. K. W. and Webb, J. C., "Dispersion-Relation-Preserving Finite Difference Schemes for Computational Acoustics", *Journal of Computational Physics*, Vol. 107, 1993, pp. 262–281.

[9]Tam, C. K. W., Webb, J. C., and Dong, Z., "A study of the short wave components in computational acoustics", *Journal of Computational Acoustics*, Vol. 1, 1993, pp. 1–30.

[10]Shang, J. S., "High-Order Compact-Difference Schemes for Time-Dependent Maxwell Equations", *Journal of Computational Physics*, Vol. 153, 1999, pp. 312–333.

[11]Vasilyev, O. V., Lund, T. S., and Moin, P., "A General Class of Commutative Filters for LES in Complex Geometries", *Journal of Computational Physics*, Vol. 146, 1998, pp. 82–104.

[12]Aumann, P., Barnewitz, H., Schwarten, H., Becker, K., Heinrich, R., Roll, B., Galle, M., Kroll, N., Gerold, T., Schwamborn, D., and Franke, M., "MEGAFLOW: Parallel complete aircraft CFD", *Parallel Computing*, Vol. 27, No. 4, 2001, pp. 415–440.

[13]Kroll, N., Rossow, C.-C., Becker, K., and Thiele, F., "MEGAFLOW — A numerical flow simulation system", ICAS-Paper 98-2.7.4, 1998.

[14]Kroll, N., Rossow, C.-C., Becker, K., and Thiele, F., "The MEGAFLOW project", *Aerospace Science and Technology*, Vol. 4, No. 4, 2000, pp. 223–237.

[15]Lummer, M., Grogger, H. A., and Delfs, J. W., "Using RANS Mean Flow Fields in Numerical Aeroacoustics Simulations (CAA)", *NATO RTO-AVT Symposium on Aging Mechanisms and Control, Part A — Development in Computational Aero- and Hydro-Acoustics, Manchester, UK*, 8–11 Oct. 2001.

TIME-ACCURATE SIMULATIONS AND ACOUSTIC ANALYSIS OF SLAT FREE-SHEAR-LAYER: PART II

Mehdi R. Khorrami[*]
Bart A. Singer[†]
David P. Lockard[**]

NASA Langley Research Center
MS 128, Hampton, VA

Abstract

Unsteady computational simulations of a multi-element, high-lift configuration are performed. Emphasis is placed on accurate spatio-temporal resolution of the free shear layer in the slat-cove region. The excessive dissipative effects of the turbulence model, so prevalent in previous simulations, are circumvented by switching off the turbulence-production term in the slat cove region. The justifications and physical arguments for taking such a step are explained in detail. The removal of this excess damping allows the shear layer to amplify large-scale structures, to achieve a proper non-linear saturation state, and to permit vortex merging. The large-scale disturbances are self-excited, and unlike our prior fully turbulent simulations, no external forcing of the shear layer is required. To obtain the farfield acoustics, the Ffowcs Williams and Hawkings equation is evaluated numerically using the simulated time-accurate flow data. The present comparison between the computed and measured farfield acoustic spectra shows much better agreement for the amplitude and frequency content than past calculations. The effect of the angle-of-attack on the slat's flow features and radiated acoustic field are also simulated and presented.

1. Introduction

Experimental studies in both the US and Europe by researchers such as Meadows et al.,[1] Hayes et al.,[2] Dobrzynski et al.,[3,4] and Davy and Remy[5] have verified that the high-lift devices are significant contributors to airframe-radiated sound in the mid- to high-frequency range. In particular, the leading-edge slat and the side edges of the flaps have been identified as dominant noise sources. NASA, in collaboration with industrial and academic partners, has embarked on a major research program to enhance our fundamental understanding of airframe noise sources and then to apply this knowledge to develop effective noise-reduction technologies that do not compromise aerodynamic efficiency. The present computational study is part of a larger effort to understand the relevant aeroacoustic flow features associated with a leading edge slat in high-lift settings. Specifically, attention is directed towards accurate numerical simulations of the complex unsteady flow field in a slat-cove region.

In a series of in-house experiments conducted in the Low Turbulence Pressure Tunnel (LTPT) at NASA Langley Research Center (LaRC), aeroacoustic studies of a generic, Energy Efficient Transport (EET) wing were performed. The three-element, high-lift configuration was comprised of a slat, a main element, and a flap (Fig.1). The model's stowed chord was

[*]Research Scientist, Computational Modeling and Simulation Branch, Associate Fellow AIAA
[†]Assistant Branch Head, Computational Modeling and Simulation Branch, Senior Member AIAA
[**]Research Scientist, Computational Modeling and Simulation Branch, Senior Member AIAA

approximately ten percent relative to the mean aerodynamic chord of a Boeing 757. Acoustic measurements were obtained using a microphone array. Detailed discussion of the array location and orientation in the LTPT facility can be found in references 6 and 7. The experiments were carried out at several distinct angles of attack, a flap deflection angle of 30° and a slat deflection angle of 30°. During wind tunnel entries in 1998 and 1999, both aerodynamic and acoustic measurements were obtained. The 1998 entry involved a part-span flap that had a slightly different profile than the full-span flap employed in the 1999 entry. However, important parameters such as the slat's geometry, settings, and aerodynamic loading were unchanged for both entries, and the corresponding radiated sound fields (except for minor differences) remained nearly identical.

Sample microphone array measurements of the EET slat are shown in Fig. 2. The displayed spectra are in 1/12th-octave bands. The flow Mach number is 0.2, corresponding to a typical approach condition, and the Reynolds number (based on the stowed chord) is 7.2 million. The measurements show high sound levels in the lower frequency range followed by a gradual drop in the levels as the mid-frequency range is approached. In the vicinity of 50 *kHz*, the spectra display a rise in sound amplitude that seems to be tonal in nature. This high-frequency tonal feature was studied in detail by Khorrami, et al.[8] and Singer et al.[6] who found vortex shedding from the finite-thickness trailing edge to be its source. The occurrence of vortex shedding at a slat trailing edge was confirmed by Takeda et al.[9] using the Particle Image Velocimetry (PIV) technique to map the flow field of a European designed high-lift model. Although this tone is significant at model scale, its importance for a full-scale aircraft is likely to be diminished because of the smaller trailing-edge bluntness relative to boundary-layer thickness on a full-scale slat. Even if the tone exists at full scale, its source is now understood and strategies for its elimination are straightforward.

More central to our current effort is the behavior of the sound sources in the 1,000Hz to 10,000Hz frequency band range. In this range, the sound levels exhibit a gradual but noticeable increase as the angle of attack is decreased. PIV measurements of differing slat flow fields by Paschal et al.[10] and Takeda et al.[9,11] also exhibited marked changes with variations in the angle of attack. More precisely, they found that at relatively high angles of attack, the fluctuating velocity field emerging through the slat gap is confined to a region of narrow spatial extent that is adjacent to the lower segment of the slat's wake. At low angles of attack, the fluctuating field becomes more energetic and is spread over most of the gap width. The energetic structures pumped through the gap appear to be mostly large-scale co- or counter-rotating vortex pairs. Clearly, a significant change in the dynamics of the slat-cove flow field occurs as the angle of attack is reduced. The underlying intricacies responsible for this flow alteration as well as any links that they may have to the increase in the radiated acoustic field still remain unresolved and deserve a careful study.

The present paper continues our effort towards understanding noise sources associated with a leading-edge slat in a high-lift setting. Our previous research focused on accurate Unsteady Reynolds Averaged Navier-Stokes (URANS) simulations of the slat-cove flow field and the computations of the resulting acoustic farfield.[7] These simulations were performed for a single angle of attack of 8 degrees. In reference 7 (hereafter referred to as KSB), the amplification of instabilities by the slat free-shear layer was shown to produce the radiated noise in the lower frequency range. Those earlier simulations, conducted in a fully turbulent mode, proved to be overly dissipative, and, thus, artificially decreased the radiated acoustic signature. In the current study, we present a simple strategy to partially remedy this shortcoming. The effectiveness of the approach is shown via numerical simulations and a comparison between the computed sound field and acoustic array measurements. Here we also extend the previous simulations, explaining the effect of angle-of-attack variation on the shear-layer instability modes, the dynamics of the cove flow field, and the radiated acoustic field.

2. Computational Procedure

Based on the EET model tested, the current simulations are performed for two-dimensional flows. A complete discussion of the numerical approach such as flow solver, high-lift geometry, grid distribution, and the expected numerical accuracy was provided by KSB and will not be repeated. Moreover, the computational framework of URANS plus Ffowcs Williams and Hawkings used in the present study to obtain the farfield acoustic noise was explained in detail in references 6-7, and thus omitted here. Following the work of KSB, the turbulence model employed is the 2-equation Shear Stress Transport (k-ω) model of Menter[12] with one major alteration as explained in the following sections.

3. Zonal Approach

3.1 Past Deficiencies

The fully turbulent simulations of KSB required explicit forcing of the shear layer to excite and maintain the large-scale structures. The location of the forcing was on the slat surface two to three local boundary layer heights away from the cusp. The amplitude of the forcing corresponded to 3% of the freestream velocity. Figure 3 shows a snapshot of the spanwise vorticity field in the slat cove area for the fully turbulent forced case. The vorticity contours clearly display the spatial location of the free-shear layer. Notice that the shear layer is a good amplifier of the initial perturbations that grow rapidly, roll-up the shear layer and form discrete vortices. Unfortunately, the fully turbulent computations were overly diffusive, causing rapid dissipation of the rolled-up vortices within a short spatial distance (see Fig. 3). To circumvent these excessive diffusive effects (due to the turbulence model), a simple remedy based on physical arguments is advocated and pursued. It is argued that, in the cove region, the established flow field is quasi-laminar but highly unsteady. Accordingly, the production term associated with the turbulence model is switched off in a limited zone that encloses the cove area. Figure 4 presents the grid distribution in the vicinity of the leading edge slat. The grid lines shown by a lighter color shading (mainly the cove area) highlight the extent of the region

where turbulence production is turned off. We emphasize that convection of the existing turbulence field into, out of, or within this region is uninhibited. A short justification for our approach follows.

3.2 Physical Justifications

Because of a strong favorable pressure gradient and a short travel distance, the slat boundary layer between the leading edge stagnation point and cusp experiences rapid acceleration and is extremely thin. For all practical purposes, at the point of separation (cusp), the boundary layer is laminar and in all likelihood will not be fully turbulent, even up to flight Reynolds numbers. Also, the separated free shear layer is initially laminar. In such free shear flows, the overall dynamics of the flow field are governed by the growth of the large-scale structures that are the manifestation of the eigenmodes of the system. The underlying instability mechanism is inviscid (inflectional) in nature; hence, simulation of the unsteady evolution of these structures should not be encumbered by the introduction of an eddy viscosity designed for statistically steady fully turbulent flow. The growth rate and frequency of the large-scale structures depend on the magnitude of the vorticity across the shear layer and the thickness of the layer. Although the overall loading of the slat sets the magnitude of the vorticity shed at the cusp, the shear-layer thickness is one of the few parameters that depends on the viscosity and the state of the boundary layer at the point of separation. Nevertheless, whether one assumes a turbulent or laminar initial state, only a minor shift in the frequency of the rolled-up vortices is expected as long as the mean shear layer thickness does not change appreciably. An important aspect of the slat flow field is the recirculating zone in the cove area. The velocity magnitudes in this zone are relatively small. Hence, the encountered flow field has a low Reynolds number. As in the case of a shallow cavity, some, if not the majority, of the large scale structures become trapped in this zone, setting up an unsteady flow field. Although the established recirculating flow may not be truly laminar, it is not fully turbulent, either. Based on the above observations, we surmise that the cove flow field (including the free shear layer), driven by the large-scale, substantially inviscid structures, behaves in an unsteady, quasi-laminar manner. In these circumstances, the effect of a turbulence model is neutral at best and detrimental in most instances. Under these unique situations, the diffusive effects of the turbulence model may be bypassed knowing full well that the pertinent features of the flow field are not altered significantly.

4. Results and Discussions

Following the work presented in KSB, the numerical results are normalized with respect to the stowed chord and free stream speed of sound, density, and molecular viscosity. Similarly, the current nondimensional time step of $\Delta t = 4.116\times10^{-4}$ (corresponding to 200 points per period for a 7.5kHz model-scale signal) matches the time step employed by KSB. All simulations are performed for a Mach number $M = 0.2$ and a Reynolds number $Re = 7.2\times10^{6}$.

4.1 URANS Simulations

To provide a direct comparison with the previous computations and to understand the effects of angle-of-attack variation, simulations for three angles of 8, 6, and 4 degrees were performed. The selected angles encompass typical aircraft approach conditions when airframe noise is loudest.

4.1.1 Eight Degree Case

A sample plot of the instantaneous spanwise vorticity field from the partially laminar simulation at 8-degree angle of attack is shown in Fig. 5. In contrast to the fully turbulent simulations (Fig. 3), the current computations display extremely complex and highly nonlinear flow dynamics. In Fig. 5, important stages such as shear layer undulation, roll-up, and the formation of discrete vortices are vividly depicted. It is emphasized here that unlike the fully turbulent case, the shear layer is self-exciting and no external forcing is used. Absent in Fig. 5 is the premature dissipation of the large-scale structures. In a significant departure from Fig. 3, the vorticity field shows the convection and coalescence of the vortices as they approach the reattachment point. At the reattachment point,

most of the vortices turn inward and get trapped in the cove recirculating flow field. Once trapped, these vortices move very slowly towards the slat cusp. Their proximity to the slat bottom surface cause the boundary layer to separate, forming vortices of opposite sign vorticity. The growing disturbances of the shear layer interact with the arriving vortices and thus establishing a feedback loop. A feature worth noticing is the absence of vorticity in the center of the recirculating zone. Contrary to the simulations of KSB, occasionally a vortex does escape through the slat gap, and the released vorticity is always of positive sign. However, the cycle appears random, and we have been unable to discern any recognizable pattern. For the present angle of attack, vortices that do escape are severely deformed by the accelerating local flow before leaving the gap very close to the bottom surface adjacent to the trailing-edge wake. This behavior closely mimics the PIV measurements of gap flow unsteadiness reported in references 9-11.

Better insight into the general migration path of the shear-layer large-scale structures is gained from the averaged flow field. A long-time average of the spanwise vorticity field is plotted in Fig. 6. In excess of 30,000 time steps were used to generate the average. To put the length of the data record in perspective, the convective travel time between the slat's cusp and its trailing edge is approximately 1,200-1,300 time steps. Several prominent features are worth noting in Fig. 6. The vorticity contours highlight the presence and location of the cove free shear layer. The layer is well defined and mildly spreading. The large-scale (instability modes) structures follow migratory paths that fall within a fairly narrow spatial band. Vortices ingested by the recirculating zone travel within a ring that borders the slat's bottom surface and the shear layer interior side, leaving the zone's center devoid of any significant levels of vorticity. Inside the gap, adjacent to the slat surface, moderate levels of vorticity are indicated. The large width of this layer precludes its association with the vorticity of the local boundary layer. The magnitude of vorticity in the noted layer suggests that a fair amount of cove generated flow disturbances pass through the gap confirming the trends deduced from the experimental measurements.[9-11] Finally, observe that negative sign vorticity is confined to the boundary layer on the slat bottom surface. The boundary-layer thickness increases moderately as the slat cusp is approached.

4.1.2 Six Degree Case

An instantaneous snapshot of the vorticity field for the 6-degree case is shown in Fig. 7. Although the angle of attack is reduced a mere two degrees from the previous case, a remarkable shift in the underlying flow dynamics takes place. The particular frame displayed in Fig. 7 was chosen to highlight some of the important changes. The first distinguishable feature is the presence of a very large and strong vortex of positive sign vorticity near the center of the recirculating zone. Unlike the 8-degree case (Fig. 5), within this zone, some of the trapped shear-layer vortices amalgamate and emerge as the center vortex. Once established, the vorticity in this vortex is constantly replenished by the newly ingested shear-layer vortices. The recirculation vortex possesses a somewhat jittery motion resulting in very irregular annular paths. The presence and the movement of the center vortex significantly modify the shear-layer development. A prominent effect is a more severe boundary layer separation on the slat bottom surface with the consequence of forming larger and stronger vortices of opposite sign vorticity. In most instances, the passage of these vortices over the cusp region disrupts the normal development of the shear layer causing instant roll-up of the separated layer. In other words, the mechanism for generating the shear-layer discrete vortices is toggled between promoting growth of convective instability modes and forcing the instant roll-up of the separated boundary layer at the cusp (Fig. 7).

Once released at the cusp, typically a negative sign vortex is paired up with an opposite sign vortex while moving upward towards the reattachment point. Although not depicted in Fig. 7, occasionally, a significant incursion into the freestream by the discrete vortices takes place. However, careful frame-by-frame scrutiny of the unsteady cove flow failed to produce any evidence of vortices colliding with the main element leading edge. Another distinguishing feature of Fig. 7 is the pumping of negative sign

vorticity through the gap. Recall that in the 8-degree case only positive vorticity was observed to leave the gap. Figure 7 clearly shows the ejection process for two co-rotating vortices (carrying negative vorticity) and some positive-vorticity lumps. Note that the vortices are only moderately deformed, and, unlike at the higher angles, they do maintain their structures. Moreover, the ejected vorticity field is spread over a significant portion of the gap width. Both of these observations tend to corroborate the PIV measurements obtained at angles of attack of 4 and 5 degrees by Paschal et al.[10] and Takeda et al.[9,11]

The long-time averaged spanwise vorticity field for the 6-degree case is shown in Fig. 8. More than 35,000 time steps were used in the averaging process. Figure 8 suggests that the prominent features of the averaged field are different than those displayed in Fig. 6. Except for near the slat cusp, the vorticity contours provide evidence of a much diffused shear layer. Due to large amplitude and highly erratic motion of the recirculation vortex, the paths of the shear-layer vortices are no longer confined to a band of limited spatial extent. Moreover, a fair amount of negative sign vorticity is released at the cusp; this negative vorticity then becomes entangled within the shear layer. Therefore, in a long-time averaging process, substantial spreading and cancellation of the shear layer vorticity field occurs. Similar arguments can be applied to explain the lack of high vorticity levels in the gap region. On the other hand, the concentrated region of vorticity at the center of the recirculating zone (Fig. 8) maps the extent of the area where the center vortex is most active. Lastly, Fig. 8 shows lifting of the negative vorticity layer from the slat surface as the slat cusp is approached. This lifting is due to more pronounced boundary layer separation at an earlier stage, formation of large negative sign vortices, and subsequent generation of secondary and tertiary vortices.

Analysis of the simulation for the 4-degree angle-of-attack produced results that are somewhat similar to the 6-degree case described above. Although a few differences exist, no dramatic changes in the cove flow dynamics (such as those observed between 8-degree and 6-

degree cases) were found. Overall, the large-scale structures in the cove flow are slightly more energetic and the movement of the vortices more chaotic compared to the 6-degree results.

4.2 Acoustic Analysis

Unsteady flow data on a surface enclosing the wing elements and the slat-cove region are used as input to the code described by Lockard[13] for the solution of the Ffowcs Williams and Hawkings[14] equation to calculate the noise radiated below the airfoil. Full discussions of the acoustic procedure and the orientation of the data surfaces are provided by KSB. For each angle of attack, in excess of 35,000 time steps are simulated of which (after discarding the initial transient part) the last 32,768 time steps are kept for processing purposes. Except for the 8-degree case, each data record is sub-divided into four equal segments of 8,192 time steps. Each segment is run through the acoustic solver, and the four outputs averaged before converting to 1/12th octave bands. Unfortunately, for the 8-degree angle, the first two segments of the input data record were corrupted during processing. Therefore, only the last two segments of 8,192 could be used. As a result, the averaged data are constructed using the remaining two available segments.

Figure 9 shows the comparison between the computed and measured noise spectra for the 8-degree angle of attack case. Also shown in the figure is our previously obtained spectrum from the fully turbulent simulation. The prominent tonal feature centered near 38,000Hz (due to vortex shedding at the slat trailing edge) was previously the subject of extensive studies.[6,8] Accordingly, we limit our discussion to frequencies below 20,000Hz. A cautionary note is warranted in the interpretation of Figures 9-11. As pointed out earlier, the URANS simulations are conducted in a 2D fashion. To compute the farfield noise, a perfect spanwise correlation in the nearfield unsteady signal is assumed. No doubt, in an actual experiment, three-dimensional effects are present. Under such conditions, the spanwise correlation is less than perfect. Therefore, a 2D acoustic computation potentially overestimates the noise significantly. Our main emphasis has been on identifying the noise generation mechanisms and not on producing a perfect prediction technique.

A careful examination of Fig. 9 reveals several similarities between the experimental acoustic and computational acoustic spectrums. For instance, both suggest a noise minimum in the vicinity of 20,000 Hz. In the low- to mid-frequency range, both computed spectra exhibit some of the proper measured trends, but the partially laminar spectrum is on average 5 to 6 dB higher in amplitude. In particular, a noise peak in the 3,000 to 3,500 Hz range is apparent. Because of the 2D nature of the simulations, the predictions should be significantly higher in amplitude than the experimental results. Hence, even though the turbulent simulation results appear to be in reasonable agreement with the experiment, they are really too low. We are working to quantify the influence of the spanwise correlation on the results.

A Comparison between the computed and measured acoustic spectra for the 6-degree case is plotted in Fig. 10. At this angle of attack, the peak in the computed spectrum is shifted to lower frequencies and occurs between 1,500Hz and 2,500Hz. The decay with frequency and the frequency of the noise minimum are very similar between the computation and the experiment. The three computed spectra are displayed in Fig. 11. In accordance with the measured trend (Fig. 2), decreasing the angle-of-attack from 8 degrees to 6 degrees produces higher acoustic amplitude. In lowering the angle further, no substantial change in the acoustic amplitude is observed. This is not totally unexpected. Recall that the analysis of the simulated flows showed only minor effects in the time evolution of the cove flow when angle of attack was lowered from 6 degrees to 4 degrees.

5. Conclusions

An aeroacoustic analysis of a generic, three-element high-lift configuration was undertaken. As a continuation of our past effort, the present research was focused on the time-evolution and dynamics of the slat's cove flow and the corresponding separated free shear layer. New two-dimensional, unsteady Reynolds Averaged Navier-Stokes simulations were performed in an attempt to remedy the shortcomings of our previous simulations, and also to understand the effects of angle-of-attack variation on the radiated slat noise. To circumvent the excessive dissipative effects of the turbulence model in our past investigation, a simple zonal approach (whereby the turbulence production term is turned off) was advocated and implemented. The removal of this excess damping allowed the shear layer to amplify large-scale structures, achieve a non-linear saturation state, and promote vortex merging. It also allowed the cove to develop a richer and more complex recirculating flow field and to establish a feedback loop within the recirculation zone.

Simulations for angles of attack of 8, 6, and 4 degrees were conducted. Careful analysis of the simulated database revealed significant changes in the prominent features of the cove and gap flow fields with reductions in the angle of attack, corroborating past PIV measurements. Using the unsteady RANS data as input, solutions of the Ffowcs Williams and Hawkings equation were calculated to yield the farfield acoustics. Comparisons between the computed and measured acoustic spectra showed much better agreement for the amplitude and frequency content than previous calculations. Overall, the computed acoustic spectra leave little doubt that the slat free shear layer is the prominent noise producing mechanism in the lower frequencies.

References

1. Meadows, K. R., Brooks, T. F., Humphreys, W. M., Hunter, W. H., and Gerhold, C. H., "Aeroacoustic Measurements of a Wing-Flap Configuration," AIAA Paper 97-1595, 1997.

2. Hayes, J. A., Horne, W. C., Soderman, P. T., and Bent, P. H., "Airframe Noise Characteristics of a 4.7% Scale DC-10 Model," AIAA Paper 97-1594, 1997.

3. Dobrzynski, W., Nagakura, K., Gehlhar, B., and Buschbaum, A., "Airframe Noise Studies on Wings with Deployed High-Lift Devices," AIAA Paper 98-2337, 1998.

4. Dobrzynski, W. and Pott-Pllenske, M., "Slat Noise Source Studies for Farfield Noise Prediction," AIAA Paper 2001-2158, May 2001.

5 Davy, R. and Remy, H., "Airframe Noise Characteristics on a 1/11 Scale Airbus Model," AIAA Paper 98-2335, 1998.

6. Singer, B. A., Lockard, and D. P., Brentner, K. S., "Computational Aeroacoustic Analysis of Slat Trailing-Edge Flow," AIAA J. Vol. 38, No. 9, September, pp. 1558-1564, 2000.

7. Khorrami, M. R., Singer, B. A., and Berkman, M. E., "Time-Accurate Simulations and Acoustic Analysis of Slat Free-Shear Layer," AIAA Paper 2001-2155, May 2001.

8. Khorrami, M. R., Berkman, M. E., and Choudhari, M., "Unsteady Flow Computations of a Slat with a Blunt Trailing Edge," AIAA J., Vol. 38, No. 11, November, pp. 2050-2058, 2000.

9. Takeda, K., Zhang, X., and Nelson, P.A., "Unsteady Aerodynamics and Aeroacoustics of a High-Lift Device Configuration," AIAA Paper 2002-0570, January 2002.

10. Paschal, K., Jenkins, L., and Yao, C., "Unsteady Slat Wake Characteristics of a 2-D High-Lift Configuration," AIAA Paper 2000-0139, January 2000.

11. Takeda, K. Ashcroft, G.B, and Zhang, X., "Unsteady Aerodynamics of Slat Cove Flow in a High-Lift Device Configuration," AIAA Paper 2001-0706, January 2001.

12. Menter, F., "Improved Two-Equation k-ω Turbulence Models for Aerodynamic Flows," NASA TM 103975, 1992.

13. Lockard, D. P., "An Efficient, Two-Dimensional Implementation of the Ffowcs Williams and Hawkings Equation," *Journal of Sound and Vibration*, Vol 229, No. 4., pp. 897-911, 2000.

14. Ffowcs Williams, J. E. and Hawkings, D. L., "Sound Generation by Turbulence and Surfaces in Arbitrary Motion," *Philosophical Transactions of the Royal Society of London A*, Vol 342, pp. 264-321, 1969.

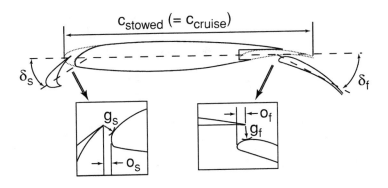

Fig. 1 Cross-sectional view of three-element EET high-lift system. Model stowed chord is 0.55mm.

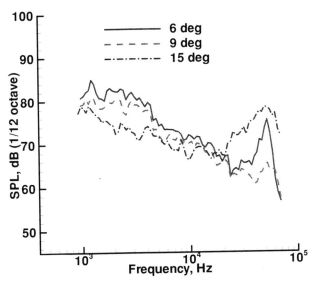

Fig. 2 Measured acoustic spectra for slat in 1/12th-octave bands. Test Parameters are: slat deflection angle of 30°, flap deflection angle of 30°, Mach number of 0.2.

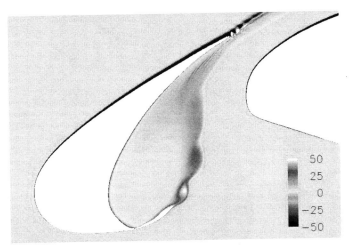

Fig. 3 Simulated instantaneous spanwise vorticity field for fully turbulent 3% forced case.

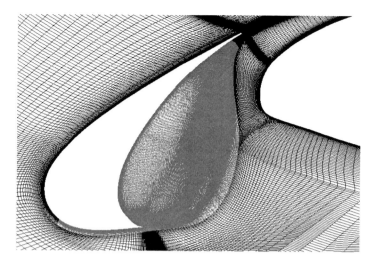

Fig. 4 Grid distribution in vicinity of slat. Every other point is shown. Lighter color grids highlight zones where turbulence production is turned off.

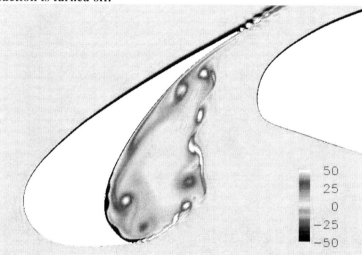

Fig. 5 Simulated instantaneous spanwise vorticity field for partially laminar case. Angle of attack is 8°.

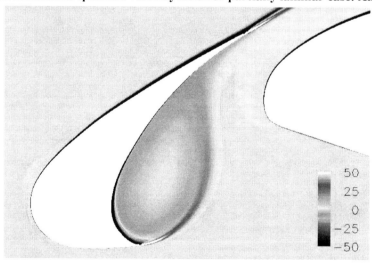

Fig. 6 Simulated averaged spanwise vorticity field for partially laminar case. Angle of attack is 8°.

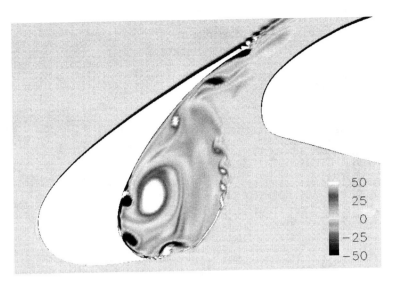

Fig. 7 Simulated instantaneous spanwise vorticity field for partially laminar case. Angle of attack is 6°.

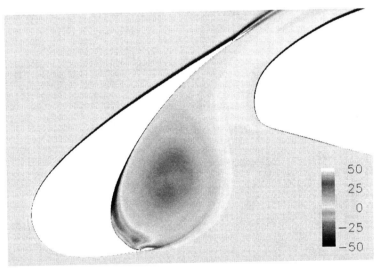

Fig. 8 Simulated averaged spanwise vorticity field for partially laminar case. Angle of attack is 6°.

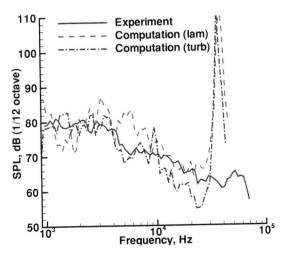

Fig. 9 Comparison of acoustic spectra for slat in 1/12th-octave bands. Angle of Attack is 8°.

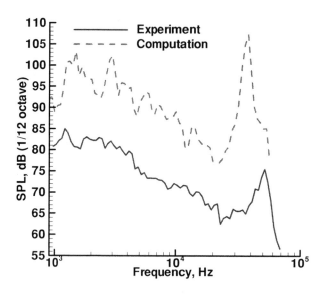

Fig. 10 Comparison of measured and computed acoustic spectra for slat in 1/12th-octave bands. Angle of attack is 6°.

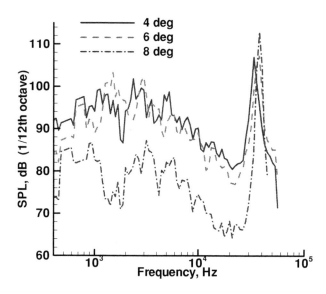

Fig. 11 Comparison of computed acoustic spectra for slat in 1/12th-octave bands.

A COMPARISON OF FFOWCS WILLIAMS-HAWKINGS SOLVERS
FOR AIRFRAME NOISE APPLICATIONS

David P. Lockard*
NASA Langley Research Center
Hampton, VA

This paper presents a comparison between two implementations of the Ffowcs Williams and Hawkings equation for airframe noise applications. Airframe systems are generally moving at constant speed and not rotating, so these conditions are used in the current investigation. Efficient and easily implemented forms of the equations applicable to subsonic, rectilinear motion of all acoustic sources are used. The assumptions allow the derivation of a simple form of the equations in the frequency-domain, and the time-domain method uses the restrictions on the motion to reduce the work required to find the emission time. The comparison between the frequency domain method and the retarded time formulation reveals some of the advantages of the different approaches. Both methods are still capable of predicting the far-field noise from nonlinear near-field flow quantities. Because of the large input data sets and potentially large numbers of observer positions of interest in three-dimensional problems, both codes utilize the message passing interface to divide the problem among different processors. Example problems are used to demonstrate the usefulness and efficiency of the two schemes.

Nomenclature

c_o	ambient speed of sound
f	integration surface defined by $f = 0$
F_i	dipole source terms
H	Heaviside function
i	$\sqrt{-1}$
M_i	local source Mach number vector, v_i/c
M	Mach number, $|M_i|$
$\hat{n}_i$	Outward directed unit normal vector
p	pressure
$\mathbf{Q}$	monopole source term
Q_i	components of vector in Eq.(6)
Q_n	$Q_i \hat{n}_i$
r_i	radiation vector, $x_i - \xi_i$
r	magnitude of radiation vector, $|r_i|$
t	time
u_i	Cartesian fluid velocity components
v_i	Cartesian surface velocity components
x, y, z	Cartesian observer coordinates

Greek:

α_1, α_2	mapped surface coordinates
β	$\sqrt{1 - M^2}$
$\delta(f)$	Dirac delta function
δ_{ij}	Kronecker delta
ρ	fluid density
τ	retarded or emission time, $t - r/c_o$
ξ, η, ζ	Source coordinates

Superscript:

$'$	perturbation quantity (e.g. $\rho' = \rho - \rho_o$)
$\hat{}$	unit vector
$\cdot$	time derivative

Subscript:

e	emission or retarded quantity
o	freestream quantity
r	inner product with $\hat{r}_i$
ret	quantity evaluated at retarded time τ
n	inner product with $\hat{n}_i$

Introduction

Despite recent advances in computational aeroacoustics, numerical simulations that resolve wave propagation from near-field sources to far-field observers are still prohibitively expensive and often infeasible. Integral techniques that can predict the far-field signal based solely on near-field input are a means to overcome this difficulty.

The Ffowcs Williams and Hawkings[1] (FW-H) equation is a rearrangement of the exact continuity and Navier-Stokes equations. The time histories of all the flow variables are needed, but no spatial derivatives are explicitly required. The solution to the FW-H equation requires a surface and a volume integral, but the solution is often well approximated by the surface integral alone. Singer et al.[2] and Brentner and Farassat[3] have shown that when the surface is in the near field of a solid body, the FW-H approach correctly filters out the part of the solution that does not radiate as sound, whereas the Kirchhoff method produces erroneous results. Many applications of the FW-H and Kirchhoff methods can be found in the area of rotorcraft acoustics.[4–7] The FW-H method has typically been applied by having the integration surface coincide with solid bodies, but the method is still applicable when the surface is

---

*Research Scientist, Senior Member, AIAA

off the body and permeable. The codes developed in this work are valid for both cases.

For three-dimensional flows, the time-domain FW-H formulations developed by Farassat[8] are efficient and amenable to numerical computations. Some simplifications are applied here based on restrictions of the surface motion, but the development follows that of Farassat very closely. The frequency-domain version of the FW-H uses the form of the equations developed by Lockard[9] for two-dimensional problems. However, the derivation was done using Cartesian tensor notation, and is equally valid in three-dimensions as long as the appropriate Green function is employed.

The remainder of the paper describes the time- and frequency-domain formulations in enough detail to show the similarities and differences between the methods. A discussion of various parallelization strategies follows. Finally, two example problems are used to demonstrate the utility and efficiency of the schemes. The last example involves a noise calculation based on a large-scale CFD computation of a landing gear.

Governing Equations

The FW-H equation can be written in differential form[10] as

$$\left(\frac{\partial^2}{\partial t^2} - c_o^2 \frac{\partial^2}{\partial x_i \partial x_i}\right)\left(H(f)\rho'\right) =$$

$$\frac{\partial^2}{\partial x_i \partial x_j}\left(T_{ij} H(f)\right)$$

$$- \frac{\partial}{\partial x_i}\left(F_i \delta(f)\right) + \frac{\partial}{\partial t}\left(Q \delta(f)\right) \quad (1)$$

where

$$T_{ij} = \rho u_i u_j + P_{ij} - c_o^2 \rho' \delta_{ij}, \quad (2)$$

$$F_i = \left(P_{ij} + \rho u_i(u_j - v_j)\right)\frac{\partial f}{\partial x_j}, \text{ and} \quad (3)$$

$$Q = \left(\rho_o v_i + \rho(u_i - v_i)\right)\frac{\partial f}{\partial x_i}. \quad (4)$$

The contribution of the Lighthill stress tensor, T_{ij}, to the right-hand side is known as the quadrupole term. The dipole term F_i involves an unsteady force, and Q gives rise to a monopole-type contribution that can be thought of as an unsteady mass addition. The function $f = 0$ defines the surface outside of which the solution is desired. The normalization $|\nabla f| = 1$ is used for f. The total density and pressure are given by ρ and p, respectively. The fluid velocities are u_i, while the v_i represent the velocities of the surface f. The Kronecker delta, δ_{ij}, is unity for $i = j$ and zero otherwise. The ambient speed of sound is denoted by c_o. A prime is used to denote a perturbation quantity

relative to the free-stream conditions denoted by the subscript o. The Cartesian coordinates and time are x_i and t, respectively. The usual convention, which is followed here, involves a quiescent ambient state with f prescribed as a function of time so that it always surrounds a moving source region of interest. $H(f)$ is the Heaviside function which is unity for $f > 0$ and zero for $f < 0$. The derivative of the Heaviside function $H'(f) = \delta(f)$ is the Dirac delta function, which is zero for $f \neq 0$, but yields a finite value when integrated over a region including $f = 0$. The inviscid part, $P_{ij} = p\delta_{ij}$, of the compressive stress tensor P_{ij} is used in this work.

Equation 1 is typically solved using a Green function technique. The temporal and spatial convolution of the free-space Green function with the source terms yields the solution for ρ'. In the farfield, $p' = c_o^2 \rho'$. The three-dimensional Green function[10] is

$$G(x_i, t; \xi_i, \tau) = \frac{\delta(\tau - t + r/c_o)}{4\pi r} \quad (5)$$

where $r_i = x_i - \xi_i$ is the radiation vector, and $r = |r_i|$. Because of the delta function, the solution to equation 1 can be manipulated into various forms, some of which are amenable to numerical solution such as formulation 1A of Farassat.[8] An alternative approach is to solve the FW-H equation in the frequency domain. In this work we follow the frequency-domain approach of Lockard[9] that is restricted to uniform, rectilinear motion, but other methods can be used that still allow general motion. In the following sections, the current implementations of these methods are discussed.

Time-Domain Method

A concise, time-domain solution to equation 1 that is applicable to nondeforming, porous surfaces can be obtained from the derivation of Farassat[11] using the variables

$$Q_i = (\rho_o - \rho)v_i + \rho u_i, \text{ and}$$
$$L_i = p\hat{n}_i + \rho u_i(u_j - v_j)\hat{n}_j \quad (6)$$

as proposed by Di Francescantonio.[6] The integral solution is given by

$$4\pi\rho'(x_i, t) = \quad (7)$$

$$\int_{f=0}\left[\frac{\dot{Q}_j\hat{n}_j}{r(1 - M_r)^2} + \frac{Q_j\hat{n}_j(r\dot{M}_r + c_o(M_r - M^2))}{r^2(1 - M_r)^3}\right]_{\text{ret}} ds$$

$$+ \int_{f=0}\left[\frac{\dot{L}_j\hat{r}_j}{c_o r(1 - M_r)^2} + \frac{L_j\hat{r}_j - L_i M_i}{r^2(1 - M_r)^2}\right]_{\text{ret}} ds$$

$$+ \int_{f=0}\left[\frac{L_j\hat{r}_j(r\dot{M}_j\hat{r}_j + c_o(M_j\hat{r}_j - M^2))}{c_o r^2(1 - M_r)^3}\right]_{\text{ret}} ds + p'_Q$$

1808

where p'_Q is the quadrupole term, which is neglected in this work. $M_i = v_i/c_o$ is the local Mach number vector, and the superscripted caret ($\hat{}$) denotes a unit vector. The outward directed unit normal vector is given by $\hat{n}_i$. The subscript ret denotes evaluation at the retarded or emission time τ. For uniform, rectilinear motion, the normals are not functions of time, so finding $Q_n = Q_i \hat{n}_i$ and $\dot{Q}_i \hat{n}_i$ is sufficient because $\partial/\partial t(Q_n) = \hat{n}_i \partial/\partial t(Q_i) + Q_i \partial/\partial t(\hat{n}_i) = \dot{Q}_i \hat{n}_i$. The dot above a variable indicates a time derivative. Hence, only four variables and their time derivatives are required to compute the kernel functions in equation 7. The time derivatives are computed using fourth-order, central differences. In the current application, the coordinates of the surface and the flow field data are known at the grid points of meshes on a series of surface patches that comprise the complete, closed surface surrounding all sources. The normals are determined using the grid metrics on the patches, which are computed using fourth-order, central differences. Because each surface patch has two independent indices, only two variables (α_1, α_2) are required to describe the variation on the mapped surface. The normal is computed from the outer product

$$n_i = \{\partial x/\partial \alpha_1, \partial y/\partial \alpha_1, \partial z/\partial \alpha_1\} \times$$
$$\{\partial x/\partial \alpha_2, \partial y/\partial \alpha_2, \partial z/\partial \alpha_2\}. \qquad (8)$$

Whether the normal points inward or outward is dependent on the ordering of the data. The current code reads a file which either specifies a source point within each surface or the correct sign of the normal on each surface. When the surfaces come from CFD data, it is usually possible to deduce which direction the normal will point. However, a visual inspection of the normals is always a good practice because incorrect signs are common and can cause errors that are difficult to recognize.

One of the more computationally intensive parts of a time-domain calculation is the determination of the retarded time τ. For general motion, a root-finding technique must be employed. However, for uniform, rectilinear, subsonic motion, the Garrick triangle[12] uniquely determines the emission time as

$$r_e = \frac{r}{1-M^2}\left(M\cos(\theta) + \sqrt{1 - M^2 \sin^2(\theta)}\right)$$
$$\tau = t - r_e/c_o \qquad (9)$$

where r_e is the distance between the source and the observer at the time of emission τ. The angle between the surface velocity vector v_i and the radiation vector r_i is θ. The $\cos(\theta)$ can be determined from the inner product of the vectors. The variables Q_n, L_i and their time derivatives must then be interpolated to the retarded time. This is an intensive part of the calculation because the interpolation is performed for every grid point, retarded time, and observer position. Changing the indexing of data to increase cache

reuse, loop unrolling, and inlining of the interpolation routine decreased the total run time by half.

Once the kernel functions in equation 7 have been determined, Gaussian quadrature is used to perform the spatial integration over the surface. Because this integration is performed repeatedly for each observer and retarded time, parts of the integral that are independent of time and observer position are precalculated and stored. The integration is performed by linearly interpolating the data from the four corners of each cell using three-dimensional shape functions commonly employed in finite elements.[13] Defining the mapped coordinates as (α_1, α_2), the elemental area, dS, is the magnitude of the normal as specified in equation 8. The value of the elemental area at each Gaussian quadrature point is then stored for reuse. The values of the shape functions at each of the quadrature points are also precalculated and stored. Typically, only four quadrature points are required over each cell. Four points will integrate quadratic functions exactly. Although the function being integrated may be of higher order, a quadratic approximation is usually sufficient provided the surface shape is well behaved. Additional quadrature points and higher-order reconstructions within each cell have not been found to be very beneficial. Part of the reason may be the oscillatory nature of the kernel function. The integration of a linear approximation of a sinusoid is often not much different from the quadrature of a higher-order fit. Grid refinement is typically much more influential on the solution quality than the order of the integration.

Because of the need to sample the source data at the retarded time, one cannot arbitrarily choose observer times. A separate code was written to determine the valid range of observer times based on a given range of input data. The Garrick triangle[12] can be used to uniquely determine the minimum and maximum reception times using equations 9 to solve for t given τ.

Impenetrable Surfaces

In many practical applications, the data for the FW-H solver is obtained on solid surfaces, and the equations can be greatly simplified thereby decreasing the computational and memory requirements. The simplifications are especially advantageous for the uniform, rectilinear motion case. For impenetrable surface data, $u_j = v_j$ and equations 6 simplify to

$$Q_i = \rho_o v_i \text{ and } L_i = p\delta_{ij}\hat{n}_j. \qquad (10)$$

Note that Q is independent of time. Furthermore, the normals $\hat{n}_j$ are only a function of space. Hence, only the time history of the pressure and its time derivative are needed when the viscous terms are neglected in P_{ij}. All of the source terms are linear, yet the method has been shown to give correct results when the surface data is in the nonlinear near field.[2] The failings of the Kirchhoff method for problems with solid surfaces is clearly not due to its source terms being linear, but rather the assumptions used to derive the equation.

Frequency-Domain Method

Several frequency-domain formulations of the FW-H equation have been reported in the literature.[14] Here, the method proposed by Lockard[9] for two-dimensional flows will be extended to three-dimensions. Although this development is restricted to surfaces in rectilinear motion at constant speed, it is still useful for airframe noise, where these assumptions are usually valid. The motion of the surface is assumed to be governed by $f = f(\mathbf{x} + \mathbf{U}t)$ where the components of $\mathbf{U}$ are constant velocities describing the motion of the surface. An application of the Galilean transformation from $(\mathbf{x}, t)$ to $(\mathbf{y}, \bar{t})$,

$$
\begin{aligned}
y_i &= x_i + U_i t, \quad \bar{t} = t, \\
\frac{\partial}{\partial x_i} &= \frac{\partial}{\partial y_i}, \quad \frac{\partial}{\partial t} = \frac{\partial}{\partial \bar{t}} + U_i \frac{\partial}{\partial y_i},
\end{aligned} \quad (11)
$$

to equation 1 leads to the convected wave equation

$$
\left(\frac{\partial^2}{\partial \bar{t}^2} + U_i U_j \frac{\partial^2}{\partial y_i \partial y_j} \right. \quad (12)
$$
$$
\left. + \quad 2 U_i \frac{\partial^2}{\partial y_i \partial \bar{t}} - c_o^2 \frac{\partial^2}{\partial y_i \partial y_i} \right) \left(H(f)\rho' \right) =
$$
$$
\frac{\partial^2}{\partial y_i \partial y_j} \left(T_{ij} H(f) \right) - \frac{\partial}{\partial y_i} \left(F_i \delta(f) \right) + \frac{\partial}{\partial \bar{t}} \left(Q_n \delta(f) \right)
$$

where, after the transformation, the F_i and Q_n become

$$
\begin{aligned}
F_i &= \left(p\delta_{ij} + \rho(u_i - U_i)(u_j + U_j) + \rho_o U_i U_j \right) \hat{n}_j, \\
Q_n &= \left(\rho(u_i + U_i) - \rho_o U_i \right) \hat{n}_i.
\end{aligned} \quad (13)
$$

The Lighthill stress tensor T_{ij} is unchanged, and $f = f(\mathbf{y})$ is now only a function of the spatial coordinates. The surface velocities v_i have been replaced by $-U_i$, which can be inferred from inspection of $f(\mathbf{x} + \mathbf{U}t) = 0$. Note that this implies that the mean flow is in the positive direction (or equivalently that the surface moves in the negative direction) when $U_i > 0$. The v_i used throughout the time-domain formulation are of opposite sign and should not be confused with the U_i. Equation 12 is now in a convenient form to perform the Fourier analysis. With application of the Fourier transform pair

$$
\mathcal{F}\{q(t)\} = q(\omega) = \int_{-\infty}^{\infty} q(t) \exp(-i\omega t) dt \text{ and}
$$

$$
\mathcal{F}^{-1}\{q(\omega)\} = q(t) = \frac{1}{2\pi} \int_{-\infty}^{\infty} q(\omega) \exp(i\omega t) d\omega, \quad (14)
$$

equation 12 becomes

$$
\left(\frac{\partial^2}{\partial y_i \partial y_i} + k^2 - 2i M_i k \frac{\partial}{\partial y_i} \right.
$$
$$
\left. - M_i M_j \frac{\partial^2}{\partial y_i \partial y_j} \right) \left(H(f) c_o^2 \rho'(\mathbf{y}, \omega) \right) =
$$
$$
\frac{\partial}{\partial y_i} \left(F_i(\mathbf{y}, \omega) \delta(f) \right) - i\omega Q_n(\mathbf{y}, \omega) \delta(f)
$$
$$
- \frac{\partial^2}{\partial y_i \partial y_j} \left(T_{ij}(\mathbf{y}, \omega) H(f) \right). \quad (15)
$$

The wavenumber is defined by $k = \omega/c_o$, the Mach number $M = U/c_o$, and complex number $i = \sqrt{-1}$. Note that the transform has been applied to the groupings T_{ij}, F_i, and Q because the equation is linear in these terms. However, the desirable properties of the FW-H are maintained because all of the nonlinear products are included before the transformation is applied. In a numerical implementation, the products are formed first, and then a fast Fourier transform (FFT) is applied. As a caution, the FFT must use the sign convention of equations 14, or the derivation must be modified appropriately. The Green function for equation 15 when $M < 1$ can be obtained from a Prandtl-Glauert transformation. Denoting the three-dimensional source coordinates as (ξ, η, ζ), and the observer position as (x, y, z) the Green function[15] is

$$
G(x, y, z; \xi, \eta, \zeta) = \frac{-1}{4\pi d} \exp^{(-ik(d - M\bar{x})/\beta^2)}
$$

where

$$
\begin{aligned}
\bar{x} &= (x - \xi)\cos\alpha\cos\phi + (y - \eta)\sin\alpha \\
&+ (z - \zeta)\cos\alpha\sin\phi, \\
\bar{y} &= -(x - \xi)\sin\alpha\cos\theta + (y - \eta)\cos\alpha \\
&+ (z - \zeta)\sin\alpha\sin\phi, \\
\bar{z} &= -(x - \xi)\sin\phi + (z - \zeta)\cos\phi,
\end{aligned}
$$

and

$$
d = \sqrt{\bar{x}^2 + \beta^2(\bar{y}^2 + \bar{z}^2)} \quad (16)
$$

The angles are defined such that $\tan\phi = W/U$, $\sin\alpha = V/M$, and $M = \sqrt{U^2 + V^2 + W^2}/c_o$. The Prandtl-Glauert factor is $\beta = \sqrt{1 - M^2}$. The solution to equation 15 for $M < 1$ can now be written as

$$
H(f) c_o^2 \rho'(\mathbf{y}, \omega) = -\int_{f=0} F_i(\boldsymbol{\xi}, \omega) \frac{\partial G(\mathbf{y}; \boldsymbol{\xi})}{\partial y_i} \, dl
$$
$$
- \int_{f=0} i\omega Q_n(\boldsymbol{\xi}, \omega) G(\mathbf{y}; \boldsymbol{\xi}) \, dl
$$
$$
- \int_{f>0} T_{ij}(\boldsymbol{\xi}, \omega) H(f) \frac{\partial^2 G(\mathbf{y}; \boldsymbol{\xi})}{\partial y_i \partial y_j} \, d\boldsymbol{\xi}. \quad (17)
$$

As has already been stated, the quadrupole contribution, represented by the last term in equation 17, is typically neglected because its influence is often small. Furthermore, the calculation is somewhat involved and expensive. Certain flows exist where the quadrupole cannot be ignored, such as those containing significant refraction of waves by shear layers and wakes. As long as the integration surface is placed outside of all regions where T_{ij} is large, the quadrupole contribution is substantially included by the surface sources even though the quadrupole integration is not performed. This is also true for the time-domain formulation.

The frequency-domain solution process involves calculating the surface normals and forming the products in F_i and Q for all time at each point on the surface just as in the time-domain version. However, the F_i and Q_n functions are Fourier transformed, and the surface integrations are performed for each frequency of interest instead of for each observer time. An inverse FFT can be used to recover the acoustic signal in the time domain. For truly periodic problems one merely uses a single period of the flow data as input to the FW-H code. However, for more complicated, aperiodic flows, windowing the data is required. The windowing should be applied to F_i and Q_n after their mean values are subtracted. The subtraction has no effect on the calculated noise because the derivatives of G all contain ω, and equation 17 shows that there is no contribution to the noise at $\omega = 0$ when the quadrupole term is neglected. The minimal amount of time data typically available from a computational aeroacoustics calculation may lead to some inaccuracies in the windowed FFT, but short time records are often just as much of an impediment for time-domain formulations because information about the frequency content is usually desired.

When the input to FW-H code is from a harmonic, linearized Euler solver, F_i and Q_n should also be linearized because the amplitudes from the linearized code may not be physical. If they are too large, the nonlinearities in the source terms can produce erroneous results. One must be careful when performing the linearization because the perturbation velocities u_i are not necessarily small. For instance, on a solid surface $u_i = -U_i$. Only a minor change in the code allows one to have a single code that is useful for input from linear and nonlinear flow solvers. The frequency domain approach is particularly efficient for harmonic data because only a single frequency needs to be calculated, and the FFT's do not need to be performed.

A disadvantage of this particular frequency-domain formulation is that the source and observer are always a fixed distance apart, and all Doppler effects are lost. In a time-domain calculation, the distance between the observer and the source can be changed for each time step to simulate a flyover condition. Most CFD computations and experiments are carried out in a laboratory frame with the ob-

server distances fixed, so this is not a major issue. However, comparisons with actual flight data should include the Doppler effects.

Impenetrable Surfaces

As was shown for the time-domain formulation, the frequency-domain version can also be significantly simplified when the input data is obtained on solid surfaces. For impenetrable surface data, $u_j = -U_j$ and equations 13 simplify to

$$Q = -\rho_o U_i \hat{n}_j \text{ and } F_i = p\delta_{ij}\hat{n}_j. \qquad (18)$$

Note that Q is steady in time and has no impact on the frequency domain solution. Hence, only the time history of the pressure is needed. One only needs to determine the Fourier transform of the pressure and scale that result by the appropriate normal to obtain the F_i terms. The savings in memory and computational requirements are so great that the solid surface formulation should be employed whenever possible. In the current implementation, different versions of two subroutines are called depending on the case being run. Although some additional coding is required, run times can be reduced by 60% and the memory load by over 70%.

Parallel Implementation

Although one normally thinks of acoustic analogy computations as being extremely efficient, calculations involving long time records and many observers can quickly become expensive. The cost of computing the time history at a single point using the FW-H may actually exceed that of a standard CFD method. However, the FW-H approach allows the observer location to be anywhere outside of the source region, whereas the CFD method must have grid points from the source to the observer. The cost involved with all those intermediate points and the errors incurred in the long range propagation make standard CFD an inappropriate choice for most far-field noise computations. Still, when mapping out the directivity in three-dimensions, hundreds of observer locations may be required. In the realistic problem of a landing gear given in the examples section, the FW-H computation of a single observer using the porous surface formulation requires seven minutes on an SGI 250MHz R10K processor. The input record contains 4096 time steps at 82,219 grid points, which consumes 1.4 GB of disk space. Mapping out a directivity is a time consuming process when performed serially. This motivated the modification of the code to use the Message Passing Interface (MPI) to perform parallel computations. Other researchers[16] have used MPI in conjunction with acoustic analogy methods.

FW-H solvers are ideal candidates for parallelization because the calculation of the signal at each observer is independent, and the contributions from each portion of the data surface combine linearly. Even the computations at each time step or frequency are independent. Hence, one has many choices of how to split the problem. Some initial testing was done with different processors dealing with different observers. However, this requires that each processor have access to the entire data record for all the surface patches. In the landing gear case, 181 patches comprise the total surface. Either all of the nodes have to read all the data, or one node must read it and broadcast it to all the others. The total record for the landing gear is expected to be over 10 GB on a medium mesh, and over 60 GB for a fine mesh. Either reading or passing that much data is not reasonable. This same problem occurs when different processors handle different frequencies or time steps. The other option is to divide the problem by surface patches, and sum all of the contributions at the end. Each processor only needs to read the data for the particular patches assigned to it. Hence, the data is only read once and only passed if the data is not directly accessible by all the nodes.

Two paradigms were used to investigate the parallel implementation. First, a standard load-balancing approach was used. The size of each of the patches was read, and the largest patch assigned to the processor with the least points until all the patches were assigned. This strategy is commonly employed in multiblock CFD codes. This approach worked well when all of the processors were identical and dedicated. However, because the code only passes a very minimal amount of data, it is typically run over a standard network on the second processor of SGI Octane workstations in the lab. These machines vary in speed, and sometimes both processors are in use when the job starts. Occasionally, one of the processors would take much longer than all of the others to complete. To circumvent this problem, the master-slave paradigm employed by Long and Brentner[17] was used. Here, one node does no work other than to tell requesting nodes what patch they should process. Again, the largest patches are assigned first so that small patches are being used when the job nears completion and the variability in processor speed is important. This paradigm worked extremely well and has resulted in a nearly linear speed up on an SGI Origin. Although the master node does not do any useful work, it needs to respond quickly to the requests from worker nodes to keep them from becoming idle. The master's job can be assigned to a slow node or to a dual processor machine that also has a slave process.

In a heterogeneous environment where one is trying to use idle machines, the master-slave paradigm is preferred. Furthermore, the load-balanced approach and master-slave approach only affect a single subroutine in the code, so it is very easy to switch between the two depending on the local operating environment.

Test Examples

Monopole in Flow

As a first demonstration of the current implementations of the three-dimensional FW-H equation, the field from a monopole source is computed in the far field using the present technique. The source moves in the $-x$ direction at Mach 0.5. An equivalent flow involves a fixed source at the origin in a uniform flow in the $+x$ direction. The complex potential for the monopole is given by Dowling and Ffowcs Williams[15] as

$$\phi(x, y, z, t) = A \frac{1}{4\pi d} \exp^{i(\omega t - k(d - Mx)/\beta^2)}. \quad (19)$$

The variables needed in the FW-H equation are obtained from the real parts of $p' = -\rho_o(\partial\phi/\partial t + U_o\partial\phi/\partial x)$, $u'_i = \partial\phi/\partial x_i$, and $\rho' = p'/c_o^2$. Equation 19 is written in a laboratory frame where the flow is moving over a stationary source. The source terms in the FW-H equation are calculated from the flow variables evaluated over two periods on the surface. For this case, $M = U_o/c_o = 0.5$, $\omega l/c_o = 4\pi/46$, $A/(lc_o) = 0.01$ and the integration surface is a cube that extends from $-5l$ to $5l$ in all three coordinate directions. The reference length is l. Fifty uniformly spaced points are used on each side of the box. Figure 1(a) compares the directivity from the calculations to the analytic solution in the $z = 0$ plane. Figure 1(b) makes a similar comparison for the time history at $(50l, 0, 0)$. The agreement is excellent, demonstrating that the formulations are valid for problems with a uniform mean flow. Similar agreement was found when each of the six sides of the cube comprising the data surface were deformed to look like a Gaussian bell provided enough points were provided to adequately resolve the variation. The calculations were performed in single precision, which appears sufficient as long as the acoustic signal on the surface is not less than five orders of magnitude smaller than the mean. A lack of smoothness in a time-domain formulation solution is an indication of a precision problem.

Landing Gear

This example involves the calculation of the noise generated by the unsteady flowfield surrounding a landing gear. An aerodynamic and acoustic analysis of a similar landing gear was performed by Souliez et al.[18] The near field in this problem is highly nonlinear, and different parts shed vorticity at different frequencies. Figure 2(a) shows an instantaneous snapshot of the perturbation pressure on all of the solid surfaces. The freestream Mach number is 0.2, and the gear is mounted on a flat plate. The reference length is the diameter of the wheels which is 3.7 in (0.09398 m). The input data for the acoustic calculation is obtained from a three-dimensional, time-dependent

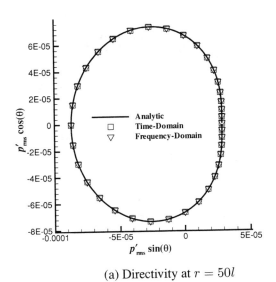

(a) Directivity at $r = 50l$

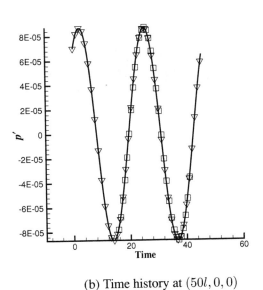

(b) Time history at $(50l, 0, 0)$

Fig. 1   Solution comparisons for a monopole in a $M = 0.5$ flow. The pressure is nondimensionalized by $\rho_o c_o^2$

CFD solution using the code CFL3D.[19,20] CFL3D was developed at NASA Langley Research Center to solve the three-dimensional, time-dependent, thin-layer Reynolds-averaged Navier-Stokes (RANS) equations using a finite-volume formulation. The CFD data used in this work is discussed in more detail in the paper by Li *et al*.[21]

The noise calculation involves 181 total patches comprising the data surface. All of the patches are on solid surfaces, so only the pressure histories are needed. 147 patches are on the gear itself and 31 are on the plate above the gear. So far, over 24,000 nondimensional time samples of $l/c_o\Delta t = 0.02$ have been collected, but only half of the data is sufficiently free of transients to be useful for acoustic calculations. The transient problem is exacerbated by

high-frequency sources that are growing through most of the time record. Some of the waves from these sources can be seen on the door in Figure 2(a). Figure 2(b) shows the time history of the pressure on the oleo in the contraction just below the door as indicated by the arrow in Figure 2(a). The time history shows the complex, intermittent character of the signal. The large amplitude oscillations occur around one kHz (model scale) at varying intervals and irregular durations. Riding on top of the signal are high frequency oscillations generated by resonances in small, triangular shaped spaces between the yokes and the door. These spaces are found on the upper and lower yokes in both the upstream and downstream junctures with the door. Unfortunately, the signals took a long time to saturate, so the calculation had to be run much longer than anticipated to eliminate the transients. The upstream and downstream cavities are slightly different in size, so the resonances occur at 20.5 kHz in the upstream cavity and at 25.4 kHz in the downstream one.

Beyond the intermittency in the signal, another complication for obtaining spectral information about the solution is the predominantly low frequency content of the gear. Very long sampling times are needed to resolve these frequencies. Although the time-domain code can exactly calculate the signal at the observer, the lack of long sampling times is a problem when the spectral content is needed. Nonetheless, the comparison of the spectra at an observer directly beneath the gear from the two FW-H codes is encouraging. The observer is $12l$ away from the gear. Figure 3(a) shows that the spectral content is nearly identical. In both cases, a hamming window was applied to minimize the effects of the aperiodic signal on the FFT's. The time histories in Figure 3(b) are also similar. The curves are offset because the frequency-domain calculation does not include the effect of the zero or steady mode. All of the primary features of the signal can be observed in both results. Some discrepancy should be expected because the effect of the window is already included in the frequency domain results because the window is applied to the input data. However, the window is applied to the time-domain results after the calculation, so its effect is not seen in Figure 3(b).

Three different data records were used to investigate the influence of the duration and the particular time interval used. Because of the complexity of the time histories on the gear, some variation should be expected, but drastic changes would indicate an improper sample length or that the flow has yet to eliminate transients. These sorts of variations were observed in many of the initial calculations. However, the comparison in Figure 4 shows only minor differences between the three calculations. A time sample of 8192 was used, which represents the time required for the flow to pass by a wheel 32 times. The full record was used, then it was subdivided into two records of 4096 samples.

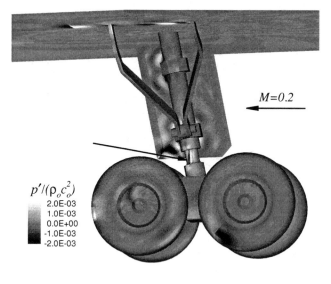

$p'/(\rho_o c_o^2)$
2.0E-03
1.0E-03
0.0E+00
-1.0E-03
-2.0E-03

(a) Perturbation pressure on solid surfaces

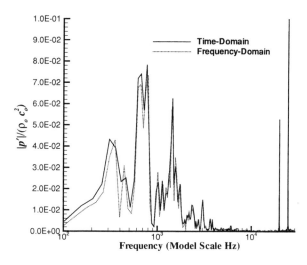

(a) Spectra

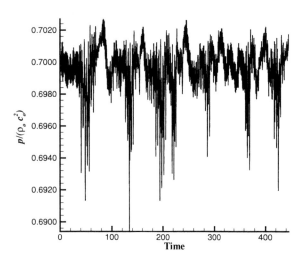

(b) Time history on the oleo

Fig. 2   CFD results for a landing gear in a $M = 0.2$ flow.

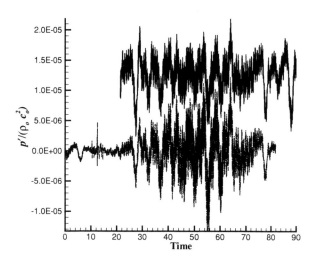

(b) Time history

Fig. 3   FW-H results for an observer directly below a landing gear in a $M = 0.2$ flow.

The comparison between the results for the full record and the latter record is very good. Somewhat more discrepancy is observed with the results for the first 4096 samples, but it is still within the variation that should be expected for such a complex flow. Even though there are not as many samples available from the computation as one can obtain from an experiment, the power spectral density should be calculated by averaging over the different samples to obtain a single answer, which should be stationary.

One of the concerns with the CFD calculation was the accuracy of the solution on the wall above the landing gear. Although the plate doesn't produce any significant fluid mechanic fluctuations that would act as sound sources, it does reflect acoustic signals, and some of the vorticity shed by the side bars interacts with the wall. The grid on the

plate in the CFD calculation coarsens very quickly away from the gear, so the accuracy of high frequency signals is likely to be very poor over much of the plate. To investigate the impact of the accuracy on the plate, the FW-H solvers were run with the wall ignored and the gear surfaces mirrored about the plate. Figure 5 shows the comparison with results obtained by including and excluding the wall. At lower frequencies, the case including the wall has much higher levels than either the no wall or mirrored cases indicating that the signal on the wall is an important source of noise. The results in the figure are from the frequency-domain code, but very similar results were obtained from the time-domain code. Figure 5(b) zooms in on the high frequency tones. For the tones, the wall and no wall re-

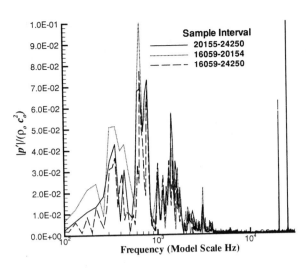

Fig. 4 FW-H results for an observer directly below a landing gear in a $M = 0.2$ flow. Calculations from frequency-domain code comparing effect of sample length.

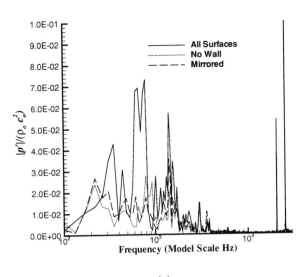

(a)

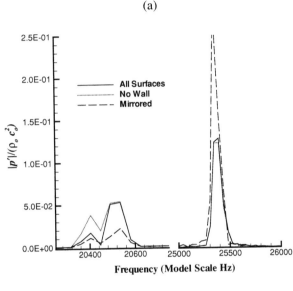

(b)

Fig. 5 FW-H results for an observer directly below a landing gear in a $M = 0.2$ flow. Results from frequency-domain code comparing the effect of including the wall and mirroring the data.

sults are nearly identical which supports the idea that the high-frequency signals on the wall are artificially dampened rapidly so that they have little impact on the acoustic calculation. The mirrored result is lower at 20.5 kHz and significantly higher at 25.4 kHz. The variability in the effect of mirroring with frequency is likely caused by interference effects which would be minimized for observers farther from the gear.

Because of the complexity of the landing-gear geometry and the various locations of the sources, one would expect the observer location to be important. Figure 6 compares the spectra for observers at three locations. All of the observers are $12l$ from the gear. The first location is directly beneath the gear. The other two observers are at the same vertical and streamwise locations as the wheels, but on opposite sides. The observer on the oleo side doesn't have the door in the way to obscure some of the sources on the oleo and yokes. This is most evident for the 25.4 kHz tone in Figure 6(b). Both side observers see much stronger tone signals indicating that the yoke resonances primarily radiate horizontally. Part of the reason that the strength of the tones observed underneath the gear is much less may be because of blockage by the truck and wheels. The 20.5 kHz tone has the same amplitude for both side observers. The reason for the lack of influence of the door on this tone has not been investigated. At lower frequencies, the signal beneath the gear has a larger amplitude indicating that the wheels and truck are best observed from below. The portion of the signal around 1.4 kHz is completely absent for the side observers. As expected, there is a significant directivity associated with the gear, but the complex interplay of source location, geometry, and observer position needs further investigation.

Performance

In the landing gear calculations, all of the frequencies were calculated in the frequency domain code, and an equivalent number of time steps in the time domain code. Table 1 shows timing results for the serial runs with 4096 samples and all 181 surfaces. These calculations involved solid surface data, so the impenetrable surface simplifications were employed. Run times are more than doubled if the surface is assumed to be penetrable. All of the frequencies were calculated by the frequency-domain code, and an equivalent number of observer times in the time-domain code. When all of the data is computed, the frequency-

1815

spectra is primarily concentrated at low frequency and at a few select tones. The number of frequencies computed could be significantly reduced in the frequency domain code. However, fewer temporal samples could be calculated in the time-domain code as long as the tones could be neglected. The time-domain code also has the advantage that one only needs to calculate the new portions of the observer signal as new input data is made available. Because the FFT's are performed on the input for the frequency-domain code, there is a minimum sample length necessary to produce reasonable results.

Code	CPU Time (s)
Time Domain	1089
Frequency Domain	425

Table 1 CPU time comparison of serial computations of a landing gear signal for one observer from 4096 time samples on 181 patches with 82,219 grid points. Calculations performed on a 250 MHz, R10k SGI Octane.

Code	Observers	CPU Time (s)
Time Domain	1	88.0
	3	128.1
Frequency Domain	1	56.5
	3	85.0

Table 2 CPU time comparison of parallel computations of a landing gear signal from 4096 time samples on 181 patches with 82,219 grid points. Sixteen SGI Octane worker nodes of nonuniform speed were used in the master-slave calculations.

For problems the size of the landing-gear calculation, the computations are normally performed in parallel using MPI. Because of the high utilization of machines dedicated for parallel calculations, the master-slave paradigm was used to take advantage of the second processor on sixteen SGI Octanes in the lab. The processor speeds varied from 195 to 250 MHz. The master node was attached to a RAID system that stored the input data. Table 2 shows the timing results for calculations involving one and three observers. The speedup from the serial case is clearly not linear, but the run times have been significantly reduced. Furthermore, much of the time is spent doing file input and output. The master node is not capable of reading the data fast enough to satisfy all of the worker nodes. In this problem, a total of 1.4 GB of data must be read and transferred across the network. When the code first starts, all of the worker nodes simultaneously try to access their data from the master. Distributing the data before the calculation would be more efficient, but having the data in one place is much more convenient. Furthermore, as the number of observers increases, the work to disk access ratio improves resulting in better efficiency as can be seen from the three observer cases in table 2. The point of this example is not to show that perfect efficiency has been obtained,

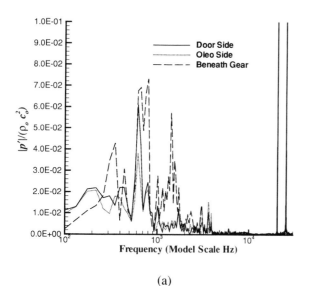

(a)

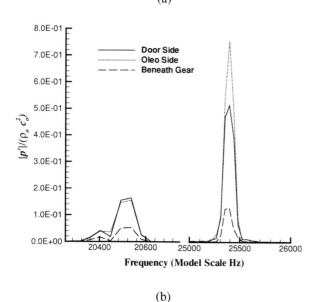

(b)

Fig. 6 FW-H results for an observer directly below a landing gear in a $M = 0.2$ flow. Results from frequency-domain code comparing the effect of observer location. All observers are $12l$ from the gear. The side observers have the same vertical location as the wheels.

domain code is considerably faster. However, the ordering of the input data was kept the same for both codes so they could share input files. The ordering used is more natural for the frequency-domain code which must perform FFT's on the time records. The time-domain code must interpolate the source terms to the retarded time, and this is done much more efficiently when the data is ordered such that the variable index varies fastest. The current code rearranges the data internally to obtain the preferred ordering. Even accounting for this extra work, the frequency-domain code would still be more efficient. Furthermore, the gear

but rather to demonstrate that the MPI implementation has enabled directivity mappings of thousands of observer locations to be performed relatively quickly on machines that are typically idle.

Conclusions

Two different formulations of the three-dimensional Ffowcs Williams and Hawkings equation for sources in uniform, subsonic, rectilinear motion have been presented. They are efficient enough to be used to perform far-field predictions from large data sets provided by either computation or experiment. Comparisons of the solutions for two example problems showed excellent agreement between the frequency- and time-domain formulations. Although the frequency-domain version of the code is somewhat faster, both algorithms are efficient enough to be used for computations involving large data sets when MPI is used to distribute the problem to many computers. Each formulation has different advantages that make it more attractive for certain classes of problems, but our tests have shown that they produce basically equivalent results for the problems investigated.

References

[1]Ffowcs Williams, J. E. and Hawkings, D. L., "Sound generation by turbulence and surfaces in arbitrary motion," *Philosophical Transactions of the Royal Society of London A*, Vol. 342, 1969, pp. 264–321.

[2]Singer, B. A., Lockard, D. P., Brentner, K. S., and Lilley, G. M., "Simulation of Acoustic Scattering from a Trailing Edge," *Journal of Sound and Vibration*, Vol. 230, No. 3, 2000, pp. 541–560.

[3]Brentner, K. S. and Farassat, F., "An Analytical Comparison of the Acoustic Analogy and Kirchhoff Formulation for Moving Surfaces," *AIAA Journal*, Vol. 36, No. 8, 1998, pp. 1379–1386.

[4]Lyrintzis, A. S., "The Use of Kirchhoff's Method in Computational Aeroacoustics," *ASME Journal of Fluids Engineering*, Vol. 116, 1994, pp. 665–675.

[5]Baeder, J. D., Gallman, J. M., and Yu, Y. H., "A Computational Study of the Aeroacoustics of Rotors in Hover," *Journal of the American Helicopter Society*, Vol. 42, No. 1, 1997, pp. 39–53.

[6]Di Francescantonio, P., "A New Boundary Integral Formulation for the Prediction of Sound Radiation," *Journal of Sound and Vibration*, Vol. 202, No. 4, 1997, pp. 491–509.

[7]Strawn, R. C. and Biswas, R., "Computation of Helicopter Rotor Noise in Forward Flight," *Journal of the American Helicopter Society*, Vol. 40, No. 3, 1995, pp. 66–72.

[8]Farassat, F., "Linear Acoustic Formulas for Calculation of Rotating Blade Noise," *AIAA Journal*, Vol. 19, No. 9, 1981, pp. 1122–1120.

[9]Lockard, D. P., "An Efficient, Two-Dimensional Implementation of the Ffowcs Williams and Hawkings Equation," *Journal of Sound and Vibration*, Vol. 229, No. 4, 2000, pp. 897–911.

[10]Crighton, D. G., Dowling, A. P., Ffowcs Williams, J. E., Heckl, M., and Leppington, F. G., *Modern Methods in Analytical Acoustics*, chap. 11, Springer-Verlag, London, 1992.

[11]Farassat, F. and Succi, G. P., "The Prediction of Helicopter Discrete Frequency Noise," *Vertica*, Vol. 7, No. 4, 1983, pp. 309–320.

[12]Garrick, I. E. and Watkins, E. W., "A Theoretical Study of the Effect of Forward Speed on the Free Space Sound Pressure Field Around Helicopters," TR 1198, NACA, 1954.

[13]Cook, R., Malkus, D., and Plesha, M., *Concepts and Applications of Finite Element Analysis*, chap. 6, John Wiley & Sons, Inc., 1989, pp. 176–180.

[14]Guo, Y., "Application of the Ffowcs Williams/Hawkings Equation to Two-Dimensional Problems," *Journal of Fluid Mechanics*, Vol. 403, January 2000, pp. 201–221.

[15]Dowling, A. P. and Ffowcs Williams, J. E., *Sound and Sources of Sound*, chap. 9, Horwood Publishing, Westergate, 1983, pp. 207–208.

[16]Ozyoruk, Y. and Long, L. N., "A New Efficient Algorithm for Computational Aeroacoustics on Parallel Computers," *Journal of Computational Physics*, Vol. 125, 1996, pp. 135–149.

[17]Long, L. N. and Brentner, K. S., "Self-Scheduling Parallel Methods for Multiple Serial Codes with Application to Wopwop," AIAA-2000-0346, 1996, Presented at the 38th AIAA Aerospace Sciences Meeting, Reno, NV, Jan 10-13.

[18]Souliez, F. J., Long, L. N., Morris, P. J., and Sharma, A., "Landing Gear Aerodynamic Noise Prediction Using Unstructured Grids," AIAA Paper 2002-0799, Presented at the 40th AIAA Aerospace Sciences Meeting, Reno, NV, Jan 14-17, 2002.

[19]Rumsey, C., Biedron, R., and Thomas, J., "CFL3D: Its History and Some Recent Applications," TM 112861, NASA, May 1997, presented at the Godonov's Method for Gas Dynamics Symposium, Ann Arbor, MI.

[20]Krist, S. L., Biedron, R. T., and Rumsey, C., "NASA Langley Research Center: Aerodynamic and Acoustic Methods Branch," *CFL3D User's Manual (Version 5)*, 1997.

[21]Li, F., Khorrami, M. R., and Malik, M. R., "Unsteady Simulations of a Landing-Gear Flow Field," AIAA Paper 2002-2411, Eighth AIAA/CEAS Aeroacoustics Conference, Breckenridge, CO, June 17–19, 2002.

AIAA 2002-2581

Validation of a Prediction model for Aerodynamic Noise from Aircraft Landing Gear

M.G.Smith (1) and L.C.Chow (2)

(1) ISVR University of Southampton, England
(2) Airbus UK, Filton, Bristol, England.

Abstract

The continued development of quiet engines is now giving rise to situations where airframe noise is comparable with engine noise at approach. The landing gear is a major contributor to airframe noise, and this paper outlines development and testing of a semi-empirical noise model for predicting the benefit of noise control fairings. The model is based on non-dimensional source spectra derived from a data base of full-scale tests on A320 landing gear installed in the DNW wind tunnel and is used to predict the noise reduction potential of a variety of fairings installed on the main and noise gears from an A340 aircraft . The model is found to give good agreement with data and this gives confidence that it may be used as an engineering tool to optimise fairing design. The paper also discusses the way in which the model can provide a framework for incorporating CFD data in the design process and also number of factors which complicate the comparison of noise data from wind tunnel and flyover tests.

1. Introduction

Aircraft landing gears are geometrically very complex and although much progress is currently being made [1], Computational Aeroacoustics methods are still some way from being sufficiently developed and rapid to provide the engineering design guidance which is needed to optimise noise control treatment. As a result it is necessary to resort to the semi-empirical modelling methods of this paper. The model described here was first developed by ISVR and British Aerospace and published in 1998 [2], but has been further developed and tested as part of the EC funded RAIN (Reduction of Airframe and Installation Noise) project. [3]

2. Outline of the noise model

The experimental data used in the development of the model were obtained by Dobrzynski and Buchholz using an A320 landing gear installed in the DNW wind tunnel. [4] The data were supplied with corrections already applied for wind tunnel effects such as the shear layer, background noise, convective amplification and geometrical factors such as the orientation of the gear leg relative to the flow and the microphone array. The correction for shear layer, due to Amiet, was probably the most difficult to determine accurately since there is an assumption that the noise arises from a point source. [5] The tests comprised 21 build configurations including tests on two wheel and four wheel gear together with a number of partial fairings, and with a range of flow speeds from 40 m/s to 78 m/s for each build. The data provided an excellent basis for an empirical noise model as the large fairings completely removed particular noise sources whereas more recent tests have worked with more practical fairings.

Noise data were recorded using an array of far-field microphones covering a range of polar angles from 65° to 135°, and a range of azimuthal angles from -20° to +22°. Some source location techniques were also applied.

In order to use the data for noise source modelling it was non-dimensionalised on the basis of known scaling laws to reveal the underlying source characteristics. The frequency, f, was converted to a non-dimensional Strouhal number, $S = f \, D / U$, using the actual free flow velocity, U, for each test and a standard dimension of $D = 1$ metre, which roughly corresponds to a typical wheel diameter.

The source data were further smoothed by collapsing data obtained at a range of flow speeds using a U^6 law and taking the median value at each Strouhal number. This had the effect of eliminating tones, and gave a set of characteristic curves from which the effect of flow velocity and tones had been removed, but which retained the effect of polar and azimuthal directivity.

The basis of the noise model was to use a number of empirical constants to fit standard source characteristics to particular classes of components such as struts, wheels, etc.. The characteristic shape of each spectrum is a 'haystack' with a peak centred at the natural vortex shedding frequency of the component given by $f_N = S_N U/d$ where d is a typical dimension. For struts where d is taken as strut diameter then S_N is typically 0.2 .[6] The 'breadth' of the haystack was one of the parameters fitted in the model.

The basic scaling law for acoustically compact sources developed by Curle[6] is

$$ I \quad \alpha \quad \frac{\rho U_0^6 \ell^2}{c^3 R^2} \quad (1) $$

where ℓ is the length of the component, U_0 is flow velocity and R is observer radius.

When applied to noise from a strut the intensity was taken to scale as length, l_s, times diameter, d_s, the mean square far-field pressure, P_s^2, at observer radius R has been expressed in the form:

$$ p_s^2 = (\rho c^2)^2 \frac{M^6}{4\pi R^2} \ell_s d_s (F_s(S_s) + F_d(S_d)) $$

(2)

$F_s(S_s)$ is a non-dimensional spectral shape function associated with the basic structural element and $F_d(S_d)$ is the spectral shape function associated with small components attached to the strut, so called dressings, which have been shown to generate significant high frequency noise. This scaling law derivation may be repeated for each source type, as described in reference 2, resulting in a different non-dimensionalised source spectrum for each source type.

The overall level of the landing gear noise during a flyover is then given by

$$ L = 10\log_{10}(D_w(\sum_s P_s^2 + P_w^2 + P_g^2 + P_h^2)) $$
$$ + 10\log_{10} C + R\alpha - 94 $$

(3)

where C is the convective amplification factor which for a point dipole source is given by $C = (1-M\cos\theta)^{-4}$, α is the atmospheric attenuation constant and D_w is a directivity function to account for effects such as installation of the gear under the wing.

Contained within this expression are a number of empirical constants for each source type which must be extracted using the experimental database and again reference 2 describes how this was done.

One of the assumptions inherent in this model is that all struts obey the same scaling law and this introduces a number of subtle effects which could be introduced into the model if required.

- The noise source may be Reynolds number dependent and this is different for each component
- Some struts may be in clean flow whereas others are in dirty flow.
- The Amiet shear layer correction will be different for each component
- The convective amplification factor C is a function of local flow over each component. This may differ significantly from the mean incident flow over the whole gear because of aerodynamic interference between components and because of the 'blockage' effect of the landing gear in the wind tunnel core flow.

The first two effects restrict the applicability model only to geometrically 'similar' gears. The other effects may affect the accuracy of the model, particularly with respect to directivity.

5. Comparison of the model with test data

The model was has been compared with a range of recent test data for A340 landing gears, the experimental details of which are described in [4]. This is a significant test for the model since the experiments included both the nose landing gear and the main landing gears which are geometrically quite different. For each gear the tests comprised measurements on a baseline configuration and then a series of tests with noise control fairings fitted, including a low noise configuration in which as much of the gear as possible was covered within the constraints of being practicable for deployment of the gear on an aircraft.

Nose gear results from the DNW:
Figure 1 shows the predicted breakdown of noise from the nose landing gear into 14 individual components. In the transformation to the low noise configuration 4 of these sources were suppressed entirely and 5 others were reduced in level resulting in a predicted 3.1 dBA change compared with a measured overall reduction of 2.4 dBA.

The predicted and measured difference spectra between the baseline configuration and the low noise configuration are shown in figure 2. The measured result is the spatial average attenuation over the 20?? far-field microphones, and the figure also shows the +/- one standard deviation from the mean. Since we are working with level differences the statistics have been calculated directly from the dB attenuations.

Agreement between predictions and measurements is quite satisfactory, but the best test of the model is whether it can predict changes such as intermediate builds. Two such results are given in figure 3 where the change due to adding or removing an individual fairing are shown (Note that the reference configuration is not the same in each graph).

For both cases there is a reasonable correlation between the measured and predicted changes. For the fairing A the prediction underestimates the measured attenuation and this was shown in the measurements to be partly due to a high speed flow over one component in the baseline configuration. Covering the component with a fairing gives a greater than expected noise reduction from the fairing. The effect of this high speed flow can be simulated in the model.

For fairing B the prediction slightly overestimates the attenuation. In this case there is a strong possibility that the wake from the fairing is impinging on other components causing their noise contribution to increase, thus reducing the effectiveness of the fairing. This effect is discussed further below.

Main gear results from the DNW
Figure 4 displays the predicted components level breakdown of noise from the main landing gear. In the transformation to the low noise configuration 4 of these 14 sources were suppressed entirely and 8 others were reduced in level. The measured overall reduction of 3.6 dBA compared with a predicted change of 3.7dBA.

The difference between the baseline and low noise configurations and the effect of individual fairings are given in figures 5 and 6 respectively. Again there is a reasonable correlation between the predictions and measurements.

The accuracy of these predictions gives some confidence that the model is a good representation of the landing gear and this opens up two possible uses. Firstly the model can be used to 'fill in' the experimental matrix so that tests for which there was insufficient wind tunnel time can be simulated. This will help to identify treatments that were not cost effective. Secondly the model can be used to suggest what further measures should be implemented to gain further noise reductions. In the case of the main landing gear the dominant remaining sources are the wheels, the drag stay and the doors.

Comparison with flyover test data
In order to compare the model with flyover data it is necessary to use equation 2 for both the nose and main landing gears and also add in the contribution from other sources. One such result is shown in figure 7. This case is for an aircraft without slats and flaps deployed so that the contribution from other sources is relatively low. At this overhead position the convective amplification correction is 0 dB.

The predictions for the landing gear in the wind tunnel were in excellent agreement and so the agreement with the flyover data is not quite as good as might have been expected. Possible reasons for this are a) the assumption that the baseline aircraft noise is unchanged may be inaccurate (e.g. the low frequency peak at has changed significantly), b) there are noise sources present in the test build that were present in neither the baseline flyover test nor the wind tunnel test on the landing gears (e.g. the mid frequency peak) c) there is a stronger than expected installation effect under the wing.

For this case the main landing gears are the dominant source though it should be noted that when the high lift devices are deployed the flow circulation around the wing significantly reduces the flow over the main landing gears. This was discussed in more detail in our previous paper.[2]

When comparing the directivity of the landing gear noise in flight with data taken in the wind tunnel data a number of subtle effects should be taken into account, particularly for gears installed beneath a wing where the flow circulation around the wing reduces the local flow over the gear[2].
- The local convective amplification is dependent on local flow velocity rather than the aircraft velocity.
- Below the aircraft the flow speed relative to the aircraft progressively increases to the speed of the aircraft. By considering this to occur at a shear layer, as in the wind tunnel, a correction analogous to the Amiet correction could be applied.
- The convective amplification correction to be applied is that for angle to the aircraft at the emission time of the noise.

6. Design optimisation
One of the side effects of fairings is that high speed flow may be deflected onto other components resulting in an increase in their noise level and thus diminishing the effectiveness of the fairings. Given that the noise output of any component varies with the 6th power of locally incident flow velocity it may be seen that the total power output of the landing gear is likely to be proportional to the spatially averaged 6th power of flow velocity, $\langle U^6 \rangle$.

Supposing that a set of fairings covers some proportion, p, of the components in a gear (so that the flow over them is reduced to zero), but that the flow over the remaining components is increased by a factor, f , where f = <U^6>$^{1/6}$/U$_0$. Then it is easy to show that the change in sound power output of the gear will be given by:

$$\Delta dB = 10\log_{10}(1-p)f^6$$

a contour map of how this function varies with p and f is shown in figure 9 and is best explained by a number of examples.

- Covering half the components without increasing the flow over other components (p=0.5, f=1.0) gives a 3dB reduction
- With p=0.9 and f=1.0 there is a 10dB reduction
- If half the components are covered, but the flow is doubled on other component (p=0.5, f=2.0) the level increases by 15 dB
- With p = 0.5 a increasing f from 1.0 to 1.2 would more than wipe out the 3dB potential gain from the fairings.

This analysis emphasis the importance of CFD predictions as integral part of the noise modelling process.

7.0 Conclusions

The model described in this paper has been shown to provide a reasonably accurate component level breakdown of landing gear noise and as such is a useful tool for engineering level design analyses.

The fact that the model works is an indication that the sources are essentially independent. This means that a CFD model could usefully be used in the design process to control flow to minimise the spatially averaged 6th power of incident flow velocity. This is likely to be the key to successful implementation of noise control fairings.

Acknowledgements

The authors would like to acknowledge the contribution of the European Commission in partially financing the work described in this paper and also the many and varied contributions of the partners in the RAIN project consortium.

List of Symbols

I	Sound intensity
ρ	density of air
c	speed of sound
U	local flow velocity
U$_0$	free stream velocity
M	flow Mach No.
R	radial distance from source to observer

ℓ , d	typical component length and diameter
ℓ_s , d$_s$	length and diameter of a strut or fairing
S$_s$	Strouhal number for strut noise, based on strut diameter
S$_d$	Strouhal number for dressing noise, based on typical dressing diameter
D$_w$	directivity due to installation under a wing
$p_s^2, p_w^2, p_h^2, p_g^2$	mean square far-field pressure due to the strut, wheel, hub or wheel gap sources.

References

1. Souliez, F.J., Long, L.N., Morris, P.J., Sharma, A. Landing Gear Aerodynamic Noise Prediction using Unstructured Grids, AIAA 2002-0799

2. Smith, M.G., Chow, L.C., Prediction Method for Aerodyanmic Noise from Aircraft Landing Gears, AIAA 98-2228

3. Chow, L.C., Mau, K., Remy, H. Landing Gears and High Lift Devices Airframe Noise Research, AIAA 2002-2408

4. Dobrzynski, W., Chow, L.C., Guion, P., Shiells, D. Research into Landing gears Airframe Noise Reduction. AIAA 2002-2409

5. Dobrzynski, W. and Buckholz, H. Full Scale Noise Testing on Airbus Landing Gears in the German Dutch Wind Tunnel, AIAA-97-1597, May 1997.

6. Amiet, R.K. Correction of Open Jet Wind Tunnel Measurements for Shear Layer Refraction, AIAA Paper No. 75-532, March 1975.

7. Curle, N. The influence of Solid Boundaries upon Aerodynamic Sound. Proc. Royal Soc., Vol. A231, pp.505-514, 1955.

8. Dowling, A.P. and Ffowcs Williams, J.E. Sound and Sources of Sound, Ellis Horwood, 1983

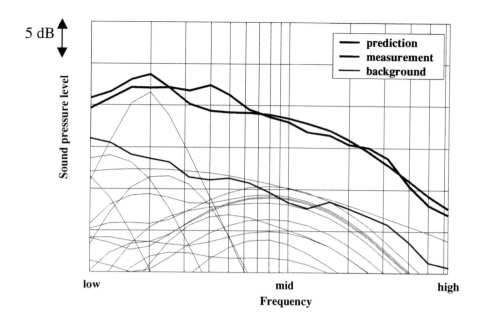

Figure 1 Component level breakdown of noise from the nose landing gear

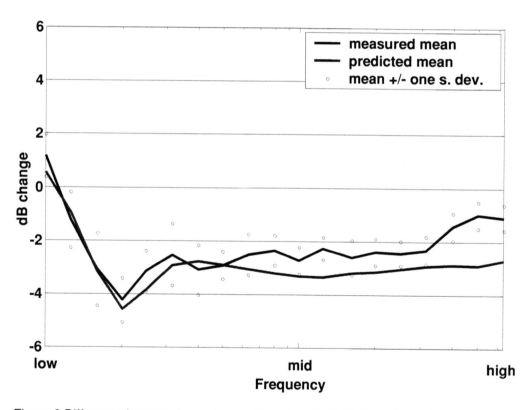

Figure 2 Difference between low noise and baseline A340 NLG configurations

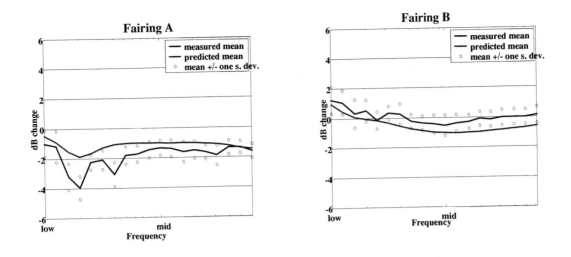

Figure 3 Effect of individual NLG fairings in RAIN tests

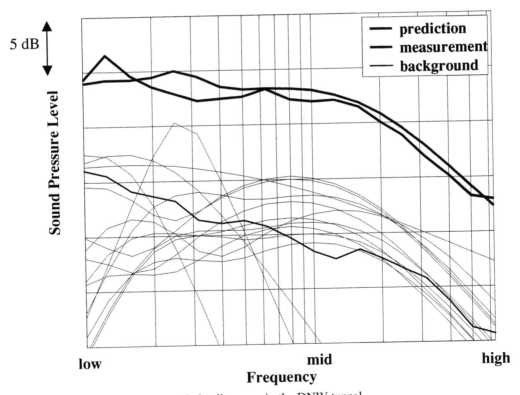

Figure 4 Prediction of baseline main landing gear in the DNW tunnel

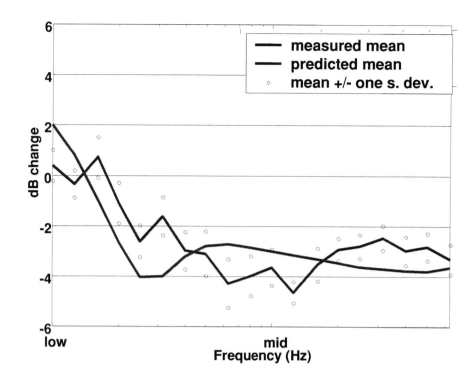

Figure 5 Prediction of the difference between the main landing gear low noise and baseline configurations

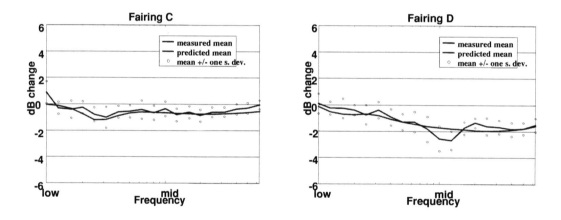

Figure 6 Effect of individual MLG fairings in RAIN tests:

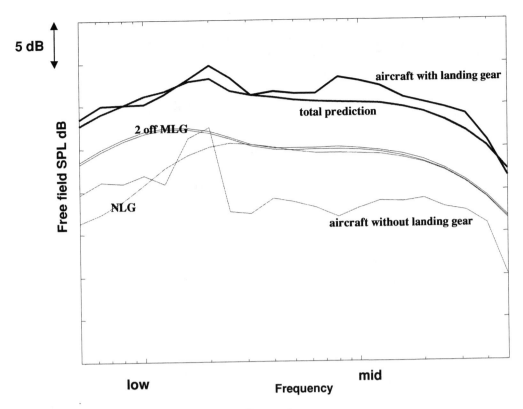

Figure 7 comparison of the model with A340 flyover data

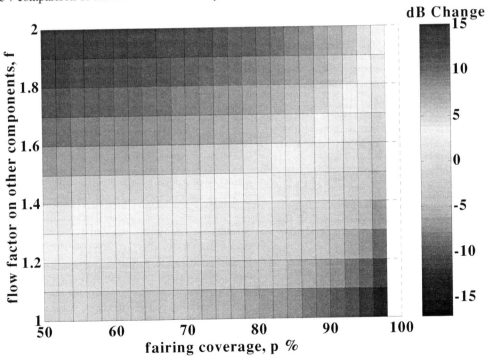

figure 8 Contour plot of change in level due to partial covering of a landing gear with resultant flow increase over other components

AIAA 2002-2582

ACOUSTIC SOURCE TERMS FOR THE LINEAR EULER EQUATIONS ON CONSERVATIVE FORM

Mattias Billson*, Lars-Erik Eriksson*† and Lars Davidson*

* *Department of Thermo and Fluid Dynamics, Chalmers University of Technology, SE-412 96 Göteborg, Sweden*

† *Volvo Aero Corporation, Military Engines Division, SE-461 81 Trollhättan, Sweden*

A rather novel approach to predict jet noise is the Stochastic Noise Generation and Radiation (SNGR) method. The SNGR method uses the linear Euler equations as an acoustic analogy together with source terms which are modeled. In other studies (Bechara[1] and Bailly[2]) the Euler equations on primitive form are used. In the present work the linear Euler equations on conservative form are used. Due to this, new source terms have to be derived for the conservative set of equations. A formal derivation of the correct source terms for the linear Euler equations on conservative form is presented. Simplified versions of the derived source terms are also developed. To validate the derived source terms a direct simulation of a forced 2D mixing layer is carried out. The solutions to the linearized Euler equations with source terms are compared to the solution of the direct simulation and show a good agreement. All simulations are performed using Tam and Webb's[3] fourth order DRP scheme and a four step fourth order Runge-Kutta time marching technique. Artificial selective damping introduced through the numerical scheme is used to avoid spurious waves. Absorbing boundary conditions based on characteristic variables, Engquist and Majda,[4,5] are used at the free boundaries and a buffer layer is added at the outflow.

Introduction

Using a Navier Stokes solver for the near field combined with an acoustic analogy for the far field is quite common in aeroacoustics. There are a variety of analogies which could be used, Lighthill's[6] analogy for free turbulence in a homogeneous medium, Lilley's analogy,[7] Curle's[8] extension to Lighthill's analogy for the presence of solid walls just to mention a few. Lighthill's analogy is most often solved as an integral solution and limited by the assumption of sound generation and radiation in a homogeneous medium and the same holds for Curle's extension to Lighthill's analogy. Although Lilley's analogy does include refractional effects it is somewhat sensitive to the way the source terms are evaluated.[9] The linear Euler equations with source terms are not limited by the homogeneous medium assumption and can handle refractional effects and reflection at solid boundaries. The scalar wave equation governs acoustic wave propagation but not entropy and vorticity waves. The linear Euler equations on the other hand govern both acoustic propagation as well as entropy and vorticity waves.

This work is a part of the evaluation and de-velopment of the SNGR (Stochastic Noise Generation and Radiation) method originally presented by Bechara[1] and further developed by Bailly.[2] The present work focus on the formulation of source terms for the linear Euler equations. Bailly[2] use a formulation of the linear Euler equations based on $(\rho', \rho u', \rho v', \rho w', p')$ as solution variables. In that formulation, the source terms only enter the momentum equations. The formulation of the linear Euler equations used in the present work is entirely based on conservative variables, $(\rho', (\rho u)', (\rho v)', (\rho w)', (\rho e_0)')$. In this formulation the source terms enter not only the momentum equations but also the energy equation. The correct formulation of the source terms for the linear Euler equations on conservative form are derived below. It is shown that the source terms not only depend on the unsteady Reynolds stresses but also on unsteady total enthalpy. This causes some problems in the SNGR method. In the present formulation of the SNGR,[2] only velocity fluctuations are modeled, assuming that all other variables are constant. For this reason different simplifications of the source terms are derived.

The use of a forced 2D mixing layer as a test case for different methods of sound prediction was first presented by Colonius.[9] Colonius performed a direct numerical simulation of a free mixing layer forced at its first three harmonics. The results were used and compared with Lilley's acoustic analogy.[7] Later Bogey[10] made a sound prediction with LES and Lighthill's analogy on a free mixing layer excited by the first two harmonics. The results were in both cases in good agreement between the direct simulations and the analogies. To validate the derived source terms a forced mixing layer is computed by direct simulation using a 2D compressible Navier-Stokes solver. The solution from the direct simulation provides a reference solution (time average) and is used to evaluate the source terms for the linear Euler equations which are solved and the results are compared. Comparisons of the computational results using the different source terms with direct simulation of a forced free mixing layer are presented and discussed.

Theory

In this section a derivation of the linearized Euler equations and energy equation on conservative form with source terms is presented. The derivation starts with the Euler equations and is a rewriting of the full Euler equations in a way that the left hand side of the equations are the linear Euler equations. The remaining non-linear terms in this derivation are put in the right hand side and form the source terms.

Start with the compressible Euler equations on conservative form.

$$\frac{\partial \rho}{\partial t} + \frac{\partial \rho u_j}{\partial x_j} = 0 \tag{1}$$

$$\frac{\partial \rho u_i}{\partial t} + \frac{\partial}{\partial x_j}(\rho u_i u_j + p\delta_{ij}) = 0 \tag{2}$$

$$\frac{\partial \rho e_0}{\partial t} + \frac{\partial}{\partial x_j}(\rho h_0 u_j) = 0 \tag{3}$$

where $(\rho, \rho u, \rho v, \rho w, \rho e_0)$ are the density, the x, y and z momentum and total internal energy per unit volume; ρh_0 is the total enthalpy per unit volume. Introducing a decomposition of the variables in a time averaged part and a fluctuating part as

$$
\begin{aligned}
\rho &= \rho + \rho' \\
u_i &= \widetilde{u}_i + u_i'' \\
p &= p + p' \\
e_0 &= \widetilde{e}_0 + e_0'' \\
h_0 &= \widetilde{h}_0 + h_0''
\end{aligned}
\tag{4}
$$

where bar denotes time averaged and prime fluctuating variable. The average of for example u_i is a Favre time average defined by

$$\widetilde{u}_i = \frac{\rho u_i}{\rho} \tag{5}$$

and the double prime is the fluctuation associated with the Favre time averaged velocity.

The momentum can be decomposed in two ways

$$
\begin{aligned}
\rho u_i &= \overline{\rho u_i} + (\rho u_i)' = \rho \widetilde{u}_i + (\rho u_i)' \quad \text{or} \\
\rho u_i &= \rho(\widetilde{u}_i + u_i'') = \rho \widetilde{u}_i + \rho u_i''
\end{aligned}
\tag{6}
$$

$$\Rightarrow (\rho u_i)' = \rho' \widetilde{u}_i + \rho u_i'' \tag{7}$$

The first decomposition in equation 6 is done by time averaging ρu_i and the second by Favre averaging u_i. Both are valid and will be used in the following derivation. Combined they give equation 7. The same holds for ρe_0 and ρh_0 which gives the following equalities

$$
\begin{aligned}
(\rho e_0)' &= \rho' \widetilde{e}_0 + \rho e_0'' \\
(\rho h_0)' &= \rho' \widetilde{h}_0 + \rho h_0''
\end{aligned}
\tag{8}
$$

Furthermore

$$
\begin{aligned}
\rho h_0 u_j &= \rho(\widetilde{h}_0 + h_0'')(\widetilde{u}_j + u_j'') \\
&= \rho \widetilde{h}_0 \widetilde{u}_j + \rho \widetilde{h}_0 u_j'' + \rho h_0'' \widetilde{u}_j + \rho h_0'' u_j''
\end{aligned}
\tag{9}
$$

$$\Rightarrow \overline{\rho h_0 u_j} = \rho \widetilde{h}_0 \widetilde{u}_j + \overline{\rho h_0'' u_j''} \tag{10}$$

Taking the time average of the continuity equation 1 gives

$$\frac{\partial \rho}{\partial t} + \frac{\partial \rho u_j}{\partial x_j} = 0 \tag{11}$$

Subtraction of equation 11 from equation 1 results in the continuity equation for the fluctuations

$$\frac{\partial \rho'}{\partial t} + \frac{\partial (\rho u_j)'}{\partial x_j} = 0 \tag{12}$$

Averaging the inviscid momentum equation 2 gives

$$\frac{\partial \rho \widetilde{u}_i}{\partial t} + \frac{\partial}{\partial x_j}(\rho \widetilde{u}_i \widetilde{u}_j + \overline{\rho u_i'' u_j''} + p\delta_{ij}) = 0 \tag{13}$$

and subtracting the resulting equation 13 from 2 gives an equation for the fluctuations

$$
\frac{\partial \rho u_i - \rho \widetilde{u}_i}{\partial t} + \frac{\partial}{\partial x_j}(\rho u_i u_j - \rho \widetilde{u}_i \widetilde{u}_j - \overline{\rho u_i'' u_j''} + (p - p)\delta_{ij}) = 0
\tag{14}
$$

Using equation 6 on the first term and expanding $\rho u_i u_j$ gives

$$
\begin{aligned}
&\frac{\partial (\rho u_i)'}{\partial t} + \\
&\frac{\partial}{\partial x_j} (\rho' \widetilde{u}_i \widetilde{u}_j + \rho u_i'' \widetilde{u}_j + \rho u_j'' \widetilde{u}_i + \\
&\rho u_i'' u_j'' - \rho \widetilde{u_i'' u_j''} + p' \delta_{ij}) = 0
\end{aligned}
\tag{15}
$$

Using equation 7 on the second term and rewriting the resulting equation by moving all non-linear terms to the right hand side gives

$$
\begin{aligned}
&\frac{\partial (\rho u_i)'}{\partial t} + \\
&\frac{\partial}{\partial x_j} (\widetilde{u}_j (\rho u_i)' + \widetilde{u}_i (\rho u_j)' - \rho' \widetilde{u}_i \widetilde{u}_j + p' \delta_{ij}) = \\
&- \frac{\partial}{\partial x_j} (\rho u_i'' u_j'' - \rho \widetilde{u_i'' u_j''})
\end{aligned}
\tag{16}
$$

Equation 16 is the linearized momentum equation on the left hand side with source terms on the right hand side. That the left hand side of 16 is the linearized momentum equation can be seen through differentiation of the term $\rho u_i u_j$ as

$$
\begin{aligned}
\mathrm{d}(\rho u_i u_j) &= \mathrm{d} \left(\frac{(\rho u_i)(\rho u_j)}{\rho} \right) \\
&= u_i \mathrm{d}(\rho u_j) + u_j \mathrm{d}(\rho u_i) - u_i u_j \mathrm{d}(\rho)
\end{aligned}
\tag{17}
$$

Now we proceed to derive the linear equation for total energy. Averaging the inviscid energy equation (equation 3) gives

$$
\frac{\partial \rho e_0}{\partial t} + \frac{\partial}{\partial x_j} (\rho h_0 u_j) = 0
\tag{18}
$$

and subtracting equation 18 from equation 3

$$
\frac{\partial (\rho e_0)'}{\partial t} + \frac{\partial}{\partial x_j} (\rho h_0 u_j - \rho h_0 u_j) = 0
\tag{19}
$$

Inserting the expressions 9 and 10 into equation 19 keeping the linear terms on the left side and moving the non-linear terms to the right hand side gives

$$
\begin{aligned}
&\frac{\partial (\rho e_0)'}{\partial t} + \frac{\partial}{\partial x_j} (\rho' \widetilde{h}_0 \widetilde{u}_j + \rho \widetilde{h}_0 u_j'' + \rho h_0'' \widetilde{u}_j) = \\
&- \frac{\partial}{\partial x_j} (\rho h_0'' u_j'' - \rho \widetilde{h_0'' u_j''})
\end{aligned}
\tag{20}
$$

Using the decomposition 7 and 8, equation 20 can now be rewritten on the form

$$
\begin{aligned}
&\frac{\partial (\rho e_0)'}{\partial t} + \frac{\partial}{\partial x_j} (\widetilde{h}_0 (\rho u_j)' + \widetilde{u}_j (\rho h_0)' - \rho' \widetilde{h}_0 \widetilde{u}_j) = \\
&- \frac{\partial}{\partial x_j} (\rho h_0'' u_j'' - \rho \widetilde{h_0'' u_j''})
\end{aligned}
\tag{21}
$$

where the left side is the linear energy equation and the right hand side contains all non-linear terms. The resulting linear Euler equations with source terms are here summarized

$$
\begin{aligned}
&\frac{\partial \rho'}{\partial t} + \frac{\partial (\rho u_j)'}{\partial x_j} = 0 \\
&\frac{\partial (\rho u_i)'}{\partial t} + \\
&\frac{\partial}{\partial x_j} (\widetilde{u}_j (\rho u_i)' + \widetilde{u}_i (\rho u_j)' - \rho' \widetilde{u}_i \widetilde{u}_j + p' \delta_{ij}) = \\
&- \frac{\partial}{\partial x_j} (\rho u_i'' u_j'' - \rho \widetilde{u_i'' u_j''}) \\
&\frac{\partial (\rho e_0)'}{\partial t} + \\
&\frac{\partial}{\partial x_j} (\widetilde{h}_0 (\rho u_j)' + \widetilde{u}_j (\rho h_0)' - \rho' \widetilde{h}_0 \widetilde{u}_j) = \\
&- \frac{\partial}{\partial x_j} (\rho h_0'' u_j'' - \rho \widetilde{h_0'' u_j''})
\end{aligned}
\tag{22}
$$

The linear Euler equations above, equations 22, have been derived from the Euler equations without approximations or assumptions of the nature of the flow. The equations above are in fact still the non-linear Euler equations. But if one argue that the right hand side of equations 22 is in some way known, then the equations on the left hand side are the linear Euler equations. The right hand side could for example be given by a large eddy simulation or DNS which also provides the reference solution for the linear Euler equations. The equations 22 would then be an analogy for acoustic generation and radiation.

Unlike scalar wave operators, the linear Euler equations also supports vorticity and entropy waves. This is both an advantage and a disadvantage for the linear Euler equations as an analogy. The advantage is that entropy and vorticity waves generated by the source term are indeed governed by the linear Euler equations. The disadvantage is that this may cause instabilities. Stability analysis of the linear Euler equations show that vorticity and entropy waves can in some cases grow without bound in the presence of mean shear. The near field solution would then be dominated by this homogeneous solution instead of the forced solution which is sought for. This does not necessarily mean that the far field solution is affected by these instabilities. The instabilities will not radiate sound and contaminate the far field as long as the acoustic characteristic variables are not too strongly coupled with the vorticity and entropy characteristic variables. There were no problems with instabilities in the simulations presented in the present work but it is important to know that control of entropy and vorticity waves may be necessary in some flows to avoid potential problems.

Approximations of source terms

One of the purposes of this work is to evaluate the effect of simplifications of the source terms in the linear Euler equations. In the SNGR only the velocities are modeled. This means that fluctuations of total enthalpy and density are not known. The first step in simplifying the source terms is to rewrite and approximate the heat source term in the energy equation. Begin by identifying

$$\rho h_0'' = \left(\frac{p}{\rho} - \widetilde{\left(\frac{p}{\rho}\right)} \right) \frac{\gamma}{(\gamma-1)} + \frac{1}{2}\rho \left(u_k u_k - \widetilde{u_k u_k} \right) \quad (23)$$

The first term can be written in terms of temperature. The first Reynolds term can be decomposed in Favre averages of velocities and the associated fluctuations. The last term can also be decomposed and rewritten in the same manner. After some algebra the following expression is obtained

$$\rho h_0'' = \rho C_p T'' + \rho \widetilde{u}_k u_k'' + \frac{1}{2}\rho \left(u_k'' u_k'' - \widetilde{u_k'' u_k''} \right) \quad (24)$$

which leads to

$$\rho h_0'' u_j'' = \rho C_p T'' u_j'' + \rho \widetilde{u}_k u_k'' u_j'' + \frac{1}{2}\rho \left(u_k'' u_k'' - \widetilde{u_k'' u_k''} \right) u_j'' \quad (25)$$

If we neglect trippel correlations of velocities we obtain

$$\rho h_0'' u_j'' = \rho C_p T'' u_j'' + \rho \widetilde{u}_k u_k'' u_j'' \quad (26)$$

and thus

$$\rho h_0'' u_j'' - \overline{\rho h_0'' u_j''} = C_p \left(\rho T'' u_j'' - \overline{\rho T'' u_j''} \right) + \widetilde{u}_k \left(\rho u_k'' u_j'' - \overline{\rho u_k'' u_j''} \right) \quad (27)$$

The following notation is introduced

$$\begin{aligned} \mathcal{T}_{ij} &= \rho u_i'' u_j'' - \overline{\rho u_i'' u_j''} \\ \mathcal{Q}_j &= C_p \left(\rho T'' u_j'' - \overline{\rho T'' u_j''} \right) \end{aligned} \quad (28)$$

Then the simplified source terms for the linear Euler equations can be written as

$$\begin{aligned} \text{Continuity} &= 0 \\ \text{Momentum} &= -\frac{\partial}{\partial x_j}\left(\mathcal{T}_{ij} \right) \\ \text{Energy} &= -\frac{\partial}{\partial x_j}\left(\mathcal{Q}_j + \widetilde{u}_i \mathcal{T}_{ij} \right) \end{aligned} \quad (29)$$

The next step in the simplification of the source terms is to neglect temperature fluctuations. The source terms are then

$$\begin{aligned} \text{Continuity} &= 0 \\ \text{Momentum} &= -\frac{\partial}{\partial x_j}\left(\mathcal{T}_{ij} \right) \\ \text{Energy} &= -\frac{\partial}{\partial x_j}\left(\widetilde{u}_i \mathcal{T}_{ij} \right) \end{aligned} \quad (30)$$

In the last step of simplifications of the source terms fluctuations of density are neglected, i.e.

$$\begin{aligned} \text{Continuity} &= 0 \\ \text{Momentum} &= -\frac{\partial}{\partial x_j}\rho \left(u_i' u_j' - \overline{u_i' u_j'} \right) \\ \text{Energy} &= -\frac{\partial}{\partial x_j}u_i \rho \left(u_i' u_j' - \overline{u_i' u_j'} \right) \end{aligned} \quad (31)$$

where the primed velocities now are fluctuations associated with the ordinary time averaged velocities.

Numerical simulation and validation of theory

Numerical scheme

The code for direct simulation and the linear Euler code are based on the same numerical scheme. The convective terms are discretized with a six point stencil. The coefficients of Tam's[3] fourth order dispersion relation preserving finite difference scheme is converted to the equivalent finite volume coefficients. The diffusive terms in the direct simulation code are discretized using a compact second order scheme. A fourth order four step Runge-Kutta time marching technique is used for the time stepping. Artificial selective damping is used to prevent spurious waves from the boundaries and regions with stretching to contaminate the solution. The manner in which the artificial selective damping is introduced is described in Eriksson.[11]

Boundary Conditions

The mixing layer consists of an upper stream with a Mach number of $M_1 = 0.5$ and a lower stream with Mach number $M_2 = 0.25$. At the interface between the two streams a hyperbolic-tangent profile is used as inflow boundary profile. The inlet streamwise profile is

$$u_{in} = \frac{U_1 + U_2}{2} + \frac{U_1 - U_2}{2} \tanh\left(\frac{2y}{\delta_\omega(0)}\right) \qquad (32)$$

where U_1 and U_2 are the upper and lower velocities respectively. The initial vorticity thickness $\delta_\omega(0)$ defines the thickness of the incoming velocity profile, see figure 1. The velocity at the inflection point is defined by $U_0 = (U_1 + U_2)/2$. The spanwise velocity v_0 is set to zero at the inlet. The pressure and density are constant over the inlet and are set to normal atmospheric conditions. The Reynolds number for this flow based on the initial vorticity thickness $\delta_\omega(0)$ is $Re_\omega = \delta_\omega(0)U_0/\nu = 1.58 \times 10^5$.

The absorbing boundary conditions used are based on local analysis of characteristic variables, Engquist and Majda.[4,5] The boundary conditions handle radiation boundaries quite well as long as the outgoing waves to be absorbed are not at too high incidence angle and they are exact and non-reflecting for waves normal to the boundary. The amount of reflection from the radiation boundary is very small for these boundary conditions. The same holds for the inlet boundary. The reason for this is that the only disturbances reaching these boundaries are acoustic waves with comparably small amplitudes. At the outflow boundary, however, there are vorticity and entropy waves as well as acoustic waves convected through the boundary. The large difference in energy of the vorticity and entropy waves leaving the computational domain at the outflow compared to the acoustic waves cause a major problem. Although most of the energy in the outgoing vorticity and entropy waves is absorbed and only a small portion of the energy is reflected back into the computational domain, the reflected part comes back as acoustic waves contaminating the solution.

To aid the absorbing boundary conditions at the outflow region a buffer region is applied at the last section of the computational domain. The mesh is also stretched in the flow direction in this region to help attenuate disturbances through the artificial dissipation in the numerical scheme. This method of taking care of outgoing disturbances was successfully used by Colonius[9] and Bogey et al.[10] The term added to the governing equations is

$$\frac{\partial Q}{\partial t} = \cdots - \frac{c\sigma(x,y)}{\Delta x}(Q') \qquad (33)$$

where

$$\sigma(x,y) = \sigma_{max}\left(\frac{x - x_0}{x_{max} - x_0}\right)^2 \qquad (34)$$

Q denotes the solution vector and $\sigma_{max} = 0.1$; x_0 and x_{max} are the beginning and end of the buffer

region. The disturbance Q' is in the direct simulation computed as $Q - Q^*$. The term Q^* is a time average calculated using a low pass filter where the average from time step n is calculated from the average at time step $n - 1$ and the solution at time step n as

$$Q^*_{(n)} = \alpha Q^*_{(n-1)} + (1 - \alpha)Q_{(n)} \qquad (35)$$

where α is a number close to one (further details below).

The parabolic shape of $\sigma(x,y)$ ensures that the damping term will not cause reflections into the computational domain. The stretching of the mesh in the buffer region is also done gradually with very small amount of stretching at the beginning and more aggressive once the damping term in the buffer region is larger.

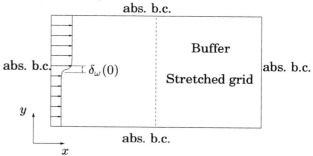

Fig. 1 Computational domain

Forcing

A two-dimensional laminar shear layer is unstable by nature and will start to break up if the computational domain is long enough. This process might take some time though and the laminar part of the shear layer can be quite long in the streamwise direction. The acoustic field produced in this process will also be more or less stochastic with peaks in the spectra for the frequencies corresponding to the natural instability frequencies of the shear layer. To get better control of the shear layer and to make it break up faster, forcing is applied at the inflow boundary. This forcing is done using the inflow absorbing boundary conditions. The incoming vorticity characteristic variable is modulated at the fundamental frequency of the incoming profile. The resulting forcing enters the spanwise inflow velocity component as

$$v_{in} = v_0 + A\sin(\omega_0 t) \qquad (36)$$

where A is the amplitude of the forcing. The forcing is only applied in the region of the hyperbolic-tangent profile. Since the forcing is included as a part of the absorbing boundary conditions, the forcing does not interfere with the absorbing property of the boundary condition and the amount of spurious waves created by the forcing is kept to a minimum. An important detail is that the forcing added in the direct simulation is also added in the linear Euler simulation. The reasoning behind this is that unless this is done, the boundary condition for the linear Euler simulation is not consistent with the sources evaluated from the direct simulation. The result from not using forcing in the linear Euler simulation is growing instabilities.

Bogey[10] computed the fundamental frequency based on the instability theory of Michalke[12] as

$$f_0 = 0.132 \left[\frac{U_0}{\delta_\omega(0)} \right] \qquad (37)$$

The shear layer is forced at two frequencies. The fundamental frequency f_0 and half the fundamental frequency $f_0/2$. In this way the forcing at the fundamental frequency will induce the creation of vortices at a frequency of f_0 which are convected downstream by the convection velocity. The second forcing at half the fundamental frequency will in turn induce a process where two successive vortices start to roll up around each other. This pair of vortices will after a short period of time start to merge and form a larger vortex. The frequency of this pairing will be denoted $f_p = f_0/2$ and the pairing time $T_p = 2T_0$. In this work, $A = 0.2$ for the forcing at the fundamental frequency f_0 and $A = 0.1$ for $f_0/2$.

Computational Setup

The computational mesh consists of 551×261 (x, y) mesh points. The physical size of the mesh is $0 \leq x \leq 6$ and $-3 \leq y \leq 3$, equivalent of $0 \leq x \leq 300\delta_\omega(0)$ and $-150\delta_\omega(0) \leq y \leq 150\delta_\omega(0)$ for $\delta_\omega(0) = 0.02[m]$. The mesh is uniform in the streamwise direction for the first 451 points with a cell length of $\Delta x = 0.375\delta_\omega(0)$. The last hundred points are used to build the buffer region in which the mesh is stretched and damping terms are added to the equations. The last cell at the outflow boundary has a cell length of $\Delta x = 4.1\delta_\omega(0)$. In the spanwise direction the mesh points are concentrated to the mixing region and stretched towards the outer boundary. The minimum cell height in the mixing region is $\Delta y = 0.164\delta_\omega(0)$ and increases slowly to $\Delta y = 0.3\delta_\omega(0)$ at $|y| \approx 5\delta_\omega(0)$. The stretching continues all the way to the boundary where the cell height is $\Delta y = 3.0\delta_\omega(0)$. With a fundamental frequency f_0 of 789Hz the emitted sound waves have a wavelength of $\lambda = 0.87[m]$ which correspond to $14\Delta y$ in the outer region so the propagating sound is well resolved in the entire domain. How the wavelength is related to the fundamental frequency will be discussed when presenting the results below.

Direct Simulation

The direct simulation started with the hyperbolic-tangent profile as initial solution. To achieve a periodic solution the simulation was run for 30 000 time steps at CFL = 0.5 which is equivalent to 40 pairing periods T_p. During this time the low-pass filter average (equation 35) was sampled with increasing value of the factor α. For the last 20 periods $\alpha = 0.9999$ was used before α was finally set to 1.0. This to ensure that the reference solution for the buffer layer would be representative of the true time average of the flow in the buffer layer. The sampling of the solution was then performed during 18432 time steps. With a fixed time step at CFL ≈ 0.5 this is equivalent to 24 periods with 768 time steps per period. In each time step a limited part of the solution called the source region was saved. The source region was defined as $-20\delta_\omega(0) \leq y \leq 20\delta_\omega(0)$ and $0 \leq x \leq 300\delta_\omega(0)$. The total amount of disk space required for this simulation was about 30 Gigabytes and the sampling took about 20 hours on an alpha XP-900 466 MHz processor.

Linear Euler Simulation

The linear Euler simulation used the solution from the direct simulation as initial solution and was performed during 18432 time steps. The time averaged solution from the direct simulation was used as reference solution. At each time step the solution from the direct simulation was used to evaluate the source terms. After the initial disturbances had left the computational domain the solutions could be compared. This procedure was repeated with all four sets of source terms; the full source terms (equation 22), the temperature based (equation 29), constant temperature (equation 30) and constant density source terms (equation 31).

Acoustic Solution

The far field acoustic solution is displayed by the dilatation $\partial u_i/\partial x_i$. It is favorable to use dilatation as acoustic variable instead of pressure. The pressure in the direct simulation has a tendency to fluctuate in the computation at a very low frequency. The reason for this is probably associated with the absorbing boundary conditions. This makes it hard to compare the direct simulation with the linear Euler solutions. The dilatation is in the far field related to pressure as

$$\Theta = \frac{\partial u_i}{\partial x_i} = -\frac{1}{c_0^2 \rho_0} \left(\frac{\partial p}{\partial t} + u_i \frac{\partial p}{\partial x_i} \right) \qquad (38)$$

Given that the drift in pressure is linear in time the dilatation will show a non-zero but constant time average. This seems to be confirmed with the results of the dilatation of the time averaged solution which show a nearly constant and non-zero dilatation in the whole domain. The dilatation of the direct simulation is thus instead compared to the dilatation of the fluctuations of the linear Euler solutions. Vorticity is used to display the near field of the mixing layer.

Results

Figure 2 shows a snapshot of the vorticity in the near field and the dilatation in the far field for the direct simulation and the linear Euler simulation with full source terms (equation 22). The solutions seem to be very similar. The phase and amplitude also seem to be correct. Some wiggles that are visible in the direct simulation are absent in the linear solution. The reason for this is probably non-linearities in the direct simulation. The solutions from the linear Euler simulations using the simplified sources (equations 29-31) are not shown due to the fact that it is hard see any difference in the solutions compared to the full source term simulation.

a) Direct simulation

b) Linear Euler simulation with full source terms

Fig. 2 Vorticity and dilatation for direct simulation and linear Euler equations using the full source terms, equation 22.

Figure 3 shows the instant pressure fluctuation at a line at $x = 2.0[m]$ and $0.5 \leq y \leq 3.0[m]$ for the direct simulation and the different linear Euler solutions. The average pressure has been corrected for the solution to the direct simulation to avoid the problem with the drift in the average pressure. The phase and amplitude of the linear Euler solutions are in good agreement with the direct simulation except very near the mixing layer. The deviation in this region is probably a result of the error in the time averaged pressure. The solutions for the different source terms are clearly very similar.

Figure 4 shows a pairing of two vortices at four different stages. The time difference between two subsequent figures from (a) to (d) is equivalent to one fourth of a pairing period. The pairing takes place at half the fundamental frequency so the pairing period time is $T_p = 2T_0$. During this time the merging vortices complete one half rotation around each other. The vortex pair is a rotating quadrupole and has as such four lobes. Thus, the merging process results in one full period of sound emitted at a period time of T_p, i.e. at the pairing frequency f_p of the mixing layer. The resulting wavelength of the emitted sound is $\lambda = c_0/f_p = 341.56/394.5 =$

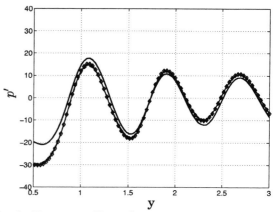

Fig. 3 Pressure disturbance at $x = 2.0[m]$, $0.5 \leq y \leq 3[m]$. **Solid line: direct simulation; others: different source terms**

$0.86[m]$. It is during this time that most of the sound is generated and emitted.

So far the results are similar to the ones achieved by Bogey.[10] But because the physical region in this simulation is relatively a little longer than the one in Bogey,[10] there is room for merged vortices to continue emitting sound as they are convected downstream. This is evident from figure 4 where one can see that there are two regions where more sound is produced than elsewhere. This gives a slightly biased directivity with two lobes in the lower and upper regions and it is especially clear in the upper half of the computational domain.

Figure 5 shows the directivity of the time average of the square of the dilatation. Two lobes of directivity for the lower and upper regions are clearly marked at $\varphi \approx \{-95°, -54°, 39°, 76°\}$. This asymmetry in the directivity is a result of the different velocities in the upper and lower halves of the computational domain. One can again see that there are very small differences in the solutions for the different source terms.

Conclusions

The exact source terms for the linear Euler equations and the inviscid linear energy equation has been derived from the non-linear Euler equations and inviscid energy equation. Simplifications of the source terms have also been presented. These source terms have been validated through numerical simulations. The solutions from the direct simulations and the solutions from the proposed equations are in good agreement. Some differences are present but the cause is believed to be due to effects of the boundary conditions. The differences are very small between the solutions from the different source terms. Even when the source terms are based only on velocity fluctuations and all other instationary effects are neglected, the solution was nearly exactly the same as for the full source terms. This implies that the major source of sound

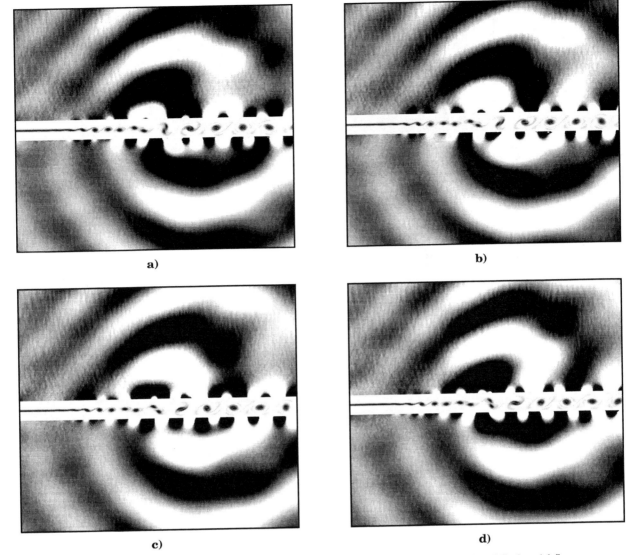

Fig. 4   Vorticity and dilatation for direct simulation. $0 \leq x \leq 3.26$, $-1.5 \leq y \leq 1.5$

in this flow is fluctuations of vorticity. Whether this is true at higher Mach numbers or with larger differences in temperature remains to be seen.

References

[1] Bechara, W., Bailly, C., and Lafon, P., "Stochastic Approach to Noise Modeling for Free Turbulent Flows," *AIAA Journal*, Vol. 32 , No. 3, 1994, pp. 455–463.

[2] Bailly, C. and Juvé, D., "A Stochastic Approach To Compute Subsonic Noise Using Linearized Euler's Equations," *AIAA Journal*, Vol. 99-1872, 1999.

[3] Tam, C. and Webb, J., "Dispersion-Relation-Preserving Finite Difference Schemes for Computational Acoustics," *J. Comp. Physics*, Vol. 107, 1993, pp. 262–281.

[4] Engquist, B. and Majda, A., "Absorbing Boundary Conditions for the Numerical Simulation of Waves," *Mathematics of Computation*, Vol. 31, 1977, pp. 629–651.

[5] Engquist, B. and Majda, A., "Radiation Boundary Conditions for Acoustic and Elastic Wave Calculations," *Communications on Pure and Applied Mathematics*, Vol. 32, 1979, pp. 313–357.

[6] Lighthill, M., "On sound generated aerodynamically, I. General theory," *Proc. Roy. Soc.*, Vol. A 211, 1952, pp. 564–587.

[7] Lilley, G., "On the noise from jets," *AGARD CP-131*, 1974.

[8] Curle, J., "The influence of solid boundaries upon aerodynamic sound," *Proc. Roy. Soc.*, Vol. A 231, 1965, pp. 505–514.

[9] Colonius, T., Lele, S., and Moin, P., "Sound generation in a mixing layer," *Journal of Fluid Mechanics*, Vol. 330, 1997, pp. 375 – 409.

[10] Bogey, C., Bailly, C., and Juvé, D., "Numerical Simulation of Sound Generated by Vortex Pairing in a Mixing Layer," *AIAA Journal*, Vol. 38 No. 12, 2000.

[11] Eriksson, L., "Development and validation of highly modular flow solver versions in G2DFLOW and G3DFLOW," Internal report 9970-1162, Volvo Aero Corporation, Sweden, 1995.

[12] Michalke, A., "On the inviscid instability of the hyperbolic-tangent velocity profile," *Journal of Fluid Mechanics*, Vol. vol 19, 1964.

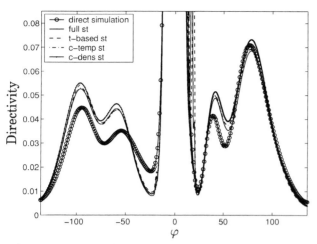

Fig. 5 **Directivity displayed as time average of square of dilatation at an arc around** $x_0 = 2.0$, $y_0 = 0$ **with radius** $r = 1.0$ **at angles** $-135 \leq \varphi \leq 0$ **degrees from the** x-**axis and** $x_0 = 1.6$, $y_0 = 0$ **with radius** $r = 1.0$ **at angles** $0 \leq \varphi \leq 135$ **degrees. Direct simulation, full source terms (full st); temperature based (t-based st); constant temperature (c-temp st); constant density (c-dens st).**

AIAA 2002-2583

Parallelization Strategy for an Explicit Computational Aeroacoustics Code

R. Hixon*
ICOMP, University of Toledo
Mail Stop 54-3
NASA Glenn Research Center
Cleveland, OH 44135
email: Duane.R.Hixon@grc.nasa.gov

M. Nallasamy**
QSS Group, Inc.
Mail Stop 500-QSS
NASA Glenn Research Center
Cleveland, OH 44135
email: fsnals@grc.nasa.gov

S.D. Sawyer***
Mechanical Engineering Department
The University of Akron
Akron, OH 44325-3903
email: ssawyer@uakron.edu

Abstract

In this work, the development of a sixth-order compact-differencing Computational Aeroacoustics (CAA) code utilizing explicit time stepping is described. The focus of this work is on the efficient parallelization of an explicit time stepping procedure. Since explicit time stepping methods must be closely synchronized to retain time accuracy, the parallel performance of a general explicit code is limited by the number of messages that must be passed between the processors during each time step. In this work, a method for minimizing the number of messages passed each time step is described and the initial results for the performance of this method will be shown.

* Senior Research Associate, Member AIAA.
** Senior Member AIAA.
*** Assistant Professor, Member AIAA.

1. Introduction

With the wide availability of low-cost personal computers (PCs), the focus of large-scale computing has shifted from programming for supercomputers utilizing relatively few, high-performance processors linked by specialized, high-performance hardware to programming for distributed clusters of computers utilizing many lower-performance processors, loosely coupled together by Ethernet connections using either the PVM or MPI communication libraries.[1]

This shift has resulted in a need for algorithms and implementations that require as few data-passing messages as possible from outside processors.[2] Also, for computational efficiency, it is preferable to initiate a message pass and continue to calculate locally while the message is passing (latency hiding), as opposed to d e processor waiting idle for the message data to arrive.[3] For steady-state, or low–order accurate unsteady implicit methods, d e calculation need not be closely synchronized between processors; thus, messages may contain data that has been lagged behind one iteration and sent while the current iteration is progressing.

For explicit time–accurate marching methods, such as the optimized Runge–Kutta and Adams–Bashforth schemes commonly used in CAA codes, the parallelization problem is complicated by the need for high accuracy during the spatial derivative calculations in the time step, as well as the close synchronization required. In the past, this has resulted in codes that do not parallelize well due to the high number of messages passed at each time step. This work is focused on exploring means of reducing the number of messages passed at each time step.

2. Governing Equations and]

The code solves the Navier–Stokes equations, which are written in Cartesian coordinates as:

$$\frac{\partial Q}{\partial t}+\frac{\partial(E-E_v)}{\partial x}+\frac{\partial(F-F_v)}{\partial y}+\frac{\partial(G-G_v)}{\partial z}=0 \tag{1}$$

where Q is the vector of conserved properties, E, **F,** and G are the inviscid fluxes, and E_v, F_v, and G_v are the viscous fluxes.

To solve these equations on a body–fitted grid, the Cartesian (x,y,z,t) equations are converted to generalized curvilinear coordinates (ξ, η, ζ, τ). In chain–rule form, Equation (1) becomes:

$$\frac{\partial Q}{\partial t}=-\left|\begin{array}{c}\frac{\partial\xi}{\partial t}\frac{\partial Q}{\partial\xi}+\frac{\partial\eta}{\partial t}\frac{\partial Q}{\partial\eta}+\frac{\partial\zeta}{\partial t}\frac{\partial Q}{\partial\zeta}\\+\frac{\partial\xi}{\partial x}\frac{\partial(E-E_v)}{\partial\xi}+\frac{\partial\eta}{\partial x}\frac{\partial(E-E_v)}{\partial\eta}\\+\frac{\partial\zeta}{\partial x}\frac{\partial(E-E_v)}{\partial\zeta}\\+\frac{\partial\xi}{\partial y}\frac{\partial(F-F_v)}{\partial\xi}+\frac{\partial\eta}{\partial y}\frac{\partial(F-F_v)}{\partial\eta}\\+\frac{\partial\zeta}{\partial y}\frac{\partial(F-F_v)}{\partial\zeta}\\+\frac{\partial\xi}{\partial z}\frac{\partial(G-G_v)}{\partial\xi}+\frac{\partial\eta}{\partial z}\frac{\partial(G-G_v)}{\partial\eta}\\+\frac{\partial\zeta}{\partial z}\frac{\partial(G-G_v)}{\partial\zeta}\end{array}\right| \tag{2}$$

In this formulation, the spatial differencing is performed using either second–order explicit, sixth–order explicit [4], 7–point explicit Dispersion Relation Preserving (DRP)[5], or sixth–order prefactored compact differences.[6] To stabilize the scheme, and to remove spurious waves from the solution, constant–coefficient tenth–order artificial dissipation utilizing filtering stencils presented by Kennedy and Carpenter[7] is added to the equations, denoted by the term $\Delta_{10}Q$. The resulting equation is written as:

$$\Delta Q=\frac{\partial Q}{\partial t}+\Delta_{10}Q \tag{3}$$

The **time** stepping method used is Habashi and Stanescu's[8] 2N storage variant of Hu's[9] Low–Dissipation and –Dispersion

Runge–Kutta (LDDRK) 5–6 scheme. This scheme has d e form:

$$\tilde{Q}_l = \alpha_{l,m}\tilde{Q}_l + \Delta t \Delta Q_l$$
$$Q_l = Q_l + \beta_{l,m}\tilde{Q}_l \qquad (4)$$
$$t_l = t_{0,m} + c_{l,m}\Delta t$$

The coefficients for this scheme are given in Reference 8.

3. Code Structure

The governing Navier–Stokes equations consist of time derivatives, spatial derivatives, and source terms. To solve these equations for an unsteady flow using a time marching method, a grid is constructed to encompass the physical domain of interest, an initial condition is specified for the flow variables, and the solution is then marched in time.

To march in time using an explicit time marching scheme, spatial derivatives are computed for the flow at the current time level; from these spatial derivatives, the time derivative can be computed and the solution is then advanced one step in time, where this process is repeated. In this way, the unsteady solution can be obtained for a given length of time.

The spatial grid used by the code is block–structured. Each block can have arbitrary surface patches on each block face. These surface patches can be connectivity patches (where two computational blocks interface in the interior of the computational domain) or boundary condition patches (where the boundary of the computational domain lies, and inflow, outflow, or wall boundary conditions must be specified).

The code is written in Fortran 90, taking advantage of the computational efficiency, dynamic memory, and data structures in this language. For portability, the code uses no extensions to the language. For message passing, the Message Passing Interface (MPI)[10,11] is used; several open–source implementations of MPI are freely available, such as MPICH[12,13] and LAM/MPI.[14,15] To verify the portability of the code between platforms, operating systems, compilers, and MPI implementations, it is tested on SGI Octanes (IRIX 6.5, SGI F90, SGI MPI and MPICH), Intel Pentium 4's (Red Hat Linux 7.3, Intel IFC, LAM/MPI and MPICH), and Apple G4's (Macintosh OS-X, Absoft F90, LAM/MPI).

The main computational work of the code for a given block can be split into these seven areas:

1) grid metric calculation
2) flux calculation
3) artificial dissipation calculation
4) flux derivate calculation
5) boundary condition calculation
6) flow time update
7) block communications

The first five areas of work are actually very similar. The grid metrics calculations require spatial derivatives of the grid variables. The flux calculations, for a viscous calculation, requires spatial derivatives of the flow variables. For inviscid fluxes, only flow information at the grid point is required. For artificial dissipation, the code uses a constant-coefficient tenth–order stencil. Thus, the artificial dissipation calculation requires a spatial derivative. The flux derivative calculation, whereby the time derivative is obtained, requires a spatial derivative. The boundary conditions usually require spatial derivatives as well.

Thus, the basic object in the code is a 'spatial derivative volume', in which we wish to compute the values of the spatial derivatives. To define fully a 'spatial derivative volume', we arrive at three volumes. The first volume is the 'interior volume', which is defined as the volume where the computed spatial derivative will be used by the code. The second volume, which encompasses the first as a subset, is the 'derivative volume', which is defined as the volume in which the spatial derivative is computed. The third and largest volume is the 'total volume', which contains all of the variable data that is necessary for a spatial derivative to be computed in the 'derivative volume'. This 'spatial derivative volume' object is illustrated in Figure 1.

From this object, we can then build up. The next level of objects are the 'boundary condition volumes', which contain 'spatial derivative volumes' as well as any other information such as mean flow data or source data that are required to define the boundary condition.

The next higher object is the 'block volume', which is a grid block that may contain a number of 'boundary condition volumes' as well as a 'spatial derivative volume' of its own. These 'block volumes' may be of different types, and this will be discussed further in the next section.

The highest object is the 'node volume', which is a group of blocks that are on a processor in a parallel cluster of computers. The total topology consists of an array of 'node volumes' dimensioned to the number of processors in the calculation.

Figure 2 illustrates the data structure hierarchy in the code.

4. Parallelization Strategy

4.1 Old Parallelization Strategy

The code is written as a structured multiblock solver, which requires communication between the blocks to calculate spatial derivatives. In a previous code using the same numerical scheme and solving the same equations[16], messages were sent between the blocks whenever spatial derivatives were needed. The algorithm for a time step was:

1) *Message Pass for Q (5 variables).*
2) Calculate viscous and inviscid fluxes and spatial dissipation.
3) *Message Pass for fluxes (12 variables).*
4) Calculate ΔQ.
5) Update Q.

In this method, no additional work was performed on each block, at the cost of two message passes per RHS calculation. On shared–memory machines such as SGI Origins, this algorithm worked very well. However, on distributed–memory clusters, such as the ICOMP Macintosh cluster, the overhead from the message-passing caused an efficiency reduction when the code was run on more than 8 processors.

Figure 3 illustrates the communications used in this parallelkation strategy. In Figure 3, the data required to compute a spatial derivative in Block 3 is denoted by crosshatching. It can be seen that Block 3 is communicating with Blocks 1, 2, 4, 5, and 6 every time a spatial derivative is needed.

4.2 New Parallelization Strategy

The new parallelization method is to calculate data in the buffers themselves. Figure 4 illustrates the data buffers that are necessary for one of the data buffers to calculate the fluxes required to calculate the time Update for the interior of Block **3**. In Figure 4, the buffers 3.1.1, 3.1.2, and 3.1.3 are needed for buffer 3.1 to calculate the viscous fluxes. The inviscid and viscous fluxes are calculated in buffer 3.1 and transferred, along with the flow variables. Using this data, Block **3** can calculate the derivatives required to determine the time update, and can then update the flow variables.

The flow chart for the new parallelization strategy is:

1) *Local Data Pass: Q (Type 2 -> Type 1, Type 1-> Type 0), x(Type 2-> Type 1, Type 1-> Type 0) if needed.*
2) Calculate grid metrics, if needed (Types 0, 1 do this).
3) Calculate viscous and inviscid fluxes (Types 0, 1 do this).
4) *Local Data Pass: Viscous and inviscid fluxes (Type 1 -> Type 0).*
5) Calculate time update and spatial dissipation (Type 0 only).
6) *Message Pass: AQ (Type 0-> Type 1, Type 0-> Type 2) (5 variables), Δx (Type 0-> Type 1, Type 0-> Type 2) (3 variables) if needed.*
7) Update *Q (Types 0, 1, 2 do this)*

In the flow chart, the numbers in parenthesis refer to the block types that must perform each step. These block **types** are defined in Section *5.*

In this way, the message passing is reduced to *5–8* variables once per time step. This **is,** however, at the cost of extra work on **each** processor and added complexity of **initial** setup. The questions raised in this work, and which we propose to answer more clearly in future work, **are:**

1) *Does the reduction in message passing speed up the code more than the increase in* **work** *on each processor slows it down?*
2) **How** *efficient is the code on distributed memory machines as compared to shared memory machines?*

5. Block Data Transfer and Buffer Blocks

Whenever a grid block (block 1) **has** a boundary that connects to another grid block (block 2), the total volume of grid block 1 must contain data from the neighboring grid block 2 in order to compute the spatial derivative at the boundary of grid block 1. There are three data transfers that may occur during a single time derivative calculation:

1) grid data transfer (to compute the grid metrics),
2) flow data transfer (to compute the artificial dissipation and viscous fluxes),
3) flux data transfer (to compute the flux derivatives, and thus the time derivative).

If the blocks are both on the same processor, the data can be transferred directly between the blocks **as** needed during the time derivative calculation process. However, if the blocks are on different processors, messages that contain the data must be passed between the processors.

The way in which these messages are passed determines how efficient the **parallel** performance of the code **is.** The message passing process **consists** of two stages: message initiation and data transfer. Message initiation requires essentially a fixed amount of CPU time, and data transfer is a function of the amount of data (message length) in the message. The data transfer rate increases with the message length until the network maximum data transfer rate is reached, whereupon the data transfer rate remains at the maximum.

Thus, for parallel efficiency, we prefer to have as few messages as possible (minimum number of initiations) that are as long as necessary (maximum data transfer rate). *Also*, nonblocking messages should be used if possible. **This** type of message allows computation to proceed while the message is being passed, reducing the perceived overhead involved in message passing; this **is** known as 'latency hiding'.

As discussed in the previous section, each block requires data from the neighboring blocks in order to compute spatial derivatives. **This** data is taken from the neighboring block and placed in the 'total volume' of the local block. The data that is required in the total volume of the local block becomes available on the neighboring block at different times during the time derivative calculation process. For example, the flux data that **is** required in **step 4 only** becomes available at the end of step **2**, while the flow data is available at d e start of d e step and is required at the beginning of step **2**.

This leads to two possibilities. First, there can **be** multiple message passes during the time derivative calculation process, each with smaller messages. The other choice is to define 'buffer blocks' on the local node, which perform only part of d e time derivative calculation. **In this** terminology, we have 'updating blocks', which actually calculate the time derivative of the flow data, and 'buffer blocks', which do not.

'Updating blocks' are the original topology that the user has input, while 'buffer blocks' are smaller constructs designed to allow the 'updating blocks' to correctly calculate the time derivatives. Thus, each 'buffer block' is associated with a single 'updating block', which is its parent. However, the 'buffer block' receives its interior data from an 'updating block' on another processor.

These 'buffer blocks' may themselves have 'buffer blocks' associate with them; **this** occurs in the case of viscous flow calculations. The code defines an 'updating block' **as** a Type 0 block the first level of buffer blocks are Type 1 blocks, the next level Type **2**, etc.

Note that only one message pass is required for each time derivative calculation using this method, at the cost of increased computation and complexity during the time derivative calculation. **This** complexity is hidden from the user, however. The code is designed to automatically generate the correct buffer blocks for each block **as** well **as** the correct boundary conditions for each buffer block. In addition, the message passing for each processor is automatically defined.

6. Test P b   d Results

The problem that testing was performed on was the case of a **2–D** inviscid cascade. In **this** problem, 27 stator vanes are in the computational domain. The inflow and outflow boundary conditions are the **2–D Giles**[17] conditions, while the Hixon curvilinear inviscid wall condition **is** used on the solid surface.[18] The inflow enters at a Mach number of **0.43** at a 36 degree angle, and is turned to a zero degree exit angle.

The grid has five blocks per passage, for a total of 135 blocks. Each passage has an H–grid at the top and the bottom, with a C–grid wrapped around the stator vane. This topology results in a six–way grid singularity point upstream of the leading edge of the airfoil. Each passage has 9312 points, for a total of 251,424 points in the computational grid.

The test case was run on two parallel machines: a cluster of six Dell Dimension Pentium 4 machines, as well as on a dual–processor SGI Octane. The Dell cluster consists of three 1700 MHz and three 1800 MHz machines, each with 768 MB of PC800 RDRAM, connected by an 8–port Netgear 1000T Ethernet' switch. The SGI Octane has two 250 MHz R10000 processors and 2 GB of RAM.

This test gives an indication of the code performance at the extremes of the hardware spectrum. The Dell cluster has high performance CPUs and lower performance networking, while the SGI has lower performance CPUs and high performance networking. Also, it must be emphasized that these are initial performance results; the code has not been profiled and optimized for computational efficiency yet.

Since the parallel decomposition routines were not implemented when this data was taken, the domain of 135 blocks were split across the processors by assigning blocks to each node. Though the code has routines to split blocks in order to more evenly balance the computational load, these routines were not used.

For these tests, three cases were run on each platform. In the first case, the blocks were assigned in input order to the nodes; this ensured that each node would communicate only with its nearest neighbor with the minimum message length. However, the computational load was not necessarily balanced. This case is labeled 'best' in the results.

In the second test case, labeled 'passage', the domain was split passage–by–passage between the processors. Since each passage is five grid blocks, the algorithm assigned five blocks to a processor, then moved to the next one, and so on. In this case again, each node communicated only with its nearest neighbors, but the. surface area of communication was much larger than the first test case.

In the third test case, labeled 'worst', the grid is split by cycling through the grid, placing a block on each processor until the blocks are all assigned. This method has the maximum amount of communication as well as the largest surface area.

Figure 5 shows the load balancing efficiency for these test cases. The ratio shown is the minimum number of Type 0 block points on a node divided by the maximum number of Type 0 block points on a node. For the 'best' and 'passage' tests, the ratio is over 0.8, while the 'worst' case drops to a ratio of 0.21 for five nodes. This poor efficiency is due to the fact that each passage has five blocks, with the smallest block having 21% of the points of the largest block. Since the algorithm is cycling through the grid, one no& receives all of the smallest blocks while another receives all of the largest blocks; thus, this very poor load balancing is due to the simple algorithm used for the initial testing.

Figure 6 shows the results for these tests on the Intel Linux cluster, while Figure 7 shows the initial results on a dual–processor SGI Octane workstation. For these test cases, LAM/MPI was used on the Intel cluster, and the proprietary SGI MPI was used on the Octane workstation.

For the single node case, the advantage of the Intel over the SGI is apparent, with the Intel Pentium 4 1700 MHz machine running the code seven times faster than the 250 MHz R10000 SGI. Interestingly, this is almost identical to the difference in processor speed.

As the code is run in parallel, the effects of the message passing and the parallel decomposition are seen in Figures 6 and 7. With the best parallel decomposition strategy, the Intel cluster parallelizes the problem reasonably well. However, the worst parallel decomposition strategy slows the calculation greatly, making six processors run slower than three with the best decomposition strategy.

Figure 7 shows the limited results obtained on the dual–processor SGI Octane workstation. The SGI is less affected by the various parallelkation strategies; this is partly due to the improved message passing of the SGI, and also partly due to the relatively slow CPU hiding the effect of the message passing.

Figure 8 plots the parallel overhead of each machine for the best and passage cases. The parallel overhead is defied as:

$$Overhead = np \frac{(CPU\,time)_{np}}{(CPU\,time)_1}$$

(5)

where np is the number of processors used.

In Figure 8, the advantages of the SGI's high–bandwidth communcation in the box become apparent, particularly for the passage test. As discussed earlier, two effects are interacting here. Figure 8 is nondimensionalized to illustrate the effect of communication to computation. The SGI has higher–bandwidth communications and a slower CPU; thus, the CPU is less likely to be waiting for data that is in transit. On the other hand, the Intel has slower communications and a faster CPU; thus it is more likely to be waiting for data that is in transit.

Figure 8 also shows the effect of the parallel decomposition strategy. For the Intel cluster, the best decomposition used averaged about a 10–20% parallel overhead, while the passage decomposition resulted in 50–60% parallel overhead. This result illustrates the importance of an effective parallel decomposition routine.

The fiial results of interest are the timings of each spatial differencing method for the same grid. The code was run 50 steps on a single processor using each spatial differencing method, and the results for the single best time step were:

Explicit 2nd order: **5.216 s.**
Explicit 6th order: **6.289 s.**
Explicit 7–point DRP (4th order): **5.994 s.**
Prefactored compact 6th order: **7.022 s.**

One interesting point is that the high–order schemes do not have a very large CPU cost penalty compared to the explicit second-order scheme. Also, the compact 6th order scheme did not have a very large CPU cost penalty compared to the explicit schemes.

7. Conclusions and Future Directions

This work reports the initial results from a parallel, high–accuracy **CAA** code. The code has been designed for minimum communication and minimum

1842

synchronization, at the cost of increased work on each parallel processor. This strategy was used to tailor the code for running on loosely-coupled clusters of computers.

Initial results from this work are promising, and the work will continue in these areas in the future:

1) Validating the code on benchmark problems.
2) Adding boundary conditions and functionality to the code.
3) Optimizing the code on a single processor.
4) Efficient parallel decomposition.

Acknowledgements

This work was conducted at the NASA Glenn Research Center, with Edmane Envia as the Technical Monitor. The authors would like to thank Danielle Koch for generating the grid used in these tests.

References

1) *Beowulf Cluster Computing with Linux*, edited by T. Sterling, MIT Press, Cambridge, MA, **2002**.

2) Wilkinson, **B.** and Allen, **M.**, *Parallel Programming*, Prentice Hall, Upper Saddle River, NJ, **1999**.

3) Gropp, **W.**, Lusk, E., and Skjellum, A., *Using MPI: Portable Parallel Programming with the Message-Passing Interface*, MIT Press, Cambridge, MA, **1994**.

4) Gustafsson, B., Kreiss, H.-O., and Oliger, J., *Time Dependent Problems and Difference Methods*, John Wiley and Sons, New York, **1995**, p. **492-495**.

5) Tam, C. K. W. and Webb, J. C., 'Dispersion-Relation-Preserving Finite-Difference Schemes for Computational Acoustics', *Journal of Computational Physics*, Vol. **107**, 1993, pp. **262-281**.

6) Hixon, R., 'Prefactored Small-Stencil Compact Schemes', *Journal of Computational Physics*, Vol. **165**, **2000**, pp. **522-541**.

7) Kennedy, C. A. and Carpenter, **M.** H., 'Several New Numerical Methods for Compressible Shear-Layer Simulations', *Applied Num. Math.*, Vol. **14**, 1994, pp. **397-433**.

8) Stanescu, D. and Habashi, W. G., "2N-Storage Low Dissipation and Dispersion Runge-Kutta Schemes for Computational Acoustics', *Journal of Computational Physics*, Vol. **143**, No. **2, 1998**, pp. **674-681**.

9) Hu, **F. Q.**, Hussaini, M. **Y.**, and Manthey, J. L., 'Low-Dissipation and Low-Dispersion Runge-Kutta Schemes for Computational Acoustics', *Journal of Computational Physics*, Vol. **124**, No. **1**, 1996, pp. **177-191**.

10) Snir, M., Otto, S., Huss-Lederman, S., Walker, D., and Dongarra, J., *MPI-The Complete Reference: Volume 1, The MPI Core*, MIT Press, Cambridge, MA, **1998**.

11) Gropp, **W.**, Huss-Lederman, S., Lumsdaine, A., **Lusk**, E., Nitzberg, B., Saphir, W., and Snir, M., *MPI-The Complete Reference: Volume 2, The MPI Extensions*, MIT Press, Cambridge, MA, **1998**.

12) Gropp, **W.**, Lusk, E., Doss, N., and Skjellum, A., 'A High-Performance, Portable Implementation of the (MPI) Message Passing Interface Standard', *Parallel Computing*, Vol. 22, No. 6, 1996, pp. **789-828**.

13) MPICH web site: http://www-unix.mcs.anl.gov/mpi/mpich/indexold.html

14) Burns, G., Daoud, R., and Vaigl, J., "LAM: An open cluster environment for MPI,' in *Proceedings of Supercomputing Symposium '94* (J. W. Ross, ed.), pp. 379–386, University of Toronto, 1994.

15) LAM/MPI web site: http://www.lam-mpi.org/

16) Hixon, R., Mankbadi, R. R., and Scott, J. R., 'Validation of a High–Order Prefactored Compact Code on Nonlinear Flows with Complex Geometries', AIAA Paper 2001–1103, Reno, NV, January 2001.

17) Giles, M. B., 'Nonreflecting Boundary Conditions for Euler Equation Calculations', *AIAA Journal,* Vol. 28, No. 12, 1990, p. 2050–2057.

18) Hixon, R., 'curvilinear Wall Boundary Conditions for Computational Aeroacoustics', AIAA Paper 99–2395, Los Angeles, CA, June 1999.

Figures

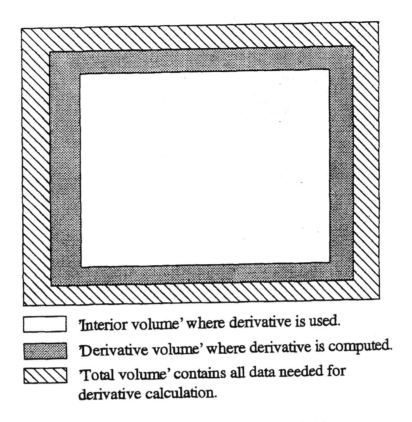

☐ 'Interior volume' where derivative is used.

▨ 'Derivative volume' where derivative is computed.

▨ 'Total volume' contains all data needed for derivative calculation.

Figure 1: 'SpatialDerivative' volume definitions

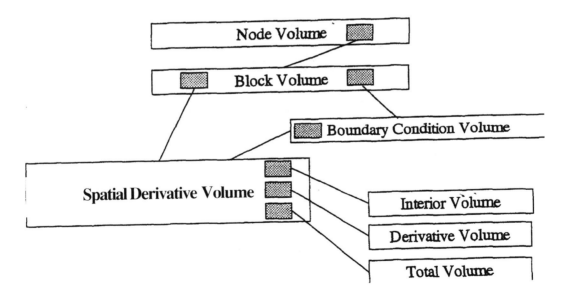

Figure 2: Code Data Structure

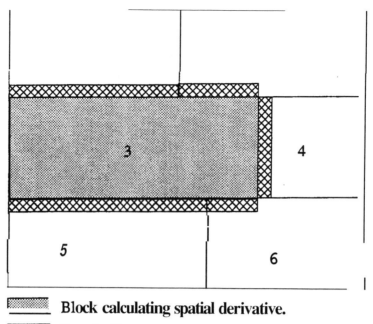

Block calculating spatial derivative.

Data buffers required for derivative calculation.

Figure 3: Communications Needed for Spatial Derivative Calculation

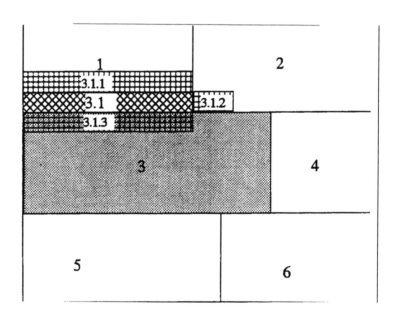

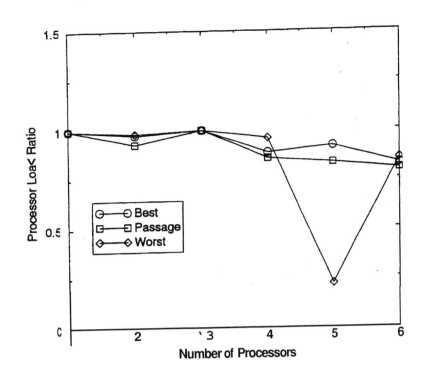

Figure 5: Load Balancing Efficiency of Test Cases

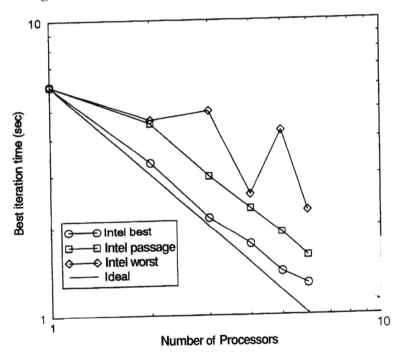

Figure 6: Performance of Unoptimized Code on Intel Cluster

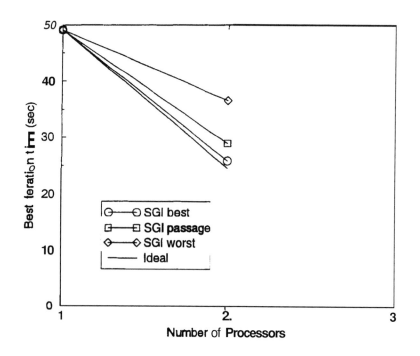

Figure 7: Performance of Unoptimized Code on SGI Octane

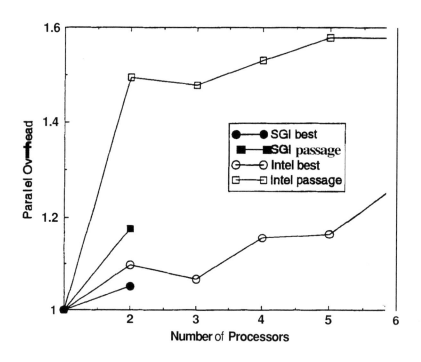

Figure 8: Parallel Overhead of Unoptimized Code

AIAA 2002-2584

ON THE USE OF CHARACTERISTICS IN COMPUTATIONAL AEROACOUSTICS

Johan B.H.M. Schulten*

National Aerospace Laboratory NLR, 8300 AD Emmeloord, The Netherlands

Abstract

Although most CAA schemes for the numerical simulation of sound propagation in flows offer significant superiority compared to standard CFD methods, their performance still crucially depends on a sufficient number of grid points per wavelength. For a given grid density only waves of a length scale beyond a certain limit can be resolved accurately. Even for harmonic sound the shortest wavelengths are not always known in advance of solving the problem and accuracy has to be established by systematic grid refinement. For non-smooth wave shapes most numerical schemes suffer from spurious dispersion. This behavior occurs even under the ideal conditions of small amplitude, plane sound waves in a uniform background fluid. The present paper outlines an alternative method that is able to model the propagation under these conditions exactly, irrespective of the number of points per wavelength or wave shape. The method is based on the concept of characteristics, i.e. the propagation directions of the pressure waves. Unlike fixed grid methods, the coordinates of the data points are found by tracking the characteristics during the solution process. The implementation of non-reflecting boundary conditions is exceptionally straightforward. The method is illustrated by two- and three-dimensional benchmark cases.

Nomenclature

c	= speed of sound
$\mathbf{i}$	= unit vector
$\mathbf{M}$	= vector mean flow Mach number
M	= scalar mean flow Mach number
p	= pressure
r	= radial coordinate
t	= time
u	= axial velocity
v	= velocity
$\mathbf{W}$	= reference system velocity
$\mathbf{x}$	= absolute position vector
x, ξ	= axial coordinate
ρ	= mass density

Subscripts

0	= mean value
a	= acoustic
h	= hydrodynamic
r	= normal to wave front
q, s	= parallel to wave front

Superscript

*	= dimensional quantity

Introduction

Traditionally, the theoretical modeling of sound propagation is based on analytical methods. Only in the last decade computers have become sufficiently powerful to consider a fully numerical approach of real life problems. Attempts to use standard second order accurate CFD (Computational Fluid Dynamics) numerical schemes for sound propagation almost invariably yield disappointing results. Unless a large number of grid points (typically 50 or more) per wavelength is adopted, the simulations suffer from severe spurious dissipation and dispersion.

This shortcoming of CFD methods promoted the rise of Computational AeroAcoustics (CAA) in the nineties of the last century. This discipline studies the efficient and accurate numerical simulation of sound propagation and generation in flows.

One of the most successful CAA methods that emerged is Tam & Webb's DRP (Dispersion Relation Preserving) scheme[1]. It is a high order explicit finite difference method that can be easily applied to a variety of aeroacoustic problems. The DRP-scheme yields accurate results for only 8 grid points per wavelength. Compared with some 50 points required for common CFD methods this implies a reduction factor of 6 in 1D problems and a spectacular factor of more than 200 in 3D problems. Reviews on the state of the art in CAA can be found in references[2,3,4].

*Research Fellow, Aeroacoustics Department P.O.Box 153, E-mail: schulten@nlr.nl, Senior Member AIAA.

Generally speaking, CAA numerical schemes are dissipation-free, high order schemes, optimized for minimum numerical dispersion. Although these methods require much less points per wavelength to achieve a certain level of accuracy than the standard CFD methods, they still have their limits. Sometimes the wave shapes to be studied are not smooth and contain higher harmonics, for which the grid density is still too coarse.

The present paper addresses the possibilities of using characteristics (propagation directions in space-time) for numerical modeling of sound wave propagation. Unlike the CAA-methods mentioned above, the method of characteristics does not use a fixed grid. Instead, the propagation vector of the wave fronts is tracked in space-time for all initial data points. This approach is similar to the concepts of wave fronts and rays that were developed by Huygens and Fermat[5] in the 17th century. However, in the present study we will not need the high frequency assumption of ray acoustics.

The method also follows the basic ideas of Riemann's theory[6] to solve the general nonlinear problem of gas dynamics in one space dimension. Along the characteristics the so-called Riemann invariants, or characteristic variables, are constant. The extension to multiple space dimensions is non-trivial, since the characteristic variables are no longer constant along the characteristic (hyper) surfaces. It will be shown that their variation readily follows from the flow equations.

After some simple examples to introduce the method, the general formulation in two and three dimensions will be derived. In this paper only linear problems with a uniform background flow will be addressed. In the numerical simulation a standard 4th order Runge-Kutta scheme[7] is used for integration along the characteristic direction. An important advantage of the present method is that the implementation of non-reflective boundary conditions, as well as outflow conditions is almost trivial, also in higher dimensions. The method will be illustrated by two- and three-dimensional benchmark cases.

Simple 1D theory and examples

Let us consider a perturbed homentropic fluid without mean flow in one space dimension. Ignoring thermal conductivity and viscosity, the flow equations reduce to the Euler equations. Using the mean fluid density and speed of sound and some arbitrary length (or time step) to make the Euler equations nondimensional, we obtain:

$$\frac{\partial p}{\partial t} + \frac{\partial u}{\partial x} = 0 \qquad (1)$$

$$\frac{\partial u}{\partial t} + \frac{\partial p}{\partial x} = 0 \qquad (2)$$

As can be readily verified, this set of equations has the following analytical solution

$$p(x,t) = p_R(x - t, 0) + p_L(x + t, 0) \qquad (3)$$

and

$$u(x,t) = p_R(x - t, 0) - p_L(x + t, 0) \qquad (4)$$

where $p_R(x,0)$ and $p_L(x,0)$ are the initial values of the right running and left running pressure waves. As first step in the method of characteristics Eq.(1) and Eq.(2) are summed, which yields:

$$\frac{\partial(p + u)}{\partial t} + \frac{\partial(p + u)}{\partial x} = 0 \qquad (5)$$

Similarly, the subtraction of Eq.(1) and Eq.(2) yields:

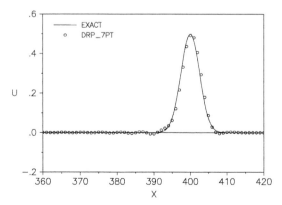

Fig.1   Gaussian pulse $t = 400$, DRP scheme

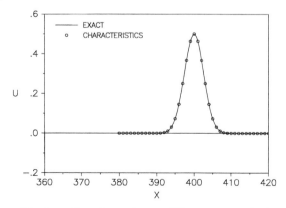

Fig.2   Gaussian pulse $t = 400$, present method

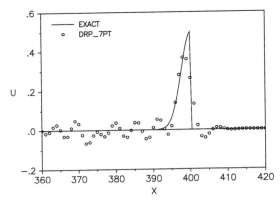

Fig.3   Half a Gaussian pulse $t = 400$, DRP scheme

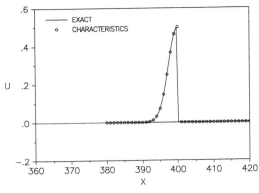

Fig.4   Half a Gaussian pulse $t = 400$, present method

$$\frac{\partial(p - u)}{\partial t} - \frac{\partial(p - u)}{\partial x} = 0 \qquad (6)$$

Now, from Eq.(5) it is obvious that the increase of quantity $(p+u)$ in time dt is compensated by an equal decrease in space dx . In other words the quantity is constant along lines dx/dt = 1, which are called the forward characteristics because they advance with time.

As a result, along the forward characteristics:

$$\left[\frac{\mathrm{d}(p + u)}{\mathrm{d}t}\right]_{\mathrm{d}x/\mathrm{d}t=1} = 0 \qquad (7)$$

i.e., quantity $(p+u)$ propagates forward with (nondimensional) unit velocity. It can be shown that this quantity is the nondimensional, linear perturbation equivalent of the forward Riemann invariant[6]:

$$u^* + \frac{2}{\gamma-1}c^* = \left[M + u + \frac{2}{\gamma-1} + p\right]c_0^* \qquad (8)$$

where γ is the ratio of specific heats of the medium. Quite similarly, we have along the backward characteristics:

$$\left[\frac{\mathrm{d}(p - u)}{\mathrm{d}t}\right]_{\mathrm{d}x/\mathrm{d}t=-1} = 0 \qquad (9)$$

Let us illustrate this result by means of the first Cat.1 benchmark problem of the first CAA Workshop[8] : the propagation of a forward propagating Gaussian pulse with the exact solution:

$$u(x,t) = 0.5\exp\left[-(\ln 2)\left(\frac{x - t}{3}\right)^2\right] \qquad (10)$$

The problem is given as an initial value problem at $t = 0$ with $p(x,0) = u(x,0)$. As follows from Eq.(1) or Eq.(2), then there is only a right running wave. In Fig.1 the result of Tam & Webb's scheme with unit spacing and a time step $\Delta t = 0.2$ is shown for $t = 400$. The time step is scaled on unit spacing of the data points and the speed of sound. Therefore, Δt is identical to the CFL number in this case. Obviously, the result is quite good with only some weak dispersion.

The result of solving Eq.(7) for the advancing characteristic variable, given in Fig.2, is independent of the time step and can be obtained from a single time step of 400. Indeed, this problem is so simple that the numerical solution by Runge-Kutta integration of Eq.(7) seems to be pointless. Apart from being discrete it perfectly mimics the analytical solution given by Eqs.(3) and (4). Also, it clearly demonstrates the difference with fixed grid methods since the original data points are shifted to the right over a distance of 400. As may be expected, the result is accurate to machine precision.

As shown in Fig.3 things dramatically change for the DRP scheme if a discontinuous waveform is taken. It is clear that the DRP scheme is unfit to handle the halved Gaussian pulse properly. In fact the large content of short waves in this shape cannot be resolved with the present grid spacing. In contrast to this, the characteristics method simulates the propagation of half a Gaussian pulse equally well as the complete pulse, as demonstrated in Fig. 4. The method does not try to approximate time or space derivatives of the wave, but directly uses the characteristic directions to propagate the signal, irrespective of its shape. Our goal will be to preserve this outstanding quality of the characteristics method in higher dimensions and for more general flow conditions. A modeling is sought that will automatically yield the accuracy observed in this section, at least when the wave fronts tend to become planar and the background uniform.

Extension to multi-dimensions

In Arbitrary Lagrangian-Eulerian (ALE) formulation[9] the equations for small perturbations of an inviscid compressible flow with a uniform background read as follows.

Continuity:

$$\frac{\partial \rho}{\partial t} + (\mathbf{M} - \mathbf{W}) \cdot \nabla \rho + \nabla \cdot \mathbf{v} = 0 \qquad (11)$$

Momentum:

$$\frac{\partial \mathbf{v}}{\partial t} + (\mathbf{M} - \mathbf{W}) \cdot \nabla \mathbf{v} + \nabla p = \mathbf{0} \qquad (12)$$

Energy:

$$\frac{\partial p}{\partial t} + (\mathbf{M} - \mathbf{W}) \cdot \nabla p + \nabla \cdot \mathbf{v} = 0 \qquad (13)$$

where $\mathbf{W}$ is the reference system velocity and $\mathbf{M}$ the vector background flow Mach number. The variables are made dimensionless in the same way as in the previous section.

Obviously, for $\mathbf{W} = \mathbf{0}$ the Euler equations are obtained, while for $\mathbf{W} = \mathbf{M}$ the Lagrangian flow description is recovered. It will prove useful to make use of both flow descriptions.

Note that the presence of an energy equation implies that we do no longer require a homentropic flow. In the latter case the energy equation becomes identical to the continuity equation. As a result, the system of equations will, besides acoustic waves, also describe entropy perturbations, which are convected with the mean flow.

Formally, we have as many scalar momentum equations (12) as there are spatial dimensions. Now consider for a moment a system of plane waves in three dimensions. Of course, physically this is completely equivalent to the situation of the 1D waves in the previous section. A coordinate rotation such that the x-axis becomes normal to the wave fronts, i.e. in the direction of ∇p, is sufficient to make this perfectly clear.

However, unlike the one-dimensional problem, the flow equations Eqs.(11) through (13) for the multi-dimensional problem admit the existence of nontrivial zero-pressure velocity fields $\mathbf{v}_b$, corresponding to vorticity perturbations. For a vanishing pressure perturbation Eqs.(12) and (13) reduce to

$$\nabla \cdot \mathbf{v}_h = 0 \qquad (14)$$

and

$$\frac{\partial \mathbf{v}_h}{\partial t} + (\mathbf{M} - \mathbf{W}) \cdot \nabla \mathbf{v}_h = \mathbf{0} \qquad (15)$$

Clearly, any velocity field satisfying Eqs. (14) and (15) can always be added to the complete system given by Eqs.(11) through (13). Eq.(14) expresses the incompressibility of these velocity fields which are therefore also called "hydrodynamic". The purely convective character of this hydrodynamic velocity is stated by Eq.(15). In general the amplitude of the hydrodynamic field has to be set by the boundary (inflow) conditions or the initial values.

Usually, we have a non-zero pressure gradient and then we can introduce a local, coordinate system (r,q,s):

$$\begin{aligned} \mathbf{i}_r &= \frac{\nabla p}{|\nabla p|}, \\ \mathbf{i}_r \cdot \mathbf{i}_q &= 0, \quad \mathbf{i}_r \cdot \mathbf{i}_s = 0, \quad \mathbf{i}_s \cdot \mathbf{i}_q = 0 \end{aligned} \qquad (16)$$

Now let us denote the "acoustic velocity" coupled with pressure perturbation by $\mathbf{v}_a$. It can be readily shown that $\mathbf{v}_a$ must be irrotational.

Substitution of $\mathbf{v} = \mathbf{v}_a + \mathbf{v}_b$ in the momentum equation Eq. (12) reveals that $\mathbf{v}_a = v_a \mathbf{i}_r$. Then, in the Lagrangian description $(\mathbf{W} = \mathbf{M})$, normal to the wave front the momentum equation Eq.(12) reduces to the <u>scalar</u> equation:

$$\frac{\partial v_a}{\partial t} + \frac{\partial p}{\partial r} = 0 \qquad (17)$$

The divergence of the acoustic velocity becomes:

$$\nabla \cdot \mathbf{v}_a = \frac{\partial v_a}{\partial r} + v_a \nabla \cdot \mathbf{i}_r \qquad (18)$$

Now, Eq.(13) + Eq.(17) yields:

$$\frac{\partial (p + v_a)}{\partial t} + \frac{\partial (p + v_a)}{\partial r} = -v_a \nabla \cdot \mathbf{i}_r \qquad (19)$$

and similarly Eq.(13) − Eq.(17) yields:

$$\frac{\partial (p - v_a)}{\partial t} - \frac{\partial (p - v_a)}{\partial r} = -v_a \nabla \cdot \mathbf{i}_r \qquad (20)$$

As a result we have along the advancing characteristic:

$$\left[\frac{\mathrm{d}(p + v_a)}{\mathrm{d}t} \right]_{\mathrm{d}\mathbf{x}/\mathrm{d}t = \mathbf{M} + \mathbf{i}_r} = -v_a \nabla \cdot \mathbf{i}_r \qquad (21)$$

and along the receding characteristic:

1852

$$\left[\frac{d(p - v_a)}{dt}\right]_{dx/dt = \mathbf{M} - \mathbf{i}_r} = -v_a \nabla \cdot \mathbf{i}_r \qquad (22)$$

Along the convective characteristic ($dx/dt = \mathbf{M}$) Eq.(13) − Eq.(11) yields:

$$\left[\frac{d(p - \rho)}{dt}\right]_{dx/dt = \mathbf{M}} = 0 \qquad (23)$$

and Eq. (15) :

$$\left[\frac{d\mathbf{v}_h}{dt}\right]_{dx/dt = \mathbf{M}} = \mathbf{0} \qquad (24)$$

Note that the characteristic variables in Eqs. (23) and (24) are <u>invariants</u> (also in multi-dimensions!). Just like the original Eqs.(11) through (13) for the five primitive variables, Eqs.(21) through (24) form a system of six scalar equations for six characteristic variables. However, the three components of $\mathbf{v}_h$ are not mutually independent because they have always to satisfy the incompressibility condition of Eq.(14).

Figure 5 gives a picture of the three types of characteristics in an Eulerian r,t-plane. Note that the skewness of the system depends on the r-component of the background flow velocity vector. In the Lagrangian frame the acoustic characteristics become symmetric about the convective characteristics which then are vertical. Note that primitive variables can only be evaluated at the intersection points of three characteristics. Hence, time step and spatial step (in r) are necessarily equal. Since the background flow vector in general does not point in the direction normal to the wave fronts this triple intersection only occurs in the Lagrangian frame.

In the degenerate case of a vanishing pressure field it is no longer possible to determine a normal

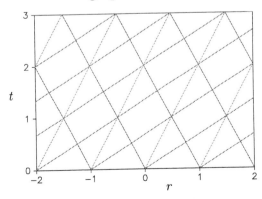

Fig.5   Characteristics in Eulerian frame;
—— **advancing,** —— **receding,** —— **convective**
(projected)

to the wave fronts and Eqs.(21) and (22) become irrelevant. Inspection of the remaining Eqs.(23) and Eq.(24) shows that in that case the solution of these equations is trivial and can be performed in any convenient coordinate system.

In general the right hand sides of Eqs.(21) and (22) have to be computed numerically. However for cylindrically ($n_{\dim} = 2$) and spherically ($n_{\dim} = 3$) symmetric waves they can be evaluated analytically and then Eqs.(21) and (22) reduce to :

$$\left[\frac{d(p + u)}{dt}\right]_{d\xi/dt = M+1} = (1 - n_{\dim})\frac{u}{\xi - Mt} \qquad (25)$$

and

$$\left[\frac{d(p - u)}{dt}\right]_{d\xi/dt = M-1} = (1 - n_{\dim})\frac{u}{\xi - Mt} \qquad (26)$$

where ξ is a coordinate axis through the center. The radius of curvature of the wave fronts is given by $|\xi - Mt|$.

Non-reflecting boundary conditions

Boundary conditions play a crucial role in CAA and often are more difficult to model than the sound dynamics inside the domain. A comprehensive review on boundary conditions in CAA has been given by Tam[10].

In the present method boundary conditions at domain boundaries are very easily imposed. Acoustically non-reflective boundaries are obtained by just requiring the incoming characteristic variable to be zero.

Note that for acoustic waves incident from outside the domain the wave front orientation is implied in the components of the acoustic velocity $\mathbf{v}_a$, which is also to be prescribed at the exposed boundaries.

As shown by Eqs.(23) and (24), inflow conditions are given by simply prescribing p - ρ and $\mathbf{v}_h$ at the inflow boundary. Outflow conditions are automatically satisfied by the solution.

Numerical implementation
Initial conditions

In the present method a problem is basically solved as the evolution in time from a given situation to the situation some time later. If a harmonic problem is to be solved, it has to be treated as a transient problem in which the situation changes from some trivial steady situation to a fully periodic situation. The 'situation' is given as a set of data in a given domain. For the present method the initial data have to be given in the form of the characteristic variables, see Eqs.(21) through (24). For programming it is convenient if the data points are positioned along isobars *(s,q)* and normal directions *(r)*. Figure 6 gives an example of a (part of a) circular system that could be the result of a cylindrical or spherical expansion. In any case the unit normal vector on the wave fronts $\mathbf{i}_r$ has to be available or computable from the data.

It is not necessary to fill the whole domain with data points at the starting time. This is because the method constructs its own coordinates during the time stepping procedure to follow. In a pure initial value problem the data are given in a certain subdomain (for instance a central pulse) from which the full domain is gradually filled as time proceeds.

A slightly different type of problem is to be solved when the medium within the domain is at rest in the beginning and perturbations enter the domain from outside. Then, there are no data points at all inside the domain at the start but the domain is gradually filled from the exposed sides. Again, it is convenient if the data points of the incident field are wave front oriented.

Time stepping

Before a time step can actually be taken, the possible change of the wave front orientation has to be evaluated and the unit propagation vector $\mathbf{i}_r$ has to be updated. To this end, a second order accurate central difference pressure gradient is taken for all data points.

Next, the divergence of the updated vector field $\mathbf{i}_r$ has to be established in all data points. Instead of trying to compute the divergence from its definition by numerical differentiation we will use Gauss' divergence theorem:

$$\int_V \nabla \cdot \mathbf{A}\,dv = \oint_S \mathbf{n} \cdot \mathbf{A}\,ds \qquad (27)$$

Here $\mathbf{A}$ is a vector field, V a volume, S the enclosing surface and $\mathbf{n}$ the outward unit normal vector. Applying the 2D version of Eq. (27) to vector field $\mathbf{i}_r$ and a small volume enclosing the point *(i,j)* considered we obtain:

$$\int_V \nabla \cdot \mathbf{i}_r\,dv = \Delta s_{i+1} - \Delta s_{i-1} \qquad (28)$$

where Δs is the arc length between characteristics j+1 and j-1. Since the volume is approximated by $\left(\Delta s_{i+1} - \Delta s_{i-1}\right) R_i$, with R_i the local radius of curvature of the isobar, the average value of the divergence of $\mathbf{i}_r$ is given by

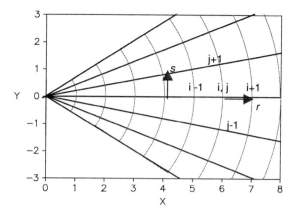

Fig.6   Isobars (——) and projected characteristics (——) for curvilinear wave fronts

$$\overline{\nabla \cdot \mathbf{i}_r} \approx \frac{1}{R_i} \qquad (29)$$

which is exact for cylindrically symmetric cases as shown by the result found earlier in Eqs.(25) and (26). However, in general the radius of curvature of the isobars is not known in advance and has to be found numerically. Therefore in the implementation of the method R_i is computed from the intersection of neighboring vectors $\mathbf{i}_r$.

The actual time integration of Eqs.(21) through (24) is performed by the classical fourth order Runge-Kutta method[7]. As shown in Fig.5, the initial spacing in r determines the time step, which necessarily results in a unit CFL number in *r*-direction. For convenience only uniform spacing of isobars is considered in this paper.

Renumbering of characteristics

From Fig.5 it is quite clear that after each time step the advancing characteristic *RR* (Right running) has moved a corresponding step forward in r and the receding characteristic *LR* (Left running) a step backward. To reallocate the characteristic variables to the same spatial coordinates, a renumbering is necessary after each time step as follows:

$$
\begin{aligned}
RR_i &= RR_{i-1}, & LR_i &= LR_{i+1} \\
x_i &= x_{i-1} \\
y_i &= y_{i-1}
\end{aligned}
\qquad (30)
$$

Note that for every characteristic direction *j* two data points travel out of the domain in each time step. This is essentially the radiation from the domain into the outside world. To keep the number of data points constant, at the same time a new advancing characteristic RR_{imin} is added at the lower *r*-boundary of the domain and a receding characteristic LR_{imax} at the upper *r*-boundary. The

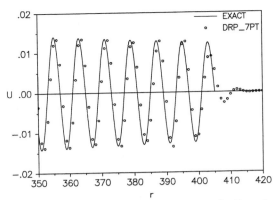

Fig.7   Spherical waves at $t = 400$, $\omega = \pi/4$, Tam & Webb DRP scheme

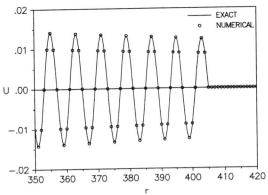

Fig.8   Spherical waves at $t = 400$, $\omega = \pi/4$, present method

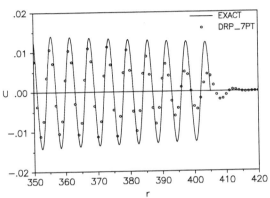

Fig. 9   Spherical waves at $t = 400$, $\omega = \pi/3$, Tam & Webb DRP scheme

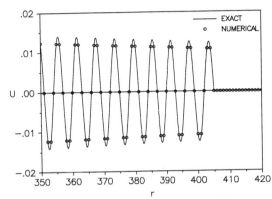

Fig. 10   Spherical waves at $t = 400$, $\omega = \pi/3$, present method

corresponding values of the characteristic variables follow from the boundary conditions.

Finally, the transformation to fixed frame of reference is established by shifting the data points over the distance covered by convection. Similarly to the above, new data points are introduced at the upstream boundary whenever data points are convected out of the domain at the downstream boundary.

Quasi-1D problems in 2D and 3D
Vibrating sphere

As an example of the potential of the present method we give here the solution of the second Cat.1 benchmark problem of the first CAA Workshop[8]. This is a problem in which the sound field of a vibrating sphere is simulated. The radius of the sphere is 5 units and the vibration is switched on at $t = 0$. For comparison with the state of the art in CAA, Fig.7 gives the results of the Tam & Webb Dispersion Relation Preserving (DRP) scheme for $t = 400$. The frequency has been chosen such that there are 8 grid points per wavelength. Obviously, the results are quite good at some wavelengths behind the advancing front.

However, in the vicinity of the outer front discrepancies appear. In Fig.8 the results of the present characteristics method are given. Clearly, there is no visible difference with the exact solution.

As shown in Fig.9, the results of the DRP scheme degrade considerably when the frequency is increased such that there are 6 points per wavelength left. In contrast to this, the results of the present method shown in Fig.10 still coincide perfectly with the exact solution. Indeed, the method is insensitive to the number of points per wavelength.

Gaussian pulse in 2D

The Category 3 benchmark problem of the first CAA workshop[8] has become a very popular test case. Basically it is the two-dimensional, symmetric variant of the Gaussian pulse in one dimension, discussed earlier. Besides a Gaussian pulse in the pressure, the full benchmark problem also contains perturbations in density and velocity corresponding to a vortex. The analytical solution can be found in references 1 or 8. Here we will use only the pressure pulse to check the present method. One of the interesting aspects of this initial value problem is that both inward and out-

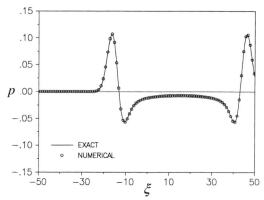

Fig. 11   Cylindrical Gaussian pulse $t = 30$, $M = 0.5$

ward running waves occur. Because $u = 0$ at $t = 0$, they start with equal strength, see Eqs.(25) and (26).

Figure 11 shows the results of the method after 30 time units from the start in the center. Due to a mean flow Mach number of 0.5 the pulse is convected downstream whilst expanding. Again, there is no visible difference between the numerical and the exact results. It must be noted that the DRP-scheme is also quite capable to produce very good results[1,8] for this smooth problem. However, the present method typically is a factor of 30 faster than the DRP-method for this problem. There are two obvious reasons for this. First, the unit time step is much larger than the maximum time step for stability in the DRP-scheme ($\Delta t \approx 0.2$). Secondly, the spatial stencil used to compute the pressure gradient is much more compact (only four neighboring points) than in the DRP-scheme.

Gaussian pulse in 3D

Another test case is the expansion of a spherical Gaussian pulse. The general exact solution for any spherically symmetric pressure pulse is given by

$$p(\xi, t) = \frac{\xi - (1 + M)t}{2(\xi - Mt)} p[\xi - (1 + M)t, 0]$$
$$+ \frac{\xi + (1 - M)t}{2(\xi - Mt)} p[\xi + (1 - M)t, 0] \tag{31}$$

Starting with the same pulse as in the 2D example, we solve Eqs.(25) and (26) numerically .The solution for $M = 0.5$ after 30 time units is presented in Fig.12. Compared to the cylindrical pulse in Fig.11 the amplitude has decreased much faster and also the inner region has virtually returned to undisturbed conditions.

Triangular pulse in 3D

A more challenging problem is the expansion in three dimensions of a triangular pressure pulse. Let the pressure at $t = 0$ be given by:

$$\begin{aligned} p &= 1 - |\xi|/10, & |\xi| \le 10 \\ p &= 0, & |\xi| > 10 \end{aligned} \tag{32}$$

Then the exact solution is readily obtained from Eq.(31). As shown in Fig.13, the method of characteristics produces a result of similar quality as for the smooth pulse in Fig.12. Note that the original discontinuity in the pressure derivative in $x = 0$ completely disappears during the expansion.

Some propagation problems in 2D

All problems in the previous section were symmetric and could be solved from Eqs.(25) and (26). These equations have a simple right hand side, which can be readily computed. Usually, problems do not exhibit symmetry and we will have to solve the more general Eqs.(21) through.(24). As discussed in a previous section the right hand side in Eqs. (21) and (22) involves serious computation.

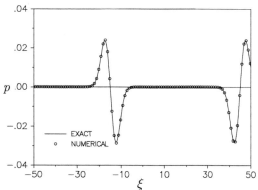

Fig. 12   Spherical Gaussian pulse, $t = 30$, $M = 0.5$

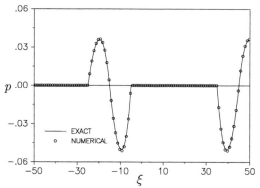

Fig.13   Spherical wave from triangular pulse, $t = 30$, $M = 0.5$

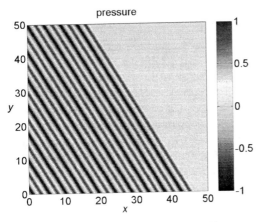

Fig.14 Oblique plane wave, incident field prescribed at left and lower boundaries, $t = 40$, $M = 0$

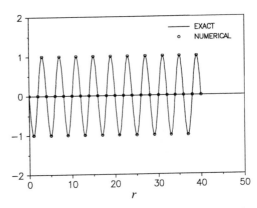

Fig. 15 Pressure along normal to oblique wave fronts in Fig.12, four points per wavelength

Oblique plane waves in 2D

A well-known situation is a domain in which we have to compute the sound field for given boundary conditions. One of the simplest problems possible is a rectangular domain exposed to a system of plane waves propagating through the domain. The present method is tested on this problem and the results are shown in Fig.14. A system of plane waves propagating at an angle of 30 degrees with the horizontal axis enters the lower left corner of the domain at $t = 0$. As shown in Fig.14, at $t = 40$ the left and lower boundaries are fully exposed to the wave system. At the right and upper faces nonreflecting boundary conditions are imposed.

Figure 15 presents the pressure along the propagation direction passing through the origin. It is clear that there is a perfect agreement with the exact solution. This problem may look an oversimplified test case, but most numerical schemes have great difficulty to compute this transient problem for a comparable grid density.

Cylindrical Gaussian pulse

A similar test case can be constructed for a cylindrical Gaussian pulse, as discussed before, but now propagating through a rectangular domain whilst expanding. As shown in Fig.16, we consider a domain with a lower left corner (50,50). The pulse has its center at the origin outside the domain and the time starts at $t = 0$. The exact characteristic variables along the exposed faces are computed every time level (d$t = 1$). The field propagates freely into the domain and computes its own propagation vector at every time level.

From Figs.16 ($t = 100$) and 17 ($t = 130$) it appears that the pulse indeed expands without any reflection from the boundaries. Also the circular symmetry is impeccably maintained.

The pressure field along the diagonal given in Fig.18 confirms the very good agreement with the exact solution.

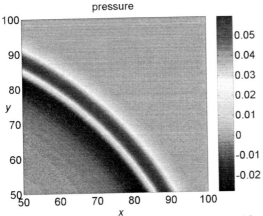

Fig. 16 Gaussian pulse in 2D, $t = 100$, $M = 0$, incident field prescribed at left and lower boundaries

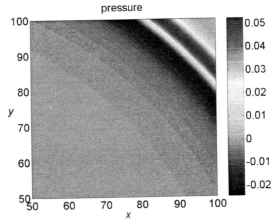

Fig.17 Gaussian pulse in 2D, $t = 130$, $M = 0$, incident field prescribed at left and lower boundaries

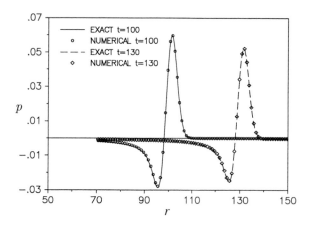

Fig. 18   Pressure along the diagonal in Figs.14 and 15

At the same time it is fair to say that still considerable difficulties have to be surmounted before the method will be applicable to more complex problems. These problems may concern a non-uniform background flow, reflection on hard obstacles, diffraction effects and nonlinearity.

Nevertheless it may be concluded that the method of characteristics has properties that make them very attractive for application in computational aeroacoustics. Its most promising features are the insensitivity to the wave shape, the absence of dissipation and dispersion errors, and the implementation of non-reflecting boundary conditions.

Acknowledgement

The author wishes to thank his colleague Dr. Ronald Nijboer for many stimulating and helpful discussions. His comments on the first draft of the manuscript led to significant improvements in the present paper.

Concluding remarks

In this paper the method of characteristics is used to compute sound propagation and radiation numerically. Unlike traditional CAA schemes the present method is not based on a fixed grid. Instead the solution is marched in time by following the propagation vectors, i.e. the characteristics. In this respect the method has some similarity with classical ray acoustics. However, the present method is more general and does not require the high frequency assumption.

As shown by two- and three-dimensional benchmark examples, the total absence of numerical dispersion and dissipation leads to very accurate numerical results. The interesting point is that this property also holds for waves of highly irregular shape, including discontinuities.

Exact non-reflecting boundary conditions are easily implemented in a most natural way. This feature alone would already justify further research on the application of the method in more complex problems.

Computationally, the method is very efficient: typically a factor of 30 faster than the DRP-method in the 2D Gaussian pulse benchmark[8].

References

[1]Tam, C.K.W., Webb, J.C., "Dispersion-Relation-Preserving Finite Difference Schemes for Computational Acoustics", *Journal of Computational Physics,* Vol.107, Aug. 1993, pp. 262-281.

[2]Tam, C.K.W., "Computational Aeroacoustics: Issues and Methods", *AIAA Journal,* Vol. 33, No.10, Oct. 1995, pp. 1788-1796.

[3]Lele, S.K, "Computational Aeroacoustics: A Review", AIAA Paper 97-0018, Jan. 1997

[4]Colonius, T., "Lectures on Computational Aeroacoustics", VKI Lecture series 1997-07: *Aeroacoustics and Active Noise Control,* Sept. 1997

[5]Pierce, A.D., *ACOUSTICS-An Introduction to its Physical Principles and Applications,* McGraw Hill, New York, 1981

[6]Toro, E.F., *Riemann Solvers and Numerical Methods for Fluid Dynamics,* 2nd edition, Springer, Berlin 1999

[7]Press, W.H., Flannery, B.P., Teukolsky, S.A., Vetterling, W.T., *Numerical Recipes,* Cambridge University Press, 1989

[8]Hardin, J.C. et al., "ICASE/LaRC Workshop Benchmark Problems in Computational Aeroacoustics (CAA)", NASA Conference Publication 3300, May 1995.

[9]Margolin, L., Introduction to "Arbitrary Lagrangian-Eulerian Computing Method for All Flow Speeds", *J. Comp. Phys.,* 135 (1997), pp. 198-202.

[10]Tam, C.K.W., "Advances in Numerical Boundary Conditions for Computational Aeroacoustics", *Journal of Computational Acoustics,* Vol.6, No.4, 1998, pp. 377-402

LARGE SCALE FREQUENCY DOMAIN NUMERICAL SIMULATION OF AIRCRAFT ENGINE TONE NOISE RADIATION AND SCATTERING

D. Stanescu,[†] M.Y. Hussaini[†] and F. Farassat[‡]

† CSIT, Florida State University, Tallahassee, Florida, 32306.

‡ NASA Langley Research Center, Hampton, Virginia 23681.

INTRODUCTION

The engines represent a major source of aircraft noise both at take off and landing. For the large turbofan engines used nowadays on commercial aircraft, fan noise dominates in particular during approach flight and landing, when the thrust force necessary from the jet is relatively small. The tonal noise generated by fan rotor-stator interaction as cylindrical duct modes is radiated from the fan inlet and exhaust and is scattered by the various surfaces surrounding the nacelle, such as fuselage and wing. Eventually both the direct and the scattered field propagate to the far field through the complex mean flow around the aircraft. Earlier studies of fan inlet noise propagation either incorporate only the effects of the nacelle boundary layer [4] or consider the flow around the nacelle axisymmetric and inviscid [10, 8]. However, the non-uniform flow around the nacelle and the relative positions of the nacelle, fuselage and wing offer the designer a range of options for reducing the noise footprint of an aircraft. A numerical simulation of the phenomenon, which is a very convenient alternative to experiments at least in the initial design stage, represents a large-scale computational problem which becomes feasible using the recent developments in computational methods for advanced architecture computers.

Time-domain methods have been proposed by various authors, including the present ones [9, 12, 14], to address this problem. Under that approach, it is straightforward to have a full nonlinear model for the sound propagation, based on the inviscid flow (Euler) equations, that applies both for take-off and landing. The use of an explicit low-storage time integration method avoids the need to store and solve a matrix at each time step, thus keeping the computer memory requirements relatively low. In this paper we present a different and complementary methodology based on the frequency domain solution of the linearized full potential equation. The possibility to solve for the acoustic field in one step as a boundary value problem must in this case be weighed against the difficulty of finding the solution of a system of equations with complex coefficients. As the size of this system increases rapidly with the frequency, a direct solution even using sparse solvers is precluded by the large memory requirements. An efficient method for its iterative solution must be devised.

The paper first introduces the governing equations for the sound propagation problem. A new treatment of the radiation boundary conditions in the form of an augmented, perfectly matched layer (PML) equation, is then presented. This new equation allows us to have the radiation boundaries relatively close to such scattering surfaces as the tip of the wing, thus making the study of actual three-dimensional configurations feasible. After a brief description of the spectral element discretization that yields the linear system of equations for the degrees of freedom of the problem, the paper discusses the methodology used to solve this system iteratively on distributed-memory computers. Numerical results obtained for two generic configurations are then presented, and some conclusions are provided at the end of the paper.

GOVERNING EQUATIONS

For the short times of propagation that we are interested in, we assume that there is no dissipation of acoustic energy, so that the inviscid flow equations can be used to model the process. For an irrotational flow the continuity equation can be written as

$$\frac{\partial \rho}{\partial t} + \nabla \cdot (\rho \nabla \Phi) = 0 \qquad (1)$$

where ρ is the fluid density, and the potential Φ is related to the velocity by $\mathbf{V} = \nabla \Phi$. For convenience, the flow variables are non-dimensionalized with respect to ρ_∞ and c_∞, the far field values of the density and speed of sound, respectively, and dimensions with respect to R, the fan blade tip radius. Using the isentropic assumption, the momentum equation can be reduced to an algebraic equation relating the density and the velocity potential,

$$\rho = \left[1 - (\gamma - 1) \left(\frac{\partial \Phi}{\partial t} + \frac{(\nabla \Phi)^2 - M^2}{2} \right) \right]^{\frac{1}{\gamma - 1}} \qquad (2)$$

where M is the far field Mach number and γ the specific heats ratio. Consider the unsteady flow field resulting from the superposition of small acoustic perturbations, denoted by a prime, on a steady mean flow denoted by an overbar: $\rho = \bar{\rho} + \rho'$ and $\Phi = \bar{\Phi} + \Phi'$. The partial differential equation governing the acoustic

perturbations is

$$\frac{\partial \rho'}{\partial t} + \nabla \cdot (\bar{\rho} \nabla \Phi' + \rho' \nabla \bar{\Phi}) = 0 \qquad (3)$$

where

$$\rho' = -\frac{\bar{\rho}}{\bar{c}^2} \left[\frac{\partial \Phi'}{\partial t} + \nabla \bar{\Phi} \cdot \nabla \Phi' \right]. \qquad (4)$$

For a frequency domain approach, the acoustic potential is considered to be of the form $\Phi' = \phi(x, y, z) \exp(i\omega t)$. Denoting by $\bar{f} = \bar{\rho}/\bar{c}$, it can be found that the equation governing ϕ, written in a form that will be useful for the derivation of the perfectly matched layer equation later on, is

$$\begin{aligned} \phi + \frac{\nabla \bar{\Phi} \cdot \nabla \phi}{i\omega} - \frac{\nabla \cdot (\bar{\rho} \nabla \phi)}{\bar{f}(i\omega)^2} + \\ \frac{\nabla \cdot (\bar{f} \phi \nabla \bar{\Phi})}{\bar{f}} + \frac{\nabla \cdot (\bar{f} \nabla \bar{\Phi} \cdot \nabla \phi \nabla \bar{\Phi})}{\bar{f}(i\omega)^2} = 0 \end{aligned} \qquad (5)$$

RADIATION BOUNDARY CONDITIONS

To obtain solutions in a relatively small computational domain, when sources may be placed relatively close to the domain boundaries, we construct a PML for the equation governing the Fourier transform $\tilde{\Phi}$ of the time dependent acoustic potential. Since its introduction by Berenger[2], the PML method has been increasingly used by researchers (e.g. Hayder, Hu and Hussaini [6]), as it allows reflections from the artificial boundaries to be decreased by orders of magnitude compared to other techniques. For previous work on the Euler equations in the time domain, on which the subsequent development is based, we refer to Hu [7]. To avoid a lengthy presentation, the construction of the PML method for the wave equation and its reduced form, the Helmholtz equation, are presented in the one-dimensional setting. Then we address the three-dimensional case for both the advective and non-advective acoustics case.

Let us consider the one-dimensional wave

equation in the form,

$$\frac{\partial^2 \Phi'}{\partial t^2} - \frac{\partial^2 \Phi'}{\partial x^2} = 0, \qquad (6)$$

which can also be written as a system of first-order partial differential equations,

$$\begin{aligned}
\frac{\partial q}{\partial t} - \frac{\partial u}{\partial x} &= 0, \\
\frac{\partial u}{\partial t} - \frac{\partial q}{\partial x} &= 0,
\end{aligned} \qquad (7)$$

where $q = \partial \Phi'/\partial t$ and $u = \partial \Phi'/\partial x$. Non-trivial wave solutions of the form $Q = [q, u]^T = Q_0 e^{i(\omega t - kx)}$ exist only for $\omega^2 - k^2 = 0$, which is the dispersion relation for this system. In the PML method, the system is replaced with the following damped system

$$\begin{aligned}
\frac{\partial q}{\partial t} - \frac{\partial u}{\partial x} + \sigma_x q &= 0, \\
\frac{\partial u}{\partial t} - \frac{\partial q}{\partial x} + \sigma_x u &= 0,
\end{aligned} \qquad (8)$$

which has the dispersion relation $(\omega - i\sigma_x)^2 - k^2 = 0$. The wave number k will now have an imaginary part for any driving frequency ω, so that the waves will become evanescent. We note however that, in order to obtain the dispersion relation for the new system, σ_x was supposed to be constant, a condition never satisfied in actual applications of the PML technique (it is at most piecewise constant). Taking the Fourier transform of the damped system, one obtains

$$\begin{aligned}
i\omega \tilde{q} - \frac{\partial \tilde{u}}{\partial x} + \sigma_x \tilde{q} &= 0, \\
i\omega \tilde{u} - \frac{\partial \tilde{q}}{\partial x} + \sigma_x \tilde{u} &= 0.
\end{aligned} \qquad (9)$$

One can now obtain $\tilde{u}$ from the second equation and substitute it in the first, to get

$$\tilde{q} - \frac{1}{G_x^2} \frac{\partial^2 \tilde{q}}{\partial x^2} = 0 \qquad (10)$$

where $G_x = i\omega + \sigma_x$ is a constant. It can be easily seen that Φ' satisfies a similar equation, and the dispersion relation for this scalar equation is the same as that of the damped system.

Let us now turn to the three-dimensional case and suppose that the PML can be situated in a region where the mean flow is uniform and aligned for convenience with the x-axis. Since $\bar{f} = 1$ and $\nabla \bar{\Phi} = M\hat{x}$ (due to non-dimensionalization) in this region, the time dependent acoustic potential is governed by the convected wave equation, obtained by using Eq. (4) in Eq. (3),

$$\begin{aligned}
&\frac{\partial^2 \Phi'}{\partial t^2} + 2M \frac{\partial^2 \Phi'}{\partial x \partial t} - \\
&(1 - M^2) \frac{\partial^2 \Phi'}{\partial x^2} - \frac{\partial^2 \Phi'}{\partial y^2} - \frac{\partial^2 \Phi'}{\partial z^2} = 0.
\end{aligned} \qquad (11)$$

Using a Prandtl-Glauert transformation of the form

$$\begin{aligned}
\tau = t + M\beta^2 x; \quad \xi &= \beta^2 x; \\
\eta = \beta y; \quad \zeta &= \beta z,
\end{aligned} \qquad (12)$$

where $\beta = \sqrt{1/(1 - M^2)}$, the equation is further reduced to the three dimensional wave equation,

$$\frac{\partial^2 \Phi'}{\partial t^2} - \frac{\partial^2 \Phi'}{\partial \xi^2} - \frac{\partial^2 \Phi'}{\partial \eta^2} - \frac{\partial^2 \Phi'}{\partial \zeta^2} = 0. \qquad (13)$$

Since $\partial/\partial t = \partial/\partial \tau$, we can conveniently set $\Phi'(\tau, \xi, \eta, \zeta) = \phi(\xi, \eta, \zeta)\exp(i\omega\tau)$ and get the Helmholtz equation for ϕ,

$$\phi - \frac{1}{(i\omega)^2} \frac{\partial^2 \phi}{\partial \xi^2} - \frac{1}{(i\omega)^2} \frac{\partial^2 \phi}{\partial \eta^2} - \frac{1}{(i\omega)^2} \frac{\partial^2 \phi}{\partial \zeta^2} = 0. \quad (14)$$

The PML equation in the new coordinate system can now be developed using the same technique as in the one-dimensional case, and is found to be

$$\phi - \frac{1}{G_\xi^2} \frac{\partial^2 \phi}{\partial \xi^2} - \frac{1}{G_\eta^2} \frac{\partial^2 \phi}{\partial \eta^2} - \frac{1}{G_\zeta^2} \frac{\partial^2 \phi}{\partial \zeta^2} = 0, \quad (15)$$

with $G_\xi = i\omega + \sigma_x$, etc. Considering plane wave solutions of the form $\phi = \phi_0 e^{-i(k_\xi \xi - k_\eta \eta - k_\zeta \zeta)}$, it can be verified that the solution to the dispersion relation now reads

$$\begin{aligned}
k_\xi &= (\omega - i\sigma_\xi)\cos(\theta_\xi), \\
k_\eta &= (\omega - i\sigma_\eta)\cos(\theta_\eta), \\
k_\zeta &= (\omega - i\sigma_\zeta)\cos(\theta_\zeta), \\
\cos^2(\theta_\xi) &+ \cos^2(\theta_\eta) + \cos^2(\theta_\zeta) = 1.
\end{aligned} \qquad (16)$$

The PML boundary condition for advective acoustics is now simply obtained by transforming this equation back to (x, y, z) coordinates.

SPECTRAL ELEMENT DISCRETIZATION

The spectral element method is used to discretize equation (5). While it contains as particular cases both the linear and the non-serendipity quadratic finite element methods, it offers an advantage related to grid generation. Indeed, in our approach, once a linear finite element grid is constructed around a configuration of interest, we can change the driving frequency and consequently change the polynomial degree used in the approximation (in order to meet the requirements in the minimum number of points per wavelength) by simply specifying it in the input file, without needing to generate a different grid. The application of the spectral element method to the governing equation leads to a discrete system of the form $A \{\phi\} = \{b\}$, where $\{\phi\}$ is the vector of point values of the complex-valued acoustic potential ϕ. Briefly stated, the computational domain Ω is partitioned into a set of non-overlapping hexahedra Ω_e, $e = 1, \ldots, E$. Within each element, a polynomial of degree N approximates the solution. The system is obtained from the variational statement of equation (5) which can be expressed as follows: find $\phi \in \mathbf{V}$ such that

$$\int_\Omega \mathbf{F} (\phi, \phi_x, \phi_y, phi_z; \psi, \psi_x, \psi_y, \psi_z) \, d\Omega = 0 \quad (17)$$

holds for each $\psi \in \mathbf{V}$. Here $\mathbf{V}$ is the complex vector space of functions that are continuous on the closure of Ω and whose restriction to an element is a complex polynomial of degree at most N in the three independent variables. The integral can be evaluated by summing up the individual contributions of all the elements. For each element, the respective contribution is computed by mapping the element onto the master element $\Omega_M = [-1, 1]^3$ and expressing the integrands in terms of Chebyshev polynomials [13] through the Lobatto quadrature points.

LINEAR SOLVER

The resulting algebraic system is of appreciable size even for low values of the driving frequency ω. Since the memory usually available even on the most performant CPUs is far from sufficient for storing the matrix in sparse matrix format, the computations have to use either a shared-memory or a distributed-memory machine for storage and solution. We chose to use a distributed-memory model, as most shared-memory machines can also be used under this model, with the code using the Message Passing Interface (MPI) standard. Each processor stores in this case a number of lines in the matrix. However, distribution of the matrix over several processors precludes construction of powerful ILU-type preconditioners, as they require massive communication among processors. Without a powerful preconditioner, iterative methods for the solution of the system are bound to fail, as the matrix usually has a very large condition number and is indefinite. To address this issue, we used a parallel Schur-complement [11] approach which is briefly described below. Let us consider the computational domain Ω divided in a number P of sub-partitions, each of which is assigned to a processor, and denote by $\mathcal{B}$ the union of all the surfaces that have two neighboring subpartitions. In the most general case, for each p there will be a number of unknown ϕ values located on $\mathcal{B}$. The vector of unknowns is partitioned as

$$\{\phi\} = \left\{ \phi_I^1 \ldots \phi_I^P \; \phi_B \right\} \quad (18)$$

where ϕ_I^p denotes all the unknowns in subpartition p not located on $\mathcal{B}$. The right-hand side vector $\{b\}$ is partitioned accordingly. The matrix A can then be written in the form

$$A = \begin{pmatrix} A_{II}^1 & 0 & \ldots & A_{IB}^1 \\ 0 & A_{II}^2 & \ldots & A_{IB}^2 \\ . & . & . & . \\ A_{BI}^1 & A_{BI}^2 & \ldots & A_{BB} \end{pmatrix} \quad (19)$$

and straighforward elimination of the terms below the main diagonal leads to

$$\begin{pmatrix} A_{II}^1 & 0 & \cdots & A_{IB}^1 \\ 0 & A_{II}^2 & \cdots & A_{IB}^2 \\ \cdot & \cdot & \cdot & \cdot \\ 0 & 0 & \cdots & S \end{pmatrix} \begin{Bmatrix} \phi_I^1 \\ \phi_I^2 \\ \cdot \\ \phi_B \end{Bmatrix} = \begin{Bmatrix} b_I^1 \\ b_I^2 \\ \cdot \\ b_S \end{Bmatrix} \tag{20}$$

where $b_S = b_B - \sum_p A_{BI}^p (A_{II}^p)^{-1} b_I^p$. The problem has thus been reduced to solving a reduced system with matrix $S = A_{BB} - \sum_p A_{BI}^p (A_{II}^p)^{-1} A_{IB}^p$ for the points on $\mathcal{B}$ only, followed by a solution on each domain of the interior problem. The matrix S is much denser than the original matrix A and its direct computation and storage is not efficient or even possible. However, for an iterative method, only the action of S on a vector is needed, and once the sparse, distributed, matrix A_{BB} is formed, this action can be computed by matrix-vector multiplications and solutions with A_{II}^p which are local operations on processor p and do not require communications, followed by accumulation in the global vector ϕ_B. All computations can be conveniently implemented by use of the high level primitives in the PETSc [1] package for efficient solution of partial differential equations.

Finding a preconditioner for S is a difficult task, as the entries of this matrix are never explicitly computed, however we found that even a simple preconditioner based on the diagonal part of A_{BB} leads to much faster convergence than iterating on the original matrix A with a diagonal preconditioner, as will be shown in the results section. All cases presented herein use this preconditioner.

NUMERICAL EXAMPLES

The computations presented here have been performed in order to study the parallel performance of the method as well as to gain physical insight into the influence of the fuselage and/or other surfaces on the sound field of a nacelle. We consider two cases of increasing geometrical complexity. Lengths have been non-dimensionalized in all cases using the radius of the inlet duct, R, as reference value. The same amplitude of the incoming acoustic mode was used for all computations of the propagation of that mode in different configurations. For all cases the flight Mach number $M = 0.2$ and the fan face Mach number is 0.35. The mean flow has been computed using the same spectral element method to solve the potential equation (incompressible flow model). The reduced frequency $\omega_r = \omega R/c_\infty = 4$, and we only show here results for plane wave and mode (1,0) propagation.

Nacelle alone

The first computation was performed for the sound field radiated from an axisymmetric bellmouth nacelle with an incoming plane wave specified on the source plane. The radius of the leading edge of the bellmouth has been chosen to be 1/4 of the radius of the inlet duct, and no centerbody (hub) is present in the nacelle. The grid has $E = 9068$ elements for this case, and we used quadratic elements, for which the total number of points in the discretization raises to $M = 78130$. Figure 1 presents the SPL contours computed in this case. As can be noticed, the SPL contours do not have axial symmetry. This is due to the fact that the computation was slightly underresolved (about four points per wavelength) and performed on a non-axisymmetric grid (the computational domain is a box in 3D space). SPL contours for the mode (1,0) case are plotted in figure 2. This case was run on the same grid but using quartic elements.

Fuselage-wing-nacelle configuration

The geometry used for the previous case was augmented with a wing of elliptic cross-section, slightly swept and mounted below the nacelle. The center of the ellipse defining the cross-section of the wing is situated in the plane $z = -3$. A grid of $E = 22843$ elements was generated in this case We present preliminary results for radiation of a plane wave at reduced frequency $\omega_r = 4$. Quartic elements have been used in this case, with the total number of discretization points in the domain being $M = 1,512,216$. The number of nonzero entries in the matrix is in this case $318,540,948$, so that the storage required to store only the nonzero structure with double precision for the complex numbers is 6 Gigabytes. Fig. 3 shows the Mach number distribution on the solid surfaces of the configuration. Note that the symmetry plane of the fuselage is fully equivalent to a solid surface both for the potential flow and the acoustic models. Fig. 4 shows the real acoustic potential contours on the surface. The region inside the PML is also included in this figure, thus damping of the waves can be noticed towards the limits of the computational domain (in that region the solution does not make physical sense). The convergence history of the linear solver using the Schur complement approach is presented in figure 5. We used the TFQMR [5] iterative method in both cases, with the diagonal part of A as preconditioner for the full matrix and the diagonal of A_{BB} as preconditioner for the Schur complement computation. As can be noticed, the use of the Schur complement approach drastically reduces the number of iterations, and consequently the computing time, for this relatively large test case. Figure 6 shows the SPL contours for the plane wave case, and figure 7 for the mode (1,0) case.

An useful way to visualize the effects of the fuselage and the wing on the sound field radiated by the nacelle alone is to extract the SPL data in specific regions of the computational domain, not only on the solid surfaces. Such data is presented in figure 8, extracted along the line $y = 0$, $z = 0$ in front of the nacelle. In the abcissa the non-dimensional distance from the source plane (situated at $x = 0$) is used. While the SPL due to the nacelle alone decreases monotonically along this line, the reflection of the main lobe on the surface of the fuselage produces a significant increase in SPL starting from $d = |x| = 3$. This increase is larger than 10dB, and is rather impossible to compute correctly without considering the exact geometric configuration of the airplane.

Conclusions

A method for computing sound radiation from turbofan engines which accounts for mounting effects has been developed. The method, based on the linearized full-potential equation, can be used to obtain the sound field of this type of engines when in the proximity of the fuselage and wing, and thus study the effect that a change in the configuration has on the noise footprint of the aircraft. Further work will be devoted to improving the efficiency of the complex Schur-complement matrix solution, as well as addressing more complicated configurations and mean flow fields.

Acknowledgements

The support of the first author by NASA grant NAG-1-01031 is gratefully acknowledged.

References

[1] Balay, S., Gropp, W.D., McInnes, L.C. and Smith, B.F., "PETSc Users Manual", ANL-95/11 Revision 2.1.1, Argonne National Laboratory, 2001.

[2] Berenger, J.-P., "A Perfectly Matched Layer for the Absorbtion of Electromagnetic Waves", *J. Comp. Physics*, Vol. 114, 185-200 (1994).

[3] Canuto, C., Hussaini, M.Y., Quarteroni, A., and Zang, T.A., *Spectral Methods in Fluid Dynamics*, Springer-Verlag (1988).

[4] Dougherty, R.P., "Nacelle Acoustic Design by Ray Tracing in Three Dimensions", AIAA Paper 96-1773, State College, PA.

[5] Freund, R.W., "A transpose-free quasi-minimal residual algorithm for non-Hermitian linear systems", *SIAM J. Sci. Comput.*, Vol. 14, 470-482 (1993).

[6] Hayder, H.E, Hu, F.Q., and Hussaini, M.Y., "Towards perfectly absorbing

boundary conditions for the Euler equations", *AIAA Journal*, Vol. 37, 912-918 (1999).

[7] Hu, F.Q., "On Absorbing Boundary Conditions for Linearized Euler Equations by a Perfectly Matched Layer", *J. Comp. Physics*, Vol. 129, 201-219 (1996).

[8] Nallasamy, M., "Computation of Noise Radiation from Fan Inlet and Aft Ducts", *J. of Aircraft*, Vol. 34, No. 3, 387-393 (1997).

[9] Ozyoruk, Y. and Long, L.N., "Computation of Sound Radiating from Engine Inlets", *AIAA Journal*, Vol. 34, No. 5, 894-901 (1996).

[10] Parrett, A.V., and Eversman, W., "Wave Envelope and Finite Element Approximations for Turbofan Noise Radiation in Flight", *AIAA Journal*, Vol. 24, No. 5, 753-760 (1986).

[11] Smith, B., Bjorstad, P., Gropp, W., "Domain Decomposition: Parallel Multilevel Methods for Elliptic Partial Differential Equations", Cambridge Univ. Press, 1996.

[12] Stanescu, D., Ait-Ali-Yahia, D., Habashi, W.G. and Robichaud, M., "Multidomain Spectral Computations of Sound Radiation from Ducted Fans", *AIAA Journal*, Vol. 37, 296-302 (1999).

[13] Stanescu, D., Ait-Ali-Yahia, D., Habashi, W.G. and Robichaud, M., "Galerkin Spectral Element Method for Fan Tone Radiation Computations", AIAA Paper 2000-1912, Lahaina, HI.

[14] Stanescu, D., Hussaini, M.Y. and Farassat, F. "Aircraft Engine Noise Scattering - A Discontinuous Spectral Element Approach", AIAA Paper 2002-0800, Reno, NV.

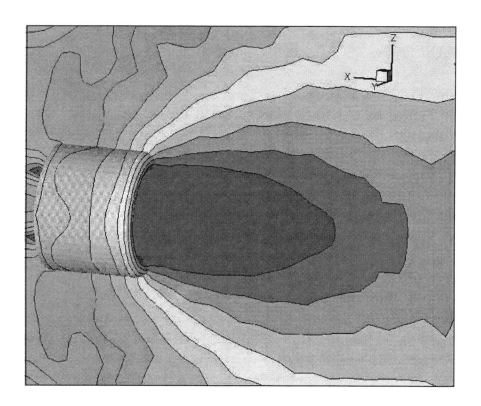

Fig. 1: SPL contours for the nacelle, plane wave radiated at $\omega = 4.0$.

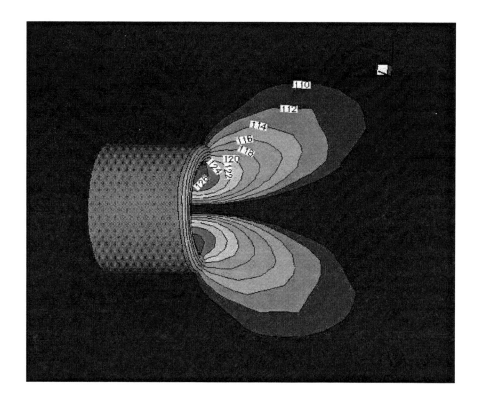

Fig. 2: SPL contours for the nacelle, mode (1,0) radiated at $\omega = 4.0$.

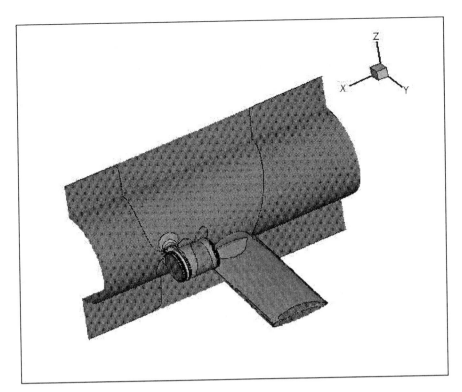

Fig. 3: Mach number contours for the fuselage-wing-nacelle case. 15 contours from 0.2 to 0.4 shown.

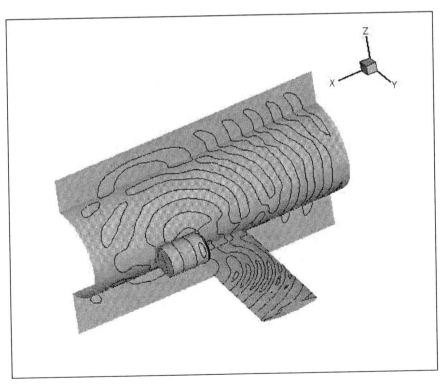

Fig. 4: Real acoustic potential contours for the fuselage-wing-nacelle case, plane wave radiated at $\omega = 4.0$.

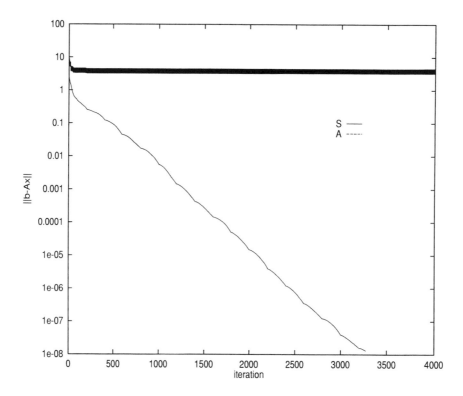

Fig. 5: Convergence history for the fuselage-wing-nacelle case, Schur complement (S) versus iterations on the full matrix (A).

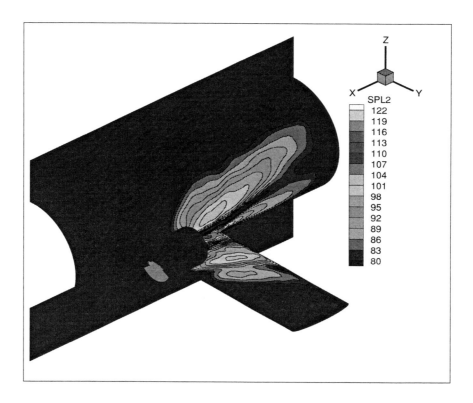

Fig. 6: SPL contours for the fuselage-wing-nacelle case, plane wave radiated at $\omega = 4.0$.

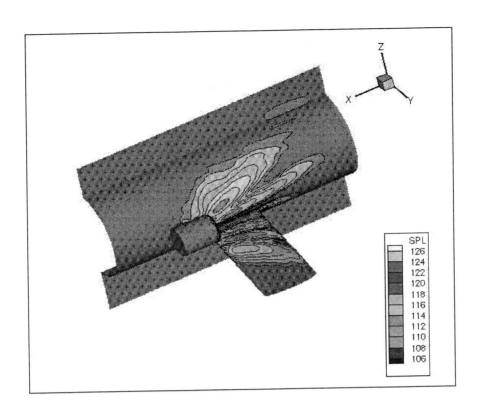

Fig. 7: SPL contours for the fuselage-wing-nacelle case, mode (1,0) radiated at $\omega = 4.0$.

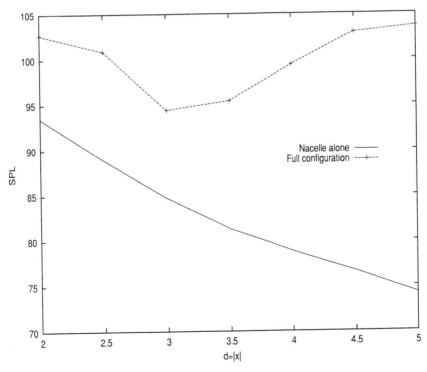

Fig. 8: SPL variation along the nacelle axis for mode (1,0) radiated at $\omega = 4.0$. Nacelle alone versus full configuration case.

A Frequency-Domain Numerical Method for Noise Radiation from Ducted Fans

Y. Özyörük,* E. Alpman†
Department of Aerospace Engineering
Middle East Technical University, 06531 Ankara, Turkey

V. Ahuja‡
Combustion Research and Flow Technology, Inc.
Dublin, PA 18917, USA

L. N. Long§
Department of Aerospace Engineering
Pennsylvania State University, University Park, PA 16802, USA

Abstract

This paper describes a frequency domain numerical method for predicting noise radiation from ducted fans, including acoustic treatment and nonuniform background flow effects. The method solves the Euler equations linearized about a mean flow in the frequency domain. A pseudo-time derivative term is added to the frequency domain equations so that a time marching technique can be employed to drive the acoustic field to steady state explicitly. This approach makes distributed parallel computing more viable for equations of this type and allows use of well known convergence acceleration techniques, such as multigrid, to obtain the solutions efficiently. Simulations of the JT15D and a generic engine are shown at various operating conditions with comparison to results from time domain studies and available experimental data.

*Assoc. Prof.
†Graduate Assistant, presently at the Department of Aerospace Engineering, Penn State University
‡Research Scientist, Senior Member, AIAA
§Professor, Assoc. Member, AIAA

1 Introduction

In an ambitious effort to reduce noise levels in modern turbofan engines considerable research has been done towards the development of advanced liner technologies. Traditional liners used to attenuate noise in turbofan engines generally consisted of arrays of Helmholtz resonators constructed by bonding fine wire mesh screens to honeycomb like cavity backed perforates. Not surprisingly, most of the liners constructed in this manner were tuned to resonate with a single dominant frequency. Under NASA's Advanced Subsonic Technology (AST) noise reduction program several advanced turbofan duct liner concepts have been developed. These include passive acoustic liners with increased degrees of freedom such as double layers, triple layers and parallel element liners[1]. However, a study on liner performance revealed that passive liners with increased degrees of freedom such as triple layer perforates showed only 2-3 percent improvement for inlets and between 6-10 percent improvement for fan ducts over 1992 technology[2]. Better liner designs can be facilitated through a better understanding of the fundamental mechanics of non-linear physical phenomena such as fluid acoustic coupling that are associated with liner resonant cavities. Furthermore, issues related to performance of liner materials at grazing flow incidence and varying flow conditions need to be addressed and understood in order to both predict the radiated fan noise accurately and design more effective liner technology. For this to be facilitated liner performance needs to be analyzed in conjunction with fan noise for engine inlet and exhaust configurations. Till recently, liner analysis was based on empirical models and experimental observations while sound propagation from engine nacelles and exhausts was looked at with radiation and duct propagation codes using hard wall assumptions. In this paper we bring about a synthesis of the two problems of liner analysis and sound radiation from engine inlets.

Most of the computational analysis performed in the area of high bypass ratio engine acoustics fall into two broad categories: Direct time domain approaches [1, 2, 3, 4, 5, 6] have become popular and most of the methods in this group are a result of the maturation of computational fluid dynamic algorithms that can be applied to aeroacoustic problems. The main advantage of time domain methods is the ability to handle multi-frequency sources in one single simulation. Nonlinear effects are also accounted for in time domain methods through the solution of the full Euler or Navier-Stokes equations. The authors Özyörük and Long [1] developed a parallel, 3-D Euler solver to predict forward-radiated noise of ducted fans. This was later followed by an effort to predict the integrated forward and aft radiated noise from turbofan engines [6]. However, the main drawback of time domain methods relates to treatment of frequency dependent lining materials. In the past such treatment of acoustic soft walls with frequency dependent impedance values has been limited to frequency domain methods. However, the authors [7] have devised and successfully used a z-transform based formulation for a frequency dependent impedance condition in time domain calculations. The continuing work of the present authors with time domain methods have become quite mature including many realistic effects.

At the other end of the spectrum are frequency domain methods that represent a second class of noise prediction methods for aircraft engines. Eversman and his co-workers developed a finite-element code based on the Galerkin method [8, 9]. Later, they included acoustic treatment effects in their numerical model [10] and extended it to calculate both

fore and aft radiation [11]. Hence this code became widely used (e.g. Ref. [12]). Eversman's code is based on the solution of the velocity potential equation in the frequency domain including nonuniform background flow effects. This code used the wave envelope technique to find far-field sound in its early developments [9] but later a Kirchhoff integration technique was also incorporated into it [13]. The aft radiation version of this code models the shear-layer emanating from the shroud for including its refraction effects on sound propagation based on some kinematic approximations. While frequency domain methods are not as efficient as the time domain methods for broadband noise predictions, and are cumbersome to use for multi-frequency noise sources, they provide important insight into the functioning of liner materials that are generally tuned to resonate at a single frequency or a narrow band of discrete frequencies. Furthermore, the use of frequency domain methods eliminates questions regarding the accurate resolution of temporal characteristics associated with the prediction algorithm.

The goal of this paper is twofold. The first is to develop a parallel, frequency domain code that includes the effects of nonuniform background flows and acoustic treatment. This code resorts only to the linearization of the Euler equations about a mean flow that comes from computational fluid dynamics (CFD) solutions, so that its refraction effects on sound propagation are included in computations more realistically. This is particularly important for aft radiation from turbofans, where the shear layer emanating from the shroud of the engine causes significant refraction of the emitted sound waves. The other goal is to validate our time domain methodology for fore and aft radiation (including impedance characteristics) against results from our frequency domain approach.

The present frequency domain approach is described in the next section. Although work is also continued to solve aft radiation problems, in the present paper only forward radiation simulations are presented. Simulations are performed for the JT15D engine inlet and a generic inlet and compared to available solutions and experimental data. It is demonstrated that the developed code is capable of making accurate forward radiation predictions.

2 Mathematical Model

2.1 Governing Equations

The 3-D, time dependent, linearized Euler equations are transformed into the frequency domain assuming perturbations of the primitive dependent variables are of the form

$$\mathbf{Q}'(\mathbf{x},t) = \text{Re}\{\hat{\mathbf{Q}}(x,r,\omega)\,e^{i\omega t + im\theta}\} \qquad (1)$$

where

$$\begin{aligned}
\mathbf{Q}' &= [u', v', w', p']^T, \\
\hat{\mathbf{Q}} &= [\hat{u}, \hat{v}, \hat{w}, \hat{p}]^T,
\end{aligned} \qquad (2)$$

and $i = \sqrt{-1}$; u', v', w' are the velocity perturbations in the cylindrical x, r, θ coordinate directions, respectively; p is the pressure; and a hat on a variable indicates a complex quantity. In Eq. (1) ω is the circular frequency and the integer m represents the azimuthal mode number.

Upon substitution of Eq. (1) into the Euler equations linearized about a nonuniform, axisymmetric flow, in cylindrical coordinates the equations governing the amplitudes of the complex flow perturbations become

$$i\omega\hat{u} + u_0\frac{\partial \hat{u}}{\partial x} + v_0\frac{\partial \hat{u}}{\partial r} + \hat{u}\frac{\partial u_0}{\partial x} + \hat{v}\frac{\partial u_0}{\partial r}$$
$$+ \frac{1}{\rho_0}\frac{\partial \hat{p}}{\partial x} - \frac{\hat{p}}{\rho_0^2 c_0^2}\frac{\partial p_0}{\partial x} = 0 \qquad (3)$$

$$i\omega\hat{v} + u_0\frac{\partial \hat{v}}{\partial x} + v_0\frac{\partial \hat{v}}{\partial r} + \hat{u}\frac{\partial v_0}{\partial x} + \hat{v}\frac{\partial v_0}{\partial r}$$
$$+ \frac{1}{\rho_0}\frac{\partial \hat{p}}{\partial r} - \frac{\hat{p}}{\rho_0^2 c_0^2}\frac{\partial p_0}{\partial r} = 0 \qquad (4)$$

$$i\omega\hat{w} + u_0\frac{\partial \hat{w}}{\partial x} + v_0\frac{\partial \hat{w}}{\partial r} + \frac{im}{\rho_0 r}\hat{p} + \frac{v_0\hat{w}}{r} = 0 \qquad (5)$$

$$i\omega\hat{p} + u_0\frac{\partial \hat{p}}{\partial x} + v_0\frac{\partial \hat{p}}{\partial r} + \hat{u}\frac{\partial p_0}{\partial x}$$
$$+ \hat{v}\frac{\partial p_0}{\partial r} + \gamma p_0\left(\frac{\partial \hat{u}}{\partial x} + \frac{\partial \hat{v}}{\partial r} + \frac{\hat{v}}{r} + \frac{im}{r}\hat{w}\right)$$
$$+ \gamma\hat{p}\left(\frac{\partial u_0}{\partial x} + \frac{\partial v_0}{\partial r} + \frac{v_0}{r}\right) = 0 \qquad (6)$$

where $[\rho_0, u_0, v_0, p_0]^T$ represent the nonuniform, axisymmetric flow states. Note that the above equations contain derivatives only in 2-D (x,r) and

the periodic, azimuthal variations have been transformed only to source-like terms multiplied by im. Hence, the 3-D field of a single spinning mode needs to be solved only in the (x,r) coordinates, reducing the computational expense of full 3-D simulations greatly.

Equations (3-6) are transformed into a body-fitted curvilinear coordinate system through the mappings

$$x = x(\xi, \eta); \; r = r(\xi, \eta), \qquad (7)$$

where (x,r) are the axial and radial coordinates, and (ξ, η) are the curvilinear coordinates.

2.2 Boundary Conditions

2.2.1 Fan-Face Conditions

Exact cylindrical duct eigensolutions are used at the fan face to excite the acoustic field, which is assumed to be a deviation from the mean field. Acoustic pressure at a constant x plane in a circular annular duct is given by

$$\hat{p}(r,\theta) = \sum_{m,\mu} A_{m\mu}[J_m(k_{m\mu}r)$$
$$+ Q_{m\mu}Y_m(k_{m\mu}r)]\,e^{i(m\theta)} \qquad (8)$$

where m and μ are the azimuthal and radial mode orders, respectively; $A_{m\mu}$ is the amplitude of the (m,μ) mode; J_m and Y_m are the mth order Bessel functions of the first and second kind, respectively; $k_{m\mu}$ are the eigenvalues that make the transcendental equation zero resulting from the wall condition, $\partial\hat{p}/\partial r|_{wall} = 0$; $Q_{m\mu} = -J'_m(\sigma k_{m\mu})/Y'_m(\sigma k_{m\mu})$ in which a prime indicates a derivative with respect to r and σ is the hub-to-tip ratio. When there is no centerbody (i.e., $\sigma = 0$), $Q_{m\mu}$ is zero. The azimuthal mode order m is found using the rotor-stator interaction theory of Tyler and Sofrin [14]. According to this theory the circumferential mode order m is given by $m = nB + sV$, where B and V are the numbers of rotor blades and stator vanes, respectively, n is the time harmonic index and s is any integer number. The number of rotor blades, number of exit guide vanes and the rotor speed are entered as part of the input to the code, and the modes that are cut-on are automatically determined based on the local mean flow conditions at the source plane, which is usually taken as the fan face. Outflow boundary conditions are applied at the source plane in conjunction with Eq. (8).

2.2.2 Hard-Wall Conditions

Consistent with the Euler equations fluid particles are let slip at a hard wall under the influence of pressure fluctuations. Numerically the normal component of the contravariant velocity perturbation is set to zero. That is, on an orthogonal mesh at the wall,

$$\hat{V}_C = \eta_x \hat{u} + \eta_r \hat{v} = 0 \qquad (9)$$

The value of the tangential contravariant velocity perturbation $\hat{U}_C = \xi_x \hat{u} + \xi_r \hat{v}$ is extrapolated from the interior solution. The azimuthal velocity $\hat{w}$ is also extrapolated from the interior solution. The pressure perturbation is then found from the normal momentum balance given, assuming the grid lines are orthogonal at the wall, as

$$\partial \hat{p}/\partial \eta = -[2\rho_0 v_{0,t} \hat{v}_t + (\hat{p}/c_0^2) v_{0,t}^2]$$
$$\times [\eta_x^2 + \eta_r^2]^{-1/2} R^{-1} \qquad (10)$$

where $v_{0,t}$ and $\hat{v}_t$ are the mean tangential velocity and tangential velocity perturbation, respectively, c_0 is the local speed of sound ($c_0^2 = \gamma p_0/\rho_0$), and R is the radius of wall curvature, which may be found using the transformation metrics at the wall.

2.2.3 Impedance Condition

Acoustic impedance condition is applied on acoustically treated surfaces (liner). Because fluid particles are allowed to slip at a wall and because a non-zero normal velocity exists on an acoustic treatment panel, the same momentum equations as the interior are solved, but the energy equation is replaced with the impedance condition equation, given as [15]

$$i\omega \hat{p} + \mathcal{L}_0 \hat{p} = -i\omega Z(\omega) \hat{v}_n \qquad (11)$$

where $\hat{v}_n$ is the normal component of the velocity perturbation, $Z(\omega)$ is the frequency dependent impedance. The spatial operator $\mathcal{L}_0$ of Eq. (11) is given in the curvilinear coordinates by

$$\mathcal{L}_0 = U_{0,C} \, \partial/\partial \xi + \nabla \eta \cdot \partial \mathbf{V}_0/\partial \eta \qquad (12)$$

where ξ is the grid line along the surface, $U_{0,C}$ is the mean tangential contravariant velocity and $\mathbf{V}_0$ is the mean velocity. The last term of the $\mathcal{L}_0$ operator is neglected in the present paper since its value is usually small on low curvature surfaces.

The equation governing the normal velocity perturbation can be written at the wall as

$$i\omega \hat{v}_n + U_{0,C} \frac{\partial \hat{v}_n}{\partial \xi} + |\nabla \eta| \left[\frac{v_{0,n}}{\partial \eta} \hat{v}_n \right.$$
$$\left. + \frac{1}{\rho_0} \frac{\partial \hat{p}}{\partial \eta} - \frac{\hat{p}}{\rho_0^2 c_0^2} \frac{\partial p_0}{\partial \eta} \right] + \frac{2 v_{0,t} \hat{v}_t}{R} \qquad (13)$$

where $v_{0,n}$ and $v_{0,t}$ are the mean normal and tangential velocities, respectively, and $\hat{v}_t$ is the tangential velocity perturbation. Upon substitution of the normal velocity perturbation from Eq. (13) into Eq. (11), an equation governing the pressure perturbation along the lined surface is obtained in the following form:

$$A \frac{\partial^2 \hat{p}}{\partial \xi^2} + B \frac{\partial \hat{p}}{\partial \xi} + C \frac{\partial \hat{p}}{\partial \eta} + D\hat{p} + E = 0 \qquad (14)$$

where

$$A = \frac{U_{0,C}^2}{i\omega Z} \qquad (15)$$

$$B = \frac{U_{0,C}}{i\omega Z} \left[2i\omega + \frac{\partial U_{0,C}}{\partial \xi} + |\nabla \eta| \frac{\partial v_{0,n}}{\partial \eta} \right] \qquad (16)$$

$$C = -|\nabla \eta|/\rho_0 \qquad (17)$$

$$D = \frac{i\omega}{Z} + \frac{|\nabla \eta|}{Z} \frac{\partial v_{0,n}}{\partial \eta} + \frac{|\nabla \eta|}{\rho_0^2 c_0^2} \frac{\partial p_0}{\partial \eta} \qquad (18)$$

$$E = -2 v_{0,t} \hat{v}_t / R \qquad (19)$$

Eq. (14) requires information of the tangential velocity perturbation. Therefore, the interior solution is obtained prior to the solution of this equation, so that the tangential velocity perturbation may be extrapolated to the soft wall from the interior solution.

2.2.4 Far-Field Conditions

Non-reflecting boundary conditions are solved on the exterior far-field boundaries. The boundary condition operator of Bayliss and Turkel [16] is used on the inflow boundary. This is similar to that proposed later by Tam and Webb [17]. At an outflow boundary, the linearized momentum equations are solved for the velocity perturbations, but the radiation operator is applied to the pressure perturbation as suggested by Ref. [17]. All far-field boundary conditions are also transformed to the frequency domain and recast in cylindrical coordinates so that the same mapping transformations as the interior apply to them.

2.3 Discretizations

A direct discretization of the governing equations and the far-field boundary conditions would result in a large linear system of equations in the complex unknowns $\hat{u}, \hat{v}, \hat{w}$, and $\hat{p}$. Solution of such equation systems is not usually efficient in distributed computing environments. The suitability of the explicit algorithms to parallel computing can, however, be exploited for solution of the present frequency domain equations by introducing a pseudo time derivative to and discretizing them explicitly. This approach allows use of well known explicit time integration methods and well known convergence acceleration techniques for rapid solutions of the equations of this type.

The interior and the far-field boundary equations are written in the form

$$\frac{d\hat{\mathbf{Q}}}{d\tau} + \mathbf{R}(\hat{\mathbf{Q}}) = 0 \qquad (20)$$

where $\mathbf{R}(\hat{\mathbf{Q}})$ represents the semi-discretized governing equations and the far-field boundary conditions in curvilinear coordinates and the first term is the pseudo time derivative term added to the equations. A four-stage Runge-Kutta time integration scheme is employed to drive the solution to a steady harmonic state iteratively. Spatial derivatives are evaluated using fourth-order accurate finite differences in general but in the developed code second-order accurate differences are also available as an option. It should be noted that since here the amplitudes of the perturbations are solved at a grid point, not their instantaneous values in time, the demand on discretization accuracy may be relaxed. Because central schemes lack of diffusion, artificial dissipation is used to suppress the development of spurious waves. A fourth-order, constant coefficient dissipation model was used in all the computations presented in the paper. The Runge-Kutta scheme is

given by

$$
\begin{aligned}
\hat{\mathbf{Q}}^{(0)} &= \hat{\mathbf{Q}}^n, \\
\hat{\mathbf{Q}}^{(1)} &= \hat{\mathbf{Q}}^n - \frac{1}{4}\Delta\tau[\mathbf{R}(\hat{\mathbf{Q}}^{(0)}) - \mathbf{D}(\hat{\mathbf{Q}}^{(0)})] \\
\hat{\mathbf{Q}}^{(2)} &= \hat{\mathbf{Q}}^n - \frac{1}{3}\Delta\tau[\mathbf{R}(\hat{\mathbf{Q}}^{(1)}) - \mathbf{D}(\hat{\mathbf{Q}}^{(0)})] \\
\hat{\mathbf{Q}}^{(3)} &= \hat{\mathbf{Q}}^n - \frac{1}{2}\Delta\tau[\mathbf{R}(\hat{\mathbf{Q}}^{(2)}) - \mathbf{D}(\hat{\mathbf{Q}}^{(0)})] \\
\hat{\mathbf{Q}}^{n+1} &= \hat{\mathbf{Q}}^n - \Delta\tau[\mathbf{R}(\hat{\mathbf{Q}}^{(3)}) - \mathbf{D}(\hat{\mathbf{Q}}^{(0)})]
\end{aligned}
$$

$$(21)$$

where superscript n shows the iteration step, $\Delta\tau$ is the pseudo time step size from an iteration step to the next, and $\mathbf{D}(\hat{\mathbf{Q}})$ is artificial dissipation.

In the present work the solution is stored at the cell centers, rather than the nodal points on the mesh. As a result of this, the wall conditions are applied between a fictitious point inside the wall and the first interior grid point off the wall. This procedure requires interpolation of data to the wall points. Third-order interpolation is used for fourth-order accuracy. Extrapolations of tangential contravariant velocities to a wall are also done to third-order accuracy.

2.4 Far-Field Predictions

Farfield sound is computed using a modified version of the Kirchhoff method that was previously developed by the authors [1]. In this method the Kirchhoff formula given by Farassat and Myers [18] is integrated using a forward time binning approach. At the end of a frequency domain computation, a 3-D Kirchhoff surface is constructed by revolving a curve (a grid line or a set of grid lines) from the 2-D grid 360° around the engine axis and the computed acoustic data on this curve is discretely distributed over the constructed Kirchhoff surface for one wave period according to Eq. (1). Then the discrete data on the Kirchhoff surface are integrated for specified far-field observer locations using the aforementioned Kirchhoff method.

2.5 Parallelization

Distributed computing approach is used in the present study. In this approach the computational

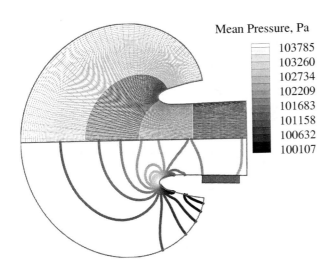

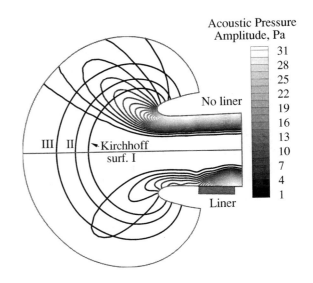

Figure 1: JT15D mesh and mean pressure contours: $M_\infty = 0.204$, $\dot{m} = 15$ kg/s.

Figure 2: Contours of acoustic pressure amplitude for the JT15D inlet: Upper half without liner, lower half with liner having $Z/\rho_\infty c_\infty = 4.01 - 1.60i$. Source (6,0) mode at 2100 Hz, $M_\infty = 0.204$, $\dot{m} = 15$ kg/s.

grid is divided into smaller domains and each subdomain is assigned to a different processor that is on a network. The necessary data exchange across a shared boundary between two neighboring subdomains is realized via library routines from the Message Passing Interface (MPI) standard.

3 Results and Discussion

3.1 Radiation from the JT15D Inlet

The present method was tested considering first the small JT15D turbofan inlet that has been studied both computationally and experimentally [9, 19, 1]. This engine has a fan with 53.5 cm diameter and its hub-to-tip ratio is approximately 0.37, but the centerbody was neglected in the computations. Two different cases are presented here. These are the spinning (6,0) and (13,0) modes with and without acoustic treatment and with flow.

3.1.1 (6,0) mode

This mode was computed at a blade passing frequency (BPF) of 2100 Hz, a free-stream Mach number of 0.204, and a mass flow rate ($\dot{m}$) of 15 kg/s. The computational mesh was divided into 4 subdomains for parallel processing, as shown in Fig. 1. The pressure contours of the computed mean flow are also shown in this figure. It is clear that due

to the deceleration of the flow at the leading edge of the inlet cowl, the mean pressure has increased values, while over the outside surface of the inlet the mean pressure has decreased values due to acceleration of the flow there. Such variations in the background flow cause refraction of acoustic waves, and therefore, must be taken into account properly for accurate radiation predictions.

Contours of the computed acoustic pressure amplitudes are shown in Fig. 2, upper half for the hard wall case and the lower half for a lined-wall case with specific resistance and reactance values of 4.01 and −1.60, respectively. The liner length was taken as 24 cm and it was located as shown in Fig. 2. Sound absorbing effects of the liner are evident from the plotted contours of acoustic pressure amplitude. As indicated earlier, far-field predictions are realized through Kirchhoff surface integrations. For assessing the effect of the Kirchhoff surface placement on far-field predictions, three different Kirchhoff surfaces were considered. These are illustrated in Fig. 2. The integrations were performed for a 50-m radius arc from the inlet mouth. The resultant sound pressure levels (SPL) are shown in Fig. 3. A hard-wall flanged duct analytical solution [20] is also shown in the figure. Computations resulted the peak radiation at an angle of 49° from the inlet axis. The analytical solution was scaled to match the present solution at this angle. It is indicated by

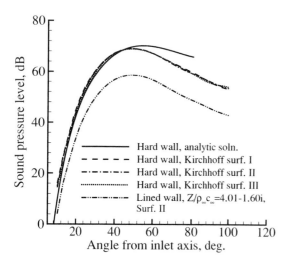

Figure 3: Farfield sound pressure levels of the JT15D inlet: Source (6,0) mode, BPF=2100 Hz, $M_\infty = 0.204$, $\dot{m} = 15$ kg/s.

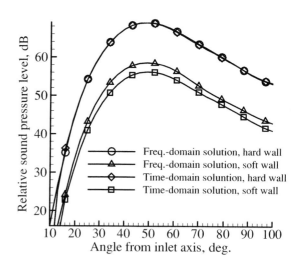

Figure 4: Comparison of the far-field solutions of the frequency and time domain methods: JT15D inlet, source (6,0) mode, BPF=2100 Hz, $M_\infty = 0.204$, $\dot{m} = 15$ kg/s.

Fig. 3 that the computed results and the analytical solution are in good agreement for the radiated sound directivity. Also all the three Kirchhoff surface locations yielded nearly identical results. Consequently, Kirchhoff surface location II was chosen for the other JT15D calculations. Comparison of the SPL plots of the hard and soft-wall cases indicates that the employed liner provided a 10.5 dB reduction in the peak radiation of the (6,0) mode at the specified frequency and flow conditions. The frequency domain computations are also compared to the results of the time domain code of Ref. [21] in Fig. 4. Hard-wall solutions given by both methods were matched at the peak radiation angle, and then the soft-wall solutions were plotted relatively. This was done since it was difficult to match the source plane amplitudes of both solutions. It is clear that the frequency domain and time domain directivities agree excellently for the hard-wall inlet, but about a 2-3 dB difference occurred between the soft-wall solutions of both methods.

3.1.2 (13,0) mode

The second test case considered involves the radiation of the (13,0) mode from the JT15D inlet at the same flow conditions as the preceding case. However, the BPF was set to 3150 Hz so that the computed results could be compared to the avail-

able experimental data of Heidelberg *et al.* [19]. At these conditions the mode cut-off ratio is 1.045. It is usually quite difficult to numerically capture and propagate acoustic waves that have cut-off ratios close to unity. Therefore, to minimize numerical error build up, fourth-order discretization was used for the spatial derivatives. Also since the peak pressure value of the (13,0) mode occurs at the duct wall and the pressure decays relatively rapidly away from the wall, the centerbody was not considered to be important, although the experimental data of Ref. [19] was obtained with a centerbody. The liner had a length of 8 cm in the experiments, and it was located just upstream of the fan-face as shown for the present configuration in Fig. 5. However, it should also be noted that the experimental data of Ref. [19] were acquired at a static test condition (i.e. zero free-stream velocity) in which the mean Mach number reached about 0.147 at the source plane in the inlet. In the present computations the same mesh and the background flow as those used for the (6,0) mode of the preceding section were used (Fig. 1) and in this flow the mean Mach number reached about 0.160 at the source plane.

SPL contours of the computed acoustic field is shown in Fig. 5. The upper half shows the contours for the hard-wall case, while the lower half for the lined-wall with specific resistance and reac-

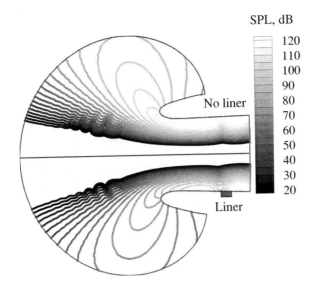

Figure 5: Contours of sound pressure level for the JT15D inlet: Upper half without liner, lower half with liner having $Z/\rho_\infty c_\infty = 0.638 + 0.5i$. Source (13,0) mode at 3150 Hz, $M_\infty = 0.204$, $\dot{m} = 15$ kg/s.

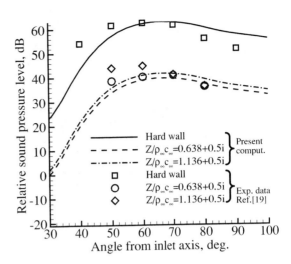

Figure 6: Farfield sound pressure levels of the JT15D inlet: Source (13,0) mode, BPF=3150 Hz, $M_\infty = 0.204$, $\dot{m} = 15$ kg/s.

tance values of 0.638 and 0.5, respectively. There appears to have occurred a standing wave in the duct resulting in a low acoustic pressure region just ahead of the fan face. This could be expected due to the reflections of the waves from the inlet mouth as a result of the changing sectional impedances due to the cross sectional area change. The sound attenuation effects of the liner is evident from the SPL contours shown in Fig. 5. The Kirchhoff surface location II of the preceding case was used for the far-field predictions, which are shown in Fig. 6 together with the experimental data of Ref. [19] for two different liner impedance values. It is clear that the present solution and the experimental data agree quite well on the general attenuation rates although the main lobe was predicted by the present method at a higher angle from the inlet axis. The shift to lower angles seen in the predictions of the directivity pattern of the far-field sound is probably because of the flow and geometry differences between the computations and experiment. In the static tests the flow just outside the nacelle was in the opposite direction than that in flight and away from the nacelle there was no flow at all. The above comparisons should be repeated with equivalent flow conditions and inlet geometry to the experiment to remove the shift in the predicted main lobe direction.

3.2 Radiation of (6,0) and (6,1) Modes from a Generic Engine

Computed results for far-field radiation from a generic engine inlet are presented in this section. This inlet has a diameter of 55.9 cm at the fan stage and the hub-to-tip ratio is 0.35. The free-stream Mach number and the mass flow rate were taken as 0.2 and 17.8 kg/s, respectively. With the selected fan configuration and operating conditions, the spinning (6,0) and (6,1) modes were cut on at 2BPF, 3120 Hz. Unlike the results of the previous sections, the solutions were obtained with the centerbody of the engine. The amplitudes of the two modes were set such that their modal shapes were both multiplied by the same reference pressure.

The computational mesh and the mean flow pressure contours are shown together in Fig. 7. The acoustic field resulted from the (6,0)+(6,1) modes with an arbitrarily set 45 deg phase difference is demonstrated in Fig. 8. The upper half of the contours is for the hard-wall inlet and lower half for the lined inlet with a specific impedance value of $4.01 - 1.01i$. The liner location is also illustrated in this figure. It is clear that the acoustic fields of the hard and soft-wall inlets are very similar. In fact, only an insignificant attenuation was caused by this liner. This is illustrated in Fig. 9 in the far-field SPL plots of the (6,0)+(6,1) modes. Also

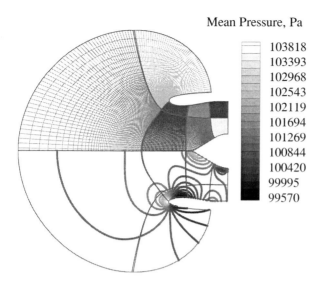

Figure 7: Generic engine mesh and the mean pressure contours: $M_\infty = 0.2$, $\dot{m} = 17.8$ kg/s.

shown in this figure are a hard-wall flanged duct analytical solution, soft-wall solution corresponding to the aforementioned location (denoted as position I in the figure) but with a specific impedance value changed to $2.17 - 1.98i$, and the solution with this impedance value but with the liner location moved near the fan face (denoted as position II). The analytical solution and the present hard-wall solutions were matched at the peak SPL value of the radiated lobe that was predicted closer to the inlet axis. It is clear that the present solution and the analytical solution agree well on the shape of this lobe, but the peak value of the other lobe was underpredicted. This difference may be acceptable since the analytical solution is for a flanged, uniform duct and the flow speed through and outside the duct is assumed the same. It is interesting though the liner impedances and locations did not change the radiated sound field significantly. The reason for this can be better understood if the contours of the acoustic pressure amplitudes that are shown in Fig. 8 are examined more closely. It is clear that more intense sound field exists away from the inlet wall. This is due to the (6,1) mode itself and due to the cancellation or reinforcement of its sound field with that of the (6,0) mode. As a result the liner was not able to attenuate the (6,1) mode, which in turn dominated the far-field sound. As indicated above no relative scalings of the (6,0) and (6,1) modes were made.

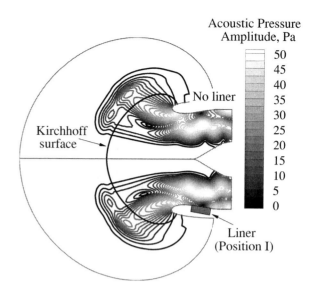

Figure 8: Contours of acoustic pressure amplitude for the generic inlet: Upper half without liner, lower half with liner having $Z/\rho_\infty c_\infty = 4.01 - 1.01i$. Source (6,0)+(6,1) modes with 45° phase difference, 2 BPF=3120 Hz, $M_\infty = 0.2$, $\dot{m} = 17.8$ kg/s.

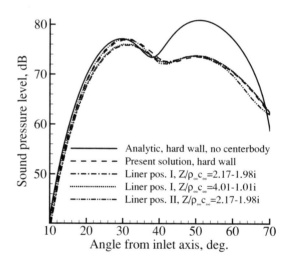

Figure 9: Farfield sound pressure levels of the generic engine: Source (6,0)+(6,1) modes with 45° phase difference, 2 BPF=3120 Hz, $M_\infty = 0.2$, $\dot{m} = 17.8$ kg/s.

In order to show how much the (6,0) mode component was actually attenuated by the liners, this mode was also considered alone. The resulting acoustic field in the inlet is shown in Fig. 10 and the far-field SPL plots are shown in Fig. 11. It is clear that the present hard-wall solution and the corresponding flanged duct solution agree well for the (6,0) mode. It is also clear that the liner with a specific impedance value of $2.17-1.98i$ yielded more

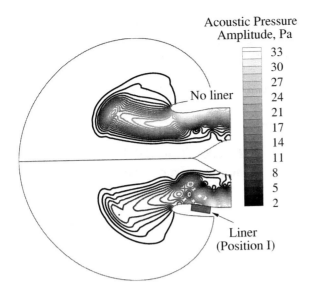

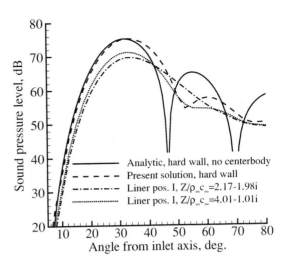

Figure 10: Contours of acoustic pressure amplitude for the generic inlet: Upper half without liner, lower half with liner having $Z/\rho_\infty c_\infty = 2.17 - 1.98i$. Source (6,0) mode only, $2\,\mathrm{BPF}=3120$ Hz, $M_\infty = 0.2$, $\dot{m} = 17.8$ kg/s.

Figure 11: Farfield sound pressure levels of the generic engine: Source (6,0) mode only, $2\,\mathrm{BPF}=3120$ Hz, $M_\infty = 0.2$, $\dot{m} = 17.8$ kg/s.

attenuation than that with a value of $4.01 - 1.01i$. Also the peak radiated SPL, which occurred around 32° from the inlet axis, was reduced by a value of about 6 dB by the former liner value, while this reduction remained limited to 4 dB by the latter one.

4   Convergence and Computational Performance

The developed code was run on a cluster of Pentium III, 700 MHz processors. Most of the runs required about 30 thousand steps for the acoustic field to converge. Each calculation took about 4-5 hrs. Although the convergence seems slow, we are expecting to be able to accelerate it by implementing a convergence acceleration technique, such as a multigrid method.

5   Conclusions

A frequency domain method has been developed for predicting sound fields of ducted fans. The method is based on the solution of the frequency domain form of the Euler equations linearized about an axisymmetric non-uniform background flow. Solu-

tions are carried out employing an explicit pseudo time marching technique, which allows solutions of equations of this type on parallel computers. Although it has not been implemented yet, a well known convergence acceleration technique may readily be incorporated into the present approach due to its explicit nature. Example solutions were carried out for the JT15D engine inlet and for a generic engine at various conditions. It was demonstrated by comparing these simulations to available analytical solutions and experimental data that the developed method accurately predicts the forward arc far-field sound of ducted fans.

References

[1] Özyörük, Y., and Long, L. N. Computation of sound radiating from engine inlets. *AIAA Journal*, **34(5)**, pp. 894–901, May 1996.

[2] Spence, P. L. Ducted fan noise prediction using wave envelope analysis and the Kirchhoff formula. AIAA Paper 97-1651-CP, *Proceedings of the 3th AIAA/CEAS Aeroacoustics Conference*, Atlanta, Georgia, USA, May 1997, pp.539–549.

[3] Rumsey, C. L., Biedron, R. T., Farassat, F., and Spence, P. L. Ducted-fan engine acoustic

predictions using a Navier-Stokes code. *Journal of Sound and Vibration*, **213(4)**, pp. 643–664, 1998.

[4] Shim, I. B., Kim, J. W., and Lee, D. J. Numerical study on radiation of multiple pure tone noise from an aircraft engine inlet. AIAA Paper 99-1831, 5th AIAA/CEAS Aeroacoustics Conference and Exhibit, Bellevue, Washington, USA, May 1999.

[5] Stanescu, D., Ait-Ali-Yahia, D., Habashi, W. G., and Robichaud, M. P. Multidomain spectral computations of sound radiation from ducted fans. *AIAA Journal*, **37(3)**, pp. 296–302, 1999.

[6] Ahuja, V., Özyörük, Y., and Long, L. N. Computational simulations of fore and aft radiation from ducted fans. AIAA Paper 2000-1943, 6th AIAA/CEAS Aeroacoustics Conference and Exhibit, Hawaii, USA, June 2000.

[7] Özyörük, Y., Long, L. N., and Jones, M. G. Time-domain numerical simulation of a flow-impedance tube. *Journal of Computational Physics*, **146(1)**, pp. 29–57, October 1998.

[8] Astley, R. J., and Eversman, W. Wave envelope and finite element schemes for fan noise radiation from turbofan inlets. AIAA Paper 83-0709, 1983.

[9] Eversman, W., Parrett, A. V., Preisser, J. S., and Silcox, R. J. Contributions to the finite element solution of the fan noise radiation problem. *Transactions of the ASME*, **107**, pp. 216–223, 1985.

[10] Eversman, W., and Roy, I. D. Ducted fan acoustic radiation including the effects of nonuniform mean flow and acoustic treatment. AIAA Paper 93-4424, 1993.

[11] Eversman, W. Aft fan duct acoustic radiation. CEAS/AIAA Paper 95-155, June 1995.

[12] Nallasamy, M., Sutliff, D. L., and Heidelberg, L. J. Propagation of spinning acoustic modes in turbofan exhaust ducts. *Journal of Propulsion and Power*, **16(5)**, pp. 736–743, 2000.

[13] Roy, I. D., and Eversman, W. Far-field calculations for turbofan noise. *AIAA Journal*, **39(12)**, pp. 2255–2261, December 2001.

[14] Tyler, J. M., and Sofrin, T. G. Axial flow compressor noise studies. *SAE Transactions*, **70**, pp. 309–332, 1962.

[15] Myers, M. K. On the acoustic boundary condition in the presence of flow. *Journal of Sound and Vibration*, **71(3)**, pp. 429–434, 1980.

[16] Bayliss, A., and Turkel, E. Far field boundary conditions for compressible flow. *Journal of Computational Physics*, **48**, pp. 182–199, 1982.

[17] Tam, C. K. W., and Webb, J. C. Dispersion-relation-preserving finite difference schemes for computational acoustics. *Journal of Computational Physics*, **107**, pp. 262–281, 1993.

[18] Farassat, F., and Myers, M. K. Extension of Kirchhoff's formula for radiation from moving surfaces. *Journal of Sound and Vibration*, **123**, pp. 451–460, 1988.

[19] Heidelberg, L. J., Rice, E. J., and Homyak, L. Acoustic performance of inlet suppressors on an engine generating a single mode. AIAA Paper 81-1965, 1981.

[20] Rice, E. J., and Heidmann, M. F. Modal propagation angles in a cylindrical duct with flow and their relation to sound radiation. AIAA Paper 79-0183, 1979.

[21] Özyörük, Y. Parallel computation of forward radiated noise of ducted fans including acoustic treatment. *AIAA Journal*, **40(3)**, pp. 450–455, March 2002.

ACOUSTIC INSERTION LOSS MEASUREMENT OF HQ-TUBE LINER

H. W. Kwan, E. Chien, J. Yu, S. Chiou, S. Byrne
Goodrich Aerostructures Group
850 Lagoon Drive, M/S 107X
Chula Vista, CA 91910
Ph: 619-691-2070
FAX: 619-691-3050
h.kwan@goodrich.com

R. A. Burdisso
Vibration and Acoustics Laboratories
Virginia Tech
Blacksburg, VA 24061-0238
Ph: (540) 231-7355
FAX: (540) 231-8836
rburdiss@vt.edu

ABSTRACT

A new advanced passive acoustic liner system for large turbofan engines is presented. The passive system consists of the integration of traditional single-layer liners with multiple arrays of Herschel-Quincke waveguides, i.e. HQ-liner concept. This system has the potential of offering superior noise reduction capability for a large turbofan engine inlet with reduced cost and weight over the current multi-layer liner structures. The main goal of this work is to experimentally demonstrate the HQ-liner's ability to attenuate noise in the acoustic/flow environment found in real systems. To this end, multiple configurations of HQ-liner systems were tested in a rectangular duct under high intensity noise and high grazing flow. This work summarizes the acoustic insertion loss measurement test results for the HQ-tube liner. The development and validation of HQ-liner models are also underway and will be reported in the near future.

INTRODUCTION

Noise has been an environmental issue associated with the commercial airline industry since the introduction of the aircraft turbofan engine. The fan is one of the greatest noise sources of turbofan transport aircraft. Considerable effort has been dedicated to reduce the rotor/stator and rotor/strut interaction fan tone sources at the engine design level, i.e. cut-off Blade Passage Frequency (BPF) configurations, as well as using passive duct liners. Today, due to more stringent community noise regulations, additional noise reduction is needed. The use of ultra-high-bypass ratio engines for jet noise reduction in the future will further result in dominant fan noise component. The shorter inlet ducts and the lower blade passage frequencies expected for these engines make traditional passive liners used to suppress fan noise less effective. Because of these difficulties, new novel engine noise control methods have been investigated in recent years, including Active Noise Control (ANC) and Herschel-

Quincke (HQ) Tube concepts.

Active noise control has recently been considered as a potential technique to reduce fan tone noise[1-5]. Over the last few years, it has been demonstrated that ANC techniques are capable of controlling a few radial modes (e.g. 2 to 4) of a single circumferential order. For significant elimination of the fan tone, multiple arrays of control sources are required to attenuate additional radial modes. This leads to a large number of control variables, with great complexity. Moreover, the implementation of active control systems requires continuous monitoring of the duct modes that usually leads to a system with a large number of sensors. The large number of actuators and sensors can result in a system with low reliability. Thus, despite the recent advances in active noise control methods for controlling the BPF tone and harmonics, the complexity of these systems imply that practical implementation may still be many years away. Furthermore, it has been reported that simply reducing the BPF tone and harmonics, i.e., without any reduction in the broadband levels, may result in little or no reduction in the EPNL, which is the metric used to quantify aircraft flyover noise.[6,7] Thus, it is likely that a noise control methodology which controls fan tone noise control in combination with broadband noise control will have to be implemented to produce an effective noise control solution for turbofan engines.

Recently, a novel approach to control both tonal and broadband noise from turbofan engines was developed.[8] The approach consists of installing circumferential arrays of Herschel-Quincke (HQ) waveguides in the inlet or bypass duct of the turbofan engine. A HQ waveguide is essentially a hollow side-tube that travels along (but not necessarily parallel to) the engine axis and attaches to the inlet at each of the two ends of the tube. The HQ concept as applied to a turbofan engine inlet is illustrated in Figure 1, where a single circumferential array of HQ-tubes is positioned on an engine inlet. The additional sound path produced by the HQ tubes generates an anti-phase sound wave that cancels the fan acoustic energy. Because of the circumferential variation of the acoustic pressure on the inlet wall, an array of independent HQ tubes is necessary to account for and preserve the circumferential variation in the pressure. With a circumferential array of independent tubes, the acoustic pressure from tube to tube has the same variation as the circumferential variation in the inlet. This is critical to the implementation of the concept to result in significant sound cancellation, i.e., when the sound in the tubes and in the inlet recombine out-of-phase, the sound at the exit of the tubes must be out-of-phase and of the same circumferential variation as the sound in the inlet.

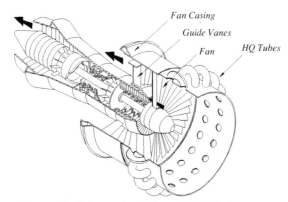

Figure 1: Schematic of Herschel-Quincke concept applied to the inlet of a turbofan engine.

The HQ technique has recently been demonstrated at Virginia Tech on a small Pratt & Whitney JT15D operational turbofan engine.[9-11] The results showed blade passage frequency (BPF) tone sound power reductions of up to 8.6 dB with two arrays of tubes. It was also demonstrated that the concept resulted in good broadband noise reduction. However, these experiments were limited in several aspects that made extrapolation of the results for large turbofan engines difficult. The noise source was artificially generated by implementing exciter rods upstream of the fan that resulted in 3-4 radial modes of circumferential order $m=1$. The inlet flow speed was low at ~ 40 m/s. The engine was operated over a small range of speeds. Thus, the HQ-technology was later experimentally evaluated on the inlet of a production Honeywell TFE731-60 engine.[12] The HQ-system was designed to control the BPF tone at approach condition. However, the system was also tested at cruise, cutback, sideline, and full power settings. The results again demonstrated the potential of the approach as an effective noise control device for turbofan engines. Thus, the HQ tube approach has the potential for overcoming many of the drawbacks associated with ANC methods (e.g., no moving parts,

no additional power supply, etc.). It is more reliable and still provides the suppression of multiple fan modes on a turbofan engine.

The HQ validation efforts on the previously noted engines were limited to hard wall inlets. However, the implementation of HQ technology will be in conjunction with currently used passive liners. In order to further explore potential application of the HQ innovation, a program has been initiated to investigate the integration of HQ-tubes with state-of-the-art liners. This HQ-liner system is a totally new noise-attenuation system, for which no prior study exists. Part of this effort is to develop and demonstrate the HQ-liner's ability to attenuate tone noise while maintaining or improving the attenuation characteristics of the traditional liner. The investigation involves both the development of a liner analysis model and the experimental test in a high sound intensity/ high grazing low duct environment for realistic evaluation. The key results from the experimental program are described here.

EXPERIMENTAL SETUP

The approach used in this study consists of installing HQ tubes (waveguide) in a rectangular lined duct as schematically illustrated in Figure 2. Two HQ tubes are positioned on the back of a liner placed in a wall of the rectangular duct. The duct is assumed to have a uniform flow in the same direction as sound propagation, i.e. flow/noise duct facility. Thus, this configuration is more representative of the conditions in the engine by-pass duct rather than the inlet duct.

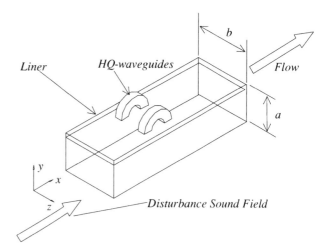

Figure 2: Schematic of rectangular flow/noise duct facility with a liner and HQ-waveguides.

Insertion Loss Test Facility and Measurements
The Goodrich Aerostructures air/noise flow duct facility was used to measure the acoustic insertion loss

of the test samples. The test section of the duct is rectangular, with a cross section of 0.127 by 0.1 m and 1.22 m in length, and is connected by aerodynamic transition ducts to two reverberant rooms at either end of the duct as shown in Figure 3. Noise sources placed inside the upstream chamber generate the disturbance sound field. Overall sound pressure levels up to 147 dB were achieved at the upstream reverberant room. For each test sample, five different airflow velocities between 0.2 and 0.6 Mach number at the test section were used.

(a)

(b)

Figure 3: (a) Overall view of flow duct test facility and (b) Test section.

The sound pressure level (SPL) of the test section was measured at three locations: 0.15, 0.3, and 0.45 m from the leading edge of a hard-walled test section. The overall SPL at the test section reached 137 dB. The sound pressure level inside the tube was also monitored using two microphones mounted 0.025 m from each tube opening.

The airflow velocity inside the tube was measured by two different methods. A flow visualization approach was used by placing red dots inside the tube wall. The second method mounted a total pressure probe and a static pressure probe 0.025 m from the forward opening of the tube to measure the air flow velocity inside the tube. The test results show that no steady airflow exists inside the HQ tubes for the flow duct test.

The method used for measuring the acoustic insertion loss (IL) was calculated by comparing the sound pressure levels (SPL) in the upstream and downstream reverberant rooms at different airflow velocities. First, hard walls were mounted at the test section, and the SPL differences (i. e., attenuation IL(H), between the upstream and downstream rooms) were measured at different airflow velocities. This set of data is used as a baseline. Second, after replacing the hard walls with the test samples, the same procedure was performed, and the attenuation, IL(S), was measured. Finally, the acoustic insertion loss of the test samples is estimated from the difference IL(S) - IL(H). The insertion losses presented in the experimental result section are the average of three tests.

Liner-HQ-waveguide Integration
Since the goal of this effort is to investigate the performance of HQ-liner systems, a key task was to study practical ways to integrate the HQ-waveguides with the liner. To this end, the HQ-tubes were mounted on the back skin of the liner as shown in Figure 4. Thus, the liner's honeycomb forms part of the waveguide. The advantage of this implementation is that the manufacturing practice of current liners does not need to be altered. Thus, the test sample fabrication criteria included (i) smooth airflow surface for the waveguide, (ii) an airtight connection between the tube and liner back skin, (iii) easily interchangeability of components, and (iv) a reasonable cost.

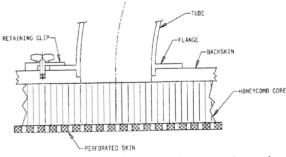

Figure 4: Liner-HQ-waveguide integration and mounting device.

Though the liner core should not acoustically affect the HQ-tube system, the part of the honeycomb core structure forming the tube was removed to investigate its effect, referred as the "no core" configuration. Figures 5(a) and (b) show the implementation of the liner-HQ system with and without core, respectively.

(a)
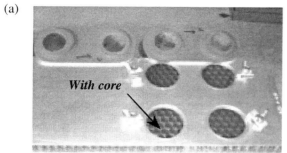

(b)
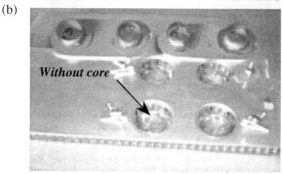

Figure 5: HQ-liner (a) with and (b) without core.

In all experimental configurations, two HQ tubes were used in combination with the liners. The liner dimensions were 0.61 m in length by 0.127 m width. It is important to note that the cross sectional areas of the four HQ-tube interfaces with the duct represents a very small area as compared to the total liner surface. The largest HQ-tube cross-sectional area used was 10.5 cm^2 that resulted in a total interface area of 42 cm^2 that represents only 5.4 % of the liner area of 774.7 cm^2.

Parametric studies were also conducted for the HQ-tube on a hard walled duct. The details of the resulting implementation of the HQ-tube on a hard walled duct are shown in Figure 6. The purpose of these tests was to investigate the effect of parameters such as tube length, tube cross sectional area, and the properties of the screen used at the tube-duct interfaces, referred to as skin in Figure 6.

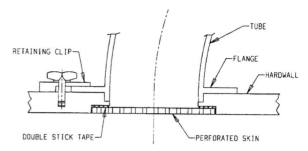

Figure 6: Hard wall HQ-waveguide mounting device

Two types of interface skins, two tube lengths, and two tube areas were tested. Different screen impedances of the interface skins were investigated. Table 1 shows the parameters tested for the HQ-tubes. All test samples were fabricated at Goodrich Aerostructures.

Table 1: HQ-tube parameters tested.

Parameter	Range
Tube length	0.14 m and 0.152 m
Tube area	0.00101 and 0.00105 m^2
Perforate skin POA	From 10% to 30%
Mesh skin	From 10 to 50 Rayls

The HQ-tubes were tested in conjunction with both perforate and linear single-degree-of-freedom (SDOF) liners. Linear liners are commonly used in turbofan engine nacelle treatment.

The main difference between these liners is that the resistance of the linear liner is basically independent of the grazing flow speed at ~ 1.1ρc, whereas the resistance of the perforate liner is a function of flow speed ranging from 0.7 to 1.9ρc for M=0.2 to 0.6, respectively. Another difference between these two liners is that the resistance of the linear liner at high flow speeds (M $\geq$ 0.4) is lower than that of the perforate liner. The reactive components of both liners are very similar.

EXPERIMENTAL RESULTS

The experimental configurations evaluated consisted of liners only, HQ tubes on a hard wall duct, and HQ tubes with liners. The case of a liner mounted on one side and HQ tubes mounted on the opposite duct sidewall was also tested. A total of 66 configurations were evaluated. Due to the sheer magnitude of the total number of test configurations, only typical plots and comparison plots are shown here. The measured acoustic insertion loss data is presented in a one-third-octave bandwidth form. In addition, to have a single metric that describes the attenuation of the different configurations, the overall insertion loss was also computed. This overall insertion loss was estimated assuming equal energy in all frequency bands.

Liner System

The goal of this research is to determine the performance of HQ tubes integrated with liners as compared to liners only as such the performance of the liners alone is presented in this section to define the baseline results. The insertion losses for the perforate liner are plotted in Figure 7. From the test results, a maximum attenuation is found around 2000 Hz. The attenuation gradually reduces as the flow speed increases. The linear liner shows similar trends. The maximum attenuation at the 2000 Hz band is basically the same for both liners at flow speeds M≥0.3.

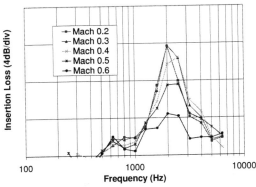

Figure 7: Insertion loss for perforate liner.

HQ-waveguide on a hard wall

Results for two parallel HQ-tubes on a hard-walled duct are presented. From the multiple tube parameters studied, the most significant results correspond to the investigation of the effect of interface skin placed at the HQ tube-duct interfaces (see Figure 6 and Table 1). The acoustic resistance of the perforate screens is very sensitive to flow speed. On the other hand, the resistances of the mesh screens are almost independent of flow speed. As expected, the resistance of the large POA perforate is both less sensitive to flow speed and lower than the lower POA perforate. The mass reactances for both of the perforate and mesh screens are about the same except the lower POA perforate reactance is slightly higher at higher frequencies.

Figure 8 shows the insertion loss results for the case of an interface skin made from lower POA perforate. The results show good attenuation around 1000 and 2000 Hz at low speeds that correspond to the 1st and 2nd tube resonances. The frequencies of these narrow band attenuations are slightly lower for the lower POA

screen as compare to that of the large POA screen. This is because of the higher reactance of the lower POA screen. On the other hand, attenuation at the tube resonances is not evident for the mesh screens. The narrow band sound attenuation results show significant variability at high frequencies for both the perforate and the mesh screens.

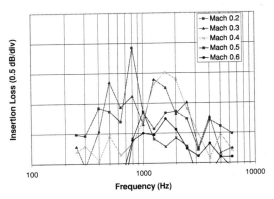

Figure 8: Insertion loss for HQ-tube on a hard wall – interface skin perforate lower POA.

Many of the HQ-hard wall configurations tested show negative insertion loss at frequencies below 800 Hz and above 2000 Hz. The increase in noise is particularly severe for the high resistance mesh. No follow-up experiments were performed to investigate the increase in noise (i.e. negative IL) due to the HQ-tubes. A potential source of the noise generated by the tubes is on the mounting of the HQ-tube screens (see Figure 6). If these screens are not perfectly flush with the duct wall, any irregularity (i.e. step) will probably trigger flow separation and behave as an aerodynamic noise source, in particular at high flow speeds. Another noise contribution could be related to potential vibration of the interface screens excited by the turbulent boundary. This vibration would then results in an increase in the transmitted noise. The mesh screens are probably more susceptible to this problem because they were not bonded to a perforate backing, resulting in a very flexible structure.

The overall insertion loss is an effective metric to define the performance of the systems. To this end, the overall insertion loss for the various HQ-liner configurations were computed and compared to the liner only cases. The overall insertion loss comparison for the different interface screens is shown in Table 2. In general, the HQ tubes with perforate screens provide better attenuation than HQ tubes with mesh screens. The lower POA screen showed slightly better overall sound attenuation in most flow speeds than the large POA screen. The high resistance mesh screen clearly outperforms the low resistance one. These are rather unexpected results because in general low resistance was assumed to be preferable for the HQ systems to yield a highly resonant system and better noise attenuation. It is interesting to note that the overall insertion loss is better as the screen resistance increases. For example, the overall IL at M=0.4 for the low POA, high rayls, large POA, and low rayls screens are ~0.54, 0.49, 0.24 and 0.03 dB, respectively. On the other hand, the normalized resistances are 1.3, 1.1, 0.55, and 0.4, respectively. The overall insertion losses become insignificant as flow speed increased in both of the comparisons.

A main concern in these computations is that the results show an increase in the overall noise levels (negative insertion loss) at high flow speeds, i.e. M≥0.5. In fact, the low resistance mesh results show negative IL at virtually all flow speeds which is concerning.

Table 2: Overall insertion loss for HQ tubes for different interface screens.

Flow speed [M]	Perforate low POA	Perforate large POA	Mesh high rayls	Mesh low rayls
0.2	0.73	0.59	0.43	-0.41
0.3	0.69	0.60	0.34	-0.15
0.4	0.54	0.24	0.49	0.03
0.5	-0.28	-0.10	0.13	-0.05
0.6	-0.19	-0.17	-0.16	-0.04

HQ-liner Configurations

Figures 9 and 10 shows the insertion loss for the perforate and linear liners with two HQ-tubes, respectively. The liner core was not removed in these cases. From the results in these figures, a maximum attenuation is found around 2000 Hz for both perforate and linear liner-HQ systems. Once again the performance decreases as the Mach number increases. These results have the same trends as for the liner only cases shown in Figure 7. This is because the attenuation of the liner-HQ system is dominated by the liner performance, i.e. the area of liner is 18 times the area of the tube-duct interfaces. At first inspection, it is difficult from these figures to clearly identify important performance differences between these liner-HQ configurations. Similarly, comparing the results of the liner-HQ system to the liner only case in Figure 7 again does not show, at first instance, clear differences.

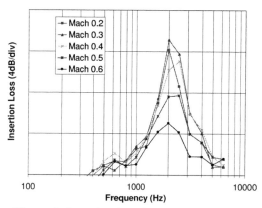

Figure 9: Insertion loss for perforate liner with two HQ-tubes mounted on back skin.

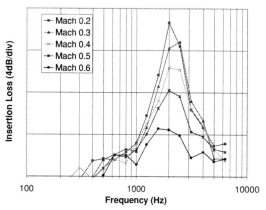

Figure 10: Insertion loss for linear liner with two HQ-tubes mounted on back skin.

For better identification of the performance of the liner-HQ system, the difference in insertion loss between the liner-HQ and liner only systems is plotted. Figure 11 shows the difference in acoustic insertion loss measurements between the perforate liner with two HQ tubes (with core) and the perforate liner only. It is clear that the HQ-tubes can provide up to a few dBs (~2 dB) at selected frequency bands (near tube resonance) while reducing the liner area by only about 5%. These results indicate that HQ tubes can enhance the perforate liner performance over a wide Mach number range (up to 0.5). It also shows additional attenuation at the 2nd harmonic tone (2 kHz) where the liner also has the best attenuation. This implies that the HQ-technology has the potential of improving the performance of liners.

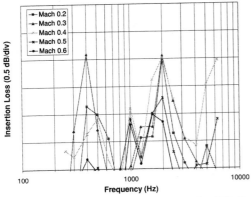

Figure 11: Insertion loss difference for HQ-liner and liner only – Perforate liner case.

The results for other HQ-liner configurations tested show very similar characteristics. However, the special configuration of placing the HQ-tubes at the opposite wall from the liner (not true liner-HQ integration as compared to mounting the tubes on the liner back skin) showed remarkable improvement over the liner only case as shown in Figure 12. The results in this figure show attenuation improvements up to 3.5 dBs over four sets of frequency bands (including high frequencies). This suggests that the HQ approach have significant potential for its implementation in the by-pass duct of turbofan engines to attenuate aft radiation.

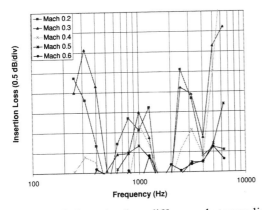

Figure 12: Insertion loss difference between linear liner with HQ at opposite side and linear liner only.

Table 3 presents the overall insertion losses for the perforate liner-HQ system with and without the core cutout and the perforate liner alone. The perforate liner-HQ without core shows better overall sound attenuation than the liner only case at all flow speeds, but as the Mach number increases the insertion loss improvement becomes more insignificant. The results also show that the perforate liner-HQ system without a core shows better performance than the system with a core. It is also interesting to point out that though the HQ-tubes alone result in a negative IL (increase in

noise) at flow Mach 0.5 and 0.6, when combined with the liner (with the core cut-out) the system, however, outperforms the liner only case (see Table 2).

Table 3: Overall insertion loss for perforate liner.

Flow speed [M]	Perforate Liner	Perforate HQ-Liner with core	Perforate HQ-Liner without core
0.2	1.81	1.91 (2%)	2.36 (13%)
0.3	1.66	2.10 (11%)	2.41 (19%)
0.4	1.86	2.28 (10%)	2.62 (19%)
0.5	1.93	1.76 (-4%)	2.11 (4%)
0.6	1.07	0.88 (-4%)	1.11 (1%)

Table 4 shows the overall insertion loss for the linear liner-HQ system with core, the HQ tubes mounted opposite to the liner, and the linear liner alone. The result for the linear liner with HQ-tubes at the opposite side outperforms the linear liner-HQ system in the mid range of flow speeds (M= 0.2 and 0.4). At a flow speed of M=0.3, the linear liner and HQ at opposite side system shows an overall insertion loss of ~3.27 dBs as compared to ~1.61 dB of the liner only case, i.e. the HQ yielded a remarkable 1.66 dB improvement. This represents an improvement of 46% in acoustic energy reduction by the HQ over the liner using only 5% of the liner area. The percentage improvements are shown in parentheses in both Tables 3 and 4.

Table 4: Overall insertion loss for linear liner.

Flow speed [M]	Linear Liner	Linear HQ-Liner with core	Linear Liner HQ opposite side
0.2	2.08	3.00 (23%)	3.18 (29%)
0.3	1.61	2.50 (22%)	3.27 (46%)
0.4	2.55	2.63 (2%)	3.04 (12%)
0.5	2.20	2.28 (2%)	2.05 (-4%)
0.6	1.34	0.91 (-10%)	1.20 (-4%)

It should be pointed out that the poor results observed in the experiments at high flow velocities, i.e. Mach 0.5 and 0.6, could be a result of aerodynamic noise generated by the growth of the boundary layer in the duct connecting both chambers.

CONCLUSIONS

The innovative implementation of the Herschel-Quincke tubes concept in conjunction with a passive liner for the reduction of noise was experimentally investigated using a lined rectangular duct. A key objective of this research was to evaluate if the HQ-tubes can enhance the performance of liners. To this end, a large number of liner-HQ configurations were tested in the rectangular flow duct facility at Goodrich. The test configurations investigated included liner only, HQ tubes on a hard walled duct, and liner-HQ tube systems. Two types of single-degree-of-freedom liners commonly used in treatment of turbofan engines were tested; i.e. a perforate and a linear liner. The HQ-tubes mounted on a hard walled duct were tested to investigate the effect of various types of face screens used at the tube-duct interfaces. Finally, the configurations of the lined wall with HQ tubes were tested to investigate the performance of the HQ tubes in conjunction with liners. In the liner-HQ configurations, the HQ-tube was mounted on the back of the liner, which is a potential practical implementation of this concept. Test configurations where the HQ-tubes were placed on the opposite side of the lined walled were also investigated.

The results of the HQ-tubes on a hard walled duct showed slightly better overall sound attenuation for high resistance face screens at the tube-duct interfaces as compared to lower resistance ones. This conclusion is opposite to the general belief that low resistance is preferred to allow for a highly resonant tube. This is probably true for the attenuation of broadband noise rather than pure tones. The control of tonal noise, i.e. BPF, 2BPF, etc., will most probably require a low resistance screen for a highly resonant system.

By comparing the attenuation of the liner-HQ to the liner only system, the impact of the HQ-tubes was assessed. The overall sound attenuation results show that the HQ-tubes significantly improves the performance of the liner only in particular at low flow speeds, i.e. $M \leq 0.4$. In a number of configurations, the improvement in noise reduction due to the tubes is remarkable in view of the fact they take only 5% of the liner area. However, the performance degrades as the flow speed increases. In particular, the effect of the HQ-tubes is detrimental (decreases liner performance) at the high flow speeds, i.e. $M \geq 0.5$.

The overall conclusion of this work is that the HQ-liner integration shows much promise as a new technology for noise control of turbofan engines. Future effort will be in further developing this technology, testing in a realistic state-of-the-art engine noise facility, and to address producibility issues.

ACKNOWLEDGMENTS

The Goodrich Aerostructures Group financially supported this work, and it is gratefully acknowledged. The technical support from all team members at Goodrich and VPI is much appreciated.

REFERENCES

1. Walker, B. E., and Hersh, A. S., "Application of active Helmholz resonator technology to plane wave duct acoustics," CEAS/AIAA-95-163, presented at the 1st Joint CEAS/AIAA Aeroacoustic Conference, Munich, Germany, vol. 2, June 1995, pp. 1115-1120.

2. Smith, J. P. and Burdisso, R. A., "Active Control of Inlet Noise From a Turbofan Engine Using Inlet Wavenumber Sensors," CEAS/AIAA-99-1808, presented at the 5th CEAS/AIAA Aeroacoustics Conference, Seattle, WA, May 1999.

3. Burdisso, R.A., Fuller, C.R., Smith, J.P., "Experiments on the Active Control of a Turbofan Inlet Noise using Compact, Lightweight Inlet Control and Error Transducers," CEAS/AIAA-95-028, 1995, pp. 177-185.

4. Smith, J.P., Burdisso, R.A., and Fuller, C.R., "Experiments on the Active Control of Inlet Noise From Turbofan Jet Engine Using Multiple Circumferential Control Arrays," AIAA 96-1792, 1996.

5. Joseph, P., Nelson, P.A., and Fisher, M.J., "Active Control of Turbofan Radiation Using an In-Duct Error Sensor Array," *Proceedings of Active 97*, pp. 273-286, August 21-23, Budapest, Hungary 1997.

6. Kraft, R. E., Janardan, B. A., Kontos, G. C., and Gliebe, P. R., "Active Control of Fan Noise – Feasibility Study. Volume 1: Flyover System Noise Studies," NASA CR 195392, October, 1994.

7. Kraft, R. E., Janardan, B. A., Gliebe, P. R., and Kontos, G. C., "Active Control of Fan Noise – Feasibility Study. Volume 4: Flyover System Noise Studies, Part 2," NASA CR 198512, September 1996.

8. Burdisso, R. A. and Smith, J. P., "Fan Noise Reduction from Turbofan Engines Using Adaptive Hershel-Quincke Tubes," US Patent No. 6,112,514, September 2000.

9. Smith, J. P. and Burdisso, R. A., "The Application of the Herschel-Quincke Tube Concept for the Reduction of Tonal and Broadband Noise From Turbofan Engines," VPI report VPI-ENGR.98.167, prepared for NASA under grant # NAG-1-1980 and proposal # 98-0448-10, 1998.

10. Burdisso, R. A. and Smith, J. P., "Control of Inlet Noise from Turbofan Engines Using Herschel-Quincke Waveguides," AIAA-2000-1994, 6th AIAA/CEAS Aeroacoustics Conference, Maui, Hawaii, USA, 12-14 June 2000.

11. Smith, J. P. and Burdisso, R. A., "Experiments With Fixed and Adaptive Herschel-Quincke Waveguides on ohe Pratt And Whitney JT15D Engine" NASA/CR-2002-211430, 2002.

12 Smith, J. P. and Burdisso, R. A., "Experimental Investigation of the Herschel-Quincke Tube Concept On The Honeywell TFE731-60 Engine," NASA/CR-2002-211431, 2002

AIAA 2002-2590

The Absorption of Sound by Helmholtz Resonators with and without Flow

Iain D.J. Dupère,* Ann P. Dowling,†

Cambridge University Engineering Department,
Trumpington Street, Cambridge CB2 1PZ, England

Abstract

Helmholtz resonators are commonly used as absorbers of incident acoustic power. Theoretical and experimental investigations have been performed in the four cases of no mean flow, grazing mean flow, bias mean flow and a combination of grazing and bias mean flows. In the absence of a mean flow, the absorption coefficient (defined as the proportion of incident energy absorbed) is a non-linear function of the acoustic pressure and high incident acoustic pressures are required before the absorption becomes significant. In contrast, when there is a mean flow present, either grazing or bias, the absorption is linear and thus absorption coefficient is independent of the magnitude of the acoustic pressure, and absorption is obtained over a wider range of frequencies. Non-linear effects are only discernible very close to resonance and at very high amplitude. With grazing mean flow, there is the undesirable effect that sound can be generated over a range of frequencies due to the interaction between the unsteadily shed vorticity waves and the downstream edge of the aperture. This production is not observed when there is a bias flow because here the vorticity is shed all around the rim of the aperture and swept away by the mean flow. When there is both a grazing mean flow and a mean bias flow, we find that only a small amount of bias mean flow, compared with grazing mean flow, is required to destroy the production of acoustic energy.

Introduction

Concern for the environment has resulted in increased legislative pressure on industrial gas turbine manufacturers to reduce pollutant emissions. This in turn has led to the adoption of lean premixed combustion systems. Lean premixed combustion offers many advantages in this respect such as lower soot and CO. Furthermore, combustion takes place at lower temperatures than conventional combustion systems, resulting in a dramatic reduction in thermal NOx emission. Unfortunately lean premixed combustion also suffers from some serious difficulties resulting from increased susceptibility to external disturbances

---

*Research Associate, Acoustics Lab.

†Professor of Mechanical Engineering,

and acoustic perturbation and reduced flame stability. Moderate coupling between acoustic fluctuations and heat release can lead to unacceptable noise levels, whilst strong coupling can lead to self excited oscillations, the amplitude of which is so great that structural damage can occur.

There is, therefore, a clear need for practical methods of controlling the oscillations. In this project, the first six months of which are reported here, the performance of acoustic absorbers both with and without flow is investigated.

Helmholtz Resonators

Introduction

A commonly used device to absorb acoustic energy is a Helmholtz resonator. Resonance is established when the mass of the plug of air in the neck oscillates against the large volume of air in the chamber. At resonance small pressure perturbations give rise to large oscillating mass fluxes in the neck. These in turn induce large viscous losses and so narrow band sound absorption is achieved for frequencies close to resonance. Classical analysis[10] uses a lumped element approach in which the specific geometry of the resonator is ignored and theory developed based upon the lumped effects of a neck of finite length and area and a cavity of fixed volume, giving a resonant frequency of $\omega = \bar{c}\sqrt{\frac{S}{Vl}}$, where S and l are the area and effective length of the neck (including end effects) respectively and V is the volume of the chamber.

The large acoustic absorption associated with Helmholtz resonators makes them suitable for the control of shock waves,[38] boundary layer turbulence[15,16] and acoustic noise.[23] In this paper our main objective is to study the acoustic absorption of Helmholtz resonators, using a lumped parameter approach to quantify the response of the resonator itself, together with a non-linear model[2] for the absorption in the absence of flow and a linear vortex shedding model[20] to quantify the absorption in the presence of a variety of mean flows.

Theory

Consider the Helmholtz resonator depicted in figure (1). A high amplitude incident sound wave, A, propagates from left to right in a pipe of cross sectional area

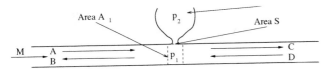

Fig. 1 Helmholtz resonator with incident and transmitted acoustic waves.

A_1 towards a Helmholtz resonator of volume V and neck cross sectional area S where it is partly reflected and partly transmitted into the downstream section of the pipe to give new waves B and C respectively. Downstream of the resonator the transmitted wave C interacts with a downstream boundary to produce a second incident wave $D = RC$, where R is the reflection coefficient describing the downstream boundary to be determined by experiment. A low Mach number flow (which may be zero), of speed U and Mach number M propagates along the pipe. The viscous effects are assumed to be negligible except in the region near the resonator neck.

The stagnation enthalpy is assumed to be continuous at the neck of the resonator:

$$B_1 = A(1+M) + B(1-M) = C(1+M+R(1-M)) \qquad (1)$$

Equation (1) is tested experimentally (see Appendix for description of experiment), the results of which are shown in figure (2) where it is seen that the error shown to be small, with the greatest errors found when the kulites or the opening are near a pressure node.

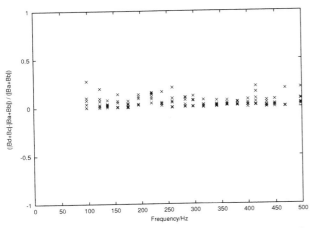

Fig. 2 The change in stagnation enthalpy at the opening non-dimensionalized in terms of the upstream stagnation enthalpy.

The mass flow rate associated with this velocity, $\bar{\rho}Su_1$, is balanced by a change in mass in the resonator chamber:

$$\bar{\rho}Su_1 = V\frac{\partial \rho}{\partial t} = i\omega V\frac{p_2}{\bar{c}^2} \qquad (2)$$

where $\bar{c}$ is the mean speed of sound. The variation of $|u_1/p_2|$ with frequency is shown in figure (3), whilst the variation of the phase of u_1/p_2 is shown in figure (4).

and the solid line represents theory. The agreement between the experiment and the theory for the magnitude is good at all frequency with the greatest error occuring near nodes. The agreement for the phase is excellent.

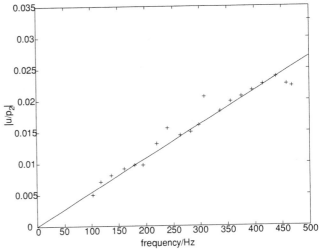

Fig. 3 The variation of $|u_1/p_2|$ with frequency .

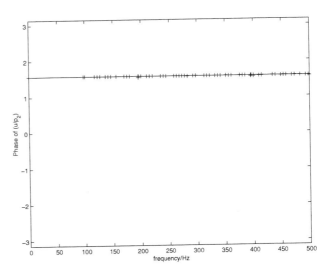

Fig. 4 The variation of the phase of u_1/p_2 with frequency.

The acoustic velocity into the resonator, u_1, can be related to the acoustic waves in the pipe either side of the resonator using conservation of mass:

$$\bar{\rho}A_1\left(\frac{A-B}{\bar{\rho}\bar{c}}\right) = \bar{\rho}Su_1 + \bar{\rho}A_1\left(\frac{C-D}{\bar{\rho}\bar{c}}\right) \qquad (3)$$

Equations (1), (2) and (3) relate the acoustic waves to the pressure and velocity in the resonator chamber. In order to determine the response of the system to an incident acoustic wave, we need to relate the acoustic resonator velocity, u_1, to the pressure difference across it, and hence to the pressure at the opening. This response differs depending upon whether we have a mean flow or not. We consider both of these separately.

In the absence of a mean flow, we use the non-linear model of Cummings[2,3] and write:

$$p_1 - p_2 = l\frac{\partial u_1}{\partial t} + \frac{c}{2}u_1|u_1| \tag{4}$$

$$= i\omega l u_1 + \frac{c}{2}u_1|u_1| \tag{5}$$

for harmonic waves, where ω is the angular frequency, l is the effective length of the Helmholtz resonator neck and c is the discharge coefficient describing the non-linear behaviour of the resonator. Both the effective neck length, l, and the discharge coefficient, c, are to be determined experimentally.

Substituting for p_2 into equation (5):

$$p_1 = u_1 i\left(\omega l - \frac{\bar{c}^2\bar{\rho}S}{\omega V}\right) + \frac{c}{2}u_1|u_1| \tag{6}$$

For low amplitude oscillation, the non-linear real part of the right hand side of equation (6) is small and so no absorption of sound energy occurs. The imaginary part then gives resonance at the frequency given by classical theory.

Non-linear equation (6) is solved numerically for the acoustic velocity, u_1, for a given neck pressure amplitude, p_1, which can also be related to the downstream waves C and D using equation (1). Equation (3) together with equation (1) can then be solved to give the incident and reflected waves A and B.

The non-linear model developed above is characterized by two parameters, the effective neck length, l, and the discharge constant, c. The former determines the resonant frequency, whilst the latter determines the acoustic absorption. For simplicity we assume that both the effective length and the discharge coefficient are independent of frequency and amplitude of oscillation. As there are two unknowns, the effective length is determined by using a least square fit of experimental data on equation (6), giving an effect length of 30mm; corresponding to overall end corrections of $1.6r$ (based upon the longest portion of the neck). The end correction varies significantly as a result of changes in geometry and flow conditions.[4,9,26,30,31] Most authors, however, report values between the values of 1.2 and $1.6r$ reported by Rayleigh and Helmholtz. The value obtained here was found to be almost independent of frequency, although some deviation was seen at frequencies below 150Hz. This was probably due to experimental error since the spacing between the kulites is small in comparison with the wavelength at these frequencies and so the processing is more susceptible to measured errors in the phases between kulites. Moreover since frequencies below 150Hz are well below the resonant frequency, errors in the effective length have little effect upon predictions of the absorption. The variation of effective length with amplitude is less than 0.5% except for the highest amplitude studied

was observed resulting in a 5% increase in the resonant frequency. This is consistent with Ih[26] who found a slight increase in the resonant frequency with neck pressure amplitude, for relatively long physical neck lengths.

Having determined the effective length of the neck, the linear part of equation (6) can be subtracted from the right hand side to leave the non-linear term. Figure (5) shows the variation of the measured non-linear term with frequency for rig 1. As expected, the non-linear term is only significant near resonance and large neck pressure amplitudes give rise to larger non-linear response. The discharge coefficient can now be determined and is plotted as a function of frequency in figures (6) and (7) for rigs 1 and 2 respectively. Unlike the effective length, the discharge coefficient is not constant and significant variation is seen away from resonance. This variation, however, is almost certainly due to experimental errors since the non-linear term is itself insignificant at those frequencies. Moreover, since the non-linear term is insignificant, any error in the discharge coefficient at these frequencies will not affect predictions of the absorption. To test the sensitivity of the non-linear term to changes in the discharge coefficient we plot the predicted non-linear term as a function of frequency for discharge coefficients of 1.8 and 2.4. The results are shown in figure (8) which is for a sound pressure level at the neck of 135dB on rig 1 with an open-end. Equivalent results for rig 1 with a closed-end and a sound pressure level of 133dB are shown in figure (9). Also shown (solid line) are the experimentally derived values using the effective length obtained from the least square fit. Both values of discharge coefficient give reasonable agreement with experiment, with the experimental falling between the two values. As a result, good predictions should be achieved provided a discharge coefficient of approximately 2 is used.

Figure (7) shows the measured values of the discharge coefficient for rig 2. As higher amplitude neck pressure fluctuations are used, the deviation in discharge coefficient is small for a wider range of frequency and for the different amplitudes. As for rig 1, the measured value is approximately 2. Both these agree well the contraction coefficient, $C_c = \sqrt{\eta/c} \approx \sqrt{1/c}$, for a sharp-edged circular orifice of .66 (see, for example, Massey[29]). For consistency a constant value of 2 is taken in all the subsequent calculations.

So far the experimental results have confirmed the validity of the assumptions used in the theory and enabled us to specify values for the two characteristic parameters: effective neck length, l, and discharge coefficient, c. Of more interest, however, is the effectiveness of the Helmholtz resonator as an acoustic energy absorber, which we now consider.

Before comparing the predicted and measured ab-

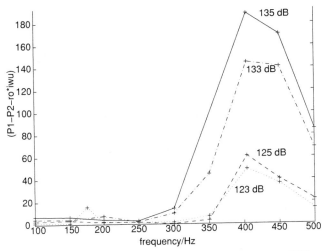

Fig. 5 The difference between the pressure difference and the linear term ($i\omega l u_1$); i.e. the measured non-linear term; as a function of frequency for rig 1.

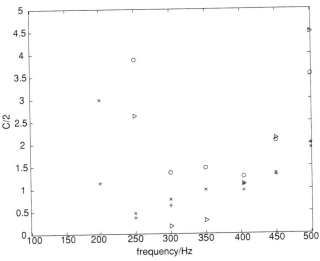

Fig. 6 The predicted value of $c/2$, the non-linear coefficient, as a function of frequency for rig 1 with neck sound pressure levels of 123dB (○), 125dB (▷), 133dB (×) and 135dB (+).

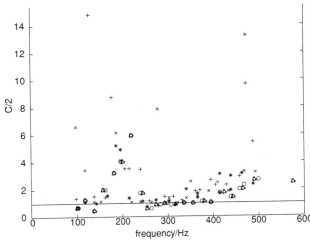

Fig. 7 The predicted value of $c/2$, the non-linear coefficient, as a function of frequency for rig 2 with acoustic neck sound pressure levels of 150dB (+), 155dB (×), 160dB (○), 165dB (△) and 170dB (▷).

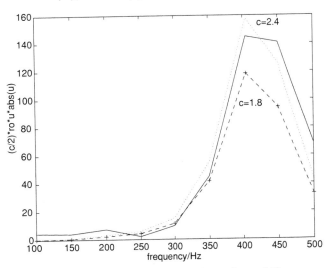

Fig. 8 The effect of varying the value of the non-linear coefficient, C, on the predicted non-linear term for an incident pressure amplitude of 135dB on rig 1 with an open end. The solid line represents the experimental measurements.

sorption coefficients, we first check that the presented theory gives good predictions of the unsteady neck velocity, u_1. To do this we substitute the values of the effective length, l, and the discharge coefficient, c, obtained above, into equation (6) which is solved iteratively for u_1. The results are shown in figure (10) which shows results for sound pressure levels of 133dB (rig 1 with a closed-end) and 135dB (rig 1 with an open-end). The figures also show the measured values (dashed line). The agreement is excellent.

Since we now have confidence in the model's ability to predict the unsteady neck velocity, we use equations (1) and (3) together with the unsteady neck velocities we obtain from equation (6) to predict the four acoustic waves; A, B, C and D; for a range of sound pressure

levels. As we are interested in the absorption of acoustic energy, we choose to present our results in terms of the absorption coefficient. This is defined as the fraction of incident energy which is absorbed.

$$\text{I.e. } \Delta = 1 - \left(\frac{|B|^2 + |C|^2}{|A|^2 + |D|^2} \right) \quad (7)$$

Figures (11) and (12) show the variation of absorption coefficient, Δ, with frequency for sound pressure levels up to 135dB on rig 1 with an open end and with a closed end respectively. The solid line represents the theory, whilst the dashed line represents the experimental measurements. The agreement is excellent except at low frequencies. There the energy contained in the incident sound field is small. Since

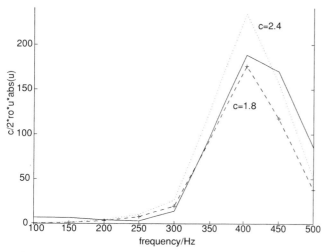

Fig. 9 The effect of varying the value of the non-linear coefficient, C, on the predicted non-linear term for an incident pressure amplitude of **133dB** on rig 1 with an closed end. **The solid line represents the experimental measurements.**

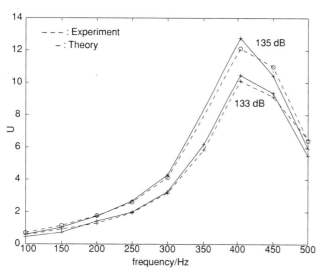

Fig. 10 Comparison between the measured and predicted acoustic velocity, u_1, as a function of frequency at pressure amplitudes of **133 and 135dB** on rig 1.

the absorption coefficient is obtained by dividing by this quantity, a small error in the amount of absorption in the experiment leads to a spuriously large amount of absorption when non-dimensionalized as in figures (11) and (12). This is confirmed by re-plotting the measured absorptions in a dimensional form, i.e. before they are divided by the incident acoustic energy. This is shown in figure (13). Notice that the apparent absorption at low frequencies seen in figures (11) and (12) is absent from this dimensional plot.

Higher amplitude neck pressures were obtained using rig 2 which used a different Helmholtz resonator. Amplitudes of between 155dB and 170dB were measured and comparison between the predicted and measured absorption coefficients is seen in figures (14) —

Figures (11) — (16) suggest that very large absorptions can be obtained; up to 80% for a sound pressure level of 170dB. Even at 133dB the absorption is nearly 50% in a closed-ended pipe of this configuration and nearly 60% for a sound pressure level of 135dB in an open-ended pipe of the configuration used in rig 1. It should be noted, however, that all the results displayed in figures (11) — (16) also include a distinct minimum. This results from a pressure node at the neck of the Helmholtz resonator. This has two effects. The first, and most obvious, is that the sound pressure levels found in practice will be low near this frequency. Secondly, at frequencies near this condition the incident pressure amplitudes need to be large in order to achieve the required sound pressure level. The incident unsteady velocities will, therefore, be very large as they are near an anti-node. The unsteady velocity into the resonator, u_1, however, is solely a function of the neck pressure amplitude (see equation (6)) and so will not be affected by the presence of the node. Hence the actual amount of acoustic absorption will be small in comparison with the incident sound energy and so the absorption coefficient will be small.

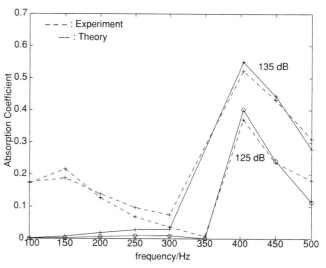

Fig. 11 Comparison between the measured and predicted absorption coefficient as a function of frequency for pressure amplitudes of **125dB** and **135dB** in rig 1 with an open end.

To confirm the effect of the node, an additional experiment was done on rig 2 with the end left open and with a neck pressure sound pressure of 170dB. As the sound waves are generated in a different way, using unsteady flow through a router, than for rig 1, the physics will change slightly as there will be a small mean flow along the pipe. This is, however, likely to be small, so we expect the behaviour will be similar. Comparison between the predicted and measured absorption in this case are shown in figure (17) where the symbols represent the measured values and the solid line represents the predicted behaviour. As before the

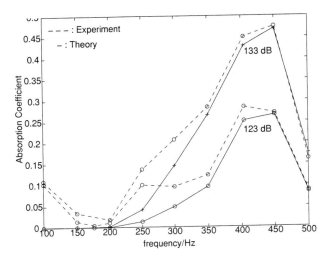

Fig. 12 Comparison between the measured and predicted absorption coefficient as a function of frequency for pressure amplitudes of 123dB and 133dB in rig 1 with a closed end.

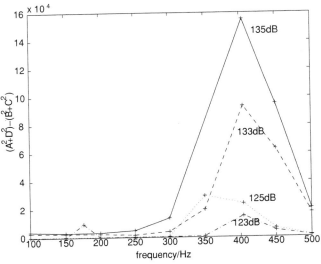

Fig. 13 The variation of the dimensional absorption with frequency for closed and open-ended pipes on rig 1 with pressure amplitudes of 123dB, 125dB, 133dB and 135dB.

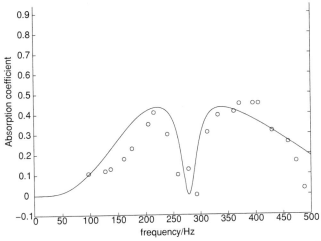

Fig. 14 Comparison between the measured and predicted absorption coefficient as a function of frequency for an incident sound pressure amplitude of 155dB in rig 2 with a closed end.

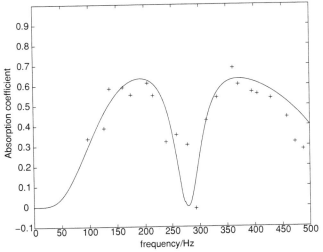

Fig. 15 Comparison between the measured and predicted absorption coefficient as a function of frequency for an incident sound pressure amplitude of 165dB in rig 2 with a closed end.

agreement is good, despite the small mean flow. The behaviour is also the same with the only main difference being the position of the pressure node which has moved to a frequency of 350Hz.

To summarize the predicted behaviour of the Helmholtz resonator, figure (18) shows the predicted absorption coefficients as a function of frequency for sound pressure levels of between 120 and 185dB, in steps of 5dB. With a sound pressure level at the neck of 120dB, absorption occurs only over a very narrow frequency range and the maximum absorption is less than 10% of the incident acoustic energy. In common with all sound pressure levels, there is a minimum in absorption at a frequency of about 275Hz, which corresponds to the frequency at which a pressure node exists in pipe at the neck opening. This results in no absorption as discussed above. As a result there are two maxima in absorption either side of the node.

As the sound pressure level at the neck is increased, absorption is seen to occur over a broader frequency range, although still with zero absorption at the pressure node. The two frequencies at which peak absorption occurs also move further from the node on either side. In addition the magnitude of the peaks increase. When the sound pressure level reaches 185dB, i.e. just above one atmosphere fluctuation, absorption occurs over a frequency range of about 800Hz, with a peak absorption coefficient of about 82%. As the natural frequency of the Helmholtz resonator is above that of the absorption minimum, notice that the absorption is not symmetric, with the absorption dropping more slowly with frequency as the frequency is increased

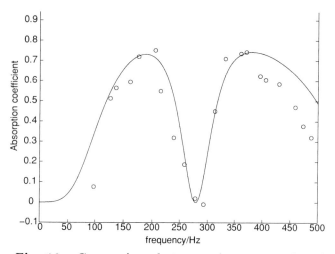

Fig. 16 Comparison between the measured and predicted absorption coefficient as a function of frequency for an incident sound pressure amplitude of 170dB in rig 2 with a closed end.

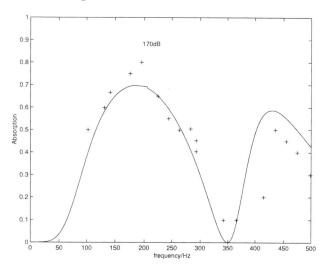

Fig. 17 Comparison between the measured and predicted absorption coefficient as a function of frequency for an incident sound pressure amplitude of 170dB in rig 2 with an open end.

above the second maximum, than is seen by decreasing the frequency below the first maximum. This feature is also evident in the absorption curves for lower sound pressure levels.

In the next section, we discuss the effects of a mean flow.

Linear Theory

In the presence of a mean flow, the acoustical shed vorticity at the trailing edge of the Helmholtz resonator neck opening is swept away by the presence of the flow. Thus a vortex sheet is established which is close to the trailing edge. Such a vortex sheet is a dipole source of sound whose phase relationship with the incident sound energy is such that energy is transferred from the acoustic waves into the vortical part of the flow field where it is eventually dissipated

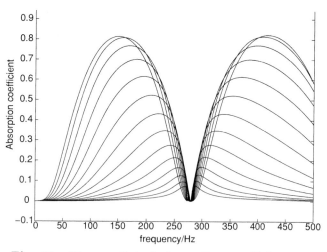

Fig. 18 The predicted absorption coefficient as a function of frequency for a range of incident sound pressure amplitudes from 120dB to 185dB in rig 2.

as heat. This mechanism for acoustic absorption is proportional to the inlet amplitude and so the absorption coefficient is independent of inlet amplitude and can be significant even for modest levels of excitation.[12–14, 20, 22, 25, 39] Here we consider the response of a Helmholtz resonator to an incident sound field in the presence of three different types of mean flow: cross flow, flow through the neck (bias flow) and a combination of cross flow with bias flow.

Powell[33] identified the Coriolis or vorticity impulse term, $\nabla.(\vec{\omega} \wedge \vec{u})$, as the most significant source of sound in a low Mach number, high Reynolds number flow. Here $\vec{\omega}$ represents the shed vorticity and $\vec{u}$ represents a flow velocity. This is an attractive idea because the source region in which the vorticity is non-zero is a much smaller region than the one in which the Lighthill stress tensor[27, 28] is non-zero. Moreover, the vorticity field is easier to obtain; such as from CFD, a simple model or experiment. Powell's derivation is not, however, strict in terms of the acoustic analogy.[27, 28] A more rigorous derivation is given by Howe[18] and Doak[5–8] who identify the the stagnation enthalpy, rather than the pressure, as the fundamental acoustic variable.

Howe[20] derived a simple model for the vorticity impulse source term in which $\nabla.(\vec{\omega} \wedge \vec{u})$ is linearized and simplified to $\nabla.(\vec{\omega}' \wedge \bar{u})$, where the prime and the overbar represent the fluctuating and mean part respectively. This approximation is valid when the thickness of the unsteadily shed vortex sheet is small in comparison with the thickness of the mean vortex sheet[20] and when the mean vorticity strength is small in comparison with the angular frequency.[12] Howe obtains the unsteady vorticity field by assuming that an infinitely thin vortex sheet is shed from the trailing edge whose strength is determined by the Kutta condition. The use of the unsteady Kutta condition in unsteady flows is now well established (see Crighton[1] for

and has been applied to a range of problems including sound absorption by perforated plates,[20–22,25,39] nozzles,[19] linings,[25,34] slits[11,17,21,35] and sudden area changes,[13,14]in the presence of either a normal or a tangential mean flow. It is found to agree well with experiments.

Here we use the Powell-Howe concept of vortex sound and Howe's model for the vorticity impulse term for all three flows. The results are quantified, following Howe,[20,24] in terms of the Rayleigh conductivity for the neck:

$$u_1 = \left(\frac{p_1 - p_2}{\overline{\rho} i \omega S} \right) \kappa \qquad (8)$$

substituting for p_2 we have:

$$u_1 = \left(\frac{p_1 \kappa}{\overline{\rho} i \omega S - i\kappa \frac{\overline{c}^2 S}{\omega V}} \right) \qquad (9)$$

For a known complex function κ, equation (9) can be combined with equations (3) and (1), to obtain the four acoustic waves A, B, C and D. With a mean flow in the pipe, the energy is in terms of the stagnation enthalpy rather than the acoustic pressure[32] and so the absorption coefficient is defined as:

$$\Delta = 1 - \frac{|B|^2(1-M)^2 + |D|^2(1+M)^2}{|A|^2(1+M)^2 + |C|^2(1-M)^2} \qquad (10)$$

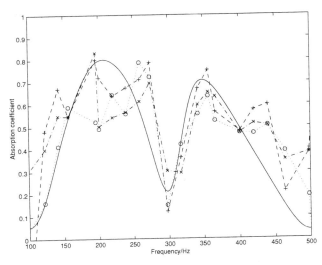

Fig. 19   Comparison between theory and experiment for a uniform mean cross flow of Mach number 0.04; — theory, +- - -+ experimental measurements at 155dB, ×- - -× experimental measurements at 150dB, ○···○ experimental measurements at 145dB.

Figure (19) shows the measured absorption coefficient as a function of frequency for mean flow Mach number of 0.04 with neck sound pressure levels of 145, 150 and 155dB. The Rayleigh conductivity used in the theory is that calculated by Howe et al[24] with a correction to allow for the physical length of the neck. The

pressure amplitude for most of the frequency range at which the absorption is significant. Since the mechanism for sound absorption is now linear, the amplitude of the acoustic velocity in the neck is restricted by a real part of the linear neck impedance. Thus neck sound pressure level needs to be larger to give rise to the large acoustic velocities required for the non-linear mechanism to give significant absorption and so the prediction is good even at these high amplitudes. An absorption coefficient of between 0.4 and 0.6 is achieved for most of the frequency range of interest. Also seen in this plot is reduced absorption near a pressure node, just as we saw in the no flow results.

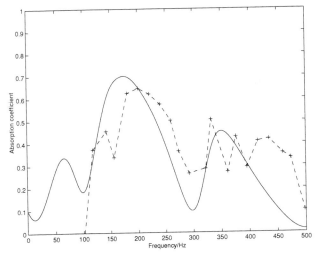

Fig. 20   Comparison between theory and experiment for a uniform mean cross flow of Mach number 0.027; — theory, +- - -+ (experimental measurements).

Figure (20) shows the measured and predicted absorption coefficient as a function of frequency for mean cross flow Mach number of 0.027. The sound pressure level at the neck is 155dB. Significant absorption occurs over a frequency range of 100 to 500Hz. The prediction is good at most frequencies, although there is a slight discrepancy near the Helmholtz resonator frequency at around 175Hz. This is due to non-linear effects which are only important near the resonant frequency. This is confirmed by figure (21) which shows the variation in the acoustic impedance, u_1/p_1, with frequency in the presence of a mean cross flow Mach number of 0.027 and at neck sound pressure levels of 135dB to 160dB. For frequencies above about 300Hz, the acoustic neck impedance is almost independent of neck sound pressure level. It is only at frequency around 175Hz that any variation is noticeable. As expected, near this frequency the acoustic impedance reduces with amplitude.

Figure (22) shows the measured absorption coefficient as a function of frequency for mean flow Mach

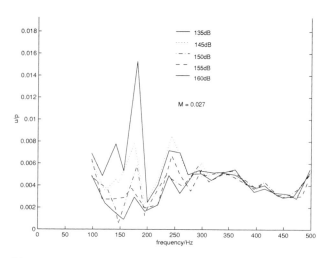

Fig. 21 The measured acoustic impedance, u_1/p_1, as a function of frequency for neck sound pressure levels of 135dB to 160dB in the presence of a uniform mean flow with Mach number 0.027. — 135dB,160dB, ··· 145dB, -·-·- 150dB, - - - 155dB

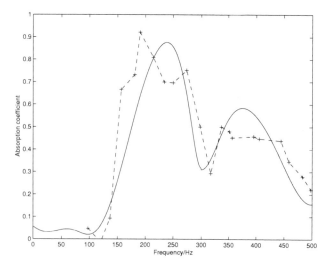

Fig. 22 Comparison between theory and experiment for a uniform mean cross flow of Mach number 0.054; — theory, +- - -+ (experimental measurements).

number of 0.054. Save for the very high amplitudes, the absorption coefficient is once again independent of amplitude for much of the frequency range. Near resonance, the absorption coefficient is greater than 80% even for a neck sound pressure level of 135dB. As in figures (19) and (20), the presence of a pressure node near 300Hz, is seen to significantly reduce the absorption.

When the flow is a bias flow rather than a cross flow, the results are qualitatively similar as seen in figure (23). Here the Rayleigh conductivity is obtained from Howe's solution for the response of an aperture with a bias flow to acoustical forcing,[20] with a correction for the physical length of the neck as for the cross flow effect. There is, however, one crucial dif-

with a bias flow. With a cross flow, the trailing edge (i.e. the upstream edge) is associated with the absorption of incident sound due to the coherent shedding of vorticity at the lip. However, when the vortex sheet which convects across the face of the resonator reaches the downstream edge it also interacts with this edge. Since the phase depends upon the distance travelled, the convection speed and the frequency, there will be a range of Strouhal numbers in which this interaction will increase rather than decrease the incident sound field resulting in net generation. This is not observed in figures (19), (20) and (22) for two reasons. First the frequency range for which this occurs is at frequencies higher than shown in the figures. Secondly the physical length of the neck is not insignificant in the experiment and this serves to reduce the generation effect. Nevertheless it is evident simply from blowing across a bottle that Helmholtz resonators can generate sound as well as absorb it. In contrast, when the flow is merely a bias flow, all the vorticity is swept away from the edge and so the resonator only absorbs sound and never generates it.

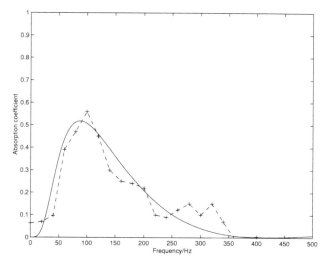

Fig. 23 Comparison between theory and experiment for a uniform mean bias flow of Mach number 0.02; — theory, +- - -+ (experimental measurements).

A similar effect can be produced by combining a mean cross flow with a small amount of mean bias flow. When this occurs the mean bias flow ensures that the vortex sheet is displaced from the downstream edge when it convects past it and so the interaction is greatly reduced. To quantify this, we perform a new calculation for an aperture in an infinitely thin plate in the presence of a mean cross flow combined with a small mean bias flow. The calculation is based upon Howe et al's calculation for the response with a mean cross flow,[24] but with the angle at which the vortex is shed changed to reflect the bias flow and with the imposition of a mean position-dependent displacement.

nus the imaginary part of the Rayleigh conductivity (i.e. the part responsible for production or generation) for cross flow only (···), through flow only (—), a bias flow which is 5% of the cross flow velocity (- - -), and 10% through flow (-·--··-). Clearly only a small amount of bias flow is required to destroy the generation of the aperture. Comparison between the measured and predicted absorption coefficient is shown in figure (25), which is qualitatively similar to figure (23).

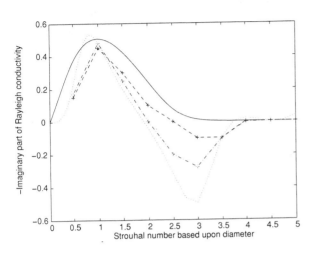

Fig. 24   A graph showing the variation in the imaginary part of the Rayleigh conductivity with Strouhal number for through flow only (—), cross flow only (···), 5% through flow (- - -), and 10% through flow (-·--··-).

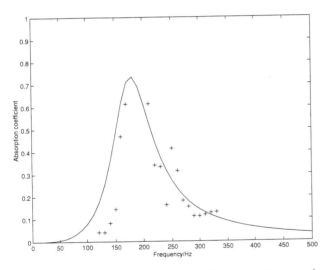

Fig. 25   Comparison between theory and experiment for a uniform mean cross flow of Mach number 0.04 combined with a bias flow Mach number of 0.004; — theory, + (experimental measurements).

With flow it appears that absorption occurs over a broader frequency range, and that this frequency range is a function of the mean flow Mach number. The absorption is high and independent of acoustic neck pressure amplitude except near resonance where

There is also some evidence that the presence of a pressure node can destroy the absorption just as it did in the non-linear regime.

Conclusions

In this paper we have described in detail the use of Helmholtz resonator as an absorber of acoustic energy. In particular, a theory has been developed, based upon Cummings' non-linear model of an orifice,[2,3] to describe the acoustical absorption of a Helmholtz resonator at high amplitude with no mean flow. The predictions made using this theory are compared with experiments for sound pressure levels up to 170dB, with good agreement at all amplitudes. The Helmholtz resonator was shown to be an effective absorber of high amplitude sound with absorptions of 75% for sound pressure levels at the neck of the resonator of 170dB. The location of the resonator was, however, shown to be crucial as pressure nodes near the resonator opening result in no acoustic absorption.

In the presence of a mean flow, acoustic absorption occurs over a wider frequency range. The effect of the flow is to sweep the acoustically shed vorticity away from the trailing edge of the neck opening and absorption is achieved which is proportional to the incident acoustic energy (i.e. the absorption coefficient is independent of the amplitude). The linear absorption results in greatly reduced acoustic neck velocities and so the non-linear absorption is not significant except at very high acoustic amplitudes near resonance.

Appendix: Experimental Arrangement

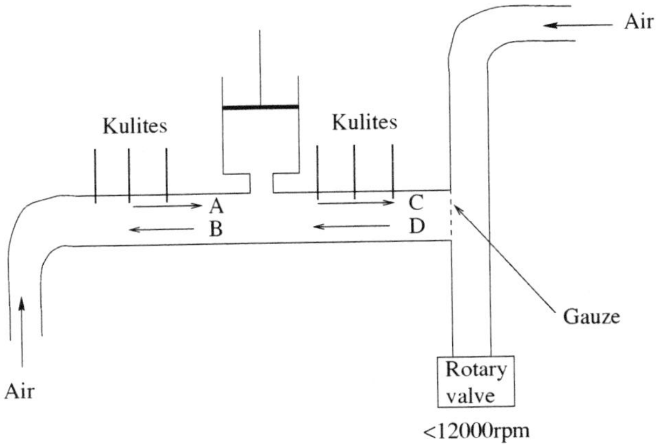

Fig. 26   Experimental rig used for high amplitude incident waves, with an without mean flow.

The experimental arrangement is illustrated in figure (26). Incident acoustic waves are generated in two ways. To produce high amplitudes air is blown through a rotary valve at single frequencies in the range 50Hz to 500Hz (rig 2). At low amplitudes the T-junction and rotary valve is replaced by a loudspeaker (rig 1). The readings from each kulite are processed to give the 4 acoustic waves using the two

viding a check. The kulites are calibrated in the way suggested by Seybert and Ross.[36] The spacing of the kulites is chosen to be 11cm which is less than half the wavelength at all frequencies whilst being sufficient to obtain distinguishable measurements. The first kulite is positioned 45mm from the resonator ensuring that the 1st radial harmonic has decayed by at least 62dB by the first kulite.

References

[1] D.G. CRIGHTON. The Kutta condition in unsteady flow. *Annual Review of Fluid Mechanics*, 17:pp411–445, 1985.

[2] A CUMMINGS. Acoustic nonlinearities and power losses at orifices. *AIAA Journal*, 22:pp786–792, 1984.

[3] A CUMMINGS. Transient and multiple frequency sound transmission through perforated plates at high amplitude. Technical Report 84-2311, AIAA, 1984.

[4] N.S DICKEY and A. SELAMET. Helmholtz resonators: One-dimensional limit for small cavity length to diameter ratios. *Journal of Sound and Vibration*, 195(3):pp512–517, 1996.

[5] P.E. DOAK. Momentum potential-theory of energy flux carried by momentum fluctuations. *Journal of Sound and Vibration*, 131:pp67–90, 1989.

[6] P.E. DOAK. Fluctuating total enthalpy as a generalised acoustic field. *Acoustical Physics*, 41:pp677–685, 1995.

[7] P.E. DOAK. Errata to fluctuating total enthalpy as a generalised acoustic field (**41**, pp677-685. *Acoustical Physics*, 42:p650, 1996.

[8] P.E. DOAK. Fluctuating total enthalpy as a generalised acoustic field. *Theoretical and Computational Fluid Dynamics, Special Volume in Honour of Sir James Lighthill*, 10:pp115–133, 1998.

[9] A. DORIA. A simple method for the analysis of deep cavity and long neck acoustic resonators. *Journal of Sound and Vibration*, 232(4):pp823–833, 2000.

[10] A.P. DOWLING and J.E. FFOWCS WILLIAMS. *Sound and Sources of Sound*. Ellis Horwood, 1983.

[11] A.P. DOWLING and I.J. HUGHES. Sound absorption by a screen perforated with a regular array of slits. *Journal of Sound and Vibration*, 156:pp387–405, 1992.

[12] I.D.J. DUPÈRE. *Sound Vortex Interaction in Pipes*. PhD thesis, University of Cambridge, 1997.

[13] I.D.J. DUPÈRE and A.P. DOWLING. The absorption of sound near abrupt area expansions. *AIAA Journal*, 38(2):pp193–202, 2000.

[14] I.D.J. DUPÈRE and A.P. DOWLING. The absorption of sound near abrupt axi-symmetric area expansions. *Journal of Sound and Vibration*, 239(4):pp709–730, 2001.

[15] K.P. FLYNN and R.L. PANTON. The interaction of Helmholtz resonators in a row when excited by a turbulent boundary layer. *Journal of the Acoustical Society of America*, 87(4):pp1482–1488, 1990.

[16] K.P. FLYNN, R.L. PANTON, and D.G. BOGARD. Effect of Helmholtz resonators on boundary layer turbulence. *AIAA Journal*, pages pp1857–1858, 1990.

[17] Y. FUKUMOTO and M. TAKAYANA. Vorticity production at the edge of a slit by sound waves in the presence of a low Mach number bias flow. *Physics of Fluids*, A3:pp3080–3082, 1991.

[18] M.S. HOWE. Contributions to the theory of aerodynamic sound, with application to excess jet noise and the theory of the flute. *Journal of Fluid Mechanics*, 71:pp625–673, 1975.

[19] M.S. HOWE. Attenuation of sound in a low Mach number nozzle flow. *Journal of Fluid Mechanics*, 91:pp209–229, 1979.

[20] number flow through a circular aperture. *Proceedings of the Royal Society of London*, A366:pp205–223, 1979.

[21] M.S. HOWE. The influence of vortex shedding on the diffraction of sound by a perforated screen. *Journal of Fluid Mechanics*, 97:pp641–653, 1980.

[22] M.S. HOWE. On the diffraction of sound by a screen with circular apertures in the presence of a low Mach number grazing flow. *Proceedings of the Royal Society of London*, A370:pp523–544, 1980.

[23] M.S. HOWE. *Acoustics of Fluid Structure Interactions*. Cambridge University Press, 1998.

[24] M.S. HOWE, M.I. SCOTT, and S.R. SIPCIC. The influence of tangential mean flow on the Rayleigh conductivity of an aperture. *Proceedings of the Royal Society of London*, A452:pp2303–2317, 1996.

[25] I.J. HUGHES and A.P. DOWLING. The absorption of sound by perforated linings. *Journal of Fluid Mechanics*, 218:pp299–335, 1990.

[26] J.-G. IH. On the inertial end correction of resonators. *Acustica*, 78:pp1–15, 1993.

[27] M.J. LIGHTHILL. On sound generated aerodynamically. I. General theory. *Proceedings of the Royal Society of London*, A211:pp564–587, 1952.

[28] M.J. LIGHTHILL. On sound generated aerodynamically. II. Turbulence as a source of sound. *Proceedings of the Royal Society of London*, A222:pp1–32, 1954.

[29] B.S. MASSEY. *Mechanics of Fluids*. Van Nostrand Reinhold, sixth edition, 1989.

[30] J. MOHRING. Helmholtz resonators with large aperture. *Acustica*, 85:pp751–763, 1999.

[31] P.A. MONKEWITZ and N.-M. NGUYEN-VO. The response of Helmholtz resonators to external excitation. part 1. single resonators. *Journal of Fluid Mechanics*, 151:pp477–497, 1985.

[32] C.L. MORFEY. Acoustic energy in non-uniform flows. *Journal of Sound and Vibration*, 14(2):pp159–170, 1971.

[33] A. POWELL. Theory of vortex sound. *Journal of the Acoustical Society of America*, 36:pp177–195, 1964.

[34] M.C. QUINN and M.S. HOWE. On the production and absorption of sound by lossless liners in the presence of mean flow. *Journal of Sound and Vibration*, 97(1):pp1–9, 1984.

[35] M.C. QUINN and M.S. HOWE. Absorption of sound at a slot in a splitter plate in a mean flow duct. *Journal of Fluid Mechanics*, 168:pp1–30, 1986.

[36] A.F. SEYBERT and D.F. ROSS. Experimental determination of acoustic properties using a two microphone random excitation technique. *Journal of the Acoustical Society of America*, 61:pp1362–1370, 1977.

[37] A.F. SEYBERT and B. SOENARKO. Error analysis of spectral estimates with application to the measurement of acoustic parameters using random sound fields in ducts. *Journal of the Acoustical Society of America*, 69:pp1190–1199, 1981.

[38] N. SUGIMOTO. Propagation of nonlinear acoustic waves in a tunnel with an array of Helmholtz resonators. *Journal of Fluid Mechanics*, 244:pp55–78, 1992.

[39] I.L. VER. Practical examples of noise and vibration: case history of consulting projects. *Noise Control Engineering Journal*, 35:pp115–125, 1990.

ENVIRONMENTAL MONITORING VIA INFRASOUND

Jay C. Hardin and Mikhail Gilinsky
Hampton University
Hampton, VA

Abstract

A "shooting method" for locating the source of infrasonic sound waves in the atmosphere is presented. This geometric acoustics method is based upon analysis of microphone (or microbarograph) array measurements to provide an initial estimate of the source location and ray direction. A ray is then propagated through the atmosphere from the estimated source position and its point and angle of return to the Earth's surface are determined. Based upon comparison with the known measurements, the initial source position and angle estimates are refined and the integration iterated until convergence is obtained. The method appears to be very rapid to implement and limited in accuracy only by the timeliness of the input sound speed and velocity profiles in the atmosphere.

Introduction

Sound waves at frequencies lower than can be heard by a normal person (i.e. sound occurring at frequencies less than about 20 Hz) are called "infrasound". There are many, both natural and manmade, sources of infrasound in the environment. For example, severe storms, volcanic eruptions, earthquakes, avalanches, airflow over mountains, microbaroms (standing wave patterns in the ocean), and meteors are all natural sources of infrasound while wind turbines, supersonic aircraft, rocket launches, satellite re-entry and chemical and nuclear explosions are all manmade sources of infrasound. Perhaps the most important property of infrasound is that there is very little natural dissipation of sound at these low frequencies. Hence, infrasound tends to propagate for very long distances before it dissipates and can thus be used to monitor distant events. For this reason, infrasonic arrays are now being set up around the world to monitor compliance with the Comprehensive Nuclear Test Band Treaty that has been ratified by many nations of the world. However, such infrasonic arrays can be utilized for many other environmental monitoring purposes as well.

One area of particular interest is evaluation of weather conditions. As an example, in the 1980's, a study was carried out at NASA's Langley Research Center of infrasound generation by microbursts (intense, local downflows of air) as an aircraft safety alert system [1]. If an aircraft encounters a microburst on landing approach, the aircraft experiences more lift in which case the pilot has a tendency to reduce the angle of attack in order to remain on the proper glide slope. Upon exiting the microburst, the aircraft may then not have sufficient lift to remain aloft and crashes have resulted. The idea was that infrasonic arrays could be installed at airports to alert pilots to such dangers. Although other means for aircraft safety alerts were subsequently installed on aircraft, the study demonstrated the feasibility of locating atmospheric phenomena by monitoring their infrasonic emissions.

A similar potential application could be to the monitoring of aircraft wake vortices near airports which is of considerable current interest [2]. The interaction of the vortices with the ground plane produces a characteristic infrasonic signature which could be employed to track the vortices. Studies of another application, the detection of bolides (meteors) entering our atmosphere from space were carried out in the 1990's, particularly by Los Alamos National Laboratory [3].

The approach presented herein envisions utilizing data from arrays of specially designed low-frequency microphones (microbarographs). The Infrasound Experts Group of the Geneva Conference on Disarmament Ad Hoc Committee on a Nuclear Test Ban recommended that such arrays consist of four microphones, one each at the vertices of an equilateral triangle with sides in the range 1-3 kilometers and one in the center of the triangle [4]. Although the present approach could be developed for such an array, as will be seen below, the authors of this study recommend an array of five microphones, four in the form of a cross with a fifth at the center. The idea of utilizing such data for source location is certainly not new. In fact, the Prototype International Data Center, in operation since 1998, has been developing an automatic and interactive data processing system for highly-impulsive sources in any terrestrial environment [5]. However, that system, as presently implemented, allows only for source location based upon intersecting azimuths, without taking into account the phase (tropospheric, stratospheric, or thermospheric turning points) of the received signal. Gibson et al [6] note that "the ability to identify infrasound phases, and to include the appropriate travel time and bearing refraction corrections for each arrival into localization procedures, would dramatically improve localization performance". The approach described herein explicitly employs the phase of the infrasonic signal in the analysis and thus should be able to produce improved location estimates.

Garces et al [7] studied the variability of the lower atmosphere and its effect on the propagation of infrasonic waves and concluded that "studies should focus on solving the inverse problem for infrasonic source locations using the most realistic propagation models available". Fortunately, an extensive amount of work has been accomplished on the propagation of infrasound in the atmosphere and models are fairly mature. Brown et al [5] discuss the techniques presently being utilized at the Prototype International Data Center. A 3-D propagation model based upon the Eikonal equations, similar to that employed herein, is in place and a seasonal atmospheric model is presently being incorporated. Gibson et al [6] describe a propagation tool kit, called InfraMAP, which was developed for the Department of Defense and includes three different propagation models: A 3-D ray theory model, Pierce's normal mode model [8], and a 2-D parabolic equation model, as well as two empirical atmospheric models. Norton et al [9] have taken a parabolic equation underwater propagation model developed for the U.S. Navy and applied it to infrasonic propagation in the atmosphere. The limiting factor in such codes appears to be in obtaining timely atmospheric data.

This paper presents a "shooting method" for infrasonic source location which utilizes a 3-D geometric acoustics model for propagation and fully accounts for the phase of the received signal. If a direct signal is received from a nearby source, the indicated source elevation angle will be small, while larger estimated source elevation angles lead to the suspicion of an echo from an atmospheric turning point for sources at or near the surface of the Earth. Such points can be predicted from the sound speed and wind velocity data.

Source Location Theory

Consider an acoustic source at the point (x,y,z) in an ambient medium and three microphones, one each at the origin, the point $(d,0,0)$ and the point $(0,d,0)$ respectively, in a Cartesian coordinate system as shown in Figure 1:

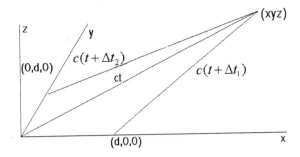

Fig 1: Source Location Geometry

Without loss of generality, to be explained later, assume that x, y, and z are all greater than or equal to zero. The source generates acoustic waves which travel out in all directions from the source at constant speed c. An acoustic wave generated by the source at time t=0 will arrive at the origin at time t, at the point (d,0,0) at time $t + t_1$, and at the point (0,d,0) at time $t + t_2$. These time differences t_1 and t_2 will be assumed to be measured and known.

Applying the distance formula to this geometry yields the three equations

$$x^2 + y^2 + z^2 = c^2 t^2$$
$$(x - d)^2 + y^2 + z^2 = c^2(t + t_1)^2 \qquad (1)$$
$$x^2 + (y - d)^2 + z^2 = c^2(t + t_2)^2$$

which govern the location of the source position. The first two of equations (1) may be solved for the travel time t yielding

$$t = \frac{d^2 - 2dx - c^2 t_1^2}{2c^2 t_1} \ge 0 \qquad (2)$$

while the first and third may be solved to yield

$$t = \frac{d^2 - 2dy - c^2 t_2^2}{2c^2 t_2} \ge 0 \qquad (3)$$

These two solutions must be equal which provides a causality requirement on the source position. Introducing the normalized variables $\tilde{x} = x/d, \tilde{y} = y/d$ and $\tilde{z} = z/d$ as well as the parameters $a = d/c\,t_1$ and $b = d/c\,t_2$ and equating (2) and (3) shows that

$$\frac{ct}{d} = a(\tilde{x} - \frac{1}{2} + \frac{1}{2a^2}) = b(\tilde{y} - \frac{1}{2} + \frac{1}{2b^2}) \ge 0 \ (4)$$

which must be satisfied at the normalized source position $(\tilde{x}, \tilde{y}, \tilde{z})$.

a. Delay Time Constraints

Note that equation (4) implies that if $\tilde{x} > 1/2 - 1/2a^2$, as will usually be the case in applications, then a<0. Similarly, if $\tilde{y} > 1/2 - 1/2b^2$, then b<0. The parameters a and b are, of course, not independent.

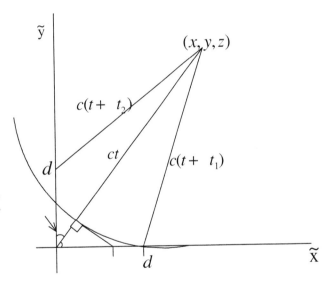

Fig.2 Delay Time Constraints

Considering Figure 2 and applying the Law of Cosines to the triangle passing through the origin, the source position and the point (d,0,0) shows that $a^2 \le 1$. Similarly, applying the Law of

Cosines to the triangle passing through the origin, the source position and the point $(0,d,0)$ shows that b^2 1. Finally, let , and be the direction cosines of the vector from the origin to the source point. An arc of radius $c(t + t_1)$ from the source point intersects this vector at a distance of $c| t_1 |$ from the origin. The tangent line to this arc at the intersection crosses the x-axis at d . Hence, it can be seen that

$$\cos = \frac{c| t_1 |}{d} > \frac{c| t_1 |}{d} = \frac{1}{|a|}$$

Similarly, $\cos > 1/|b|$. Thus, the constraint that

$$\frac{1}{a^2} + \frac{1}{b^2} < \cos^2 + \cos^2 \quad \cos^2 + \cos^2 + \cos^2 = 1$$

(5)

can be obtained.

b. Source Location Hyperboloids

Utilizing equation (2) in the first or second of equations (1) yields

$$(\tilde{x} \quad \frac{1}{2})^2 / A^2 \quad \tilde{y}^2 / B^2 \quad \tilde{z}^2 / B^2 = 1$$

(6)

where $A^2 = 1/4a^2$ and $B^2 = (a^2-1)/4 a^2$. Equation (6) may be recognized as a hyperboloid with the $\tilde{x}$ axis as the transverse axis. The source position must lie on this hyperboloid. Similarly, utilizing equation (3) in the first or third of equations (1) yields

$$(\tilde{y} \quad \frac{1}{2})^2 / C^2 \quad \tilde{x}^2 / D^2 \quad \tilde{z}^2 / D^2 = 1 \quad (7)$$

where $C^2 = 1/4b^2$ and $D^2 = (b^2 - 1)/4b^2$. Equation (7) may be recognized as a hyperboloid with the $\tilde{y}$ axis as the transverse axis. Likewise, the source position must lie on this hyperboloid. Hence, the source position must lie on the intersection of the two hyperboloids given by equations (6) and (7). Further, the source position must satisfy the causality constraint given by equation (4) which, in terms of the parameters A, B, C and D, becomes

$$(\tilde{y} \quad 2D^2) = \frac{C}{A}(\tilde{x} \quad 2B^2) \quad (8)$$

This relation as well as the projections in the $\tilde{x}$ $\tilde{y}$ plane of the hyperboloids given by equations (6) and (7) are shown in Figure 3:

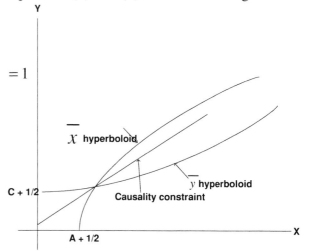

Fig 3: Source Location Relations in $\tilde{x}$ $\tilde{y}$ Plane

Note that the linear equation (8) defines the source plane (plane in which the source must lie) as well as two of the direction cosines to the source from any point on the line in the $\tilde{x}$ $\tilde{y}$ plane, i.e.

$$\cos_s = \frac{A}{\sqrt{A^2 + C^2}} \sin_s$$

$$\cos_s = \frac{C}{\sqrt{A^2 + C^2}} \sin_s$$

(9)

where s is the angle that the incoming ray from the source makes with the z-axis.

c. Intersection of Hyperboloids

The source location has been shown above to lie on the intersection of the two hyperboloids and to satisfy the causality constraint. In order to determine the form of the intersection, consider the change of variables

$$\tilde{x} = 2B^2 + \frac{A \quad C}{\sqrt{A^2 + C^2}}$$

$$\tilde{y} = 2D^2 + \frac{C + A}{\sqrt{A^2 + C^2}}$$

$$\tilde{z} = \tilde{z}$$

which places the origin of the coordinate system at the point $(\tilde{x}, \tilde{y}) = (2B^2, 2D^2)$ and then rotates it through an angle $= \tan^{-1} C/A$ with respect to the $\tilde{x}\ \tilde{y}$ axes. Thus, the $axis$ in the direction of the causality constraint, given by equation (8), along which the intersection will lie, and the $axis$ is perpendicular to it. Utilizing this change of variables in either equation (6) or equation (7) and setting $= 0$ yields

$$\frac{(\quad {}_0)^2}{S^2} \quad \frac{\tilde{z}^2}{R^2} = 1 \qquad (10)$$

where

$${}_0 = \frac{2(AB^2 + CD^2)\sqrt{A^2 + C^2}}{B^2 \quad C^2}$$

$$R^2 = B^2 + \frac{4B^2(AC + D^2)^2}{B^2 \quad C^2}$$

$$S^2 = \frac{(A^2 + C^2)R^2}{B^2 \quad C^2}$$

Note that R^2 and S^2 are both nonnegative since

$$B^2 \quad C^2 = \frac{(a^2 \quad 1)}{4a^2} \quad \frac{1}{4b^2} = \frac{1}{4} \quad 1 \quad \frac{1}{a^2} \quad \frac{1}{b^2} > 0$$

by equation (5). Thus, equation (10) may be recognized as a hyperbola as shown in Figure 4:

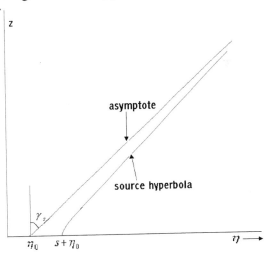

Fig 4: Altitude Hyperbola in Source Plane

which must be satisfied by the altitude of the source. Note that for large distances, which will ordinarily be the case in practice, the hyperbola approaches its asymptote given by

$$\tilde{z} = \frac{R}{S}(\quad {}_0) \qquad (11)$$

Thus, the direction cosine toward a distant source from the point $(\ ,\ ,\tilde{z}) = (\ {}_0, 0, 0)$ is given by

$$\cos {}_s = \frac{R}{\sqrt{R^2 + S^2}} \qquad (12)$$

This relation, along with equations (9) completely define the direction to a distant source from the point

$$\tilde{x} = x/d = 2B^2 + \frac{A_0}{\sqrt{A^2 + C^2}}$$

$$\tilde{y} = y/d = 2D^2 + \frac{C_0}{\sqrt{A^2 + C^2}} \qquad (13)$$

$$\tilde{z} = z/d = 0$$

This fact will be utilized in the development of the "shooting method".

The Shooting Method

At this point, one might well question what the previous analysis for an ambient medium with constant speed of sound has to do with the real atmosphere where there are winds and where the temperature and, hence, the sound speed varies with position. In actuality, this ambient analysis will be employed only to produce initial conditions for what will be deemed a "shooting method" to determine the location of the source of incoming radiation. Consider a set of five microphones in the form of a cross as shown in Figure 5:

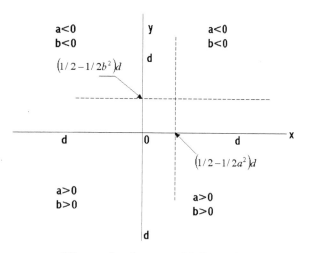

Figure 5: Assumed Microphone Array

Considering only the microphones at the origin, at the point (d,0,0) and at the point (0,d,0) for the moment, if the parameters a and b are measured, then the quadrant in which the source lies is essentially determined by the signs of a and b. As

can be seen in the figure, the causality constraint, equation (4), shows that unless $0 \le x \le (1/2 - 1/2a^2)d$ or $0 \le y \le (1/2 - 1/2b^2)d$ or both, which is unlikely, the source quadrant can be assigned based upon a knowledge of the signs. Once the source quadrant has been determined, then one can consider only the three microphones in that quadrant and the previous analysis applies. Similar considerations can be developed for other arrays of microphones.

a. Atmospheric Turning Points

When an infrasonic source on or near the surface of the Earth radiates to a distant microphone on the surface of the Earth, the microphone is ordinarily in a "shadow zone" where there is very little direct radiation from the source. This phenomenon is due not only to the curvature of the Earth, but also to the fact that the speed of sound normally initially decreases with altitude which causes the sound waves to be refracted upward away from the surface of the Earth. Although "creeping waves" which travel along the surface of the Earth do exist [10], they are subject to high dissipation and their amplitude is usually very weak. Thus, numerous studies [See, for example, 5,10,11] indicate that the primary infrasonic radiation arriving at the microphone is due to the existence of atmospheric turning points where outgoing radiation is refracted back toward the surface of the Earth. Thus, the source elevation obtained previously is not toward the actual source, but toward the point where the source radiation refracted from a turning point in the atmosphere.

The existence of such turning points can be understood through the following analysis. Although the wavelengths of infrasound, > 100 feet, are large compared to those ordinarily considered in acoustics, the ones of interest in atmospheric monitoring are still small compared to the length scales of mean atmospheric changes. Thus, geometrical or "ray" acoustics may be employed in the analysis of atmospheric infrasound. Ray acoustics is based upon the idea that sound moves through the medium at the speed of sound plus the speed of the medium. Thus, if $\mathbf{v}(\mathbf{x},t)$ and $c(\mathbf{x},t)$ are the wind velocity and speed of sound respectively at the point $\mathbf{x}$ in the medium at time t, then the velocity of a point on a wavefront is given by [10]

$$\frac{d\mathbf{x}}{dt} = \mathbf{v}(\mathbf{x},t) + \mathbf{n}(\mathbf{x},t)c(\mathbf{x},t) \qquad (14)$$

where $\mathbf{n}(\mathbf{x},t)$ is the normal vector to the wavefront. The change in the normal vector as the wavefront propagates satisfies

$$\frac{d\mathbf{n}}{dt} = \ c\ \ \ \nabla\ \mathbf{v}\ \mathbf{n} + \mathbf{n}(\mathbf{n}\quad c + \mathbf{n}\ (\ \nabla\ \mathbf{v}\ \mathbf{n})) \qquad (15)$$

From equation (14), it can be seen that if the initial normal vector lies in a plane through which there is no crosswind, i.e. the wind velocity vector lies in the same plane, then the velocity of the point on the wavefront will also be in that plane. In this case, a sound ray from the source would travel from the source to a receiver at the point given by equation (13) in the source plane given by equation (8). Further, as can be seen from equation (15), if the speed of sound and the wind velocity were constant, the normal vector would not change and the ray paths would be straight lines. In this general discussion, the velocity vector and speed of sound have been allowed to be time dependent. However, such data is typically not available for the atmosphere. In further analysis, the velocity vector and speed of sound will be taken to depend only upon altitude.

The ray paths in the atmosphere are not generally straight lines because both the wind velocity and sound speed vary with altitude. Such variation can lead to the existence of turning points in the atmosphere. For example, consider the case where there is no crosswind through the source plane given by equation (8). Then, the infrasonic radiation arriving at the observer location, equation (13), will have traveled in the source plane shown in Figure 4. For simplicity,

also neglect any vertical component of velocity in this plane. Then, letting $\mathbf{x} = d$ and recalling that $z = d\tilde{z}$, equation (14) shows that a point on the wavefront will satisfy

$$\frac{dx}{dt} = u(z) + lc(z)$$
$$\frac{dz}{dt} = nc(z) \qquad (16)$$

where $\mathbf{v}(\mathbf{x}) = u(z)\mathbf{i}$ is the wind velocity vector and $\mathbf{n} = l\mathbf{i} + n\mathbf{k}$ is the normal vector. Equation (15) then becomes

$$\frac{dl}{dt} = nl(l\frac{du}{dz} + \frac{dc}{dz})$$
$$\frac{dn}{dt} = \ l^2(l\frac{du}{dz} + \frac{dc}{dz}) \qquad (17)$$

and combining the first of equation (17) with the second of equations (16) yields

$$\frac{dl}{dz}\quad \frac{1}{c}\frac{dc}{dz}l = \frac{1}{c}\frac{du}{dz}l^2$$

This is a Bernoulli equation [13] which may be solved by standard methods to yield

$$l(z) = \frac{c(z)}{k\quad u(z)} \qquad (18)$$

where the constant k is given by

$$k = \frac{c(0)}{l(0)} + u(0)$$

and z=0 is the point where the wavefront originated. The wave direction will become horizontal and, thus, a turning point will occur whenever $l(z) = \pm 1$. The speed of sound and wind velocity varies with time, particularly seasonally. At times, a turning point exists in the stratosphere (~50 km altitude) which is primarily responsible for infrasonic reflections [5,10,11]. At all times, there are at least one and sometimes two such points in the thermosphere (~120 km altitude).

b. Initial Source Position Estimate

Assuming the source location to be on or near the surface of the Earth, a particularly simple model of the situation can be developed by replacing the speed of sound and wind velocity below the turning point by average values, i.e. $c(z) \approx \overline{c}$ and $u(z) \approx \overline{u}$. Then, as discussed above, the ray paths will be straight lines and the situation in the source plane will be as shown in Figure 6:

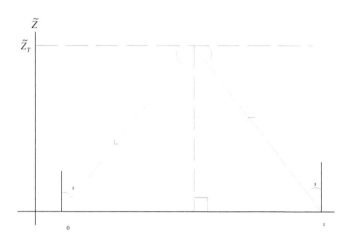

Fig 6: Simplified Model in Source Plane

A turning point exists at the altitude $\tilde{z}_T = z_T / d$. The angle, θ_s, between the incoming ray and the vertical was obtained in equation (12) above. The angle of incidence, , at the point of refraction must be equal to the angle of reflection by the "law of mirrors" [10]. Thus, by equilateral triangles, the angle between the outgoing ray at the source position, θ_s, and the vertical must also be θ_s. Hence the initial direction cosine at the source position is $l(0) = \sin \theta_s$ and the altitude of the turning point can be obtained from equation (18), i.e.

$$c(z_T) \approx u(z_T) = \frac{c(0)}{\sin \theta_s} \approx u(0) \qquad (19)$$

Once the turning point has been obtained, equation (16) may readily be integrated to show that

$$x(t) = (\overline{u} \approx \overline{c} \sin \theta_s) t + x(0)$$
$$z(t) = \overline{c} \cos \theta_s t \qquad (20)$$

Thus, the time taken for the ray to reach the turning point is

$$t_P = \frac{z_T}{\overline{c} \cos \theta_s}$$

and the horizontal distance traveled during this time is

$$\frac{R_S}{2} = \left| x(t_P) \approx x(0) \right| = \left| \overline{u} \approx \overline{c} \sin \theta_s \right| t_P \qquad (21)$$

where R_S is the range in the source plane given by equation (8) from the point given by equation (13). Thus, an initial estimate of the source position as well as the initial ray direction has been obtained.

c. Numerical Iteration Technique

In order to implement the "shooting method", the best available sound speed and velocity data as a function of space and time are utilized in equations (14) and (15). Thus, all the complications of variable sound speed and wind velocity are included, in particular any crosswind component through the source plane. These ordinary differential equations are then integrated forward in time utilizing the estimate of the source position and ray direction developed above as initial conditions. The position and angle at which the ray again strikes the ground are then compared with the known measurements. Thus, a ray is "shot" from the estimated source position and evaluated as to how well it agrees with the known data. If the comparison is not favorable, the integration is then iterated by revising the initial source position and/or ray direction estimates until adequate convergence is obtained.

This "shooting method" takes its name from the Shooting Method which has been employed in the solution of two point boundary value problems in differential equations. As with such problems, the perturbation of the initial source location estimate is a matter of trial and error which improves with experience. The accuracy of the technique in converging to the true source location is highly dependent upon the timeliness and accuracy of the sound speed and wind velocity data.

An Example

In order to demonstrate the technique, an example has been devised and numerically computed. The speed of sound in the atmosphere has been assumed given by the expression

$$c(z) = 0.012z^2 \quad 5.3z + 340 \qquad (22)$$

in meters per second where z is in kilometers. This profile is shown in Figure 7:

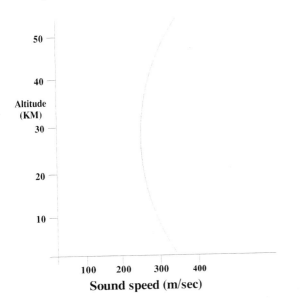

Figure 7: Sound Speed Profile

which is somewhat reminiscent of the actual profile in the lower atmosphere [10]. For simplicity, the wind velocity has been taken to have a component only in the x-direction and the profile has been assumed to be linear, i.e.

$$u(z) = 0.83z \qquad (23)$$

with z in kilometers as shown in Figure 8.

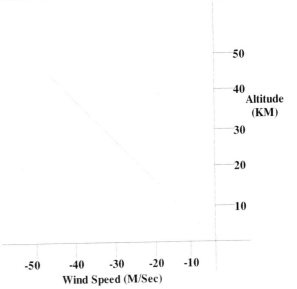

Figure 8: Wind Speed Profile

Note that the wind speed reaches values of the order of Mach number 0.1 near the altitude of 50 kilometers.

The microphones have been taken to be separated by the distance d=2 km, which is on the order of the proposed monitoring stations [4] and to each measure a time delay of 3.39 seconds, i.e. $t_1 = t_2 = 33\mathcal{9}$ seconds. Thus, $a = b = \sqrt{3}$ and the direction cosines to the source from the position $(\tilde{x}, \tilde{y}, \tilde{z}) = (1,1,0)$, given by equation (13), are $\cos{_s} = \cos{_s} = \cos{_s} = 1/\sqrt{3}$ as shown by equations (9) and (12). Note that the source plane makes an angle of 45 degrees with both the x and y axes and thus the velocity only in the x-direction assumed above will represent a cross wind through the source plane.

The turning point analysis, given by equation (19) with the sound speed and velocity profiles of equations (22) and (23) predicts a turning point near an altitude of 50 km. Thus, the time to the turning point is near 3 and 1/2 minutes and the range to the source, R_s, given by equation (21) is near 141.4 km. Hence the estimated source position is

$$x(0) = \frac{AR_s}{\sqrt{A^2 + C^2}} + d = 101.41$$

$$y(0) = \frac{CR_s}{\sqrt{A^2 + C^2}} + d = 101.41 \qquad (24)$$

$$z(0) = 0$$

in kilometers from the origin of the microphone array and the ray leaving that point would be estimated to have direction cosines

$$l(0) = \cos_s = 1/\sqrt{3}$$

$$m(0) = \cos_s = 1/\sqrt{3} \qquad (25)$$

$$n(0) = \cos_s = 1/\sqrt{3}$$

For the assumed sound speed and velocity profiles, the governing ray tracing equations, given by equations (14) and (15) are

$$\frac{d\tilde{x}}{d\tilde{t}} = \tilde{u} + l\tilde{c} \qquad \frac{dl}{d\tilde{t}} = nlF$$

$$\frac{d\tilde{y}}{d\tilde{t}} = m\tilde{c} \qquad \frac{dm}{d\tilde{t}} = nmF \qquad (26)$$

$$\frac{d\tilde{z}}{d\tilde{t}} = n\tilde{c} \qquad \frac{dn}{d\tilde{t}} = (n^2 \quad 1)F$$

where $\tilde{u} = u/c(0), \tilde{c} = c/c(0), \tilde{t} = c(0)t/d$ and

$$F = l\frac{d\tilde{u}}{d\tilde{z}} + \frac{d\tilde{c}}{d\tilde{z}}.$$ Equations (26) were programmed on a spread sheet and solved with $\tilde{t} = 0.5$ and the initial conditions given by equations (24) and (25). The results were

$$
\begin{aligned}
\tilde{x}(102) &= 11.17916 \\
\tilde{y}(102) &= 3.901344 \\
\tilde{z}(102) &= .0.140876 \\
l(102) &= .0578967 \\
m(102) &= .0578967 \\
n(102) &= 0.572569
\end{aligned}
\qquad (27)
$$

Thus, as shown in Figure 9, the ray missed its mark of $(\tilde{x}, \tilde{y}, \tilde{z}) = (1,1,0)$, but the incoming direction cosines were very close to the expected value of $l = m = n = 1/\sqrt{3} = .0577$. Thus, having calibrated the "Kentucky windage" for the situation, the miss values from the origin given by equation (27) were added to the initial conditions of equation (24) and the calculation iterated. Such iteration is very simple on a spread sheet as the computation is rerun almost as fast as the initial conditions are changed. The result was that the ray came in at the origin as shown in Figure 9, rather than at the position (1,1,0). Thus, a third iteration was calculated by adding one to the $\tilde{x}$ and $\tilde{y}$ initial conditions. This resulted in the solution

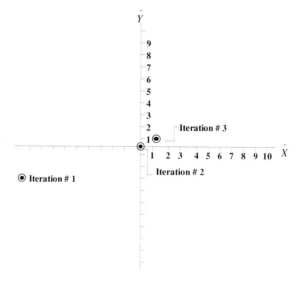

Fig 9: Iteration Results

$$\tilde{x}(102) = 1.000001$$

$$\tilde{y}(102) = 1$$

$$\tilde{z}(102) = 0.140876$$

$$l(102) = .0578967$$

$$m(102) = .0578967$$

$$n(102) = .0572569$$

as shown in Figure 9 which was deemed converged. Hence the initial conditions would be the predicted source location. This example is admittedly contrived and simpler than the real world situation would be. However, it does illustrate the simplicity and accuracy of this technique in locating the source of incoming infrasonic radiation. More complicated sound speed profiles, wind velocity components and incoming ray angles are readily accommodated.

Conclusions

A "shooting method" for the location of the source of atmospheric infrasonic radiation has been developed. The technique is based upon extensive analysis of measured data to provide initial estimates of the source location and ray angle as well as an iterative 3-D geometric acoustics approach to converge to the actual source location. The method fully accounts for atmospheric turning points (phases) and appears limited in accuracy only by the timeliness of the input sound speed and wind velocity data.

References

1. Zuckerwar, A.J.: Infrasonic Emissions from Local Meteorological Events: A Summary of Data Taken Throughout 1984. NASA TM 87686, 1986.

2. Rubin, W.L., Burnham, D.C., Spitzer, E.A. and Rudis, R.P.: Robust Low Cost Airport Wake Vortex Sensor, J. of Aircraft, Vol.37, No.3, pp. 377-382, 2000.

3. ReVelle, D.O. and Whitaker, R.W.: Infrasonic Detection of a Leonid Bolide: 1998 November 17, Meteoritics and Planetary Science, Vol.34, pp.995-1005, 1999.

4. Blandford, R.R.: Design of Infrasonic Arrays, AFTAC-TR-97-013, 1997.

5. Brown, D.J., Wang, J., Katz, C.N., Gault, A. and LeBras, R.: Infrasonic Processing at the Prototype International Data Center, 21st Seismic Research Symposium, Las Vegas, NV, September 21-24, 1999.

6. Gibson, R., Norris, D. and Farrel, T.: Development and Application of an Integrated Infrasound Propagation Modeling Tool Kit, 21st Seismic Research Symposium, Las Vegas, NV, September 21-24, 1999.

7. Garces, M., Hanson, R., Lindquist, K., Drob, D., and Picone, M.: Variability of the Lower Atmosphere and its Effect on the Propagation of Infrasonic Waves, 21st Seismic Research Symposium, Las Vegas, NV, September 21-24, 1999.

8. Pierce, A.D. and Kinney, W.A.: Computational Techniques for the Study of Infrasound Propagation in the Atmosphere, Technical Report AFGL-TR-76-56, Air Force Geophysics Laboratories, Hanscom AFB, MA, 1976.

9. Norton, G.V., Kinney, W.A., Novarini, J.C., Ramsdale, D.J. and Whitaker, R.W.: Adaptation of an Underwater Acoustic Propagation Model to Infrasonic Atmospheric Propagation, 21st Seismic Research Symposium, Las Vegas, September 21-24, 1999.

10. Pierce, A.D.: Acoustics, Acoustical Society of America, Woodbury, NY, 1991.

11. Mutschlecner, J.P. and Whitaker, R.W.: Thermospheric Infrasound Signals, 21st Seismic Research Symposium, Las Vegas, NV, September 21-24, 1999.

12. Hayes, W.D., Haefeli, R.C. and Kulsrud, H.E.: Sonic Boom Propagation in a Stratified Atmosphere, With Computer Program, NASA CR-1299, 1969.

13, Cunningham, W.J.: Introduction to Nonlinear Analysis, McGraw-Hill Book Company, New York, 1958.

APPLICATION AND VERIFICATION OF TIME DOMAIN IMPEDANCE BOUNDARY CONDITIONS IN MULTI-DIMENSIONAL ACOUSTIC PROBLEMS

Shi Zheng[*], Mei Zhuang[†]
Department of Mechanical Engineering
Michigan State University, East Lansing, MI 48823
Tel: (517)353-9450 Fax: (517)353-1750 Email: zhuangm@egr.msu.edu

Abstract

Broadband time domain impedance boundary conditions are implemented in multi-dimensional acoustic problems. A series of acoustic wave propagation problems in one, two and three-dimensions with an impedance boundary are then solved as test cases both analytically and numerically. The numerical results of all the three acoustic problems agree very well with those of the analytical solutions. To the authors' knowledge, it is the first time that the analytical solution to the three-dimensional problem of this kind is derived analytically. The impedance boundary condition is also tested against the single frequency time domain boundary condition to gain further confidence. Finally, it is demonstrated that the impedance boundary condition is stable under both uniform and sheared mean flow conditions with other test cases.

Introduction

Aeroacoustic problems in liner technology are an important category of the application of computational aeroacoustics (CAA). Because of the limitations of the frequency domain simulations, the time-domain impedance boundary conditions in CAA applications have been exploited in the past few years. Since the impedance boundary conditions are best dealt with in the frequency domain, it is desirable to convert characteristics of impedance in frequency domain into the time domain so that the information can serve as a well-posed boundary condition for the linearized Euler equations. Several approaches of converting the conventional frequency domain impedance condition into the time domain have been carried out.[1-4] Tam and Auriault[1] derived an equivalent of the impedance boundary condition and have proved the well-posedness

and stability of their impedance boundary conditions. They also claimed that these conditions are also stable even in the presence of mean flows, but no numerical evidence has ever been presented. The work of Özyörük and Long[2, 3] used the z-transform to formulate the impedance in the z-domain and then an inverse z-transform to provide the time-discretized impedance boundary condition in the time domain. Furthermore, instead of a direct inverse of impedance of the frequency domain into the time domain, Fung and Ju[4] use the inversion of the corresponding reflection coefficient and then implement boundary operators for the time domain prediction of wave reflection. In this paper, the time domain impedance boundary condition developed by Tam and Auriault[1] is implemented for multi-dimensional acoustic problems. The results of numerical simulation of the selected one-, two- and three-dimensional wave propagation problems are then verified by the analytical solutions. To the authors' knowledge, the analytical solution of the selected three-dimensional wave propagation problem is derived for the first time. The impedance boundary condition is also tested against the single frequency time domain boundary condition to gain further confidence. Finally, the impedance boundary condition is shown to be stable under both uniform and sheared mean flow conditions with other test cases.

Formulation of the Problem

In this section, we formulate the three physical problems that will be solved both analytically and numerically in the following sections. The impedance problems are generalized as a three-dimensional case, which can later be adapted to the one- or two-dimensional case. The three-dimensional problem is schematically shown in Figure 1.

---

[*] Graduate Assistant

[†] Associate Professor, Senior Member AIAA

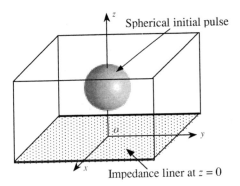

Figure 1. Schematic of the three-dimensional problem

The governing equations are the three-dimensional nondimensionalized linearized Euler equations,

$$\frac{\partial}{\partial t}\begin{bmatrix} u \\ v \\ w \\ p \end{bmatrix} + \frac{\partial}{\partial x}\begin{bmatrix} p \\ 0 \\ 0 \\ u \end{bmatrix} + \frac{\partial}{\partial y}\begin{bmatrix} 0 \\ p \\ 0 \\ v \end{bmatrix} + \frac{\partial}{\partial z}\begin{bmatrix} 0 \\ 0 \\ p \\ w \end{bmatrix} = 0 \qquad (3.1)$$

for $-\infty < x < \infty$, $-\infty < y < \infty$ and $z \geq 0$. It is noted that the continuity equation has been dropped since it is essentially the same as the energy equation when the problem is nondimensionalized. As shown in Figure 1 an initial spherical pulse is centered at $(0, 0, z_s)$. The impedance liner is applied on the boundary plane at $z = 0$. The impedance is characterized by Z, which relates in frequency domain the acoustic pressure $\hat{p}$ and the normal velocity $\hat{v}_n$ (positive when pointing into the impedance liner) at the impedance wall through

$$\hat{p} = Z\hat{v}_n \qquad (3.2)$$

In all the three test cases, a broadband acoustic pressure pulse is initially introduced with zero initial velocity components. For the three-dimensional case, a spherical Gaussian pulse is used,

$$p_0(R) = e^{-BR^2} \qquad (3.3)$$

where R is the distance to the pulse center at $S(0,0,z_s)$ and B is a constant ($B = \ln 2/25$). For the two-dimensional case, a two-dimensional version of equation (3.3) is used, which is cylindrical in a three-dimensional sense. For the one-dimensional test problem, a broadband disturbance is generated by the following initial pressure condition,[1]

$$p_0(x) = \exp[-0.0044(x - 83.333)^2] \\ * \cos[0.444(x - 83.333)] \qquad (3.4)$$

Mathematical Derivation of the Analytical Solution

In this section we are going to discuss the analytical solutions to the problems that have been formulated in the previous section.

In general the analytical solutions are considered to be the superposition of the incident wave and its reflection by the impedance wall. The incident wave is or is part of the solution to the Euler equations in free space. Since the impedance properties are given in frequency domain and in terms of planar waves, a broadband incident wave need to be decomposed into harmonic waves and a non-planar incident wave need to be decomposed into planar waves. Then the reflection of each of the harmonic planar incident wave can be determined. The total reflected wave is in a form of an integral of the reflected harmonic planar waves. This is the general idea for deriving the analytical solutions to our problems. The analytical solutions to the one- and two-dimensional problems have been shown in the previous work,[2,4] where the authors might have used different mathematical techniques but generally follow the same idea as stated previously. To the authors' knowledge the analytical solution of the three-dimensional test problem have not been derived before. Therefore only the analytical solution for the three-dimensional problem is derived following the above idea. A similar approach can be used to derive the analytical solutions for the one- and two-dimensional problems.

The acoustic field in the semi-infinite space ($-\infty < x < \infty$, $-\infty < y < \infty$ and $z \geq 0$) with an initial spherical wave centered at $S(0,0,z_s)$ is composed of three components, i.e., the outgoing wave, which diverges from the sphere center, the incoming wave, which converges to the sphere center and the reflected wave by the impedance wall. These components are examined in some details as follows.

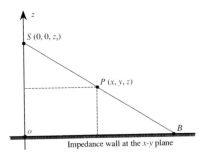

Figure 2. Determination of the existence of the incoming wave at point $P(x, y, z)$

The outgoing and the incoming waves are the same components as those in free space, except that the incoming wave is not present everywhere all the time due to the existence of the wall while the outgoing wave is always unaffected by the wall. To illustrate how to determine the existence of the incoming wave at a point for a given time, a point $P(x, y, z)$ below the center of the spherical wave $S(0, 0, z_s)$ with $z < z_s$, is considered as shown in Figure 2. Point B is at the intersection of line SP and the impedance plane at $z = 0$. If we let BP denote the distance between points B and P, the initial incoming wave is passing through point P at time $t < BP$ (the speed of sound is 1). At time $t = BP$, the initial incoming wave on radius BS has just passed through point P. Therefore, at $t > BP$ there is no incoming wave at point P. At points with $z \geq z_s$ it is obvious that the incoming wave is always present. The reflected wave is the outgoing wave, or incident wave with respect to the wall, after being bounced back by the wall. Depending on the location of a point, the total acoustic wave at the point is the sum of the outgoing and the reflected waves or these two waves and the incoming wave.

The outgoing and incoming waves can be determined by solving the Euler equations (3.1) in free-space. For simplicity, the problem is solved in the form of the velocity potential φ with spherical symmetry[5] with the result as in equation (4.1)

$$\varphi(R, t) = \frac{f(R - t)}{R} - \frac{f(R + t)}{R} \quad (4.1)$$

where $R = \sqrt{x^2 + y^2 + (z - z_s)^2}$ and f is an even function. For the initial condition [equation (3.3)], f is given as

$$f(r) = -\frac{1}{4B} \exp(Br^2), \text{ for } -\infty < r < \infty.$$

This solution in equation (4.1) can be readily interpreted as the superstition of an outgoing wave

$$\varphi_{out}(R, t) = \frac{f(R - t)}{R} \quad (4.2)$$

and an incoming wave

$$\varphi_{in}(R, t) = -\frac{f(R + t)}{R} \quad (4.3)$$

The reflected wave is determined by considering the incident or outgoing wave φ_{out} in equation (4.2) being reflected by the impedance wall. As stated in the beginning of this section, the broadband spherical outgoing wave must be decomposed into harmonic planar components to study the effects of the impedance wall. This decomposition process is done in

the following two steps (can be done in the reverse order). First by resolving function $f(R - t)$ into its Fourier transform, the broadband outgoing spherical wave φ_{out} is decomposed into harmonic outgoing spherical waves

$$\varphi_{our}(R, t) = \int_{-\infty}^{\infty} \hat{f}(k_0) \frac{\exp[ik_0(R - t)]}{R} dk_0 \quad (4.4)$$

where $\hat{f}(k_0)$ is defined by the Fourier transform

$$\hat{f}(k_0) = \frac{1}{2\pi} \int_{-\infty}^{\infty} f(x) \exp(-ik_0 x) dx$$

and $\exp[ik_0(R - t)]/R$ in the integrand of equation (4.4) represents a harmonic outgoing spherical wave with an angular frequency/wavenumber k_0 (the speed of sound is unity). Since $f(R - t)$ is an even function, its Fourier transform $\hat{f}(k_0)$ must be real and also even.[6] This allows the integration in equation (4.4) to be performed only over the non-negative range of angular frequency/ wavenumber k_0 with the real part unchanged,

$$\varphi_{out}(R, t) = 2\int_{0}^{\infty} \hat{f}(k_0) \exp(-ik_0 t) \frac{\exp(ik_0 R)}{R} dk_0 \quad (4.5)$$

For the sake of convenience, the time dependence is separated from the harmonic spherical wave, which will then be represented only by the term $\exp(ik_0 R)/R$ in the following derivation.

As the second step of the decomposition process, a harmonic spherical wave $\exp(ik_0 R)/R$ with a non-negative angular frequency/wavenumber k_0 is decomposed into harmonic planar waves, using Weyl's integral,[7, 8]

$$\frac{\exp(ik_0 R)}{R}$$
$$= \frac{i}{2\pi} \int_{-\infty}^{\infty} \int_{-\infty}^{\infty} \exp\{i[k_x x + k_y y + k_z(z - z_s)]\} \frac{dk_x dk_y}{k_z},$$
$$\text{for } z > 0 \quad (4.6)$$

where $\exp\{i[k_x x + k_y y + k_z(z - z_s)]\}$ represents a harmonic planar wave with $k_z = \sqrt{k_0^2 - k_x^2 - k_y^2}$. It is noted that k_z could be complex-valued since both k_x and k_y change from $-\infty$ to ∞ with k_0 fixed.

By now, the broadband spherical incident wave has been decomposed into harmonic planar waves and thus it is ready to incorporate the effects of the impedance wall on each of these harmonic plane incident waves. Using the method of mirror image, the reflected wave of each of the harmonic planar waves in the integrand of equation (4.6) by the impedance wall is determined to be

$$C_r(k_0,k_z)\exp\{i[k_x x + k_y y + k_z(z+z_s)]\} \quad (4.7)$$

where the reflection coefficient $C_r(k_0,k_z)$ is determined from the impedance properties characterized by $Z(\omega)$ defined by equation (3.2),

$$C_r(k_0,k_z) = \frac{Z(k_0)(k_z/k_0)-1}{Z(k_0)(k_z/k_0)+1}$$

Corresponding to equation (4.6), the reflected harmonic (non-planar) outgoing wave is then obtained by integrating the reflected harmonic plane waves in equation (4.7).

$$\varphi_{k_0,refl}(x,y,z,k_0) = \frac{i}{2\pi}\int_{-\infty}^{\infty}\int_{-\infty}^{\infty} C_r(k_0,k_z)$$
$$* \exp\{i[k_x x + k_y y + k_z(z+z_s)]\}\}\frac{dk_x dk_y}{k_z} \quad (4.8)$$

Similarly, the reflected wave of the outgoing wave in equation (4.5) is obtained by integrating the reflected harmonic (non-planar) wave in equation (4.8)

$$\varphi_{refl}(x,y,z,t) = 2\int_0^{\infty}\hat{f}(k_0)\exp(-ik_0 t)\varphi_{k_0,refl}(R,k_0)dk_0 \quad (4.9)$$

By changing the variables of integration and separating the real and the imaginary parts of equation (4.8), we have

$$\text{Re}[\varphi_{k_0,refl}(x,y,z,k_0)]$$
$$= k_0\int_{-1}^{0} C_1\sin(k_0 z'\zeta - \beta_1)J_0[k_0 r\sqrt{1-\zeta^2}]d\zeta$$
$$+ k_0\int_0^{\infty}C_2\cos(\beta_2)\exp(-k_0 z'\xi)J_0[k_0 r\sqrt{1+\xi^2}]d\xi$$

and

$$\text{Im}[\varphi_{k_0,refl}(x,y,z,k_0)]$$
$$= k_0\int_{-1}^{0} C_1\cos(k_0 z'\zeta - \beta_1)J_0[k_0 r\sqrt{1-\zeta^2}]d\zeta$$
$$+ k_0\int_0^{\infty}C_2\sin(\beta_2)\exp(-k_0 z'\xi)J_0[k_0 r\sqrt{1+\xi^2}]d\xi$$

where J_0 is the Bessel function of the first kind of order zero and C_1, β_1, C_2 and β_2 are defined in the following relations

$$C_1 = |C_r(k_0,-k_0\zeta)|, \quad C_r(k_0,-k_0\zeta) = C_1\exp(i\beta_1),$$
$$C_2 = |C_r(k_0,ik_0\xi)|, \quad C_r(k_0,ik_0\xi) = C_2\exp(i\beta_2).$$

With the real part and the imaginary part separated for equation (4.8), the numerical evaluation of the integral equation will be easier.

By taking the derivatives of the velocity potential, the acoustic pressure and the components of the particle velocity can be determined. Specially, the acoustic pressures associated with the outgoing, incoming and reflected waves are determined from equations (4.2), (4.3) and (4.9),

$$p_{out}(x,y,z,t) = -\frac{\partial}{\partial t}\varphi_{out}(x,y,z,t) = \frac{f(R-t)}{R} \quad (4.10)$$

$$p_{in}(x,y,z,t) = -\frac{\partial}{\partial t}\varphi_{in}(x,y,z,t) = -\frac{f(R+t)}{R} \quad (4.11)$$

$$p_{refl}(x,y,z,t) = -\frac{\partial}{\partial t}\varphi_{refl}(x,y,z,t)$$
$$= 2i\int_0^{\infty}k_0\hat{f}(k_0)\exp(-ik_0 t)\varphi_{k_0,refl}(x,y,z,k_0)dk_0 \quad (4.12)$$

with the real part given as

$$\text{Re}[p_{ref}(x,y,z,t)]$$
$$= 2\int_0^{\infty}k_0\hat{f}(k_0)[\sin(k_0 t)\text{Re}(\varphi_{k_0,refl}) - \cos(k_0 t)\text{Im}(\varphi_{k_0,refl})]dk_0 \quad (4.13)$$

Thus the total acoustic pressure is the sum of two equations (4.10) and (4.13) or three equations (4.10), (4.11) and (4.13), depending on the existence of the incoming wave. Numerical integration has to be performed to evaluate equation (4.13). The analytical solution is then compared with that of the numerical solution obtained from the following section.

Numerical Formulation

Modeling of Broadband Time Domain Impedance boundary condition

The impedance is modeled by the broadband time domain impedance boundary condition proposed by Tam and Auriault[1] when the impedance is of the Helmholtz resonator type and thus can be characterized in the form

$$Z(\omega) = R_0 - i(X_{-1}/\omega + X_1\omega). \quad (5.1)$$

where R_0, X_{-1} and X_1 are parameters that reflect the impedance properties. We take the same values as in reference 1 for the parameters R_0, X_{-1} and X_1, or equivalently, 0.2, -0.4758 and 2.0938 respectively in the dimensionless form in the current study. The broadband time domain impedance boundary condition for the impedance model (5.1) is derived as[1]

$$\frac{\partial p}{\partial t} = R_0\frac{\partial v_n}{\partial t} - X_{-1}v_n + X_1\frac{\partial^2 v_n}{\partial t^2} \quad (5.2)$$

where p and v_n are the acoustic pressure and the normal acoustic velocity at the impedance wall in the time domain. Equation (5.2) is discretized and used as the impedance boundary condition for the numerical solution. It is noted that the discretized forms of equation (5.2) are different for the cases of different numbers of dimensionalities due to the difference in the governing equations. Reference 1 presents the complete discretized form of equation (5.2) with DRP scheme for the one-dimensional case. For the two- and the three-dimensional cases, proper modification is necessary.

Nonreflecting Radiation Boundary Conditions

Since the physical problem is formulated in a semi-infinite space and the computational domain has to be finite, it is required that the waves be able to leave the computational domain without being reflected, just as they travel inside the physical domain, where the medium is homogeneous and thus non-reflective. This physical condition is being approximated using the non-reflecting radiation boundary conditions

$$\left(\frac{1}{c}\frac{\partial}{\partial t}+\frac{\partial}{\partial r}+n\frac{1}{r}\right)U=0 \qquad (5.3)$$

where n equals to 0, 1/2 and 1 for the one-, two- and three-dimensional cases, respectively. The flux vector is given as $U=[\vec{v}^{T},p]^{T}$, where $\vec{v}$ denotes the vector form of the particle velocity. r is the distance between the current boundary point and a fixed point inside the computational domain. It is the absolute value of the only spatial coordinate for the one-dimensional case, the radial coordinate in the polar coordinate system for the two-dimensional case and the radial coordinate in the spherical coordinate system for the three-dimensional case, with the origin of each coordinate system being at the fixed point.

It is noted that except for the one-dimensional case, the non-reflecting radiation boundary conditions are rigorously valid only when the boundaries are infinitely far from the locations of 'sources', which coincide with the origin (the fixed point) with respect to these boundaries. Therefore, the use of such boundary conditions in the numerical practice, where the boundaries are only finitely far from the 'sources', will introduce errors. However, our numerical practice shows that even a moderate distance can be considered far enough from the acoustic source such that the error introduced is very small and thus does not affect the solution characteristics.

Broadband Dispersion-Relation-Preserving (DRP) Upwind Scheme

For the current investigation, the fourth-order, seven-point stencil optimized upwind DRP scheme with the parameters chosen as $\beta_{0}=\pi/2$, $\lambda=0.0374$, and

$\sigma=0.2675\pi$ [9] is used for the numerical simulation of the Euler equation. The approximation coefficients used in the scheme for the interior and boundary points are the same as those listed in reference 9. The accuracy and the robustness of the scheme have been verified for acoustic wave propagation problems with various geometry and boundary conditions by the previous work of Zhuang and Chen.[9]

Comparison of the Numerical and the Analytical Solutions

The results from the numerical simulations are compared with the analytical solutions for the three selected wave propagation problems. For the one-dimensional case, the reflected wave propagating away from the impedance boundary is shown in Figure 3 at $t=140.1$. Since the time is long enough for the acoustic pulse to hit the impedance boundary and reflect away from it, the acoustic energy at this time has been suppressed due to the energy absorption of the impedance. As it is shown the agreement between the analytical and the numerical solutions is excellent. For the two-dimensional case, the acoustic pressure distribution along the impedance wall at $t=20$ is calculated for the modified Gaussian pulse form[4] and compared with that of the analytical solution in Figure 4. The agreement between the numerical solution and the analytical solution is considered very good although it is not as perfect as in the one-dimensional case. In addition, the pressure contours in the computational domain at the same time are plotted in Figures 5(a) and 5(b) for the analytical and numerical solutions respectively. For the three-dimensional case, the acoustic pressure along the x-axis, which is on the impedance wall, at $t=20$ and $t=30$ is shown in Figures 6(a) and 6(b). As we can see, the numerical solutions approximate the analytical solutions reasonably well for the three-dimensional case. In summary, the numerical implementation is verified by the results of the three test cases. It is worth mentioning that in solving the same impedance problems, the numerical solutions spend much less time than the analytical solutions for the two- and three-dimensional cases.

Comparison of the Results of the Single Frequency and Broadband Time Domain Impedance Boundary Conditions

The single frequency time domain impedance boundary condition for the one-dimensional linearized Euler equations is available in reference 1. Here we present

1916

such a boundary condition in the two-dimensional setting.

$$\frac{\partial u}{\partial x} + \frac{\partial v}{\partial y} = R\frac{\partial p}{\partial x} + X\Omega u \text{ for } X < 0, \qquad (7.1)$$

$$p = Ru - \frac{X}{\Omega}\frac{\partial p}{\partial x} \text{ for } X \geq 0. \qquad (7.2)$$

where R and X are related to the acoustic impedance by the relation $Z = R - iX$.

Although a problem involving only a single frequency component could be solved in frequency domain, solving it in time domain may serve as a good test case to check the broadband time domain impedance boundary conditions as well as the numerical code.

The configuration of the test problem is the same as the previous two-dimensional one, except that instead of an initial Gaussian pulse, a source term in the form $\exp\{-(\ln 2)[(x-32)^2 + y^2]/25\}\sin(\omega t)$ is added on the right hand side of the energy component in equation (3.1). The problem is solved using both the single frequency and the broadband time domain boundary conditions. The results are shown in Figure 7. We can see that for an angular frequency at $\omega = 0.7854$, which is equivalent to $PPW = 8$, the results in Figure 7(a) given by the two boundary conditions are very similar, with only a slight difference. For a lower angular frequency at $\omega = 0.3142$, which is equivalent to $PPW = 20$, the results in Figure 7(b) are perfectly identical to each other. This implies that the small difference for the former case is due to the grid resolution and thus proves the consistency in the two impedance boundary conditions. Therefore, by the comparison, we have gained more confidence in the broadband time domain boundary condition.

Application of the Broadband Time Domain Impedance Boundary Condition

Up to now, we have been discussing about the time-domain impedance boundary conditions when no mean flow is present and have verified that the boundary conditions produce stable and accurate results. In the following, as an extra topic of the paper, we will test the stability of the time domain impedance boundary conditions in the presence of mean flows. Two test cases are considered in a two-dimensional setting with an impedance wall at $y = 0$. The governing equations are the linearized Euler equations with mean flows. The boundary condition in equation (5.2) is discretized in accordance to the governing equations. At $t = 0$, a Gaussian pressure pulse is introduced in a uniform

mean flow of $M_x = 0.8$ and in a sheared mean flow with a profile of $M_x(y) = 0.8\sin[(\pi/2)(y/100)]$ for the two cases respectively. The case with no mean flow present is also considered for the purpose of comparison. The initial state for all three cases is shown in Figure 8(a). The acoustic pressure fields at $t = 75$ are shown in Figures 8(b) ~ (d) for all the three cases. In obtaining these solutions using the broadband time domain impedance boundary condition, no instability has ever occurred. Thus the results of these examples substantiate Tam's claim that the time domain solutions of the linearized Euler equations with mean flows and the impedance boundary condition (5.2) are stable.[1]

Conclusions

The analytical solution of a three-dimensional initial and impedance boundary problem is derived and evaluated together with those of the one- and two-dimensional problems. With the analytical solutions and numerical experiments, the broadband time domain boundary conditions prove to be both accurate and numerically stable in solving the three-parameter impedance boundary problems, even in the presence of mean flows. Having been verified, the numerical implementation can be further applied to other more practical acoustic problems involving impedance liners, for which analytical or experimental solutions are not always possible.

References

1. Tam, C.K.W., and Auriault, L., Time-Domain Impedance Boundary Conditions for Computational Aeroacoustics, *AIAA Journal*, Vol. 34, No. 5, 1996, pp917-923.

2. Özyörük, Yusuf and Long, Lyle N., A Time-Domain Implementation on Surface Acoustic Impedance Condition with and without Flow, AIAA 96-1663, 2nd AIAA/CEAS Aeroacoustics Conference, State College, PA, May 1996.

3. Özyörük, Yusuf, Long, Lyle N. and Jones, Michael G., Time-Domain Numerical Simulation of a Flow-Impedance Tube, *Journal of Computational Physics*, Vol. 146, 1998, pp.29-57.

4. Fung, K.-Y. and Ju, Hongbin, Impedance and Its Time-Domain Extensions, *AIAA Journal*, Vol. 38, No. 1, 2000, pp30-38.

5. Whitham, G.B., *Linear and Nonlinear Waves*, John Wiley & Sons, Inc, 1974.

6. Arsac, J., *Fourier Transforms and the Theory of Distributions*, Prentice-Hall, Inc, 1966.

7. Poritsky, H., Extension of Weyl's Integral for Harmonic Spherical Waves to Arbitrary Wave shapes, *Communications on Pure and Applied Mathematics*, Vol. IV, 1951, pp33-42.

8. Roseau, M, *Asymptotic Wave Theory*, North-Holland Publishing Company, 1976.

9. Zhuang, M. and Chen, R. F., "Applications of High-Order Optimized Upwind Schemes for Computational Aeroacoustics," *AIAA Journal*, Vol. 40, No. 3, March 2002, pp. 443-449.

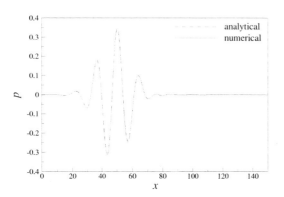

Figure 3. Comparison for the one-dimensional case at $t = 140.1$

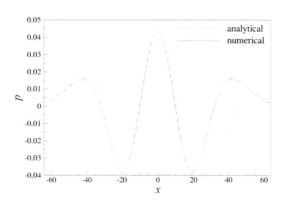

Figure 4. Comparison for the two-dimensional case: acoustic pressure along the impedance wall at $t = 20$

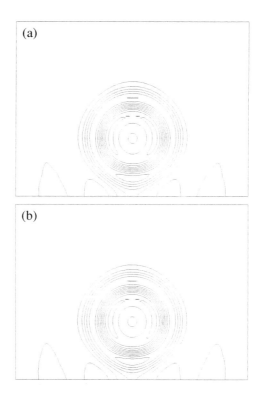

Figure 5. Comparison for the two-dimensional case: acoustic pressure in the computational domain at $t = 20$. (a) analytical solution, (b) numerical solution.

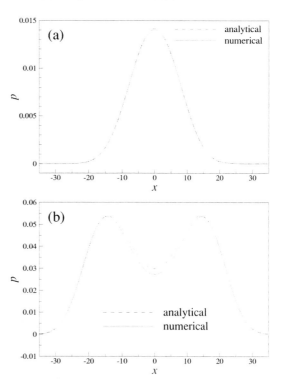

Figure 6. Comparison for the three-dimensional case: acoustic pressure along the x-axis at (a) $t = 20$ and (b) $t = 30$.

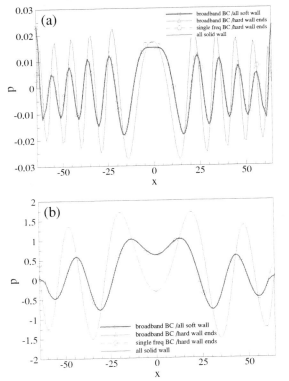

Figure 7. Acoustic pressure along the wall calculated with the single frequency and broadband time domain impedance boundary conditions: (a) $\omega = 0.7854$ (*PPW* = 8); (b) $\omega = 0.3142$ (*PPW* = 20).

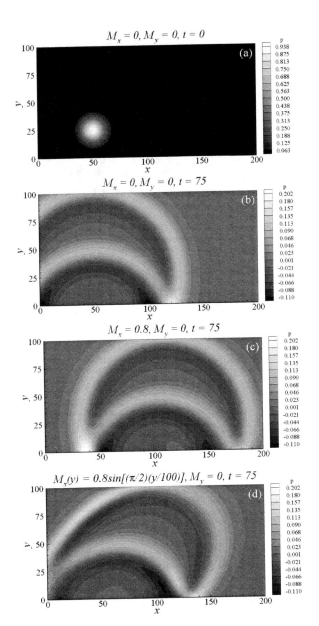

Figure 8. (a) The initial acoustic pressure field at $t = 0$ for all the mean flow conditions. The acoustic pressure fields at $t = 75$ under different mean flow conditions: (b) no mean flow, $M_x = M_y = 0$; (c) uniform mean flow, $M_x = 0.8$, $M_y = 0$ and (d) sheared mean flow, $M_x(y) = 0.8 \sin\left[(\pi/2)(y/100)\right]$, $M_y = 0$.

AIAA 2002-2594

Numerical Prediction of Minor Losses in High Amplitude Acoustic Resonators

Said Boluriaan[*] and Philip J. Morris[†]

Department of Aerospace Engineering

The Pennsylvania State University

University Park, PA 16802, U.S.A.

A time accurate high order numerical simulation performed on parallel computers is used to study the minor losses due to an abrupt change in a resonator cross-sectional area. A finite amplitude standing wave is established in the resonator using two different types of driver. In one case the entire resonator is shaken and in the other a line source is used to simulate the effect of a piston. It is found that a net pressure difference is generated across the change in cross-sectional area. It is argued that this is due to minor loss coefficients being different in one half cycle than the other in an oscillatory flow. This net pressure difference is almost constant along the resonator. The results of the numerical simulation are in very good agreement with the results of a complementary experiment for a wide variety of operating conditions. It is found that a quasi-steady approach underpredicts the minor losses. An empirical relationship is defined for the minor losses based on the results of the numerical simulation. An approach based on the second law of thermodynamics is also used to examine the loss of availability due to the minor losses.

Introduction

IN recent years, thermoacoustic engines and refrigerators have improved in efficiency and have increased their range of applicability. However, the efficiency of such devices is limited by thermoviscous losses, and these losses become more significant as such devices become more efficient. Thermoviscous losses are due mostly to viscous dissipation in the vicinity of solid boundaries and minor losses. Minor losses are an additional pressure drop associated with the transition between channels and sharp changes in the direction of the flow.

Although the energy dissipation associated with the minor losses has a significant adverse effect on the overall efficiency of the thermoacoustic device, it is not the only reason that a study of minor losses is of interest. Recently, Swift et al.[1] made use of a jet pump to suppress unwanted streaming in a traveling wave engine or refrigerator. A jet pump develops an adverse pressure gradient that is almost entirely based on the minor losses. This pressure gradient interrupts the flow and suppresses the streaming. Although the streaming suppression improves the device efficiency, the presence of the jet pump itself contributes to extra energy dissipation and so has negative effect on the efficiency. A clear understanding of the minor losses is essential in order to optimize the jet pump design.

Minor losses have been studied and well documented for steady state flows:[2] however, for unsteady flows the physics behind these losses, and the methods to determine pressure differences associated with them, are not well understood. Since there is no dependable model for minor losses in unsteady flows at the moment, most investigators use the Iguchi hypothesis (see Swift[3]) in order to account for them. This hypothesis assumes that for low frequency oscillatory flows the same relation that is used for steady state flow may be used. The Iguchi hypothesis provides a crude estimate and does not take into account effects such as the frequency of the flow oscillations and the phase differences between velocity and pressure.

The focus of the present paper is on the minor losses due to an abrupt change in a resonator cross-sectional area. In a previous study by the authors,[4] the acoustics and flow field of such a resonator were examined. The results of that numerical simulation successfully captured nonlinear effects such as streaming and radiation pressure. It was also shown that a net pressure difference due to the minor losses was developed. The present paper uses the same approach and configuration to perform a parametric study and to extend the simulation to a wider variety of operating conditions including different source strengths, boundary conditions, and types of drivers. The results are compared against experimental data obtained in a complementary study that is being conducted at Penn State. Ultimately, the goal of the present research is to obtain a correlation between pressure losses (or other relevant flow variables) due to a sudden change in cross-sectional area for all the different geometries and operating conditions that are involved in the problem.

In the next section minor losses are introduced and the state of the art in the analysis of minor losses in

---

[*]Post-Doctoral Research Associate, Member, AIAA

[†]Boeing/A. D. Welliver Professor, Fellow, AIAA

both steady and oscillatory flows is reviewed briefly. Then the technical approach of the present paper is discussed. This includes the governing differential equations that are to be solved, the numerical scheme, and the modeling of the driver. This is followed by the results of the numerical simulations and a comparison with the available experimental measurements. Finally, some conclusions are drawn.

Minor Losses

Minor losses appear in a flow path in many ways: junctions; bends; valves; and elbows, to name just a few. Here, we are particularly interested in the minor losses associated with a sudden change in flow cross sectional area, as illustrated in Fig. 1(a). In the following sections, the more familiar steady flow minor losses are reviewed briefly first, and then minor losses in oscillatory flows are considered.

Steady Flow

Consider a flow passage with a sudden change in cross-sectional area as shown in Fig. 1(a). The question is: for a viscous fluid flow, how much "extra" total energy losses for a "given" mass flow rate would occur due to the change in flow cross-sectional area. Since the mass flow rate is fixed, the velocity averaged over the channel cross-section at sections 1 and 2 in the presence and absence of the minor losses remains unchanged. Therefore, the total energy dissipation due to the minor losses is translated into a static pressure drop between the two locations. Thus, a simple static pressure difference measurement between points 1 and 2 can provide a fairly accurate representation of the minor loss between the two points. However, the measurement locations must be chosen carefully to ensure that no measurement takes place in the region with high vortical motions in the vicinity of the junction. For example, currently, the ASME standards[5] suggest that pressure data for flow pass an orifice be taken 2.5 tube diameters before and 8 tube diameters after the junction to measure the "permanent" pressure drop.

The pressure drop associated with minor losses in a steady flow may be represented as a power series in velocity:

$$\Delta p_{m\ell} = \xi_1 V + \xi_2 V^2 + \xi_3 V^3 + \cdots \qquad (1)$$

where V is a velocity scale relevant to the problem. For almost all of the cases of practical interest, the first two terms on the right hand side provide an adequate correlation. The minor loss coefficient, k, is then "defined" as:

$$k = \frac{\Delta p_{m\ell}}{\rho_o V^2/2} = \frac{K_1}{Re} + K_2 \qquad (2)$$

where ρ_o is a reference mean density, and the Reynolds number, Re, is defined as:

$$Re = \frac{VL}{\nu} \qquad (3)$$

Here, L is a relevant length scale and ν is the kinematic viscosity of the fluid. For a fluid with constant molecular properties, K_1 and K_2 in Eq. 2 are constant. Equation 2 is the basis of the "Two-K" model proposed by Hooper.[6,7] For a flow with low Reynolds number, say $Re < 25$, the first term on the right hand side of Eq. 2 is dominant and the pressure drop varies linearly with velocity. Examples are creeping flow, lubrication, flow inside capillary tubes, fluid flow modeling of dashpots and shock absorbers, and so on. This result is consistent with laminar viscous flow inside tubes or closed conduits.

For a flow with high Reynolds number, one can neglect the first term in Eq. 2 and writes the pressure drop as:

$$\Delta p_{m\ell} = \frac{1}{2} k \rho_o V^2 \qquad (4)$$

For sufficiently high Reynolds number, the minor loss coefficient, k, is independent of the Reynolds number and the pressure drop varies with the velocity squared. Almost all of the fluid flow problems that are of interest in thermoacoustics and fluid mechanics fall into this category.

For practical applications, Eq. 4 provides an easy correction to the use of the Bernoulli equation for viscous flows:

$$\left(\frac{p}{\rho_o} + \frac{1}{2}V^2 + gz \right)_1 = \left(\frac{p}{\rho_o} + \frac{1}{2}V^2 + gz \right)_2 + \frac{\Delta p_{m\ell}}{\rho_o} \qquad (5)$$

where g is the acceleration due to gravity and z is the height from a reference level. A positive $\Delta p_{m\ell}$ requires a flow from location 1 to location 2. Each term in Eq. 5 represents energy per unit mass. Therefore, the power loss due to the minor losses is given by:

$$\dot{\mathcal{W}} = U \Delta p_{m\ell} \qquad (6)$$

where U is the volume velocity, which is a constant for a given mass flow rate in incompressible flow.

In general, the minor loss coefficients cannot be evaluated analytically. However, the case of a sudden expansion is an exceptional case in which it is possible to use the momentum equation in the axial direction to estimate the pressure drop and consequently the minor loss coefficient within a good accuracy:[8]

$$\Delta p_e = \frac{1}{2} \rho_o V_1^2 \left[1 - \left(\frac{S_1}{S_2} \right) \right]^2 \qquad (7)$$

and

$$k_e = \left[1 - \left(\frac{S_1}{S_2} \right) \right]^2 \qquad (8)$$

where S_1 and S_2 are flow cross-sectional areas at locations 1 and 2 respectively, and the subscript e emphasizes that the results are for a sudden expansion. In the derivation of Eqs. 7 and 8 no assumption has

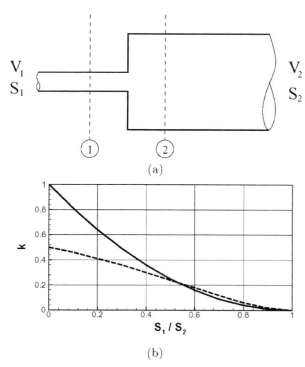

(a)

(b)

Fig. 1　(a) Schematic of a flow passage with a sudden change in cross-section (b) Minor loss coefficients as a function of the ratio of the cross-sectional area. Solid line: sudden expansion, plotted using Eq. 8; dashed line: sudden contraction, experimental data from Streeter.[9]

been made with respect to the shape of the flow cross-section. So, they may be applied to flow inside ducts of arbitrary cross section.

In almost all other cases the minor loss coefficients have to be determined either experimentally or through a numerical simulation based on the Navier-Stokes equations. Figure 1(b) shows the minor loss coefficients for two cases of a sudden expansion and a sudden contraction as a function of the cross-sectional area ratio. These are the two cases that are of particular interest in the present paper.

It is also instructive to examine minor losses from the point of view of the second law of thermodynamics. This provides a different but equally valid perspective for the case of steady flow. However, for oscillatory flow, it may open a new avenue in this field, as discussed in the next section. As flow passes the junction, energy is neither lost nor dissipated. Energy indeed is conserved. What is referred to as the "energy dissipation" is in fact exergy destruction or lost of availability. Availability is a measure of the maximum capacity of an energy system to perform useful work as it proceeds to a specified final state in equilibrium with its surroundings.[10] Exergy is a thermodynamic property that is defined as:

$$\psi = (h^o - T_o s) - (h_o - T_o s_o) \tag{9}$$

where ψ is the exergy per unit mass, s is the specific en-

tropy, T is temperature and a subscript o denotes the ambient condition. The total enthalpy, or methalpy, is defined as:

$$h^o = h + \frac{1}{2}|\mathbf{V}|^2 + gz \tag{10}$$

where h is the specific enthalpy and $\mathbf{V}$ is the velocity vector. Equation 9 determines the maximum reversible work per unit mass that can be done in a given thermodynamic state. The exergy change between locations 1 and 2 in Fig. 1(a) may be written as:

$$\begin{aligned} \Delta\psi &= \psi_2 - \psi_1 \\ &= (h_2 - h_1) - T_o(s_2 - s_1) \\ &\quad + \frac{1}{2}\left(V_2^2 - V_1^2\right) + g(z_2 - z_1) \end{aligned} \tag{11}$$

Recall the following thermodynamic relationship:

$$T\mathrm{d}s = \mathrm{d}h - \mathrm{d}p/\rho \tag{12}$$

For an isentropic process, i.e., reversible and adiabatic, $\mathrm{d}s=0$. If an additional assumption of incompressibility is also added, integration of Eq. 12 between locations 1 and 2 in Fig. 1 yields:

$$h_2 - h_1 = \frac{p_2 - p_1}{\rho} \tag{13}$$

and Eq. 11 reduces to:

$$\Delta\psi = \frac{p_2 - p_1}{\rho} + \frac{1}{2}\left(V_2^2 - V_1^2\right) + g(z_2 - z_1) \tag{14}$$

Since a reversible process is assumed, there is no loss of exergy, $\Delta\psi = 0$, and the Bernoulli equation is retrieved. Although the analysis here assumes an adiabatic process, it is straightforward to show that Eq. 14 also holds for a reversible isothermal process.[11]

In the presence of minor losses $\Delta\psi$ is no longer zero and represents the loss of exergy in the junction. A change in exergy not only takes into account the pressure drop, but also accounts for all sources of irreversibility. Therefore, working with $\Delta\psi$ may well lead to a more appropriate measure of minor losses. It can be shown, for example, that the change in exergy in a simple adiabatic pipe flow is proportional to the pressure drop associated with the viscous friction.[12] Here, we attempt to relate exergy to the pressure drop across a sudden change in cross-sectional area. For an adiabatic process with no external work, the first law of thermodynamics requires that the total enthalpy be conserved:

$$\mathrm{d}h^o = 0 \tag{15}$$

Equation 15 is a simple energy balance and it is valid with or without minor losses. Then Eq. 12 may be written as:

$$T\mathrm{d}s = -\mathrm{d}\left(\frac{1}{2}V^2 + gz\right) - \frac{\mathrm{d}p}{\rho} \tag{16}$$

For an adiabatic inviscid flow, the process may be considered isentropic:

$$0 = -\mathrm{d}\left(\frac{1}{2}V^2 + gz\right) - \left(\frac{\mathrm{d}p}{\rho}\right)_{inv} \quad (17)$$

and for a viscous flow:

$$T\mathrm{d}s = -\mathrm{d}\left(\frac{1}{2}V^2 + gz\right) - \left(\frac{\mathrm{d}p}{\rho}\right)_{vis} \quad (18)$$

where the subscripts inv and vis signify inviscid or viscous flow respectively. It was stated earlier that the analysis assumes a given mass flow rate and configuration. Therefore, the change in kinetic and potential energies are similar for both inviscid and viscous flows. Subtracting Eqs. 17 from 18 yields:

$$T\mathrm{d}s = \left(\frac{\mathrm{d}p}{\rho}\right)_{inv} - \left(\frac{\mathrm{d}p}{\rho}\right)_{vis} \quad (19)$$

Equation 19 may be integrated from the entrance to the exit to relate entropy change to the pressure difference. In the case of an ideal gas, $\rho T = p/R$. So that,

$$\Delta s = s_{out} - s_{in} = R\left[\ln\left(\frac{p_{out}}{p_{in}}\right)_{inv} - \ln\left(\frac{p_{out}}{p_{in}}\right)_{vis}\right] \quad (20)$$

In general, the change in entropy is due to heat transfer and irreversibilities. Since an adiabatic process is assumed, the entropy change, Δs, is in fact entropy generation, s_{gen}, due to the minor losses. If $\Delta p = (p_{in} - p_{out}) \ll p_{in}$:

$$s_{gen} = R\frac{\Delta p_{vis} - \Delta p_{inv}}{p_{in}} \quad (21)$$

It is noteworthy to examine Δp_{inv} and Δp_{vis} more closely. Δp_{inv} is the static pressure difference before and after the junction in Fig. 1(a). It is *not* associated with any loss of available work or exergy destruction. It is the pressure difference given in Eq. 14 with $\Delta\psi = 0$. Δp_{vis}, on the other hand, has two components; one is much like Δp_{inv} and has to do with the change in cross-sectional area. The other is due to the pressure lost because of the minor losses in the junction. The numerator of Eq. 21, therefore, represents the pressure lost due to minor losses and the equation itself shows that the entropy generation in the junction is proportional to this pressure loss.

The preceding analysis has assumed an ideal gas as the working fluid. It is straightforward to show from Eq.19 that for an incompressible fluid,

$$s_{gen} = \frac{\Delta p_{vis} - \Delta p_{inv}}{\rho T_{in}} \quad (22)$$

A combination of the first and second laws of thermodynamics may be used to relate the entropy generation to the change in exergy. For a steady flow with no heat transfer it can be written as,[13]

$$T_o s_{gen} = \Delta\psi = \psi_{in} - \psi_{out} \quad (23)$$

where the exergy, ψ, is defined in Eq. 9. Therefore, the loss of available work, or exergy destruction, is proportional to the entropy generation which itself is directly proportional to the pressure loss due to minor losses.

The power loss, or loss of available work due to minor losses, then can be calculated as:

$$\dot{W} = \dot{m}T_o s_{gen} = T_o \dot{S}_{gen} \quad (24)$$

In the case of incompressible flow, Eq. 24 is identical to Eq. 6. However, Eq. 24 is rather general and can be used in unsteady as well as steady flow and with or without heat transfer. The case of unsteady flow with an emphasis on oscillatory flow is discussed in the next section.

Oscillatory Flow

Unlike steady flow, the minor losses in unsteady flows are not well understood. The fact that the flow quantities are time dependent adds an extra dimension to the problem and makes analysis complicated. For instance, parameters such as the frequency and wavelength of the oscillations, the relaxation time, and phase differences between flow variables that were irrelevant to steady flow, now play important roles in transient flows. There are many different classes of time dependent flows. In this paper only oscillatory flows are considered.

At present, minor losses in oscillatory flows are treated using the steady flow relations and their associated experimental results. For example, in the case of a sudden change in cross-sectional area, Eq. 4 is adopted as the basis for analysis, and it is assumed that this equation may be applied instantaneously throughout the oscillation cycle. Suppose that the minor loss coefficients for sudden expansion and sudden contraction are k_e and k_c respectively. In the quasi-steady approach it is assumed that these coefficients take the same value as they do in a steady flow. Therefore, in the half of a cycle in which the flow goes from 1 to 2 in Fig. 1a the pressure drop associated with minor losses may be written as:

$$\Delta p_e(t) = p_1(t) - p_2(t) = \frac{1}{2}\rho_o k_e v(t)^2 \quad (25)$$

and for the next half cycle the flow experiences a sudden contraction. So, the associated pressure drop is taken to be:

$$\Delta p_c(t) = p_1(t) - p_2(t) = -\frac{1}{2}\rho_o k_c v(t)^2 \quad (26)$$

where ρ_o is the mean density and $v(t)$ is the instantaneous particle velocity. Backhaus and Swift[14] assumed that the first order instantaneous particle velocity takes the form of $v(t) = v_1 \sin\omega t$ where v_1 is the amplitude of the velocity oscillation to the linear order. Then the time average of the pressure difference in a complete cycle may be calculated as:

$$\overline{\Delta p} = \frac{1}{8}\rho_o(k_e - k_c)v_1^2 \qquad (27)$$

The pressure differences Δp_e and Δp_c may be called "the instantaneous pressure drop due to the first order velocity,[14]" and $\overline{\Delta p}$ is a time averaged pressure build up due to the fact that the minor loss coefficient in a sudden expansion is different from that for a sudden contraction.

The difference in minor loss coefficients in Eq. 27 is almost always a positive value (see Fig. 1), which suggests that the minor losses in this case develop a positive pressure difference in favor of location 1. In other words for a given pressure at point 2, the pressure at point 1 in a viscous flow is higher than that in an inviscid flow. This net pressure build up due to the minor losses provides a mechanism for streaming suppression. Equation 27 may also be obtained by direct use of Eq. 4 with a velocity scale equal to $v_1/2$. Equation 27 was originally developed to estimate minor losses for a traveling wave where the first order particle velocity amplitude is a constant. However, in a standing wave resonator, the particle velocity amplitude varies from point to point.

It is clear from Eq. 27 that as flow undergoes a sudden expansion, it contributes positively to $\overline{\Delta p}$ and as it undergoes a sudden contraction its contribution is negative. However, in both directions minor losses result in energy dissipation and this is the penalty that has to be paid to obtain the net pressure difference, $\overline{\Delta p}$. The power dissipation associated with the minor losses may be calculated using Eq. 6. Again, it is assumed that the steady flow relation may be used instantaneously, and a time average is then performed to calculate the average power lost during an acoustical cycle:

$$\dot{W} = U\Delta p = \frac{\rho_o S_1}{3\pi}|v_1|^3(k_e + k_c) \qquad (28)$$

Several assumptions have to be made in the above analysis that have to be examined critically. First, the analysis implicitly assumes a low frequency excitation. This allows us to assume that the flow in each half a cycle reaches a quasi steady condition, and therefore the application of Eq. 4 is legitimate for an unsteady flow. This obviously is not the case for high frequency oscillations: not only because the flow is far from the quasi-steady condition, but also because the minor losses are implicitly assumed to be associated with the shear viscosity. However, this may not be the dominant dissipation mechanism for high frequency oscillations. Second, the velocity scale has been chosen to be the particle velocity amplitude. This may not be the best choice for a velocity scale, as in the presence of acoustic streaming other velocity scales appear in the flow field that may be more relevant to the minor loss calculations.

These shortcomings of the simplified analysis given by Eq. 27 are no strangers to the thermoacoustics community. Swift[15] states that the application of Eq. 27 results in a minor loss estimate that is significantly different from the experimental data. However, this equation does provide a qualitative understanding of some aspects of the minor losses in an oscillatory flow. The analysis suggests that there must be a build up in pressure difference where the minor loss coefficients are different in one half cycle than the other. This argument is supported by experimental measurements. As will be shown, this is the key element to the analysis given in the present paper.

An approach based on the second law of thermodynamics may also be used to study the power loss associated with the minor losses in an oscillatory flow. Recall that the pressure loss in the steady flow is proportional to the entropy generation rate as given in Eq. 21. In general, the entropy generation rate may be written as:[13]

$$\dot{S}_{gen} = \frac{dS}{dt} - \sum_{i=0}^{N} \frac{\dot{Q}_i}{T_i} - (\dot{m}s)_{in} + (\dot{m}s)_{out} \qquad (29)$$

Equation 29 signifies the methods by which entropy may be generated. The first term on the right hand side represents the time rate of change of total entropy inside the control volume. The second term indicates the effect of heat transfer. The last two terms account for the entropy transport due to mass flux through the control surface. The rate at which the available work is lost is then given as:

$$\dot{W} = T_o \dot{S}_{gen} \qquad (30)$$

which is the power lost due to minor losses. Equation 29 may also be time averaged to calculate the averaged rate of entropy generation during an acoustical cycle. Equation 30 then gives the averaged power loss.

The above thermodynamic analysis assumes an equilibrium condition. It assumes that the relaxation times for all thermodynamic processes are very short compared to any time scale relevant to the problem. The relaxation frequency for air (a combination of Oxygen, Nitrogen, and water vapor) at normal conditions is of order of kilohertz.[16] Therefore, for any excitation in that frequency range or above the thermodynamic relations that are given here should be used with caution.

The determination of the pressure difference due to minor losses is found numerically in the present paper. The details of the simulation are given in the next section.

Technical Approach

In this section, first the governing differential equations that are used in the present numerical simulation are introduced. Then the computational domain and the grid are described. This is followed by a description of the numerical scheme and the parallel implementation of the code. Finally, the source models for the driver are explained.

Governing Differential Equations

In the study of minor losses, it is the viscous effect in the vicinity of the solid walls and in the shear layer regions that are mainly responsible for the energy dissipation and pressure losses. Therefore, the full Navier-Stokes equations need to be used to simulate the key processes realistically. In compact form, the dimensionless equations in two dimensions may be written,

$$\frac{\partial \mathbf{Q}}{\partial t} + \frac{\partial \mathbf{E}}{\partial \xi} + \frac{\partial \mathbf{F}}{\partial \eta} = \mathbf{S} \qquad (31)$$

in a generalized coordinate system, where

$$\mathbf{Q} = \frac{1}{J} \left\{ \begin{array}{c} \rho \\ \rho u \\ \rho v \\ \rho E_t \end{array} \right\},$$

$$\mathbf{E} = \frac{1}{J} \left\{ \begin{array}{c} \rho U \\ \rho U u + \xi_x p - (\xi_x \tau_{xx} + \xi_y \tau_{xy}) \\ \rho U v + \xi_y p - (\xi_x \tau_{xy} + \xi_y \tau_{yy}) \\ (\rho E_t + p) U - \xi_x \beta_x - \xi_y \beta_y \end{array} \right\},$$

$$\mathbf{F} = \frac{1}{J} \left\{ \begin{array}{c} \rho V \\ \rho V u + \eta_x p - (\eta_x \tau_{xx} + \eta_y \tau_{xy}) \\ \rho V v + \eta_y p - (\eta_x \tau_{xy} + \eta_y \tau_{yy}) \\ (\rho E_t + p) V - \eta_x \beta_x - \eta_y \beta_y \end{array} \right\} \quad (32)$$

and $\mathbf{S}$ represents the source term. The variables ρ, p, and E_t are the density, pressure, and total energy respectively. The total energy is defined as

$$E_t = \frac{p}{\rho (\gamma - 1)} + \frac{|\mathbf{u}|^2}{2} \qquad (33)$$

where γ is the ratio of specific heats and $\mathbf{u}$ is the velocity vector. Time and the two Cartesian velocity components are t, u, and v respectively. $U = \xi_x u + \xi_y v$ and $V = \eta_x u + \eta_y v$ are the contravariant velocities. The speed of sound in the free stream is chosen as the velocity scale since it is more convenient to view the velocity in terms of Mach number for aeroacoustic calculations. Other thermodynamic variables are non-dimensionalized by their corresponding values in the free stream. The fluid medium is assumed to be an ideal gas, so the ideal gas law and the Navier-Stokes equations form a complete set of equations that may be solved for the dependent variables, $\mathbf{Q}$. With the use of Stokes hypothesis, the viscous terms in Eqn. (32) are

given by

$$\tau_{xx} = \frac{2 M \mu}{3 Re} \left[2 \left(\xi_x \frac{\partial u}{\partial \xi} + \eta_x \frac{\partial u}{\partial \eta} \right) - \left(\xi_y \frac{\partial v}{\partial \xi} + \eta_y \frac{\partial v}{\partial \eta} \right) \right],$$

$$\tau_{yy} = \frac{2 M \mu}{3 Re} \left[2 \left(\xi_y \frac{\partial v}{\partial \xi} + \eta_y \frac{\partial v}{\partial \eta} \right) - \left(\xi_x \frac{\partial u}{\partial \xi} + \eta_x \frac{\partial u}{\partial \eta} \right) \right],$$

$$\tau_{xy} = \frac{M \mu}{Re} \left[\xi_y \frac{\partial u}{\partial \xi} + \eta_y \frac{\partial u}{\partial \eta} + \xi_x \frac{\partial v}{\partial \xi} + \eta_x \frac{\partial v}{\partial \eta} \right],$$

$$\beta_x = u \tau_{xx} + v \tau_{xy} + q_x,$$

$$\beta_y = u \tau_{xy} + v \tau_{yy} + q_y, \qquad (34)$$

where $M = u_\infty / c_\infty$ is the Mach number, $Re = \rho_\infty u_\infty L / \mu_\infty$ is the Reynolds number, and μ is the coefficient of viscosity. c_∞, u_∞, ρ_∞, and μ_∞ are the reference speed of sound, velocity, density, and the viscosity coefficient respectively. L is an appropriate length scale depending on the problem to be solved. The heat transfer terms model heat conduction with Fourier's law. For example, the x component of the heat flux is given by

$$q_x = \frac{M \mu}{(\gamma - 1) Re Pr} \left(\xi_x \frac{\partial T}{\partial \xi} + \eta_x \frac{\partial T}{\partial \eta} \right). \qquad (35)$$

where Pr is the Prandtl number, which is approximately 0.72 for air, and γ is taken as 1.4. The coefficients of viscosity, μ, and thermal conductivity, k, are related to the thermodynamic variables using Sutherland's formula. The Prandtl number is then used to determine the coefficient of thermal conductivity once μ is known. In the current implementation, these equations are solved in generalized coordinates in conservative form to facilitate the treatment of curvilinear boundaries and grid stretching.

Computational Domain and Grid

Figure 2 shows the computational domain. The dimensions are all scaled with respect to the length of the larger channel. A viscous solid wall boundary condition (no slip condition) is enforced on the channel walls. Both adiabatic and isothermal boundary conditions may be used. When a line source is used to drive the acoustic field, it is placed as shown by the dashed line in Fig. 2. Otherwise, a shaker is used. The details of the drivers are given below.

The code uses a structured rectangular grid. In order for the code to capture the flow quantities inside the boundary layers accurately, the grid is clustered close to the walls. The grid is also clustered in the vicinity of the shear layer in the larger channel. A total of 52941 grid points are used. The details of the mesh that is used are given by Morris et al.[4]

Numerical Scheme and Parallel Implementation

In the present simulation a finite difference scheme is used in which the Navier-Stokes equations are discretized with the fourth-order Dispersion Relation Preserving (DRP) scheme developed by Tam and Webb.[17]

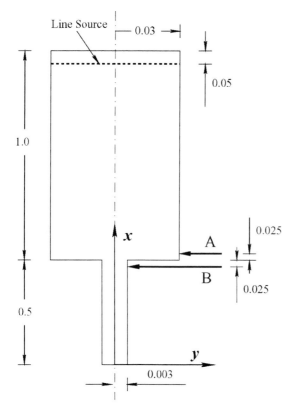

Fig. 2 Sketch of the computational domain. Not to scale

The solution advances in time using explicit fourth-order Runge-Kutta integration.

The code is written in Fortran 90. The computations are performed in parallel on 16 processors. The Message Passing Interface (MPI) library is use to communicate among the processors. A two dimensional domain decomposition and a multiblock structure are adopted. The details of the parallel implementation are given by Morris *et al.*[4] For the grid used in the present study, it takes about 20 hours of wall clock CPU time per acoustical cycle to perform the computations on 16 processors.

Source Model for the Driver

In order to establish a standing wave inside the resonator, it should be excited at its resonance frequency. This is done by a driver. In practice, it is possible to drive the resonator in a number of different ways: a piston may be used, a subwoofer may be installed at one end, or the whole resonator may be shaken. Physically and mathematically each of these drivers defines a different problem, which may have different flow field patterns. However, all of them may be used to establish a quarter wavelength standing wave inside the smaller channel. The resonance condition in the larger channel might be quite different. For a shaker or a piston that is installed at the end of the larger channel, the pressure fluctuations in that vicinity behave more closely to an anti-node. On the other hand, for a subwoofer this region acts more like a pressure node. Whether it is possible at all to have a perfect standing wave in both channels at the same time remains to be determined by both experiments and numerical analysis.

In the simulations presented in this paper two of the three techniques, a shaker and a piston, are modeled and investigated. The effect of the piston is modeled by a line source that is applied on the right hand side of the continuity equation as a periodic mass source. A corresponding source term must also be added to the energy equation to account for the fact that the mass source adds energy to the system and to ensure that the source only generates acoustic waves. The source term on the right hand side of Eq. 31 then becomes:

$$\mathbf{S} = \frac{1}{J} \left\{ \begin{array}{c} S_p \\ 0 \\ 0 \\ \left[\frac{\gamma p}{\rho(\gamma-1)} - \frac{1}{2}(u^2 + v^2)\right] S_p \end{array} \right\}, \quad (36)$$

with,

$$S_p = A_p \exp(-\ln 2/\alpha^2(x - x_s)^2)\sin(\omega t) \quad (37)$$

where x is the axial location and x_s is the source position. The parameter α defines the Gaussian envelope half width and is taken to be 0.05 for the current simulations. ω is the source frequency and it corresponds to the quarter wavelength resonant frequency of the smaller channel. The parameter A_p is the source amplitude. This source description is equivalent to that used by Tam and Dong.[18]

In the second method, the resonator is excited by shaking the whole apparatus. The problem is then reformulated in a coordinate system attached to the resonator. The resultant effect is an extra body force that may be treated as the source term in Eq. 31:

$$\mathbf{S} = \frac{1}{J} \left\{ \begin{array}{c} 0 \\ -\rho a_x \\ -\rho a_y \\ -\rho(u a_x + v a_y) \end{array} \right\}, \quad (38)$$

where a_x and a_y are the components of the acceleration due to shaking in the x and y directions, respectively. In the present simulations, the resonator is only shaken in the x axis direction using a simple harmonic motion. Therefore, $a_y = 0$ and the source becomes:

$$\mathbf{S} = \frac{1}{J} \left\{ \begin{array}{c} 0 \\ A_s \rho \omega^2 \sin \omega t \\ 0 \\ A_s \rho u \omega^2 \sin \omega t \end{array} \right\}, \quad (39)$$

where A_s is the displacement amplitude of the vibration and ω is the shaking frequency.

	Adiabatic BC	Isothermal BC
Piston	$A_p = 0.05$ $A_p = 0.10$	$A_p = 0.05$ $A_p = 0.10$ $A_p = 0.25$
Shaker	$A_s = 0.001$ $A_s = 0.002$	$A_s = 0.001$ $A_s = 0.002$

Table 1 Simulation summary. A_p is the line source amplitude in Eq. 37. A_s is the displacement amplitude of the shaker's vibration in Eq. 39.

Results

In the present study a series of simulations are performed. In these simulations two types of boundary conditions, namely adiabatic and isothermal, and two types of drivers, a shaker and a line source to simulate the effect of a piston, are considered. In each case, the code is run for different source amplitudes. A summary of the simulation conditions is given in Table 1.

An initial transient time is needed before a standing wave is established in the resonator. This transient time is found to be a function of the boundary conditions, being shorter in the isothermal case. In all cases, after about 15 to 20 acoustical cycles almost all initial transient effects have passed, and a reasonable statistically stationary state is reached.

Figure 3 shows a comparison between the root mean square of pressure along the centerline for some of the different cases studied. The solid lines represent the results for an isothermal boundary condition for the cases where a line source is used to model the driver. The numbers on the plot represent the source amplitude. The dashed lines correspond to the results for adiabatic boundary conditions. Two plots are shown for the adiabatic case. One is for the case with a line source as the driver and the other is the result where the resonator is shaken in the axial direction.

A number of observations can be made regarding Fig. 3. First, it can be seen that in all cases a quarter wavelength standing wave resonance is established in the smaller channel. The pressure anti-node is at the end wall as expected. However, the pressure node is slightly inside the smaller channel. The pressure anti-node location depends both on the oscillation amplitude and the boundary condition that is used. For an isothermal boundary condition, it appears that the pressure anti-node is significantly inside the smaller channel for low amplitude oscillations. As the source amplitude increases, the location of the pressure anti-node moves slightly closer to the junction.

The second observation that can be made is regarding the relative pressure amplitude between the isothermal and adiabatic boundary condition cases. It is clear from the figure that for a given source amplitude, the adiabatic boundary conditions result in a much higher RMS pressure, which is higher by a factor of four in the smaller channel. The difference in

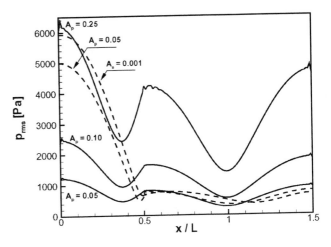

Fig. 3 Pressure root mean square along the centerline for different cases. —— : Isothermal boundary condition; – – – : adiabatic boundary condition. A_p and A_s indicate the line source amplitude that simulates the piston and the shaker displacement amplitude, respectively.

the larger channel is very small. This clearly has to do with the cooling effect provided by the isothermal boundary condition. The cooling is more effective in the smaller channel where the channel walls are closer and the thermal penetration depth is a considerable portion of the channel width. On the other hand, in the larger channel the thermal penetration depth is insignificant compared to the channel width, and also the total thermal inertia of the larger channel is high enough to keep the effect of wall cooling to a minimum. Though, as the source amplitude increases, the RMS pressure in the larger channel does increase accordingly.

The third observation is that the results for a line source and a shaker for a given boundary condition are alike, regardless of the fact that the two source representations are completely different. In the case of a line source, the source is applied to the continuity and energy equations. This is a mass source that periodically adds and subtracts mass to the computational domain. It is intended to mimic a piston whose motion may be seen as a mass source. Furthermore, the source is localized along a very thin line: the dashed line in Fig. 2. On the other hand, the shaker is modeled by a source applied to the momentum and energy equations. This is a source in the form of a body force, and it is not localized. It is applied everywhere in the solution domain. Although these two models are fundamentally different, they provide very comparable results.

The fourth observation is the unusual behavior of the RMS pressure close to the end walls in the case of the isothermal boundary condition. This is a numerical error and has to do with the fact that an isothermal boundary condition requires a very steep temperature gradient close to the wall. This can be explained by a simple analysis. Consider the flow associated with a standing wave near the end wall of a resonator. The velocity in the direction normal to the wall is very small and may be neglected. In the absence of the wall and real fluid effects, the pressure and temperature fluctuations are given by the standing wave values, denoted by p_1^s and T_1^s respectively. The subscript 1 denotes a first-order quantity and the superscript s indicates a standing wave. For ideal gases they are related by,[4]

$$\frac{T_1^s}{T_o} = \frac{\gamma - 1}{\gamma} \frac{p_1^s}{p_o} \qquad (40)$$

where, p_o and T_o are the mean pressure and temperature respectively. For a real fluid, the one-dimensional, first-order energy equation may be written,

$$\rho_o c_p \frac{\partial T_1}{\partial t} = \frac{\partial p_1}{\partial t} + \frac{\partial^2 T_1}{\partial x^2} \qquad (41)$$

where c_p is the specific heat at constant pressure. If periodic solutions are assumed of the form,

$$T_1(x,t) = \hat{T}_1(x) \exp(i\omega t) \qquad (42)$$

Then the variation of the temperature fluctuation with distance from the wall is given by,

$$\hat{T}_1(x) = C \exp\left[-(1+i)\, x/\delta_\kappa\right] + \frac{\hat{p}^s}{\rho_o c_p} \qquad (43)$$

where $\hat{p}^s$ is the amplitude of the standing wave pressure and the thermal penetration depth $\delta_\kappa = \sqrt{2\kappa/\omega}$ with the thermal diffusivity $\kappa = k/\rho_o c_p$. For large distances from the wall,

$$\hat{T}_1(x) \rightarrow \frac{\hat{p}^s}{\rho_o c_p} = \hat{T}^s \qquad (44)$$

where Eq. 40 has been used to introduce the amplitude of the standing wave temperature $\hat{T}^s$.

The constant C is determined using the boundary condition at the end wall. For an adiabatic boundary condition, $\partial \hat{T}_1/\partial x = 0$ at $x = 0$. This requires that $C = 0$ and the temperature fluctuation is equal to the standing wave temperature, $\hat{T}^s$. Thus, there is no change in the temperature fluctuation close to the end wall and no special grid treatment is required. On the other hand, for an isothermal boundary condition, $\hat{T}_1 = 0$ for $x = 0$. Thus,

$$\hat{T}_1 = \hat{T}^s \left\{ 1 - \exp\left[-(1+i)\, x/\delta_\kappa\right] \right\} \qquad (45)$$

The temperature fluctuation far from the plate, i.e., as $x \rightarrow \infty$, is identical to the adiabatic case: but, the temperature fluctuation has to vanish on the wall from the far field value within one to two thermal penetration depths. This results in a steep temperature gradient close to the wall which is difficult to capture numerically. In the present simulations, no attempt

was made to cluster the grid near the end walls. This results in the small oscillations in the root mean square pressure seen in Fig. 3.

The pressure variation in the resonator consists of two components. One component is associated with the finite amplitude of the acoustic field and has no dependence on the fluid viscosity or the minor losses. This part is similar to the pressure difference given in Eq. 14 or Δp_{inv} in Eq. 21 which is a function of flow geometry and is reversible. This inviscid pressure variation may be determined using a second order analysis of the Bernoulli equation:[19]

$$\langle p - p_{ref} \rangle = \frac{1}{2\rho_o c_o^2} \langle p'^2 \rangle - \frac{1}{2} \rho_o \langle u'^2 \rangle + C \qquad (46)$$

where $\langle\ \rangle$ denotes the time averaged value, p_{ref} is a constant reference pressure, and C is a constant in space and time that depends on the constraints of the problem at hand such as boundary conditions or conservation of mass or volume. It may also depend on the fluid physical properties such as the ratio of the specific heats, γ.[19] The second component of the pressure variation in the resonator is the contribution of the minor losses. This component is a result of energy dissipation due to the generation of vorticity, which is a direct consequence of the fluid viscosity, and is an irreversible phenomenon. The simplified analysis that led to Eq. 27 suggests that the minor losses can build an extra pressure above and beyond the Bernoulli pressure due to the fact that the minor loss coefficient is different when the flow undergoes a sudden expansion than the coefficient for a sudden contraction. Figure 4 shows the mean pressure variation along the channel centerline with respect to a reference pressure for the case with adiabatic boundary conditions and a line source amplitude equal to 0.05. The dashed line is the inviscid pressure difference based on Eq. 46. The solid line is the result of the numerical simulation for viscous fluid flow. The extra pressure that is built in the smaller channel is almost independent of the location as shown in Fig. 5.

Figure 6 shows the corresponding result for a case with isothermal boundary condition. This is an extreme case with a source amplitude equal to 0.25. It can be seen that the two plots are again almost identically matched in the larger channel. The excess pressure over the Bernoulli pressure is clearly seen in the smaller channel, although in this case their difference varies slightly along the smaller channel.

In all of the results presented here it should be recalled that a synthetic jet is established in the larger channel just downstream the junction. This causes the small oscillations in the mean pressure near the junction, (see Morris et al.[4]).

The outcome of the preceding results provides an excellent opportunity for an accurate measurement of pressure difference due to the minor losses. Usually it

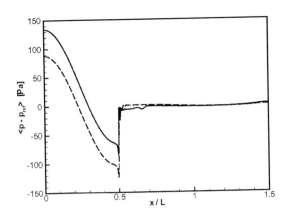

Fig. 4 $<p - p_{ref}>$ along the channel centerline where p_{ref} is a reference pressure. ———— : Viscous flow numerical simulation; – – – : second order inviscid calculation (Eq. 46).

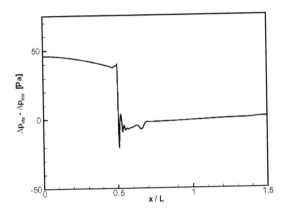

Fig. 5 The difference between viscous pressure difference and the Bernoulli pressure along the centerline for an adiabatic boundary condition.

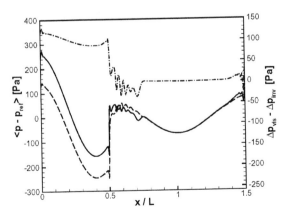

Fig. 6 Pressure variation along the centerline for an isothermal boundary condition and a very high source amplitude. – – – : Bernoulli (inviscid) pressure; ———— : Viscous pressure; – · – · – : Difference between viscous and inviscid pressure. The pressure difference should be read from the right axis.

is difficult to make reasonably accurate pressure measurements along the resonator side wall and especially in the vicinity of the junction. However, since the difference in inviscid and viscous pressure does not vary significantly along the smaller channel, the measurement can be made at the end wall of the smaller channel. On that wall, the fluid normal velocity is clearly zero (both for viscous and inviscid flow) and $\langle u'^2 \rangle$ vanishes in Eq. 46. If the time history of the pressure is measured on the end wall, then its RMS value and DC shift may be determined easily. Then Eq. 46, with $\langle u'^2 \rangle = 0$ may be used to determine Δp_{inv}, and the DC shift itself is the Δp_{vis}.

Such experimental measurements are presently being conducted at Penn State by Mr. Andy Dollar and Prof. Anthony Atchley in the Graduate Program in Acoustics. Figure 7 shows a comparison between their experimental measurements and the results of a variety of simulations. In this figure, the excess pressure, $\overline{\Delta p}$, is plotted as a function of a scaled RMS pressure for a point on the end wall of the smaller channel. The dashed line, with a slope of one, represents the Bernoulli pressure. This line is based on Eq. 46. The Bernoulli pressure may also be viewed as Δp_{inv}. The filled square symbols show the results of the experimental data. The solid line is the best linear fit to the experimental results. The solid line is forced to pass through the origin as it is expected that when $\langle p'^2 \rangle = 0$, no excess pressure on the wall should be observed. All other open symbols on the figure show the results of the present numerical simulations for different cases. These cases are described in the figure's caption.

Figure 7 shows clearly that an excess pressure over the Bernoulli pressure is produced due to the minor losses. The results of the numerical simulations are in a very good agreement with the experimental data. Considering the fact that the geometry of the experimental apparatus and that of the numerical simulation are not completely identical, the agreement between the results is quite impressive and encouraging.

An empirical relationship can be defined based on the numerical simulation and the experimental results:

$$\Delta p_{vis} = \frac{1}{2} K \frac{\langle p'^2 \rangle}{\rho_o c_o^2} \qquad (47)$$

or:

$$\Delta p_{m\ell} = \Delta p_{vis} - \Delta p_{inv} = \frac{1}{2}(K-1) \frac{\langle p'^2 \rangle}{\rho_o c_o^2} \qquad (48)$$

The coefficient K may be estimated from Fig. 7 as 1.5.

It is instructive to compare this result with Eq. 27 that is derived on the basis of the Iguchi hypothesis. Notice that $\overline{\Delta p}$ in Eq. 27 is in fact the excess pressure over the Bernoulli pressure. From Fig 1 the value of $(k_e - k_c)$ may be estimated as 0.35 for the present

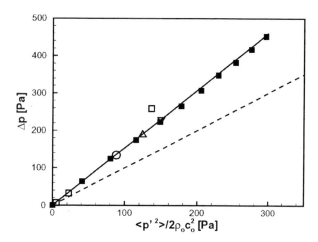

Fig. 7 Pressure difference in the smaller channel as a function of a scaled RMS pressure on the end wall. $---$: Bernoulli pressure calculated from Eq. 46; ■ : experimental data; —— : best linear fit to the experimental results; ○ : simulation-adiabatic boundary condition using a line source; □ : simulation-isothermal boundary condition using a line source; △ : simulation-adiabatic boundary condition using a shaker; ▽ : simulation-isothermal boundary condition using a shaker

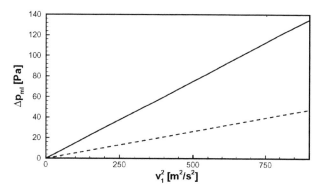

Fig. 8 A comparison between $\overline{\Delta p}$ obtained by Iguchi hypothesis and the correlation given in the present paper. $---$: Eq. 27, —— : Eq. 48.

geometry. As mentioned earlier, in the case of a standing wave resonator, v_1 in Eq. 27 is space dependent. Here, the maximum value of v_1 is used. The results are plotted in Fig. 8 by a dashed line. The correlation given in Eq. 48 is shown by a solid line. The results of the numerical simulations and experiments are not shown again as they obviously follow the solid line. It can be seen that although the maximum possible v_1 is assumed, the Iguchi hypothesis and Eq. 27 for those cases studied in the present paper underpredicts $\Delta p_{m\ell}$. However, it is fair to say that Eq. 27 can predict the general behavior of the $\overline{\Delta p}$ correctly: only an adjustment in $(k_e - k_c)$ is necessary. This can be provided either by experiment or numerical simulation.

Equation 48 could be written in terms of v_1 or an RMS velocity if a plane wave behavior is assumed.

However, it is not a good idea to use the maximum particle velocity amplitude as the working parameter since its location moves considerably in different cases. On the other hand, the maximum value of the RMS pressure is always at the end wall, and it can be measured easily and accurately.

Within the framework of the Iguchi hypothesis, the analysis given in this paper may be used to determine the minor loss coefficients in a sudden expansion and contraction individually. Equation 27 shows that the pressure difference due to minor losses is a function of the difference in the minor loss coefficients. It is rewritten here for convenience,

$$\Delta p_{m\ell} = \frac{1}{8}\rho_o(k_e - k_c)v_1^2 \qquad (49)$$

On the other hand, the power loss in Eq. 28 depends on the sum of minor loss coefficients:

$$\dot{\mathcal{W}} = T_o \dot{S}_{gen} = \frac{\rho_o S_1}{3\pi}|v_1|^3(k_e + k_c) \qquad (50)$$

The above equations provide two relations for two unknowns, k_e and k_c, if all other parameters are known. For example in the case of an adiabatic boundary condition with a line source as the driver, the numerical simulation determines $\Delta p_{m\ell}$ to be 45.5 Pa. The average power loss due to the minor losses can be calculated from the average rate of entropy generation across the junction during an acoustical cycle. A control volume is considered around the junction that extends from location A to location B in the axial direction and all the way to the channel walls in the transverse direction: see Fig. 2. The results of the numerical simulation then may be used to calculate the average rate of entropy generation using Eq. 29. For the case considered, the average rate of entropy generation inside the control volume during an acoustical cycle is calculated to be 0.024056 W/K. The maximum velocity amplitude is also estimated to be 17.1 m/s. Therefore, k_e and k_c may be calculated as 1.4 and 0.4, respectively. These values may seem higher than reasonable. This is due to the fact that Eq. 49 tends to underpredict the averaged pressure difference. The calculated value for k_e and k_c may be called "apparent" minor loss coefficients to reflect the fact that these are the values that those coefficients have to take in order for Eq. 49 to give the correct result. This can be further clarified by equating Eqs. 49 and 48, and assume a plane wave relationship between the pressure and velocity amplitude. For $K = 1.5$, it yields:

$$k_e - k_c = 1 \qquad (51)$$

It is expected that the values of both k_e and k_c will both be positive, which results in $k_e > 1$.

Conclusions

In this paper, a detailed simulation and analysis of minor losses in oscillating flows has been described.

In particular, minor losses associated with a sudden change in resonator cross sectional area have been considered. It has been shown that, in an oscillating flow, a net pressure difference is established with the pressure in the smaller channel being greater than that in the larger one. This is in addition to the Bernoulli pressure difference associated with second-order, isentropic effects. This additional net pressure difference is caused by the difference in pressure generated by minor losses between the parts of the flow cycle where the sudden change in area is associated with an expansion or a contraction. The level of the pressure difference is greater by a factor of three than that calculated using a quasi-steady (Iguchi) hypothesis. The results of the simulation have been compared with experiment and excellent agreement has been obtained.

The focus of our research at present is a study of the net pressure difference associated with minor losses in asymmetric orifices. This geometry more closely resembles that used in thermoacoustic Stirling engines. In addition, streaming associated with travelling waves is under investigation. The coupling of these two topics will lead to a better understanding of the optimization of jet pumps for streaming suppression.

Acknowledgments

The authors are grateful for access to the experimental data provided at short notice by Mr. Andy Dollar and Prof. Anthony Atchley of the Penn State Graduate Program in Acoustics. This work is supported by the Office of Naval Research.

References

[1] Swift, G. W., Gardner, D. L., and Backhaus, S., "Acoustic Recovery of Lost Power in Pulse Tube Refrigerators," *Journal of the Acoustical Society of America*, Vol. 105, No. 2, 1999, pp. 711–724.

[2] Idelchik, I. E., *Handbook of Hydraulic Resistance*, CRC Press, 1994.

[3] Swift, G., *Thermoacoustics: A Unifying Perspective for Some Engines and Refrigerators*, Los Alamos National Laboratory, 2001.

[4] Morris, P. J., Boluriaan, S., and Shieh, C. M., "Simulation of the Pressure Difference due to Minor Losses Through a Sudden Contraction and Expansion in a Resonator," *Submitted to Journal of the Acoustical Society of America*, 2002.

[5] "Fluid Meters Report," American Society of Mechanical Engineers, 1971.

[6] Hooper, W. B., "The Two-K Method Predicts Head Losses in Pipe Fittings," *Chemical Engineering*, Vol. August, 1981, pp. 96–100.

[7] Hooper, W. B., "Calculate Head Loss Caused by Change in Pipe Size," *Chemical Engineering*, Vol. November, 1988, pp. 89–92.

[8] Lighthill, M. J., *An Informal Introduction to Theoretical Fluid Mechanics*, Oxford University Press, 1986.

[9] Streeter, V. L., *Handbook of Fluid Dynamics*, McGraw-Hill, New York, 1961.

[10] American Institute of Physics, "Efficient Use of Energy," AIP Conference Proceedings No. 25, 1975.

[11] Van Wylen, G. J., Sonntag, R. E., and Borgnakke, C., *Fundamentals of Classical Thermodynamics*, John Wiley & Sons, Inc., 1994.

[12] Bejan, A., *Entropy Generation through Heat and Fluid Flow*, John Wiley & Sons, Inc., 1982.

[13] Bejan, A., *Advanced Engineering Thermodynamics*, John Wiley & Sons, Inc., 1997.

[14] Backhaus, S. and Swift, G. W., "A Thermoacoustic-Stirling Heat Engine:Detailed Study," *Journal of Acoustical Society of America*, Vol. 107, No. 6, 2000, pp. 3148–3166.

[15] Swift, G. W., "Streaming in Thermoacoustic Engines and Refrigerators," *Nonlinear Acoustics at the Turn of the Millennium*, edited by W. Lauterborn and T. Kurz, American Institute of Physics, New York, 2000, pp. 105–114.

[16] Pierce, A. D., *Acoustics: An Introduction to its physical principles and applications*, Acoustical Society of America, Woodbury, NY, 1989.

[17] Tam, C. K. W. and Webb, J. C., "Dispersion-Relation-Preserving Difference Schemes for Computational Aeroacoustics," *J. Computational Physics*, Vol. 107, No. 2, 1993, pp. 262–281.

[18] Tam, C. K. W. and Dong, Z., "Radiation and Outflow Boundary Conditions for Direct Computation of Acoustic and Flow Disturbances in a Nonuniform Mean Flow," *Journal of Computational Acoustics*, Vol. 4, No. 2, 1996, pp. 175–201.

[19] Wang, T. G. and Lee, C. P., "Radiation Pressure and Acoustic Levitation," *Nonlinear Acoustics*, edited by M. F. Hamilton and D. T. Blackstock, chap. 6, Academic Press, New York, 1998, pp. 177–204.

AIAA 2002-2596

GENERAL AVIATION IC ENGINE
DIMENSIONLESS EXHAUST NOISE SPECTRUM

Howard V. L. Patrick*
Embry-Riddle Aeronautical University
Daytona Beach, Florida 32114, USA

Hiroko Tada[†]
Honda Research and Development Company
Tochigi 321-3393, Japan

ABSTRACT

A general aviation intermittent combustion (IC) engine noise test facility is utilizedto investigate the tonal characteristics of engine exhaust noise using a Lycoming 0-320 D1D engine with a standard Cessna 172 Skyhawk exhaust system. Propeller noise is eliminated with this facility because a hydraulic dynamometer is used to absorb the power normally delivered to the propeller. Engine tests are performed at different delivered powers and shaft rotational speeds, and the far field radiated noise is measured and recorded.

This investigation determines that the magnitude and frequency of the primary engine firing frequency (EFF) tone and harmonics scale with engine power. The EFF tone scales as approximately the 4th power, 2EFF as the 12th power, 3EFF as the 16th power, 4EFF as the 20th power, and 5EFF as the 24th power of rpm. A normalized acoustic pressure and frequency are introduced resulting in a dimensionless frequency spectrum that successfully scales the EFF and significant harmonic tones. This spectrum greatly simplifies prediction of the overall sound pressure level of a very complex non-linear acoustic phenomena associated with the exhaust noise of a general aviation IC engine.

BACKGROUND

The far field radiated noise of propeller powered general aviation (GA) aircraft with IC engines is usually dominated by propeller generated noise, at least near the propeller plane of rotation[1]. With the advent of quiet three-bladed propellers specifically designed for GA aircraft[2] the reduction in engine exhaust noise becomes of interest in the development of environmentally quiet airplanes.

---

*Professor, Aerospace Engineering Dept., Senior Member of AIAA
[†]Acoustic Engineer, Engineering Development Dept. 10

For a two-bladed propeller powered with a four-cylinder and four-stroke engine, tones of propeller blade passing frequency (BPF) and multiples coincide with EFF and harmonics[3]. Because these propeller and engine tones occur at identical frequencies, the magnitude of each contributor cannot be ascertained.

To determine GA IC engine exhaust noise without propeller noise, an engine noise test facility (ENTF) is developed and is shown in Figure 1. This portable facility incorporates a hydraulic dynamometer to load the engine output shaft, and is capable of testing up to 485 kW (650 hp) GA IC engines. A detailed description of this facility, capabilities, and the far field acoustic measurement techniques is given in Reference 4. This facility consists of an engine mount frame and test-bed, dynamometer, drive-train, cooling systems, as well as electrical, instrumentation, fuel and control systems that allow for flexible engine operation. The ENTF is ideal for the acoustical evaluation of quiet GA IC engine exhaust system designs and determining their effect on engine performance.

ENGINE EXHAUST NOISE CHARACTERISTICS
A standard Cessna 172-exhaust system is acoustically evaluated using a Lycoming 0-320 DID engine. Shown in Figure 2 is a photograph of this exhaust system mounted on the engine of the test facility. It is important to note that the large cylindrically shaped expansion chamber is empty.

The far field noise measurement is performed using a laid-down microphone[4] at a distance of 50 ft from and aligned with the exhaust system exit. The microphone is positioned perpendicular to the engine propeller shaft centerline at the exhaust exit. This position is at an azimuthal angle of 90^0 from the engine shaft centerline, which is the same side as the photograph of the exhaust system shown in Figure 2. The noise is measured at various engine powers of varying shaft rotational speeds. The power measured by the dynamometer does not include the power absorbed by the exhaust system, and the test is not necessarily performed at full engine throttle.

Fig. 1. Photograph of engine noise test facility (ENTF).

Fig. 2. Photograph of engine with standard Cessna 172 exhaust system installed.

ENGINE EXHAUST NOISE SPECTRA

Tests are performed with measured power of 109.7 kW (147 hp) at 2,750 rpm, 95.5 kW (124 hp) at 2,590 rpm, 76.2 kW (102 hp) at 2,420 rpm, and 56.7 kW (76 hp) at 2,160 rpm. This experimental procedure involves running the engine at approximately constant torque but at different rotational speeds resulting in different delivered powers. Presented in Figure 3 is the engine exhaust noise frequency spectrum[5] for a Lycoming 0-320 D1D engine with standard Cessna 172-exhaust system installed at a delivered power of 109.7 kW and

2,750 rpm. The spectrum sound pressure level SPL is in decibels with respect to 20 μPa over the frequency range from 20 Hz to 2,375 Hz. Inspection of this figure reveals a spectrum curve dominated by tones at lower frequencies, and at higher frequencies the spectrum is characterized by broadband noise associated with jet noise from the hot gases exhausting into the quiescent atmosphere[6]. These tones are generated by the pulsating combustion process associated with piston powered engines. For a four-stroke engine each piston fires every two revolutions with an engine rotational speed of 2,750 rpm or 45.8 Hz, results in a fundamental firing frequency f of 22.9 Hz. The primary engine firing frequency EFF for a four-cylinder engine is four times fundamental firing frequency, or 91.6 Hz. It is important to note that the noise levels reported are 6 dB greater than in the free field because of acoustic pressure doubling[4].

Further review of the spectrum in Figure 3 indicates that multiples of the fundamental firing tone f dominate the spectrum at frequencies less than approximately 1.4 kHz. Typically, the most intense tones occur at primary engine firing frequency and multiples that are labeled on the curve as EFF, 2EFF, 3EFF, etc. The EFF tone is equal to 4f and harmonics of EFF are also multiples of 4f, e.g. EFF is 4f, 2EFF is 8f, 3EFF is 12f, etc. Examples of this spectrum dominance are the two tones at EFF with a SPL of approximately 101 dB, and 2EFF with a SPL of 95 dB while the tone at 5f has a SPL of 87 dB which is approximately 8 dB less than the 2EFF tone. The two tones EFF and 2EFF, totally dominate the acoustic energy on a non-weighted basis. The 5f, 6f, and 7f tones are clearly visible between the EFF and 2EFF tones. This tonal dominance of the exhaust noise spectrum of GA IC engines is typical[3]. Because of the focus on EFF and harmonic tones in this investigation, there is no need to analyze spectra at frequencies greater than 1,000 Hz.

The goal of this study is to establish an engine exhaust noise scaling procedure that is based upon empirical data collected using the Lycoming O-320 D1D aircraft engine with the standard Cessna 172 muffler installed. The purpose of this normalization procedure is to create a single dimensionless spectrum curve, which indicates the SPL of the EFF and harmonic tones for any delivered engine power and rotational speed combination.

Shown in Figure 4 is the noise spectrum[5] for a delivered engine power of 95.5 kW at 2,590 rpm. This spectrum range clearly shows the tonal nature of the engine exhaust noise and allows for better identification of the primary engine firing tones, which are the EFF, 2EFF, 3EFF, 4EFF and 5EFF tones. At the rotational speed of 2,590 rpm, f is 21.6 Hz and EFF is equal to 4f, which is 86.3 Hz.

Presented in Figure 5 is the noise spectrum[5] for a delivered engine power of 76.1 kW at 2,420 rpm. At engine rotational speed of 2,420 rpm, f is 20.2 Hz and EFF is 80.7 Hz. Inspection of this curve clearly shows the primary engine firing frequencies of EFF through 5EFF, where the SPL of EFF and 2EFF are 100 dB and 89 dB respectively. The noise spectrum[5] at a power of 56.7 kW at 2,160 rpm is shown in Figure 6 where f is 18 Hz, and the EFF tone is 72.0 Hz with a SPL of approximately 98 dB.

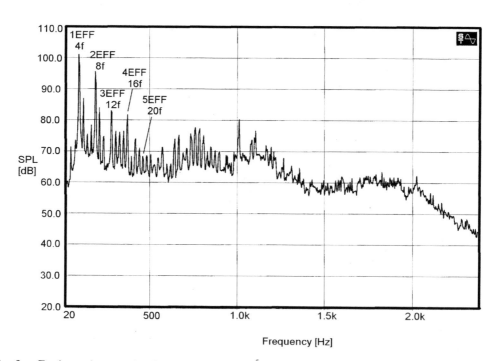

Fig. 3.   Engine exhaust noise frequency spectrum[5] for a Lycoming 0-320 D1D engine with standard Cessna 172-exhaust system installed at a delivered power of 109.7 kW (147 hp) and 2,750 rpm over a frequency range of 20-2,375 Hz.

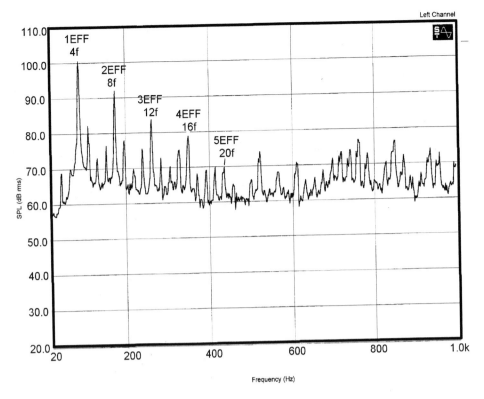

Fig. 4. Engine exhaust noise spectrum[5] for a Lycoming 0-320 D1D engine with standard Cessna 172-exhaust system at a delivered power of 95.5 kW (124 hp) and 2,590 rpm.

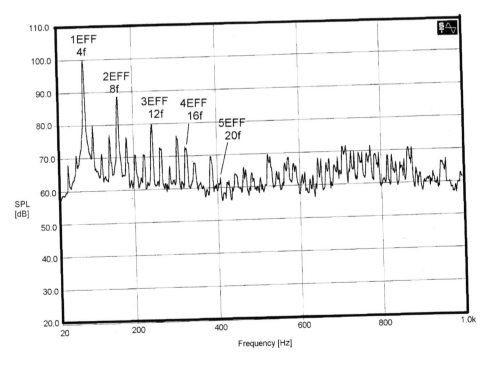

Fig. 5. Engine exhaust noise frequency spectrum[5] for a Lycoming 0-320 D1D engine with standard Cessna 172-exhaust system at a delivered power of 76.1 kW (102 hp) and 2,420 rpm.

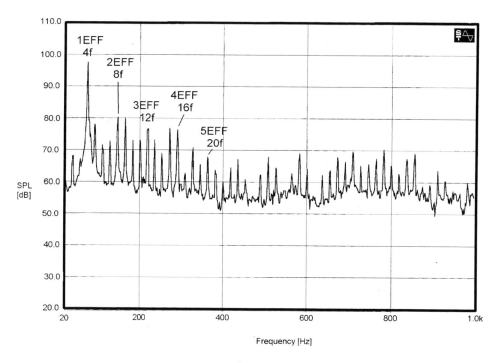

Fig. 6. Engine exhaust noise frequency spectrum[5] for a Lycoming 0-320 D1D engine with standard Cessna 172-exhaust system at a delivered power of 56.7 kW (76 hp) and 2,160 rpm.

DIMENSIONLESS SPECTRA

The magnitude and frequency of the primary engine firing tones from EFF through 5EFF at each of the four power settings are determined from inspecting Figures 3 through 6 and tabulated in Table 1. Table 1(a) lists the basic engine characteristics and test conditions for the Lycoming 0-320 D1D engine with a standard Cessna 172 exhaust system. During the test period, there is no wind and the atmospheric condition is characterized by a density altitude of 420 m with a speed of sound of 338.7 m/s.

Table 1(b) lists details of the relevant radiated noise parameters at an engine power 109.7 kW and engine rotational speed 2,750 rpm obtained from Figure 3 where the SPL and frequency of the tones of EFF though 5EFF are clearly visible. The actual mean square sound-pressure $\bar{p}^2$ is calculated from the SPL tone using Equation 1 where p_{ref} is 20 μPa.

$$ SPL = 10\log\left(\frac{\bar{p}^2}{p_{ref}^2}\right) \qquad (1) $$

The actual sound pressure $\bar{p}$ is obtained by taking the square-root of $\bar{p}^2$. Knowing the SPL for the EFF

through 5EFF tones obtained from the spectra in Figures 3 through 6, results in determining $\bar{p}$ for all of these conditions. These values of SPL and frequency for EFF through 5EFF tones at the different power and their respective engine rotational speeds as well as $\bar{p}$ are listed in Table 1.

In order to develop a scaling law that will collapse the SPL spectral curves to a single curve an appropriate dimensionless SPL and frequency is necessary. Appropriate fundamental characteristic parameters must be used that reflect an understanding of the physics of sound generation in an IC engine. For the normalizing process, M denotes the mass unit in kg, L is the characteristic length in m, and T is the characteristic time unit in seconds. Frequency has the dimension of T^{-1} therefore a characteristic speed divided by a characteristic length is necessary to achieve a unit of T. The Strouhal number S is a dimensionless frequency associated with pulsating flows, e.g. vortex shedding of flow past a cylinder[7]. S is taken to be equal to the tonal frequency f multiplied by the exhaust pipe diameter d divided by the hot gas mean flow speed through the exhaust pipe exit $\bar{U}$ as shown in Equation 2. Using $\bar{U}$ as the characteristic speed in calculating Strouhal number is based upon knowing that the pulsating hot gas flow emanating from the pipe exit is a monopole noise source[5].

$$S = fd/\overline{U} \qquad (2)$$

The mean fluid flow speed $\overline{U}$ with dimensions of [L/T] is calculated using the volumetric flow rate Q with basic units of [L^3/T]. Knowing Q allows calculation of $\overline{U}$ using Equation 3 where A_d is the cross-section area with diameter d.

$$\overline{U} = Q/A_d \qquad (3)$$

The mean mass flow rate $\dot{m}_f$ through the exhaust system is required to calculate Q using Equation 4 where ρ_{gas} is the hot exhaust gas density at the pipe exit to the atmosphere.

$$Q = \frac{\dot{m}_f}{\rho_{gas}} \qquad (4)$$

To estimate $\dot{m}_f$ it is assumed[8] that the engine has an air to fuel ratio A/F of 12 and that the specific fuel consumption sfc is $0.0577(10)^{-6}$ kg/w.s (0.4lb/hp.hr)[9]. Knowing the sfc allows estimation of $\dot{m}_f$ using Equation 5 where P is the delivered engine power in watts.

$$sfc = \frac{\dot{m}_f}{P} \qquad (5)$$

The mass flow rate of air $\dot{m}_a$ is determined knowing $\dot{m}_f$ and A/F using Equation 6.

$$\dot{m}_a = (A/F)\dot{m}_f \qquad (6)$$

The total mass flow rate through the exhaust system $\dot{m}_{tot}$ is equal to the sum of the mass flow rates of fuel and air as given in Equation 7.

$$\dot{m}_{tot} = \dot{m}_a + \dot{m}_f \qquad (7)$$

Engine exhaust temperature of a GA aircraft engine is measured about 8 cm downstream from the exhaust manifold, in the exhaust pipe. This temperature is approximately 800 ^{0}C and the exhaust gas temperature decreases rapidly along the exhaust system. Because the gas temperature at the pipe exit is unknown, it is assumed to be 500 ^{0}C and the pressure is one standard atmosphere p_{atm}. Knowing these two parameters the perfect gas law shown in Equation 8 is used to estimate the exhaust pipe exit density ρ_{gas}. This hot gas density is required to calculate the volumetric gas flow rate Q out of the pipe end using Equation 4. Knowing Q, the mean flow speed $\overline{U}$ is then calculated using Equation 3.

$$\rho_{gas} = \frac{p_{atm}}{RT} \qquad (8)$$

In summary, the procedure for estimating $\overline{U}$ requires calculating $\dot{m}_f$ using Equation 5 and then $\dot{m}_a$ is determined using Equation 6. The total gas mass flow rate $\dot{m}_{tot}$ is calculated using Equation 7. The hot gas density at the pipe exit ρ_{gas} is calculated using Equation 8, which is needed to calculate the volumetric flow rate Q using Equation 4. Finally Equation 3 is used to calculate the estimated mean flow speed out of the exhaust pipe exit $\overline{U}$. Listed in Table 1(a) is the estimated ρ_{gas}. Also listed in Table 1, Sections b through e, are $\dot{m}_{tot}$ and $\overline{U}$ at each of the engine power settings for the spectra shown in Figures 3 through 6.

The unit for sound pressure is Pa or N/m^2, with basic M, L and T units of M/LT^2. A dimensionless sound pressure $\overline{p}_{non}$ is given by Equation 9 where $\overline{p}$ is the actual acoustic pressure, $\overline{U}$ is the mean flow speed of the hot exhaust gas leaving the pipe exit, P is engine power in watts, d is exhaust pipe inside diameter in meters, and k is wave number in m^{-1} units. The rationale for using d as the characteristic length and $\overline{U}$ as the characteristic speed is that the sound emanating from the exhaust pipe exit is a monopole source associated with the pulsating flow of gas leaving the pipe exit[5]. It is obvious that the acoustical energy emanating from the pipe exit is a function of delivered engine power P. The wave number k is proportional to the inverse of the wavelength and is used to assure that $\overline{p}_{non}$ is truly dimensionless.

$$\overline{p}_{non} = \frac{\overline{p}\,d\,\overline{U}}{Pk} \qquad (9)$$

The wave number is related to the frequency of the sound wave by Equation 10, where c is the atmospheric speed of sound.

$$k = 2\pi f/c \qquad (10)$$

The dimensionless sound pressure level SPL$_{non}$ is given by Equation 11 using units of decibels with the reference pressure equal to unity, and $\bar{p}_{non}^2$ is the mean square value of the dimensionless pressure.

$$SPL_{non} = 10\log \bar{p}_{non}^2 \qquad (11)$$

As a result of implementing these dimensionless quantities, the frequency spectrum can be modified using Strouhal number as the dimensionless frequency and SPL_{non} as the dimensionless sound pressure level. Implementation of these normalized quantities results in a dimensionless spectrum of the EFF and harmonic tones. Listed in Table 1 are all of the pertinent regular and dimensionless parameters.

In summary, the Strouhal number S and the wave number k are calculated based upon the values of EEF

and harmonic frequency tones using Equations 2 and 10 respectively. Dimensionless sound pressure $\bar{p}_{non}$ is calculated using Equation 9, which is based upon the actual acoustic sound pressure $\bar{p}$ calculated using Equation 1, exhaust pipe diameter d and mean flow rate $\overline{U}$, engine power P, and wave number k. Dimensionless sound pressure level SPL_{non} is calculated using Equation 11. These parameters for the different engine power and rotational speed conditions are listed in Table 1(b) through (e). The data for 109.7 kW (147 hp) at 2,750 rpm is shown in Table 1(b), 95.5 kW (124 hp) at 2590 rpm are listed in Table 1(c), 76.1 kW (102 hp) at 2420 rpm are given in Table 1(d), and the 56.7 kW (76 hp) at 2160 rpm data are listed in Table 1(e).

Table 1. Engine Exhaust Tonal Noise Parameters.

(a) Basic engine characteristics and test conditions.

density altitude	420 m
speed of sound : c	338.7 m/s
pipe cross section area : A_d	$6.36(10)^{-3}$ m^2
engine displacement : $\forall$	$7.58(10)^{-3}$ m^3
pipe exit gas density: ρ_{gas}	0.4566 kg/m^3

(b) Engine rotational speed : 2,750 rpm

engine power : P	$109.7(10)^3$ w [147 hp]
gas mass flow rate: $\dot{m}_{tot}$	0.0963 kg/s
gas flow speed: $\overline{U}$	33.2 m/s

tone	SPL	$\bar{p}$	f	k	S	$\bar{p}_{non}$	$\bar{p}_{non}^2$	SPL_{non}
	[dB]	[Pa]	[Hz]	[m^{-1}]	[-]	[-]	[-]	[dB]
EFF	101.0	2.24	91.7	1.701	0.249	$3.59(10)^{-5}$	$1.287(10)^{-9}$	-88.9
2EFF	95.4	1.178	183.3	3.40	0.498	$9.44(10)^{-6}$	$8.91(10)^{-11}$	-100.5
3EFF	83.5	$2.99(10)^{-1}$	275	5.10	0.746	$1.597(10)^{-6}$	$2.55(10)^{-12}$	-115.9
4EFF	81.6	$2.41(10)^{-1}$	367	6.81	0.995	$9.64(10)^{-7}$	$9.29(10)^{-13}$	-120.3
5EFF	68.3	$5.20(10)^{-2}$	458	8.50	1.2429	$1.666(10)^{-7}$	$2.78(10)^{-14}$	-135.6

(c) Engine rotational speed : 2,590 rpm

engine power : P	$95.5(10)^3$ w [124 hp]
gas mass flow rate : $\dot{m}_{tot}$	0.0813 kg/s
gas flow speed: $\overline{U}$	28.0 m/s

tone	SPL [dB]	$\bar{p}$ [Pa]	f [Hz]	k [m⁻¹]	S [-]	$\bar{p}_{non}$ [-]	$\bar{p}^2_{non}$ [-]	SPL$_{non}$ [dB]
EFF	100.5	2.12	86.3	1.601	0.277	$3.49(10)^{-5}$	$1.220(10)^{-9}$	-89.1
2EFF	91.9	$7.87(10)^{-1}$	172.7	3.20	0.555	$6.43(10)^{-6}$	$4.14(10)^{-11}$	-103.4
3EFF	83.5	$2.99(10)^{-1}$	259	4.80	0.832	$1.644(10)^{-6}$	$2.70(10)^{-12}$	-115.7
4EFF	78.9	$1.762(10)^{-1}$	345	6.40	1.1096	$7.26(10)^{-7}$	$5.28(10)^{-13}$	-122.8
5EFF	70.0	$6.33(10)^{-2}$	432	8.00	1.3870	$2.09(10)^{-7}$	$4.36(10)^{-14}$	-133.6

(d) Engine rotational speed : 2,420 rpm

engine power : P	$76.1(10)^3$ w [102 hp]
gas mass flow rate : $\dot{m}_{tot}$	0.0668 kg/s
gas flow speed: $\bar{U}$	23.0 m/s

tone	SPL [dB]	$\bar{p}$ [Pa]	f [Hz]	k [m⁻¹]	S [-]	$\bar{p}_{non}$ [-]	$\bar{p}^2_{non}$ [-]	SPL$_{non}$ [dB]
EFF	100.0	2.00	80.7	1.497	0.316	$3.63(10)^{-5}$	$1.336(10)^{-9}$	-88.7
2EFF	88.7	$5.45(10)^{-1}$	161.3	2.99	0.632	$4.96(10)^{-6}$	$2.46(10)^{-11}$	-106.1
3EFF	80.0	$2.00(10)^{-1}$	242	4.49	0.947	$1.213(10)^{-6}$	$1.472(10)^{-12}$	-118.3
4EFF	72.0	$7.96(10)^{-2}$	322	5.99	1.263	$3.61(10)^{-7}$	$1.307(10)^{-13}$	-128.8
5EFF	62.7	$2.73(10)^{-2}$	403	7.49	1.579	$9.93(10)^{-8}$	$9.85(10)^{-15}$	-140.1

(e) Engine rotational speed : 2,160 rpm

engine power : P	$56.7(10)^3$ w [76 hp]
gas mass flow rate : $\dot{m}_{tot}$	0.0498 kg/s
gas flow speed: $\bar{U}$	17.14 m/s

tone	SPL [dB]	$\bar{p}$ [Pa]	f [Hz]	k [m⁻¹]	S [-]	$\bar{p}_{non}$ [-]	$\bar{p}^2_{non}$ [-]	SPL$_{non}$ [dB]
EFF	97.5	1.500	72.0	1.336	0.378	$3.05(10)^{-5}$	$9.33(10)^{-10}$	-90.3
2EFF	80.2	$2.05(10)^{-1}$	144.0	2.67	0.756	$2.09(10)^{-6}$	$4.36(10)^{-12}$	-113.6
3EFF	76.5	$1.337(10)^{-1}$	216	4.01	1.134	$9.07(10)^{-7}$	$8.23(10)^{-13}$	-120.8
4EFF	76.2	$1.291(10)^{-1}$	288	5.34	1.512	$6.58(10)^{-7}$	$4.33(10)^{-13}$	-123.6
5EFF	67.7	$4.85(10)^{-2}$	360	6.68	1.890	$1.975(10)^{-7}$	$3.90(10)^{-14}$	-134.1

Shown in Figure 7 is the SPL for EFF through 5EFF tones plotted as a function of frequency with the adjoining plotted points connected with straight lines. The curve plotted using diamond shaped points depict the tones for 109.7 kW at 2,750 rpm, square points denote tones at 95.5 kW and 2,590 rpm, triangles represent the tones for 76.1 kW at 2,420 rpm, and circles depict tones at 56.7 kW and 2,160 rpm. Inspection of the curves in this figure shows wide spacing between the curves except for the 56.7 kW curve at the 4EFF and 5EFF tones. For each curve, the point located at the smallest S represents the SPL at EFF while the point at the largest S connotes the SPL at

5EFF. The other three points represent the SPL tones at 2EFF, 3EFF and 4EFF at progressively increasing Strouhal numbers.

According to Dobrynski[1], the overall sound pressure level (OASPL) difference between two different engine rpm for the same engine is proportional to the ratio of engine rotational speed to the fourth power. However, when comparing the SPL at EFF and multiples for the data presented in Table 1, it is clear that the difference between each tone for the presented data does not always scale by this relationship. Using an arbitrary power n, the change in sound pressure level ΔSPL for each tone in decibels is given by Equation 12 where N is the engine rotational speed.

$$\Delta SPL = 10\log\left(\frac{N_2}{N_1}\right)^n \qquad (12)$$

Based upon comparing tones EFF through 5EFF in Figures 3 through 6 and listed in Table 1, it is estimated that for the EFF tone n is 4, and for 2EFF, 3EFF, 4EFF, and 5EFF, n is 12, 16, 20, and 24 respectively. For some unknown reason n is always in multiples of four.

It is known that there is significant acoustic sound absorption in exhaust conduits because of the fully developed turbulent pipe flow that exists in IC aircraft engine exhaust systems[10]. Because of the large acoustic

impedance differences between the hot exhaust gases exiting into the cold quiescent air at the exhaust pipe exit, acoustic energy is reflected back into the exhaust conduit[11]. A similar phenomenon at the exhaust exit occurs because of the turbulent mixing region between the exhaust gases and surrounding cold air[12]. All of these nonlinear flow phenomena result in attenuation of sound that increases with escalating frequency. The scaling of sound pressure level at different EFF and harmonic tones mEFF is equal to $10\log(N_2/N_1)^n$ which means that as the EFF harmonic number m increases, the exponential power of the rotational speed ratio n also increases. Based upon the three phenomena discussed it is not surprising that n increases as the harmonic number m increases.

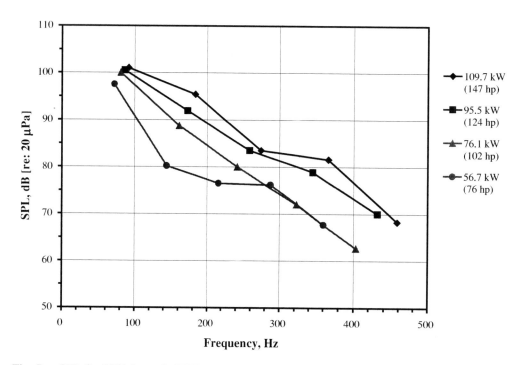

Fig. 7.   SPL for EFF through 5EFF tones plotted at a function of frequency for 109.7 kW (147 hp), 95.5 kW (124 hp), 76.1 kW (102 hp), and 56.7 kW (76 hp).

Shown in Figure 8 is the SPL_{non} plotted as a function of S. This dimensionless spectrum is based on far field acoustic measurements of the Lycoming O-320 D1D aircraft engine with standard Cessna 172 exhaust system at various power and engine rotational speed settings. In this figure, the four curves shown are based on the SPL tones at EFF, 2EFF, 3EFF, 4EFF, and 5EFF at engine power of 109.7 kW, 95.5 kW, 76.1 kW, and 56.7 kW, listed in Table 1. The plotting point configurations used in this figure are the same as used

in Figure 7 to reduce confusion when comparing curves between these two figures.

Inspection of Figure 8 indicates that the dimensionless engine exhaust noise spectrum covers the Strouhal frequency range of approximately 0.25 to 1.90, and all the curves representing different power levels are similar except for the points represented by 56.7 kW at the 4EFF and 5EFF tones. It is hypothesized that this low power level curve is not typical at these higher harmonics because the internal engine frictional losses become significant. There is little scattering of points when excluding the two points represented by the circles at S of approximately 1.5 and 1.9, which are for the low power level of 56.7 kW. Shown in Figure 8 is the author's best-fit curve that is given by Equation 13.

$$SPL_{non} = 10.56S^2 - 5.81S - 73.2 \qquad (13)$$

Comparing the typical power spectra represented by Figure 7, with the dimensionless spectrum given in Figure 8, reveals how well the normalization process collapses the data to a single curve. This dimensionless spectrum based on EFF and harmonic tones can be used to predict the exhaust noise OASPL for a Lycoming 0-320 D1D with a standard Cessna 172 exhaust system. It is possible that this curve could predict the exhaust noise of other engines but further tests must be performed to validate this possibility.

SOUND PRESSURE LEVEL PREDICTION
The engine delivered power and rotational speed as well as density altitude must be known to implement Equation 13. Assuming a four-stroke and four-cylinder engine is being used, the EFF tone is twice the rotational speed in revolutions per second, which is equivalent to frequency in Hertz. There are five quantities required to calculate the actual sound pressure level $\overline{p}$ and they are the: inside exhaust pipe diameter d, mean flow speed out of the pipe exit $\overline{U}$, delivered engine power P, and wave number k. The pipe diameter is measured in meters, k is calculated using Equation 10 and $\overline{U}$ is calculated using Equations 3 through 8. Based on knowledge of engine rotational speed the EFF and harmonic tonal frequencies are estimated, and Strouhal number S is calculated using Equation 2. The next step is to implement the curve in Figure 8 to estimate SPL_{non} using calculated S. Having determined SPL_{non} then Equation 11 is used to calculate $\overline{p}_{non}^2$, and taking the square root of this quantity, gives $\overline{p}_{non}$. The actual acoustic pressure $\overline{p}$ is determined using Equation 9 and the SPL is calculated using Equation 1. This same procedure is then used to determine the SPL at EFF harmonics up to 5EFF. Because these tones totally dominate the non-weighted noise spectrum, the OASPL is obtained by adding logarithmically the SPL for EFF and harmonic tones. Knowing the frequency and SPL at each of these tones, the A-weighted OASPL is determined by applying the A-weighted correction to each of the SPL at the correct EFF and harmonic tone frequency and adding them logarithmically.

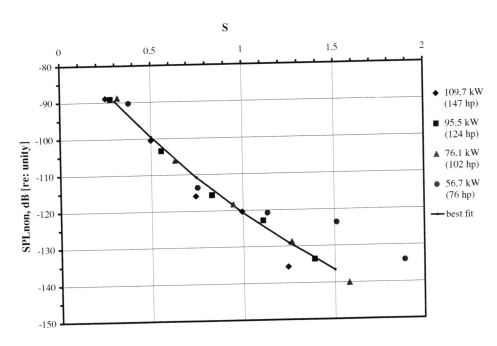

Fig. 8. Dimensionless engine exhaust noise spectrum at different engine power levels.

CONCLUSTION

This investigation shows that the far field radiated engine exhaust noise of a general aviation IC engine is dominated by the primary engine firing frequency (EFF) and harmonic tones. The magnitude of these tones scale with engine power. The EFF tone scales as approximately the 4th power, 2EFF as the 12th power, 3EFF as the 16th power, 4EFF as the 20th power, and 5EFF as the 24th power of rpm.

A normalized acoustic sound pressure level and frequency is developed that collapses the engine exhaust noise spectra based on EFF and harmonics at different power levels, to a simple second order polynomial curve when plotted in a semi-logarithmic format. This dimensionless spectrum greatly simplifies prediction of the overall sound pressure level of a very complex nonlinear acoustic phenomena associated with the exhaust noise of a Lycoming 0-320 D1D piston powered aircraft engine with a standard Cessna 172 Skyhawk exhaust system.

RECOMMENDATIONS

Further experiments are required to validate the applicability of the dimensionless engine exhaust noise spectrum used in this investigation to different general aviation aircraft IC engines and exhaust systems. Using the engine noise test facility located at Embry-Riddle Aeronautical University, acoustical evaluation of IC engine exhaust noise should be performed using larger displacement engines, exhaust systems without mufflers, and exhaust pipe of different lengths and diameters. The results of these tests will isolate the effect of sound absorption in the turbulent flow of the exhaust pipe as well as the sound reflection effects of acoustic impedance differences and turbulent mixing region at the exhaust pipe exit. It is also extremely important to design and evaluate mufflers that will significantly reduce IC aircraft engine exhaust noise and determine their impact on engine performance.

REFERENCES

1. Dobrzynski, I. W. 1994. Determination of Emission Values for Noise Emission Calculation at General Aviation Airports (German), IB 129-94/17, German Research Institute for Air and Space Travel.

2. Patrick, H. V. L., R. Finn, and C. Stich. 1997. Two and Three-Bladed Propeller Design for Reduction of Radiated Noise, AIAA Paper 97-710.

3. Maglieri, D. J., and H. H. Hubbard. 1974. Factors Affecting the Noise from Small Propeller Driven Aircraft, SAE Technical Report 750516.

4. Patrick, H. V. L., K. Lobo, and H. Tada. 1984. General Aviation Aircraft Engine Noise Test Facility, AIAA Paper No. 2000-1940.

5. Tada, H. 1999. An Intermittent-Combustion General Aviation Aircraft Engine Exhaust Noise Prediction Algorithm, MSAE Thesis, Embry-Riddle Aeronautical University.

6. Davies, P.O.A.L. 1992. Intake and Exhaust Noise, Institute of Sound and Vibration Research Technical Report, University of Southampton, England.

7. Schlichting, H. 1978. Boundary Layer Theory, 7th Ed., McGraw-Hill.

8. Stone, R. 1999. Introduction to Internal Combustion Engines, 3rd Ed., Society of Automotive Engineers (SAE).

9. Anderson, A. D. 1999. Aircraft Performance and Design, WCB/McGraw-Hill.

10. Howe, M. S. 1984. On the Absorption of Sound by Turbulence and Other Hydrodynamic Flows, Journal of Applied Mathematics, Vol. 32, pp. 187-209.

11. Alfredson, R. J. and P. O. A. L. Davies. 1970. The Radiation of Sound from an Engine Exhaust, Journal of Sound and Vibration, Vol. 13, No. 4, pp. 389-408.

12. Munt, R. M. 1977. The Interaction of Sound with a Subsonic Jet issuing from a Semi-Infinite Cylindrical Pipe, Journal of Fluid mechanics, Vol. 83, part 4, pp. 609-640.

Recent Progress Towards a Large Eddy Simulation Code for Jet Aeroacoustics

A. Uzun,[*] G. A. Blaisdell,[†] and A. S. Lyrintzis[‡]

School of Aeronautics and Astronautics
Purdue University
West Lafayette, IN 47907

In this paper, we present 3-D Large Eddy Simulation(LES) results for turbulent round jets. Our recently developed LES code is part of a Computational Aeroacoustics(CAA) methodology that will eventually couple the near field unsteady LES data with an integral acoustic formulation for the far field noise prediction of turbulent jets. The code employs high-order accurate compact differencing together with implicit spatial filtering and state-of-the-art non-reflecting boundary conditions. The classical Smagorinsky subgrid-scale(SGS) model is used for representing the effect of the unresolved scales on the resolved scales. Preliminary results obtained in our simulations seem encouraging when compared with experimental data.

Introduction

THE turbulent jet noise problem still remains one of the most complicated and difficult problems in aeroacoustics. There is a need for substantial amount of research in this area that will lead to improved jet noise prediction methodologies and aid in the design process of aircraft engines with low jet noise emissions. With the recent improvements in the processing speed of computers, the application of Direct Numerical Simulation(DNS) and Large Eddy Simulation(LES) to jet noise prediction methodologies is becoming more feasible. The first DNS of a turbulent jet was done for a Reynolds number 2000, supersonic jet at Mach 1.92 by Freund et al.[1] The computed sound pressure levels were compared with experimental data and found to be in good agreement with jets at similar convective Mach numbers. Freund[2] also simulated a Reynolds number 3600, Mach 0.9 turbulent jet using 25 million grid points, matching the parameters of the experimental jet studied by Stromberg et al.[3] Excellent agreement with the experimental data was obtained for both the mean flow field and the radiated sound. Such results clearly show the attractiveness of DNS to the jet noise problem. However, due to a wide range of length and time scales present in turbulent flows, DNS is still restricted to low-Reynolds-number flows in relatively simple geometries at present. DNS of high-Reynolds-number jet flows of practical interest would necessitate tremendous resolution requirements that are far beyond the reach of the capability of even the fastest supercomputers available today.

Therefore, as frustrating as it might seem, turbu-

lence still has to be modelled in some way to do simulations for problems of practical interest. LES, with lower computational cost, is an attractive alternative to DNS. In an LES, the large scales are directly solved and the effect of the small scales or the subgrid scales on the large scales are modelled. The large scales are generally much more energetic than the small ones and are directly affected by the boundary conditions. The small scales, however, are usually much weaker and they tend to have more or less a universal character. Hence it makes sense to directly simulate the more energetic large scales and model the effect of the small scales. LES methods are capable of simulating flows at higher Reynolds numbers and many successful LES computations for different types of flows have been performed to date. Since noise generation is an unsteady process, LES will probably be the most powerful computational tool to be used in jet noise research in the foreseeable future since it is the only way, other than DNS, to obtain time-accurate unsteady data.

One of the first attempts in using LES as a tool for jet noise prediction was carried out by Mankbadi et al.[4] They employed a high-order numerical scheme to perform LES of a supersonic jet flow to capture the time-dependent flow structure and applied Lighthill's theory[5] to calculate the far field noise. The first application of Kirchhoff's method in combination with LES to far-field jet noise was conducted by Lyrintzis and Mankbadi.[6] LES has also been used together with Kirchhoff's method[7] for the noise prediction of a Mach 2.0 jet by Gamet and Estivalezes[8] as well as for a Mach 1.2 jet with Mach 0.2 coflow by Choi et al.[9] with encouraging results obtained in both studies. Zhao et al.[10] did LES for a Mach 0.9, Reynolds number 3600 jet obtaining mean flow results that compared well with Freund's DNS and experi-

---

[*]Graduate Research Assistant, Student Member AIAA.
[†]Associate Professor, Senior Member AIAA.
[‡]Professor, AIAA Associate Fellow.

mental data. They also studied the far field noise from a Mach 0.4, Reynolds number 5000 jet. They compared Kirchhoff's method results with the directly computed sound and observed good agreement. Morris *et al.* simulated high speed round jet flows using the Nonlinear Disturbance Equations(NLDE).[11-15] In their NLDE method, the instantaneous quantities are decomposed into a time-independent mean component, a large-scale perturbation and a small-scale perturbation. The mean quantities are obtained using a traditional Reynolds Averaged Navier-Stokes(RANS) method. As in LES, they resolved the large-scale fluctuations directly and used a subgrid-scale model for the small-scale fluctuations in their unsteady calculations. In a recent paper,[16] they also report the noise from a supersonic elliptic jet. Chyczewski and Long[17] conducted a supersonic rectangular jet flow simulation and also did far field noise predictions with a Kirchhoff method. Boersma and Lele[18] did LES for a Mach 0.9 jet at Reynolds numbers of 3600 and 36000 without any noise predictions. More recently, Bogey *et al.*[19] simulated a Reynolds number 65000, Mach 0.9 jet using LES and obtained very good mean flow results, turbulent intensities as well as sound levels and directivity. Constantinescu and Lele[20] did simulations for a Mach 0.9 jet at Reynolds numbers of 3600 and 72000. They directly calculated the near-field noise using LES. Their mean flow parameters and turbulence statistics were in good agreement with experimental data and results from other simulations. The peak of the power spectra of the sound waves was also captured accurately in their calculations.

In general, the LES results in the literature are encouraging and show the potential promise of LES application to jet noise prediction. Except for the study of Choi *et al.*[9] which is not a well resolved LES, the highest Reynolds numbers reached in the LES simulations so far are still below those of practical interest. Simulations of jets at higher Reynolds numbers would be very helpful for analyzing the broad-banded noise spectrum at such high Reynolds numbers. On the other hand, none of the LES studies done so far have predicted the high-frequency noise associated with the unresolved scales. Obviously, a subgrid-scale model for noise is highly desirable. Piomelli *et al.*,[21] Rubinstein and Zhou,[22] Seror *et al.*,[23] and Zhao *et al.*[24] did some initial work on the investigation of the contribution of small-scales to the noise spectrum. More research in this area that will lead to development of subgrid-scale acoustic models is needed.

With this motivation behind the current study given, we now present the two main objectives of this research:

1. Development and validation of a versatile 3-D LES code for turbulent jet simulations. A high-order accurate 3-D LES code utilizing a robust dynamic subgrid scale model is being developed. Generalized curvilinear coordinates are used, so the code can be easily adapted for calculations in several applications with complicated geometries. Since the sound field is several orders of magnitude smaller than the aerodynamic field, we make use of high-order accurate non-dissipative compact schemes which satisfy the strict requirements of CAA. Implicit spatial filtering is employed to get rid of the high-frequency oscillations resulting from unresolved scales and boundary conditions. Non-reflecting boundary conditions are imposed on the boundaries of the domain to let outgoing disturbances exit domain without spurious reflection. A sponge zone that is attached downstream of the physical domain damps out the disturbances before they reach the outflow boundary. Significant progress towards this first goal has already been made. The current version of the LES code has the standard Smagorinsky model implemented. As will be shown in the results section, promising results were obtained with our current code.

2. Accurate prediction of the far field noise. Even though the sound is generated by a nonlinear process, the sound field itself is known to be linear and irrotational. This implies that instead of solving the full nonlinear flow equations out in the far field for sound propagation, one can use a cheaper method instead, such as Lighthill's acoustic analogy[5] or surface integral acoustic methods such as Kirchhoff's method[7] and the porous Ffowcs-Williams Hawkings (FW-H) equation.[25,26] In our future studies, the near field provided by the LES code will be supplied to a surface integral acoustic method for computing noise propagation to the far field. Results will be compared with experimental as well as computational data available in the literature.

Governing Equations

Large Eddy Simulation(LES) can be thought of as a compromise between Direct Numerical Simulation(DNS) and the Reynolds Averaged Navier-Stokes(RANS) equations. In a DNS, all the relevant scales of turbulence have to be directly computed, whereas in a RANS calculation, all the relevant scales of turbulence are modelled. In an LES, the flowfield is decomposed into a large-scale or resolved-scale component ($\bar{f}$) and a small-scale or subgrid-scale component (f_{sg}),

$$f = \bar{f} + f_{sg} \qquad (1)$$

The large-scale component is obtained by filtering the entire domain using a grid filter function, G, as follows

$$\bar{f}(\vec{x}) = \int_V G(\vec{x}, \vec{x}') f(\vec{x}') d\vec{x}' \qquad (2)$$

The filtering operation removes the small-scale or the subgrid-scale turbulence from the Navier-Stokes equations. The resulting governing equations are then solved directly for the large-scale turbulent motions while the effect of the subgrid-scales are computed using a subgrid-scale model, such as the classical Smagorinsky model[27] or the more sophisticated dynamic model proposed by Germano et al.[28]

For compressible flows, the large-scale component is written in terms of a Favre-filtered variable

$$\tilde{f} = \frac{\overline{\rho f}}{\bar{\rho}} \tag{3}$$

The Favre-filtered unsteady, compressible, non-dimensionalized Navier-Stokes equations formulated in conservative form are solved in this study. The continuity equation is given by

$$\frac{\partial \bar{\rho}}{\partial t} + \frac{\partial \bar{\rho} \tilde{u}_i}{\partial x_i} = 0 \tag{4}$$

The momentum equation is

$$\frac{\partial \bar{\rho} \tilde{u}_i}{\partial t} + \frac{\partial \bar{\rho} \tilde{u}_i \tilde{u}_j}{\partial x_j} + \frac{\partial \bar{p}}{\partial x_i} - \frac{\partial}{\partial x_j}(\hat{\sigma}_{ij} - \tau_{ij}) = 0 \tag{5}$$

where the resolved shear stress tensor is given by

$$\hat{\sigma}_{ij} = \frac{2\tilde{\mu}}{Re}\left(\tilde{S}_{ij} - \frac{1}{3}\tilde{S}_{kk}\delta_{ij}\right) \tag{6}$$

with the Favre-filtered strain rate tensor defined as

$$\tilde{S}_{ij} = \frac{1}{2}\left(\frac{\partial \tilde{u}_j}{\partial x_i} + \frac{\partial \tilde{u}_i}{\partial x_j}\right) \tag{7}$$

The subgrid-scale stress tensor is modelled as

$$\tau_{ij} = -2C\bar{\rho}\Delta^2 \tilde{S}_M\left(\tilde{S}_{ij} - \frac{1}{3}\tilde{S}_{kk}\delta_{ij}\right) + \frac{2}{3}C_I\bar{\rho}\Delta^2 \tilde{S}_M^2 \delta_{ij} \tag{8}$$

where

$$\tilde{S}_M = \left(2\tilde{S}_{ij}\tilde{S}_{ij}\right)^{1/2} \tag{9}$$

and C, C_I are the model coefficients, and Δ is the filter width or the eddy viscosity length scale. In the subgrid-scale stress equation, the first term on the right hand side is the original incompressible term in Smagorinsky's model,[27] and the second term is the compressible correction proposed by Yoshizawa[29] and implemented by Moin et al.[30]

Finally, the energy equation is

$$\frac{\partial \bar{e}_t}{\partial t} + \frac{\partial \tilde{u}_i(\bar{e}_t + \bar{p})}{\partial x_i} - \frac{\partial}{\partial x_i}\tilde{u}_j(\hat{\sigma}_{ij} - \tau_{ij}) + \frac{\partial}{\partial x_i}(\hat{q}_i + Q_i) = 0 \tag{10}$$

where the total energy is defined as

$$\bar{e}_t = \frac{1}{2}\bar{\rho}\tilde{u}_i\tilde{u}_i + \frac{\bar{p}}{\gamma - 1} \tag{11}$$

The resolved heat flux is

$$\hat{q}_i = -\left[\frac{\tilde{\mu}}{(\gamma - 1)M_r^2 RePr}\right]\frac{\partial \tilde{T}}{\partial x_i} \tag{12}$$

and the subgrid-scale heat flux is modelled as

$$Q_i = \frac{-C\bar{\rho}\Delta^2 \tilde{S}_M}{Pr_t}\frac{\partial \tilde{T}}{\partial x_i} \tag{13}$$

The ideal gas relation

$$\bar{p} = \frac{\bar{\rho}\tilde{T}}{\gamma M_r^2} \tag{14}$$

and Sutherland's law for the molecular viscosity $\tilde{\mu} = \mu(\tilde{T})$ are also used in these equations with the Sutherland constant and the reference temperature chosen as $110K$ and $288K$, respectively.

The three coefficients for the subgrid-scale models are C, C_I and the turbulent Prandtl number, Pr_t. In the standard Smagorinsky model with compressibility corrections, these coefficients are set to constant values based on previous studies. It is also possible to represent these coefficients as functions of space and time, and compute them dynamically as part of the flowfield simulation.[28,30]

In order to do direct numerical simulations using these Favre-filtered equations, all spatially filtered variables can be replaced by their unfiltered forms and the subgrid-scale stress tensor and the subgrid-scale heat flux terms are simply set to zero.

The equations given so far are formulated in Cartesian coordinates. For problems involving complex geometries, the form of the governing equations in generalized curvilinear coordinates should be used. Extension of the equations from Cartesian coordinates to generalized curvilinear coordinates is straightforward and will not be presented here. In this work, we use the governing equations formulated in curvilinear coordinates and solve the discretized equations using the methods described in the next section.

Numerical Methods

We first transform a given non-uniformly spaced curvilinear computational grid in physical space to a uniform grid in computational space and solve the discretized governing equations on the uniform grid. To compute the spatial derivatives at interior grid points away from the boundaries, we employ the non-dissipative sixth-order compact scheme of Lele.[31] For boundary points, we apply the third-order one-sided compact scheme and for the points next to the boundaries, we use the fourth-order central compact scheme formulation.

Spatial filtering is sometimes used as a means of suppressing unwanted numerical instabilities that can arise from the boundary conditions, unresolved scales and mesh non-uniformities. In our study, we considered two different filters. We initially used the following fourth-order compact filter developed by Lele[31]

$$\beta\hat{\phi}_{i-2} + \alpha\hat{\phi}_{i-1} + \hat{\phi}_i + \alpha\hat{\phi}_{i+1} + \beta\hat{\phi}_{i+2} = a\phi_i$$
$$+b(\phi_{i+1} + \phi_{i-1}) + c(\phi_{i+2} + \phi_{i-2})$$
$$+d(\phi_{i+3} + \phi_{i-3}) \quad (15)$$

where ϕ_i and $\hat{\phi}_i$ represent the solution variable and the spatially filtered solution variable at point i, respectively and the coefficients are given by

$$\alpha = 0.652247, \qquad \beta = 0.170293$$

$$a = \frac{2 + 3\alpha}{4}, \quad b = \frac{9 + 16\alpha + 10\beta}{32} \quad (16)$$

$$c = \frac{\alpha + 4\beta}{8}, \quad d = \frac{6\beta - 1}{32}$$

The application of this filter results in a penta-diagonal system of equations. It was determined by Zhao[32] that filtering at and near the boundaries is not necessary and therefore, this filter is used on grid points $i = 5$ through $i = N - 4$ where N is the total number of grid points along the grid line.

The second filter we considered is the following sixth-order tri-diagonal filter used by Visbal and Gaitonde[33]

$$\alpha_f\hat{\phi}_{i-1} + \hat{\phi}_i + \alpha_f\hat{\phi}_{i-1} = \sum_{n=0}^{3} \frac{a_n}{2}(\phi_{i+n} + \phi_{i-n}) \quad (17)$$

where

$$a_0 = \frac{11}{16} + \frac{5\alpha_f}{8}, \quad a_1 = \frac{15}{32} + \frac{17\alpha_f}{16},$$

$$a_2 = \frac{-3}{16} + \frac{3\alpha_f}{8}, \quad a_3 = \frac{1}{32} - \frac{\alpha_f}{16} \quad (18)$$

The parameter α_f must satisfy the inequality $-0.5 < \alpha_f < 0.5$. A less dissipative filter is obtained with higher values of α_f within the given range. With $\alpha_f = 0.5$, there is no filtering effect. Since this filter has a 7-point right-hand side stencil, it obviously cannot be used at near-boundary points. Instead, one-sided, sixth-order equations given by Visbal and Gaitonde[33] are used for near-boundary points. The boundary points, $i = 1$ and $i = N$ are left unfiltered.

The solution is normally filtered in every spatial direction at the end of every time step. In DNS calculations, filtering is typically used to maintain numerical stability. The filter eliminates all the scales that cannot be resolved by the finite difference scheme. Hence, in LES calculations, the filter is treated as the grid filter.

The standard fourth-order explicit Runge-Kutta scheme is used for time advancement. For boundary conditions, we initially employed Thompson's non-reflecting boundary conditions[34] on all boundaries of

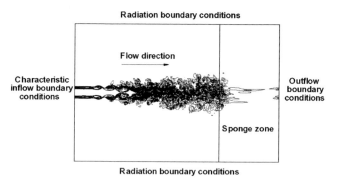

Fig. 1   Schematic of the boundary conditions.

the domain except for the inflow boundary. However, during our 3-D turbulent round jet simulations at a Reynolds number of 36000(based on jet diameter), we discovered that Thompson's boundary conditions actually did not provide the correct entrainment flow physics on the boundaries of a Cartesian grid. Hence, we decided to switch to the boundary conditions of Tam and Dong.[35] The original two-dimensional boundary conditions of Tam and Dong were recently extended to 3-D by Bogey and Bailly.[36] The 3-D radiation boundary conditions formulated in spherical coordinates are applied on the lateral boundaries of the computational domain illustrated in figure 1. It should be noted that Tam and Dong's radiation boundary conditions are formulated for boundaries to which only acoustic disturbances reach. The lateral boundaries of figure 1 are therefore suitable for the application of these boundary conditions. However, radiation boundary conditions cannot be applied on the outflow boundary of figure 1 since there are entropy and vorticity waves in addition to acoustic waves crossing this boundary. Instead, Tam and Dong's outflow boundary conditions are imposed on the outflow boundary.

For the outflow boundary, we use the sponge zone method proposed by Colonius *et al.*[37] In this method, a sponge zone is attached downstream of the physical domain. We apply grid stretching and explicit filtering in this exit zone to dissipate the vortices present in the flowfield before they hit the outflow boundary. We then use Tam and Dong's outflow boundary conditions without any modification at the end of the sponge zone. This method has been shown to be quite effective in minimizing reflections from the outflow boundary.

The inflow boundary is responsible for both allowing the outgoing acoustic waves to leave the domain as well as generating disturbances that trigger the growth of instabilities in the flowfield. For the inflow boundary conditions, we apply a procedure based on characteristics.[32]

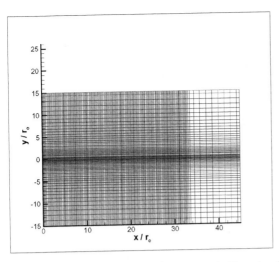

Fig. 2 The $x-y$ section of the computational grid used in the $Re_D = 36000$ simulation. (Every 2nd node is shown.)

Results

Before doing any 3-D simulations, we studied a 2-D planar mixing layer problem to test the various numerical algorithms implemented in our 3-D LES code. Our 2-D results compared well with the available experimental and computational data in the literature.

The first 3-D LES test case we considered is a turbulent round jet at a Mach number of 0.9. The Reynolds number of the jet is

$$Re_D = \frac{\rho_j U_j D_j}{\mu_j} = 3600 \quad (19)$$

where ρ_j, U_j, μ_j are the jet centerline density, velocity and viscosity at the nozzle exit, respectively and D_j is the jet diameter. This is the same test case studied by Freund[2] in his DNS. We obtained promising results in this simulation. Due to space restrictions, we will skip the details of this test case here.

For our second test case, we studied a turbulent round jet at a Reynolds number of 36000. The stretched Cartesian grid used in this test case had $350 \times 128 \times 128$ points in the x, y, and z directions respectively. Figures 2 and 3 illustrate the $x-y$ and $y-z$ sections of our grid. The domain extends to about $45r_o$ in the streamwise direction and from $-15r_o$ to $15r_o$ in the transverse y and z directions, where r_o is the jet radius. In the x direction, the physical region ends at around $x = 32r_o$. The grid spacing along the x direction in the physical portion of the grid is uniform and about $0.10r_o$. The minimum grid spacing in the y and z directions is about $0.05r_o$ around the jet centerline. Exponential grid stretching is applied along the transverse directions such that the maximum spacing around the external boundaries is about $0.66r_o$.

For the inflow forcing in this test case, we applied the same kind of forcing used by Constantinescu and Lele[20] in their LES calculations. In this forcing,

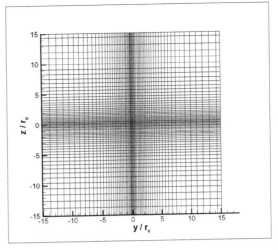

Fig. 3 The $y-z$ section of the computational grid used in the $Re_D = 36000$ simulation. (Every 2nd node is shown.)

time-harmonic fluctuations are imposed on the mean streamwise velocity on the inflow boundary as follows:

$$v_x(r) = \frac{1}{2}U_o \left[1 - \tanh\left[b\left(\frac{r}{r_o} - \frac{r_o}{r} \right) \right] \right] (1 + \alpha \sin(2\pi St\, t)) \quad (20)$$

where the Strouhal number, $St = 2r_o f/U_o$ is 0.9, r_o is the jet radius, U_o is the mean jet centerline velocity on the inflow boundary, f is the frequency of the perturbations, $b = 3.125$ is the shear layer thickness parameter, and the amplitude of the sinusoidal oscillations, α is 0.005. Randomly generated perturbations are applied on the azimuthal velocity component using the following equation

$$v_\theta'(r, \theta) = 0.025 U_o\, \epsilon \exp\left(-3\left(1 - \frac{r}{r_o} \right)^2 \right) \quad (21)$$

where ϵ is a random number between -0.5 and 0.5. The exponential function in the above equation localizes the perturbations within the shear layer region only. Both the mean azimuthal velocity and the mean radial velocity on the inflow boundary are zero. We did not impose any fluctuations on the radial velocity component.

As will be explained below, we did several runs in this test case. For all the simulations presented in this section, we used 128 processors on Indiana University's IBM-SP research computer. Each run required about 3 days to complete. For every simulation, we ran a total of 50000 time steps during which an acoustic wave travelling at the ambient sound speed moved a distance of about 37 times the domain length in the streamwise direction. The initial transients exited the domain over the first 10000 time steps. We then collected the flow statistics over the other 40000 time steps. Although a value of $C = 0.012$ was used for our $Re_D = 3600$ simulation, the Smagorinsky co-efficient at this higher Reynolds number (36000) was chosen as $C = 0.018$ in an *ad hoc* manner. As the Reynolds number is increased, the dissipative length scales are hardly resolved on relatively coarse grids, hence all the dissipation has to come from the SGS model. We did a Kolmogorov length scale analysis and determined that our coarsest grid resolution for this Reynolds number was between 50 and 60 times the local Kolmogorov length scale. Assuming that the upper limit of the dissipative length scales is 60 times the Kolmogorov length scale,[38, 39] we see that we hardly resolved any of the dissipative length scales in portions of the flow where the local length scales were very small. We believe that a larger coefficient should represent the effect of the dissipative length scales on the large scales more accurately at high Reynolds numbers on a relatively coarse grid. For comparison, Bogey *et al.*[19] used a larger constant of $C = 0.18^2 = 0.0324$ in their LES calculation for a jet at a Reynolds number of 65000. We kept the compressibility correction constant at $C_I = 0.0066$, and the turbulent Prandtl number at $Pr_t = 0.7$, same as the values used in the $Re_D = 3600$ simulation.

As mentioned previously, we discovered some entrainment flow problems with Thompson's boundary conditions during the runs done in this test case. Since we are dealing with a round jet problem, the ambient fluid that is entrained by the jet should be coming in radially towards the jet centerline along the boundaries of the $y - z$ section of the grid that was previously shown in figure 3. However, it was found that with Thompson's boundary conditions, the entrained fluid came in at almost normal angles pretty much everywhere along the boundaries except at the corners. Clearly, this is not physical. Hence, starting from the current test case, we decided to employ the state-of-the-art Tam and Dong's boundary conditions which solved the entrainment problem.

Figure 4 shows the instantaneous contours of vorticity magnitude on the $x - z$ plane. The jet is initially laminar, then the transition process starts and the jet becomes fully turbulent after its potential core breaks up.

In order to study the effect of spatial filtering on our results, we did a run using the 4th-order accurate implicit penta-diagonal filter as well as another run using the 6th-order accurate implicit tri-diagonal filter with $\alpha_f = 0.49$. The solution was filtered once in each spatial dimension at the end of every time step in both runs. Figures 5 through 9 summarize the mean flow results obtained with the 4th-order accurate penta-diagonal filter. Our results are compared with the experimental data of Hussein *et al.*[40] for an incompressible jet at $Re_D = 95500$ as well as that of Panchapakesan *et al.*[41] for an incompressible jet at $Re_D = 11000$. In figure 5, we plot the streamwise

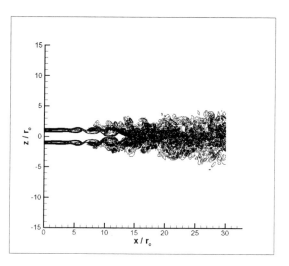

Fig. 4 **Instantaneous contours of vorticity magnitude on the $x - z$ plane at $y = 0$, $Re_D = 36000$. 30 levels shown.**

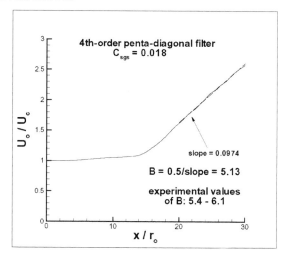

Fig. 5 **Inverse of the mean streamwise velocity on the centerline normalized by the jet inflow velocity, 4th-order accurate filter, $C_{sgs} = 0.018$.**

variation of the inverse of the mean centerline velocity normalized by the jet inflow velocity. After transition to turbulence, we get a linear growth. The slope of the line can be used to compute the jet decay coefficient and our value is around 5.13. Experimental values of the jet decay coefficient are in between 5.4 and 6.1. The reason for our low value will be explained shortly. The growth of the half-velocity radius, illustrated in figure 6, also shows a linear growth in the turbulent region of the jet, consistent with experimental observations. The slope of the linear line which is defined as the jet spreading rate, is about 0.0918. Experimental values for the jet spreading rate range from 0.086 to 0.096. Mean streamwise velocity profiles at two downstream locations are plotted in figure 7. From this figure, it can be observed that the profiles of our compressible jet at the two downstream locations collapse onto each other fairly well and exhibit

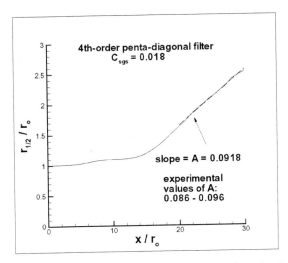

Fig. 6 Half-velocity radius normalized by the jet radius, 4th-order accurate filter, $C_{sgs} = 0.018$.

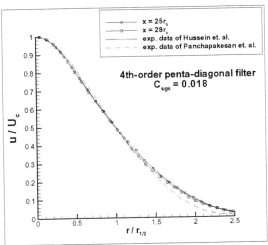

Fig. 7 Normalized mean streamwise velocity profiles and comparison with experimental data, 4th-order accurate filter, $C_{sgs} = 0.018$.

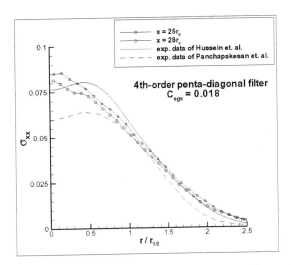

Fig. 8 Normalized Reynolds stress σ_{xx} profiles and comparison with experimental data, 4th-order accurate filter, $C_{sgs} = 0.018$.

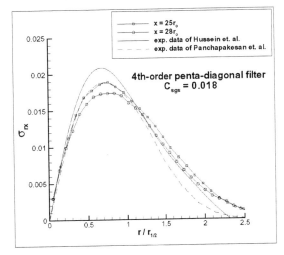

Fig. 9 Normalized Reynolds stress σ_{rx} profiles and comparison with experimental data, 4th-order accurate filter, $C_{sgs} = 0.018$.

self-similarity which is consistent with experimental observations. Our results are also in very good agreement with the experimental profiles of incompressible jets. We also compared our Reynolds stresses with the available experimental data of Hussein $et\ al.$[40] and Panchapakesan $et\ al.$[41] The normalized Reynolds stresses in cylindrical coordinates are defined as follows:

$$\sigma_{xx} = \frac{\overline{v_x' v_x'}}{U_c^2} \quad \sigma_{rr} = \frac{\overline{v_r' v_r'}}{U_c^2}$$

$$\sigma_{\theta\theta} = \frac{\overline{v_\theta' v_\theta'}}{U_c^2} \quad \sigma_{rx} = \frac{\overline{v_r' v_x'}}{U_c^2} \quad (22)$$

where v_x', v_r', v_θ' are the axial, radial and azimuthal components of the fluctuating velocity, respectively, U_c is the mean jet centerline velocity at a given axial location, and the overbar denotes time-averaging. In order to compare our Reynolds stresses with the ex-

perimental data, we transformed our Reynolds stresses from the Cartesian coordinate system to the cylindrical coordinate system. The transformation process was trivial and the details of it will be skipped here. Figures 8 and 9 plot our computed Reynolds stresses and compare them with the experimental data. From these plots, we see that our Reynolds stress profiles also exhibit self-similarity, consistent with experimental evidence, and our data are again in fairly good agreement with experiment.

Figures 10 through 14 summarize the mean flow results obtained with the 6th-order accurate tri-diagonal filter. In general, the two sets of results obtained with different filters do not seem to differ much although the Reynolds stress profiles computed with the 6th-order filter match the experimental profiles of Hussein $et\ al.$[40] slightly better. The jet decay coeffi-

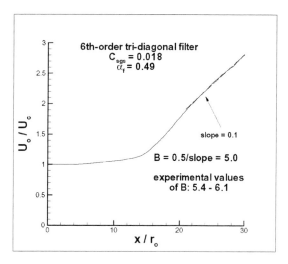

Fig. 10 Inverse of the mean streamwise velocity on the centerline normalized by the jet inflow velocity, 6th-order accurate filter, $C_{sgs} = 0.018$, $\alpha_f = 0.49$.

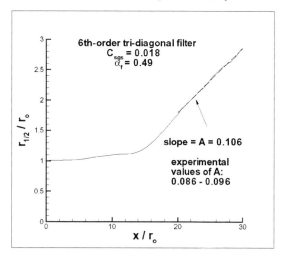

Fig. 11 Half-velocity radius normalized by the jet radius, 6th-order accurate filter, $C_{sgs} = 0.018$, $\alpha_f = 0.49$.

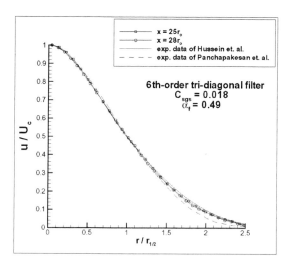

Fig. 12 Normalized mean streamwise velocity profiles and comparison with experimental data, 6th-order accurate filter, $C_{sgs} = 0.018$, $\alpha_f = 0.49$.

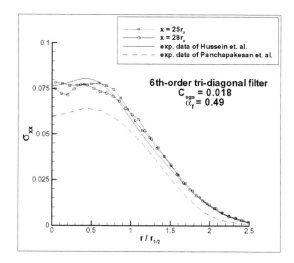

Fig. 13 Normalized Reynolds stress σ_{xx} profiles and comparison with experimental data, 6th-order accurate filter, $C_{sgs} = 0.018$, $\alpha_f = 0.49$.

cients obtained in both runs are a bit low relative to the experimental values. The jet spreading coefficient obtained with the 4th-order accurate filter is just below the upper limit of the experimental values while the one obtained with the 6th-order accurate filter is slightly larger. The mean streamwise velocity profiles as well as the Reynolds stress profiles in both cases compare fairly well with experiment.

We also investigated the effect of the Smagorinsky coefficient on the mean flow properties. We did a new run using $C = 0.019$ and the 6th-order filter with $\alpha_f = 0.49$. The mean flow results for this simulation are plotted in figures 15 through 19. As can be seen from these results, a slightly larger Smagorinsky coefficient results in a jet decay coefficient of 5.76 which is within the range of experimental observations. The jet decay coefficient obtained with $C = 0.018$ was 5.0, a bit smaller than the lower limit of experimen-

tal data. The reason for this difference is believed to be the fact that with a higher SGS model coefficient, the jet loses more of its energy into dissipation and does not have as much energy left to spread out. Furthermore, with increasing jet decay coefficient, the jet spreading rate gets smaller. This is justified by the fact that a jet spreading rate of 0.106 is obtained with $C = 0.018$ while a value of 0.086 is obtained with $C = 0.019$. Hence, the jet decay coefficient as well as the jet spreading rate are directly affected by the SGS model constant. Another interesting fact is that even though the simulation with $C = 0.019$ produced a jet decay coefficient and a jet spreading rate in good agreement with experiment, we see that the Reynolds stress profiles in this simulation have significantly changed relative to the ones obtained in the simulation done with $C = 0.018$. This must be due to the too dissipa-

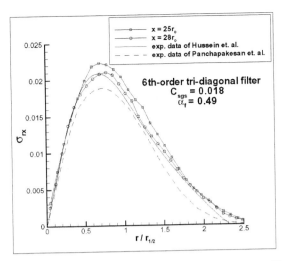

Fig. 14 Normalized Reynolds stress σ_{rx} profiles and comparison with experimental data, 6th-order accurate filter, $C_{sgs} = 0.018$, $\alpha_f = 0.49$.

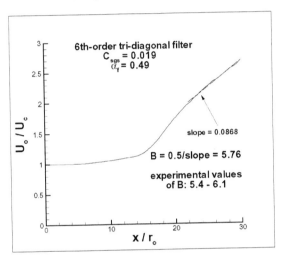

Fig. 15 Inverse of the mean streamwise velocity on the centerline normalized by the jet inflow velocity, 6th-order accurate filter, $C_{sgs} = 0.019$, $\alpha_f = 0.49$.

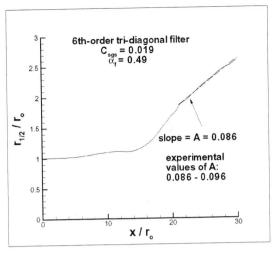

Fig. 16 Half-velocity radius normalized by the jet radius, 6th-order accurate filter, $C_{sgs} = 0.019$, $\alpha_f = 0.49$.

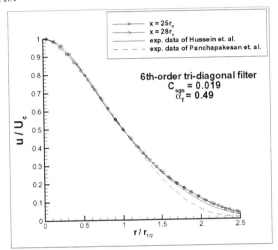

Fig. 17 Normalized mean streamwise velocity profiles and comparison with experimental data, 6th-order accurate filter, $C_{sgs} = 0.019$, $\alpha_f = 0.49$.

tive nature of the Smagorinsky SGS model. A slight increase in the model coefficient provides more dissipation but at the same time it suppresses more of the turbulence and subsequently causes a significant change in the Reynolds stresses.

Finally, in order to see how much the filtering parameter α_f affects the mean flow results, we did a simulation using $\alpha_f = 0.45$ in our 6th-order tridiagonal filter with the Smagorinsky coefficient chosen as $C = 0.018$. Shown in figures 20 through 24 are the results obtained in this run. It is easily observed that the lower value of the filtering parameter qualitatively has the same effect as increasing the Smagorinsky coefficient. This makes sense since the lower values of α_f correspond to a more dissipative filter. The dissipation coming from the filter at this value of α_f seems to be causing noticeable changes in the Reynolds stress

profiles relative to the ones obtained using $\alpha_f = 0.49$ with $C = 0.018$.

Concluding Remarks - Future Work

As part of a jet noise prediction methodology, we have developed and tested a 3-D Large Eddy Simulation code. So far, our main concern was the validation of the LES code, therefore studies related to the aeroacoustics of turbulent jets have not been performed yet. In our initial 3-D test cases, we performed turbulence simulations on grids consisting of about 6 million grid points in reasonable amounts of run time of less than 4 days using up to 128 processors on SGI Origin 2000 and IBM SP parallel computers. Calculations were done for turbulent jets at Reynolds numbers of 3600 and 36000. Acceptable mean flow results were obtained in our simulations and we believe we gathered enough evidence towards the validation of our LES

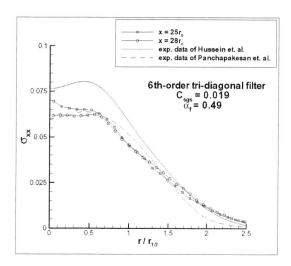

Fig. 18 Normalized Reynolds stress σ_{xx} profiles and comparison with experimental data, 6th-order accurate filter, $C_{sgs} = 0.019$, $\alpha_f = 0.49$.

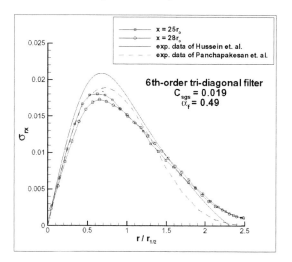

Fig. 19 Normalized Reynolds stress σ_{rx} profiles and comparison with experimental data, 6th-order accurate filter, $C_{sgs} = 0.019$, $\alpha_f = 0.49$.

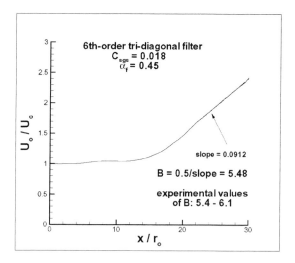

Fig. 20 Inverse of the mean streamwise velocity on the centerline normalized by the jet inflow velocity, 6th-order accurate filter, $C_{sgs} = 0.018$, $\alpha_f = 0.45$.

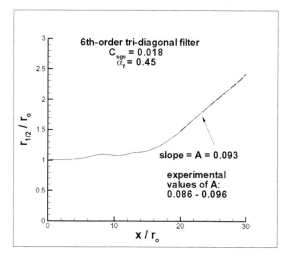

Fig. 21 Half-velocity radius normalized by the jet radius, 6th-order accurate filter, $C_{sgs} = 0.018$, $\alpha_f = 0.45$.

code. However, we found that the Smagorinsky SGS model is too dissipative and the mean flow results are sensitive to the particular choice of the model constant. The effect of different grid filters on the results was also studied. In general, the 4th-order penta-diagonal filter results and the 6th-order tri-diagonal filter with $\alpha_f = 0.49$ results do not differ much. Yet, the more dissipative tri-diagonal filter with $\alpha_f = 0.45$ has similar effects as increasing the SGS model constant.

In our future work, we will implement a dynamic SGS model that is applicable to inhomogeneous turbulent flows in complex geometries. Currently, one model under consideration for implementation into our code is the localized dynamic SGS model by Kim and Menon.[42–44] This model is based on the subgrid kinetic energy which is computed by solving a transport equation. The model coefficients are determined using a localized dynamic procedure. This is actually a one-equation SGS model. Unlike the algebraic Smagorinsky model, it does not require the assumption of local equilibrium between the SGS energy production and dissipation rate. As a result, the model allows non-negligible kinetic energy to remain unresolved in the small scales. This implies that the computational grids to be used with this model can be relatively coarser than those that would be needed with an algebraic SGS model.

Our eventual goal in this study is to accurately capture the noise field generated by the turbulent mixing of the jet and compute the sound propagation to the far field. For this purpose, the near-field data computed by our LES code will be coupled with a surface integral acoustic method. Surface integral acoustic methods based on the Kirchhoff and the porous Ffowcs Williams-Hawkings (FW-H) formulations have been

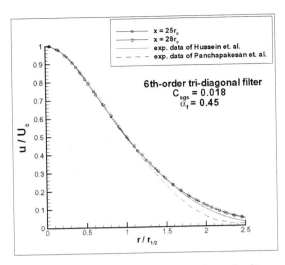

Fig. 22 Normalized mean streamwise velocity profiles and comparison with experimental data, 6th-order accurate filter, $C_{sgs} = 0.018$, $\alpha_f = 0.45$.

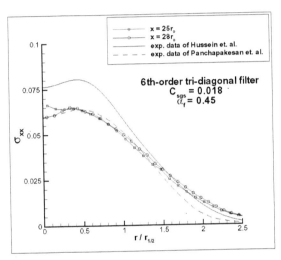

Fig. 23 Normalized Reynolds stress σ_{xx} profiles and comparison with experimental data, 6th-order accurate filter, $C_{sgs} = 0.018$, $\alpha_f = 0.45$.

widely used in Computational Aeroacoustics (CAA) to date. Although Kirchhoff's method has been used in jet noise problems before, the porous FW-H equation has not been widely applied to this problem yet. One disadvantage of the Kirchhoff method is that the control surface must be chosen to be in the linear flow region since Kirchhoff's formulation is based on the linear wave equation and does not include nonlinear flow effects. The location of the linear region is not well defined and is problem dependent. However, the FW-H formulation is based on the conservation laws of fluid mechanics rather than on the wave equation. The FW-H formulation includes nonlinearities and hence the integration surface can be placed in the nonlinear regions of the flow field if the quadrupole source is included. The quadrupole source term accounts for nonlinear effects such as nonlinear wave propagation, variations on

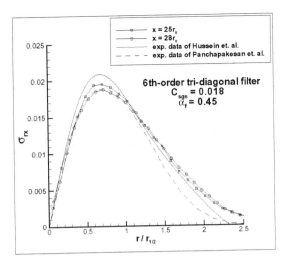

Fig. 24 Normalized Reynolds stress σ_{rx} profiles and comparison with experimental data, 6th-order accurate filter, $C_{sgs} = 0.018$, $\alpha_f = 0.45$.

the local sound speed and noise generated by shocks, vorticity and turbulence in the flow field. Brentner and Farassat[45] showed that if the quadrupole term is neglected outside the control surface, the FW-H solution is less sensitive than the Kirchhoff method to the placement of integration surface. They also showed that the FW-H formulation is equivalent to the Kirchhoff formulation when the integration surface is located in the linear flow region. Hence, our efforts will be concentrated on the application of the FW-H method to jet noise prediction. In order to avoid boundary effects, the control surface needed for the FW-H method will be kept outside the jet flow, but inside the boundaries of the computational domain used in LES calculations. The quantities needed on the control surface will be provided by the LES code.

Acknowledgments

This work is sponsored by the Indiana 21st Century Research & Technology Fund and was also partially supported by National Computational Science Alliance under the grant CTS010032N, and utilized the SGI Origin 2000 computer systems at the University of Illinois at Urbana-Champaign. Some of the computations were performed on the IBM-SP research computers of Indiana University and Purdue University.

References

[1]Freund, J. B., Lele, S. K., and Moin, P., "Direct Numerical Simulation of a Mach 1.92 turbulent jet and its sound field," *AIAA Journal*, Vol. 38, No. 11, November 2000, pp. 2023–2031.

[2]Freund, J. B., "Noise Sources in a low-Reynolds-number turbulent jet at Mach 0.9," *Journal of Fluid Mechanics*, Vol. 438, 2001, pp. 277–305.

[3]Stromberg, J. L., McLaughlin, D. K., and Troutt, T. R., "Flow Field and Acoustic properties of a Mach Number 0.9 Jet at a low Reynolds Number," *Journal of Sound and Vibration*, Vol. 72, No. 2, 1980, pp. 159–176.

[4] Mankbadi, R. R., Hayder, M. E., and Povinelli, L. A., "Structure of supersonic jet flow and its radiated sound," *AIAA Journal*, Vol. 32, No. 5, May 1994, pp. 897–906.

[5] Lighthill, M. J., "On the Sound Generated Aerodynamically: I, General Theory," *Proc. Royal Soc. London A*, Vol. 211, 1952, pp. 564–587.

[6] Lyrintzis, A. S. and Mankbadi, R. R., "Prediction of the far-field jet noise using Kirchhoff's formulation," *AIAA Journal*, Vol. 1, No. 2, 1996, pp. 1–4.

[7] Kirchhoff, G. R., "Zur Theorie der Lichtstrahlen," *Annalen der Physik und Chemic*, Vol. 18, 1883, pp. 663–695.

[8] Gamet, L. and Estivalezes, J. L., "Application of Large-Eddy Simulations and Kirchhoff method to jet noise prediction," *AIAA Journal*, Vol. 36, No. 12, December 1998, pp. 2170–2178.

[9] Choi, D., Barber, T. J., Chiappetta, L. M., and Nishimura, M., "Large Eddy Simulation of high-Reynolds number jet flows," AIAA Paper No. 99-0230, January 1999.

[10] Zhao, W., Frankel, S. H., and Mongeau, L., "Large Eddy Simulations of Sound Radiation from Subsonic Turbulent Jets," *AIAA Journal*, Vol. 39, No. 8, August 2001, pp. 1469–1477.

[11] Morris, P. J., Wang, Q., Long, L. N., and Lockhard, D. P., "Numerical Predictions of High Speed Jet Noise," AIAA Paper No. 97-1598, May 1997.

[12] Morris, P. J., Long, L. N., Bangalore, A., and Wang, Q., "A Parallel Three-Dimensional Computational Aeroacoustics Method Using Nonlinear Disturbance Equations," *Journal of Computational Physics*, Vol. 133, 1997, pp. 56–74.

[13] Morris, P. J., Long, L. N., Scheidegger, T. E., Wang, Q., and Pilon, A. R., "High Speed Jet Noise Simulations," AIAA Paper No. 98-2290, 1998.

[14] Morris, P. J., Long, L. N., and Scheidegger, T., "Parallel computations of high speed jet noise," AIAA Paper No. 99-1873, 1999.

[15] Morris, P. J., Scheidegger, T. E., and Long, L. N., "Jet noise simulations for circular nozzles," AIAA Paper No. 2000-2080, June 2000.

[16] Boluriaan, S., Morris, P. J., Long, L. N., and Scheidegger, T., "High speed jet noise simulations for noncircular nozzles," AIAA Paper No. 2001-2272, May 2001.

[17] Chyczewski, T. S. and Long, L. N., "Numerical prediction of the noise produced by a perfectly expanded rectangular jet," AIAA Paper No. 96-1730, May 1996.

[18] Boersma, B. J. and Lele, S. K., "Large Eddy Simulation of a Mach 0.9 Turbulent Jet," AIAA Paper No. 99-1874, May 1999.

[19] Bogey, C., Bailly, C., and Juvé, D., "Computation of the sound radiated by a 3-D jet using Large Eddy Simulation," AIAA Paper No. 2000-2009, June 2000.

[20] Constantinescu, G. S. and Lele, S. K., "Large Eddy Simulation of a Near Sonic Turbulent Jet and its Radiated Noise," AIAA Paper No. 2001-0376, January 2001.

[21] Piomelli, U., Streett, C. L., and Sarkar, S., "On the computation of sound by large-eddy simulations," *Journal of Engineering Mathematics*, Vol. 32, 1997, pp. 217–236.

[22] Rubinstein, R. and Zhou, Y., "Characterization of Sound Radiation by Unresolved Scales of Motion in Computational Aeroacoustics," Tech. Rep. NASA/CR-1999-209688, ICASE Report No. 99-39, ICASE, NASA Langley Research Center, October 1999.

[23] Seror, C., Sagaut, P., Bailly, C., and Juvé, D., "On the radiated noise computed by large-eddy simulation," *Physics of Fluids*, Vol. 13, No. 2, February 2001, pp. 476–487.

[24] Zhao, W., Frankel, S. H., and Mongeau, L., "Effects of Spatial Filtering on Sound Radiation from a Subsonic Axisymmetric Jet," *AIAA Journal*, Vol. 38, No. 11, November 2000, pp. 2032–2039.

[25] Williams, J. E. F. and Hawkings, D. L., "Sound Generated by Turbulence and Surfaces in Arbitrary Motion," *Philosophical Transactions of the Royal Society*, Vol. A264, 1969, pp. 321–342.

[26] Crighton, D. G., Dowling, A. P., Williams, J. E. F., Heckl, M., and Leppington, F. G., *Modern Methods in Analytical Acoustics: Lecture Notes*, Springer–Verlag, London, 1992.

[27] Smagorinsky, J. S., "General Circulation Experiments with the Primitive Equations," *Monthly Weather Review*, Vol. 91, No. 3, March 1963, pp. 99–165.

[28] Germano, M., Piomelli, U., Moin, P., and Cabot, W., "A Dynamic Subgrid-Scale Eddy Viscosity Model," *Physics of Fluids A*, Vol. 3, No. 7, July 1991, pp. 1760–1765.

[29] Yoshizawa, A., "Statistical Theory for Compressible Turbulent Shear Flows, with Application to Subgrid Modeling," *Physics of Fluids*, Vol. 29, No. 7, July 1986, pp. 2152–2164.

[30] Moin, P., Squires, K., Cabot, W., and Lee, S., "A Dynamic Subgrid-Scale Model for Compressible Turbulence and Scalar Transport," *Physics of Fluids A*, Vol. 3, No. 11, November 1991, pp. 2746–2757.

[31] Lele, S. K., "Compact Finite Difference Schemes with Spectral-like Resolution," *Journal of Computational Physics*, Vol. 103, No. 1, November 1992, pp. 16–42.

[32] Zhao, W., *A Numerical Investigation of Sound Radiated from Subsonic Jets with Application to Human Phonation*, Ph.D. thesis, School of Mechanical Engineering, Purdue University, West Lafayette, IN, June 2000.

[33] Visbal, M. R. and Gaitonde, D. V., "Very high-order spatially implicit schemes for computational acoustics on curvilinear meshes," *Journal of Computational Acoustics*, Vol. 9, No. 4, 2001, pp. 1259–1286.

[34] Thompson, W. K., "Time-Dependent Boundary Conditions for Hyperbolic Systems, II," *Journal of Computational Physics*, Vol. 89, No. 1, August 1990, pp. 439–461.

[35] Tam, C. K. W. and Dong, Z., "Radiation and Outflow Boundary Conditions for Direct Computation of Acoustic and Flow Disturbances in a Nonuniform Mean Flow," *Journal of Computational Acoustics*, Vol. 4, No. 2, 1996, pp. 175–201.

[36] Bogey, C. and Bailly, C., "Three-dimensional non-reflective boundary conditions for acoustic simulations: far field formulation and validation test cases," *Acta Acustica*, soon to appear.

[37] Colonius, T., Lele, S. K., and Moin, P., "Boundary Conditions for Direct Computation of Aerodynamic Sound Generation," *AIAA Journal*, Vol. 31, No. 9, September 1993, pp. 1574–1582.

[38] Pope, S. B., *Turbulent Flows*, Cambridge University Press, 2000.

[39] Piomelli, U., Scotti, A., and Balaras, E., "Large Eddy Simulations of Turbulent Flows, from Desktop to Supercomputer (Invited Talk)," Vector and Parallel Processing - VECPAR 2000, 4th International Conference, Porto, Portugal, Selected Papers and Invited Talks, June 2000.

[40] Hussein, H. J., Capp, S. C., and George, W. K., "Velocity measurements in a high-Reynolds-number, momentum-conserving, axisymmetric, turbulent jet," *Journal of Fluid Mechanics*, Vol. 258, 1994, pp. 31–75.

[41] Panchapakesan, N. R. and Lumley, J. L., "Turbulence measurements in axisymmetric jets of air and helium. Part 1. Air jets." *Journal of Fluid Mechanics*, Vol. 246, 1993, pp. 197–223.

[42] Kim, W.-W. and Menon, S., "A new dynamic one-equation subgrid-scale model for large eddy simulations," AIAA Paper No. 95-0356, January 1995.

[43] Kim, W.-W. and Menon, S., "An Unsteady Incompressible Navier-Stokes solver for Large Eddy Simulation of Turbulent Flows," *International Journal for Numerical Methods in Fluids*, Vol. 31, 1999, pp. 983–1017.

[44] Kim, W.-W. and Menon, S., "LES of Turbulent Fuel/Air Mixing in a Swirling Combustor," AIAA Paper No. 99-0200, January 1999.

[45] Brentner, K. S. and Farassat, F., "Analytical Comparison of the Acoustic Analogy and Kirchhoff Formulation for Moving Surfaces," *AIAA Journal*, Vol. 36, No. 8, August 1998, pp. 1379–1386.

AIAA 2002-2599

COMPREHENSIVE 3D UNSTEADY SIMULATIONS OF SUBSONIC AND SUPERSONIC HOT JET FLOW-FIELDS. PART 1: AERODYNAMIC ANALYSIS.

N. Lupoglazoff[*], A. Biancherin[†], F. Vuillot[‡], G.Rahier[*]
ONERA, Châtillon, France

Abstract

This paper presents numerical simulations of subsonic and supersonic hot jets, conducted at ONERA and aimed at the prevision of radiated jet noise. This first paper describes the aerodynamic part of this work, the acoustic part being related in a second paper. Full 3D unsteady simulations are performed with a parallel version of the ONERA MSD code. At this point no turbulence modeling is used : large scale structures are directly captured by the Navier-Stokes solver while the numerical scheme dissipates smaller scales. Grid construction is central to this work. The grid incorporates the nozzle and contains a refined portion intended to properly compute the jet region, including the propagation of acoustic waves. Away from the jet region the grid cell size is continuously increased, in order to allow the numerical scheme to dissipate the acoustic waves before they reach the domain external boundaries. One objective of grid construction is to avoid having boundary conditions close to the jet region, where natural instability waves must be free to appear. Parallel computations on 5 processors of ONERA NEC SX5 vector computer permitted to run a typical computation, compatible with statistical and acoustical processings, during one week-end. Means and RMS results for both subsonic and supersonic jets are compared to experimental results or empirical laws. Detailed analyses of the nozzle exit regions are provided and instability waves are identified. More classical RANS (k, ε) computations have also been performed for the supersonic case and are compared to the averaged 3D unsteady results. For the subsonic case a grid sensitivity study was carried out on a refined grid. Results obtained on both grids are compared. Results demonstrate that jet destabilization is obtained naturally without the need of external forcings. Analysis indicates that the computed unsteady fields are realistic and compare well with expected jet behaviors. One cause of concern is that the computed potential cones are consistently shorter than expected (of the order of 30% shorter). Explanations of this result and the consequences on the radiated noise are still under investigation.

Presentation

Future commercial aircrafts will face increasing regulations concerning noise emissions. In that context, jet noise is of particular concern, especially for high speed aircrafts at take-off, such as the next generation supersonic airplane. In France, several research programs have been initiated to study the problems faced by such vehicle. These include research activities on the prevision of supersonic and subsonic jet noise.

Jet noise has received much attention[e.g. 1, 2] in the past years: direct simulation have been attempted[3, 4], as well as simulations using some type of LES techniques[5-12], arguing that large turbulent structures are responsible for most of the acoustic emission of jets and that fine scale turbulence is less critical. Historically supersonic jets were first considered, due to the larger noise emissions and somewhat simpler boundary conditions for the numerical procedure. Larger noise emission minimizes the difficulty in predicting jet noise: acoustic sources are intense and more easily captured by the simulation. However, subsonic jets are closer to the actual problem of an airplane during take-off, since the jets are more likely to be subsonic under such conditions. This implies

that the tools developed and validated against supersonic jet conditions must also be capable of treating subsonic jets with less marked noise sources.

The present work has been carried out in the framework of an ONERA internal federative research project dedicated to the next generation supersonic transport aircraft, in connection with other national research programs concerned with the ATSF (Avion de Transport Supersonique du Futur) implying several national research laboratories such as ECL (Ecole Centrale de Lyon) and ISL (Institut de Saint-Louis).

ONERA DSNA department has a strong expertise in both advanced CFD and acoustics tools that permits to consider actual CAA applications. Jet noise is naturally part of this expertise and it was decided to initiate a comprehensive analysis of jet noise, including the full computation of the unsteady aerodynamic field, including the nozzles generating the jets, and the coupling with acoustic radiation codes, to extrapolate the aerodynamic computations to the far-field acoustic domain.

The work is presented in two companion papers. The first paper presents the aerodynamic analysis of the jet zone, while the second paper concentrates on the acoustic analysis. For both papers, the case of a

---

[*] Research scientist, DSNA department
[†] PhD student, DSNA department
[‡] Deputy head, DSNA department, Senior member

supersonic jet is first considered. This permitted to validate the procedure against experimental results obtained by Seiner & Ponton [13], for the case of a hot supersonic jet. The procedure was then applied to the case of a hot subsonic jet described in several ONERA publications and papers [14-17].

This first paper presents the numerical procedure that has been followed to obtain 3D unsteady Navier-Stokes solutions in the jet region. Both supersonic and subsonic cases followed similar tracks and were built with similar strategies. Results are compared to experimental data as well as to results from more classical RANS approaches (supersonic case). Grid sensitivity analysis was performed on the subsonic case. These computations served as input data for the second paper [17] that presents the results of the acoustic analysis.

Numerical procedure

At the beginning three main ideas were posed as guide lines. The first idea was that the aerodynamic computations should include the nozzle flow at the origin of the jet. Indeed, past works showed that when only the jet domain is considered, some form of perturbations must be externally incorporated into the computation to permit jet destabilization. In return, the perturbation can alter the radiated field, with the presence of additional spectral components that are difficult to remove from the computed radiated field. An other difficulty is the possible sensitivity of the computational results to the perturbations. For instance, the length of the potential core, the amplitude of the fluctuating field, as well as its spatial distribution can be affected. By moving the boundary conditions away from the critical jet origin location, it was anticipated that the instability waves, at the origin of the jet destabilization, would be allowed to evolve more naturally to produce realistic flow fields.

The second idea was to use parallel computing together with ad hoc choice of the grid size to permit a typical computation, producing acoustically useable data (i.e. several hundreds of D/U time units, where D is the nozzle exit diameter and U the nozzle exit axial velocity), in less than a week-end. Preliminary estimations concluded that a 2 millions point grid could produce such data in less than 100 hours of computation on one processor of the ONERA NEC SX5 16 processor supercomputer. Using 5 processors of this computer will then reduce the machine time to 20 hours that should easily fit in a week-end. CPU speed of over 12 GFlops was indeed attained.

The third idea was to use the numerical scheme to naturally damp the fluctuations before they reach the external boundaries of the computational domain. Indeed numerical wave reflections at boundaries is a difficult point for direct simulations of unsteady flow fields. Absorbing boundaries and/or sponge zones were often used in the past. However such treatments may pose some problems in practice to assure robustness and proper continuity properties for the numerical solution. Here, it was decided to use external grid which would contain cells of regularly increasing size as the external boundaries are approached, up to extra large cells that cannot propagate the fluctuating fields generated inside the grid zones with finer cells. This combination of fine and large cell sizes should ensure a flow field freed of unwanted wave reflections.

With these ideas in mind, both supersonic and subsonic grids were constructed. It was decided to use ONERA MSD code in its MSD 2.3.1 version, dated April 2001 [19]. This code is a referenced code intensively used, both for research and industrial activities, in the field of energetics and propulsion. It is a multi-domain, finite volume, parallel code with multi-species, reactive, two-phase flow capabilities, working on block structured meshes. The MSD code proposes several time and space integration schemes, up to second order implicit ADI time scheme and third order flux splitting spatial scheme. Preliminary tests showed that such combination of schemes was capable of correctly propagating acoustic wave down to 16 grid points per wavelength.

Test case definition

In order to be able to compare both the aerodynamic and the acoustic results to actual measurements, the following test cases were retained.

Supersonic jet

The Seiner & Ponton jet was selected. Reference[13] presents numerous results for various supersonic jets with different jet temperatures. We selected the cases of a cold (313 K) and hot (1370 K) Mach 2 jets. Since the exact geometry of the nozzle could not be found in the literature, we modified the geometry of the Eggers cold jet case to define a nozzle with the same throat and exit diameters as the Seiner & Ponton nozzle. The Eggers nozzle geometry was obtained from the Nasa web site (http://www.lerc.nasa.gov/www/wind/valid/homepage.html). The cold flow case was used for preliminary RANS computations and will not be detailed here. The hot flow case was selected, as in the work of L. Gamet [5], as the relevant test case, since most of the acoustic measurements presented in [13] concern this case. The corresponding hot jet characteristics are D_j= 9.144 cm , V_j=1120 m/s and $(Re)_j \approx 10^6$.

Subsonic jet

In the past years, a large amount of works was carried out at ONERA on hot subsonic jet noise[14-17]. From this large data base, we selected the case of subsonic hot jet (Mach number of 0.7) with the following characteristics:

Nozzle exit diameter: 80 mm
Stagnation temperature: 900 K
Stagnation pressure: 1,4 atm.
Jet exit velocity: 410 m/s

The corresponding Reynolds number is close to $1.2 \ 10^6$. The actual nozzle, used in the tests was recovered. After detailed geometric analysis of its internal and external shapes, a point CAO file was generated and input to the ICEM-CFD grid generation software that was used to generate the grid.

Grid constructions

Initial grids

Both supersonic and subsonic jet grids were constructed in the following manner:

- Domain 1: comprises the nozzle internal volume.
- Domain 2: consists of the upstream external domain close to the nozzle external wall.
- Domain 3 is a small domain extending from nozzle exit plane to a downstream plane located at 4R (i.e. 2D) from the nozzle lips. This location at 4R from the exit plane was chosen from experience of past LES simulations which had to be started away from the highly sheared flow at nozzle exit.
- Domain 4 is formed of the upstream external domain, extending to the external boundaries. boundaries.
- Domain 5 is a large downstream domain, comprising the jet itself and extending to external boundaries.

The grids were constructed in 2D, then the grid plane was rotated around the axis to produce 3D grids. 61 planes were used in all cases.

Depending on the case, these domains were assembled in 5 sets to equilibrate the processor loads. In particular, domain 5 had to be split in smaller domains to permit proper load balancing.

Both 3D grids were close to the 2 millions grid points limit (1,6 millions). Each grid comprised a refined zone extending axially to 26D from the nozzle exit plane and transversally between 2D (nozzle end) and 4D (26D end). In this refined zone the grid was sized such as to permit to properly capture the sheared flow as well as the propagation of the acoustic waves, up to a frequency corresponding to a Strouhal number of 0.3. Outside this zone, the scheme is not expected to propagate the waves without alterations. This is not a problem, since the control surfaces, used for the acoustic treatments are located inside the refined zone.

Figures 1 and 2 present the supersonic and subsonic jet grids.

Refined grid

For the subsonic case, a grid refinement study was performed, using the first results from the aerodynamic and acoustic analyses. The grid size in the refined zone was halfed in directions x and r. The small domain 3 was non longer needed and was merged into domain 5. The refined zone was extended radially (between 4D and 5D) and shortened axially (17D). This grid contains 2,4 millions grid points. Its cut-off frequency in the refined zone corresponds to a Stouhal number of 0.6. The number of cells in the refined zone increased from 629 280 to 1 399 320.

Initial and boundary conditions

Boundary conditions implementation was eased by the choice to include the nozzle domain into the computational domain. Indeed, only nozzle upstream conditions had to be specified in the form of stagnation conditions. Other conditions were simply conditions at the external boundaries. For subsonic outflow boundaries, the static pressure was specified, while for inflow boundaries, stagnation conditions were specified. The MSD code automatically shifts from inflow to outflow conditions, according to the sign of the normal flow velocity. No supersonic outflow boundaries were found to exist in all the computations presented.

Computations were started from rest and carried out with a first order implicit time scheme with local time stepping until the flow field was established. Computations were then shifted to the second order implicit time scheme with a constant time step. In all computations, the third order spatial scheme was used.

Results

Both subsonic and supersonics computations produced naturally unsteady jets without the need to introduce any form of forcing. These were analyzed from time averaged fields (mean flow fields) and fluctuating fields. For the latter fields, RMS fields were produced a from : $U_{RMS} = (<U^2> - <U>^2)^{1/2}$.

Instantaneous fields were also used, either as still images (snap shots) of the flow or as animations, when several instantaneous fields were used to create motion pictures of the flow field. In addition, numerical transducers were located inside the computational domain to provide high resolution time and spectral analyses.

Supersonic jet

A typical run permitted to acquire 44 ms of data (i.e. 539 D/U). This was used to evaluate the statistics of the unsteady field and served as input for the acoustic analysis [18]. For this case, more classical RANS computations were also performed on both the 2D and 3D grids. Two versions of the (k, ε) turbulence model were used. The first one is the standard model, while the second one uses modified C_ε constants, to take care of the axisymmetry of the case (see [20], note that this adjustment was done on a cold flow case). Figure 3 presents the evolution of the axial velocity along the jet center line for all the computations performed. The modified (k, ε) model shows the best agreement with experimental results. Please note that further constant adjustment for this hot flow case would have produced an even better agreement. The 3D Navier-Stokes (3D-NS) results exhibit a shorter (30%) potential core, comparable with the standard (k, ε) results. To check the influence of the implicit procedure, an explicit time integration scheme was used and did not improve this result. Figure 4 presents the jet radial expansion ratios from R_{05} and b coefficients given in [13] for the 1114 K case only. R_{05} is the ratio of the jet radius at the half velocity point to the nozzle radius and $b = R_{05} - h$ where h is the normalized radial extension of the potential core. While overall results show satisfactory trends, 3D-NS results overpredict jet expansion, in a way similar to the standard (k, ε) results. The 3D-NS results are further illustrated by the following figures :

- Figure 5 presents the mean and RMS fields of the axial velocity.
- Figure 6 shows a constant velocity surface that shows the large scale structures that dominate the jet turbulence.
- Figure 7 presents instantaneous pressure and temperature fields.

A detailed analysis of the pressure field at the nozzle exit clearly shows the presence of instability waves, as illustrated on figs. 8 and 9. In particular oblique waves are clearly visible on fig. 8. On fig. 9, two wave fronts are visible with angles θ=37 deg. and θ'=56 deg. These values can be compared with those of supersonic instability waves of convective Mach number $M_c = V_j/(c_j + c_a) = 1.249$, and to Kelvin-Helmholtz instability waves of convective Mach number $M'_c = (V_j + c_j)/(c_j + c_a) = 1.873$, where c_a and c_j are ambient and jet speeds of sound and V_j the jet velocity. With $\theta = \cos^{-1}(1/M_c)$, we obtain $\theta = 37$ deg. and $\theta' = 58$ deg., in good agreement with values read from fig.9.

Finally, fig. 10 presents the spectral density for one selected numerical transducer placed in the jet (x=15.5D and y=0.45D). The spectral content is found to be broad banded, and the frequency range corresponds to the expected range.

Subsonic jet

The initial grid was first used and produced results that were judged realistic enough to proceed with first acoustic analysis, as described in [18]. However these results showed that the refined zone could be optimized to concentrate grid points in the jet region. A refined grid was thus constructed, as explained above. This grid produced a time step roughly two times shorter and required twice as much time iterations in order to provide comparable time exploration for statistical and acoustic treatments.

These computations on the refined mesh could be run in two consecutive week-ends. Typical computation accumulated data over 72 ms (370 D/U time units). This was judged sufficient for statistical treatment and acoustic analysis, described in [18].

Figure 10 presents the axial and radial mean axial velocity profiles for both grids, compared to empirical laws proposed in [15]. As for the supersonic case, jet expansion is too rapid but the qualitative agreement is satisfactory. Grid refinement produced only limited improvements, as can be seen on fig. 10. As expected, jet mixing occurs sooner than for the supersonic jet (fig. 3). For the subsonic case, the above convective Mach numbers take the following values: $M_c = 0.44$ and $M'_c = 1.075$ ($\theta' = 21$ deg.).

Figure 11 displays the mean and RMS axial velocity fields for the initial grid (similar pictures were obtained on the refined grid). Again, overall behavior is correct and maximum RMS fluctuations reach 20% of the jet velocity.

Figure 12 presents the computed instantaneous pressure fields. Clear evidence of acoustic emission are visible with no marked differences between the two grids.

Some details of the flow at the nozzle exit are presented on fig. 13, where an instantaneous constant pressure surface (102200 Pa) is displayed. Again, instability waves can be observed. The differences between the two grids are more marked, despite clear similarities appear. Instabilities are initiated on a short wave-length mode, which exhibits a rather high degree of symmetry (n=0 mode), more apparent on the refined grid. The details of the subsonic jet are quite different from the supersonic case. In particular, unstable waves appear much sooner, almost at the nozzle lip and the corresponding modes are close to n=0 modes (i.e. symmetry around the jet axis).

The next figures (figs. 14 and 15) illustrate further the pressure field at the vicinity of the nozzle lip. The refined grid seems to better describe the initial instability mode and to preserve for a longer distance the n=0 mode, while the initial grid evolves more rapidly to an antisymmetric (n=1) mode. However the incidence of such fine details on the radiated noise is not quite clear yet and will be discussed in [18]. Assuming a mean convective velocity close to $V_j/2$, wave-lenghts observed of figs. 14 and 15 can be converted to Stouhal numbers based on nozzle diameter and jet velocity. First estimations yielded a Strouhal number for the initial instability mode slightly above 2. This mode rapidly evolves towards a mode with a Strouhal number close to unity, less than a nozzle diameter downstream.

Finally, fig. 16 presents the spectral density for one selected numerical transducer, placed in the jet (x=6D and y=0.5D). Again the spectral content is found to be broad banded and the frequency range corresponds to the expected range. It is interesting to compare figs. 9 and 16 that illustrate the difference between supersonic and subsonic jets. As expected, the subsonic jet produces a less intense pressure field with a broader frequency range with less marked lower frequencies.

Conclusions

Supersonic and subsonic hot jets were computed aiming at far field noise predictions, through coupling with acoustic solvers. Special attention was given to grid construction. In particular, the nozzle flow fields were incorporated into the computational domains and grid coarsening was used to damp the fluctuating fields before they reach the external boundaries. This permitted to avoid using external forcing to destabilize the jets and produced clear, reflection free, unsteady fields. The grids comprised refined domains to carry out the 3D Navier-Stokes solution, comprising the generated acoustic waves, away from the jet zone, in order to couple the aerodynamic computations to acoustic solvers for far field radiated noise predictions. The use of parallel computing rendered possible fast turn out for the computational runs and real time analysis of the results, both from the aerodynamic and acoustic point of view. Realistic data were produced and the analysis provided details of the early jet destabilization process. In the near future, these will be compared to linear stability theory results, in order to better understand the jet destabilization process. Grid refinement study was carried out for the subsonic case and confirmed the results obtained on the initial grid, with minor improvements. These first computations helped to determine the conditions for realistic unsteady jet flow computations and for efficient coupling with acoustic propagation codes through surface integration methods. Future works will addresses coupling through volume integrals and noise source identification

Acknowledgments

The authors want to acknowledge the role of G. Elias and O. Piccin in choosing and recovering the subsonic nozzle geometry and fruitful discussions with Ch. Bailly (ECL), D. Sipp, B. Poirée (SPAé), J. Haertig (ISL), G. Casalis, S. Lewy and T.H. Lê, as well as appreciated assistance and advices of G. Chaineray and M.-P. Errera in conducting the parallel computations.

References

[1] P. J. Morris, L. N. Long, T. E. Scheidegger, Q. Wang, A. R. Pilon. "High Speed Jet Noise Simulations.", AIAA 98-2290, 4th AIAA/CEAS Aeroacoustics conference, 1998, Toulouse, France.

[2] H. Shen, C. K. W. Tam, "Numerical simulation of the generation of axisymetric mode jet screech tones", AIAA J., Vol.36, No.10, Oct. 1998.

[3] J. B. Freund, S. K. Lele, P. Moin, "Direct simulation of a mach 1.92 jet and its sound field", AIAA 98-2291, 4th AIAA/CEAS Aeroacoustics conference, 1998, Toulouse, France.

[4] J. B. Freund "Noise sources in a low Reynolds number turbulent jet at Mach 0.9", J. Fluid Mech. (2001), vol. 438, pp. 277-305.

[5] F.Bastin, P. Lafon, S. Candel, "Computation of jet mixing noise due to coherent structure: the plane jet case," J. Fluid Mech, (1997) Vol.335, pp. 261-304.

[6] L. Gamet, J. L. Estivalezes, "Application of Large Eddy Simulation and Kirchhoff Method to Jet noise Prediction", AIAA J., Vol.36, No. 12, 1998, pp. 2170-2178.

[7] B. J. Boersma, S. K. Lele, "Large eddy simulation of a Mach 0.9 turbulent jet," AIAA 99-1874, 5th AIAA/CEAS aeroacoustic conference, May 99, Bellevue, WA.

[8] C. Seror, P. Sagaut, C. Bailly, D. Juvé, "Sound generated by high speed rectangular jet using large eddy simulation," 7ème Internationnal Congress on sound and vibration, 4-7 juillet 2000, Germany.

[9] R. R. Mankbadi, S. H. Shih, R. Hixon, L. A. Povinelli, "Direct computation of jet noise produced by large-scale axisymmetric structures," J. of Propulsion and Power, Vol.16, No.2, March-April 2000, pp. 207-215.

[10] W. Zhao, S. H. Frankel, L. Mongeau, "Effects spatial filtering on sound radiation from a subsonic axisymmetric jet," AIAA J, vol.38, No.11, Nov. 2000, pp 2032-2039.

[11] C. Bogey, C. Bailly, D. Juvé, "Computation of the sound radiated by a 3-D jet using large eddy simul,ation" AIAA 2000-2009, 6th AIAA/CEAS aeroacoustic conference, June 2000, Lahaina, Hawai.

[12] C. Seror, "Simulation des grandes échelles pour la prédiction du bruit des écoulements turbulents," Thèse, novembre 2000, Université de Paris-sud Orsay.

[13] J. M. Seiner, M; K. Ponton, "The effects of temperature on supersonic jet noise émission," DGLR/AIAA n° 92-02-046.

[14] C. Dahan, G. Elias, A. Lelarge, "Structures cohérentes dans un jet chaud localement subsonique", Congrès de la société française de physique, juin 1975.

[15] S. Candel, "Champ aérodynamique d'un jet chaud subsonique et structure cohérente", Rapport ONERA, 1974.

[16] C Dahan, "Emission acoustique de structures cohérentes dans un jet turbulent," Note technique ONERA, décembre 1976.

[17] J. F. Amphoux de Belleval, "Relation du champ acoustique d'un jet chaud avec sa turbulence et son émission infrarouge," Publication ONERA, 1976, European Space Agency.

[18] A. Biancherin, N. Lupoglazoff, G. Rahier, F. Vuillot, "Comprehensive 3D unsteady simulations of subsonic and supersonic hot jet flow-fields. Part 2:

acoustic analysis," AIAA 2002-2600, 8th AIAA/CEAS Aeroacoustics Conference & Exhibit, June 17-19 2002, Breckenridge, CO.

[19] G. Chaineray et al., "MSD 2.3.1 Notice d'utilisation", MSDH / NU001 - 3.0, mars 2001.

[20] G. Turpin, J. Troyes, "Validation of a two-equation turbulence model for axisymetric reacting and non-reacting flows," AIAA 2000-3463, 36th AIAA/ASME/SAE/ASEE Joint Propulsion Conference & Exhibit, July 17-19, 2000, Huntsville, Alabama, USA.

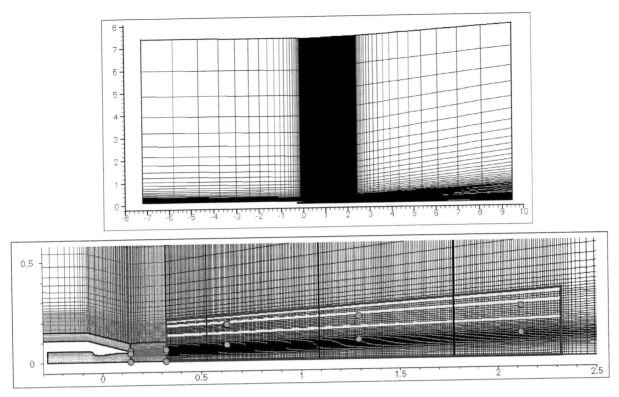

Figure 1: Supersonic jet grid. Overall computational domain (top) and details of the nozzle and jet zone (bottom). Axes are labeled in m. Red limit indicates the refined grid. Green circles show the numerical transducer locations. Yellow lines indicate integration surfaces for acoustic treatment.

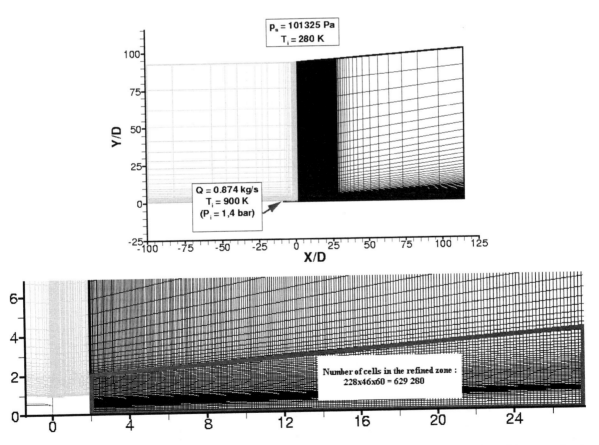

Figure 2: Subsonic jet grid. Overall computational domain (top) and details of the nozzle exit and jet zone (bottom). Red limit indicates the refined grid

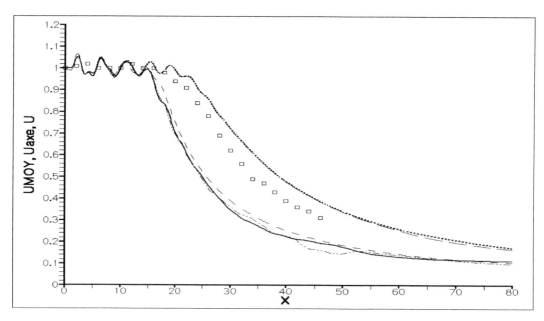

Figure 3 : Axial profils of mean axial velocity (relative to jet velocity) as function of distance from the nozzle (relative to nozzle radius). Modified (k, ε) : dots (3D) and long dashed (2D) ; Standard (k, ε) : short dashed (2D) ; 3D Navier-Stokes : solid (implicit) and dash dots (explicit).

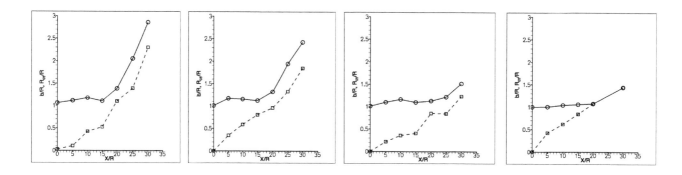

Figure 4 : Expansion factors $R_{0.5}$ (solid) and b (dashed). From left to right : 3D Navier-Stokes ; Standard (k, ε) ; Modified (k, ε) , Experiment at 1114 K.

Figure 5 : Constant velocity surface

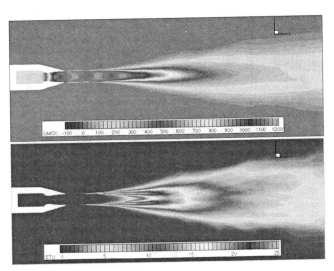

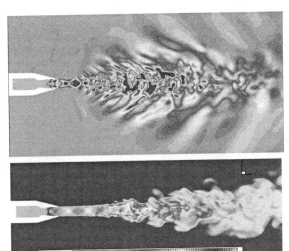

Figure 6 : Mean (m/s) and fluctuating (% of jet velocity) axial velocity fields

Figure 7 : Examples of instantaneous fields. Pressure (top) and temperature (bottom)

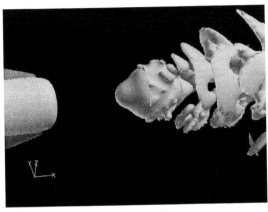

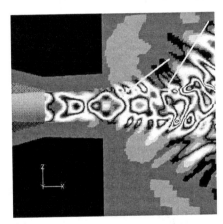

Figure 8 : Details of the pressure field at nozzle exit. Constant pressure surface (left) ; Schlieren like representation (right) showing wave propagation angles θ and θ' .

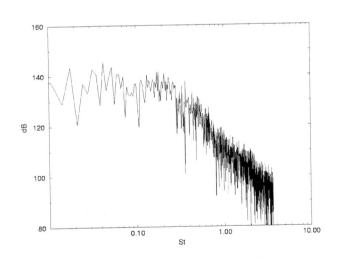

Figure 9 : Spectral content of one numerical pressure transducer located in the jet (x=15.5D, r=0.45D

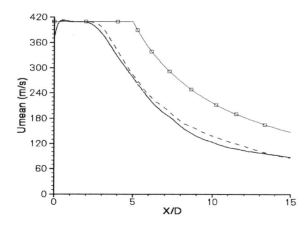
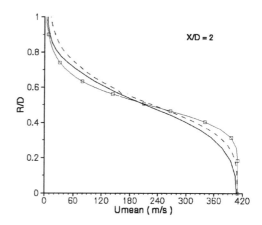

Figure 10 : Axial (left) and radial at x/D=2 (right) profiles of the mean axial velocity, compared to empirical laws (symbols) ; initial (black solid) and refined (red dashed) grids.

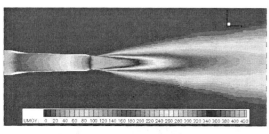
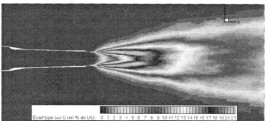

Figure 11 : Mean (m/s) and fluctuating (% of jet velocity) axial velocity fields

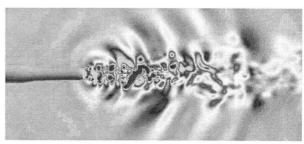
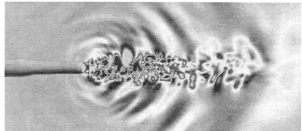

Figure 12 : Instantaneous pressure fields. Coarse (top) and fine (bottom) grids

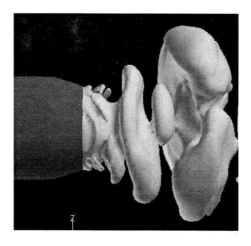
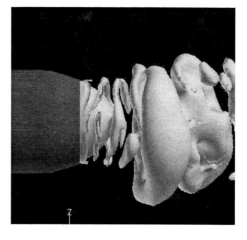

Figure 13 : Details of the pressure field (102200 Pa surface) at the nozzle exit. Coarse (left) and fine (right) grids.

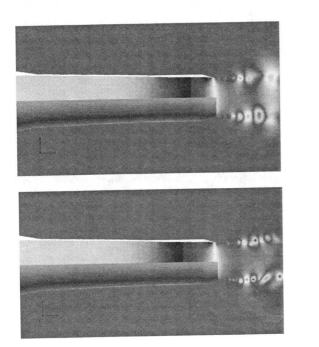

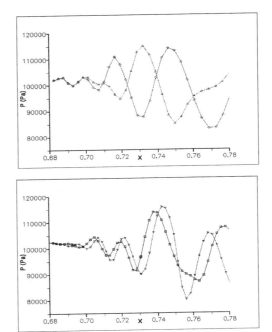

Figure 14 : Details of the pressure field at the nozzle exit. Coarse (top) and fine (bottom) grids.

Figure 15 : Axial evolutions of the pressure at the nozzle exit at r = ±R. Coarse (top) and fine (bottom) grids

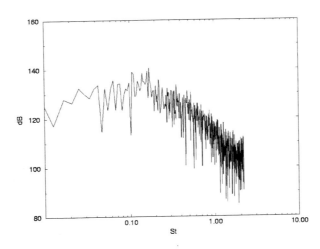

Figure 16 : Spectral content of one numerical pressure transducer located in the jet (x=6D, r=0.5D

AIAA 2002-2600

COMPREHENSIVE 3D UNSTEADY SIMULATIONS OF SUBSONIC AND SUPERSONIC HOT JET FLOW-FIELDS. PART 2: ACOUSTICS ANALYSIS.

A. Biancherin[*], N. Lupoglazoff[‡], G.Rahier[†], F. Vuillot[‡]

ONERA, Châtillon, France

Abstract

This paper presents the acoustic analysis of the hot subsonic and supersonic jets aerodynamic simulations described in Part I. Acoustic predictions are performed using the flow-fields provided by the 3D unsteady Navier-Stokes computations, for both supersonic and subsonic hot jets. Two surface integral formulations are used: the Kirchhoff method and the Ffowcs Williams and Hawkings (FW-H) equation on a porous surface. Integrations are performed on conical control surfaces as much as possible enclosing the jet and its mixing layers. The influence of the formulation and of parameters, such as control surface location and extent, open or closed nature of the control surfaces, on acoustic far field predictions is first investigated. The results show that the chosen control surfaces are far enough from the jets for FW-H and Kirchhoff calculations starting from pressure but not well suited for Kirchhoff calculations starting from density, in the present cases of hot jets. Comparisons with direct CFD results in the near field confirm this analysis and validate FW-H and Kirchhoff (pressure) radiated noise predictions. The results also show that an open control surface at its upstream and downstream ends can be used in practice. Closed control surface benefits appear only for acoustic predictions at low angle from the jet axis. However such surfaces intersect the jet and are not compatible with Kirchhoff calculations. Far field predictions are then compared with experiments for both supersonic and subsonic jets. The sound directivity and the Strouhal number of the maximum level in the spectral density as a function of the angle of observation are rather well predicted. However, the maximum noise level is overestimated. A deeper analysis of these aeroacoustic predictions is in progress. An example of improvement of CFD/acoustic jet computations is presented.

Presentation

Future commercial aircrafts will face increasing regulations concerning noise emissions. In that context, jet noise is of particular concern, especially for high speed aircrafts at take-off, such as the next generation supersonic airplane. In France, several research programs have been initiated to study the problems faced by such vehicle. These program include research activities on the prevision of supersonic and subsonic jet noise.

Jet noise has received much attention[e.g. 1, 2] in the past years: direct simulation have been attempted [3-4], as well as simulations using some type of LES techniques [5-12], arguing that large turbulent structures are responsible for most of the acoustic emission of jets and that fine scale turbulence is less critical. Historically supersonic jets were first considered, due to the larger noise emissions and somewhat simpler boundary conditions for the numerical procedure. Larger noise emission minimizes the difficulty in predicting jet noise: acoustic sources are intense and more easily captured by the simulation. However, subsonic jets are closer to the actual problem of an airplane during take-off, since the jets are more likely to be subsonic under such conditions. This implies that the tools developed and validated against

supersonic jet conditions must also be capable of treating subsonic jets with less marked noise sources.

The present work has been carried out in the framework of an ONERA internal federative research project dedicated to the next generation supersonic transport aircraft, in connection with other national research programs concerned with the ATSF (Avion de Transport Supersonique du Futur) implying several national research laboratories such as ECL (Ecole Centrale de Lyon) and ISL (Institut de Saint-Louis).

ONERA DSNA department has a strong expertise in both advanced CFD and acoustics tools that permits to consider actual CAA applications. Jet noise is naturally part of this expertise and it was decided to initiate a comprehensive analysis of jet noise, including the full computation of the unsteady aerodynamic field, including the nozzles generating the jets, and the coupling with acoustic radiation codes, to extrapolate the aerodynamic computations to the far-field acoustic domain.

The work is presented in two companion papers. The first paper presents the aerodynamic analysis of the jet zone, while the second paper concentrates on the acoustic analysis. For both papers, the case of a supersonic jet is first considered. This permitted to validate the procedure against experimental results obtained by Seiner & Ponton [13], for the case of a hot

---

[*] PhD student, DSNA department
[†] Research scientist, DSNA department
[‡] Deputy head, DSNA department, Senior member

supersonic jet. The procedure was then applied to the case of a hot subsonic jet described in several ONERA publications and papers [14-18].

This second paper will present the acoustic calculations performed starting from the unsteady flow-fields provided by the aerodynamic simulations described in the first paper [19].

Acoustic formulations

The acoustic predictions are performed using surface integral formulations. Two approaches have been used: the Kirchhoff method[20] and the integration of the Ffowcs Williams and Hawking (FW-H) equation on a porous surface[21]. Both approaches allow to determine the pressure radiated by a volume of perturbed fluid starting from the perturbation field on a closed control surface surrounding this volume. They may thus be well suited for noise prediction of isolated jets for which a control surface enclosing the mixing layer should contain all the noise sources. These surface integral methods have been preferred to the volume integration of the Lighthill quadrupoles[22] for these first jet noise analyses (conducted separately of the aerodynamic simulation) because they require to save CFD data only on surfaces.

Both Kirchhoff and FW-H surface formulations as well as their physical meaning are presented in the reference[23]. In particular, the theoretical consequences of a control surface not enclosing all non-negligible noise sources are discussed. We only recall here that the input data of FW-H calculations are the density, the pressure and the velocity components u, v, w of the fluid on the control surface whereas the input data of Kirchhoff calculations are limited to the density (termed K-ρ hereafter) or the pressure (termed K-p) and its gradient on this surface.

The present acoustic calculations have been carried out using the KIM code developed at ONERA for helicopter rotor, turbomachinery compressor, airfoil and jet noise predictions. The formulas in the time domain and the original fully non-compact integration technique implemented in this code are also described in details in the reference [23].

Application to the test case

The 3D unsteady aerodynamic study of two hot jet configurations has been described in the first part of this work[19]. The configurations correspond to a supersonic (case 1) and a subsonic (case 2) hot jets, with axisymmetric geometries (see figs. 1 and 2 and table below).

	D $(10^{-3}m)$	M	U_{jet} $(m.s^{-1})$	T_i (K)	R_e
Case 1	91.44	2	1120	1370	$1.0\ 10^6$
Case 2	80	0.7	410	900	$1.2\ 10^6$

The supersonic jet case is described in Seiner & Ponton[13]: experimental acoustic data are given in this reference. The subsonic jet case comes from past ONERA experimental studies [14-18].

As described in[19], the Navier-Stokes computations relied on grid definitions allowing for proper acoustic propagation in the near jet region, up to a frequency corresponding to a Strouhal number of 0.3. Away from the jet region the grids are coarsened so that acoustic waves cannot reach the external boundaries, thus avoiding spurious reflexions.

In order to provide the necessary inputs for acoustic calculations of the far fields, several integration surfaces were inbedded into the grids (fig. 3). These conical surfaces are located in the near field, at different positions relative to the jet axis (fig. 5). The influence of the surface position on the radiated noise will be studied. The following surfaces were considered:

Supersonic jet (case 1)
- Surface S1 :
from R=1.4D at X=2D to R=2D at X=23D.
- Surface S2,
from R=1.8D at X=2D to R=3D at X=23D.
- Surface S3,
from R=2.1D at X=2D to R=3.5D at X=23D.

Subsonic jet / initial mesh (case 2)
- Surface S2,
from R=1.70D at X=0 to R=3.18D at X=28D.
- Surface S3,
from R=1.94D at X=0 to R=3.83D at X=28D.
Subsonic jet / refined mesh (case 3)
- Surface S2,
from R=2.39D at X=0 to R=3.55D at X=28D.
- Surface S3,
from R=3.54D at X=0 to R=4.46D at X=28D.

A typical aerodynamic computation consisted of 40000 time steps (80000 for case 3). The aerodynamic fields were stored on the surfaces S_i every 25 time steps, producing 1600 samples (case 3: 3200), with a time resolution of $\Delta t_e=25\Delta t$, for a total time exploration of T= 40000Δt (case 3: 80000Δt). The characteristics of the surface samplings are summarized in the table below:

	T (ms)	TU_j/D	Δt_e (μs)	f_e (Hz)	$f_e D/U_j$
Case 1	44	539	27.5	36364	3.0
Case 2	72	370	45	22222	4.3
Case 3	64	324	20	50000	9.7

For the Kirchhoff formulations only density or pressure data are required but surfaces must comprise two layers, in order to properly compute the needed pressure or density gradients. The FW-H integration uses only one layer but requires five variables: ρ, ρu, ρv, ρw and p.

Figure 4 shows the far field observation points for the supersonic case. Numerical pressure transducers are also located in the near jet region (refined zone of the grid, see [19]) and will be used to compare the predicted radiated pressure with the direct Navier-Stokes solution. The far field transducers are located on circular arcs from the nozzle exit (R=40D, supersonic case and R=75D, subsonic case) and correspond to experimental microphone locations. The jet noise directivity will be compared to experimental measurements at these far field locations.

Validation of the calculation procedure
Influence of the integration surface
All the integration surfaces S_i are considered for the three different acoustic computations (FW-H, K-ρ, K-p) and the stability of the radiated field is examined. On fig. 6 the results of the FW-H formulation are presented, for the supersonic jet, in the form of time history of the radiated pressure, at location (R=40D and Φ=60 deg.). The results show little influence of the surface location. The same behavior was obtained for the K-p integration, based on the pressure. However, the results of the K-ρ formulation, based on the density, exhibited a marked influence of the choice of the integration surface.

Figure 7 shows the spectral analysis of the pressure signals of fig. 6. The spectral density is based on band averaged analysis (500 Hz = 14 Δf_c). Again the stability of the FW-H formulation is apparent for the three integration surfaces.

Similar results were obtained for the case of the subsonic jet and are not presented here.

Influence of the formulation
Figures 8 and 9 present, respectively for the supersonic and the subsonic jets, the comparison of the rsults predicted of the three acoustic calculations K-ρ, K-p and FW-H. Averaged spectral densities are presented, as obtained from integration surface S2. It is clear that the K-ρ method over estimates the low frequency part of the spectrum (below 1.2 kHz).

Figures 10 and 11 represent, again for both the supersonic and subsonic jets, the averaged spectral densities as obtained from the near jet region. The chosen observation point is located above surface S2, in the refined zone, so that acoustic radiated fields can be compared to direct Navier-Stokes solution (same sampling rate was used in all approaches). Again the K-ρ methods differs in the low frequency range. Other approaches compare well, indicating consistent results. These differences in tendencies between the formulations of K-ρ and K-p can be explained from fig. 12. Indeed, three graphs respectively represent a spectral density of pressure p/p_0, of density ρ/ρ_0 and temperature T/T_0 along a line extracted from surface S2. Significant levels are visible in the low frequency end of the spectrums, for both density and temperature

while the pressure plot does not contain such low frequencies. It is believed that hot spots crossing S2 are responsible for low frequency density fluctuations that pollute the K-ρ radiated field. On fig. 13 the noise level directivities, obtained from the three methods of surface integrations, are compared. Exept for the K-ρ approach, good agreements are observed. The low frequency content of the K-ρ predictions results in an almost isotropic directivity. Indeed, when the temporal signals computed from the K-ρ approach are band filtered (1-15 kHz) the K-ρ results match with those of the K-p and FW-H calculations.

Secondary influences
The surfaces of control defined previously for the two jets were characterized by their position relative to the axis. Other parameters likely to disturb the acoustic prediction of the jet are analyzed in this chapter. In the case of the subsonic jet, the length of surface S2 was modified (L=15D, L=20D and L=28D). Figure 14 presents the directivity patterns obtained, for each length and for the FW-H formulation. The three control surfaces lead to similar results, especially for L = 20D and L = 28D, showing that these control surfaces include most of the noise sources. Some low frequency sources, located in the downstream part of the jet are not included in the 15D control surface. Figure 15 shows that, for a low angle of observation, the pressure radiated by these sources is out of phase with the low frequency part of the pressure radiated from the upstream sources. It is thus logical that the 15D control surface which does not take into account this phase compensation, leads to slightly higher levels for some angles of observation.

The surface integral methods theretically require closed surfaces. However until now, the considered cones were let open at their ends. The influence of open surfaces on the radiated fields was studied. Open and closed surfaces of varied lengths, were used. For instance, fig. 16 shows the difference in the radiated field between closed and open surfaces of length 20D, using the FW-H method. It is interesting to compare fig.16 with fig. 17, which displays, for the same surface, the K-p results. The closed surface results in higher levels in directions normal to the added vertical ends. It is believed that this is due to pollution of the pressure field caused by vortical structures going through the downstream end.

Visualization of synthesis
Figure 18 is an image extracted from a motion picture that presents both the near field Navier-Stokes pressure field and the acoustic radiated field. This figure allows to visualize the pressure fluctuations in the jet (dominated by convective structures) and their propagative component outside the jet.

Comparisons with experiment

The validated acoustic procedures are then applied to both supersonic and subsonic jets and the acoustic predictions are compared to published far-field experimental data.

Supersonic jet

The directivity of the acoustic radiation of the supersonic jet is displayed on fig. 13. Computed acoustic field is characterized by a maximum noise level close to 50 deg.. That is in good agreement with the experimental data[13]. However, the maximum level is over-estimated by almost 8 dB. The first explanation for this over-estimation can be linked to the aerodynamic computations. Indeed, it has been mentioned in [19] that the computed potential cone is shorter than the experimental measurements. The following actions can be proposed to attempt to improve the aerodynamic solution:

- grid refinement in the jet region to better describe the finer structures that may condition the evolution of jet mixing. That was carried out for the subsonic jet and the first results are presented in the continuation of the article.

- decrease the jet Reynolds number in order to scale up the jet turbulent structures, relative to the grid resolution

- incorporate some form of turbulence modeling to better describe the unresolved scales.

Figures 19 and 20 show spectra in far field for several angles of observation. They respectively present the computed acoustic fields and experimental results. The evolutions of the predicted spectra are similar to those given in[13] . However the computed spectrums exhibit an insufficient filling in the medium and high frequency range. This is consistent with the grid sizing which has been set to propagate the waves correctly up to a Strouhal number of 0.3 (see [19]) corresponding to frequencies lower than 3kHz. This explanation is illustrated by fig. 21 which presents the Strouhal numbers corresponding to the maximum of spectral density of the radiated pressure for several angles of observation.

Subsonic jet

Comparisons similar to those carried out for the jet supersonic are made in the case of the subsonic jet. Figure 22 summarizes the directivities predicted by the formulations of FW-H and K-p and the experimental directivity detailed in an ONERA internal report[17]. The first remark is that the angle of the maximum level differs from the experiment (around 40 deg. for calculation and approximately 30 deg. for measurements). The noise levels are also over-estimated. Same reasons as for the supersonic jet are evoked: they could be of aerodynamic nature and linked to a shorter potential cone, as discussed in [19].

Like the supersonic jet, comparisons of spectra for several angles of observation are carried out

between calculations (fig. 23) and the experimental data (fig. 24). Global agreement is observed, while computed spectra under-predict the higher frequency range. Again this result was expected from the grid design that limits the resolvable frequencies to Strouhal numbers less than 0.3.

Finally the influence of the grid was analyzed, using aerodynamic results obtained for the subsonic jet on a refined grid (see [19]). The refined grid has grid size halfed in directions x and r in the near jet region. Figure 25 presents the directivity diagram computed from the two grid solutions, using the FW-H formulation, compared to the experimental results. Slight improvements are visible for the refined grid that may be linked to slightly improved aerodynamic solution. However, the improvements remain relatively limited, indicating that the grid issue may not be sufficient to explain the observed discrepencies.

Conclusions

Acoustic calculations have been performed starting from the flow-fields provided by 3D unsteady Navier-Stokes computations, for both supersonic and subsonic hot jets. The radiated noises have been calculated using two surface integral formulations: the Kirchhoff method and the FW-H equation on a porous surface. Integration have been performed on conical control surfaces surrounding the jet using the ONERA acoustic code KIM.

The influence of the formulation and of parameters of the calculation on the acoustic predictions has been first investigated. This parametric study showed that:

- the chosen control surfaces are located far enough from the jets for FW-H and K-p methods but appear not well suited for the K-ρ method, in the present cases of hot jets. Indeed, the density fluctuations on the control surface contains a non propagative part which is linked to hot spots crossing the surface. It was demonstrated that these non propagative perturbations highly affect the noise predictions at low frequency. The consequences of this non uniform flow on the integration surface are quite negligible when using FW-H and K-ρ methods for theoretical reasons which are examined and will be explained in a future paper.

- although the acoustic formulations require a closed control surface, an integration surface opened at its upstream and downstream ends can be used in practice. A closed control surface may benefits only acoustic predictions at low angle from the jet axis. Furthermore it can not be used for K-ρ because of the well-known non propagative pressure perturbations induced on the downstream closing surface by the crossing vortices.

-the comparison of the predicted radiated pressure with direct CFD results in the near field confirms the validity of the FW-H and the K-p calculations for the present test cases.

The predictions have been then compared with experimental data in far field, for both supersonic and subsonic jets.
- the sound directivity is rather well predicted but the maximum noise level is overestimated: about 8 dB for the supersonic jet and about 7 dB for the subsonic jet. This discrepancy between calculations and experiment may be the consequence of computed potential cones consistently shorter than expected. As a first attempt of improvement, complementary computations of the subsonic jet have been performed using a finer CFD grid. They lead to a longer potential cone and a lower maximum noise level.
- the Strouhal number of the maximum level in the spectral density, as a function of the angle of observation, is in agreement with experiment. On the other hand, the medium and high frequencies of the radiated noise are underestimated. It is a logical consequence of the CFD grid cell size only adapted (in this first study) to the capture of the large scale structures of the jet flow-field and to the acoustic wave propagation in the near field.

In conclusion, these first acoustic calculations using surface integral formulations have brought much interesting and encouraging results. The next step of the acoustic study will consist in calculating the Lighthill quadrupoles distribution in the jet flow-field for a deeper analysis of the noise sources.

Acknowledgments
The authors want to acknowledge the role of G. Elias and O. Piccin in choosing and recovering the subsonic nozzle geometry and fruitful discussions with J. Prieur, S. Lewy and D. Gely.

References
[1] P. J. Morris, L. N. Long, T. E. Scheidegger, Q. Wang, A. R. Pilon. "High Speed Jet Noise Simulations.", AIAA 98-2290, 4th AIAA/CEAS Aeroacoustics conference, 1998, Toulouse, France.

[2] H. Shen, C. K. W. Tam, "Numerical simulation of the generation of axisymetric mode jet screech tones", AIAA J., Vol.36, No.10, Oct. 1998.

[3] J. B. Freund, S. K. Lele, P. Moin, "Direct simulation of a mach 1.92 jet and its sound field", AIAA 98-2291, 4th AIAA/CEAS Aeroacoustics conference, 1998, Toulouse, France.

[4] J. B. Freund, "Noise sources in a low-Reynolds-number turbulent jet at Mach 0.9.", J. Fluid Mech, (2001) Vol.438, pp. 277-305.

[5] F.Bastin, P. Lafon, S. Candel, "Computation of jet mixing noise due to coherent structure: the plane jet case," J. Fluid Mech, (1997) Vol.335, pp. 261-304.

[6] L. Gamet, J. L. Estivalezes, "Application of Large Eddy Simulation and Kirchhoff Method to Jet noise Prediction", AIAA J., Vol.36, No. 12, 1998, pp. 2170-2178.

[7] B. J. Boersma, S. K. Lele, "Large eddy simulation of a Mach 0.9 turbulent jet," AIAA 99-1874, 5th AIAA/CEAS aeroacoustic conference, May 99, Bellevue, WA.

[8] C. Seror, P. Sagaut, C. Bailly, D. Juvé, "Sound generated by high speed rectangular jet using large eddy simulation," 7ème Internationnal Congress on sound and vibration, 4-7 juillet 2000, Germany.

[9] R. R. Mankbadi, S. H. Shih, R. Hixon, L. A. Povinelli, "Direct computation of jet noise produced by large-scale axisymmetric structures," J. of Propulsion and Power, Vol.16, No.2, March-April 2000, pp. 207-215.

[10] W. Zhao, S. H. Frankel, L. Mongeau, "Effects spatial filtering on sound radiation from a subsonic axisymmetric jet," AIAA J, vol.38, No.11, Nov. 2000, pp 2032-2039.

[11] C. Bogey, C. Bailly, D. Juvé, "Computation of the sound radiated by a 3-D jet using large eddy simul,ation" AIAA 2000-2009, 6th AIAA/CEAS aeroacoustic conference, June 2000, Lahaina, Hawai.

[12] C. Seror, "Simulation des grandes échelles pour la prédiction du bruit des écoulements turbulents," Thèse, novembre 2000, Université de Paris-sud Orsay.

[13] J. M. Seiner, M; K. Ponton, "The effects of temperature on supersonic jet noise émission," DGLR/AIAA n° 92-02-046.

[14] C. Dahan, G. Elias, A. Lelarge, "Structures cohérentes dans un jet chaud localement subsonique", Congrès de la société française de physique, juin 1975.

[15] S. Candel, "Champ aérodynamique d'un jet chaud subsonique et structure cohérente", Rapport ONERA, 1974.

[16] C Dahan, "Emission acoustique de structures cohérentes dans un jet turbulent," Note technique ONERA, décembre 1976.

[17] Gely D.,internal report ONERA, December 2001.

[18] J. F. Amphoux de Belleval, "Relation du champ acoustique d'un jet chaud avec sa turbulence et son émission infrarouge," Publication ONERA, 1976, European Space Agency.

[19] N. Lupoglazoff, A. Biancherin, F. Vuillot, G. Rahier, "Comprehensive 3D unsteady simulations of subsonic and supersonic hot jet flow-fields. Part 1: aerodynamics analysis," AIAA 2002-2599, 8th AIAA/CEAS Aeroacoustics Conference & Exhibit, June 17-19 2002, Breckenridge, CO.

[20] Golstein M.E.,"Aeroacoustics," Mc Graw Hill International Book Compagny, 1976.

[21] Ffowcs Williams J.E. and Hawkings D.L.,"Sound Generation by Turbulence and Surfaces in Arbitrary Motion," Philo. Trans. Royal Society of London, Vol. 264, A1151, pp. 321-342, May 1969.

[22] Lighthill M.J.,"On Sound Generated Aerody-namically, I: General Theory," Proceedings of the Royal Society of London, Vol. A221, pp. 564-587, 1952.

[23] Prieur J., Rahier G., "Aeroacoustic Integral Methods and Efficient Numerical Implementation, "Aerospace Science and Technology, Vol. 5, No. 7, pp. 457-468, October 2001.

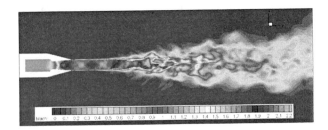

Figure 1 – Example of instantaneous mach fields.
Supersonic jet.

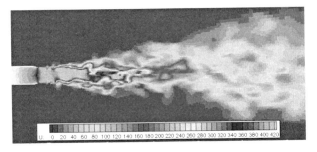

Figure 2 – Example of instantaneous axial velocity fields.
Subsonic jet.

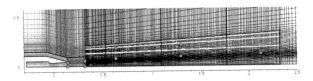

Figure 3 – Supersonic jet grid. Overall details of the nozzle
and jet zone. Red limit indicates the refined grid. Green
circles show the numerical transducter locations. Yellow
lines indicate integration surfaces for acoustic treatment.

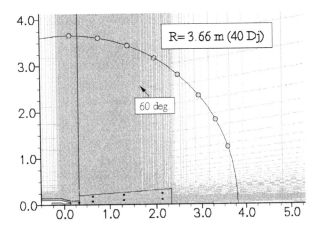

Figure 4 – Supersonic jet grid detail.
Yellow circles indicate microphones situated on a circle of
radius of 40D.

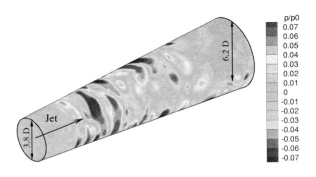

Figure 5 – Example of instantaneous pressure fluctuation
field on a control surface surrounding the supersonic jet.

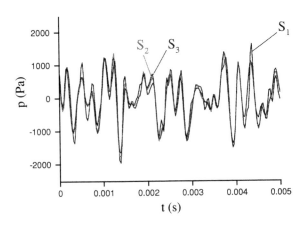

Figure 6 – Time history of the pressure radiated in the far
field by the supersonic jet. Calculations using FW-H
formulation and different integration surfaces.

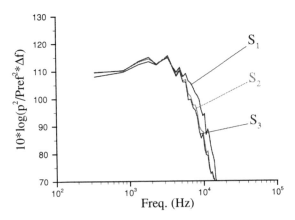

Figure 7 – Spectral density of the pressure radiated in the far
field by the supersonic jet. Calculations using FW-H
formulation and different integration surfaces.

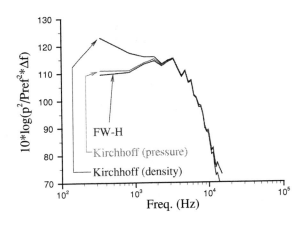

Figure 8 – Spectral density of the pressure radiated in the far field by the supersonic jet. Comparisons between Kirchhoff calculations starting from density, starting from pressure and FW-H calculations (control surface: S_2)

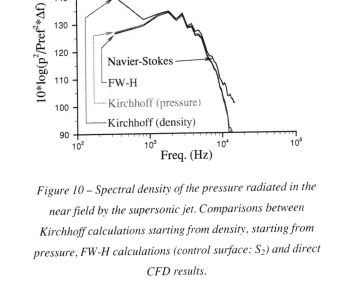

Figure 10 – Spectral density of the pressure radiated in the near field by the supersonic jet. Comparisons between Kirchhoff calculations starting from density, starting from pressure, FW-H calculations (control surface: S_2) and direct CFD results.

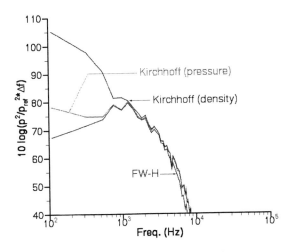

Figure 9 – Spectral density of the pressure radiated in the far field by the subsonic jet. Comparisons between Kirchhoff calculations starting from density, starting from pressure and FW-H calculations (control surface: S_2).

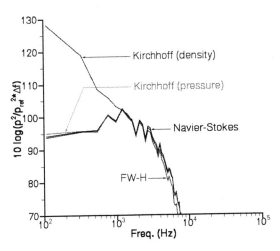

Figure 11 – Spectral density of the pressure radiated in the near field by the subsonic jet. Comparisons between Kirchhoff calculations starting from density, starting from pressure, FW-H calculations (control surface: S_2) and direct CFD results .

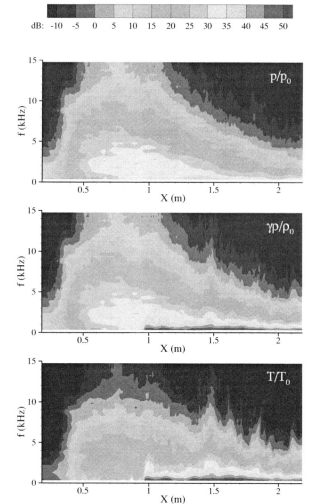

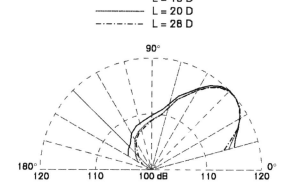

L = 15 D
L = 20 D
L = 28 D

Figure 14 – Noise directivities comparison of contrôle surfaces of different length. Ffowcs Williams and Hawkings calculations. Subsonic jet.

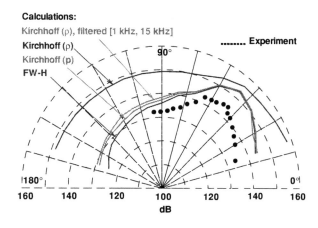

Figure 12 – Spectral density of the pressure, density and temperature along a axial generator of the control surface S₂.

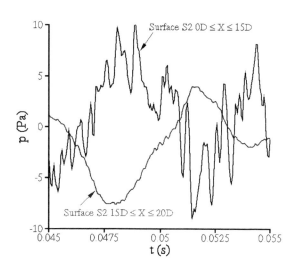

Figure 15 –Contribution of the two parts of the contrôle surface S2 to the pressure radiated at 150 deg. Ffowcs Williams and Hawkings calculations. Subsonic jet.

Calculations:

Kirchhoff (ρ), filtered [1 kHz, 15 kHz]

Kirchhoff (ρ)
Kirchhoff (p)
FW-H

········· **Experiment**

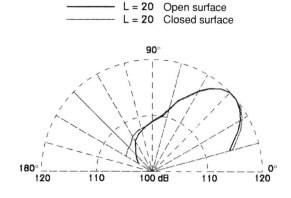

L = 20   Open surface
L = 20   Closed surface

Figure 13 – Noise directivity of the supersonic jet. Comparisons between Kirchhoff calculations starting from density (ρ), starting from pressure (p), FW-H calculations (control surface: S₂) and experiment.

Figure 16 – Noise directivities comparison between closed and open controle surfaces of length 20D. Ffowcs Williams and Hawkings calculations. Subsonic jet.

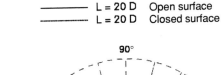

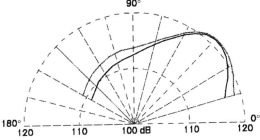

Figure 17 – Directivities comparison between closed and open controle surfaces of length 20D. Kirchhoff (pressure) calculations. Subsonic jet.

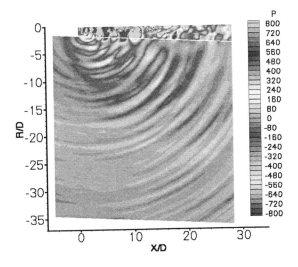

Figure 18 – Association of near field Navier-Stokes calculation and far field acoustic propagation calculation.Subsonic jet.

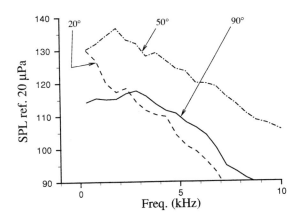

Figure 19 – Spectra of the predicted pressure radiated in far field by the supersonic jet.

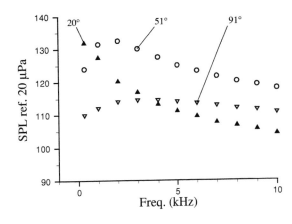

Figure 20 – Experimental spectra of the pressure radiated in far field by the supersonic jet.

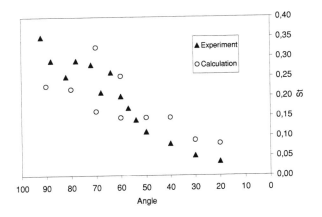

Figure 21 – Strouhal of the maximum level in the spectral density of the pressure radiated by the supersonic jet as a function of the angle of observation. Comparison with published experimental data.

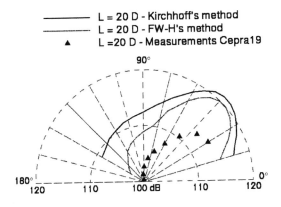

Figure 22 – Noise directivity of the subsonic jet. Comparisons between Kirchhoff calculations starting from pressure (p), FW-H calculations (control surface: S_2) and experiment.

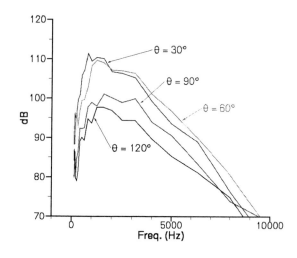

Figure 23 – Spectra of the predicted pressure radiated in far field by the subsonic jet..

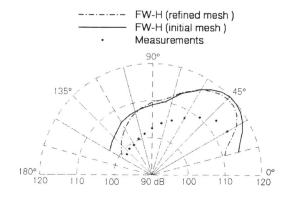

Figure 25 – Noise directivity of the subsonic jet. Comparisons between FW-H calculations using CFD refined mesh and initial mesh (control surface: S_2), and experiment.

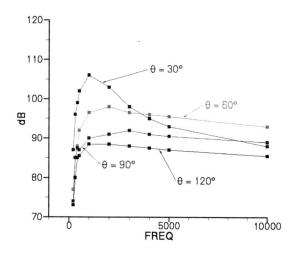

Figure 24 – Experimental spectra of the pressure radiated in far field by the subsonic jet.

LOW-DIMENSIONAL DESCRIPTION OF AN UNDEREXPANDED RECTANGULAR JET

D. Moreno[*], A. Krothapalli[†], M. B. Alkislar[‡], and L. M. Lourenco[§]

Department of Mechanical Engineering
Florida A&M University and Florida State University
2525 Pottsdamer St., Tallahassee, Florida 32310
kroth@eng.fsu.edu

The Proper Orthogonal Decomposition (POD) method is applied to the analysis of Particle Image Velocimetry (PIV) data obtained for a supersonic screeching rectangular jet. The large-scale coherent structures observed in the shock-containing region of the jet are characterized in terms of orthonormal basis functions. It was found that a large fraction of the fluctuation energy is contained within the first two modes. The essential features of the jet are captured with only two functions. Galerkin projection of the Navier-Stokes Equations on to the basis set of two principal eigenfunctions results in a low order system of dynamical equations. The solution of this system of equations describes the dynamics of the large-scale coherent structures. The simulation results compare reasonably well with the experiments.

1. INTRODUCTION

This paper is motivated by our attempt to provide a method of velocity field data analysis aimed at obtaining low–dimensional approximate description of high speed jets. The velocity field data is obtained experimentally using the Particle Image Velocimetry (PIV) technique. Recent developments in the statistical technique of proper orthogonal decomposition (POD) seems to offer some hope to capture the spatial as well as temporal behavior of energetic large-scale structures in a variety of shear flows. Data analysis using POD is often conducted to extract "mode shapes" or basis functions, from experimental data for subsequent use in Galerkin projections that yield low-dimensional models[1]. This enables one to build efficient reduced order models based on the first few dynamically important POD modes, thus serving as potential substitute for computationally intensive simulations. This paper concentrates on the data analysis aspect followed by the ensuing reduced-order modeling. As a first attempt in this endeavor, we focus on the flow field of an underexpanded rectangular jet that is dominated by coherent large-scale structures generated by the inherent global instability set up by a feed back mechanism[2,3].

The POD method was originally suggested by Lumely[4] to extract organized large-scale structures from turbulent flows. The method provides a set of optimized orthonormal basis functions for an ensemble of data. The most important property of POD is its optimality in the sense that it provides the most efficient way of capturing the dominant features of an infinite dimensional process with only few functions. For this reason POD has been in extensive use to examine turbulent flows, particularly in the analysis of Direct Numerical Simulation (DNS) data[5-10]. In the present study, the method is applied to PIV data SET obtained from the measurements of synoptic velocity field of a screeching rectangular jet. The detailed discussion of the jet characteristics are given in a recent paper by Krothapalli et al.[11]

2. THEORETICAL BACKGROUND

2.1. POD Method

In the present study, the procedure outlined in Berkooz et al.[12] is followed. The idea behind POD is to find a basis function { } in which the ensemble data $\{u_i\}$ is optimally represented. In this paper, u_i is considered a real random vector of length M with temporal and spatial dependence. Thus, we are looking for a function that maximizes the inner product with u_i, which is given as

$$\frac{\max \left\langle |u, \ |^2 \right\rangle}{\| \ \|^2} \tag{1}$$

where < > represents an ensemble average, | | denotes

[*] Centro de Investigaciones en Optica A.C.,Mexico.
[†] Don Fuqua Professor, Associate Fellow AIAA
[‡] Research Associate, Member AIAA
[§] Professor, Member AIAA

the modulus and $\| \ \|$ is the second norm. This is a problem of calculus of variations and the solution can be represented as

$$\int_D \langle u(x)u^*(x')\rangle \phi(x')dx' = \lambda \phi \tag{2}$$

where (*) represents the complex conjugate. Thus, the optimal basis are given by the eigenfuction $\{\phi\}$ of the integral equation (2) whose kernel is the average autocorrelation function defined by

$$R_{ij}(x,x') = \langle u_i(x)u_j(x')\rangle \tag{3}$$

Then, equation (2) can be expressed as

$$\int_D R_{ij}(x,x')\phi_j^{(n)}(x')dx' = \lambda^{(n)}\phi_i^{(n)}(x) \tag{4}$$

where D is the two-dimensional domain of the velocity field. The solution of equation (4) represents a set $\phi^{(n)}$ of basis functions for which each velocity field u_i is represented as

$$u_i = \sum_{n=1}^N a_i^{(n)}\phi^{(n)} \tag{5}$$

where a is the dot product for u and ϕ. That is, a is the projection of u in the direction represented by ϕ.

The eigenfunction ϕ can be assumed to have the form

$$\phi = \sum_{k=1}^{M} A_k u^{(k)} \tag{6}$$

In this work the data used are velocity field realizations of $n\times m$ vectors and hence a typical realization of 285×93 produces a vector length of 26,505. The corresponding autocorrelation matrix has dimensions of 26,505×26,505. The solution of the eigenvalue problem, for such a large matrix is quite cumbersome and very time consuming with the current computers. Sirovich[1] proposed an equivalent approach to overcome this difficulty in which expressions R_{ij} can be expressed as

$$R_{ij}(x,x') = \frac{1}{M}\sum_{n=1}^{M} u_i^n u_j^n \tag{7}$$

Here the M is the number of snapshots (or realizations).

If (4), (6) and (7) are combined, we obtain

$$\mathbf{CA} = \lambda \mathbf{C} \tag{8}$$

where $\mathbf{C}$ is an $M\times M$ matrix defined as

$$C_{ij} = \sum_{m=1}^{n} u^{(i)}(x_m)u^{(j)}(x_m) \tag{9}$$

with n being the number of vectors in the velocity field.

2.2. Galerkin Procedure

The Galerkin method is a discretization scheme for PDE's, which is generically categorized as one of the spectral methods or methods of weighted residuals. This method is based on the separation of variables approach and is an attempt to find an approximate solution in the form of truncated series expansion given by

$$\hat{u}(x,t) = \sum_{i=1}^{N} a_i(t)\phi_i(x) \tag{10}$$

where ϕ_i are our known eigenfunctions calculated using the POD method described earlier. Thus, the original infinite-dimensional system is approximated by a N-dimensional system where the order of the reduced model is determined by the truncation velocity, $\hat{u}$. The method then involves the projection of the truncated velocity in equation (5) on to the Navier-Stokes equations. A brief description of this procedure is given below.

Suppose we have a system governed by the PDE's

$$\frac{\partial u}{\partial t} = D(u) \qquad u: D\times(0,\infty) \to R \tag{11}$$

with appropriate boundary conditions and initial conditions, where $D( )$ is a spatial operator. On projecting the eigenfunctions, ϕ_i on to equation (11), we obtain the following expression

$$\left(\phi^{(n)}, \frac{\partial u_i}{\partial t} - D(u_i)\right) = 0, \qquad n=1,\dots,M \tag{12}$$

The above operation leads to a set of ordinary differential equations of the form

$$\frac{da_i}{dt} = F_i(a_1,\dots,a_M) \tag{13}$$

where $a = (a_1,\dots,a_M)$ and $F: \mathbf{R}^N \to \mathbf{R}^N$. By solving the reduced order model represented by the equation (13) and substituting back into equation (10) we get an approximate solution for $\hat{u}(x,t)$. This procedure will avoid solving the infinite dimensional system given by the original PDE's and it provides a practical procedure for studying the evolution of the flow field.

2.1.1. Equations of motion

The method developed by Rowley et al.[13] is followed for applying scalar-valued POD/Galerkin to compressible flows using the isentropic Navier-Stokes equations. Since, the original compressible equations are quite complicated, approximations are made to obtain a simpler set of equations that can be used for Galerkin projection. The detailed derivation of the equations can be found in Rowley *et al.*[13] The resulting equations of motion are

$$\frac{D}{Dt} + \frac{1}{2} \quad \mathbf{u} = 0$$

$$\frac{D\mathbf{u}}{Dt} + \frac{2}{1} \quad = \quad {}^2\mathbf{u} \tag{14}$$

where   is the local sound speed and $= 1.4$ and

$$\mathbf{u} = \overline{\mathbf{u}} + \sum_{n=1}^{N} a^{(n)} \,{}^{(n)}$$

The isentropic N-S in non-dimensional form are given as

$$u_t + uu_x + vu_y + \frac{1}{M^2}\frac{2}{1} \quad {}_x = \frac{1}{Re_h}(u_{xx} + u_{yy})$$

$$v_t + uv_x + vv_y + \frac{1}{M^2}\frac{2}{1} \quad {}_y = \frac{1}{Re_h}(v_{xx} + v_{yy}) \tag{15}$$

$${}_t + u \,{}_x + v \,{}_y + \frac{1}{2} \quad (u_x + v_y) = 0$$

where $Re_h = U_j h/$. Velocities have been normalized by the initial jet velocity U_j,   is normalized by the ambient sound speed, x and y by the nozzle height h, and time by h/U_j. Applying the Galerkin procedure to equation (15), a system of ODE's in the form of equation (13) is obtained.

3. EXPERIMENTAL APARATUS AND PROCEDURES

Experiments were conducted in the blow-down jet facility of the Fluid Mechanics Research Laboratory[14]. This facility is capable of generating jets with Reynolds numbers in excess of 3×10^6 with exit Mach numbers up to 2.15 and total temperatures up to 800 K. The $M_d=1.44$, convergent-divergent nozzle used in this study has a rectangular exit with 4:1 aspect ratio and 10 mm in short dimension (h).

The mean exit velocity profile with laminar boundary layers was top hat as the jet was exhausted into a quiet surrounding at ambient conditions. The jet exit Reynolds number based on the nozzle exit height and the mean exit velocity is 3.3×10^5. A Cartesian coordinate system (X, Y, Z) was chosen with its origin located at the center of the nozzle exit plane and with X axis oriented along the centerline of the jet, Y and Z axes are oriented along the short and long dimensions respectively. The measurements are confined to the central plane (XY plane) of the jet containing the small dimension of the nozzle and YZ planes at selected locations downstream of the nozzle exit. Because of the slender character of the jet flow, it is necessary to cover the entire jet in several measurement zones.

These zones may have different sizes to cover the regions of interest. In addition, they overlap on each other to ensure the coverage of the whole field and for a proper match.

Non-intrusive measurements of the velocity field were made using stereoscopic Particle Image Velocimetry (PIV). A detailed discussion of the application of the Stereoscopic PIV technique to supersonic jets is given in Alkislar[14,15]. The flow was seeded internally with submicron particles generated by a modified Wright nebulizer in the size range of 01-1 μm. Rosko fog generator was used to seed the ambient air with particle sizes 1-10 μm. A typical instantaneous velocity field obtained in the central plane containing the small dimension of the nozzle, covering the region from the nozzle exit to about 10 h, is shown in figure 1. The uniformly scaled velocity vectors superimposed with the contours of the out of plane component of the vorticity are shown in the figure. The convective velocity of vortical structures is subtracted from the whole velocity field to show the details of the shear layer. The data was obtained using an 83×136 (X, Y) Cartesian grid. The jet was operated at the underexpanded jet condition corresponding to the fully expanded jet Mach number of 1.69. The jet displays organized vortical structures that are generated by the well known feed back mechanism. The large structures in screeching jets typically appear at a periodic rate, giving raise to the opportunity of acquiring the phase locked velocity field data. The near field microphone signal is used for the timing reference for the phase averaging of the PIV data at specific phases of the driving signal as illustrated in figure 2. Corresponding to each phase there is a composite snapshot of the flow field starting at some reference time given by the microphone signal. The composite snapshots approximate reasonably the instantaneous flow field for the purposes of extracting the large-scale coherent vortical structures in the jet. PIV results

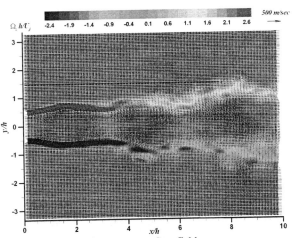

Figure 1. A typical instantaneous flow field.

suggest that thirty samples are sufficient to achieve statistical convergence of the velocity field at constant phase. The data was sampled at 22.5° intervals within the first half of the screech cycle. It was found that the selected data taken in the second half of the screech cycle was simply a reflection of the data. In total 560 instantaneous velocity fields are obtained. The details of the phase-locked system are given in Alkislar[14].

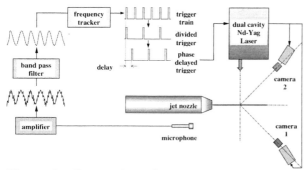

Figure 2. Illustration of phase locked system for stereoscopic PIV measurements.

4 RESULTS AND DISCUSSIONS

The global mean velocity of the flow is first obtained using 560 instantaneous velocity fields. The fluctuating velocity field realizations are then obtained from subtracting the global mean from each of the instantaneous velocity fields. The fluctuating velocity field realizations are used to compute the eigenvalues and eigenfunctions using the method outlined in section 2.1. The data covering the region $x/h = 0.1 - 32.4$ are used. At each phase, thirty-five realizations are considered. Sixteen phases within the screech cycle are used. The mean vorticity at constant phase is calculated using the expression

$$\langle \omega_z \rangle = \frac{\partial \langle v \rangle}{\partial x} - \frac{\partial \langle u \rangle}{\partial y}.$$

The contours of the normalized vorticity magnitude at four different phases within a screech cycle are shown in Figure 3. The vorticity contours seen in the figure are a clear indication of the presence of large-scale coherent vortical structures. The large vortical structures are convected downstream at half the jet exit velocity. They appear at a periodic rate at a frequency of 4200 Hz. The vortical structures are highly three dimensional in nature and as a result, the vorticity contours appear to be fragmented. The source of three-dimensionality can be attributed to the generation of streamwise vortices in the shear layers[11]. The periodic shock cell structure commonly seen in underexpanded jets is also evident in this figure. More detailed description of the large-scale structure dynamics for this flow is given in Alkislar[14].

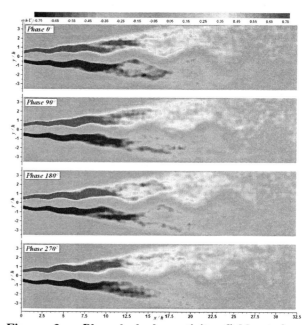

Figure 3. Phase-locked vorticity field at four consecutive phases within the screech cycle.

4.1 Energy Distribution

The energy associated with different eigenfunctions is contained in their corresponding eigenvalue, λ. In equation (8), $\mathbf{C}$ is a real symmetric matrix, it has positive real eigenvalues, and $\mathbf{A}$ can be structured in decreasing order of the corresponding eigenvalues $\lambda^1 > \lambda^2 > ,....., \lambda^n > 0$. The relative values of λ^n reflect the amount of energy in each eigenfunction (or Mode). That is:

$$E_n = \frac{\lambda^n}{\sum_{n=1}^{M} \lambda^n}$$ (10)

is a fraction of the data set energy that is contained in the direction of the nth eigenfunction ϕ.

Table 1 lists the relative energy of the eigenvalues for the first 10 modes for the axial and transverse components of the velocity and the corresponding vorticity fields. The cumulative energy of the eigenvalues is shown in Figure 4. It is observed from the data that the first two modes contain significant percent of the total energy. Accordingly, the analysis of the mode shapes to be discussed later is confined mostly to these dominant modes.

Sirovich[1] suggests that a 99 % of the total energy be used as cut off for representing the flow field accurately. On the other hand, Palacios[16] suggests a 75 % of the energy may be sufficient for a good representation of the system. As it will be shown later,

Table 1. The first 10 eigenvalues (Energy represented in percent of the total energy).

i	(u)	(v)	$(_z)$
1	45.87	57.41	39.91
2	35.43	32.00	29.76
3	4.33	1.70	4.13
4	2.66	1.44	3.25
5	2.06	1.18	3.15
6	1.57	0.92	2.40
7	1.34	0.89	2.40
8	1.20	0.86	2.19
9	1.07	0.69	2.14
10	0.96	0.57	2.03

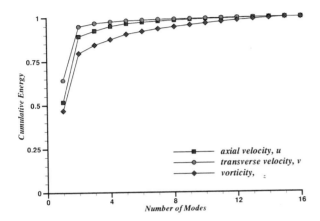

Figure 4. POD cumulative energy distribution.

the reconstruction of the vorticity field with about 75% of the energy provides a good representation of the principal characteristics of the flow field.

4.2. Mode shapes and reconstruction

The characteristics of the POD modes are now examined to understand the large-scale structure dynamics. Figure 5 presents the first three mode shapes corresponding to the axial velocity, transverse velocity and the vorticity. Also included in the figure are their experimentally determined global mean distributions. The color contours in the figure representing the mode shapes have both positive (red) and negative (blue) values. The mode shapes are simply a pattern that may not provide a direct connection to the large-scale structure physics. However, upon close examination, it is observed that the peak magnitude locations in the first two mode shapes appear to coincide with the corresponding peak periodic Reynolds stresses[14]. Hence, it is believed that the mode shape structure may have some relationship with coherent structure

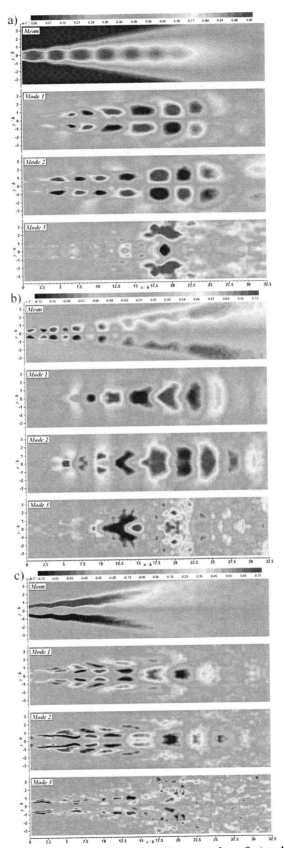

Figure 5. Average and first three modes of a) axial velocity, b) radial velocity and c) vorticity

dynamics. Indeed, it has been suggested by Lumely[4] that a high-energy eigenfunction could represent a structure in the flow field. Consequently, in the following discussion, eigenfunction, structure and pattern are used as synonymous.

Using the dominant POD mode shapes, the velocity and vorticity fields at a constant phase are reconstructed as shown in Figure 6. Reconstruction is carried out using equation (5). The original experimental data at the corresponding phase is also included in the figure for comparison. From the reconstructed data, it appears that the first two modes capture the velocity and vorticity fields with fidelity. The flow reconstruction using more than the first two modes appear to add little information. Therefore, that the two energetic modes are sufficient to capture the complete structure of the flow within the region where the large structure dynamics are most important. Based on this observation, the two dominant modes are used in the low dimensional modeling using the above-described Galerkin procedure.

4.3. Low order modeling

The scalar-valued POD/Galerkin method is applied to predict the flow field using computed eigenfunctions from POD analysis. The first two dominant modes are considered to obtain the coefficients (a_n) of the dynamical equations. A system of six equations and six unknowns is solved using the initial condition given by the first value of a_1 and a_2 at $t = 0$. They are obtained from the direct projection of the first realization on the eigenfunctions. The fourth order Runge-Kutta scheme provided in MatLab software has been utilized. The time step used in the simulation is the same as the time interval between the experimental realizations. Thus, a direct comparison between experimental data and the simulation data can be made as shown in Figure 7. Here the computed values for $a_n(t)$ are compared to the direct projection results. The simulation results shown in Figure 7 for the axial and transverse velocities and the speed of sound compare reasonably well with the direct projections of realizations on the eigenfunctions. The Crocco's relationship[17] is used to calculate the temperature, from which the speed of sound can be obtained. The calculated data is limited to the region $0 < x/h < 9$.

The spectral analysis of both the experimental and simulation $a_n(t)$ values is shown in Figure 8. It reveals that the frequency of oscillation of the simulated flow is in commensurate with the experimental data. However, the amplitude of the spectral peaks does not

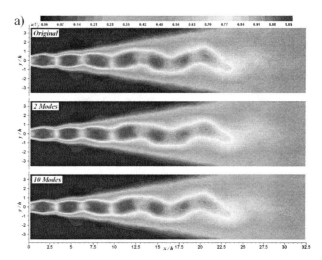

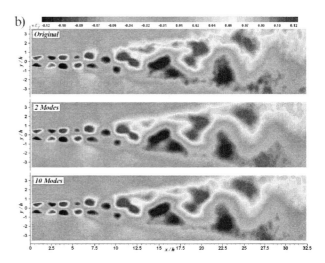

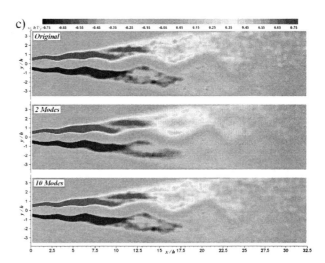

Figure 6. The comparison of original flow field with POD reconstructions. a) original, b) first 2 modes, c) first 10 modes.

1982

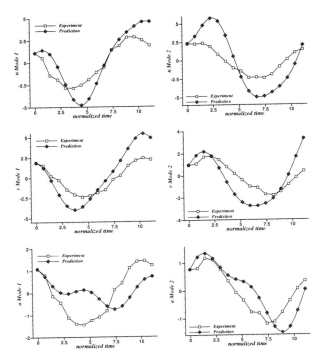

Figure 7 Time traces of first 2 modes for axial velocity, transverse velocity and sound speed in the potential core region: experimental and Galerkin prediction.

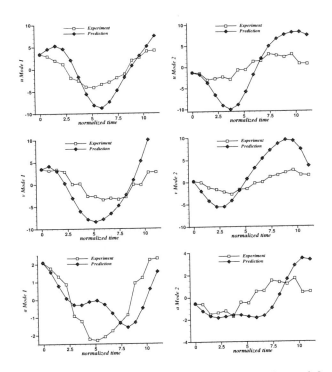

Figure 8. Time traces of first 2 modes for axial velocity, transverse velocity and sound speed in the transient region: experimental and Galerkin prediction.

agree with the simulation results showing higher amplitude. This may be due to the simplified equations of motion used in the simulation.

When the region of interest is extended up to $x/h = 15$, the simulation results begin to deviate further from the POD calculations as shown in Figure 9. This may be due to the use of isentropic Navier-Stokes equations that do not include the contributions of viscous terms, which may play an increasingly important role further downstream of the jet.

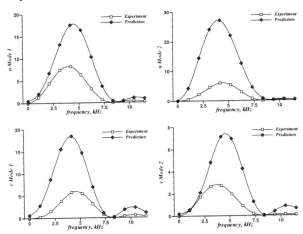

Figure 9. Comparison of spectrums of time traces of experimental results with the results of Galerkin prediction.

Figure 10 shows comparisons between the phase-averaged experimental and simulation data for four different phases. Both the axial and transverse velocity fields are included in the figure. Although there are some differences in the details, the overall flow field is captured well in the simulations. In particular, the oscillation of the jet column is captured vividly.

5. CONCLUSIONS

The use of POD method in the analysis of stereoscopic PIV data is presented here for characterizing the large-scale coherent structures in terms of the superposition of few eigenfunctions. The method captures the main features of the flow with only two modes, because most of the fluctuation energy is contained within them.

Projection of the Navier-Stokes equations on the basis set of principal eigenfunction modes, obtained from the POD method, results in a low-order system of dynamical equations. Solution of this system of equations provides a description of the coherent structure dynamics associated with the eigenfunctions. The simulation results obtained using these equations compare well with the experimental results. From this

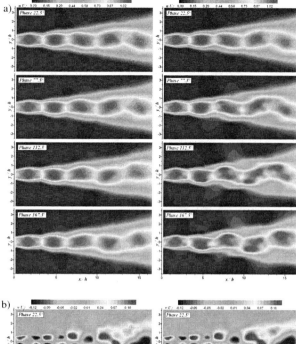

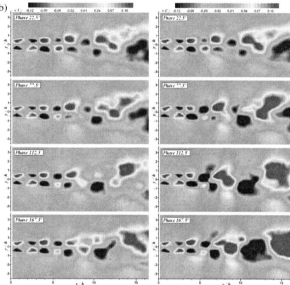

Figure 10 Comparison of experimental flow field (left) with the results of Galerkin prediction (right), a) axial velocity, b) transverse velocity.

study, it appears that the low order modeling of self-excited jet flows can be useful for predictions of global flow characteristics.

We like to thank the Office Of Naval Research (Dr. Gabriel Roy – Technical Monitor) for supporting our work on high-speed jet noise research. D Moreno wants to acknowledge CONACYT and COCYTEG in Mexico for the partial support of the post-doctoral staying.

REFERENCES

[1] Sirovich L.,"Turbulence and the dynamics of coherent structures I-III", *Quarterly Applied Mathematics*, **XLV**, 561-590 (1987).

[2] Powell, A. "On the noise emanating from a two dimensional jet above the critical pressure", *Aeronautical Quarterly*, **4**, pp. 103-122, (1953)

[3] Krothapalli, A., Baganoff D., and Hsia, Y. "On the Mechanism of Screech Tone Generation in Underexpanded Rectangular Jets", AIAA Paper 83-0727, April 1983, Atlanta.

[4] Lumley, J., "The structure of inhomogeneous turbulent flows", Atmospheric Turbulence and wave propagation, Nauca, Moccow, (1967)

[5] Aubry, N., Holmes, P., Lumley, J. L. and Stone, E., "The Dynamics of Coherent Structures in the Wall Region of a Turbulent Boundary Layer", *Journal of Fluid Mechanics*, **192**, pp. 115-173 (1988).

[6] Gordeyev, S. and Thomas, F., "Coherent Structure in the Turbulent Planar Jet. Part.1 Extraction of the Proper Orthogonal Decomposition Eigenmodes and Self-similarity," *Journal of Fluid Mechanics*, **414**, pp. 145-194 (2000)

[7] Citriniti, J. and George, W., "Reconstruction of the Global Velocity Field in the Axisymmetric Mixing Layer Utilizing the Proper Orthogonal decomposition," *Journal of Fluid Mechanics*, **418**, pp. 137-166 (2000).

[8] Bernero, S. and Fiedler, E., "Application of the particle image velocimetry and proper orthogonal decomposition to the study of a jet in a counterflow", *Experiments in Fluids*, **29** (7), pp.274-281 (2000).

[9] Graftieaux L., Michard M., and Grosjean N., "Combining PIV, POD and vortex identification algorithms for the study of unsteady turbulent swirling flows", *Measurement Science and Technology*, **12**, pp.1422-29 (2001).

[10] Patte-Rouland B., Lalizel G., Moreau J., and Rouland E., "Flow analysis of an annular jet by particle image velocimetry and proper orthogonal decomposition", *Measurement Science and Technology*, **12**, pp. 1404-12 (2000).

[11] Krothapalli, A., Alkislar, M. B. and Lourenco, L., "The Role of Large Scale Structures on the Screech Amplitude", AIAA Paper 01-2144, May 2001, Maastrich.

[12] Berkooz, G., Holmes, P., and Lumley J. "The proper orthogonal decomposition in the analysis of turbulent flows", *Annual Review of Fluid Mechanics*, **25,** 539-575 (1993).

[13] Rowley, C. W., Colonius, T. and Murray, R. M. "POD based models of self-sustained oscillations in the flow past an open cavity", AIAA Paper 2000-1969, June 2000.

[14] Alkislar, M. B., "Flow Field Measurements in a Screeching Rectangular Jet", *Ph.D. Dissertation*, Florida State University, (2001).

[15] Alkislar, M. B., Krothapalli, A. and Lourenco, L., "Stereoscopic PIV Measurements of a Screeching Supersonic Jet", *Journal of Visualization*, **3** (2), (2000).

[16] Palacios A., Gunaratne G. M., and Gorman M., "Cellular pattern formation in circular domains", *Chaos*, **7** (3)**,** 463-475 (1997).

[17] Tam, C. K. W., Chen, P. and Seiner, J. M. "Relationship Between Instability Waves and Noise of High Speed Equations", *AIAA Journal*, **30** (7), pp. 1747-1752 (1992).

SIMULATION OF JET NOISE WITH OVERFLOW CFD CODE AND KIRCHHOFF SURFACE INTEGRAL

M. Kandula*
Dynacs Inc., Kennedy Space Center, FL 32899

R. Caimi†
NASA Kennedy Space Center, FL 32899

ABSTRACT

An acoustic prediction capability for supersonic axisymmetric jets was developed on the basis of OVER-FLOW Navier-Stokes CFD (Computational Fluid Dynamics) code of NASA Langley Research Center. Reynolds-averaged turbulent stresses in the flow field are modeled with the aid of Spalart-Allmaras one-equation turbulence model. Appropriate acoustic and outflow boundary conditions were implemented to compute time-dependent acoustic pressure in the nonlinear source-field. Based on the specification of acoustic pressure, its temporal and normal derivatives on the Kirchhoff surface, the near-field and the far-field sound pressure levels are computed via Kirchhoff surface integral, with the Kirchhoff surface chosen to enclose the nonlinear sound source region described by the CFD code. The methods are validated by a comparison of the predictions of sound pressure levels with the available data for an axisymmetric turbulent supersonic (Mach 2) perfectly expanded jet.

Nomenclature

c = mean sound speed, $\sqrt{\gamma g_c R_u T / W}$, ft/s

d_j = nozzle exit diameter, ft

f = frequency, Hz

---

*Principal Investigator, Associate Fellow AIAA
†Lead Engineer, Launch Systems Testbed

g_c = gravitational constant, (lbm-ft/lbf.s^2)

k = turbulent kinetic energy

M = Mach number, V/c

m = instability mode

p = static pressure, lbf/ft^2

p' = acoustic pressure disturbance, $p - p_m$, lbf/ft^2

Q' = vector of disturbance variables

Re = Reynolds number, $\rho u_j d_j / \mu$

R_u = universal gas constant, lbf.ft/(lbm-mole R)

r = radial distance

r_j = nozzle exit radius, ft

St = Strouhal number, $f d_j / u_j$

T = temperature, R

V = velocity, m/s

u = axial velocity, ft/s

u_c = jet center-line velocity at exit, ft/s

w = radial velocity, ft/s

W = molecular weight, lbm/lbm-mole

x = axial distance from the nozzle exit, ft

z = radial distance from jet axis, ft

Greek Symbols

ε = dissipation rate of turbulent kinetic energy

μ = dynamic viscosity, lbm.ft/s

ρ = density, lbm/ft^3

γ = isentropic exponent

ω = circular frequency, radians/

ψ = angle from jet axis, deg

INTRODUCTION

Acoustic loads in a launch vehicle environment represent a principal source for inducing structural vibration and may be critical to the proper functioning of vehicle components and ground support structures and equipment in the immediate vicinity of the launch pad. A knowledge of acoustic loads, including the overall sound pressure level (OASPL), sound pressure level (SPL) spectrum, and the distribution (or correlation) of surface acoustic loads, is necessary to provide the input for vibroacoustic analysis and evaluation of structural integrity. In the design of launch vehicles, it is highly desirable that data on acoustic loads (near-field and far-field noise levels) be generated both analytically and from testing of small-scale and full-scale models. Since full-scale acoustic and vibration testing is often cost prohibitive, the option of small-scale testing combined with analysis methods remains as a practical alternative. Accurate characterization of acoustic loads on launch pad structures thus proves to be a formidable challenge.

Noise from subsonic jets is mainly due to turbulent mixing, comprising the contributions of large-scale and fine-scale structures (Lighthill[1,2]). The turbulent mixing noise is mainly broadband. In perfectly expanded supersonic jets (nozzle exit plane pressure equals the ambient pressure), the large-scale mixing noise manifests itself primarily as Mach wave radiation, caused by the supersonic convection of turbulent eddies with respect to the ambient fluid. In imperfectly expanded supersonic jets, additional noise is generated on account of broadband shock noise and screech tones.

The prediction of noise generation and propagation from exhaust jets by computational methods entails certain numerical requirements (Tam[3]). Although the existing CFD codes can predict the noise generation in the nonlinear source-field, their application to acoustic predictions for obtaining near-field and far-field sound levels results in inaccuracies due to numerical dispersion and dissipation over long propagation distances. Specialized Computational Aeroacoustics (CAA) methods were developed to resolve these numerical issues satisfactorily (Tam and Webb[4], Lele[5]). These computational methods for direct calculation of noise in the near-field and the far-field, however, require prohibitively large computational resources.

This situation motivated in recent years the application of CFD codes to model the source region (containing the sound sources), with the near-field and far-field sound predicted by either Lighthill's acoustic analogy (Lighthill[1,2]) or the Kirchhoff surface integral (Kirchhoff[6]). In Lighthill's acoustic analogy the Navier-Stokes equations are rearranged in wave-like form with Lighthill's stress tensor acting as the source term, and the near-field and far-field sound is obtained via a volume integral. This volume integral again requires large computational resources. On the other hand, the Kirchhoff method requires only a surface integral, with the Kirchhoff surface enclosing the nonlinear source region, and is chosen in a region where the linear wave equation is valid. Additionally, the Kirchhoff method does not suffer dissipation and dispersion errors when the near-field and far-field sounds are directly calculated with the CFD codes. By restricting the use of CFD methods to the nonlinear near-field region for source identification and employing Kirchhoff integration for the linear region, computational requirements are greatly reduced.

The ability to accurately predict the turbulent mixing noise sources remains as a key requirement in the overall acoustic analysis. Both the large-scale turbulence structures (instability waves) and the fine-scale turbulence represent the mixing noise sources. The large turbulence structures are responsible for Mach wave emission that is directional, and the fine-scale turbulence mixing noise is fairly uniform independent of direction. In the past the two-equation $k - \varepsilon$ turbulence model is generally used to model the sound sources. However, this model entails large computational requirements (two additional equations) and is often plagued with convergence problems in flows with shock waves and strong gradients. Furthermore, the universal constants in the turbulence model are often altered to fit the theory with the acoustic measurements. On the other hand, the simple algebraic mixing length type turbulence model cannot accurately describe the growth of the mixing layers. Thus a one-equation turbulence model seems to be an attractive choice for engineering applications. This model generally results in faster convergence and requires less computational resources.

The objective of this investigation is to predict supersonic jet acoustics on the basis of CFD/ Kirchhoff formulation in conjunction with a one-equation turbulence model. This report, based on Ref. 7, summarizes the development of a computational procedure in which the OVERFLOW CFD Navier-Stokes code (Buning et al.[8]) predicts the nonlinear source-field within the jet and application of Kirchhoff surface integral for acoustic radiation.

ANALYSIS

This method of analysis is based on the application of a CFD code for identifying the noise sources in the source-field and Kirchhoff surface integral for the propagation of sound radiation to the near-field and the far-field.

CFD Analysis

Numerical Algorithm

For the CFD analysis, the OVERFLOW code (Buning et al.[8]) of NASA Langley is used for computing the instantaneous flowfield. This code solves the three-dimensional compressible turbulent flow Navier-Stokes equations in generalized coordinates. The one-equation turbulence model of Spalart and Allmaras[9] is considered.

Boundary Conditions

To simulate the exterior (infinite boundary) acoustic problem, we need to prescribe outflow and radiation boundary conditions at the boundaries of a finite computational domain. These boundary conditions must be sufficiently transparent to the outgoing disturbances so that they exit the computational domain without significant (nonphysical) reflections. It is assumed that the boundaries are sufficiently far from the sources.

The OVERFLOW code, in its present form, is designed primarily for the prediction of steady or unsteady turbulent flowfields and used widely to model aerodynamic flows. It does not however provide the necessary time-dependent boundary conditions for handling the reflection-free acoustic propagation. Therefore appropriate modifications to the code were made to provide a set of time-dependent reflection-free boundary conditions (includes periodic inflow, outflow, and radiation).

a. Inflow Boundary Conditions

At the supersonic inflow, all data are specified, such that all time variations of the characteristic variables are set to zero because all waves are incoming waves.

b. Outflow Boundary Conditions

In general at the outflow boundary, the outgoing disturbances consist of acoustic, entropy, and vorticity waves. Here we follow Thompson's approach (Thompson[10]) based on one-dimensional characteristics analysis (Riemann variables). The amplitude of the outward propagating waves at the boundary are specified entirely from the solution within the computational domain, while the amplitude of the inward propagating waves is prescribed at the boundary. For details on the method, the original reference should be consulted.

c. Radiation Boundary Condition

At boundaries where there exist only outgoing acoustic waves, Tam and Webb[4] developed a set of radiation boundary conditions based on an asymptotic analysis (valid for large distances). These boundary conditions, originally formulated in a spherical coordinate system, when applied to a cylindrical coordinate system, are given by (Hixon et al.[11])

$$Q'_t = -\xi\left[\frac{x}{R}Q'_x + \frac{r}{R}Q'_r + \frac{Q'}{R}\right] \qquad (1a)$$

where

$$Q' = [\rho', u', w', p']^T,$$
$$\xi = c\left[\frac{x}{R}M + \sqrt{1-\left(\frac{r}{R}M\right)^2}\right], \qquad (1b)$$
$$R = \sqrt{x^2 + r^2}$$

In the above equations, Q' is the vector of disturbance variables, x the axial distance from the origin, and r the radial distance from the jet axis. The subscripts on Q' indicate partial derivatives.

Kirchhoff Code

For the acoustic radiation, the Kirchhoff code YORICK developed by Pilon and Lyrintzis[12] of Purdue University was considered. The Kirchhoff surface, enclosing the nonlinear source region, is chosen in a region where the linear wave equation is valid. Outside the Kirchhoff surface, the flow is governed by the linear equation

$$\nabla^2 p' - \frac{1}{c_\infty^2}\left(\frac{\partial}{\partial t} + u_\infty \frac{\partial}{\partial x}\right)^2 p' = 0 \quad (2a)$$

where u_∞ is the freestream (ambient) velocity. In the special case of stationary ambient ($u_\infty = 0$), it reduces to the simple wave equation. A solution to the pressure field can be expressed by the surface integrals as (Morino and Tseng[13], Lyrintzis and Mankbadi[14])

$$p'(x, y, z, t) = -\frac{1}{4\pi}$$

$$\int \left[\frac{p'}{r_0^2}\frac{\partial r_0}{\partial n_0} + \frac{1}{r_0}\frac{\partial p'}{\partial n_0} + \frac{1}{c_\infty r_0 \beta^2}\frac{\partial p'}{\partial t}\left(\frac{\partial r_0}{\partial n_0} - M_\infty \frac{\partial x_0'}{\partial n_0}\right) \right]_\tau dS_0 \quad (2b)$$

where

$$x_0 = x, \quad y_0 = \beta y, \quad z_0 = \beta z$$

$$r_0 = \left\{ (x-x')^2 + \beta^2\left[(y-y')^2 + (z-z')^2\right] \right\}^{\frac{1}{2}}$$

$$\tau = \frac{[r_0 - M_\infty(x - x')]}{c_\infty \beta^2}, \quad \beta = \left(1 - M_\infty^2\right)^{1/2}$$

In the above equations, (x, y, z) refer to Cartesian system, and the primes denote the Kirchhoff surface. The subscript 0 refers to Prandtl-Glauert transformation coordinates. The quantity M_∞ is the freestream Mach number, c_∞ the speed of sound in the freestream, $\tau = t - t'$ the retarded time, and n_0 the outward normal to the Kirchhoff surface S_0.

Thus the pressure at any instant in the region outside the Kirchhoff surface can be expressed in terms of the information prescribed on the Kirchhoff surface. The required data on pressure and its normal and temporal derivatives on the Kirchhoff surface are taken from the CFD solution.

VALIDATION TEST CASE

The CFD/Kirchhoff methodology formulated above is tested by comparing the predictions with the well-known acoustic test data of Seiner et al.[15] for Mach 2 perfectly expanded supersonic jets of air. The nozzle exit radius is 0.04572 m. Although the data cover a wide range of jet total temperature (using propane burners), detailed validation is performed here for a jet total temperature of 755 kelvin (K). Validation at other jet total temperatures will be reported in a later report. Table 1 shows the data at the nozzle exit. The jet exit velocity is 822 meters per second (m/s), and the jet exhausts into quiescent surroundings at a temperature of 280 K. Fig. 1 shows the location of the far-field measurements of the OASPL with which comparisons with the CFD results are reported.

NUMERICAL SOLUTION

CFD Solution

Axisymmetric Grid

For the CFD computations, an axisymmetric grid of size 200 x 100 x 3 (200 grid points in the axial direction, 100 grid points in the radial direction, and 3 in the azimuthal plane) is considered (Fig. 2). A grid length of 60 jet radii and a grid radius of 10 radii are considered. The grid is clustered in the radial direction near the nozzle wall to resolve the shear layer. Because of the perfectly expanded condition, uniform grid is considered adequate in the axial direction.

Flowfield Solution

At the inlet, the flow variables are specified based on the nozzle exit conditions. In addition, a periodic disturbance (axisymmetric mode) of a single frequency is also prescribed as follows:

$$u'(z) = w'(z) = A \sin(\omega t) \exp\left[-\ln(2)\left(\frac{z-h}{b}\right)^2\right] \quad (3)$$

where ω is the circular frequency of the disturbance and A the amplitude of disturbance. Based on the work of Mankbadi et al.[16], values of $b = 0.1$ and $h = 0.78361$ are considered. The amplitude A is taken to be of the order of 0.01. A value of $St = 0.2$ (based on typical peak SPL frequency for supersonic jets) is considered here for obtaining the disturbance frequency ω.

Appropriate time-dependent boundary conditions were applied to ensure reflection-free boundaries. An outflow boundary condition of Thompson type (Thompson[10]) is applied at the outflow boundary, which maintains the mean static pressure at the ambient value. An acoustic radiation boundary condition of Tam and Webb[4] is applied at the lateral boundary.

The CFD solution converges after about 8,000 time-step iterations (the code is run in a time-accurate manner) before a periodic state is established. An initial steady-state solution (based on local time-stepping, requiring about 600 iterations for convergence) has served as the starting solution for the time-accurate run. The solution is obtained on an IRIX workstation (SGI Indigo machine). About 15 hours of computing time are required for the solution to achieve a periodic state.

Acoustic Solution

After a periodic state has been established, the appropriate data from CFD, corresponding to a cycle, is communicated to the Kirchhoff code. The Kirchhoff surface is a cylindrical surface coinciding with a grid line. The radius of the Kirchhoff surface is taken as about 6 radii from the jet axis. Only the lateral surface of the cylinder is taken into account, and the cylinder ends are neglected due to the effects of nonlinearities. The data to be specified on the Kirchhoff surface include the instantaneous pressure, the pressure-time derivative, and the pressure gradient normal to the surface. The Kirchhoff code then computes the OASPL and the pressure-time signals in the near- and the far-field. From the pressure-time signals, it is possible to compute the SPL spectrum at any location with the aid of the Fast Fourier Transform (FFT).

RESULTS AND DISCUSSION

Jet Mean Flowfield

Fig. 3 shows the computed mean velocity contours in the jet. The potential core and the mixing of the turbulent shear layer are clearly displayed. A comparison of the predicted centerline mean axial velocity with the data is presented in Fig. 4. Both the data and the CFD solution suggest that the jet potential core extends to about 15 jet radii from the nozzle exit plane. The jet potential core may be defined as the axial distance where the jet centerline velocity remains at about 99% of the jet exhaust velocity. It is known that the major noise production region occurs near the end of the potential core, where the most

highly amplified instability wave reaches its maximum growth (Seiner et al.[15]).

In the velocity decay region past the core, the CFD solution predicts a slower growth relative to the measurements. This discrepancy is attributable to the accuracy of the Spalart-Allmaras one-equation turbulence model. Also, the effects of compressibility are not appropriately taken into account in this turbulence model, as it was originally developed for incompressible flows. Data on compressible shear layers indicate that compressibility tends to reduce the growth rate of the shear layers (Goebel and Dutton[17]) relative to the incompressible case, with an increase in the jet convective Mach number. For example, before the potential core closes, a jet convective Mach number M_c, which may be defined by (Freund et al.[18])

$$M_c = \frac{M_j \sqrt{T_j / T_\infty}}{1 + \sqrt{T_j / T_\infty}}$$

The reduced transverse turbulence intensity is believed to be responsible for the observed reduction in the spreading rate for compressible mixing layer. By taking into account the effects of compressibility on the turbulent kinetic energy and its specific dissipation rate into a two-equation turbulence model, the reduction in the mixing length growth rate is found to agree with the data (Kandula and Wilcox[19]).

Figs. 5 and 6 respectively display the mean static pressure and mean Mach number along the centerline of the jet. The pressure oscillation along the centerline is relatively small and shows the accuracy of the boundary conditions. The centerline Mach number variation follows the trend of the centerline velocity, as is to be expected.

Calculations show that with an increase in jet temperature, the potential core length decreases. These results are in qualitative agreement with the data of Seiner et al.[15]. As the jet temperature increases, the convective Mach number increases, and the Mach wave radiation pattern is modified, with the OASPL values generally increasing with an increase in jet temperature.

Jet Instantaneous Pressure and OASPL Contours

Fig. 7 displays the instantaneous pressure contours in the source-field, showing the directivity of Mach wave emission. The lack of significant reflection near the boundaries indicates that the outflow and the radiation boundary conditions implemented in the CFD code are satisfactory. A display of the OASPL within the jet, characterizing the nonlinear source-field, as directly computed by the CFD code, is presented in Fig. 8. Inside the jet shear layer, the pressure levels are high (as much as 180 dB), with the highest OASPL occurring about 7 jet radii downstream of the exit.

Near-Field and Far-Field Acoustic Solutions

Fig. 9 presents the OASPL contours in the near- and the far-field as computed by the CFD/Kirchhoff formulation. It is seen that the OASPL ranges from 80 dB to 130 dB in this region. The directivity of the Mach wave radiation (emission) is evident. It is generally accepted that the mechanism for Mach wave radiation is strongly connected with the amplification of instability modes, and this amplification scales with the jet convective Mach number.

The variation of the OASPL in the streamwise direction at $z/r_j = 80$ is compared in Fig. 10 with the measurements of Seiner et al.[15]. The predicted peak angle of emission of about 128 degrees is in good agreement with the data, which indicates a peak at 127 degrees. Also, the peak value of the OASPL is about 7 dB less than the measured value. There is an underprediction of the OASPL at the off-peak locations both upstream and downstream of the peak. This underprediction is primarily due to the axisymmetric simulations (axisymmetric disturbance mode $m = 0$ instability) of the present investigation. It is impossible to develop a three-dimensional helical mode instability with axisymmetric simulations. Measurements show that near the nozzle exit, axisymmetric modes seem to be dominant, and farther downstream the helical nature of the large-scale structure is dominant (Viswanathan and Sankar[20]). Also, both experiments and hydrodynamic stability analysis suggest that the $m = +1$ helical mode is dominant above a jet Mach number of about 1.4. Thus by including azimuthal mode ($m = +1$) instability in a three-dimensional analysis, predictions of sound pressure levels could be considerably improved (Gamet and Estivalezes[21]). Such three-dimensional simulations require considerably more computing resources, which are outside the scope of the present work. Further improvements in the predictions can be realized by considering inflow disturbances of various frequencies (or random disturbances).

Fig. 11 shows the corresponding comparison with the OASPL plotted as a function of the axial distance from the exit plane. The computed results of OASPL for three values of $z/r_j = 30, 55$ and 80 are displayed in Fig. 12, the

last one corresponding to the data by Seiner[15]. With increasing values of z/r_j, the peak value of OASPL decreases, and the corresponding peak angle decreases. This is to be expected in view of the directivity of Mach wave radiation. The correctness of this trend also serves to verify the Kirchhoff code implementation.

The spectral content of SPL (dB/Hz) along a direction corresponding to the maximum radiation ($x/r_j = 60, z/r_j = 80$) is displayed in Fig. 13. Fig. 14 indicates the variation of 1/3 octave SPL (dB) as a function of the frequency. A well-defined peak SPL value of about 128 dB is seen to occur at a frequency of about 2 kilohertz (kHz), which corresponds to a Strouhal number of 0.2. This value is consistent with the frequency of the imposed disturbance at the nozzle exit. Fig. 15 presents the result of Fig. 14 in a semi-log plot.

CONCLUSIONS

The CFD/Kirchhoff approach is capable of predicting the SPL spectrum and the OASPL at any location in the near-field and the far-field. The relative reduction in the computational time due to the Kirchhoff method and the axisymmetric simulation make it an attractive engineering tool. The one-equation turbulence model of Spalart-Allmaras for computing turbulent stresses affords additional reduction in the computational time and at the same time improves the robustness of the code relative to two-equation turbulence models. The peak angle of Mach wave radiation and the peak level of OASPL are satisfactorily predicted. Predictions at off-peak conditions could be substantially improved by considering three-dimensional disturbances (azimuthal mode instability) and disturbances of various frequencies.

ACKNOWLEDGEMENTS

The authors wish to thank Dr. Pieter Buning of NASA Langley Research Center for discussions with regard to the OVERFLOW code. Professor Anastasios Lyrintzis of Purdue University (School of Aeronautics and Astronautics) kindly provided the YORICK code for Kirchhoff integration. Thanks are also due to Dr. Ravi Margasahayam of Dynacs Inc., and Professor Michael Norton of the University of Western Australia for useful discussions. Detailed review of the report by Stanley Starr, Chief Engineer, Dynacs Inc. is gratefully acknowledged.

REFERENCES

1. Lighthill, M.J., On Sound Generated Aerodynamically: I. General Theory, Proc. Roy. Soc. (London), Ser. A, Vol. 211, No. 1107, pp. 564-587, March 1952.

2. Lighthill, M.J., On Sound Generated Aerodynamically: II. Turbulence as a Source of Sound, Proc. Roy. Soc. (London), Ser. A, Vol. 222, No. 1148, pp. 1-32, Feb. 1954.

3. Tam, C.K.W., Computational Aeroacoustics; Issues and Methods, AIAA J., Vol. 33, No. 10, pp. 1788-1796, 1995.

4. Tam, C.K.W., and Webb, J.C., Dispersion-Relation-Preserving Finite Difference Schemes for Computational Aeroacoustics, Journal of Computational Physics, Vol. 107, pp. 262-281, 1993.

5. Lele, S.K., Compact Finite Difference Schemes with Spectral-Like Resolution, J. of Computational Physics, Vol. 103, pp. 16-42, 1992.

6. Kirchhoff, G. R., Zur Theorie der Lichtstrahlen, Annalen der Physik und Chermie, Vol. 18, pp. 663-695, 1883.

7. Kandula, M., and Caimi, R., Simulation of Supersonic Jet Noise With the Adaptation of OVERFLOW CFD Code and Kirchhoff Surface Integral, NASA TM-2001-210263, July 2001.

8. Buning, P.G., Jesperson, D.C., Pulliam, T.H., Chan, W.M., Slotnick, J.P., Krist, S.E., and Renze, K.J., OVERFLOW User's Manual- version 1.8, NASA Langley Research Center, February 1998.

9. Spalart, P.R., and Allmaras, S.R., A One-Equation Turbulence Model for Aerodynamic Flows, AIAA-92-0439, 1992.

10. Thompson, K.W., Time-Dependent Boundary Conditions for Hyperbolic Systems II, Journal of Computational Physics, Vol. 89, pp. 439-461, 1990.

11. Hixon, R., Shih, S.-H, and Mankbadi, R., Evaluation of Boundary Conditions for Computational Aeroacoustics, AIAA J., Vol. 33, No. 11, pp. 2006-2012, November 1995.

12. Pilon, A.R., and Lyrintzis, A.S., Development of an Improved Kirchhoff Method for Jet Aeroacoustics, AIAA J., pp. 783-790, May 1998.

13. Morino, L., and Tseng, K., A General Theory of Unsteady Compressible Potential Flows with Applications to Airplanes and Rotors, in Developments in Boundary Element Methods, edited by P.K. Banerjee and L. Morino, Vol. 6, pp. 183-245, Elsevier Applied Science, Barking, England, UK, 1990.

14. Lyrintzis, A.S., and Mankbadi, R.R., Prediction of the Far-Field Jet Noise Using Kirchhoff's Formulation, AIAA J., Vol. 32, No.2, 413-416, February 1996.

15. Seiner, J.M., Ponton, M.K., Jansen, B.J., and Lagen, N.T., The Effects of Temperature on Supersonic Jet Noise Emission, AIAA 92-02-046, 1992.

16. Mankbadi, R., Hixon, H., Shih, S.H., and Povinelli, L., Use of Linearized Euler Equations for Supersonic Jet Noise Prediction, AIAA J., Vol. 36, No.2, February 1998.

17. Goebel, S.G., and Dutton, J.C., Experimental Study of Compressible Turbulent Mixing Layers, AIAA J., Vol. 29, No. 4, pp. 453-477, 1991.

18. Freund, J.B., Lele, S.K., and Moin, P., Numerical Simulation of a Mach 1.92 Turbulent Jet and Sound Field, AIAA J., Vol. 38, No. 11, November 2000.

19. Kandula, M., and Wilcox, D.C., An Examination of $k - \omega$ Turbulence Model for Boundary Layers, Free Shear Layers, and Separated Flows, AIAA 95-2317, 1995.

20. Viswanathan, K., and Sankar, L.N., Toward the Direct Calculation of Noise: Fluid/Acoustic Coupled Simulation, Vol. 33, No. 12, pp. 2271-2279, 1995.

21. Gamet, L., and Estivalezes, J.L., Application of Large-Eddy Simulations and Kirchhoff Method to Jet Noise Prediction, AIAA J., Vol. 36, No. 12, pp. 2170-2178, December 1998.

Table 1. Summary of Nozzle Conditions

Stagnation temperature, K	755
Nozzle exit diameter, m	0.09144
Exit pressure, atm	1.0
Exit temperature, K	419
Exit velocity, m/s	822
Acoustic velocity at exit, m/s	411
Nozzle exit Mach number	2.0
Exit jet Reynolds number	1.3×10^6
Ambient pressure, atm	1.0
Ambient temperature, K	280

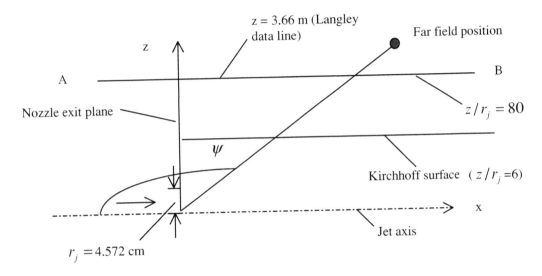

Fig. 1. Schematic of the Test Case Nozzle

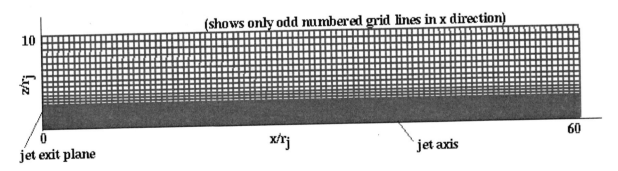

Fig. 2. Axisymmetric grid (200 x 100)

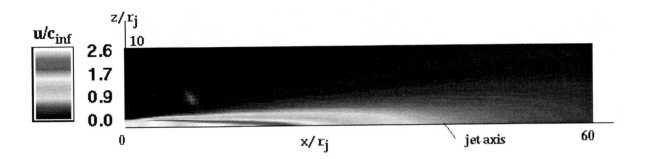

Fig. 3. Mean Axial Velocity Contours in the Jet From CFD Solution

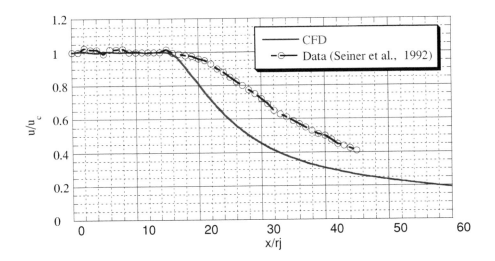

Fig. 4. Jet Centerline Variation of Axial Velocity From CFD

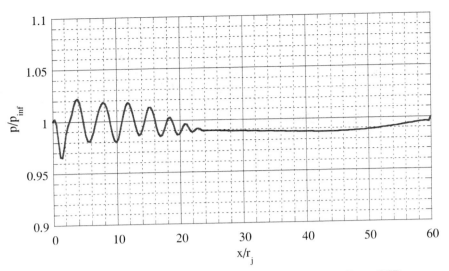

Fig. 5. Jet Centerline Variation of Static Pressure From CFD

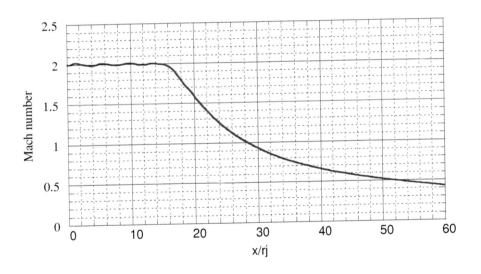

Fig. 6. Jet Centerline Variation of Mach Number From CFD

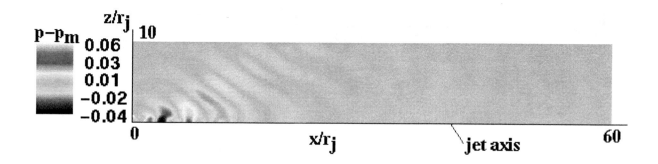

Fig. 7. Instantaneous Pressure Contours in the Jet From CFD Solution

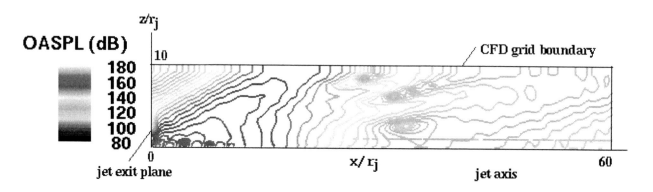

Fig. 8. Contours of OASPL in the Source-Field as Computed Directly From CFD

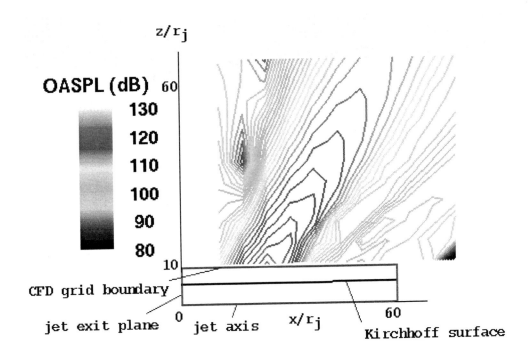

Fig. 9. Contours of OASPL Predicted From CFD/Kirchhoff Method

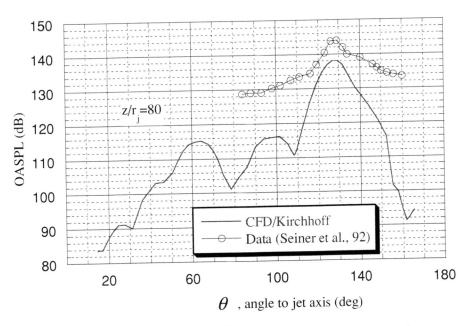

Fig. 10. Comparison of Angular OASPL Distribution at $z/r_j = 80$

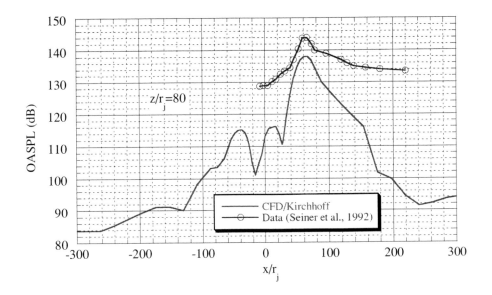

Fig. 11. Comparison of Axial OASPL Distribution at $z/r_j = 80$

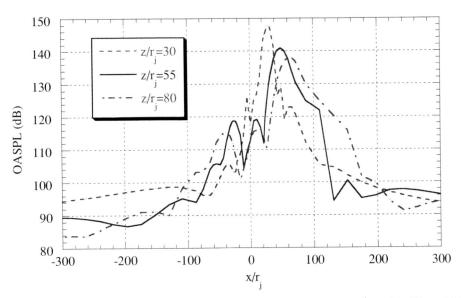

Fig. 12. Computed Axial Distributions of OASPL for $z/r_j = 30$, 55, and 80

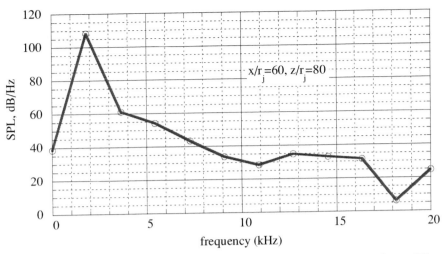

Fig. 13. Computed SPL Distribution at $x/r_j = 60$, and $z/r_j = 80$

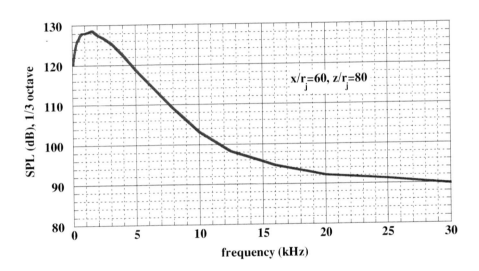

Fig. 14. Computed SPL Distribution at $x/r_j = 60$, and $z/r_j = 80$

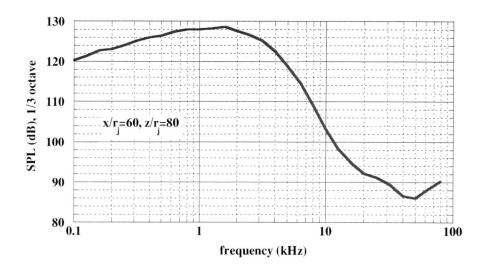

Fig. 15. Computed SPL Distribution (Semi-Log Plot) at $x/r_j = 60$, and $z/r_j = 80$

Jet Noise at Take-off and Landing[†]

Nikolai N. Pastouchenko[*] and Christopher K.W. Tam[**]
Florida State University
Tallahassee, FL 32306-4510
tam@math.fsu.edu

Abstract

During take-off or landing, the jet of an aircraft is not aligned with the direction of flight. Effectively, the jet is in forward motion at an angle of attack. This causes significant distortion of the jet flow and its turbulence intensity and characteristics. In turn, this could lead to changes in the radiated noise spectrum and directivity. A quantitative investigation of this effect is carried out using the Tam and Auriault theory for noise from the fine scale turbulence. Numerical results indicate that for high subsonic and supersonic jets, the effect is generally small; in the order of 1 to 2 dB in parts of the spectrum, even though the jet flow is greatly distorted. This finding is new and quite unexpected.

1. Introduction

When a commercial jet aircraft takes off (see figure 1) or comes down for landing, it climbs out or descends at a relatively steep angle. In this configuration, the jet moves forward at an angle of attack. In the past, most jet noise investigations, both theoretical and experimental, concentrated on noise radiation into a static environment. To account for forward flight effects, fly-over experiments were carried out. However, as far as is known, fly-over measurements were confined, invariably, to level flights over a microphone or an array of microphones. Accuracy of fly-over measurements are generally affected by outdoor meteorological conditions. To remove such uncertain influence, simulated forward flight experiments[1−4] and theoretical prediction[5−9] were performed using an open wind tunnel. However, in almost all these works, the jet was aligned in a forward flight direction at zero angle of attack. Thus these experiments and prediction models did not actually simulate the actual aircraft take-off or landing configuration.

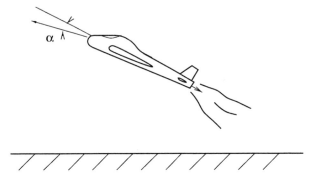

Figure 1. The take-off configuration of a jet.

For jets in forward flight at an angle of attack, the jet velocity profile becomes increasingly distorted in the downstream direction. If a circular nozzle is used, the constant velocity contours will no longer remain circular a few diameters downstream of the nozzle exit. The distortion of the jet flow will inevitably change the turbulence distribution in the jet and would, therefore, affect the radiated noise. For noise from the fine scale turbulence of the jet, the distortion of the mean flow will also affect the mean flow refraction effect. This has the potential to further modify the radiated noise spectrum and directivity.

The purpose of this paper is to assess, for the first time, the effect of angle of attack on the flow and noise radiation of a high speed jet in a take-off or landing configuration. According to Tam & Chen[10] and Tam, Golebiowski & Seiner[11] jet noise consists of two components. They are the noise from the large turbulence structures and the fine scale turbulence of the jet. Here, we will restrict our consideration to the noise from the fine scale turbulence only. The present method of investigation consists of two steps. First, we calculate the jet mean flow at an angle of attack inside an open wind tunnel. In this computation, a $k - \varepsilon$ turbulence model, Ref [12], is used to account for the turbulence of the jet flow. The computation solves the parabolized Reynolds Averaged Navier-Stokes Equations (RANS) by a marching scheme following the work of Ref [13]. Second, we calculate the radiated noise according to the theory of Tam & Auriault[14]. The computed values of k and ε from the first step are now used to provide turbulence information to the noise source function. To account for mean flow refraction, the adjoint Green's function method of Tam & Auriault[15] is employed. Since the jet profile is distorted, the adjoint Green's function will be computed numerically. In this work, it is recast as a sound scattering problem and solved by the DRP scheme[16] as described in Ref[13].

The changes in jet mean flow velocity as well as turbulence intensity, length and time scales due to angle of attack in forward flight will be reported. The effect of these changes on jet noise spectrum and directivity are investigated. The present study includes cold and hot jets at high subsonic and supersonic Mach numbers. Numerical results appear to indicate that at an angle of attack of 10 degrees or less, there are only minor changes in the jet noise spectrum; of the order of 1 to 2 dB in parts of the spectrum, even though the jet mean flow is highly distorted. This finding is unexpected but is useful from the point of view of aircraft community noise prediction.

2. Physical Model and Computational Methods

Let us consider a jet inside an open wind tunnel at an angle of attack α as shown in figure 2. Interest is in determining the noise radiated to the microphones outside the open wind tunnel and to compare the spectra and directivity with those at zero angle of attack.

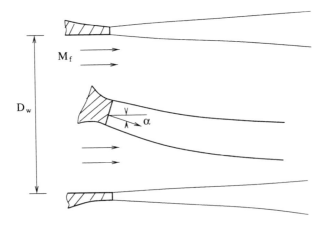

Figure 2. Jet at an angle of attack α in a simulated forward flight experiment.

Computationally, the present problem is quite similar to the forward flight effect study of Ref[9]. The major difference is that, at an angle of attack, the jet mean flow is highly distorted and three-dimensional. Because of the lack of strong upstream influence, the parabolized Reynolds Averaged Navier-Stokes equations (RANS) would be adequate for mean flow calculation. In the present investigation, the $k - \varepsilon$ turbulence model with model constants given by Thies and Tam[11] is used throughout. The parabolized RANS equations can be found in Ref[13] and will, therefore, not be repeated here. To calculate the flow and the $k - \varepsilon$ turbulence information for a jet in forward flight at an angle of attack, the computer code used in Ref[13] is used. What is required is a proper prescription of the starting conditions at the nozzle exit. Here we will let the x-axis be along the centerline of the open wind tunnel pointing in the direction of the flow as shown in figure 2. The z-axis points vertically up. The angle of attack is measured in the $x - z$ plane. The flow profiles at $x = 0$ plane are taken to be,

$$
u = \begin{cases}
u_j \cos \alpha, \\
\qquad (y^2 + z^2 \cos^2 \alpha) \leq h_1^2 \\[2ex]
u_f + (u_j \cos \alpha - u_f) \exp\left[-(\ln 2\right. \\
\quad \left. \cdot \left(\frac{(y^2+z^2\cos^2\alpha)^{\frac{1}{2}}-h_1}{b_2}\right)^2\right], \\
\qquad (y^2 + z^2 \cos^2 \alpha) \geq h_1^2 \\
\qquad \text{and } (y^2 + z^2) \leq h_2 \\[2ex]
u_\infty + (u_f - u_\infty) \exp\left[(-\ln 2\right. \\
\quad \left. \cdot \left(\frac{(y^2+z^2)^{\frac{1}{2}}-h_2}{b_2}\right)^2\right], \\
\qquad (y^2 + z^2) > h_2^2
\end{cases} \tag{1}
$$

$$
v = \begin{cases}
u_j \sin \alpha, \\
\qquad (y^2 + z^2 \cos^2 \alpha) \leq h_1^2 \\[2ex]
u_j \sin \alpha \exp\left[(-\ln 2\right. \\
\quad \left. \cdot \left(\frac{(y^2+z^2\cos^2\alpha)^{\frac{1}{2}}-h_1}{b_1}\right)^2\right], \\
\qquad (y^2 + z^2 \cos^2 \alpha) > h_1^2
\end{cases} \tag{2}
$$

$$T = \begin{cases} T_j, \\ \qquad (y^2 + z^2 \cos^2 \alpha) \le h_1^2 \\[6pt] T_f + (T_j - T_f) \exp \left[(-\ln 2) \right. \\ \qquad \left. \cdot \left(\dfrac{(y^2 + z^2 \cos^2 \alpha)^{\frac{1}{2}} - h_1}{b_1} \right)^2 \right], \\[6pt] \qquad (y^2 + z^2 \cos^2 \alpha) > h_1^2 \\ \qquad \text{and } (y^2 + z^2) \le h_2^2 \\[6pt] T_\infty + (T_f - T_\infty) \exp \left[(-\ln 2) \right. \\ \qquad \left. \cdot \left(\dfrac{(y^2 + z^2)^{\frac{1}{2}} - h_2}{b_2} \right)^2 \right], \\[6pt] \qquad (y^2 + z^2) > h_2^2 \end{cases} \qquad (3)$$

$$p = \frac{\rho_j u_j^2}{\gamma M_j^2} \qquad (4)$$

where u_j, u_f are the jet and the open wind tunnel velocities. $u_\infty = 0.02 u_j$ is added to the outside flow to support the parabolized marching scheme. T_j, T_f and T_∞ are the jet, the open wind tunnel and the ambient temperatures. b_1 is the half-width of the shear layer separating the jet and the open wind tunnel flow and b_2 is that of the shear layer between the open wind tunnel and the ambient air. h_1 and h_2 are the core radii of the jet and the wind tunnel respectively.

To account for flow refraction effect on noise radiated by the fine scale turbulence of a jet, Tam and Auriault[14] employed the adjoint Green's function. For a three-dimensional non-axisymmetric jet, Tam and Pastouchenko[13] recast the adjoint Green's function as a scattering problem after invoking the locally parallel flow approximation. The scattering problem was solved in the time domain by marching the solution to a time periodic state. In this work, the same method is used. One distinct advantage of this method is that the shear layer refraction effect of the open wind tunnel is automatically included in the computation of the adjoint Green's function.

Once the mean flow and the values of k and ε of the jet flow as well as the adjoint Green's function are found, the far field noise spectrum $S(R, \Theta, \phi, f D_j / u_j)$ can be computed by the theory of Tam and Auriault[14]. The formulas for the far field noise spectrum are,

$$S\left(R, \Theta, \frac{f D_j}{u_j}\right) = 10 \log \left[\frac{S(R, \Theta, \phi, f)}{p_{\text{ref}}^2 \left(\frac{D_j}{u_j}\right)} \right] \qquad (5)$$

$$S(R, \Theta, \phi, f) = (4\pi)^2 \left(\frac{\pi}{\ln 2}\right)^{\frac{3}{2}} \iiint\limits_{\text{jet}} \frac{A^2 q^2 \ell_s^3}{\tau_s}$$
$$\cdot \left\{ \frac{|p_a(\mathbf{x_2}, \mathbf{x}, \omega)|^2 \exp \left[\frac{-\omega^2 \ell_s^2}{\overline{u}^2 (4 \ln 2)} \right]}{1 + \omega^2 \tau^2 (1 - \frac{\overline{u}}{a_\infty} \cos \Theta)^2} \right\} d\mathbf{x_2}. \qquad (6)$$

In (6) $\mathbf{x_2}$ is the source point, and $\mathbf{x}$ is the far field measurement point with spherical coordinates (R, Θ, ϕ). The spherical coordinate system is centered at the nozzle exit with the polar axis coincides with the x-axis. Θ is the polar angle and ϕ is the azimuthal angle. Θ is related to the more often used inlet angle χ by $\chi = \pi - \Theta$. ϕ is measured from the z-axis as shown in figure 3. Also $\omega = 2\pi f$ is the angular frequency. p_{ref} is the reference pressure for the decibel scale. D_j and u_j are the fully expanded jet diameter and velocity. $\frac{f D_j}{u_j}$ is the Strouhal number. $\overline{u}$ is the mean flow velocity at the source point. a_∞ is the ambient sound speed. $p_a(\mathbf{x_2}, \mathbf{x}, \omega)$ is the adjoint Green's function. Equation (6) contains a number of turbulence quantities including q, the turbulence intensity, ℓ_s, the eddy size, and τ_s, the eddy decay time. They are related to k, the turbulence kinetic energy and ε, the dissipation rate, of the $k - \varepsilon$ turbulence model as follows:

$$\ell_s = c_\ell \ell = c_\ell \left(\frac{k^{\frac{3}{2}}}{\varepsilon} \right), \tau_s = c_\tau \tau = c_\tau \left(\frac{k}{\varepsilon} \right), q = \frac{2}{3} \overline{\rho} k$$

where $\overline{\rho}$ is the density of the jet mean flow at $\mathbf{x_2}$. c_ℓ, c_τ and A are the three constants of the theory. Their numerical values are[14]

$$c_\ell = 0.256, \qquad c_\tau = 0.233, \qquad A = 0.755.$$

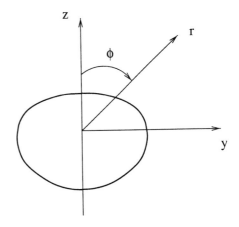

Figure 3. Definition of azimuthal angle ϕ and the $y - z$ plane.

3. Numerical Results

In this paper, the numerical values of the various jet parameters are taken to be,

$$\alpha \ (\text{angle of attack}) = 10°,$$

$$M_f \ (\text{forward flight Mach number}) = 0.2$$

$$\frac{h_1}{D_j} = 0.47, \qquad \frac{b_1}{D_j} = 0.03,$$

$$\frac{h_2}{D_j} = 9.5, \qquad \frac{b_2}{D_j} = 0.5.$$

In addition, the turbulence quantities at the $x = 0$ plane are assigned the following values,

$$\frac{k}{u_j^2} = 10^{-6}, \qquad \frac{\varepsilon D_j}{u_j^3} = 10^{-6}$$

3.1. Mean Velocity Contours

To show the significant distortion of the jet flow at 10° angle of attack, axial velocity contours at different downstream locations are plotted in the $y - z$ plane in figure 4. Shown in this figure is the case of a Mach 0.9 hot jet at a temperature ratio (T_r/T_a) of 2.8 where T_r is the jet reservoir temperature and T_a is the ambient temperature. Figures 4a to 4d show the distribution of contours of u/u_j at $x/D_j = 1.0$, 5.0, 10.0 and 20.0. Clearly, because of the jet is at an angle of attack, the flow is greatly distorted especially around the bottom side of the jet. The incoming flow (relative to the nozzle) compresses the lower part of the jet resulting in closely spaced velocity contours. What is shown in this figure is typical of all the cases examined in the present investigation. There is no question that the jet mean flow is non-axisymmetric and three-dimensional.

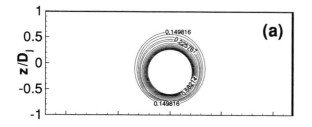

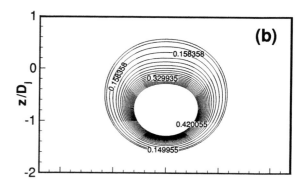

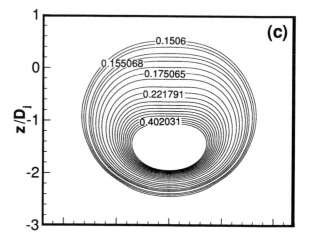

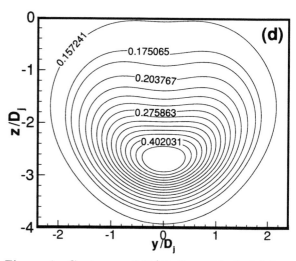

Figure 4. Contours of U/U_j for a Mach 0.9 jet at 10° angle of attack. $T_r/T_a = 2.8$, $M_f = 0.2$. (a) x/D_j = 1.0, (b) x/D_j = 5.0, (c) x/D_j = 10.0, (d) x/D_j = 20.0.

3.2. Effects on Jet Turbulence

The large distortion of the mean flow due to angle of attack also affects the distribution of turbulence intensity and its length and time scales. Figure 5 shows a comparison between the turbulence intensity distributions of a Mach 0.9 hot jet with $T_r/T_a = 2.8$ at zero angle of attack and at $10°$ angle of attack in the $x - z$ plane. An examination of these figures indicates that despite the obvious fact that the distribution is highly unsymmetric at $10°$ angle of attack, the magnitude of k/u_j^2 has not substantially changed.

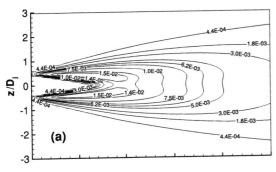

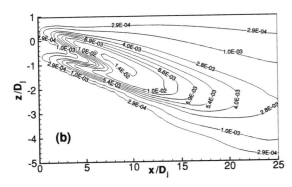

Figure 5. Contours of k/u_j^2 in the $x - z$ plane for a Mach 0.9 jet, $T_r/T_a = 2.8, M_f = 0.2$. (a) angle of attack $= 0°$, (b) angle of attack $= 10°$.

Figures 6a and 6b compare the eddy size $\ell s/D_j$. Because the thickness of the mixing layer on the bottom side of the jet is significantly reduced due to angle of attack, the eddy size is reduced. On the other hand, the thickness of the mixing layer on the top side of the jet is increased. The eddy size becomes larger. However, it is not immediately clear from this figure what the overall effect of these changes on the radiated noise could be.

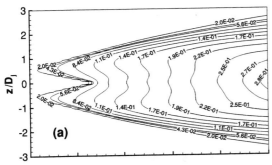

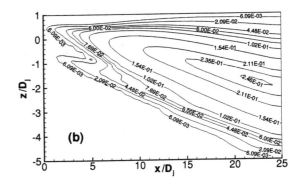

Figure 6. Contours of l_s/D_j in the $x - z$ plane for a Mach 0.9 jet, $T_r/T_a = 2.8, M_f = 0.2$. (a) angle of attack $= 0°$, (b) angle of attack $= 10°$.

Figure 7 shows contours of the eddy decay time $\tau_s u_j/D_j$ in the $x - z$ plane of the jet at zero and at $10°$ angle of attack. In the highly compressed bottom mixing layer of the jet at an angle of attack, the decay time becomes much shorter. On the other side of the jet, the turbulent eddies persist much longer before complete decay. Physically, the distortion of the jet mean flow and turbulence reduces the generation of high frequency sound on the top side of the jet mixing layer in favor of low frequency sound. The opposite is true on the bottom side. Thus it appears that there is a compensating effect on the overall noise radiated from the jet.

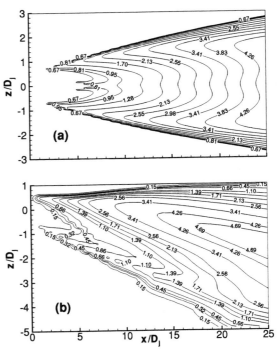

Figure 7. Contours of $\tau_s u_j/D_j$ in the $x - z$ plane for a Mach 0.9 jet, $T_r/T_a = 2.8, M_f = 0.2$. (a) angle of attack $= 0°$, (b) angle of attack $= 10°$.

3.3. Effect on Jet Noise Spectra

The effect of angle of attack on the noise spectrum and directivity for both high subsonic and supersonic jets are investigated. For directivity study, changes in the inlet angle χ as well as the azimuthal angle ϕ are included.

Figure 8 compares the calculated and measured noise spectra for a Mach 1.5 cold jet $(T_r = T_a)$ with forward flight Mach number $M_f = 0.2$. The measured data are from Norum and Brown[4]. The angle of attack is zero. The calculated noise spectrum at zero angle of attack agrees well with the measurements. Plotted in this figure also are the calculated noise spectra for 10° angle of attack at azimuthal angle $\phi = 180°$, 150° and 120°. Figure 8a shows the case at $\chi = 120°$. Figure 8b and 8c show the cases at $\chi = 90°$ and 80° respectively. based on these results, it appears that angle of attack, up to 10 degrees, has only minor effects on the radiated noise spectra.

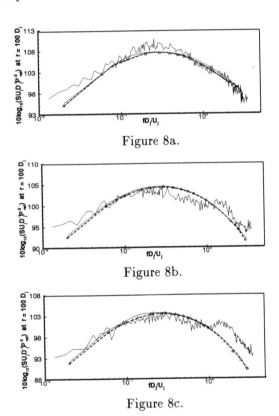

Figure 8a.

Figure 8b.

Figure 8c.

Figure 8. Comparisons of calculated and measured noise spectra for a Mach 1.5 cold jet $(T_r/T_a = 1.0)$ at $M_f = 0.2$. 10° angle of attack; - - - - - - $\phi = 180°$, ... $\phi = 150°$, Δ $\phi = 120°$. Zero angle of attack ———. (a) $\chi = 120°$, (b) $\chi = 90°$, (c) $\chi = 80°$. Experimental data (Ref. 4) at zero angle of attack.

Figure 9 is again for a cold jet $(T_r = T_a)$ but at subsonic Mach number of 0.98. The experimental data are from Ref[17]. The jet in the experiment is at zero angle of attack. The calculated noise spectra at zero angle of attack are in good agreement with measurements. Figure 9a shows the noise spectra at $\chi = 120°$ amd figure 9b those at $\chi = 90°$. Again the spectra at 10° angle of attach at different azimuthal angle ϕ remain essentially the same as those at zero angle of attack.

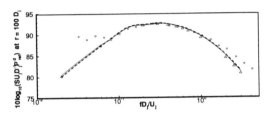

Figure 9a.

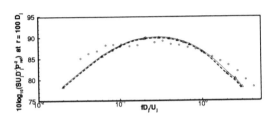

Figure 9b.

Figure 9. Comparisons of calculated and measured noise spectra for a Mach 0.98 cold jet $(T_r/T_a = 1.0)$ at $M_f = 0.2$. 10° angle of attack; - - - - - - $\phi = 180°$, ... $\phi = 150°$, Δ $\phi = 120°$. Zero angle of attack ———. (a) $\chi = 120°$, (b) $\chi = 90°$. ○ experimental data (Ref. 17) at zero angle of attack.

Figures 10 and 11 are similar to figures 8 and 9 except that the jets are hot. Figures 10a and 10b at Mach 0.9 and temperature ratio 2.8 suggest that at $\chi = 60°$ and 90° there is a reduction of low frequency noise up to about 1.5 dB due to angle of attack. However, at $\chi = 120°$, figure 10c shows a noise increase at high frequencies, of the order up to 2.0 dB, at 10° angle of attack. Figures 11a and 11c at Mach 1.5 and temperature ratio 2.0 reveal that angle of attack can produce opposite effect in different direction of radiation. At 60° inlet angle, there is a reduction in high frequency noise. However, at 120° inlet angle, there is an increase in high frequency noise. The reduction and increase are around 1.0 to 1.5 dB.

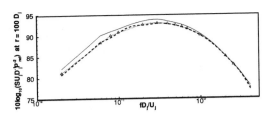

Figure 10a.

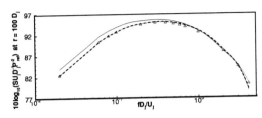

Figure 10b.

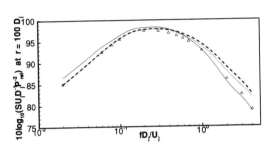

Figure 10c.

Figure 10. Calculated noise spectra for a Mach 0.9 hot jet at $T_r/T_a = 2.8$ and $M_f = 0.2$. ——— zero angle of attack; - - - - - - 10° angle of attack, $\phi = 180°$; $\cdots\cdots$ 10° angle of attack, $\phi = 150°$; $\triangle$ 10° angle of attack, $\phi = 120°$. (a) $\chi = 60°$, (b) $\chi = 90°$, (c) $\chi = 120°$.

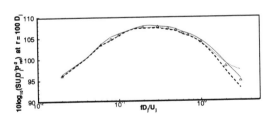

Figure 11a.

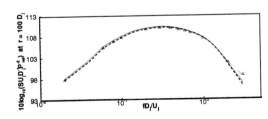

Figure 11b.

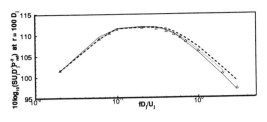

Figure 11c.

Figure 11. Calculated noise spectra for a Mach 1.5 hot jet at $T_r/T_a = 2.0$ and $M_f = 0.2$. ——— zero angle of attack; - - - - - - 10° angle of attack, $\phi = 180°$; $\cdots\cdots$ 10° angle of attack, $\phi = 150°$; $\triangle$ 10° angle of attack, $\phi = 120°$. (a) $\chi = 60°$, (b) $\chi = 90°$, (c) $\chi = 120°$.

The results of figures 8 and 9 indicate that for cold jets at high subsonic and supersonic Mach number, angle of attack up to 10° causes no more than minor changes in the noise spectra. For hot jets, it is different. An increase or a decrease of noise level up to 1.5 to 2.0 dB is possible in part of the noise spectrum. As noted in Sections 3.1 and 3.2, angle of attack can lead to a redistribution of turbulence intensity and large distortion of the mean flow. With a thinner shear layer on the bottom side of the jet there is a significant change in the mean flow refraction effect on radiated noise. In the present study, there is no indication that either the noise source redistribution or the change in mean flow refraction effect is dominant. Without a dominant mechanism associated with a jet at an angle of attack, it is not possible to anticipate by simple reasoning whether there is a noise increase or decrease. It appears that only a full calculation of the noise spectrum can provide an assessment of the effect of angle of attack at a given jet operating condition.

4. Concluding Remarks

At take-off or landing, the jet of an aircraft moves forward at an angle of attack. The effect of angle of attack on jet noise has not been investigated before. In this paper, the case of a jet at an angle of attack of 10 degree in simulated forward flight is considered. Only the effect of angle of attack on the noise from the fine scale turbulence of the jet flow is studied. Calculated results for high subsonic and supersonic jets reveal that the effect is unexpectedly small. It is not a significant factor (only about 1 to 2 dB change in noise level in some part of the spectrum for hot jets) for community noise consideration.

It must, however, be reminded that turbulent mixing noise of a jet is made up of two components. In this work, only the fine scale turbulence noise is investigated. It is likely that the distortion of the mean flow of a jet due to angle of attack could cause considerable changes in the large turbulence structures of the jet flow. This, in turn, could affect the radiated noise. The magnitude of this effect has yet to be quantified. It is hoped that such a study could be carried out either computationally or experimentally in the near future.

Acknowledgments

This work was supported by NASA Langley Research Center Grant NAG 1-2145 and the Florida State University.

References

1. Tanna, H.K. and Morris, P.J., "In-Flight Simulation Experiments on Turbulent Jet Mixing Noise," Journal of Sound and Vibration, Vol. 53, 1977, pp.389-405.

2. Larson, R.S., McColgan, C.J., and Packman, A.B.,"Jet Noise Source Modification Due to Forward Flight," AIAA Journal, Vol. 16, No.3, 1978, pp. 225-232.

3. Yu, J.C. and Dixson, N.R., "Experimental Study of Sound Radiation from Subsonic Jet in Simulated Motion," AIAA Journal, Vol. 18, No. 4, 1980, pp. 427-433.

4. Norum, T.D. and Brown, M.C., "Simulate High Speed Flight Effects on Supersonic Jet Noise," AIAA Paper 93-4388, Oct. 1993.

5. Cocking, B.J., "A Prediction Method for the Effects of Flight on Subsonic Jet Noise," Journal of Sound and Vibration, Vol. 53, 1977, pp. 435-453.

6. Stone, J.R., "On the Use of Relative Exponents for Jet Engine Exhaust Noise," NASA TM 78873, 1978.

7. Michalke, A. and Michel, U., "Relation Between Static and In-Flight Directivities of Jet Noise," Journal of Sound and Vibration, Vol. 63, 1979, pp.602-605.

8. Michalke, A. and Michel, U., "Prediction of Jet Noise in Flight from Static Tests," Journal of Sound and Vibration, Vol. 67, 1979, pp. 341-367.

9. Tam, C.K.W. and Pastouchenko, N.N., "Effects of Forward Flight on Jet Mixing Noise from Fine-Scale Turbulence," AIAA Journal, Vol. 39, No. 7, 2001, pp. 1261-1269.

10. Tam, C.K.W. and Chen, P., "Turbulent Mixing Noise from Supersonic Jets," AIAA Journal, Vol 32, Sept. 1994, pp. 1774-1780.

11. Tam, C.K.W., Golebiowski, M., and Seiner, J.M., "On the Two Components of Turbulent Mixing Noise from Supersonic Jets," AIAA Paper 96-1716, May, 1996.

12. Thies, A.T. and Tam, C.K.W., "Computation of Turbulent Axisymmetric and Nonaxisymmetric Jet Flows Using the k-e Model," AIAA Journal, Vol. 34, No. 2, 1996, pp. 309-316.

13. Tam, C.K.W. and Pastouchenko, N.N.,"Noise from Fine-Scale Turbulence of Nonaxisymmetric Jets," AIAA Journal, Vol. 40, No. 3, 2002, pp.456-464.

14. Tam, C.K.W. and Auriault, L., "Jet Mixing Noise from Fine Scale Turbulence," AIAA Journal, Vol. 37, No. 2, 1999, pp.145-153.

15. Tam, C.K.W. and Auriault, L., "Mean Flow Refraction Effects on Sound Radiated from Localized Sources in a Jet," Journal of Fluid Mechanics, Vol. 370, 1998, pp. 149-174.

16. Tam, C.K.W. and Webb, J.C., "Dispersion-Relation-Preserving Finite Difference Schemes for Computational Acoustics," Journal of Computational Physics, Vol. 107, Aug, 1993, pp. 262-281.

17. Plumblee, H. E., "Effects of Forward Velocity on Turbulent Jet Mixing Noise," NASA CR-2702, 1976.

AEROACOUSTIC MEASUREMENTS OF A WING/SLAT MODEL

Jeff M. Mendoza [*]
Honeywell Engines, Systems, and Services
Phoenix, AZ

Thomas F. Brooks [†]
William M. Humphreys [‡]
NASA Langley Research Center
Hampton, VA

Abstract

Aeroacoustic evaluations of high-lift devices have been carried out in the Quiet Flow Facility of the NASA Langley Research Center. The present paper deals with detailed flow and acoustic measurements that have been made to understand, and to possibly predict and reduce, the noise from a wing leading edge slat configuration. The acoustic database is obtained by a moveable Small Aperture Directional Array of microphones designed to electronically steer to different portions of models under study. The slat is shown to be a uniform distributed noise source. The data was processed such that spectra and directivity were determined with respect to a one-foot span of slat. The spectra are normalized in various fashions to demonstrate slat noise character. In order to equate portions of the spectra to different slat noise components, trailing edge noise predictions using measured slat boundary layer parameters as inputs are compared to the measured slat noise spectra.

List of Symbols

C_p	Coefficient of pressure
$\hat{e}$	Column steering vectors
QFF	Quiet Flow Facility
F	Transfer function for per-foot processing
$\hat{G}$	Cross-spectral matrix
h	Trailing edge thickness
m	Microphone number
M	Freestream flow Mach number
r_{mo}	Microphone to source distance
SADA	Small Aperture Directional Array
TE	Trailing edge
BL	Boundary layer
u	Local flow velocity
u_{av}	Average slat trailing edge velocity
u_g	Gap velocity
u_p	Pressure side slat TE velocity at δ_p
u_s	Suction side slat TE velocity at δ_s
U	Freestream (open-jet) velocity
w_m	Frequency dependent weighting function
W	Row matrix of w_m terms
w'_m	SADA weighting factors
α_m	Main element angle of attack
α_s	Slat angle of attack relative to main-element waterline
δ_p	Pressure side BL thickness
δ^*_p	Pressure side BL displacement thickness
δ_s	Suction side BL thickness
δ^*_s	Suction side BL displacement thickness
Ψ	Array azimuth (sideline) angle
Φ	Array elevation (over-flight) angle
Φ_{adj}	Elevation angle adjusted for shear layer effects, emission angle in retarded coordinates

---

[*] Senior Engineer, Acoustics, Member AIAA

[†] Senior Research Scientist, Aeroacoustics Branch, Associate Fellow AIAA

[‡] Research Scientist, Advanced Measurement and Diagnostics Branch, Senior Member AIAA

Introduction

Background

With the advent of high by-pass ratio fans and the rapid advances of low noise engine technologies, airframe noise sources can now dominate the aircraft noise signature under high lift conditions (Macaraeg[1]). On approach, airframe noise can be a primary offender. The airframe landing gear, flaps and flap side edges, and the leading-edge slat have been identified as key airframe noise sources (Davy and Remy[2], Hayes et al.[3], Dobrzynski et al.[4], Guo et al.[5,6], etc.). The relative importance and dominance of these noise sources over different frequency ranges depend on the trimmed airframe configuration. Progress has been made in understanding and prediction capability, in reducing airframe noise under, first, the NASA Advanced Subsonic Technology (AST) Program and, now, the NASA Quiet Aircraft Technology (QAT) program. The present paper reports results of slat noise measurements conducted in the Quiet Flow Facility (QFF) at NASA Langley Research Center.

The leading edge slat of a multi-element wing is designed to delay the onset of main element separation by alleviating the suction side pressure peak of the main element leading edge (see Figure 1 for key terminology). This is achieved by accelerating flow through the slat gap that results in an increase of the wing C_{Lmax}. More detailed descriptions of the complex flow field between the slat and main element would involve the viscous interactions of the slat wake and the main element boundary layer. With regard to operating configurations, one may anticipate that trade-offs would occur between control of acoustic emissions and that of aerodynamic performance. For example, although it has been suggested[7] that reducing the slat gap (demonstrated in the present measurements also) can attain slat noise reduction, reduced lift performance can be a consequence[8]. The gap flow field is believed to be central to the slat noise (and performance) problem. Moriarty et al.[9] measured key flow characteristics from a slat and main element model using PIV measurements. Velocities through the slat gap were found to be as high as twice the freestream value. In addition, turbulent kinetic energy levels were highest in the slat gap region where the separating shear layer reattaches to the backside of the slat. This suggests that this region is likely to be the most energetic if feedback from the slat trailing edge amplifies disturbances.

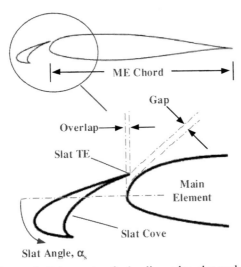

Figure 1 Schematic of a leading edge slat and wing main element leading edge.

Some early airframe noise investigations sought to separate airframe noise contributions from a 4.7% scale DC-10 model. With the reduction of localized flap sources using control devices, Hayes et al.[3] were able to observe the slat noise contribution to the overall noise. Guo et al.[5,6] also utilized the same model to define wing conditions which appear to result in significant slat noise. They demonstrated that at the moderate to low flap deflection angles slat noise dominated the spectrum. Their phased array results also identified the distributed nature of the leading edge slat source. The flap and slat are independent noise sources that would only affect one another through their mean aerodynamic influence.

In addition to full aircraft modeling, specific airframe component noise has been the subject of a number of airframe noise studies. Dobrzynski et al.[4] used a 1/10th scaled Airbus-type high lift wing to quantify wing noise sources. They found that under certain slat configurations vortex shedding from the slat edge cove resulted in excessive low frequency tonal noise in the vicinity of the slat. These tones were the result of laminar shedding off the slat cove and were reduced by boundary layer tripping just upstream of the cove leading edge. Trailing edge (TE) noise was also identified as a significant slat source and scaled to the 5th power of the freestream velocity. The wing model used in this investigation included a slat track where noise levels in the vicinity of the slat tracks or supports were typically ~ 8-10 dB higher locally than the levels in other slat regions. These effects could not be entirely dismissed from the total noise spectra for the slat region. Similarly, Storms, et al.[10] focused their aeroacoustic measurements on the leading edge slat using a high lift model consisting of several slat brackets, a main element, and a partial span outboard flap. Their large array and their processing produced phased array noise maps containing highly localized noise sources across the span of the slat and therefore could not accurately focus on other potentially key slat noise mechanisms. Their RANS computations and measurements indicated the potential for Kelvin-Helmholtz instabilities in the slat cove that grows as the flow is accelerated through the slat gap. It was conjectured that these instabilities could be part of a feedback mechanism that included the slat trailing edge vortex shedding.

A number of computational models have been developed to describe the slat noise generation and radiation problem (Guo[7,11], Khorrami, et al.[12], Singer et al.[13], and Khorrami et al.[14]). Most utilized RANS techniques to capture specific flow features pertaining to either the low frequency oscillations from the slat cove free shear layer or vortex shedding off the slat trailing edge a measured high frequency mechanism found in slat model test data from the Low Turbulence Pressure Tunnel (LTPT). Qualitative agreement with measured data was reasonably found[12,13,14]. Guo's[7] recent slat noise modeling publication utilizes a discrete vortex modeling approach to capture the unsteady flow field around the cusp and through the slat gap and subsequent acoustic interactions. The most notable results of this work are the documented slat noise radiation and Mach number scaling relation. Guo reported that for low frequency slat noise the dominant radiation direction is normal to the slat element chord and that slat trailing edge sources should scale as M^5 (findings of Guo[11]). Cove region vortical fluctuations resulted in energy radiating dominantly in the fly-over direction and normal to the main element chord. Analysis was presented indicating this mechanism could scale as $M^{2.5}$ as justified by computation for non-compact sources at high frequencies.

The recent work of Dobrzynski et al.[15] is a comprehensive presentation of slat noise measurements including scaling results and directivity. Their measured noise source amplitudes scaled as the 4.5 power of the wind tunnel velocity and the frequency scaled with the slat cove vortex dimension (approximated using the slat chord length) and wind tunnel velocity. Their directivity results support a compact dipole model of slat trailing edge noise with maximum radiation in the rear arc direction.

Present Approach

This paper discusses the results of 2-dimensional wing/slat model tests conducted in the Quiet Flow Facility. Data obtained from a Small Aperture Directional Array (SADA) of microphones positioned about the model, static pressure measurements on the model, boundary layer probe measurements in the wake of the slat, and unsteady pressure sensors on the slat and main element surfaces are used to characterize slat noise. To better isolate the true distributed slat noise source from extraneous sideplate juncture noise sources, additional processing steps are added to our standard beamforming approach. The resultant noise spectra are representative of noise from a slat with a one-foot span. This allows an examination of scaling laws, directivity, and diagnostic prediction comparisons.

Airframe Component Test and Processing

Test Set-Up and Method

The testing of various wing/slat geometries was conducted in the NASA Langley QFF. The setup is shown in Figure 2. The QFF is an open-jet facility designed for anechoic acoustic testing. For this study, a

2- by 3-foot rectangular open-jet nozzle was employed that provided up to a 0.17 Mach number flow. The 3-foot span model had a 16" chord (6% of full-scale) NACA 63_2-215 main element airfoil with a slat chord of 3.2".

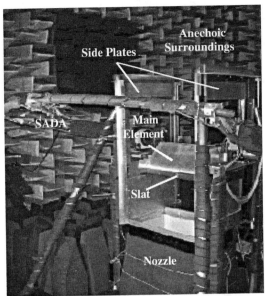

Figure 2 Wing/slat test apparatus in QFF.

The main element and slat are instrumented with static pressure ports and unsteady pressure transducers. The model is held in place via the use of vertical side plates, which were aligned and rigidly fastened to the exit of the nozzle. Appropriate acoustic foam treatments were applied to all edges and supports to reduce acoustic reflections from these surfaces. The slat geometric positions referenced to the main element are shown in Figure 3. The slat at each angle of $\alpha_S = 10°$, $20°$, and $30°$ is pivoted about a single trailing edge "notch" position of zero for the baseline case. The other notch positions, which are closer to the main element and thus serve to close off the gap, are shown. Table 1 gives the slat overlap and gap dependence on notch position. For the data presented, the main element was aligned at geometric angles of attack of $26°$ and $32°$ relative to the undisturbed flow. These large physical angles are used, in this open-jet test set-up, to duplicate the slat-area aerodynamics typical of high-lift wing/slat configurations. This method is fully discussed in the subsequent model aerodynamics section.

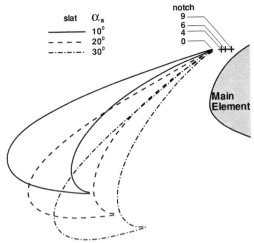

Figure 3 Slat deflections and notch settings.

Slat Position (notches)	Overlap/C %	Gap/C %
0	0.307	1.713
4	1.188	1.084
6	1.563	0.833
8	1.941	0.591
9	2.126	0.476

Table 1 Overlap and Gap percentages of chord for 20° slat condition. For the 10° slat, add 0.016% to all Overlap numbers and add 0.09% to all Gap numbers. For the 30° slat, subtract 0.061% and add 0.140%, respectively.

Acoustic directivity and spectra of selected portions of the wing/slat model were obtained using the Langley-developed SADA. The SADA consists of 33 B&K model 4138, 1/8-inch microphones with 1/4-inch preamplifiers projecting from an acoustically treated aluminum frame. The array pattern incorporates four irregular circles of eight microphones each with one microphone placed at the center of the array. Each circle was twice the diameter of the circle it encloses. The maximum radius of the array is 3.89 inches. Two small laser diode pointers are incorporated into the array frame on opposite sides of the center microphone for use in alignment.

The SADA is mounted on a pivotal boom designed such that the array could be positioned at a number of elevation and azimuth angles. While the boom pivot is not centered with the slat, the electronic steering processing fully accounted for array orientations and positions. Rotation of the boom is performed using precision DC servo rotation stages. Additional details concerning array and boom construction can be found in References 16 and 17.

Dynamic surface pressures were obtained along the centerline chord of the slat and the leading edge of the main element airfoil using Kulite model LQ-34-064-5A sensors. The positions of the flush-mounted sensors are shown in Figure 4. The chordwise distance from the leading edge is x and the spanwise distance from the center of the span is y. The chordwise position for each slat sensor at a main element angle of attack of 26° and a slat angle of 10° is given in Table 2.

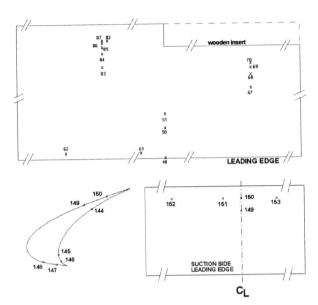

Figure 4 Unsteady pressure sensor distribution.

Kulite #	X (inches)	Y (inches)	Z (inches)
144	23.51	0.00	0.16
145	22.12	0.00	-0.50
146	22.11	0.00	-0.70
147	21.95	0.00	-0.71
148	21.63	0.00	-0.48
149	23.36	0.00	0.35
150	24.04	0.00	0.26
151	24.04	0.53	0.26
152	24.04	2.00	0.26
153	24.04	-1.00	0.26

Table 2 Sensor coordinates in tunnel coordinates.

Data Acquisition and Post Processing

The acquisition hardware used to collect data from the array microphones and surface pressure sensors consisted of a series of transient data recorders controlled by a workstation. Signals were simultaneously recorded at a sampling rate of 142.857 kHz, with 14 bits dynamic range for the 33 SADA microphones and with 12 bits for the surface pressure sensors. Two million 2-byte samples were collected for each acquisition. The microphone signals were high pass filtered at 300 Hz, and all channels employed anti-aliasing filters set to 50 kHz.

Microphone and surface pressure sensor calibration data were accounted for in the post-processing. For the SADA microphones, pistonphone and injection calibrations of amplitude and phase were conducted. Amplitude and phase calibrations for the surface pressure sensors were obtained using a miniature acoustic source capable of high frequency output that was referenced to the output of a B&K 4138 microphone.

Data processing of SADA microphone signals included the construction of cross-spectral matrices from the raw time data. The individual elements in each cross-spectral matrix were computed using Fast Fourier Transforms (FFT's) of the original data ensemble using a Hamming window. These data were segmented into 1000 non-overlapping blocks each containing 2^{13} samples yielding a frequency resolution of 17.44 Hz. Classical beamforming was performed on the cross-spectral matrices to electronically "steer" the SADA to predefined noise source locations using the equation below,

$$P(\hat{e}) = \frac{\hat{e}^T \hat{W} \hat{G} \hat{W}^T \hat{e}}{\sum\limits_{m=1}^{m_0} w_m^2} \qquad (1)$$

where w_m is a frequency dependent weighting function obtained via a unique shading algorithm providing a constant beamwidth independent of frequency (between 10 to 40 kHz). $\hat{W}$ is a row matrix containing the w_m terms, $\hat{G}$ is a cross spectral matrix, and $\hat{e}$ is a column steering vector containing terms for each microphone in the array. The output of equation (1) is the mean-squared-pressure P measured at the steering location. Mean amplitude and phase changes due to refracted sound transmission through the curved shear layer associated with the mounting of the model in the QFF were corrected and incorporated into the steering vector using Snell's law in Amiet's method. A typical mean refracted ray path is shown in Figure 5. Using equation (1), noise source distribution maps, spectra, and directivity were generated for a number of test conditions. Beamforming results were obtained at a number of pressure side elevation angle positions, which are shown on the right-hand side in Figure 6. Additional details concerning the SADA, beamforming method, shear correction, and shading algorithm can be found in References 16 and 17.

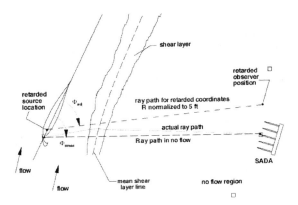

Figure 5 Typical mean reflected ray path.

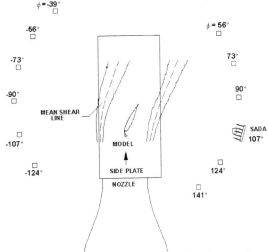

Figure 6 SADA measurement elevation angles.

Array Processing of Distributed Source Noise

A spanwise uniform flowfield over a wing and slat consisting of a pressure side slat cove and a gap between the main element and slat trailing edge will inherently produce a uniform line distribution of independent sources of noise (independent to the extent that the correlated turbulence scales are small compared to the span). In reality, the slat and main element wing are coupled by bracket structures that in some aircraft configurations can be complex and bulky, adding to the complexity of the noise sources. In the present QFF model configuration, the slat and the main element are both mounted to sideplates. Because both the slat and main element are lifting surfaces and the sideplates are not, localized vortical flow occurs near the junctures, whose interaction with the surfaces produce localized noise sources. It is the goal of the present study to examine only the uniform slat noise. For this paper a processing method is used that extracts the slat noise while suppressing the juncture noise contributions.

Figure 7 shows a typical noise map from SADA to illustrate the presence of both the distributed source and localized juncture noise sources at a particular frequency (12.5 kHz). For clarity, only the highest 10 dB contour levels are shown. A contour value at a point is the SADA output when steered to the point along a plane defined through the main element chord line. The distributed slat noise source is clearly seen along the center portion of the span. It is desired to determine spectra representing the slat noise produced by one foot of span. One possible processing method would be to incorporate the contour integration method of Reference 18. However, since a requirement of this integration method is that the source region of all major contributors to any contour area under consideration be included in the integration, one would have to determine the total noise from both the distributed slat noise and the juncture noise sources. From this total noise, one would have to subtract the juncture noise contributions. This would involve source-subtraction modeling that is not yet accomplished. Instead, a simpler method is used that takes advantage of a design (and standard processing) feature of the SADA that the main-sensing-lobe "3 dB down" spatial resolution is approximately one foot in width and that any noise contributions from the side-plate juncture are minimized when the SADA steered to the span center. This is true for a set frequency range of 10-40 kHz. At frequencies below 10 kHz, the main lobe widens. Above 40 kHz, the main lobe narrows. The extraction method used here employs this standard SADA processing and then adds additional steps to more exactly account for array characteristics in the final determination of a per-foot noise spectrum.

verified by examining maximum contour levels in the streamwise direction along the span centerline in the slat region for 12.5 kHz). A full spectrum is generated using standard SADA processing. The spectrum is then adjusted in amplitude as a function of frequency by the function F. This function is the ratio of the noise that would be perceived by a single microphone at the SADA location from a uniform distribution of independent noise sources distributed over a 1-foot span and the noise that would be perceived by the SADA from a similar uniform source but distributed over a 3.25-foot span. Thus, the adjusted measured spectrum would represent the "per-foot" spectrum of the slat noise alone. The function F is determined based on SADA response as calculated for each SADA position and orientation with respect to the slat. The extra 0.25-foot in span is added to approximately account for reflection effects from the sideplates. In comparing the basic SADA spectra to the adjusted spectra, one finds as expected that the levels between frequency range of 10-40 kHz nearly match and that the levels of the adjusted spectra are lower at frequencies less than 10 kHz because of the array main lobe broadening of which the F function accounts for. A possible source of error in this procedure is that sideplate juncture noise, of which the SADA suppresses between 10 to 40 kHz, is less suppressed at lower frequencies, however, such positive level bias is believed to be small as contour plots for lower frequencies reveal less obvious sideplate contribution.

The narrowband beamformed spectra were determined over a frequency range of 300-50000 Hz using a frequency step size of 17.45 Hz. After applying the F function, one-third Octave spectra were formed and were then normalized to a five-foot observer distance. The processing produced spectra representing slat noise from a 1-foot spanwise section, as measured by a single microphone 5 feet from the center of the span.

Model Aerodynamics

Because of the relative size of the open jet wind tunnel test section compared to that of the model, one could not properly test the complete slat / main element /flap high lift configuration. Ideally from an aerodynamic simulation standpoint, the testing for a complete model of this size would be conducted in a larger tunnel, but because of the significant acoustic measurement advantages for this QFF test arrangement, a practical testing approach was taken. Following the testing philosophy used previously in studies[17,18,19] of the flap for this model, the model was tested such as the local aerodynamics could be properly matched to represent high-lift device conditions. This is permitted

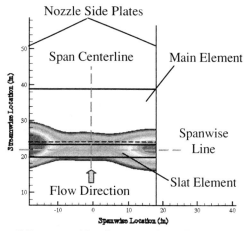

Figure 7 Pressure side (flyover) view of distributed slat noise with local discontinuities at the side plates.

The processing procedure used for this QFF configuration involves first beamforming the SADA to the center of the slat noise region (this location is

acoustically because of the independence of noise source regions. In fact, one benefit of this approach is that, because the slat, main element, and flap were not tested simultaneously, less noise sources are present and thus the interpretation of the acoustic measurements is simplified.

The model was instrumented with static pressure tabs on both the slat and main element to define the model aerodynamics in the slat region. The flap was removed from the model. Large main element angles of attack were used to compensate for the lack of lift typically generated by a main element and flap. The approach attained high-lift aerodynamics about the slat region, while knowingly compromising the main element aerodynamics downstream of approximately the quarter chord.

The pressure C_p distributions about the slat and leading edge region of the main element is shown in Figure 8 for the two main element angles and the three slat angles tested. The slat notch position was zero (see Figure 3 and Table 1) and the tunnel Mach number was 0.17. As seen, there are a relatively small number of sensors on both the slat and the main element particularly in the trailing edge of the slat and the leading edge of the main element regions. Still the anticipated high lift device character is clearly shown. For increasing slat deflection angle, the trends are for decreasing slat leading-edge suction peak and increasing slat trailing-edge suction (indicative of increasing gap velocity). If one compared the present C_p results to that of Storms et al.[10], our slat region aerodynamics for $\alpha_m = 26°$ and $32°$, correspond to approximately their $\alpha_m = 4°$ and to one less than their $8°$, respectively. Storms et al. tested beyond $\alpha_m = 16°$, so our loading was on the lighter end of their testing range.

Accurate estimates of velocities in and about the slat trailing edge were not possible using the C_p data because of the very sparse distribution of pressure ports near the edge and on the main element. However, even if one had a fine distribution, one would not be able to determine boundary layer / near wake characteristics important for evaluating the slat noise problem. Therefore, velocity survey measurements were made across the near wake of the slat trailing edge. The measurements were made using a specially constructed Pitot tube probe that consisted of parallel tube components. The probe orientations and respective traverse paths that were used are illustrated in an inset of Figure 9. The traverse path being aligned perpendicular to the main element surface is the probe orientation used for most data presented in this paper. The probe's outer diameter was .030", the inside

diameter was .018". The survey path brought the probe to within .010". This closeness was obtained by final positioning of the probe path after the probe deflection was established within the flow.

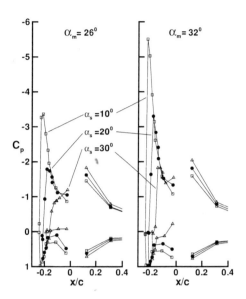

Figure 8 Slat and main element C_p distributions.

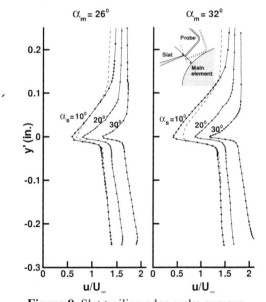

Figure 9 Slat trailing edge wake surveys.

The velocity survey results for the zero-notch reference configurations are shown in Figure 9. The y' axis is along the traverse path with positive y' on the slat suction side and negative y' on the pressure side / gap region. The data shown for slat angles $\alpha_s = 10°$, $20°$, and $30°$ are for the probe path aligned perpendicular to the main element surface. The y'=0 position was defined as corresponding to the minimum velocity value. To show the effect of probe orientation, data for $\alpha_s = 10°$ are shown for the probe path aligned perpendicular to the slat surface trailing-edge mean line. The actual velocity vector orientations, which affect these velocity amplitude measurements over the survey distance, were not determined. In general, it is seen that the velocities are higher for the larger main element angles and higher for the larger slat angles. The larger slat angles have smaller boundary layers on both the suction and pressure sides.

The slat trailing edge boundary layer / near-wake thicknesses δ_s and δ_p of the suction and pressure sides, respectively, were chosen based (somewhat subjectively) on the curvature of the velocity survey results. These values of δ_s and δ_p, along with their corresponding velocities u_s and u_p, are shown in Figure 10 to show the dependence of slat trailing edge flow on angles α_m and α_s, and gap opening. The square symbols, representing the values determined from Figure 9, show readily the trends already sited of increasing velocity and decreasing boundary layer values for larger slat angles. For each slat and main element angle condition, decreasing the gap (increasing the notch number, see Figure 3) is seen here to change the velocities somewhat. Also shown are the δ_s and δ_p values determined using the alternate velocity survey path data of Figure 9 for $\alpha_s = 10°$. Some differences can be seen as a result of the different orientation.

Subsequently, use is made of the values of displacement thicknesses δ_s^* and δ_p^*. For the baseline cases, these are given in Table 3 along with δ_s and δ_p, and the corresponding velocities u_s and u_p. The δ^*'s were determined by integration from y'=0 to the

respective δ values. Any error in the δ^* values due to lack of resolution because of probe size and distance from the edge, should be offset by ignoring the trailing edge thickness in the δ^* calculations.

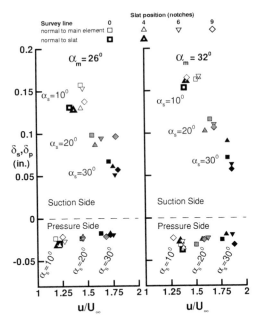

Figure 10 Boundary layer thicknesses summary as a function of relative local velocity.

α_m °	α_s °	δ_S (in.)	δ^*_S(in.)	δ_P (in.)	δ^*_P(in.)	u_S/U_∞	u_P/U_∞	u_{av}/U_∞	u_g/U_∞
26	10	.158	.0355	.024	.0065	1.44	1.18	1.31	1.28
26	20	.098	.0144	.024	.0032	1.55	1.44	1.50	1.55
26	30	.067	.0056	.018	.0021	1.71	1.63	1.67	1.75
32	10	.159	.0563	.032	.0080	1.51	1.34	1.43	1.40
32	20	.116	.0212	.032	.0031	1.65	1.50	1.58	1.60
32	30	.071	.0085	.026	.0022	1.82	1.76	1.79	1.90

Table 3 Determined values of TE near-wake thicknesses, displacement thicknesses, and associated velocities for slat at notch position of zero. M = U /c = 0.17.

Results and Discussion

Slat and Main Element Angle Variations

Figure 11 illustrates the effect of slat angle of attack on far field noise for $\alpha_m = 26°$ and M = 0.17. The low frequency noise levels (< 10 kHz) remain relatively unchanged as the slat angle is increased from 10° to 20° but ~ 5 dB more at the 30° slat deflection. Above 10 kHz the presence of a broadband hump develops with the peak increasing in level and slightly in frequency as the slat deflection angle is increased. This same basic noise trend is observed for the varying slat deflection angles with the main element setting now at 32° (see Figure 12). Again, low frequencies are less changed while the high frequency broadband spectral hump develops, but only for $\alpha_s = 30°$.

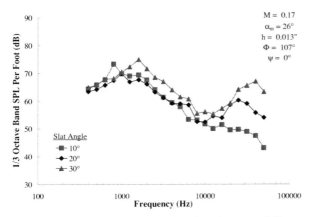

Figure 11 Effect of slat deflection for $\alpha_m = 26°$.

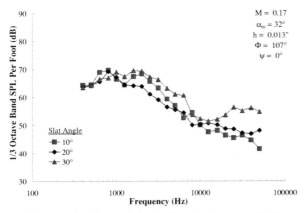

Figure 12 Effect of slat deflection for $\alpha_m = 32°$.

It is demonstrated in the section discussing trailing edge bluntness effects, that this high frequency noise increase is not likely the result of trailing edge bluntness noise. It does, however, appear that the increase is related to changes in local flow velocities. Also in a later section, it is shown that the high frequency noise is characteristic of turbulent boundary layer trailing edge (TBL-TE) scattering from the pressure side of the slat. As seen from Figure 11, there is an increase in the high frequency broadband hump of ~ 10 dB and ~ 6 dB going from 10° to 20° and 20° to 30°, respectively. The increase in gap velocity follows a similar trend as the noise where, from Table 3, the larger increase in gap velocity occurs between the 10° and 20° slat deflection cases. The higher gap velocities result in increased noise. The fact that the 32°/20° (α_m/α_s) case resulted in a higher gap velocity where u_g is 1.6U than the 26°/20° case where u_g is 1.55U (lower) yet lower high frequency noise levels implies

that the high frequency noise may not be solely due to local flow changes, but potentially due to geometric factors.

Coherence data from Kulites in the slat cove show increasingly high coherence levels in the 25 kHz region between pressure side sensors 146 and 145 as the slat angle is increased from 10° to 30°. Figure 12 shows this high level of coherence for the 26°/30° case. The relatively high level of coherence is not found between slat pressure-side sensors 146 (slat cove) and 144 (near the trailing edge) or between any of the sensors on the slat suction side, suggesting a more local acoustic event.

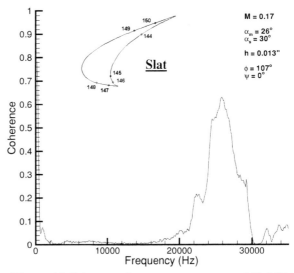

Figure 13 Coherence between cove sensors 146-145 for 26°/ 30° (α_m/α_s).

Effect of Gap Reduction

The effect of reducing the gap size is shown in Figure 14. Reducing the gap size to within ~ 1% of the main element chord significantly reduced the noise in the lower frequencies and completely closing the gap resulted in noise level reductions at all frequencies reaching as high as ~14 dB. The nearly-closed 9-notch configuration resulted in a significant amount of noise reduction below 10 kHz and not so much at the higher frequencies. Only when the gap is completely closed do significant noise reductions occur at the higher frequencies. Measured boundary layer properties and local flow velocities were not significantly altered by different gap settings (notches). Data for the 26°/20° 9-notch configuration, however, indicates a slight increase in slat trailing edge flow velocity (see Figure 10). The gap closing chokes the pressure-side flow to where the cove region may behave as a plenum and key noise producing (low frequency) structures cannot form

2017

or are attenuated. Noise reduction is expected if slat sources are indeed a result of edge scattering.

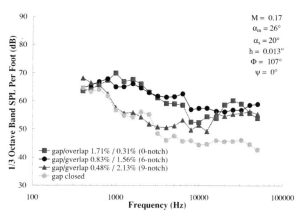

Figure 14 Varying gap/overlap for 26°/20°.

Flow Field Alterations

Flow field modifications were made in an attempt to discern the effect of the state of the boundary layer feeding the cove on the measured sound. Figure 15 compares these results containing light tripping on the suction side, with the effect of heavy tripped (90 grit sand paper) on the pressure side, of heavier tripping on both the slat and main element, a tear drop cove insert, and the use of vortex generators on the pressure side. Figure 16 is an illustration of the grit and vortex generators. The more heavily tripped cases resulted in a slight increase in noise in the 1 kHz to 10 kHz range. The teardrop insert provided some noise benefit in the low frequencies as well as the high frequency spectral hump region.

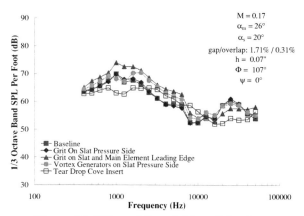

Figure 15 Effect of flow field modifications.

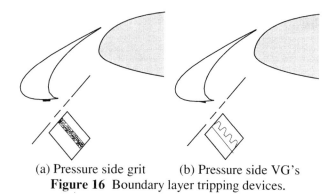

(a) Pressure side grit   (b) Pressure side VG's
Figure 16 Boundary layer tripping devices.

Mach Number Scaling

The noise effect of incident Mach number variations for the 26°/20° condition are shown in Figure 17. Characteristic of this data is the occurrence of a low frequency spectral peak followed by an approximate inverse square frequency law as consistently observed in the spectrum. Lilley[20] has reported this spectrum roll-off as a common occurrence in many shear flows. An additional characteristic of the data is the presence of spectral hump at the higher frequencies as freestream flow velocity increases. Computing Strouhal numbers based on stowed chord length and freestream flow velocity, it can be shown that the data from Figure 17 fall well within the Strouhal range reported by Gou[7] (Figure 8 in Ref. 7). Guo showed that this Strouhal range is consistent with measured full-scale aircraft data.

The data in Figure 17 was normalized based on M^5 and M^4 power laws versus a frequency adjusted to flow Mach number (scaled to M = 0.17) in Figure 18 and Figure 19, respectively. This type of frequency scaling is a Strouhal scaling where the characteristic length (slat chord is used here) is assumed unchanged by the Mach number changes. The M^5 scaling is indicative of simple scattering off the slat trailing edge. Figure 18 shows that M^5 scaling provides a reasonably good collapse of the data at all frequencies. A better collapse of the data in the mid-frequency range is found using an M^4 power scaling, see Figure 19. Dobrzynski et al.[15] found that scaling their data with $V^{4.5}$ provided the best collapse. Although $M^{4.5}$ did not better fit the measured data here, it is clear that something lower than M^5 may improve the collapse (at least in the mid-frequencies). A following section will illustrate that this Mach number scaling behavior is consistent with predictions of TE noise for isolated airfoils.

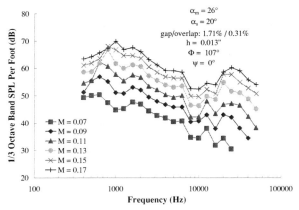

Figure 17 Mach number variations for 26°/20°.

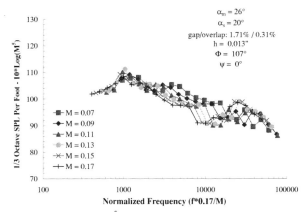

Figure 18 M^5 scaling of the 26°/20° data.

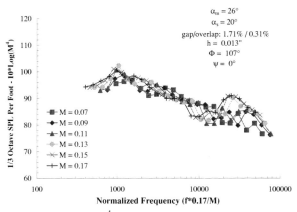

Figure 19 M^4 scaling of the 26°/20° data.

In a similar manner data for the 32°/20° configuration are presented in Figure 20 and scaled with Mach number as M^5 and M^4 in Figure 21 and Figure 22, respectively. Similar trends are found. As for the 26°/20° mid frequency data appears to scale as something other than M^5 and for this particular configuration, the mid and high frequencies better scale as M^4.

Mach number scaling using a power lower than 4 did not improve the data collapse. As indicated, Guo's[7] OASPL data scaled between M^2 and M^3, which was attributed to the non-compact high frequency sources under consideration. Measured high frequency results scale better using M^5 for the 0-notch TE configuration just presented and, it will be shown, blunt edge configurations more clearly follow an M^5 scaling. Both indicative of edge noise sources.

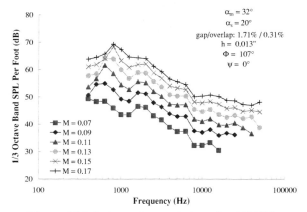

Figure 20 Mach number variations for 32°/20°.

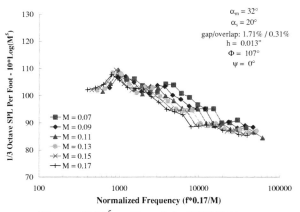

Figure 21 M^5 scaling of the 32°/20° data.

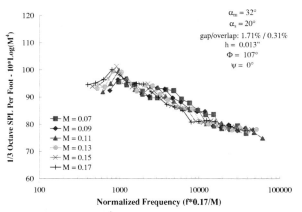

Figure 22 M^4 scaling of the 32°/20° data.

Slat Trailing Edge Bluntness

The h = 0.013" configuration was altered to investigate the effect of trailing edge bluntness on slat noise production by thickening and thinning the slat trailing edge, see Figure 23. Thinning the slat trailing edge was accomplished by extending a very thin, 0.005", but sturdy strip of tape from the slat trailing edge.

Thickness Modifications

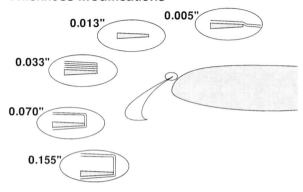

Figure 23 Slat trailing edge thickness modifications.

For the 26°/20° condition with h = 0.013", slat acoustics varied with Mach number as shown in Figure 17. Figure 24 shows the effect of Mach number for a slat thickness of h = 0.07". The thicker slat trailing edge introduced a relatively large peak in the spectrum that increases in frequency as the Mach number increases. The remaining spectral features remained relatively unchanged for this condition indicating that bluntness noise predictions could be superimposed with the estimates of other prominent noise mechanisms. Data from Figure 24 is scaled as M^5 in Figure 25. The spectral peak associated with the added slat bluntness scales well. The scaling trends at frequencies other than the shedding frequency is consistent with that of Figure 18.

Coherence data between sensors in the slat cove indicate values on the order of about $\gamma^2 \sim 0.4 - 0.6$ in the vortex shedding region and comparable levels in the 22 - 25 kHz range, similar to that indicated in Figure 13. Kulites near the trailing edge were covered or partially so. The sensors in the cove (specifically sensors 145, 146, and 147) clearly indicate the presence of a strong acoustic source emanating from the slat trailing edge. Interesting to note is that the phase difference between sensor 146 and 145 is essentially zero in the 12.5 kHz range for M = 0.17 showing that the acoustic wave front or hydrodynamic pressure pattern impinges upon these sensors nearly in phase.

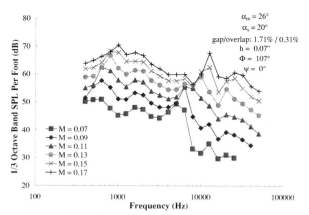

Figure 24 Effect of Mach number for h = 0.07".

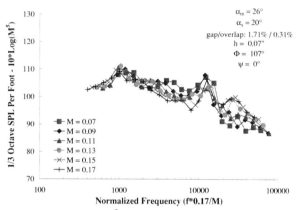

Figure 25 M^5 scaling of Figure 24 data.

The noise effects for Mach number variation for a trailing edge thickness of h = 0.155" are depicted in Figure 26 and the M^5 scaling of this data in Figure 27. As with the previous thickness condition, the bluntness adds a sharp peak to the baseline acoustic results. Peak frequencies occur at frequencies lower than the corresponding cases for h = 0.07" showing a classical Strouhal scaling with trailing edge thickness.

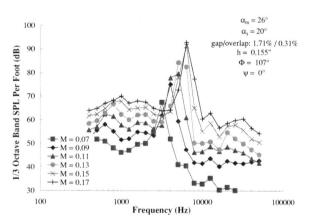

Figure 26 Effect of Mach number for h = 0.155".

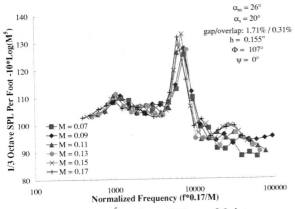

Figure 27 M^5 scaling of Figure 26 data.

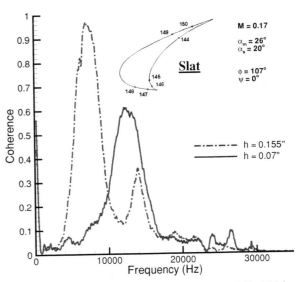

Figure 28 Coherence between cove sensors 147-145 in for h = 0.07" and h = 0.155".

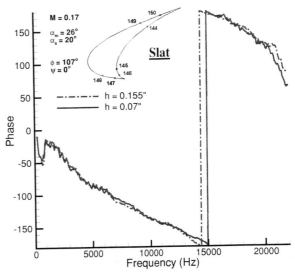

Figure 29 Phase relationship between sensors 147 and 145 for h = 0.07" and h = 0.155".

The vortex-shedding peak resulting from the thickest bluntness configuration is significantly elevated above the broadband levels of the spectrum compared to that of Figure 24 and Figure 25. This peak amplitude may be the result of acoustic reinforcement of some type at this condition. Similarly, it could be argued that the other less blunt configurations (h < 0.155") could be suppressed at their shedding frequencies resulting in lower amplitudes. Further investigation is needed to explain this behavior.

Coherence results for M = 0.17 and surface sensors 147 and 145 are presented in Figure 28 for both h = 0.07" and h = 0.155". This figure shows very strong coherence $\gamma^2 \sim 1$ for the h = 0.155" bluntness peak and sharp coherence of ~ 0.35 at ~ 14 kHz that is roughly 2x the bluntness peak frequency. The peak coherence level is reduced by ~ 40% for the h = 0.07" trailing edge thickness (TET). The phases from this sensor combination are indicated in Figure 29 where it is found that both mechanisms appear to propagate from the trailing edge region to the leading edge at an acoustic velocity (based on the straight line separation distance between sensors). Coherence between sensor 144 (pressure side near the slat TE) and sensors in the cove region show essentially no coherence at the second peak frequency for h = 0.155" of Figure 28. Also interesting to note for this condition is that the coherence from sensors on the suction side of the slat indicates a relatively high level of coherence with sensors in the leading edge region. This is in contrast to the result of the h = 0.07" case where coherence levels were relatively weak between suction side and the leading edge sensors. This may implicate a resonance mechanism with harmonics associated with some suction side instabilities that reinforce the h = 0.155" condition.

The effect of trailing edge thickness at a fixed Mach number, M, of 0.17 is shown in Figure 30. Low frequencies remain unchanged due to the added bluntness and the mid to high frequencies are affected only in the range where vortex shedding from the blunt trailing edge occurs. Strouhal scaling this data as St = fh/u$_g$ results in a Strouhal number near St ~ 0.25 at the shedding frequencies, slightly lower than St = 0.3 as reported by Lilley[20]. Based on this Strouhal number, vortex shedding resulting from thicknesses h = 0.013" and h = 0.005" would occur well outside of our acoustic data range. As a result, the high frequency spectral hump in the 25 kHz range of the h = 0.013" data (e.g., Figure 11) cannot be attributed to bluntness noise.

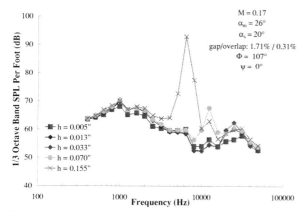

Figure 30 Effect of trailing edge thickness, M = 0.17.

Directivity

Figure 31 shows the 26°/20° directivity from pressure side elevation angles as indicated in Figure 6. The 56° elevation angle data is excluded because noise maps indicate that the SADA, at this position, was not able to accurately focus to the slat region because of severe shear layer refraction angles. Noise levels at all frequencies continuously increase as the SADA position moves from the rear wing trailing edge position (0° elevation in our nomenclature) toward the slat leading edge. The adjusted elevation range does not cover the entire pressure side arc, but it does appear that the peak overall levels may occur just beyond flyover.

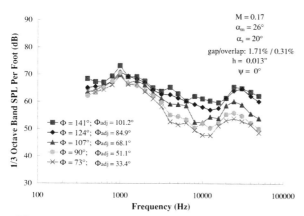

Figure 31 Elevation directivity for 0-notch setting.

Figure 32 shows directivity normalization as applied to Figure 31 data. Amplitude normalization assumes a simple dipole with convection effects utilizing adjusted angles from the shear layer refraction code and emission coordinates. The normalization does a good job of collapsing the higher frequencies. In Figure 31, the data at the low frequency end appear to collapse very well without normalization. As part of

the SADA processing, all results are corrected to a 5' observer position from the source. The spectral characteristics in the low frequency may be interpreted as the result of a nearly omnidirectional sound source.

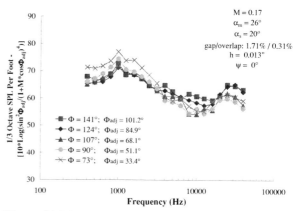

Figure 32 Directivity normalization of Figure 31 data.

Similar trends are observed for the 6-notch gap/overlap setting, see Figure 33 and Figure 34 for the non-normalized and normalized directivity results, respectively, as well as the thickest trailing edge configuration, i.e., h = 0.155" (Figure 35 and Figure 36). The bluntness peak normalized levels illustrated in Figure 36 collapse to within a few dB with this correction. As previously indicated, only a few directivity plots are shown here. All the processed slat noise data to date has shown similarity to that presented. The simple dipole normalization collapses the mid to high frequencies consistent with the expected radiation of the assumed edge scattering mechanisms.

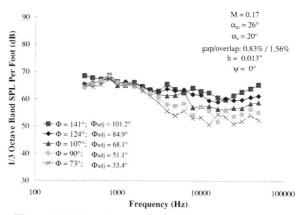

Figure 33 Elevation directivity for 6-notch setting.

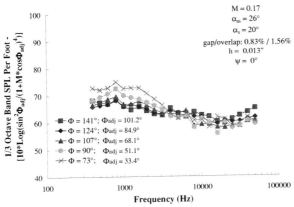

Figure 34 Directivity normalization of Figure 33 data.

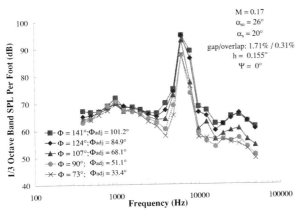

Figure 35 Elevation directivity for blunt TE.

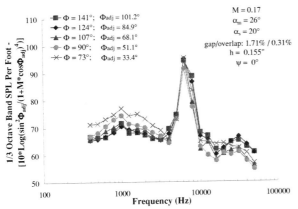

Figure 36 Directivity normalization of Figure 35 data.

Diagnostic Using Prediction Simulation

Although a prediction method for slat noise is not given here, an existing trailing edge noise prediction method can serve as a diagnostic to examine source components and their ability to explain the measured

spectra. In this section, boundary layer thickness values and velocities of Table 3 are used in the airfoil self noise prediction codes of Brooks et al.[21] and comparisons are made to measured slat noise spectra.

The airfoil self noise codes contain models for turbulent boundary layer – trailing edge (TBL-TE) noise, laminar boundary layer – trailing edge (LBL-TE) noise, blunt trailing edge (BTE) noise, and tip noise. Figure 37 shows a "prediction" where the models used are that of the TBL-TE noise and BTE noise components. The "predictions" are for an observer that is 5 feet away and normal to the chord of an isolated airfoil (no accounting is made of slat geometry nor that the line of sight of the slat TE is blocked by the main element). A comparison can be made to the spectrum of the $\alpha_m=26°/\alpha_s=20°$ case with bluntness of thickness h=0.155" for M=0.17, shown in Figure 26 and Figure 30. In Figure 37:

• The pressure side and suction side TBL-TE noise spectral components are predicted using δ_p^*, δ_s^* (rather than using the code's internally generated values) and u_p, u_s values from Table 3.

• A lower frequency spectral component to TE noise is included, which is suggested here to be representative of turbulence within the cove region passing the TE. This is calculated in the manner of pressure side TBL-TE noise using the average velocity across the gap, u_g, from Table 3 and a selected value of δ_p^*=0.25". (Note that this δ_p^* value in the code is indicative of a turbulent scale of 1" to 2.5", because of the normal δ^*/δ relationship.)

• For the spectral component due to bluntness, the BTE model uses h, δ_p^* and δ_s^*, a Ψ factor in the code equaling zero for a cusped TE, and a stream velocity u_{av} from Table 3.

• The total spectrum shown in Figure 37 is the sum of the separate components.

Additional calculated results are shown in Figure 38 and Figure 39 of spectra for the baseline cases where the BTE term is excluded (this is subsequently discussed). The same calculation procedure involving Table 3 was used. These spectra can be compared to those of Figure 11 and Figure 12, respectively. Also, in Figure 40, the $\alpha_m=26°$ / $\alpha_s=20°$ baseline case for different tunnel speeds are calculated and scaled in the manner of Figure 18 for the corresponding measured spectra.

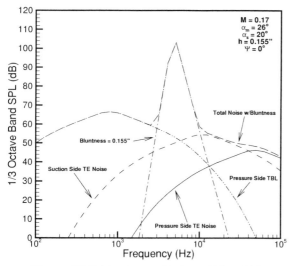

Figure 37 Self noise prediction of blunt TE.

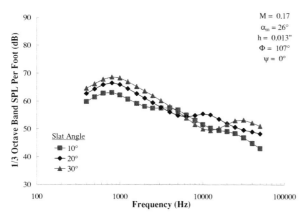

Figure 38 Self noise predictions of the effect slat angle variation for $\alpha_m = 26°$.

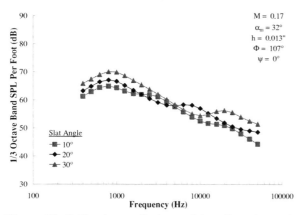

Figure 39 Self noise predictions of the effect slat angle variation for $\alpha_m = 32°$.

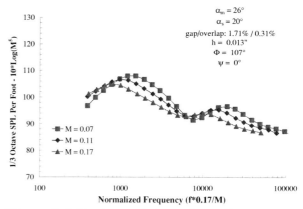

Figure 40 Self noise predictions of the effect of Mach number using M^5 noise scaling.

Clearly the calculations are greatly simplified with regard to flow detail and turbulence structure definitions, as well as geometry related acoustic effects. Still, comparing these "predictions" with data measured indicate some key mechanisms are likely captured.

- First, the low frequency component, thought by the authors to be logically related to TE noise due to the passage of cove region turbulence, appears well represented in many respects using a straight-forward application of the self noise code. But in comparing Figure 38 and Figure 39 to Figure 11 and Figure 12, respectively, this low frequency component is seen to be influenced by α_m and α_s changes, apparently because of turbulent structure changes not being accounted for in the code application.

- Second, the calculated TBL related TE noise appears to account for at least a portion of the higher frequency noise. In this high frequency range however, there seems to be a strong additive noise or noise reinforcing effect from the cove region depending on the α_m/α_s condition. In a compatible result with the measurements (comparing Figure 40 to Figure 18) the velocity scaling of the "predicted" spectra show the same observed behavior as seen for the measurement spectra, that the scaling does not closely follow the 5th power scaling law.

- Third, by comparing Figure 37 and Figure 30, one sees a general agreement with regard to the bluntness noise (BTE) calculation. For other "h" thicknesses, BTE calculations have shown generally good (if not somewhat low) peak-frequency predictions. However, the levels were substantially higher than measured. As seen in Figure 30, the measured levels at the smaller thicknesses are seen to be subdued compared to what one may expect, given the high peak level for h=0.155". A number of factors could affect this phenomenon. The TE flow behavior was not fully measured and flow skew and other distortions could serve to suppress the vortex shedding. Also, aeroacoustic feedback could suppress or reinforce the vortex shedding dependent on the frequencies. Such effects need study.

Summary and Conclusions

An extensive experimental investigation of slat noise has been conducted in the QFF of NASA LaRC. Unique array processing was developed and utilized to focus acoustic results on the distributed nature of a 2-D wing and slat model. The measured noise levels have been presented with respect to 1-foot span of the slat for an observer 5 feet away. The focus of this investigation was primarily on the broadband nature of slat noise and tying the measured noise to key slat flow features. Slat trailing edge bluntness effects were also considered. A number of germane aeroacoustic scaling results and slat acoustics have been presented. In addition, a diagnostic tool for slat noise provided successful examination of key slat noise sources. These results are summarized below:

♦ An increase in slat angle increases the high frequency noise levels where a broad spectral hump was observed. This noise increase coincides with an increase in velocity through the slat gap. Predictions using measured BL parameters indicate that the high frequency spectral hump can be partially attributed to TBL-TE noise most likely from the slat pressure side.

♦ Completely closing off the slat gap results in noise level reductions as high as 14 dB. The cove teardrop insert is also shown to be an effective noise reduction device at most frequencies.

♦ Mach number scaling using the 5th power provides the best collapse of the noise data providing strong evidence of self-noise (edge scattering) mechanisms.

♦ Thickening the slat trailing edge results apparently in a highly coherent vortex shedding source. Strouhal scaling of the bluntness data with h and u_g results in St of ~ 0.25 at the vortex shedding frequency.

♦ The thickest bluntness condition was well predicted using the airfoil self noise code of Brooks et al.[21]. Other slat trailing edge thicknesses produced slightly lower than expected noise that may implicate damping from an aeroacoustic mechanism at these vortex-shedding frequencies.

♦ A simple dipole with convection effects was used to normalize the elevation angle directivity data. This normalization provided a good collapse of the data at most frequencies. The very low frequencies arguably collapsed better without normalization potentially implying the presence of an omnidirectional source in addition to the simple dipole sources already identified.

♦ The airfoil self noise diagnostic tool appears to capture most of the salient features and trends of the measured noise data.

Measured data and analysis indicate that key slat noise components are the result of trailing edge noise from both the suction side and pressure side of the slat. Mach number scaling results and directivity show strong evidence to support this claim. The aeroacoustic database may serve to better refine prediction methods such as what was introduced here for more accurate and efficient slat noise assessments.

Acknowledgements

The authors wish to gratefully acknowledge Dr. Florence V. Hutcheson from the Aeroacoustics Branch at NASA LaRC for her assistance in some of the analysis. The authors also gratefully acknowledge Daniel J. Stead of Lockheed-Martin for data acquisition, data processing, software development, and general support.

References

1. Macaraeg, M.G., "Fundamental Investigations of Airframe Noise", *AIAA Paper 98-2224*, June 1998.

2. Davy, R., and Remy, H., "Airframe Noise Characteristics on a 1/11 Scale Airbus Model", *AIAA Paper 98-2335*, June 1998.

3. Hayes, J.A., Horne, C.W., Soderman, P.T., and Bent, P.H., "Airframe Noise Characteristics of a 4.7% Scale DC-10 Model ", *AIAA Paper 97-1594-CP, 3rd AIAA/CEAS Aeroacoustics Conference and Exhibit*, Atlanta, GA, May, 1997.

4. Dobrzynski, W., Nagakura, K., Gehlhar, B., and Buschbaum, A., "Airframe Noise Studies on Wings with Deployed High-Lift Devices ", *AIAA Paper 99-1805, 5th AIAA/CEAS Aeroacoustics Conference and Exhibit*, Bellevue, WA, May, 1999.

5. Guo, Y.P., Hardy, B., Bent, P., Yamamoto, K., and Joshi, M., "Surface Pressure Fluctuations on DC-10 High Lift System and their Correlation with Far Field Noise", NASI-20103, Task 2, NASA CRAD-9310-4872, 1998.

6. Guo, Y.P., Hardy, B., Bent, P., Yamamoto, K., and Joshi, M., "Noise Characteristics of DC-10 Aircraft High Lift Systems", NASI-20103, Task 2, NASA CRAD-9310-4893, 1998.

7. Guo, Y.P., "A Discrete Vortex Model for Slat Noise Generation", *AIAA Paper 2001-2157, 7th AIAA/CEAS Aeroacoustics Conference*, Maastricht, Netherlands, May, 2001.

8. Thomas, F.O., Nelson, R.C., and Lui, X., "Experimental Investigation of the Confluent Boundary Layer of a High-Lift System", *AIAA Journal*, Volume 38, Number 6, pp. 978-988, June, 2000.

9. Moriarity, P.J., and Heineck, J.T., "PIV Measurements Near a Leading Edge Slat", *Proceedings of the 3rd International Workshop on PIV*, 1999.

10. Storms, B.L., Hayes, J.A., Moriarity, P.J., and James, R.C., "Aeroacoustic Measurements of Slat Noise on a Three-Dimensional High-Lift System", *AIAA Paper 99-1957, 5th AIAA/CEAS Aeroacoustics Conference and Exhibit*, Bellevue, WA, May, 1999.

11. Guo, Y.P., "A Model for Slat Noise Generation ", *AIAA Paper 97-1647, 3rd AIAA/CEAS Aeroacoustics Conference and Exhibit*, Atlanta, GA, May, 1997.

12. Khorrami, M.R., Berkman, M.E., Choudhari, M., Singer, B.A.,Lockard, D.P., and Brentner, K.S., "Unsteady Flow Computations of a Slat with a Blunt Trailing Edge ", *AIAA Paper 99-1805, 5th AIAA/CEAS Aeroacoustics Conference and Exhibit*, Bellevue, WA, May, 1999.

13. Singer, B.A., Lockard, D.P., Brentner, K.S.Khorrami, M.R., Berkman, M.E., and Choudhari, M, "Computational Aeroacoustic Analysis of Slat Trailing Edge Flow", *AIAA Paper 99-1802, 5th AIAA/CEAS Aeroacoustics Conference and Exhibit*, Bellevue, WA, May, 1999.

14. Khorrami, M.R., Singer, B.A., Berkman, M.E., "Time Accurate Simulations and Acoustic Analysis of Slat Free-Shear Layer", *AIAA Paper 01-2155, 7th AIAA/CEAS Aeroacoustics Conference and Exhibit*, Maastricht, Netherlands, May, 2001.

15. Dobrzynski, W. and Pott-Pollenske, M., "Slat Noise Source Studies for Farfield Noise Prediction", *AIAA Paper 2001-2158, 7th AIAA/CEAS Aeroacoustics Conference and Exhibit*, Maastricht, The Netherlands, May, 2001.

16. Humphreys, W.M., Brooks, T.F., Hunter, W.W., and Meadows, K.R., "Design and Use of Microphone Directional Arrays for Aeroacoustic Measurements", *AIAA Paper 98-0471, 36st Aerospace Science Meeting and Exhibit*, Reno, NV, January, 1998.

17. Meadows, K.R., Brooks, T.F., Humphreys, W.M., Hunter, W.W., and Gerhold, C.H., "Aeroacoustic Measurements of a Wing-Flap Configuration", *AIAA Paper 97-1595, 3rd AIAA/CEAS Aeroacoustics Conference*, Atlanta, GA, May, 1997.

18. Brooks, T.F., and Humphreys, W.M., "Effect of Directional Array Size on the Measurement of Airframe Noise Components", *AIAA Paper 99-1958, 5th Aeroacoustics Conference*, Bellevue, WA, May, 1999.

19. Brooks, T.F., and Humphreys, W.M., "Flap Edge Aeroacoustic Measurements and Predictions", *AIAA paper 2000-1975, 6th AIAA/CEAS Aeroacoustics Conference*, Lahaina, Hawaii, June, 2000.

20. Lilley, G.M., "The Prediction of Airframe Noise and Comparison with Experiment", Journal of Sound and Vibration , 239(4), pp. 849-859, 2001.

21. Brooks, T.F., Pope, D.S., Marcolini, M.A., "Airfoil Self-Noise and Prediction", *NASA Reference Publication 1218*, July, 1989.

INFLUENCE OF SMALL STEPS ON WALL PRESSURE FLUCTUATION SPECTRA MEASURED ON TU-144LL FLYING LABORATORY

B.M. Efimtsov, A.Yu. Golubev, TsAGI, Moscow, Russia
S.A. Rizzi[†], NASA Langley Research Center, Hampton, VA, USA
A.O. Andersson, R.G. Rackl, Boeing, Seattle, WA, USA
E. V. Andrianov, Tupolev, Moscow, Russia

Abstract

Results of analyzing flight-test data of pressure-fluctuation fields in front of forward-facing steps and behind backward-facing steps are presented. The range of dimensionless step heights (normalized by boundary-layer displacement thickness) in the flight test was 0.042-0.236. The flight tests covered a mach-number range from 0.57 to 1.97. In the mach-number ranges covered by wind-tunnel tests (0.57 to 0.78 and 1.5 to 2) data agree very well with the flight data. Very importantly, the flight-test data fill in the gap previously existing for small-step pressure-fluctuations in the range of mach 0.78 to 1.5. Increased pressure-fluctuations were observed in the transonic region.

Introduction

Forward- and backward-facing steps due to manufacturing imperfections on exterior aircraft surfaces (skin-element joints, windshield and door edges, etc.) are potential sources of aerodynamically generated interior noise. Such steps are small compared to the boundary-layer thickness. As already demonstrated in wind-tunnel experiments[1,2] such steps can in flight generate local pressure-fluctuation fields with audio-frequency intensities more than one hundred times greater than those due to boundary-layer turbulence over a smooth surface. The data yielded the principal characteristics of the pressure-fluctuation fields in front of forward-facing and behind backward-facing steps, random in space and time, covering useful ranges of mach, Reynolds, and Strouhal numbers, and dimensionless step height. However, a suitable transonic (0.78 < mach < 1.5) wind tunnel was not available. The mach number range of 0.8 to 1.2 is of great interest to high-subsonic-speed passenger aircraft. Even when normalized, the pressure-fluctuation intensity from these experimental data showed a tendency to ramp up as mach 0.78 was approached. Similarly, the normalized intensity at mach 1.5 was substantially greater than the ones at mach 0.78 or 2.0. One may therefore suspect a sharp increase of pressure-fluctuation intensity in the mach-number region 0.78 to 1.5. A flight experiment on the Tupolev 144 Flying Laboratory was carried out in order to fill in this mach-number gap[3-4]. Furthermore, these data extended the range of dimensionless step heights (normalized by boundary layer displacement thickness) achieved in the wind tunnel tests, to below 0.11. This value is seen only on an aircraft's nose, whereas the behavior for much smaller values is needed for larger boundary layer thicknesses further aft. This paper presents the results of analyzing the flight-test data at small steps. The intensity distribution of spectral components of pressure fluctuations in space is investigated. Its relationships to mach, Reynolds, and Strouhal number, and dimensionless step height are compared with that obtained from the wind tunnel experiments.

General information on measurements of pressure fluctuations at steps on TU-144LL

Pressure-fluctuation fields at forward- and backward-facing steps on the Tu-144LL were realized with the use of layered metallic plates placed on the fuselage skin in two zones (Fig.1): between window apertures at a distance of ~22.5m and at a distance of ~45m from the front fuselage point. The plates were set in such a way that they partly overlapped window apertures equipped with special metallic plugs (blanks). Each of these layered metallic plates with an overall thickness of 7mm consisted of two plates of smaller thickness. Directly connected with the skin was a 4mm thick plate which held another 3mm thick plate. The connection between them was such that the 3mm plate could be easily removed. Thus, the pressure-fluctuation fields could be studied in front of forward-facing steps and behind backward facing steps of different heights (7mm and 4mm) in each of two zones on the fuselage surface.

The plates in the two zones had identical dimensions with length 758mm. The width of the lower (4mm thick) plate was 305mm and that of the upper (3mm thick) plate was 216mm. A transition in the circumferential direction from the 216mm to 305mm width was made from a sculpted filler material to avoid steps in the circumferential direction. Similarly, a transition between the lower plate and the fuselage surface effectively extended the width dimension of the lower panel to 375mm. The plates were curved to conform to the circumferential

---

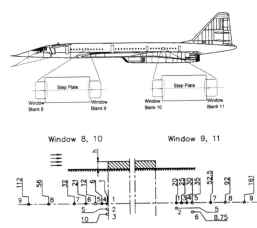

Figure 1. Disposition of window-blanks 8, 9, 10, 11 and layout of measurement points in front of forward-facing steps and behind backward-facing steps. Dimensions are in mm.

curvature of their installed locations. There was no appreciable curvature in the longitudinal direction. While plates with even larger widths would have been desirable, this was not possible due to practical considerations by Tupolev.

The plates were mounted at different distances from the nose so that test data could be obtained at different Reynolds numbers, which differed much in the same way as the two dimensionless step heights. The experimental data obtained under such conditions permit a direct evaluation of the effects of Reynolds number and dimensionless step height.

Window blanks were used in place of the windows and served as a structure through which transducers could be mounted. The window blanks had a smooth external surface and were set strictly flush with the exterior aircraft fuselage surface. The transducers for measuring pressure fluctuations in front of forward-facing steps (window blanks 8 and 10) and behind backward-facing steps (window blanks 9 and 11) were mounted through the window blanks. Details of the installation are provided in[4]. The sensitive elements of the transducers were strictly flush with the exterior window-blank surface. Only nine transducers were placed on each window blank; this was determined by the number of channels available in the signal-conditioning and measurement systems. It is evident that such a limited number of transducers cannot give complete information on the spatial characteristics of the extremely complex, substantially non-uniform fields of pressure fluctuations at the steps. Experimental data obtained in wind tunnels[1-2] were extensively used to determine transducer locations that would give maximal information about the studied fields. The locations of the pressure-fluctuation transducers (with dimensions in mm) are also shown in Fig.1.

In the flow direction, the transducers were placed such that they could cover the whole zone with large pressure fluctuations for the steps of larger height (7mm). To ensure direct comparison between the results at different step heights, identical dimensionless (normalized by the step height) coordinates were provided. The transducers were also set at points where the maximum pressure fluctuations were expected. Following the experimental results from[1-2], the maximum pressure fluctuations in front of forward-facing steps are observed right at the step. At backward-facing steps, the maximum pressure-fluctuation intensity in wind tunnel measurements was observed approximately five step heights downstream.

In the circumferential direction, the transducers were placed only in the zone of expected maximum pressure fluctuations. Three pressure-fluctuation transducers were mounted directly in front of forward-facing steps (transducers 1-3). Four transducers were mounted behind backward-facing steps with two at a distance of 20mm (transducers 1-2) and two at a distance of 35mm (transducers 5-6).

The pressure-fluctuation transducers were Kulite type XCS-062-15D. These are miniature transducers, ~16mm in length and 1.63mm in diameter. Each transducer has an external temperature-compensation module and a tube, which connects a cavity behind the sensitive element with the air space in the cabin. The sensitive element thus experiences the static pressure differential between the fuselage interior and exterior. Note however that the signal conditioning utilized a two-stage amplifier, the first of which was capacitively coupled. Thus, the DC component associated with the static pressure differential was blocked and only the fluctuating component was allowed to pass and be subsequently recorded. The sensitive element of the transducer is protected on the external side by a circular plate (1.63mm in diameter) with small circular holes through which the pressure is sensed. The holes are set in a circle of ~1mm diameter. The transducers were placed on window-blanks through nonmetallic threaded plugs, which provided electrical insulation from the window blanks. The protecting perforated plate and the exposed end of the insulating threaded plug were both set flush with the smooth exterior surface of the window blanks.

Calibration of the pressure-fluctuation transducers was performed with a calibrator specially developed by Boeing and able to generate a 150dB sinusoidal signal at 250Hz, as well as broadband noise. Calibrations were performed both before and after each flight. No differences between calibrations before and after the flight were observed. Furthermore, the results of calibrations during the flight tests practically agreed with those carried out in the laboratory.

The signal time histories from all transducers in a window-blank pair were simultaneously recorded on a Metrum RS-512 digital tape recorder. The signals were low-pass filtered at a cut-off frequency of 11.2 kHz, equal to the upper frequency of the 1/3-octave band with central frequency 10kHz.

Measurements of pressure fluctuations at the steps were made at subsonic, supersonic and transonic velocities $0.57 \leq M \leq 2.0$. In three flights, the steps were 7mm high and in the last flight, the upper (3 mm thick) panels were removed so that the steps were 4mm high. Measurements at subsonic and supersonic flight velocities were carried out during horizontal flight-path segments. At transonic velocities, there were relatively small variations of altitude and mach number.

After completing the program of flight tests, the data were downloaded from the Metrum recorder and written to CD-ROMs for subsequent analysis and modeling. Spectral and correlation analysis of signals was performed using the Lab Windows CVI software package.

Preliminary analysis of experimental data (performed while solving methodology problems) showed that in practically all the time histories subjected to further spectral and correlation analysis, the condition of statistical steady state is fulfilled. This appeared also to be valid for the regimes of small variations of mach number. The main parts of other flight regimes were repeated in order to evaluate the stability of the experimental results. In comparable flight regimes, the differences in spectral levels were no more than 1dB. Comparison between the spectra measured in flight and on the ground with engines operating at high power allows the conclusion that pressure fluctuations at all the measurement points in flight are significantly higher than sound levels due to propulsion.

Results of experimental investigations of pressure-fluctuation spectra

As with the experiments in wind tunnels[1,2,5], similarity theory was used in the present analysis. Dimensional analysis leads to the following dimensionless representation of spectral density $\Phi(\omega)$ depending on five similarity parameters:

$$\Phi(\omega)U/q^2 h = F\left(M, Re, h/\delta^*, x/h, Sh\right) \quad (1)$$

Here U is the free-flow velocity; h is step height; q is the dynamic head; M is the free-flow mach number, δ^* the boundary-layer displacement thickness; $Re = \delta^* U \nu$ is Reynolds number (ν is kinematic viscosity); $Sh = \omega h U$ is Strouhal number based on step height; x is the longitudinal distance from the step; ω is circular frequency. The dimen-

sionless spectral density is presented, as usual, as a function of Strouhal number depending on parameters M, Re, h/δ^* and x/h. Thus, at fixed locations (x/h=const) the pressure-fluctuation spectra have the same similarity criteria as the averaged characteristics of flow above the step:

$$M=const; Re=const; h/\delta^*=const \quad (2)$$

The validity of similarity condition (1) as well as the significance and completeness of the respective parameters were established in previous work[5], using a forward-facing step of greater height (in comparison with the boundary-layer displacement thickness) on a plate and on the wind tunnel wall at supersonic flow velocity. The experimental results obtained in wind tunnels[1-2] showed the validity of these parameters for pressure-fluctuation fields both in front of forward-facing steps and behind backward-facing steps of small dimensionless height. Unfortunately, the ranges of Reynolds number (Re=2.48×10^5-6.89×10^5) and of dimensionless step heights (h/δ^*=0.042-0.236) in the present flight experiments were limited. Only Reynolds numbers at the upper limit of the wide range covered in the wind tunnel experiments were commensurate with those on the Tu-144LL.

The range of dimensionless step height in the Tu-144LL experiment partly overlaps the lower end of the range in wind-tunnel experiments. The minimum values of this parameter under flight conditions are about 2.5 times less than its minimum value in wind tunnels without artificial thickening of the turbulent boundary layer. The range of mach numbers realized on Tu-144LL covers practically the whole range of interest from the standpoint of noise inside high-speed airplanes.

Spatial distribution of pressure-fluctuation spectra

Pressure-fluctuation fields at forward- and backward-facing steps are characterized by high intensity and possess significant spatial non-uniformity. The experimental data for the 4mm-high forward-facing step on window blank 10 at M=0.57; M=1.21; M=1.97 appear in Fig.2a-Fig.2c. The data in these figures are presented as the difference in pressure-fluctuation levels (ΔL) in 1/3-octave frequency bands recorded at different points in front of the step and those predicted[6], i.e. the wall pressure-fluctuation levels in the same frequency bands of the turbulent boundary layer on a smooth surface with zero mean-pressure gradient.

A comparison with the wind-tunnel experiments shows the same significant increase (up to 30 dB) in the pressure-fluctuation intensity in front of the step, but faster reduction of the frequency region of elevated pressure fluctuations (in comparison with the

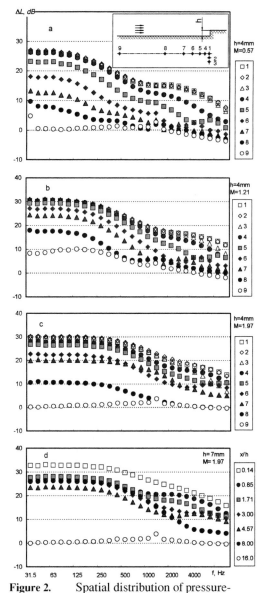

Figure 2. Spatial distribution of pressure-fluctuation intensity in front of forward-facing step.

turbulent boundary layer) as the observation-point distance to the step increases.

Note some features of the spatial distribution of pressure-fluctuation intensity within 1.5 step height's distance from the step. This area is (transducers 1-5) characterized by a small variation of low-frequency pressure-fluctuations. This is characteristic not only of subsonic and transonic velocities, but also of low supersonic flight velocities. As frequency increases, this feature vanishes and at frequencies above 2kHz we observe the same (practically equidistant) spectrum stratification as in the low-frequency region with the observation point further away from the step (at x/h≥3).

At low supersonic velocity (Fig.2b), substantially less spectrum stratification is observed at distances from the step up to x/h=8 (location 7). Nevertheless, even at location 9, the most distant from the step, the low-frequency pressure-fluctuation intensity is almost 10 dB higher than for a turbulent boundary layer on a smooth surface.

An unusual spectral shape at M=1.97 (Fig.2c) is observed at point 6 (x/h=5.25) and at point 7 (x/h=8). This seems to be connected with the separation-induced shock located between these points. This assumption is confirmed by the pressure-fluctuation spectra presented in Fig.2d, which were obtained at a larger step height (h=7mm). The elevated low-frequency levels of pressure fluctuations at location 8 (x/h=8) are characterized by a sharper decay in the high-frequency region in comparison with the high-frequency roll-off at location 7 (x/h=4.57). Probably, the shock in this case is located between locations 7 and 8, i.e. approximately in position x/h≈6, which is characteristic of step heights commensurate with the boundary layer thickness[5].

Some characteristics of the spatial distribution of pressure-fluctuation intensity in front of steps of small dimensionless height are worth noting. At small height (h/δ*≈0.066), a substantial decrease of pressure-fluctuation intensity is observed as the observation point moves away from the step (Fig.2c). We do not find as sharp a decrease of pressure-fluctuation intensity behind the shock as observed at a step height commensurate with the boundary layer thickness (Fig.2d).

Fig.3 illustrates the spatial distribution of pressure-fluctuation intensity behind backward facing steps: at the smaller step height (h=4mm) on window blank 11 at M=0.57 (Fig.3a), M=1.21 (Fig.3b) and M=1.97 (Fig.3c).

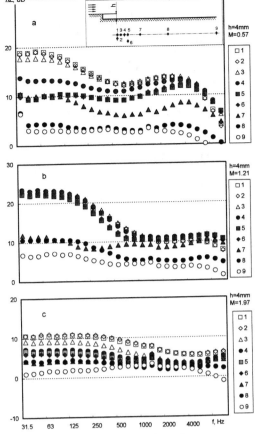

Figure 3. Spatial distribution of pressure-fluctuation intensity behind backward facing step.

These data, as well as the experimental data obtained in wind tunnels[2] show that behind a backward-facing step the region of increased pressure fluctuations is of substantially larger extent than that observed in front of forward-facing steps. As the observation point moves away from the backward-facing step, the maximum values of ΔL and their variation in the high-frequency part of the spectrum also agree with those observed in the wind tunnel experiments at M≈0.5 and M≈2. However, at low frequencies, the values of ΔL at points 1-3 obtained in flight experiments are significantly higher than those observed at M≈0.5 in the wind tunnel experiment.

The characteristics of low-frequency pressure-fluctuation behavior revealed in the flight experiment can be explained only by additional disturbances. The only supposition that can be made is that these are generated by the interaction of the flow with the front and side surfaces of the plate. This supposition is supported in a way by the correlations between the spectral components of the pressure-fluctuation field between a point directly in front of the plate and a point behind it, where attachment of the flow separated at the rear edge of the plate was expected. Con-

sidering this, the results of measurements behind a backward facing step on Tu-144LL are, strictly speaking, valid only at high frequencies, and influenced by the finite extent of the step plates at lower frequencies.

For the spectra in 1/3-octave frequency bands, measured behind the step in the zone of flow attachment at low subsonic flight velocity, a gently sloping maximum is characteristic in the high-frequency region (Fig.3a). It also manifests itself behind the attachment region downstream. A similar maximum was also observed in the wind tunnel experiment. As mach number increases, this spectral feature decreases and at M=1.5 it is no longer observed.

Let us note another observation of the measurement results behind a backward-facing step on the flying laboratory regarding the position of the zone of the separated-boundary-layer reattachment. Precisely in this zone the maximum intensity of pressure fluctuations is observed at practically all frequencies. Fig.4 illustrates a variation of the position of maximum pressure fluctuations behind the step as the flight mach number increases. At M=0.57 the maximum position approximately corresponds to x/h=5.0. At M~1.0, the maximum intensity position corresponds x/h=7.5. Further increase of the mach number results in a reverse shift of the maximum, and at M=1.96 its shift to the neighboring measurement point located at x/h=4.3 is quite evident.

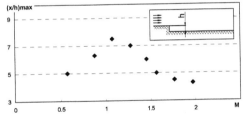

Figure 4. Shift of the intensity maximum of pressure fluctuations behind backward-facing step at different mach numbers.

One source of additional uncertainty is flow downwash. The flow visualization data on Tu-144 and directly on Tu-144LL provide evidence[4] of the presence of pronounced downwashes in the measurement zones. The most intensive downwashes were observed in the first zone located closer to the fuselage nose (on window-blanks 8 and 9).

The effect of flow downwash on pressure-fluctuations at steps remains unstudied at present. However, it is well known that downwashes disturb the flow's two-dimensionality, which can lead to changes in the wall pressure-fluctuation intensity of separated flows. As a rule, three-dimensional effects in two-dimensional separated flow cause some weakening of wall pressure fluctuations.

<u>Effect of Reynolds number on pressure-fluctuation spectra</u>

The effect of Reynolds number on the pressure-fluctuation spectra in front of forward-facing steps was determined by comparing the dependencies of dimensionless spectral density on Strouhal number (1) at slightly different values of dimensionless step height (at h=7mm on window blank 10 and at h=4mm on window blank 8). This was done at different measurement points with identical dimensionless coordinates x/h successively for each mach number. Here, as an illustration, the data on such a comparison of spectra are presented only for M=0.57 (Fig.5a), M=1.2 (Fig.5b) and M=1.97 (Fig.5c). In the measurement zone located closer to the nose (window-blank 8) at M=0.57 the pressure-fluctuation intensity in front of the step is lower than in the zone located downstream (window-blank 10). The effect decreases at M=1.2 (Fig.5b) and at M=1.97 (Fig.5c) it is practically not manifested.

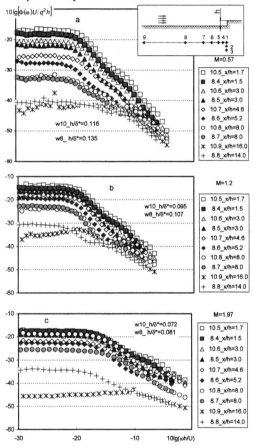

Figure 5. Effect of Reynolds number on pressure-fluctuation spectra in front of forward-facing step.

Under flight conditions of Tu-144LL corresponding to M=1.2 the flow visualization indicates significantly weaker flow downwashes than at M=0.57. At M≈2.0 the downwashes are minimal and

weak. Thus, the difference observed in the decrease of the pressure-fluctuation intensity in front of the step in the zone of window blank 8 at different mach numbers appears to correlate with the observed downwashes in this zone, and is not a function of Reynolds number. Such a conclusion is also confirmed by the results of pressure-fluctuation investigations in front of a forward-facing step obtained in the wind-tunnel experiments[1], which demonstrated a very small effect of Reynolds number over a wide range up to the values close to the minimum values encountered on Tu-144LL.

In evaluating the effect of Reynolds number on pressure fluctuations behind backward-facing steps, low-frequency spectrum components will not be used for reasons previously cited, especially in the region of the separated-flow reattachment (at 3≤x/h≤8). In the region of high Strouhal numbers one can observe much the same difference of the dimensionless spectral density of pressure fluctuations (Figs.6a,b) in the first (window-blank 9) and the second (window-blank 11) zones, as in front of the steps (Figs.5a-c). This difference can also be explained by flow downwashes, and not by a Reynolds number effect, which was not observed in the wind tunnel experiments either.

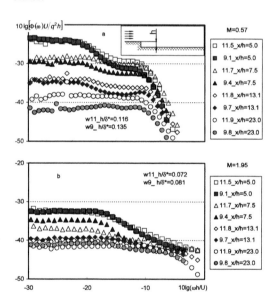

Figure 6. Effect of Reynolds number on pressure-fluctuation spectra behind backward-facing step.

<u>Effect of dimensionless step height on pressure-fluctuation spectra</u>

Fig.7a illustrates the effect of dimensionless height immediately in front of a forward-facing step on pressure fluctuation spectra for M=0.87. At small Strouhal numbers, the effect of dimensionless step

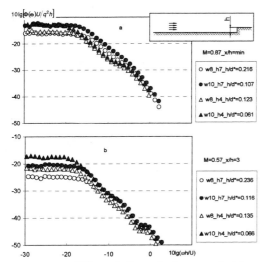

Figure 7. Effect of dimensionless step height on pressure-fluctuation spectra in front of forward-facing step.

height appears to be zero. In the region of Strouhal numbers, where a decrease in dimensionless spectral density is observed, one can clearly see stratification of dimensionless spectra relating to different values of h/δ^*, principally due to the variation in cut-off frequency (transition from constant intensity [Sh°= Strouhal to power zero] to rolling off with frequency). In this case, a higher cut-off frequency corresponds to a larger value of h/δ^*. Precisely such effects of dimensionless step height (only with a lower cut-off frequency) were revealed in the wind tunnel experiments[1]. These effects are observed at different mach numbers.

As the observation point moves upstream from a forward-facing step, the spectrum quickly changes character. Already at x/h=3 (Fig.7b) a reverse picture is observed: the dimensionless spectra are stratified in the region of small Strouhal numbers (in the area of dependence ~Sh°) and differ little in the area of spectral rolloff at higher frequencies. This picture remains practically unchanged as the observation point moves away from the step. Although not shown, it is invariant with respect to mach number, until the observation point falls in the vicinity of the separation-induced shock. Such a transformation of spectra was indeed observed in the wind-tunnel experiments.

Evaluation of the effect of dimensionless height on the pressure-fluctuation spectra, measured behind a backward-facing step, is worthwhile only for the region of high Strouhal numbers where the experimental data are not influenced by the finite step-plate size. Only some tendencies related to the effect of dimensionless step height can be reported here: increase of h/δ^* leads to some increase of spectral den-

sity in this Strouhal-number region at practically all mach numbers and to some increase of cut-off frequency at supersonic flight conditions. The latter point is illustrated by the experimental data at M=1.97 (Fig.8).

Effect of mach number on pressure-fluctuation spectra

In the experiment on Tu-144LL, the range $0.57 \leq M \leq 1.97$ was covered. Sufficiently reliable data on the mach-number effect on pressure fluctuations in front of a forward-facing step over the whole range of Strouhal numbers of practical interest were obtained. Unfortunately, only the experimental data obtained in the range of high Strouhal numbers, can be considered valid for pressure fluctuations behind backward-facing steps.

The mach-number effect on the pressure-fluctuation spectra directly in front of the step (x/h=min) on window-blank 10 at h=4mm is illustrated in Fig.9. It is clearly seen that the mach-

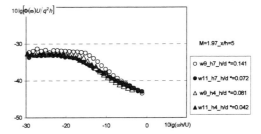

Figure 8. Effect of dimensionless step height on pressure-fluctuation spectra behind backward-facing step.

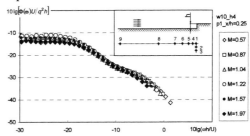

Figure 9. Effect of mach number on pressure-fluctuation spectra in front of forward-facing step.

number effect is more pronounced in the range of low Strouhal numbers where dimensionless spectral density is observed to be independent of Strouhal number. The maximum values of dimensionless spectral density in this case correspond to low supersonic flight velocities (M=1.22).

Fig.10 presents the dependence of dimensionless spectral density on mach number at fixed Strouhal number corresponding to the region where the spectral density is independent of Strouhal number. In essence, this is the dependence of the principal parameter of the prediction model of the pressure-fluctuation field in front of a forward-facing step, indicated in reference[1] as F_{mo} (see section 3).

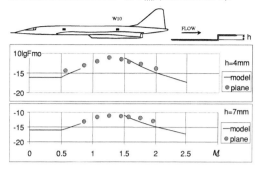

Figure 10.   Effect of mach number on maximum intensity of pressure fluctuations in front of forward-facing step.

Fig.10 also presents the dependence of F_{mo} on mach number, as obtained from wind-tunnel experiments and used in the development of the prediction model[1] of the characteristics of the pressure-fluctuation field in front of a forward-facing step of small height. In the ranges of mach number covered by wind-tunnel experiments, the flight experiment confirms the reliability the prediction model. Furthermore, the experiment on Tu-144LL permits extending this prediction model to a parameter region heretofore not studied: $0.78 \leq M \leq 1.5$.

If displayed in 1/3-octave bands, the spectrum for a backward-facing step shows a marked peak at high frequencies for low mach numbers (Fig.11). At higher mach numbers, this peak disappears. This behavior is evident in the mach-number range 0.87-1.57 not previously covered in wind-tunnel experiments. This is why the prediction model[2] presents different relations for evaluating pressure fluctuations behind backward facing steps for subsonic ($M \leq 0.78$) and supersonic ($M \geq 1.5$) flows. The new experimental material permits these two relations to be joined.

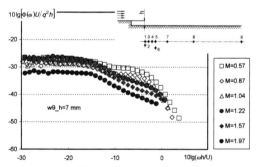

Figure 11.   Effect of mach number on pressure-fluctuation spectra behind backward-facing step.

The low-frequency part of the spectrum in Fig.11 for $M \leq 1.5$ seems to be distorted by the addi-

tional disturbances from the plate discussed above. However, the spectrum behavior at M=1.57 and M=1.97 characterized by their practically equidistant stratification indicates that the experimental data at low frequencies, obtained at M=1.97 on window blank 9 at h=7mm, possibly is reliable.

Modeling of the experimental data

The prediction models for pressure fuctuations at forward-facing steps[1] and backward-facing steps[2] can now be extended to lower non-dimensional step heights ($h/\delta^* < 0.3$) and to the transonic region based on the flight data. The form of these prediction models is

$$\Phi(x,\omega) = \frac{q^2 h}{U} F_m \Psi(M) \exp(-|x - x_m|/L) + \Phi_{b\ell}(\omega)$$

where the factor F_m describes the Strouhal-number dependence. For a forward-facing step

$$F_m = \frac{F_{m0}}{\left\{1 + (Sh/Sh_1)^{3n_1}\left[1 + (Sh/Sh_2)^{3(n_2-n_1)}\right]\right\}^{1/3}}$$

The characteristic parameters (Sh_2, n_1, n_2) remain unchanged while Sh_1, F_{mo} take on new values:
$$F_{m0} = 0.035;$$

$$Sh_1 = \Psi_1(M) \begin{cases} 0.148(h/\delta^*) & \text{at } 0.042 \leq h/\delta^* \leq 0.11; \\ 0.131(h/\delta^* - 0.11) + 0.01628 \\ \qquad \text{at } 0.11 < h/\delta^* \leq 0.3; \end{cases} \quad (3)$$

$$\Psi_1(M) = \begin{cases} 1 & \text{at } M \leq 0.8; \\ 1 + (M - 0.8)0.8 & \text{at } 0.8 < M \leq 2. \end{cases}$$

Dependence of the pressure-fluctuation spectral density on mach number is described by a modified empirical dependence extended to the whole mach-number region ($M \leq 2$).

$$\psi(M) = \begin{cases} 1 & \text{at } M \leq 0.5 \\ \dfrac{4(M/1.4)^{1.32}}{1 + (M/1.4)^4} & \text{at } 0.5 < M \leq 2 \end{cases} \quad (4)$$

The non-uniformity scale of the field is determined in the same way as for prediction model[1], and is given as an empirical dependence of dimensionless step height and mach number:

In the region of $0.042 \leq h/\delta^* \leq 0.15$

$$L/h = \max\left\{ \frac{\overline{L}_0 \psi(M)}{1 + 2.5Sh}, 2 \right\} \quad (5)$$

$$\overline{L}_0 = 0.65(h/\delta^*)^{-0.625};$$

In the region $0.15 < h/\delta^* \leq 0.3$, $L/h = \overline{L}_0 \psi(M)$.

Improvement of the prediction model for the pressure-fluctuation field behind a backward-facing step offered the opportunity to join different dependencies for spectral density at subsonic and supersonic flight velocities. A superposition of two fields with different dependencies of spectral density on mach number was used. The typical dimensionless spectrum of the first field (F_m) is described by the same relation as the one used in the prediction model[2] with modified characteristic parameters:

$$F_m = \frac{F_{m0}}{\left[\left(Sh/Sh_1\right)^{2n_1} + \left(Sh/Sh_2\right)^{2n_2}\right]^{1/2}}$$

$$F_{m0} = \begin{cases} 11\times10^{-4} & \text{at } 0.042 \le h/\delta^* \le 0.07; \\ \left[1+20\left(h/\delta^* - 0.07\right)\right]10^{-4} & \text{at } 0.07 < h/\delta^* \le 0.3; \end{cases} \qquad (6)$$

$$Sh_1 = 10^{-3};$$

$$Sh_2 = \begin{cases} 0.02 & \text{at } 0.042 \le h/\delta^* \le 0.07; \\ 0.02 + 0.08\left(h/\delta^* - 0.07\right) & \text{at } 0.07 < h/\delta^* \le 0.3; \end{cases}$$

$$n_1 = 0.01; n_2 = 0.75;$$

Dependence of pressure-fluctuation intensity on mach number for the first field is described by the following empirical relations:

$$\psi(M) = \begin{cases} 1 & \text{at } M \le 0.75; \\ 1 + 2(M - 0.75) & \text{at } 0.75 < M \le 1; \\ 1.5 & \text{at } 1 < M \le 1.5; \\ 1.5 - 2(M - 1.5) & \text{at } 1.5 < M \le 2. \end{cases} \qquad (7)$$

The typical dimensionless spectrum for the second field (quantities with *) is presented in the form:

$$F_m{}^* = \frac{F_{m0}^*\left(Sh/Sh_1^*\right)^{n_1^*}}{1+\left(Sh/Sh_1^*\right)^{n_2^*}} \qquad (8)$$

The characteristic parameters corresponding to these fields are described by the relations:

$$F_{m0}^* = F_{m0}; \quad Sh_1^* = 0.5; \qquad (9)$$

$$n_1^* = 0.2; n_2^* = 3.0$$

Dependence of pressure fluctuations on mach number for the second field is described by relations indicating its vanishing effect as M approaches 1.5.

$$\psi^*(M) = \begin{cases} 1 & \text{at } M \le 0.5; \\ 1 - (M - 0.5) & \text{at } 0.5 < M \le 1.5; \\ 0 & \text{at } 1.5 < M \le 2. \end{cases} \qquad (10)$$

The new experimental data also permit refining the location of the pressure-fluctuation intensity maximum:

$$(x/h)_{max} = \begin{cases} 5 & \text{at } M \le 0.5; \\ 5 + 5(M - 0.5) & \text{at } 0.5 < M \le 1; \\ 7.5 & \text{at } 1 < M \le 1.4; \\ 7.5 - 6(M - 1.4) & \text{at } 1.4 < M \le 2. \end{cases} \qquad (11)$$

The non-uniformity scale of the pressure-fluctuation field is unmodified from the prediction model[2].

Concluding Remarks

Spectral analysis of the results of pressure-fluctuation measurements in front of forward-facing steps and behind backward-facing steps showed that in the flight experiment on Tu-144LL a great body of experimental data of practical interest was obtained. These data confirm mainly the reliability of the wind-tunnel experimental results[1-2] from which the prediction model is built. Moreover, they permit improving this model and its extension to those regions of real parameters, which were not covered in the wind tunnel experiments. The case in point here is the region of mach numbers (0.78<M<1.5) and the region of small dimensionless (normalized by the boundary layer displacement thickness) step heights (h/δ*<0.11) for which reliable experimental data were not obtained in wind tunnels. Exactly this mach-number region, its lower part (0.78<M≤1.2) particularly, is of greatest interest for high-speed aircraft.

Acknowledgements

The authors want to thank the Boeing Company for financial support of this work and in particular S.V. Kravchenko and D.H. Reed for helpful technical discussions and organization of the work.

References

1. Efimtsov B.M. Kozlov N.M. Kravchenko S.V. Andersson A.O. "Wall pressure-fluctuation spectra at small forward-facing steps". AIAA-99-1964.

2. Efimtsov B.M. Kozlov N.M. Kravchenko S.V. Andersson A.O. "Wall pressure-fluctuation spectra at small backward-facing steps". AIAA-2000-2053.

3. Rizzi S.A., Rackl R.G. and Andrianov E.V., "Flight test measurements from the Tu-144LL structure/cabin noise experiment," NASA/TM-2000-209858, January 2000.

4. Rizzi S.A., Rackl R.G. and Andrianov E.V., "Flight test measurements from the Tu-144LL structure/cabin noise follow-on experiment," NASA/TM-2000-209859, February 2000.

5. Efimtsov B.M., Kuznetsov V.B. "Wall pressure fluctuation spectra at supersonic streamline of a forward facing step". Uchenye Zapiski TsAGI, v.20, No.3, 1989.

6. Efimtsov B.M. "Similarity criteria of wall pressure fluctuation spectra of the turbulent boundary layer". Akustichesky Zhurnal, v.30, ed.1, 1984.

AIAA 2002-2606

ABSORBING LAYERS AND RADIATION BOUNDARY CONDITIONS FOR JET FLOW SIMULATIONS

Thomas Hagstrom[*]and Igor Nazarov[†]

ABSTRACT

The radiation of energy to the far field is an essential feature of aeroacoustic phenomena. Thus any simulation of sound production by complex flows must include some domain truncation strategy. The most accurate methods currently available for constant coefficient wave propagation problems are the imposition high-order radiation boundary conditions and the attachment of reflectionless sponge layers or PMLs. For jet flow simulations, the first technique may be applied outside the jet, but its generalization to the inflow or outflow boundary is problematic. In this work we focus on the construction of improved PMLs. For the compressible Euler equations linearized about a uniform flow, we construct a new layer with no obvious theoretical defects. In particular, unlike other layer equations proposed in the literature, with ours all waves are damped, the equations are strongly well-posed, and there is no requirement that the grid be aligned with the flow. We also generalize the construction to linearizations about parallel flows. Although it is easy to develop layers with a reflectionless interface, it is not easy to force all waves to be damped, particularly when the flow profile itself has instabilitites. Nonetheless, by numerically optimizing two parameters, a layer with acceptable absorption characteristics is constructed. Some limited numerical experiments are given to illustrate its performance.

INTRODUCTION

To directly simulate aeroacoustic phenomena such as jet noise is of fundamental engineering and scientific interest. It also poses an extreme challenge to numerical methodologies. In particular, the fraction of the energy radiated to the far field is very small, and thus simulations must be very accurate.

As the problem is naturally posed on an unbounded spatial domain, a computational domain truncation must be imposed which does not lead to observable errors in the far field.

Current simulations, e.g. [4, 5], typically use a combination of low order approximate conditions [6] and an exit zone with grid stretching and filtering [3]. Our analysis and simulation of model problems over long times [10] shows that the former conditions cannot be expected to provide acceptable accuracy. As for the exit zone, its construction is ad hoc and it uses a nonnegligible fraction of the mesh. In this work we describe improved boundary conditions and reflectionless sponge layers for compressible flow calculations which we believe have the potential to significantly improve the accuracy and efficiency jet noise simulations.

The typical setup is illustrated in Figure 1. At the radiation boundaries outside the jet, linearization about a uniform flow is a reasonable assumption. In this favorable situation, highly accurate radiation boundary conditions are available [10, 12, 8, 17], as is our newly constructed PML, described below. At inflow and outflow, on the other hand, linearization about a uniform flow is obviously inaccurate. Thus the focus of our efforts is to develop an accurate treatment of these boundaries.

In Section 2 we briefly describe our results on high-order radiation boundary conditions for the Euler equations linearized about a uniform flow. We also discuss what is involved to generalize them to linearizations about a parallel flow. In Section 3, which contains the primary new results we want to report, we show how to construct PMLs for the linearized Euler equations with excellent absorption properties. Both uniform and parallel flows are considered, and some numerical experiments are presented. We conclude with a list of open problems.

[*]Department of Mathematics and Statistics, The University of New Mexico, Albuquerque, NM 87131. Work supported in part by NASA Contract NAG3-2322, NSF Grant DMS-9971772 and by ICOMP, NASA Glenn Research Center.

[†]Department of Mathematics and Statistics, The University of New Mexico, Albuquerque, NM 87131. Work supported in part by NASA Grant NAG3-2322.

RADIATION CONDITIONS

In recent years there has been remarkable progress in the construction, implementation, and analysis of convergent sequences of radiation boundary conditions for constant coefficient hyperbolic systems. (See [8] for a recent review.) Specializations of these constructions to the Euler equations linearized about a uniform flow are given in [10, 12]. We expect the conditions to be applicable to the radiation boundaries of Figure 1, and we briefly discuss them here.

The essential idea in this work is to:

(i.) Find a concrete representation of an exact radiation condition.

(ii.) Find a convergent sequence of approximations to the exact condition.

(iii.) Use auxiliary functions to conveniently implement the approximate conditions to arbitrary order.

For definiteness, we consider a flat boundary as in [10]. The proposed radiation conditions at an inflow boundary with normal x_1 take the form:

$$(\gamma - 1)\rho - T = 0, \qquad (1)$$

$$\frac{D_{\tan}}{Dt}(p + v_1) \quad + \frac{1}{2}\mathcal{R}(p + v_1)$$
$$+\frac{1 - U_1}{2}\left(\frac{\partial v_2}{\partial x_2} + \frac{\partial v_3}{\partial x_3}\right) \qquad = 0, \qquad (2)$$

$$\frac{D_{\tan}v_2}{Dt} + U_1\frac{\partial v_1}{\partial x_2} + \frac{\partial p}{\partial x_2} = 0, \qquad (3)$$

$$\frac{D_{\tan}v_3}{Dt} + U_1\frac{\partial v_1}{\partial x_3} + \frac{\partial p}{\partial x_3} = 0. \qquad (4)$$

and at outflow:

$$\frac{D_{\tan}}{Dt}(p - v_1) + \mathcal{R}p + U_1\left(\frac{\partial v_2}{\partial x_2} + \frac{\partial v_3}{\partial x_3}\right) = 0. \quad (5)$$

(Here we have nondimensionalized the variables. ρ is the density perturbation, p the pressure perturbation, T the temperature perturbation, and v_i the velocity perturbations.)

The approximation involves the operator $\mathcal{R}$:

$$\mathcal{R}w = \sum_{j=1}^{l} \psi_j, \qquad (6)$$

$$\frac{D_{\tan}^2\psi_j}{Dt^2} - \gamma_j^2(1 - U_1^2)\nabla_{\tan}^2\psi_j = \qquad (7)$$
$$-2(1 - U_1^2)\alpha_j\nabla_{\tan}^2\frac{D_{\tan}w}{Dt}.$$

The order of the approximation is increased by increasing l, that is by using more auxiliary functions. In [10] a particular approximation, i.e. a particular recipe for choosing the coefficients, is tested. For a difficult problem involving a periodic array of pressure pulses, we obtain the relative errors tabulated in Table 1. From this we reach two conclusions. First, very high order conditions can be stably implemented. Second, reasonably high order is needed for good long time accuracy. The standard conditions corresponding to $l = 0$ yield poor answers for moderate times.

It is possible in principle to generalize these conditions to linearizations about parallel flows. This could be useful for jet flows at the inflow boundary where disturbances from the mean flow may be small. The problem with our current formulation is that high-order derivatives of the mean fields are required. We are presently investigating whether or not this leads to practical difficulties, and how it might be avoided.

A second difficulty associated with the use of high-order conditions is the treatment of corners. Recently this has been studied in great detail for the wave equation [19]. We plan to look into the applicability of this analysis to the Euler system.

A PML FOR THE EULER EQUATIONS

The main alternative to accurate radiation boundary conditions is a reflectionless absorbing layer or PML. Such layers are extensively used in electromagnetics [2]. Generalizations to the linearized Euler equations have been constructed and tested [15, 13], but only lead to weakly well-posed problems [7, 14, 18]. The constructions in [1, 16] correct some of these difficulties, but introduce new ones. In what follows we systematically construct a new PML for the linearized Euler equations which avoids these difficulties.

Uniform Flows

The nondimensionalized compressible Euler equations linearized about an arbitrary, uniform flow field are given by:

$$u_t + A_1 u_{x_1} + \sum_{j=2}^{3} A_j u_{x_j} = 0, \qquad (8)$$

where

$$u = (\ \rho \quad v_1 \quad v_2 \quad v_3 \quad p\ )^T, \qquad (9)$$

2037

$$A_j = U_j I + \begin{pmatrix} 1 \\ 0 \\ 0 \\ 0 \\ \gamma \end{pmatrix} e_{j+1}^T + e_{j+1} \begin{pmatrix} 0 \\ 0 \\ 0 \\ 0 \\ \gamma^{-1} \end{pmatrix}^T . \quad (10)$$

We assume a subsonic flow and, for definiteness $U_1 > 0$.

Anticipating the construction of a layer with interface at $x_1 = 0$, we perform a Fourier-Laplace transformation with dual variables (s, ik_2, ik_3). Solutions then take the form:

$$\hat{u} = e^{\lambda x_1} \hat{\phi}, \quad (11)$$

where $(\lambda, \hat{\phi})$ solve the eigenvalue problem:

$$\left(sI + \lambda A_1 + \sum_{j=2}^3 ik_j A_j \right) \hat{\phi} = 0. \quad (12)$$

The solution is right-going if $\Re\lambda < 0$ when $\Re s > 0$ and left-going if $\Re\lambda > 0$ when $\Re s > 0$.

We find that the eigenvalues corresponding to right-going waves are:

$$\frac{\tilde{s} U_1 - \sqrt{\tilde{s}^2 + (1 - U_1^2)|k|^2}}{1 - U_1^2}, \quad -\frac{\tilde{s}}{U_1}, \quad (13)$$

and the single right-going eigenvalue is:

$$\frac{\tilde{s} U_1 + \sqrt{\tilde{s}^2 + (1 - U_1^2)|k|^2}}{1 - U_1^2}. \quad (14)$$

Here

$$\tilde{s} = s + ik_2 U_2 + ik_3 U_3, \quad |k|^2 = k_2^2 + k_3^2. \quad (15)$$

Within the absorbing layer, $x_1 > 0$, we seek a solution in the form:

$$\hat{u} = e^{\lambda x_1 + \left(\frac{\lambda}{r} - \mu\right) \int_0^{x_1} \sigma(z)dz} \hat{\phi}. \quad (16)$$

It is obvious that such solutions are continuous across the interface, so that the layer is perfectly matched for arbitrary parameter choices. Generally, we may take r and μ to be the symbols of localizable pseudodifferential operators. For the Euler equations we take r to be the symbol of a first order differential operator and μ to be a constant. For absorption we consider the real parts of the exponents. These should be negative for right-going waves and positive for leftgoing waves even for $\Re s = 0$. Generally, we will be unable to do this on the entire imaginary axis, but will attain it except at two exceptional points.

Considering λ/r it is clear that $r = \tilde{s}$ is a good choice. We get, for the rightgoing waves:

$$\frac{\lambda}{r} = -\frac{1}{U_1}, \quad (17)$$

$$\frac{\lambda}{r} = \frac{U_1}{1 - U_1^2} - \frac{1}{1 - U_1^2} \frac{\sqrt{\tilde{s}^2 + (1 - U_1^2)|k|^2}}{\tilde{s}}, \quad (18)$$

and for the leftgoing waves

$$\frac{\lambda}{r} = \frac{U_1}{1 - U_1^2} + \frac{1}{1 - U_1^2} \frac{\sqrt{\tilde{s}^2 + (1 - U_1^2)|k|^2}}{\tilde{s}}. \quad (19)$$

It can be shown that:

$$\Re \left(\frac{\sqrt{\tilde{s}^2 + (1 - U_1^2)|k|^2}}{\tilde{s}} \right) > 0, \quad \Re s \geq 0, \quad (20)$$

except on $\tilde{s} \in (-i\sqrt{1 - U_1^2}|k|, i\sqrt{1 - U_1^2}|k|)$. On that interval, however, λ itself is real. We thus conclude these have the correct sign except for the constant term associated with the acoustic modes. The latter can be eliminated by the choice of μ:

$$\mu = \frac{U_1}{1 - U_1^2}. \quad (21)$$

The exponent associated with the other modes remains negative. In the end, we have exponential decay except when $\tilde{s} = \pm\sqrt{1 - U_1^2}|k|$.

Note that within the layer:

$$\left(\frac{d}{dx} + \mu\sigma \right) \hat{u} = \frac{r + \sigma}{r} \lambda \hat{u}. \quad (22)$$

Hence $\hat{u}$ satisfies:

$$s\hat{u} + \left(1 - \frac{\sigma}{r + \sigma} \right) A_1 \left(\frac{d}{dx} + \mu\sigma \right) \hat{u} + \sum_{j=2}^2 ik_j A_j \hat{u} = 0. \quad (23)$$

Introducing the auxiliary variable:

$$\hat{w} = -\frac{\sigma}{r + \sigma} A_1 \left(\frac{d}{dx} + \mu\sigma \right) \hat{u}. \quad (24)$$

and inverting the transforms we attain our final form:

$$u_t + A_1(u_{x_1} + \mu\sigma u) + \sum_{j=2}^d A_j u_{x_j} + w = 0, \quad (25)$$

$$w_t + U_2 w_{x_2} + U_3 w_{x_3} + \sigma w + \sigma A_1(u_{x_1} + \mu\sigma u) = 0. \quad (26)$$

In [11] we will give a complete mathematical analysis of the new layer. However, we can summarize its salient features:

i. All waves (acoustic, vorticity, entropy) are damped, with none of the instabilitites discussed in [18].

ii. The equations are strongly well-posed, unlike the orginal split formulation of Hu [15, 14, 7].

iii. There is no restriction on the direction of the flow field, as in [1].

Thus, the new layer is a clear improvement, at least theoretically, over earlier formulations. Its only negative feature is that one new auxiliary variable is required for each physical variable.

A Numerical Experiment

To illustrate the properties of the new layer we solve (8) in two space dimensions with $U_1 = .3$ and $U_2 = .4$. A forcing is applied to each equation which is 1-periodic in x_2 and is given by:

$$f = (t/5)^9 (2 - t/5)^9 \sqrt{\frac{120}{\pi}} e^{-120r^2}, \qquad (27)$$

for

$$y \in (0, 1), \quad t \in (0, 10). \qquad (28)$$

Here r is measured from the center of the computational domain. The equations are discretized by eighth order central differencing in space and the standard eighth order predictor-corrector method in time. At the interface between the physical domain and the absorbing layer we use characteristic matching. The layers are also terminated with characteristic boundary conditions. To stabilize the one-sided differencing we use mesh grading as described in [9]. In the experiments shown we use a 54×50 mesh in the physical domain, which has dimensions 1×1. We consider four layers, of widths .3 and .6 on each side and maximum values of $\sigma_m = 80$ and $\sigma_m = 160$. For the experiments shown we choose a linear profile with $\sigma = 0$ at the interface. We note that it is possible (and in this case more efficient) to allow σ to be discontinuous. However, for nonperiodic problems we have found it convenient to enforce continuity when dealing with corner conditions. A reference solution is computed with a very thick layer of width 4 on each side and a maximum $\sigma_m = 160$. We choose a very small time step as the stability domain of the time-stepping scheme is quite limited, $\Delta t = 1/2000$. The total time of simulation is 25. In Tables 2-(4 we show results up through $t = 15$, beyond which the solution is negligibly small.

We observe little difference between the three fields, except for the fact that p decays more rapidly, as the vorticity mode leaves the domain more slowly. For short times, widening the layer is always advantageous. The best results are for the smaller value of

σ_m. This is explained by the fact that for larger values the decay of the solution is more rapid within the layer, leading to greater discretization error near the interface. In no instance does the solution with the layers decay in time as rapidly as the true solution, so the relative errors are eventually large. However, compared with peak values of the solution they are reasonable. In Figures 2-5 we also plot p, v_1, v_2 at $t = 5, 7, 10, 12$ for the case $w = .6$, $\sigma_m = 80$. The reflectionless interface and decay of the solution is clearly seen.

Parallel Flows

To move towards the construction of absorbing layers for a jet at the outflow (or inflow) boundary, we consider the Euler equations linearized about a parallel flow profile in two space dimensions:

$$u_t + A_1(y)u_x + A_2(y)u_y + C(y)u = 0, \qquad (29)$$

where

$$A_1 = \begin{pmatrix} U_1(y) & \bar{\rho}(y) & 0 & 0 \\ 0 & U_1(y) & 0 & \frac{1}{\bar{\rho}(y)} \\ 0 & 0 & U_1(y) & 0 \\ 0 & 1 & 0 & U_1(y) \end{pmatrix}, \qquad (30)$$

$$A_2 = \begin{pmatrix} 0 & 0 & \bar{\rho}(y) & 0 \\ 0 & 0 & 0 & 0 \\ 0 & 0 & 0 & \frac{1}{\bar{\rho}(y)} \\ 0 & 0 & 1 & 0 \end{pmatrix}, \qquad (31)$$

$$C = \begin{pmatrix} 0 & 0 & \bar{\rho}'(y) & 0 \\ 0 & 0 & U_1(y)' & 0 \\ 0 & 0 & 0 & 0 \\ 0 & 0 & 0 & 0 \end{pmatrix}. \qquad (32)$$

(Here we have chosen a slightly different nondimensionalization.)

As in the previous analysis, we may construct modal solutions:

$$\hat{u} = e^{\lambda x} \phi \qquad (33)$$

where ϕ satisfies:

$$\left(sI + \lambda A_1 + A_2 \frac{\partial}{\partial y} + C \right) \phi = 0. \qquad (34)$$

(This system must be provided with appropriate boundary conditions, a point we'll ignore for now.)

We now attempt to define layer equations with the property that modal solutions within the layer take the form:

$$\hat{q} = e^{\lambda x + \left(\frac{\lambda}{s} - \mu \right) \int_0^x \sigma(z)dz} \phi. \qquad (35)$$

Here we will take μ to be a scalar multiplication and we have exploited the fact that the tangential velocity is zero to replace r by s in analogy with the uniform flow results. For the layer interface to be reflectionless we require that ϕ be unchanged. Thus, the modal equation must be unchanged so that the layer equations are given by:

$$s\hat{u} + \frac{s}{s+\sigma}A_1\left(\frac{\partial}{\partial x} + \mu\sigma\right)\hat{u}$$
$$+A_2\left(\frac{\partial}{\partial y} + \mu'\int_0^x \sigma(z)dz\right)\hat{u} \qquad (36)$$
$$+C\hat{u} = 0.$$

Introducing a set of auxiliary variables, w, we obtain the augmented system:

$$u_t + A_1(u_x + \mu\sigma u)$$
$$+B(u_y + (\mu'\int_0^x \sigma(z)dz)u) \qquad (37)$$
$$+Cu + w = 0,$$

$$w_t + \sigma w + \sigma A_1(u_x + \mu\sigma u) = 0. \qquad (38)$$

We emphasize that by construction the interface between the layer and the physical domain is reflectionless. Our problem is to choose μ to guarantee the absorption properties. This seems a more complex issue than in the uniform flow case where we used analytic expressions for λ to find a *unique* constant value of μ for which *all* waves are damped. Moreover, the flow profiles are typically linearly unstable themselves. In the following section we will restrict ourselves to constant μ and numerically study the dependence of the spectrum of the layer equations on its value and on σ.

Dependence on μ

To better understand the choice of μ we consider a simple special case. Precisely we choose a 2π-periodic flow profile:

$$U_1(y) = M_{\text{jet}}\frac{\cos^2(y/2)}{1 + \sin^2(y/2)}, \quad \bar{\rho}(y) = 1. \qquad (39)$$

We also consider 2π-periodic solutions in x. The temporal stability of solutions in the layer may then be described by the eigenvalues, κ, of:

$$-\begin{pmatrix} (ik+\mu\sigma)A_1 + A_2\frac{\partial}{\partial y} & I \\ \sigma(ik+\mu\sigma)A_1 & \sigma I \end{pmatrix}. \qquad (40)$$

Approximating the functions by 50-term Fourier series in y and solving the resulting eigenvalue problems in Matlab for $k = 0, \ldots, 25$ yields the results in Table 5 for:

$$\kappa_S = \max_{0\leq k\leq 25}\max_{\kappa} \Re(\kappa). \qquad (41)$$

(We consider $M_{\text{jet}} = .5, .7, .9$.)

A few important conclusions follow from the tabulated results:

i. The flow itself is unstable with a growth rate ranging from .16 to .26. (This follows from κ_S for $\sigma = 0$.)

ii. The growth rate of instabilities within the layer is sensitively dependent on the choice of the parameters μ and σ. For a good choice of μ and σ not too large it was possible to make the maximum growth rate within the layer smaller than in the physical domain. However, for a bad choice it can be worse. (We have observed such instabilities in actual computations.)

iii. The growth rate within the layer generally increases with increasing σ. (Recall this is not the case for linearizations about uniform flows.) Thus we would typically fix σ and attempt to achieve convergence by increasing the layer width.

Of course much of the spectrum of the layer equations is in the far left half-plane, in contrast with the interior equations whose spectrum is mainly imaginary. This is illustrated in Figure 6, where all computed eigenvalues are plotted for each case.

We note that in many of the cases shown the fastest growing instabilities were found for $k = 25$, the largest wave number considered. Thus, actual maximum growth rates may be larger. Indeed we have observed high frequency instabilities for poorly chosen μ. Of course, it might be possible to suppress these by some artificial damping mechanism, as discussed in [15, 18].

We have just begun numerical experiments for parallel flows. As mentioned above, we have observed long time instabilities as indicated by the analysis. In Figures 7-9 we show results obtained for a good value of μ. Precisely, we consider the flow profile (39), scaled to be 1-periodic in y, with $M_{\text{jet}} = 0.5$. The numerical method, mesh, and forcing were as in the preceding example except that the order of the predictor-corrector method was 4, the time step was 1/1000, and the forcing was only applied to the pressure equation. We chose $\mu = .15$ for which we have good stability characteristics. The solution is shown for $t = 5, 10, 100$, with the latter value chosen to demonstrate that the layer is stable for very long times.

Of course these results are not entirely satisfactory. In particular, we would like to develop some theoretical guidance for choosing μ. We would also like to consider variable μ or possibly a matrix-valued function. It is difficult to see how to proceed without better analysis.

2040

CONCLUSION

In conclusion, we have made some progress in applying new methods developed in other areas of computational wave propagation to problems in aeroacoustics. In particular, for linearizations about uniform flows, we have shown how to construct and apply both high-order radiation boundary conditions and reflectionless absorbing layers or PMLs. To further their applicability, we have considered linearizations about parallel flows with some success. However, certain open issues remain. In the future we hope to:

(**i.**) Reformulate the radiation boundary conditions in a jet to avoid high order derivatives of the mean profiles;

(**ii.**) Improve our understanding of the absorption properties of PMLs;

(**iii.**) Implement and test the new methods in a non-linear setting.

References

[1] S. Abarbanel, D. Gottlieb, and J. Hesthaven. Well-posed perfectly matched layers for advective acoustics. *J. Comput. Phys.*, 154:266–283, 1999.

[2] J.-P. Berenger. A perfectly matched layer for the absorption of electromagnetic waves. *J. Comput. Phys.*, 114:185–200, 1994.

[3] T. Colonius, S. Lele, and P. Moin. Boundary conditions for direct computation of aerodynamic sound generation. *AIAA J.*, 31:1574–1582, 1993.

[4] J. Freund. Acoustic sources in a turbulent jet: a direct numerical simulation study. Technical Report AIAA 99-1858, AIAA, 1999.

[5] J. Freund. Noise sources in a low Reynolds number jet at Mach 0.9. *J. Fluid Mech.*, 438:277–305, 2001.

[6] M. Giles. Nonreflecting boundary conditions for Euler equation calculations. *AIAA Journal*, 28:2050–2058, 1990.

[7] J. Goodrich and T. Hagstrom. A comparison of two accurate boundary treatments for computational aeroacoustics. In *3rd AIAA/CEAS Aeroacoustics Conference*, 1997.

[8] T. Hagstrom. Radiation boundary conditions for the numerical simulation of waves. *Acta Numerica*, 8:47–106, 1999.

[9] T. Hagstrom. Experiments with stable, high-order difference approximations to hyperbolic initial-boundary value problems. In A. Bermudez, D. Gomez, C. Hazard, P. Joly, and J. Roberts, editors, *Proceedings of the Fifth International Conference on Mathematical and Numerical Aspects of Wave Propagation Phenomena*. SIAM, 2000.

[10] T. Hagstrom and J. Goodrich. Accurate radiation boundary conditions for the linearized Euler equations in Cartesian domains. *SIAM J. Sci. Comp.*, 2002. To appear.

[11] T. Hagstrom and J. Goodrich. A new PML for the linearized Euler equations. In preparation., 2002.

[12] T. Hagstrom, S.I. Hariharan, and D. Thompson. High-order radiation boundary conditions for convective waves. In preparation.

[13] M. Hayder, F. Hu, and M. Hussaini. Towards perfectly matched boundary conditions for Euler equations. Technical Report AIAA 97-2075, AIAA, 1997.

[14] J. Hesthaven. The analysis and construction of perfectly matched layers for the linearized Euler equations. Technical Report 97-49, ICASE, 1997.

[15] F. Hu. On absorbing boundary conditions for linearized Euler equations by a perfectly matched layer. *J. Comput. Phys.*, 129:201–219, 1996.

[16] J.-L. Lions, J. Métral, and O. Vacus. Well-posed absorbing layer for hyperbolic problems. *Num. Math.*, 2001. To appear.

[17] V. Ryaben'kii, S. Tsynkov, and V. Turchaninov. Global discrete artificial boundary conditions for time-dependent wave propagation. Technical Report 2001-14, ICASE, 2001.

[18] C. Tam, L. Auriault, and F. Cambuli. Perfectly matched layer as an absorbing boundary condition for the linearized Euler equations in open and ducted domains. *J. Comput. Phys.*, 144:213–234, 1998.

[19] O. Vacus. Mathematical analysis of absorbing boundary conditions for the wave equation: the corner problem. *Math. Comp.*, 2002. To appear.

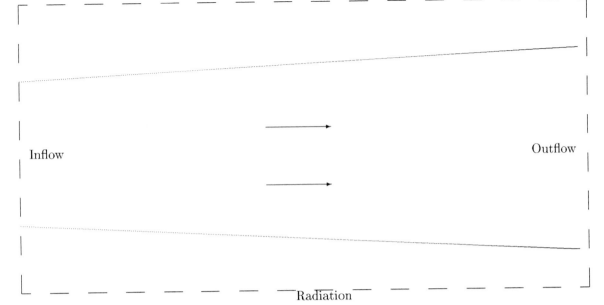

Figure 1: Boundaries for a jet flow simulation

Table 1: Relative Errors - from [10]

l	$t=1$	$t=2$	$t=4$	$t=8$	$t=16$	$t=32$	$t=64$
0	4.8(−3)	3.4(−2)	5.8(−2)	1.8(−1)	5.9(−1)	1.0(0)	1.8(0)
8	1.5(−7)	1.2(−7)	5.6(−8)	8.4(−5)	7.4(−3)	5.9(−2)	2.3(−1)
16	1.5(−7)	1.2(−7)	5.4(−8)	5.4(−8)	2.3(−4)	9.0(−3)	6.6(−2)
32	1.5(−7)	1.2(−7)	5.4(−8)	2.8(−8)	9.9(−8)	4.0(−4)	8.3(−3)
48	1.5(−7)	1.2(−7)	5.4(−8)	2.8(−8)	3.5(−8)	2.0(−5)	1.4(−3)
64	1.5(−7)	1.2(−7)	5.4(−8)	2.8(−8)	3.5(−8)	1.5(−7)	3.1(−4)
80	1.5(−7)	1.2(−7)	5.4(−8)	2.8(−8)	3.5(−8)	4.3(−8)	1.3(−4)
96	1.5(−7)	1.2(−7)	5.4(−8)	2.8(−8)	3.5(−8)	4.2(−8)	2.8(−5)
112	1.5(−7)	1.2(−7)	5.4(−8)	2.8(−8)	3.5(−8)	4.2(−8)	5.0(−7)

Table 2: L_2 pressure errors

t	$\|p\|$	$w = .3, \sigma_m = 80$	$w = .3, \sigma_m = 160$	$w = .6, \sigma_m = 80$	$w = .6, \sigma_m = 160$
1	5.3(−6)	1.1(−14)	1.0(−13)	7.6(−16)	1.1(−14)
2	1.4(−3)	1.9(−10)	3.2(−9)	7.3(−12)	1.9(−10)
3	2.0(−2)	3.5(−8)	4.0(−7)	3.2(−9)	3.5(−8)
4	7.8(−2)	1.5(−6)	1.1(−5)	1.4(−7)	1.5(−6)
5	1.3(−1)	1.2(−5)	9.1(−5)	1.1(−6)	1.2(−5)
6	9.9(−2)	3.4(−5)	3.3(−4)	3.5(−6)	3.4(−5)
7	3.6(−2)	6.2(−5)	6.8(−4)	5.1(−6)	6.2(−5)
8	4.8(−3)	1.3(−4)	9.4(−4)	3.0(−6)	1.3(−4)
9	1.2(−4)	2.2(−4)	1.2(−3)	4.1(−6)	2.2(−4)
10	8.0(−6)	3.2(−4)	1.4(−3)	7.8(−6)	3.2(−4)
11	8.3(−6)	4.0(−4)	1.3(−3)	1.4(−5)	4.0(−4)
12	8.3(−6)	3.9(−4)	6.5(−4)	2.5(−5)	3.9(−4)
13	8.1(−6)	2.8(−4)	1.7(−4)	4.4(−5)	2.8(−4)
14	7.8(−6)	2.0(−4)	2.4(−4)	6.6(−5)	2.1(−4)
15	7.5(−6)	2.1(−4)	1.8(−4)	8.6(−5)	2.3(−4)

Table 3: L_2 v_1 errors

t	$\|v_1\|$	$w = .3, \sigma_m = 80$	$w = .3, \sigma_m = 160$	$w = .6, \sigma_m = 80$	$w = .6, \sigma_m = 160$
1	5.9(−6)	8.5(−15)	7.7(−14)	5.7(−16)	8.5(−15)
2	1.9(−3)	1.7(−10)	2.7(−9)	7.0(−12)	1.1(−10)
3	3.3(−2)	3.3(−8)	4.0(−7)	3.2(−9)	3.3(−8)
4	1.5(−1)	1.6(−6)	1.1(−5)	1.5(−7)	1.6(−6)
5	3.3(−1)	1.5(−5)	1.0(−4)	1.3(−6)	1.5(−5)
6	4.1(−1)	4.2(−5)	3.9(−4)	4.4(−6)	4.2(−5)
7	2.9(−1)	6.8(−5)	8.6(−4)	7.4(−6)	6.8(−5)
8	1.2(−1)	1.7(−4)	1.4(−3)	6.3(−6)	1.7(−4)
9	2.5(−2)	3.4(−4)	2.0(−3)	6.5(−6)	3.4(−4)
10	1.9(−3)	5.7(−4)	2.5(−3)	1.2(−5)	5.7(−4)
11	2.0(−4)	7.8(−4)	2.3(−3)	2.2(−5)	7.7(−4)
12	3.0(−5)	8.5(−4)	1.4(−3)	3.9(−5)	8.6(−4)
13	5.0(−6)	7.8(−4)	5.9(−4)	6.8(−5)	7.8(−4)
14	2.1(−6)	7.6(−4)	4.7(−4)	1.1(−4)	7.6(−4)
15	1.8(−6)	6.8(−4)	3.4(−4)	1.5(−4)	6.9(−4)

Table 4: L_2 v_2 errors

t	$\|v_2\|$	$w = .3, \sigma_m = 80$	$w = .3, \sigma_m = 160$	$w = .6, \sigma_m = 80$	$w = .6, \sigma_m = 160$
1	6.0(−6)	2.6(−15)	2.1(−14)	2.0(−16)	2.6(−15)
2	2.1(−3)	1.1(−10)	1.5(−9)	5.4(−12)	1.1(−10)
3	3.8(−2)	2.4(−8)	3.1(−7)	2.6(−9)	2.4(−8)
4	1.9(−1)	1.4(−6)	9.5(−6)	1.4(−7)	1.4(−6)
5	4.5(−1)	1.4(−5)	9.2(−5)	1.2(−6)	1.4(−5)
6	5.8(−1)	4.3(−5)	3.9(−4)	4.3(−6)	4.3(−5)
7	4.4(−1)	7.3(−5)	8.9(−4)	7.5(−6)	7.3(−5)
8	1.9(−1)	1.8(−4)	1.4(−3)	6.7(−6)	1.8(−4)
9	4.0(−2)	3.5(−4)	2.0(−3)	7.7(−6)	3.5(−4)
10	2.9(−3)	5.4(−4)	2.8(−3)	1.5(−5)	5.4(−4)
11	2.0(−4)	7.0(−4)	2.9(−3)	2.6(−5)	7.0(−4)
12	3.3(−5)	7.9(−4)	1.8(−3)	4.7(−5)	7.9(−4)
13	8.5(−6)	8.0(−4)	6.7(−4)	8.2(−5)	8.0(−4)
14	5.6(−6)	7.5(−4)	6.1(−4)	1.3(−4)	7.5(−4)
15	5.1(−6)	7.0(−4)	4.8(−4)	1.9(−4)	7.2(−4)

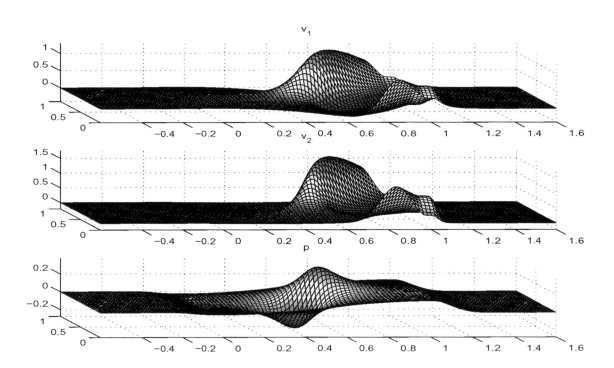

Figure 2: Solution at $t = 5$, $w = .6$, $\sigma_m = 80$

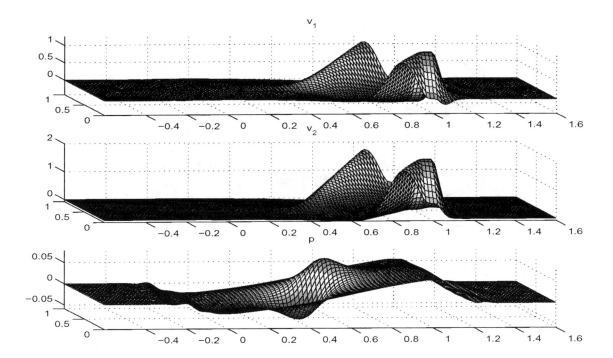

Figure 3: Solution at $t = 7$, $w = .6$, $\sigma_m = 80$

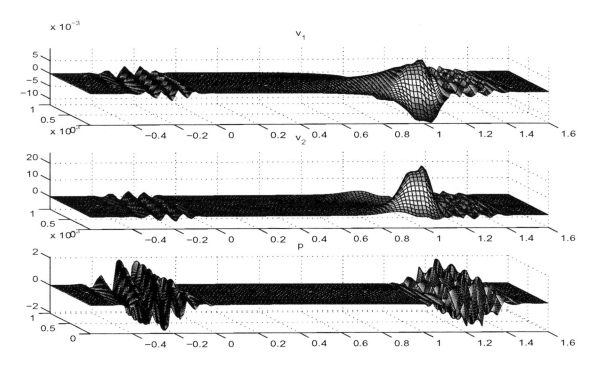

Figure 4: Solution at $t = 10$, $w = .6$, $\sigma_m = 80$

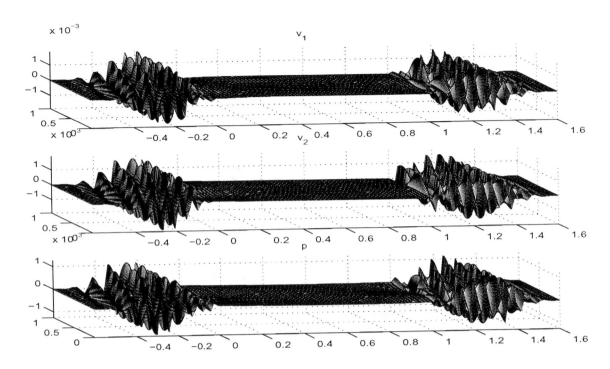

Figure 5: Solution at $t = 12$, $w = .6$, $\sigma_m = 80$

Table 5: Layer eigenvalues as a function of μ.

σ	μ	κ_S, $M_{\text{jet}} = .5$	σ	μ	κ_S, $M_{\text{jet}} = .7$	σ	μ	κ_S, $M_{\text{jet}} = .9$
0	0	1.58(−1)	0	0	2.12(−1)	0	0	2.59(−1)
50	.150	4.99(−2)	50	.200	4.06(−1)	50	.200	2.09(0)
50	.160	3.59(−2)	50	.210	3.39(−1)	50	.300	6.61(−1)
50	.170	2.64(−2)	50	.220	2.76(−1)	50	.320	5.43(−1)
50	.180	4.21(−2)	50	.230	2.16(−1)	50	.325	5.16(−1)
50	.210	1.09(−1)	50	.240	1.63(−1)	50	.330	5.44(−1)
50	.267	3.14(−1)	50	.250	1.99(−1)	50	.340	5.72(−1)
50	.400	1.11(0)	50	.260	2.38(−1)	50	.400	9.90(−1)
100	.170	5.63(−2)	100	240	3.71(−1)	100	.325	9.59(−1)

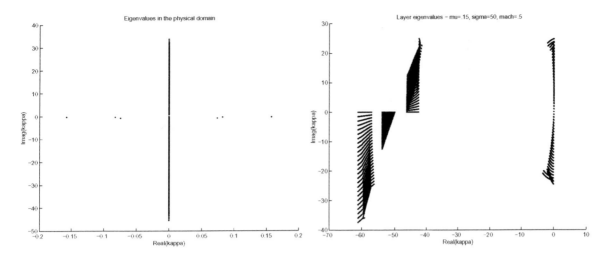

Figure 6: Eigenvalues in the jet and in the PML

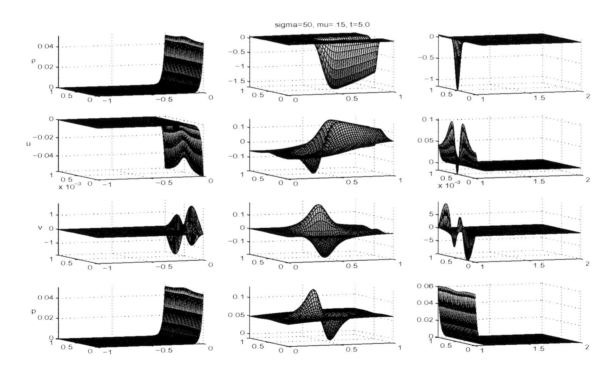

Figure 7: Solution at $t = 5$, parallel flow case

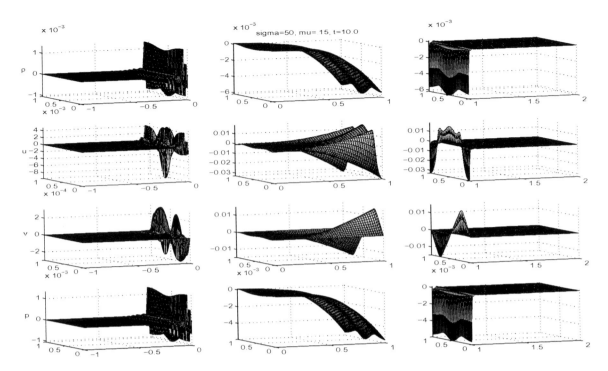

Figure 8: Solution at $t = 10$, parallel flow case

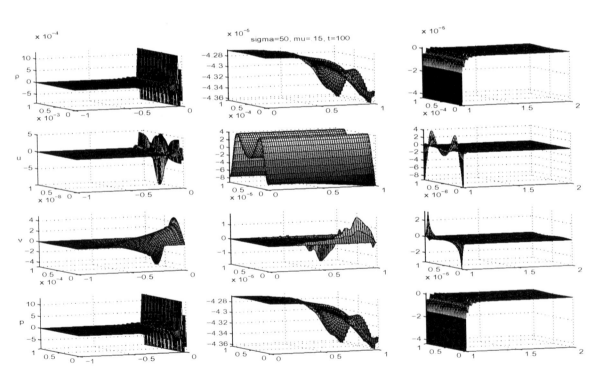

Figure 9: Solution at $t = 100$, parallel flow case

AUTHOR INDEX

A, Alan. - 569
Abbey, E. - 1568
Abdelhamid, Y. - 1143
Agarwal, A. - 1753
Ahuja, K. - 642, 916, 1265
Ahuja, V. - 1870
Akishita, S. - 424
Ali, A. - 1597
Alkislar, M. - 1304, 1977
Alpman, E. - 1870
Alvi, F. - 23
Amedin, C. - 156
Anavaradham, G. - 53
Andersson, A. - 2027
Andrianov, E. - 2027
Arakeri, A. - 591
Arakeri, V. - 1304
Arnette, S. - 1152
Arunajatesan, S. - 11, 1319
Astley, R. - 580
Atalla, N. - 156
Atassi, H. - 477, 1597, 1608
Atassi, O. - 1597
Atkins, H. - 1232
B, Brian. - 569
Babu, V. - 53
Baeder, J. - 1211
Bailly, C. - 856, 1200, 1371
Baker, N. - 580
Balakumar, P. - 1337
Barone, M. - 444
Batten, P. - 1223
Bebesel, M. - 1080
Bellucci, V. - 458
Ben Khelil, S. - 1730
Bernardini, G. - 1413
Bethke, S. - 1702
Betts, J. - 696, 1071
Bhat, T. - 961
Biancherin, A. - 1955, 1966
Biedron, R. - 406
Billson, M. - 1826
Birch, S. - 236
Blaisdell, G. - 1943
Blake, W. - 435, 1689
Bobbitt, P. - 1444
Bodony, D. - 621
Bodén, H. - 530
Bogey, C. - 856, 1200
Boluriaan, S. - 1920
Boudreau, J. - 64
Brauer, C. - 708
Bremner, P. - 1521
Bridges, J. - 212, 929, 1348
Brooks, T. - 817, 2009
Brown, S. - 186

Buchal, T. - 1683
Buchholz, H. - 796
Buehrle, R. - 186, 201
Buhler, W. - 174
Bulter, G. - 1176
Burdisso, R. - 1881
Burnside, N. - 64, 113, 1764
Byrne, S. - 1881
Böhning, P. - 1134, 1189
Cabell, R. - 1090, 1098
Caimi, R. - 1986
Cain, A. - 1
Calhoon, W. - 1319
Canabal, F. - 1434
Casalino, D. - 1464
Casalis, G. - 614
Casper, J. - 868
Cattafesta, L. - 738, 749
Celano, J. - 520
Celic, A. - 807
Chakravarthy, S. - 53, 1223
Chandrasekharan, R. - 64
Chen, X. - 844
Chien, E. - 1881
Chin, C. - 164
Chiou, S. - 1881
Choudhari, M. - 773
Chow, L. - 92, 103, 1818
Clark, L. - 406
Clarke, J. - 1424
Cox, D. - 1098
Crivellini, A. - 1382
Crouzet, F. - 1683
Czech, M. - 1143
Dahl, M. - 603, 634
Dash, S. - 1319
Davidson, L. - 1826
Davy, R. - 141
Delfs, J. - 1786
Devenport, W. - 658
Dillmann, A. - 787
Dobrzynski, W. - 103, 796
Doty, M. - 1532, 1585
Dowling, A. - 1487, 1890
Duell, E. - 1152
Dupere, I. - 1890
Duraisamy, K. - 1211
Dyson, R. - 467
Edgar, N. - 1392
Efimtsov, B. - 2027
Ehrenfried, K. - 787
Elam, K. - 940
Elhadidi, B. - 1608
Elkoby, R. - 961
Elmer, K. - 1424
Elnady, T. - 530

Envia, E. - 362, 990, 1027
Eriksson, L. - 1826
Eschricht, D. - 1505
Eversman, W. - 1243
Ewert, R. - 760
Farassat, F. - 868, 1859
Fite, E. - 1027
Flohr, P. - 458, 1702
Frendi, A. - 174, 1434
Freund, J. - 212, 245, 1312
Fuller, C. - 1071
Gaeta, R. - 642
Galland, M. - 1108, 1166
Gallman, J. - 560
Gehlhar, B. - 796
Gennaretti, M. - 1413
Gerhold, C. - 406
Gershzohn, G. - 1424
Gervais, M. - 1475
Gibbs, G. - 186, 1090, 1098
Gilinsky, M. - 1901
Gliebe, P. - 1003
Gloerfelt, X. - 856
Goldberg, U. - 1223
Golubev, A. - 2027
Golubev, V. - 634, 1382
Goody, M. - 1652
Greska, B. - 591
Grosveld, F. - 201
Guidati, S. - 708
Guillen, P. - 1730
Guion, P. - 103
Guo, Y. - 1743
Hagstrom, T. - 2036
Hamilton, J. - 580
Hanson, D. - 974
Hanson, R. - 1713
Hardin, J. - 1901
Harper-Bourne, M. - 258
Heck, J. - 1497
Heidelberg, L. - 328, 1637
Heminger, J. - 488
Henderson, B. - 1348
Herrero, C. - 1730
Hersh, A. - 520
Hilbrunner, O. - 1108, 1166
Hileman, J. - 904
Hirschberg, A. - 1325
Hixon, R. - 467, 1382, 1835
Hoffmann, F. - 1080
Horne, W. - 83, 113, 1764
Hossain, M. - 1546
Hu, F. - 1232
Hu, Z. - 228
Hubner, J. - 749
Hughes, C. - 280, 302, 377
Hughes, N. - 1546
Humphreys, W. - 2009
Hussaini, M. - 1859

Hutcheson, F. - 817
Hynes, T. - 509
Iida, A. - 1722
Imamoglu, B. - 1337
Jacob, M. - 1464
Jaeger, S. - 64, 113, 1764
James, K. - 83, 113
Jansen, K. - 1402
Janssens, M. - 1497
Jansson, D. - 749
Jeracki, R. - 280, 302
Jones, M. - 550, 1254
Joppa, P. - 349
Joseph, T. - 591
Juve, D. - 856
Kafyeke, F. - 64
Kandil, O. - 1444
Kandula, M. - 1986
Kannepalli, C. - 1319
Karabasov, S. - 509
Karbon, K. - 1515
Kato, C. - 1722
Kegerise, M. - 1098
Kenzakowsli, D. - 1319
Kerschen, E. - 1
Khavaran, A. - 212
Khorrami, M. - 128, 773, 1796
Kibens, V. - 23
Kinzie, K. - 1557
Kitchen, E. - 580
Klos, J. - 186
Kodama, H. - 1017
Konno, K. - 1637
Koop, L. - 787
Krebs, W. - 1702
Kreider, K. - 488
Krothapalli, A. - 591, 1304, 1977
Krupar, M. - 377
Kunze, C. - 435
Kunze, R. - 560
Kwan, H. - 1881
Lafon, P. - 1683
Lambert, D. - 1424
Lan, J. - 1626
Lauke, T. - 1786
Laurence, D. - 1683
Lebedev, A. - 236
Leclercq, D. - 1775
Lee, J. - 164
Lele, S. - 444, 621, 1359
Li, F. - 128
Li, X. - 1294
Lilley, G. - 773
Listerud, E. - 1243
Lockard, D. - 773, 1796, 1807
Long, L. - 1870
Lourenco, L. - 1304, 1977
Lui, C. - 1359
Lummer, M. - 1786

Lupoglazoff, N. - 1955, 1966
Lynch, D. - 435, 1689
Lyrintzis, A. - 1943
Lyubimov, D. - 236
M, Mike. - 569
Maeder, T. - 880, 1402
Maestrello, L. - 1666
Maier, R. - 1080
Maillard, V. - 1371
Malik, M. - 128
Mankbadi, R. - 603, 634, 1382
Manoha, E. - 1730
Mary, I. - 1730
Maslov, V. - 236
Massey, K. - 916, 1265
Mathur, G. - 164
Mau, K. - 92
McGuirk, J. - 1546
McLaughlin, D. - 1532, 1585
Mead, C. - 961
Meinke, M. - 760
Mendoza, J. - 2009
Michel, U. - 787, 1134, 1189, 1294, 1619
Millan, P. - 718
Miller, C. - 280, 302
Millet, C. - 614
Mineev, B. - 236
Minotti, A. - 718
Mish, P. - 658
Mizuno, A. - 1722
Moens, F. - 141
Moreau, S. - 681
Moreno, D. - 1977
Morfey, C. - 228, 844
Morgans, A. - 1487
Morino, L. - 1413
Morris, P. - 1753, 1920
Mueller, T. - 435, 1689
Mungal, G. - 1713
Musser, C. - 195
Möser, M. - 1062
Nakamura, Y. - 1017
Nallasamy, M. - 990, 1835
Nazarov, I. - 2036
Neise, W. - 1062, 1118
Nelson, J. - 1127
Nelson, P. - 844
Nesbitt, E. - 961, 1143
Neuhaus, L. - 1118
Nishida, T. - 738
Nishizawa, T. - 1017
Nozaki, O. - 1017
Odedra, J. - 23
Oerlemans, S. - 727
Osman, H. - 156
Ostertag, J. - 807
Otugen, V. - 416
Ovenden, N. - 541
Ozyoruk, Y. - 1870

Page, G. - 1546
Panda, J. - 940
Panneerselvam, S. - 53
Papamoschou, D. - 1568
Papp, J. - 1319
Pappa, R. - 201
Parrott, T. - 550, 1254
Paschereit, C. - 458
Pastouchenko, N. - 2001
Patrick, H. - 1932
Peto, J. - 23
Piet, J. - 718, 1189
Piper, G. - 1127
Podboy, G. - 377
Pott-Pollenske, M. - 796
Povinelli, L. - 1382
Prade, B. - 1702
Premo, J. - 349, 1626
Pritchard, J. - 201
Rackl, R. - 2027
Rahier, G. - 1955, 1966
Raman, G. - 1, 23, 416
Reba, R. - 880, 1402
Reinero, B. - 1764
Remy, H. - 92, 141
Ricot, D. - 1371
Rienstra, S. - 1284
Riethmuller, M. - 1325
Rizzi, S. - 2027
Roger, M. - 681, 1464
Rops, C. - 1497
Ross, J. - 23
Rossmann, T. - 1713
Rung, T. - 1505
Sagaut, P. - 1730
Samimy, M. - 904
Sandham, N. - 228
Sawyer, S. - 1835
Schein, D. - 642, 1557
Schemel, C. - 1294
Schmitz, F. - 1475
Schram, C. - 1325
Schroeder, W. - 760
Schulten, J. - 1849
Schultz, T. - 738
Schulz, J. - 1062
Scott, J. - 488, 1382
Seasholtz, R. - 940
Secundov, A. - 236
Seiner, J. - 11, 1319
Sellen, N. - 1108, 1166
Shabbir, A. - 990
Sheplak, M. - 738, 749
Sheverev, V. - 416
Shiells, D. - 103
Shivashankara, B. - 1424
Siddavaram, V. - 1304
Sijtsma, P. - 727
Siller, H. - 1619

Simon, F. - 718
Singer, B. - 1796
Singh, R. - 1515
Sinha, N. - 11
Smith, M. - 1818
Snellen, M. - 1497
Sobieski, J. - 1254
Soderman, P. - 64, 113, 1764
Solomon, W. - 642, 1557
Soteriou, M. - 880
Soukhomlinov, V. - 416
Stanek, M. - 23
Stanescu, D. - 1859
Stepaniuk, V. - 416
Stoker, R. - 1743
Storms, B. - 83
Strange, P. - 961
Strumolo, G. - 1497
Susan-Resiga, R. - 477
Sutliff, D. - 1027, 1626, 1637
Suzuki, T. - 1176
Symes, M. - 1775
Tada, H. - 1932
Tam, C. - 269, 2001
Tan, B. - 833
Tarau, C. - 416
TenPas, P. - 1392
Tesson, V. - 1585
Tewes, S. - 1080
Thiele, F. - 1294, 1505
Thorp, S. - 990
Tobias, L. - 1424
Tracy, M. - 550
Trumper, M. - 1546
Tsuchiya, N. - 1017
Tweedt, D. - 1027
Uellenberg, S. - 1143
Umesh Chandra, B. - 53
Uzun, A. - 1943
van Lier, L. - 1497
Viswanathan, K. - 893
Vuillot, F. - 1955, 1966
Wagner, S. - 708, 807
Walker, B. - 520
Walle, F. - 796
Walter, J. - 1152
Wat, J. - 1424
Watkins, J. - 1127
Watson, W. - 550, 1254
Wei, M. - 1312
Wernet, M. - 929, 1348
Wilby, J. - 1521
Woodward, R. - 280, 302, 377
Yahathugoda, I. - 424
Yamagata, A. - 1017
Yamamoto, K. - 1017, 1743
Yan, J. - 1505
Yang, Z. - 1444
Yen, J. - 1152

Yu, J. - 1881
Zhang, X. - 844
Zheng, S. - 1277, 1912
Zheng, Z. - 833
Zhuang, M. - 1277, 1912